PLANT PROPAGATION
by
TISSUE CULTURE
Part 1

The Technology

Edwin F. George Ph.D.

2nd Edition, 1993

Exegetics Limited

© 1993 Copyright of the publishers:

Exegetics Ltd.,
Edington, Wilts.
BA13 4QG , England.

First published 1984
Second (revised) edition 1993

British Library
Cataloguing in Publication Data

A catalogue record for this book is available from the British Library

ISBN 0-9509325-4-X

Printed in Great Britain by Butler & Tanner Ltd., Frome, Somerset.
All sales and other enquiries should be sent to the publishers, Exegetics Ltd.

Preface

The extent to which plants are propagatated using tissue culture techniques continues to increase; it is represented in the range of plants which can be multiplied, the large number of laboratories now using these methods, and the very many scientific papers written about the subject. What then is the value of a textbook on the subject prepared 10 years ago? Somewhat diminished, I fear; it is hardly surprising that for some time the publishers have been receiving requests for a revision of *Plant Propagation by Tissue Culture*.

Here then is the second edition, much more comprehensive than the first, but inevitably, even more bulky. Its extent is now too great to be accommodated in a single volume, and the new edition is to be published in two parts: the first describes the technology of propagating plants by tissue culture methods; the second, methods which are adopted and results which have been obtained, in practice. A criticism of the first edition was that it contained too few illustrations; I have tried to correct the situation in this revision.

These volumes are intended as encyclopaedic texts on the whole subject of propagating plants by using tissue cultures. They are consequently illustrated by many examples of published results; and are accompanied by copious references to the scientific literature, which are intended to facilitate further research by those wishing for more detailed information on the many subjects covered.

The author and publishers wish to thank all those who have helped in any way in the preparation of this book. Particular thanks is due to Dr. P. K. Evans of Southampton University, who has offered suggestions throughout the preparation of this work, and acted as critic of the written word. Dr. Evans has also kindly supplied photographs, which are used as illustrations in this volume. P. D. Sherrington and D. J. M. Puttock assisted with the preparation of the first edition, and of *Plant Culture Media*, and so have contributed to the knowledge base. We have once again used the system devised by Dr. G. S. Davy for summarising plant culture media; Dr. Davy has also contributed technical advice and support on some of the physical chemistry summarised in the book, and we warmly thank him for his help.

We express our appreciation to:

Drs. R. Barg and N. Umiel and Mssrs. Gustav Fischer, who kindly gave us permission to publish the data in Fig. 99.

Drs. S. Roest and G. S. Bokelmann and Elsevier Science Publishers B.V., who permitted us to use the data for Figs. 94 and 98.

Prof. Dr. G. Reuther and the International Society for Horticultural Science, for permission to use a modified version of a figure in *Acta Horticulturae*, and for the help received from Prof. Reuther in correcting our draft.

Dr. Guideroni and Mssrs. Martinus Nijhoff Publishers, for permission to reproduce a modified version of a figure which appeared in the journal *Plant Cell, Tissue and Organ Culture*;

Drs. J. A. McComb and I. J. Bennett for permission to publish Fig. 82, and for help in revising our original draft.

Safetech Ltd., Limerick, Ireland for permission to reproduce a drawing of their product.

Edwin George
May 1993.

"For who hath despised the day of small things ?"

Zechariah **4**: 10

"When will the book be finished? That's the question. If it is to appear next winter, I haven't a minute to lose between now and then. But there are moments when I'm so tired that I feel I'm liquefying like an old Camembert."

Gustave Flaubert (1821–1880)
(ex *Flaubert's Parrot* by Julian Barnes)

Contents

Introduction

Modern scientific investigation has extended and enhanced the methods by which plants can be propagated. Not only have traditional skills been improved, but techniques have also been found whereby the vegetative propagation of plants can be carried out advantageously in a laboratory. In many instances, growers now have a choice of which method to use: their choice will depend on the speed with which new plants are required, and the requisite cost and quality of the final product.

Plant Propagation by Tissue Culture is devoted entirely to laboratory methods of propagation. The large amount of scientific data now available has necessitated that the second edition is in two parts; this volume describes the technology, and Part II (which commences with Chapter 12) covers the practice by which plants of various kinds are multiplied. To satisfy the objective, it is usually necessary to grow small plants, plant organs or pieces of tissue aseptically on a nutritional medium, using tissue culture techniques. Newly produced shoots or plantlets are returned to the external environment and grown on to maturity or until they are suitable for sale. Plant material is thus taken from its normal growing (*in vivo*) situation, and cultured *in vitro* (meaning literally, 'in a glass' because the cultures are contained within glass or clear plastic vessels). When plant material comes out of culture it is moved into the *ex vitro* or *extra vitrum* ('out of', or 'outside' glass) environment and must once again become adapted to normal *in vivo* growth (Fig. 1). The *in vitro* multiplication of plants is also called *micropropagation* because it is necessary to handle very small parts of plants and small pieces of plant tissue, and miniature shoots and plantlets are initially derived.

The chief advantages of micropropagation are that it is usually very much more rapid than other methods of vegetative multiplication, and that it enables vegetative propagation where it is difficult or impossible by conventional techniques. In addition there are now many techniques for the genetic modification of plants *in vitro*. These also depend upon micropropagation for the regeneration and multiplication of new characteristics

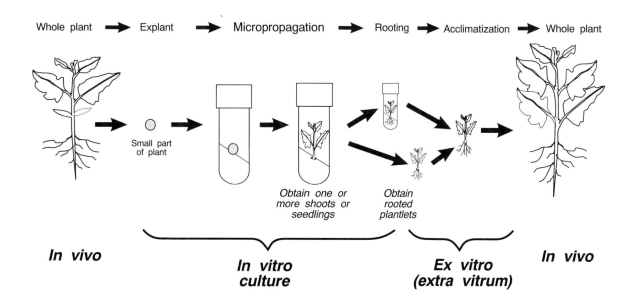

Fig. 1. The basic steps in micropropagation.

1

UNITS AND ABBREVIATIONS

UNITS OF MEASUREMENT

Most readers will be aware that the older system of metric units of measurement has now been largely replaced by the *Système Internationale d'Unité*, abbreviated in English to *SI* units. *SI* units have been used in this text, and in Chapter 7 conversions are given from some older units of measurement which are found in early plant tissue culture literature.

Units can be presented by using solidi, or negative powers, in either of the following ways:—

$$m/s \qquad m\,s^{-1} \qquad \text{(metres per second)}$$

The latter style is now considered to be correct for *SI* units, but the former less cumbersome method has been used in this text for common abbreviations, such as mg/l (mg l^{-1}). We have also expressed the molar concentration of solutions using the more concise M for molarity, instead of mol l^{-1}. Negative powers have been employed for more complex units, which are usually encountered in that form in the scientific literature, for example:—

$$\mu mol\,m^{-2}\,s^{-1}$$

Simplification

The *SI* unit of volume is the cubic metre (m^3), and not the litre, which has only temporary acceptance. In some scientific journals, concentrations are therefore now expressed as a mass (kg), or amount of substance (mol), per cubic metre; for example:

$$5\,kg\,m^{-3} \text{ (equivalent to 5 mg } cm^{-3}, \text{ or 5 mg } ml^{-1}); \text{ instead of 5 g } l^{-1} \text{ (5 g/l).}$$

Many would agree that the change is not helpful to biologists concerned with the preparation and use of solutions, and as we have not yet seen the formally correct *SI* terminology entering the plant tissue culture literature, we have continued to use the litre to describe mass per unit volume. This note is to assist you with the meaning of such unfamiliar descriptions of concentrations, should you meet them for the first time.

ABBREVIATIONS REFERRING TO MEDIA

The names of plant culture media have been shown in bold type; those of very common media have been abbreviated:

MS	**Murashige and Skoog (1962)** medium		
½**MS**	**Murashige and Skoog (1962)** medium (or salts), at one half the normal dilution		
LS	**Linsmaier and Skoog (1965)** medium	**WPM**	**Lloyd and McCown (1981) WPM** medium
SH	**Schenk and Hildebrandt (1972)** medium	**B5**	**Gamborg et al. (1968)** medium

Media supplements

CM	Coconut milk (coconut water)	AC	Activated charcoal

ABBREVIATIONS REFERRING TO GROWTH REGULATORS

Auxins commonly used in micropropagation work (see Chapter 11)

IAA	NAA	IBA
2,4-D	2,4,5-T	

'Anti-auxins' :

TIBA

Cytokinins used in micropropagation work

BAP	2-iP	kinetin

Other classes of regulant:

GA₃ (Gibberellic acid)

ABA (Abscisic acid)

Abbreviation for some other additives

DMSO	Dimethylsulphoxide, a solvent and cryoprotectant
PVP	Polyvinylpyrrolidone, used to prevent blackening.

1

Plant Tissue Culture Techniques

Plant tissue culture is the science (or art!) of growing plant cells, tissues or organs isolated from the mother plant, on artificial media. It includes techniques and methods appropriate to research into many botanical disciplines and several practical objectives. Before beginning to propagate plants by tissue culture methods, it is necessary to have a clear understanding of the ways in which plant material can be grown and manipulated in 'test tubes'. This chapter therefore describes the techniques which have been developed for the isolation and *in vitro* culture of plant material, and shows where further information can be obtained.

DEFINITIONS

Both organised and unorganised growth are possible *in vitro*.

Organised growth

Organised growth contributes towards the creation or maintenance of a defined structure. It occurs when plant organs such as the growing points of shoots or roots (apical meristems), leaf initials, young flower buds or small fruits, are transferred to culture and continue to grow with their structure preserved. Growth which is coherently organised also occurs when organs are freshly created. This may occur *in vitro* either directly upon an organ or upon a piece of tissue placed in culture (an explant), or during the culture of previously unorganised tissues. The process of *de novo* organ formation is called *organogenesis* or *morphogenesis* (the development of form).

Unorganised growth

The existence of higher plants depends on the organised allocation of functions to different parts which in consequence become *differentiated*, that is to say, modified and specialised to enable them undertake their requisite roles.

Unorganised growth is seldom found in nature, but occurs fairly frequently when pieces of whole plants are cultured *in vitro*. The tissues which are then formed, typically lack any recognisable structure and contain only a limited number of the many kinds of specialised and differentiated cells found in an intact plant. A differentiated cell is one which has developed a specialised form (morphology) and/or function (physiology). A differentiated tissue (*e.g.* xylem or epidermis) is a aggregation of differentiated cells. So far the formation of differentiated cell types can only be controlled to a limited extent in culture. It is not possible, for example to maintain and multiply a culture composed entirely of epidermal cells. By contrast, unorganised tissues can be increased in volume by subculture and can be maintained on semi-solid or liquid media for long periods. They can often also be used to commence cell suspension cultures.

Differentiation is also used botanically to describe the formation of distinct organs through morphogenesis.

TISSUE CULTURE

Cultures of unorganised tissues

'Tissue culture' is commonly used as a collective term to describe all kinds of *in vitro* plant cultures although strictly it should refer only to cultures of unorganised aggregates of cells. In practice the following kinds of cultures are most generally recognised:

Callus (or tissue) cultures. The growth and maintenance of largely unorganised cell masses which arise from the uncoordinated and disorganised growth of small plant organs, pieces of plant tissue, or previously cultured cells.

Suspension (or cell) cultures. Populations of plant cells and small cell clumps, dispersed in an agitated liquid medium.

Protoplast cultures. The culture of plant cells that have been isolated without a cell wall.

Anther cultures. The culture of complete anthers containing immature pollen microspores. The objective is usually to obtain haploid plants by the formation of *somatic embryos* (see below) directly from the pollen, or sometimes by organogenesis *via* callus. *Pollen cultures* are those initiated from pollen that has been removed from anthers.

Cultures of organised structures

Organ culture is used as a general term for those types of culture in which an organised form of growth can be continuously maintained. It includes the aseptic isolation from whole plants of such definite structures as leaf primordia, immature flowers and fruits, and their growth *in vitro*. For the purposes of plant propagation, the most important kinds of organ culture are:

- *Meristem cultures,* in which are grown very small shoot apices, each consisting of the apical meristematic dome with or without one or two leaf primordia. The shoot apex is typically grown to give one single shoot.

- *Shoot tip, or shoot cultures,* started from shoot tips, or buds, larger than the shoot apices employed to establish meristem cultures, having several leaf primordia. These shoot apices are usually cultured in such a way that each produces multiple shoots.

- *Node cultures* of separate lateral buds, each carried on a small piece of stem tissue; stem pieces carrying either single or multiple nodes may be cultured. Each bud is grown to provide a single shoot.

- *Embryo cultures,* where fertilised or unfertilised zygotic (seed) embryos are dissected out of developing seeds or fruits and cultured *in vitro* until they have grown into seedlings. Embryo culture is quite distinct from somatic embryogenesis (see below).

- *Isolated root cultures.* The growth of roots, unconnected to shoots: a branched root system may obtained.

These types of cultures are described in more detail later in this chapter.

Using tissue cultures for plant propagation

Complete new plants can be derived from tissue cultures in three ways:

- from pre-existing shoot buds or primordial buds (meristems) which are encouraged to grow and proliferate;

- following shoot morphogenesis when new shoots are induced to form in unorganised tissues or directly upon explanted tissues of the mother plant;

- through the formation of *somatic embryos* which resemble the seed embryos of intact plants, and which can grow into seedlings in the same way. This process is called *somatic embryogenesis.*

To obtain plants by the first two of these methods, it is necessary to treat shoots of an adequate size as miniature cuttings and induce them to produce roots.

The derivation of new plants from cells which would not normally have taken part in the process of regeneration, shows that plant cells are for the most part *totipotent*, *i.e.* they each retain a latent capacity to produce a whole plant. Totipotency is a special characteristic of cells in young tissues and meristems. It can be exhibited by some differentiated cells, but not those which have developed into terminally differentiated structures (*e.g.* sieve tubes or tracheids).

Theoretically, plant cells, organs, or plants, can all be cloned, i.e produced in large numbers as a population where all the individuals have the same genetic constitution as the parent. Present tissue culture techniques do not permit this in every case and irregularities do sometimes occur, resulting in genetic variants. Nevertheless, as will be described in the chapters which follow, a very large measure of success can be achieved and cultures of various kinds can be used to propagate plants.

Initiating tissue cultures

Explants

Tissue cultures are started from pieces of whole plants. The small organs or pieces of tissue that are used are called *explants*. The part of the plant (the *stock plant* or *mother plant*) from which explants are obtained, depends on:

- the kind of culture to be initiated,

- the purpose of the proposed culture, and

- the plant species to be used.

Explants can therefore be of many different kinds. The correct choice of explant material can have an important effect on the success of tissue culture.

Plants growing in the external environment are invariably contaminated with micro-organisms and pests. These contaminants are mainly confined to the outer surfaces of the plant, although, as discussed in Chapter 5, some microbes and viruses may be systemic within the tissues. Because they are started from small explants and must be grown on nutritive media which are also favourable for the growth of micro-organisms, plant tissue cultures must usually be established and maintained in aseptic conditions. Most kinds of microbial organism, and in particular bacteria and fungi, compete adversely with plant material growing *in vitro*. Therefore, as far as possible, explants must be free from microbial contaminants when they are first placed on a nutrient medium. This usually involves growing stock plants in ways that will minimise infection, treating the plant material with disinfecting chemicals to kill superficial microbes, and sterilising the tools used for dissection and the vessels and media in which cultures are grown. Some kinds of plants can, however, be micro-propagated in non-sterile environments (see Chapter 4).

Isolation and incubation

The work of isolating and transferring cultured plant material is usually performed in special rooms or inside hoods or cabinets from which micro-organisms can be excluded. Cabinets used for isolation can be placed in a draught-free part of a general laboratory, but are much better situated in a special inoculation or tranfer room reserved for the purpose. The accommodation, equipment and methods which are required for successful inoculation and transfer are described in a later chapter. Cultures, once initiated, are placed in incubators or growth rooms where lighting, temperature and humidity can be controlled. The rate of growth of a culture will depend on the temperature (and sometimes the lighting) regime adopted.

The cultural environment

Plant cultures are commenced by placing one or more explants into a pre-sterilized container of sterile nutrient medium. Some explants may fail to grow, or may die, due to microbial contamination; to ensure the survival of an adequate number, it therefore is usual to initiate several cultures at the same time, each being started from an identical organ or piece of tissue. Explants taken from stock plants at different times of the year, may not give reproducible results in tissue culture. This may be due to variation in the level of external contaminants or because of seasonal changes in endogenous (internal) growth substance levels in the stock plant (see Chapter 8).

Media

Plant material will only grow *in vitro* when provided with specialised media. A medium usually consists of a solution of salts supplying the major and minor elements necessary for the growth of whole plants, together with:

- various vitamins (optional):

- various amino acids (optional); and

- a carbon and energy source (usually sucrose).

The many alternative formulations are discussed and extensively listed in Chapters 9 and 10. Growth and development of plant cultures usually also depends on the addition of plant growth regulants to the medium. *Plant growth regulators* are compounds which, at very low concentration, are capable of modifying growth or plant morphogenesis. Many workers define a medium as a completed mixture of nutrients and growth regulators. This is a rather inflexible method, as regulants frequently need to be altered according to the variety of plant, or at different stages of culture, whilst the basic medium can stay unchanged. It is therefore recommended that nutritional and regulatory components should be listed separately. In these books, the growth regulator requirements of tissue cultures are described in Chapters 11 (this book), and Chapter 12 (in Part 2).

Plant material can be cultured either in a liquid medium or on a medium which has been partially solidified with a gelling agent. The method employed will depend on the type of culture and its objective.

Solidified media

Media which have had a gelling agent added to them, so that they have become semi-solid, are widely used for explant establishment; they are also employed for much routine culture of callus or plant organs (including micropropagation), and for the long-term maintenance of cultures. Agar is the most common solidifying agent, but a gellan gum is also widely used (Chapter 9).

Cultures grown on solid media are kept static. They require only simple containers of glass or plastic which occupy little space. Only the lower surface of the explant, organ or tissue is in contact with the medium. This means that as growth proceeds there will be gradients in nutrients, growth factors and the waste products of metabolism, between the medium and the tissues. Gaseous diffusion into and out of the cells at the base of the organ or tissue may also be restricted by the surrounding medium.

Liquid media

Liquid media are essential for suspension cultures, and are preferred for critical experiments on the nutrition, growth and cell differentiation in callus tissues. They are also used in some micropropagation work. Very small organs (*e.g.* anthers) are often floated on the top of liquid medium and plant cells or protoplasts can be cultured in very shallow layers of static liquid, providing there is sufficient gaseous diffusion. Larger organs such as shoots (*e.g.* proliferating shoots of shoot cultures) can also often be grown satisfactorily in a shallow layer of non-agitated liquid where part of the organ protrudes above the surface. However some method of support is necessary for small organs or small pieces of tissue, which would otherwise sink below the surface of a static liquid medium, or they will die for lack of aeration. Systems of support which have been found to be effective and which

can be used instead of agar-solidified media are described in Chapters 9 and 14.

Many tissues and organs, small and large, also grow well unsupported in a liquid medium, providing it is shaken or moved. Some kind of agitation is essential for suspension cultures to prevent cells and cell aggregates settling to the bottom of the flask. Other purposes served by agitation include: the provision of increased aeration, the reduction of plant polarity, the uniform distribution of nutrients and the dilution of toxic explant exudates (Lim-Ho, 1982). There are several alternative techniques:

- **Stirred or shaken cultures.** Plant cell suspensions can be cultured very satisfactorily when totally immersed in a liquid culture medium, providing it is shaken (by a rotary or reciprocating shaking machine) or stirred (*e.g.* by a magnetic stirrer) to ensure adequate aeration. This method may also be used for culturing organs of some plants (*e.g.* proliferating shoot cultures), but the fragmentation which occurs can be disadvantageous.

- **Rotated tubes.** Periodic immersion may be achieved by growing cultured material in tubes or flasks of liquid medium which are rotated slowly. Steward and Shantz (1956) devised so-called 'nipple flasks' for this purpose which had several side-arms. They were fixed to a wooden wheel which was rotated so that tissue in the arms of each flask was alternately bathed in medium and drained or exposed to the air (Fig. 2). This technique ensured that callus tissue for which they were used waswell aerated. The medium usually became turbid as cells dissociated from the callus and started a cell suspension. Flasks of this sort are seldom used to-day because of their cost. A similar alternating exposure can be achieved by placing calluses in vessels which are rotated slowly.

- **Air circulation**. Liquid medium in flasks or column bio-reactors (fermentors) can be circulated and at the same time aerated, by the introduction of sterile air. Shearing forces within air-lift reactors are much less than in mechanically-stirred vessels so that plant cell suspensions suffer less damage.

- **Drip feed.** Rather than immersing callus or organ cultures, liquid medium may be slowly dripped onto the growing tissues and afterwards drained or pumped away for recirculation. A particular advantage of this technique is the ability to grow cultures in a constant and non-depleted medium;

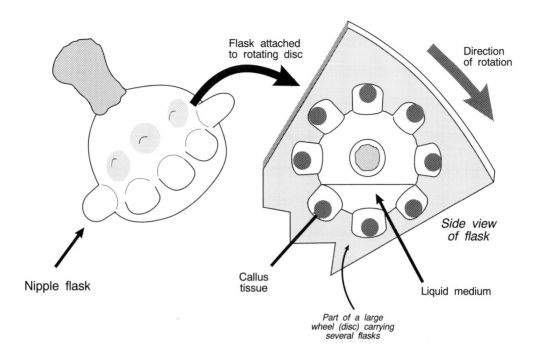

Fig. 2. A nipple flask for growing callus in a liquid medium.

nutrients can be varied frequently and rapidly and their availability controlled by altering either concentration or flow rate. Toxic metabolites, which in a closed container might accumulate and inhibit growth, can be removed continuously. As complicated apparatus is needed, the method has not been widely used.

Experimental systems. Various other ways of growing plants in or on liquid media have been devised. They include growing plant material in a mist of liquid medium (Weathers and Giles, 1987) and growing shoots and plantlets on a layer of agar supported above a liquid medium (Vermeer and Evers, 1987b). These techniques have not yet been widely adopted. The relative merits of solid and liquid media (and combinations of both) are discussed further in Chapter 7.

Problems of establishment

Phenolic oxidation

Some kinds of plants, particularly tropical species, contain high concentrations of phenolic substances which are oxidised when cells are wounded or senescent. Isolated tissue then becomes brown or black and fails to grow. The prevention of blackening, which can be a serious problem in tissue culture, is discussed in detail in Chapter 13.

Minimum inoculation density

Certain essential substances can pass out of plant cells by diffusion. Substances known to be released into the medium by this means include alkaloids, amino acids, enzymes, growth substances and vitamins (Street, 1969). The loss is of no consequence when there is a large cluster of cells growing in close proximity or where the ratio of plant material to medium is high. However when cells are inoculated onto an ordinary growth medium at a low population density, the concentration of essential substances in the cells and in the medium can become inadequate for the survival of the culture. This means that there is a minimum size of explant or quantity of separated cells or protoplasts per unit culture volume, for successful culture initiation. Inoculation density also affects the initial rate of growth *in vitro*. Large explants generally survive more frequently and grow more rapidly at the outset than very small ones. In practice minimum inoculation density varies according to the strain of plant being cultured and the cultural conditions. For commencing

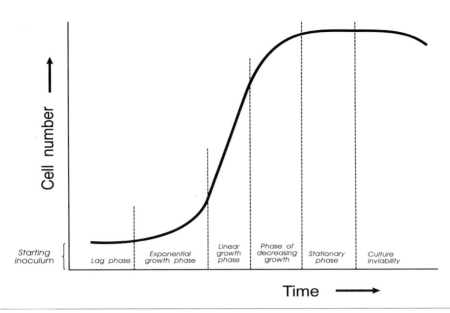

Fig. 3.   Diagram showing the phases of growth in batch suspension cultures.

suspension cultures it is commonly about $1–1.5 \times 10^4$ cells/ml.

The minimum cell density phenomenon is sometimes called a 'feeder effect' because deficiencies can often be made up by the presence of other cells growing nearby. Suspension cultures can be started from a low density of inoculum by 'conditioning' a freshly prepared medium — *i.e.* allowing products to diffuse into it from a medium in which another culture is growing actively, or adding a quantity of filter-sterilised medium which has previously supported another culture. The use of conditioned media can reduce the critical initial cell density by a factor of about 10 (Stuart and Street, 1969).

It is possible to overcome the deficiencies of plant cells at low starting densities by adding small amounts of known chemicals to a medium. For example, Kao and Michayluk (1975) have shown that *Vicia hajastana* cells or protoplasts can be cultured from very small initial inocula or even from individual cells: a standard culture medium was supplemented with growth regulators, several organic acids, additional sugars (apart from sucrose and glucose), and in particular, casein hydrolysate (casamino acids) and coconut milk.

There is often a maximum as well as a minimum plating or inoculation density for plant cells or protoplasts. In a few cases the effective range has been found to be quite narrow. With mechanically-separated cells of young sweet potato cotyledons there was no cell growth, division, or survival below or above $1.5–5.0 \times 10^5$ cells per $60\,\text{mm} \times 15\,\text{mm}$ plate (Schwenk, 1980). Some effects of inoculation density on morphogenesis are described in Chapter 8.

Patterns of growth and differentiation

A typical unorganised plant callus, initiated from a new explant or a piece of a previously-established culture, has three stages of development, namely:

- the induction of cell division;

- a period of active cell division during which differentiated cells lose any specialised features they may have acquired and become *dedifferentiated*;

- a period when cell division slows down or ceases and when, within the callus, there is increasing cellular differentiation.

These phases are similarly reproduced by cell suspensions grown in a finite volume of medium (a batch culture), where according to a variety of different parameters that can be used to measure growth (*e.g.* cell number, cell dry weight, total DNA content) an S-shaped growth curve is generally obtained (Fig. 3). There is initially:

- a *lag phase*, that is followed by,

- a period of exponential and then linear growth,

- a period when the rate of growth declines, and finally,

- a *stationary phase* when growth comes to a halt.

Some differentiation of cells may occur in cell cultures during the period of slowed and stationary growth, but it is generally less marked and less complete than that which occurs in callus cultures. Cultures cannot be maintained in stationary phase for long periods. Cells begin to die and, as their contents enter the nutrient medium, death of the whole culture accelerates. Somewhat similar patterns of growth also occur in cultures of organised structures. These also cease growth and become moribund as the components of the medium become exhausted.

Subculturing

Once a particular kind of organised or unorganised growth has been started *in vitro,* it will usually continue if callus cultures, suspension cultures, or cultures of indeterminate organs (see below) are divided to provide new explants for culture initiation on fresh medium. Subculturing often becomes imperative when the density of cells, tissue or organs becomes excessive; to increase the volume of a culture; or to increase the number of organs (*e.g.* shoots or somatic embryos) for micropropagation. The period from the initiation of a culture or a subculture to the time of its transfer is sometimes called a *passage.* The first passage is that in which the original explant or inoculum is introduced.

Suspensions regularly subcultured at the end of the period of exponential growth can often be propagated over many passages. However, many cultures reach a peak of cell aggregation at this time and aggregation often becomes progressively more pronounced in subsequent passages (Street, 1977c). Subculture is therefore more conveniently carried out during the stationary phase when cell aggregation is least pronounced. Rapid rates of plant propagation depend on the ability to subculture shoots from proliferating shoot or node cultures, from cultures giving direct shoot regeneration, or callus or suspensions capable of reliable shoot or embryo regeneration.

A further reason for transfer, or subculture, is that the growth of plant material in a closed vessel eventually leads to the accumulation of toxic metabolites and the exhaustion of the medium, or to its drying out. Thus, even to maintain the culture, all or part of it must be transferred onto fresh medium. Callus subcultures are usually initiated by moving a fragment of the initial callus (an *inoculum*) to fresh medium in another vessel. Shoot cultures are subcultured by segmenting individual shoots or shoot clusters. The interval between subcultures depends on the rate at which a culture has grown: at 25°C, subculturing is typically required every 4–6 weeks. In the early stages of callus growth it may be convenient to transfer the whole piece of tissue to fresh medium, but a more established culture will need to be divided and only small selected portions used as inocula. Regrowth depends on the transfer of healthy tissues.

Decontamination procedures are theoretically no longer necessary during subculturing, although sterile transfer procedures must still be used. However, when using shoot or node cultures for micropropagation, some laboratories do re- sterilise plant material at this stage as a precaution against the spread of contaminants (see Chapter 5). Cultures which are obviously infected with micro-organisms should not normally be for subculturing and are best destroyed.

Subculturing hazards

There are several hazards in subculturing which are discussed more fully in other chapters of this book. Several kinds of callus may arise from the initial explant, each with different morphogenic potential. Strains of callus tissue capable of giving rise to somatic embryos and others without this capability can, for instance, arise simultaneously from the culture of grass and cereal seed embryos. Careful selection of the correct strain is therefore necessary if cultures capable of producing somatic embryos are ultimately required. Timing of the transfer may also be important, because if left alone for some while, non-embryogenetic callus may grow from the original explant at the expense of the competent tissue, which will then be obscured or lost.

Although subculturing can often be continued over many months without adverse effects becoming apparent, cultures of most unorganised cells and of some organised structures can accumulate cells that are genetically changed. This may cause the characteristics of the culture to be altered and may mean that some of the plants regenerated from the culture will not be the same as the parent plant. This subject is discussed in detail in Chapter 3. Cultures may also inexplicably decline in vigour after a number of passages, so that further subculture becomes impossible.

TYPES OF TISSUE CULTURE

ORGAN CULTURES

Differentiated plant organs can usually be grown in culture without loss of integrity. They can be of two types:

- *Determinate organs* which are destined to have only a defined size and shape (*e.g.* leaves, flowers and fruits), and

- *Indeterminate organs*, where growth is potentially unlimited (apical meristems of roots and non-flowering shoots).

In the past, it has been thought that the meristematic cells within root or shoot apices were not committed to a particular kind of development. It is now accepted that, like the primordia of determinate organs such as leaves, apical meristems also become inherently programmed (or determined) into either root or shoot pathways (Wareing, 1979). The eventual pattern of development of both indeterminate and determinate organs is often established at a very early stage. For example, the meristematic protrusions in a shoot apex become programmed to develop as either lateral buds or leaves after only a few cell divisions have taken place (see Chapter 8).

Culture of determinate organs

An organ arises from a group of meristematic cells. In an indeterminate organ, such cells are theoretically able to continue in the same pattern of growth indefinitely . The situation is different in the primordium of a determinate organ. Here, as meristematic cells receive instructions on how to differentiate, their capacity for further division becomes limited.

If the primordium of a determinate organ is excised and transferred to culture, it will sometimes continue to grow to maturity. The organ obtained *in vitro* may be smaller than that which would have developed on the original plant *in vivo*, but otherwise is likely to be normal. The growth of determinate organs cannot be extended by subculture: growth ceases when they have reached their maximum size.

Organs of limited growth potential which have been cultured, include leaves (Caponetti and Steeves, 1963; Caponetti, 1972b); fruits (Nitsch, 1951, 1963; Street, 1969); stamens (Rastogi and Sawhney, 1988a); ovaries and ovules (which develop and grow into embryos) and flower buds of several dicotyledonous plant species (Table 1).

Until recently, a completely normal development was obtained in only a few cases. This was probably due to the use of media of sub-optimum composition. By experimenting with media consitituents, Berghoef and Bruinsma (1979a) obtained normal growth of *Begonia franconis* buds and were thus able to study the effect of plant growth substances and nutritional factors on flower development and sexual expression (Berghoef and Bruinsma, 1979b). Similarly, by culturing dormant buds of *Salix,* Angrish and Nanda (1982a,b) could study the effect of bud position and the progressive influence of a resting period on the determination of meristems to become catkins and fertile flowers. In several species, flowers have been pollinated *in vitro* and have then given rise to mature fruits (*e.g.* Ruddat *et al.*, 1979).

Reversal of determination. Plants cannot be propagated by culturing meristems already committed to produce determinate organs, but providing development has not proceded too far, flower meristems can often be induced to revert to vegetative meristems *in vitro*. In some plants the production of vegetative shoots from the flower meristems on a large inflorescence can provide a convenient method of micropropagation (see Chapter 2).

Table 1. Some species in which flower buds have been cultured.

Cucumis sativus	Galun *et al.* (1962)
Viscaria spp.	Blake (1966, 1969)
Nicotiana tabacum	Hicks and Sussex (1970)
Aquilegia formosa	Bilderback (1971, 1972)
Cleome iberidella	De Jong and Bruinsma (1974)
Nicotiana offinis	Deaton et al. (1980)

Culture of indeterminate organs

Meristem and shoot culture

The growing points of shoots can be cultured in such a way that they continue uninterrupted and organised growth. As these shoot initials ultimately give rise to small organised shoots which can then be rooted, their culture has great practical significance for plant propagation. Two important uses have emerged:

— Culture of the extreme tip of the shoot is called *meristem culture:* it is used as a technique to free plants from virus infections. Explants are dissected from either apical or lateral buds. They comprise a very small stem apex (0.2–1.0 mm in length) consisting of just the apical meristem and one or two leaf primordia.

— Culture of larger stem apices or lateral buds (ranging from 5 or 10 mm in length to undissected buds) is used as a very successful method of propagating plants. The terms 'shoot culture' or 'shoot tip culture' have been used for this technique (page 44).

The size and relative positions of the two kinds of explant in a shoot apex of a typical dicotyledon is shown in Fig. 4. Node culture is an adaptation of shoot culture.

If successful, meristem culture, shoot culture and node culture can ultimately result in the growth of small shoots. With appropriate treatments, these original shoots can either be rooted to produce small plants or 'plantlets', or their axillary buds can be induced to grow to form a cluster of shoots. Plants are propagated by dividing and reculturing the shoot clusters, or by growing individual shoots for subdivision. At a chosen stage, individual shoots or shoot clusters are rooted. Tissue cultured shoots are removed from aseptic conditions at or just before the rooting stage, and rooted plantlets are hardened off and grown normally. Shoot culture and node culture are discussed in greater detail in Chapter 2 and meristem tip culture is described in Chapters 2 and 5.

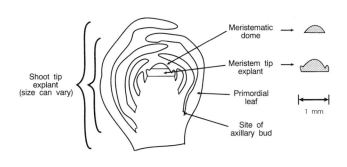

Fig. 4. A diagramatic section through a bud showing the locations and approximate relative sizes of meristematic dome, meristem tip and shoot tip explants.

Embryo culture

Objectives. Zygotic or seed embryos are often used advantageously as explants in plant tissue culture, for example, to initiate callus cultures. In embryo culture however, embryos are dissected from seeds, individually isolated and 'germinated' *in vitro* to provide one plant per explant. Isolated embryo culture can assist in the rapid production of seedlings from seeds that have a protracted dormancy period, and it enables seedlings to be produced when the genotype (*e.g.* that resulting from some interspecific crosses) conveys a low embryo or seed viabililty.

Practical uses. During the course of evolution, natural incompatibility systems have developed which limit the types of possible sexual crosses (see De Nettancourt and Devreux, 1977). Two kinds of infertility occur:

— Pre-zygotic incompatibility, preventing pollen germination and/or pollen tube growth so that a zygote is never formed;

— Post-zygotic incompatibility, in which a zygote is produced but not accepted by the endosperm. The embryo, not receiving sufficient nutrition, disintegrates or aborts.

Pre-zygotic incompatibility can sometimes be overcome in the laboratory using a technique developed by Kanta *et al.* (1962) called *in vitro* pollination (or *in vitro* fertilisation). For a description of this technique see review articles by Ranga Swamy (1977), Zenkteler (1980) and Yeung *et al.* (1981). Reviews of embryo culture have been provided by Torrey (1973), Norstog (1979) and Raghavan (1967, 1977a, 1980, 1986).

Embryo culture has been used successfully in a large number of plant genera to overcome post-zygotic incompatibility which otherwise hampers the production of desirable hybrid seedlings. For example, in trying to transfer insect resistance from a wild *Solanum* species into the aubergine, Sharma *et al.*(1980a) obtained a few hybrid plants (*Solanum melongena* × *S.khasianum*) by embryo culture. Embryo culture in these circumstances is more aptly termed *embryo rescue*. Success rates are usually quite low and the new hybrids, particularly if they arise from remote crosses, are sometimes sterile. However, this does not matter if the plants can afterwards be propagated asexually. Hybrids between incompatible varieties of tree and soft fruits (Tukey, 1934; Skirm, 1942) and *Iris* (in Reuther, 1977) have been obtained by culturing fairly mature embryos.

Techniques. Fruits or seeds are surface sterilised before embryo removal. Providing aseptic techniques are strictly adhered to during excision and transfer to a culture medium, the embryo itself needs no further sterilisation. To ease the dissection of the embryo, hard seeds are soaked in water to soften them, but if softening takes more than a few hours it is advisable to re-sterilise the seed afterwards. A dissecting microscope may be necessary to excise the embryos from small seeds as it is particularly important that the embryo should not be damaged.

Culture of immature embryos (pro-embryos) a few days after pollination frequently results in a greater proportion of seedlings being obtained than if more mature embryos are used as explants, because incompatibility mechanisms have less time to take effect. Unfortunately dissection of very small embryos requires much skill and cannot be done rapidly: it also frequently results in damage which prevents growth *in vitro*. In soybean, Hu and Sussex (1986) obtained the best *in vitro* growth of immature embryos if they were isolated with their suspensors intact. Excised embryos usually develop into seedlings precociously (*i.e.* before they have reached the size they would have attained in a normal seed — see Chapter 14).

As an alternative to embryo culture, in some plants it has been possible to excise and culture pollinated ovaries and immature ovules. Ovule culture, sometimes called 'in ovulo embryo culture', can be more successful than the culture of young embryos. Pro-embryos generally require a complex medium for growth, but embryos contained within the ovule require less complicated media. They are also easily removed from the plant and relatively insensitive to the physical conditions of culture (Thengane *et al.*, 1986). The difference between embryo and ovule culture is shown diagramatically in Fig. 5.

Because seedlings which resulted from ovule culture of a *Nicotiana* interspecific cross all died after they had developed some true leaves, Iwai *et al.* (1985) used leaves of the immature seedlings as explants for the initiation of callus cultures. Most shoots regenerated from the callus also died at an early stage, but one gave rise to a plant which was discovered later to be a sterile hybrid. Plants were also regenerated from callus of a *Pelargonium* hybrid by Kato and Tokumasu (1983). The callus in this case arose directly from globular or heart-shaped zygotic embryos which were not able to grow into seedlings.

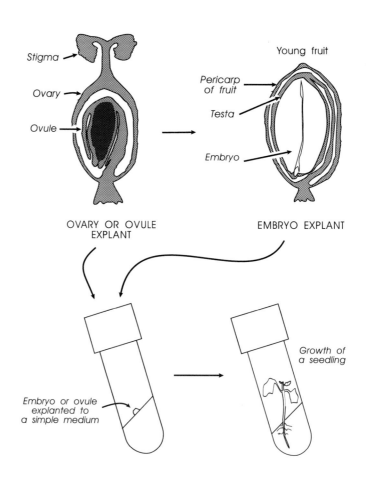

Fig. 5.   Ovule and embryo culture.

The seeds of orchids do not have functional storage organs, nor a true seed coat so dissection of the embryo would not be possible. In fact, for commercial purposes, orchid seeds are now almost always germinated *in vitro*, and growth is often facilitated by taking immature seeds from green pods (see under Orchids, Chapter 17).

Many media have been especially developed for embryo culture and some were the forerunners of the media now used for general tissue culture. In general, mature embryos require only inorganic salts supplemented with sucrose, whereas immature embryos have an additional requirement for vitamins, amino acids, growth regulators and sometimes coconut milk or some other endosperm extract. Raghavan (1977b) encouraged the incorporation of mannitol to replace the high osmotic pressure exerted on proembryos by ovular sap. Seedlings obtained from embryos grown *in vitro* are planted out and hardened off in the same manner as other plantlets raised by tissue culture (Chapter 14).

Although embryo culture is especially useful for plant breeders, it does not lead to the rapid and large scale rates of propagation characteristic of other micropropagation techniques, and so it is not considered further in this book. More details can be found in papers by: Sanders and Ziebur (1958); Raghavan (1967, 1980, 1986); Torrey (1973); Zilis and Meyer (1976); Collins and Grosser (1984), Monnier (1990) and Ramming (1990). Yeung *et al.* (1981) have suggested a basic protocol which, with modifications, should be applicable to any species.

The induction of multiple shoots from seeds is described in Chapter 2.

Isolated root culture

Root cultures can be established from root tips taken from primary or lateral roots of many plants. Suitable explants are small sections of roots bearing a primary or lateral root meristem. These explants may be obtained, for example, from surface sterilised seeds germinated in aseptic conditions. If the small root meristems continue normal growth on a suitable medium, they produce a root system consisting only of primary and lateral roots (Fig 6). No organised shoot buds will be formed.

The discovery that roots could be grown apart from shoot tissue was one of the first significant developments of modern tissue culture science. Root culture initially attracted a great deal of attention from research workers and the roots of many different species of plants were cultured successfully (see the comprehensive reviews of Street, 1954, 1957, 1969; and Butcher and Street, 1964).

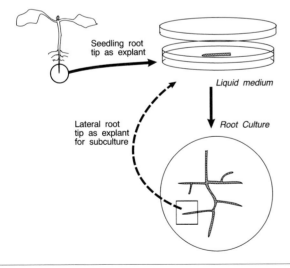

Fig. 6. Methods of root culture.

Plants fall generally into three categories with regard to the ease with which their roots can be cultured. There are some species such as clover, *Datura*, tomato and *Citrus*, where isolated roots can be grown for long periods of time, some seemingly, indefinitely (Said and Murashige, 1979) providing regular subcultures are made. In many woody species, roots have not been grown at all successfully in isolated cultures. In other species such as pea, flax and wheat, roots can be cultured for long periods but ultimately growth declines or insufficient lateral roots are produced to provide explants for subculture.

The inability to maintain isolated root cultures is due to an induced meristematic dormancy or 'senescence', related to the length of time that the roots have be growing *in vitro*. Transferring dormant meristems to fresh medium does not promote regrowth, possibly due to the accumulation of naturally-occuring auxinic growth substances at the root apex. The addition of so-called anti-auxin, or cytokinin growth regulators (see Chapter 11) can often prolong active growth of root cultures, whereas placing auxins or gibberellic acid in the growth medium, causes it to cease more rapidly. Cultures which cannot be maintained by transferring root apices, can sometimes be continued if newly-initiated lateral root meristems are used as secondary explants instead (Fig. 6).

Isolated plant roots can usually be cultured on relatively simple media such as **White (1954)** containing 2% sucrose (see Chapter 10). Liquid media are preferable, as growth in or on a solid medium is slower. This is presumably because salts are less readily available to the roots from a solidified medium and oxygen availability may be restricted. Although roots will accept a mixed nitrate/ammonium source, they will not usually grow on ammonium nitrogen alone. Species, and even varieties or strains, of plants, are found to differ their requirement for growth regulators, particularly for auxins, in the root culture medium.

Use in botanical research. Isolated root cultures have been employed for a number of different research purposes. They have been particularly valuable in the study of nematode infections and provide a method by which these parasites can be cultured in aseptic conditions. Root cultures may also be used to grow beneficial mycorrhizal fungi, and to study the process of root nodulation with nitrogen-fixing *Rhizobium* bacteria in leguminous plants. For the latter purpose, various special adaptations of standard techniques have been adopted to allow roots to become established in a nitrate-free medium (Raggio *et al.*, 1957; Torrey, 1963).

Use in micropropagation. Unlike some other cultured tissues, root cultures exhibit a high degree of genetic stability (see Chapter 3). It has therefore been suggested that root cultures could afford one means of storing the germplasm of certain species (see Chapter 6). For suitable species, root cultures can provide a convenient source of explant material for the micropropagation of plants, but they will only be useful in micropropagation if shoots can be regenerated from roots. There are however several ways in which this can be done, although they are likely to be effective in only a small number of plant genera which have a natural tendency to produce suckers, or new shoots from whole or severed roots:

1. **From direct adventitious shoots**. Adventitious shoots form readily on the severed roots of some plant species, and root cuttings are employed by horticulturalists to increase plants *in vivo* (see, for example, the review by Hodge, 1986). Shoot regeneration from roots has not been widely used as a method of micropropagation, even though direct shoot regeneration from roots has been observed *in vitro* on many plants. Sections of fleshy roots used as primary explants are especially likely to form new shoots. Adventitious shoots always develop at the proximal end of a root section while, as a rule, new roots are produced from the distal end.

   Isolated root cultures would be useful in micropropagation if shoots could be induced to form directly upon them. Unfortunately plants seem to have a high degree of genetic specificity in their capacity to produce shoots directly on isolated root cultures. Shoot induction often occurs after the addition of a cytokinin to the medium. Seeliger (1956) obtained shoot buds on cultured roots of *Robinia pseudoacacia* and Torrey (1958b), shoot buds on root cultures of *Convolvulus*. Direct shoot formation was induced in three species of *Nicotiana* and on *Solanum melongena* by Zelcer *et al.* (1983) but in *N. tabacum* and *N. petunoides* shoots were only obtained after callus formed on the roots. The most optimistic report we have seen comes fom Mudge *et al.* (1986), who thought that the shoot formation which they could induce in raspberry root cultures would provide a convenient and labour- saving method of multiplying this plant *in vitro*.

2. **From shoots or embryos originating indirectly on root callus**. Plants may also be regenerated from root-derived callus of some species *e.g.* tomato (Norton and Boll, 1954), *Isatis tinctoria* (Danckwardt-Lilliestrom, 1957); *Atropa belladonna* (Thomas and Street, 1972). Embryogenesis, leading to the formation of protocorm-like bodies, occurs in the callus derived from the root tips of certain orchids *e.g.* *Catasetum trulla* × *Catasetum* (Kerbauy, 1984a); *Epidendrum obrienianum* (Stewart and Button, 1978); *Oncidium varicosum* (Kerbauy, 1984b).

3. **By conversion of the apical root meristem to a shoot meristem**. Changing the determined nature of a root meristem, so that it is induced to produce a shoot instead of a root, is a very rare event but has been noted to occur *in vitro* in the orchid *Vanilla planifolia*. The quiescent centre of cultured root tip meristems was changed into a shoot meristem so that cultured root tips grew to produce plantlets or multiple shoots (Philip and Nainar, 1986, 1988). Ballade (1971) maintained that newly initiated root initials, arising from single nodes of *Nasturtium officinale*, could be made to develop into shoot meristems by placing a crystal of kinetin on each explant which was then transferred to a medium containing 0.05% glucose.

CULTURE OF UNORGANISED CELLS

Callus cultures

Callus is a coherent and amorphous tissue, formed when plant cells multiply in a disorganised way. It is often induced in or upon parts of an intact plant by wounding, by the presence of insects or micro-organisms, or as a result of stress. Callus can be initiated *in vitro* by placing small pieces of the whole plant (explants) onto a growth-supporting medium under sterile conditions. Under the stimulus of endogenous growth substances or growth regulating chemicals added to the medium, the metabolism of cells, which were in a quiescent state, is changed, and they begin active division. During this process, cell differentiation and specialisation, which may have been occurring in the intact plant, are reversed, and the explant gives rise to new tissue which is composed of meristematic and unspecialised cell types.

During dedifferentiation, storage products typically found in resting cells tend to disappear. New meristems are formed in the tissue and these give rise to undifferentiated parenchymatous cells without any of the structural order that was characteristic of the organ or tissue from which they were derived. Although callus remains unorganised, as growth proceeds, some kinds of specialised cells may be again formed. Such differentiation can appear to take place at random, but may be associated with centres of morphogenesis which can give rise to organs such as roots, shoots and embryos. The *de novo* production of plants from unorganised cultures is often referred to as plant *regeneration*.

Although most experiments have been conducted with the tissues of higher plants, callus cultures can be established from gymnosperms, ferns, mosses and thallophytes. Many parts of a whole plant may have an ultimate potential to proliferate *in vitro*, but it is frequently found that callus cultures are more easily established from some organs than others. Young meristematic tissues are most suitable, but meristematic areas in older parts of a plant, such as the cambium, can give rise to callus. The choice of tissues from which cultures can be started is greatest in dicotyledonous species. A difference in the capacity of tissue to give rise to callus is particularly apparent in monocotyledons. In most cereals, for example, callus growth can only be obtained from organs such as zygotic embryos, germinating seeds, seed endosperm or the seed-ling mesocotyl, and very young leaves or leaf sheaths, but so far never from mature leaf tissue (*e.g.* Green and Phillips, 1975; Dunstan *et al.*, 1978). In sugar cane, callus cultures can only be started from young leaves or leaf

bases, not from semi-mature or mature leaf blades (Fig. 7).

Even closely associated tissues within one organ may have different potentials for callus origination. Thus when embryos of *Hordeum distichum* at an early stage of differentiation are removed from developing seeds and placed in culture, callus proliferation originates from meristematic mesocotyl cells rather than from the closely adjacent cells of the scutellum and coleorhiza (Granatek and Cockerline (1979).

The callus formed on an original explant is called 'primary callus'. Secondary callus cultures are initiated from pieces of tissue dissected from primary callus (Fig. 8). Subculture can then often be continued over many years, but the longer callus is maintained, the greater is the risk

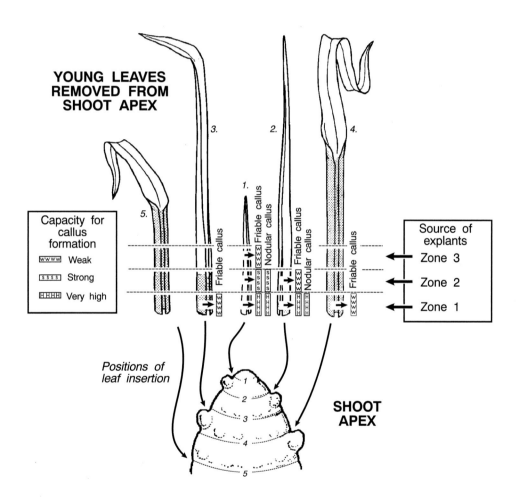

Fig. 7. The competence of young leaves of sugar cane to form callus of differing morphogenic capacity.
The bases of leaves taken from a shoot apex can form friable (practically non-morphogenic) callus or nodular (embryogenic) callus, depending on developmental stage. Embryogenic callus is only obtainable fom the bases of leaves 1 and 2. [From Guiderdoni and Demarly, 1988].

that the cells thereof will suffer genetic change (see Chapter 3).

Variability. Callus tissue is not of one single kind. Strains of callus differing in appearance, colour, degree of compaction and morphogenetic potential commonly arise from a single explant. Sometimes the type of callus obtained, its degree of cellular differentiation and its capacity to regenerate new plants, depend upon the origin and age of the tissue chosen as an explant. Loosely packed or 'friable' callus is usually selected for initiating suspension cultures (see below).

Some of the differences between one strain of callus tissue and another can depend on which part of the total package of genetic information is functioning within the cells (*epigenetic* differences). Variability is more likely when callus is derived from an explant composed of more than one kind of cell. For this reason there is often merit in selecting small explants from only morphologically uniform tissue, bearing in mind that a minimum size of explant is normally required to obtain callus formation.

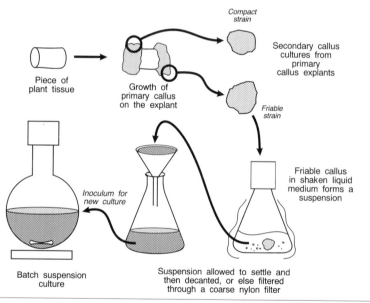

Fig. 8.   Typical steps in the initiation of callus and suspension cultures.

The genetic make up of cells is very commonly altered in unorganised callus and suspension cultures. Therefore another reason for cell strains having different characteristics, is that they have become composed of populations of cells with slightly different genotypes.

Genetic and epigenetic changes occurring in cultures are described in greater detail in Chapters 3 and 8. The growth, structure, organisation and cytology of callus is discussed in various chapters of the book edited by Street

(1977a), and also in the review by Yeoman and Forche (1980).

Suspension (cell) cultures

Unorganised plant cells can be grown as callus in aggregated tissue masses, or they can be freely dispersed in agitated liquid media. Techniques are similar to those used for the large scale culture of bacteria. Cell or suspension cultures, as they are called, are usually started by placing an inoculum of friable callus in a liquid medium (Fig. 8). Under agitation, single cells break off and, by division, form cell chains and clumps which fracture again to give individual cells and other small cell groups. It is not always necessary to have a previous callus phase before initiating suspension cultures. For example, leaf sections of *Chenopodium rubrum* floated on **Murashige and Skoog (1962)** medium in the light, show rapid growth and cell division in the mesophyll, and after 4 days on a rotary shaker they can be disintegrated completely to release a great number of cells into suspension (Geile and Wagner, 1980).

Because the walls of plant cells have a natural tendency to adhere together, it is not possible to obtain suspensions which consist only of dispersed single cells. Some progress has been made in selecting cell lines with increased cell separation, but cultures of completely isolated cells have yet to be obtained. The proportion and size of small cell aggregates varies according to plant variety and the medium in which the culture is grown. As cells tend to divide more frequently in aggregates than in isolation, the size of cell clusters increases during the phase of rapid cell division. Because agitation causes single cells, and small groups of cells, to be detached, the size of cell clusters decreases in batch cultures as they approach a stationary growth phase (see below).

The degree of cell dispersion in suspension cultures is particularly susceptible to the concentration of growth regulators in the culture medium. Auxin growth regulants increase the specific activity of enzymes which bring about the dissolution of the middle lamella of plant cell walls (Torrey and Reinert, 1961). Thus by using a relatively high concentration of an auxin and a low concentration of a cytokinin growth regulator in the culture medium, it is usually possible to increase cell dispersion (Narayanaswamy, 1977). However the use of high auxin levels to obtain maximum cell dispersion will ensure that the cultured cells remain undifferentiated. This may be a disadvantage if a suspension is being used to produce

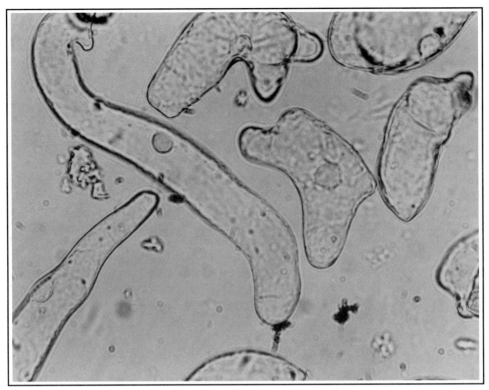

Fig. 9. Cells from a suspension culture of wheat (× 400).

secondary metabolites. Well dispersed suspension cultures consist of thin-walled undifferentiated cells (Fig. 9), but these are never uniform in size and shape. Cells with more differentiated structure, possessing, for example, thicker walls and even tracheid-like elements, usually only occur in large cell aggregates.

The growth of plant cells is more rapid in suspension than in callus cultures and is also more readily controlled because the culture medium can be easily ammended or changed. Organs can be induced to develop in cell suspensions: root and shoot initiation usually commences in cell aggregates. Somatic embryos may arise from single cells. Cells from suspensions can also be plated onto solid media where single cells and/or cell aggregates grow into callus colonies from which plants can often be regenerated.

Many different methods of suspension culture have been developed. They fall into two main types: *batch cultures* in which cells are nurtured in a fixed volume of medium until growth ceases, and *continuous cultures* in which cell growth is maintained by continuous replenishment of sterile nutrient media. All techniques utilise some method of agitating the culture medium to ensure necessary cell dispersion and an adequate gas exchange.

Batch cultures. Batch cultures are initiated by inoculating cells into a fixed volume of nutrient medium. As growth proceeds, the amount of cell material increases until nutrients in the medium are depleted or there is the accumulation of an inhibitory metabolite. Batch cultures have a number of disadvantages that restrict their suitability for extended studies of growth and metabolism, or for the industrial production of plant cells, but they are nevertheless widely used for many laboratory investigations. Small cultures are frequently agitated on orbital shakers onto which are fixed suitable containers, which range in volume from 100 ml (Erlenmeyer conical flasks) to 1000 ml (spherical flasks); the quantity of medium being approximately ⅕ of the flask volume. The shakers are usually operated at speeds from 30–180 r.p.m with an orbital motion of about 3 cm. Alternatively, stirred systems can be used.

Continuous cultures. Using batch cultures, it is difficult to obtain a steady rate of production of new cells having constant size and composition. Attempts to do so necessitate frequent sub-culturing, at intervals equivalent to the doubling time of the cell population. Satisfactorily balanced growth can only be produced in *continuous* culture, a method which is especially important when plant cells are to be used for the large scale production of a primary or secondary metabolite. Continuous culture techniques require fairly complicated apparatus. Agitation of larger cultures in bio-reactors is usually achieved by stirring with a turbine and/or by passing sterile air (or a controlled gaseous mixture) into the culture from below and releasing it through plugged vents. Mechanically-stirred reactors damage plant cells by shearing. This is minimized in air-lift reactors.

The use of suspension cultures in plant propagation. The growth of plant cells is more rapid in suspension than in callus culture and is also more readily controlled because the culture medium can be easily ammended or changed. For these reasons suspension cultures might be expected to provide a means of very rapid plant multiplication. There are two methods:

- plants may be obtained from somatic embryos formed in suspensions. Once embryos have been produced, they are normally grown into plantlets on solid media, although other methods are potentially available (Chapter 2);

- cells from suspensions are plated onto solid media where single cells and/or cell aggregates grow into callus colonies from which plants can often be regenerated.

In practice neither of these techniques has been sufficiently reliable for use in plant propagation.

Immobilised cell cultures

Plant cells can be captured and immoblised by being cultured in a gel which is afterwards solidified (see page 343). This technique has only limited application to plant micropropagation, but is now employed quite widely when plant cells are grown for the production of their secondary products or for the bio-transformation of chemical compounds (Lindsey and Yeoman, 1983).

CULTURES OF SINGLE CELL ORIGIN

Single cell clones

Cultures can be initiated from single plant cells, but only when special techniques are employed. Frequently these comprise passing suspension-cultured cells through a filter which removes coarse cell aggregates and allows only single cells and very small cell clusters to pass through. Small groups of cells are then assumed to have originated from single cells. The suspension obtained is usually plated onto (or incorporated into) a solidified medium in Petri dishes at a sufficient density to permit cell growth (see below), but with the cells sufficiently

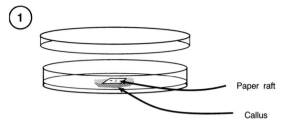

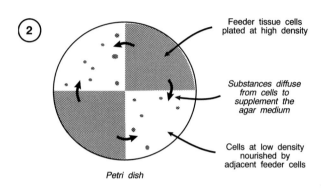

Fig. 10. Two methods of assisting the growth of cells plated at low density.

dispersed so that, when growth commences, individual callus colonies can be recognised under a binocular microscope and transferred separately to fresh medium. Cell lines originating from single cells in this way are sometimes called *single cell clones* or *cell strains*. The derivation of single cell clones was reviewed by Street (1977d).

Each cell clone has a *minimum effective initial cell density* or *minimum inoculation density*) below which it cannot be cultured. The minimum density varies according to the medium and growth regulators in which the cells are placed; it is frequently about 10–15 cells/ml on standard media. Widely dispersed cells or protoplasts will not grow because they lose essential growth factors into the surrounding medium. The minimum inoculation density can therefore be lowered by adding to a standard medium either a filtered extract of a medium in which a culture has been previously grown (the medium is then said to be *conditioned*), or special organic additives (when it is said to be *supplemented*).

Cells or protoplasts (see below) plated at a density which is insufficient for spontaneous cell division may also be nurtured into initial growth by being 'nursed' by tissue growing nearby. One way of doing this is to place an inoculum onto a filter paper disc (a *raft*) or some other inert porous material, which is then put in contact with an established callus culture of a similar species of plant, the cells of which are called *nurse cells*, and the tissue a *feeder layer*. An alternative technique is to divide a Petri dish into compartments (Fig. 10). Nurse tissues cultured in some segments assist the growth of cells or protoplasts plated in the other areas.

Another method of producing cell colonies which are very likely to have had a single cell origin has been described by Bellincampi *et al.* (1985). A filtered cell suspension with a high proportion of single cells, is cultured at high density in a medium which contains only 0.2% agar. At this concentration the agar does not solidify the medium, but keeps apart the cell colonies growing from individual cells, preventing them from aggregating. When clusters of approximately 10–15 cells have been formed, they can be plated at a dilution of 50 (20% plating efficincy) to 200 plating units/ml (60% plating efficiency) on a medium gelled with 1% agar where they grow as separate callus colonies. *Plating efficiency* is the percentage of plating units (cell aggregates in this case) which give rise to callus colonies.

Selection of cell lines. The establishment of single cell clones is one way to separate genetically different cell lines from a mixed cell population. By artificially increasing the genetic variation between cells in a culture, and then applying a specific selection pressure, resistant cell lines have been obtained (*e.g.* those resistant to certain drugs, herbicides or high levels of salt), and in some instances plants with similar resistances have then been regenerated from the resulting cells or callus.

Separated cells

Single cells can be separated directly from intact plants. They are often more easily isolated, and less liable to damage, than protoplasts, because the cell wall remains intact. Consequently single cells can be used in robust operations, such as direct physiological studies. It has been said that, for this purpose, they are more representative of differentiated tissues than cells derived from tissue cultures (Miksch and Beiderbeck, 1976); but the disruption caused by separation may induce atypical responses.

Mechanical separation. In some plant species, intact cells of certain organs can be separated by disrupting the tissue mechanically. Viable mesophyll cells, for example, can be obtained easily from *Asparagus cladodes* (Colman *et al.*, 1979) and from leaves of *Macleaya cordata* (Kohlenbach; 1966, 1967). These cells can be grown either in suspension or solid culture and induced into morphogenesis, including somatic embryo formation (Kohlenbach, 1977). Schwenk (1980, 1981) simply placed pieces of the young cotyledons of sweet potato in water inside an abrasive tube in which a vortex was created. After removing debris, a cell suspension could be obtained from which cells grew and formed callus when plated on nutrient agar.

The capacity to isolate separated cells directly from higher plants appears to be limited (Jullien and Rossini, 1977). The type of tissue used seems to be important both to permit cell separation and to obtain subsequent growth. Cells separated from the leaves, instead of from the cotyledons, of sweet potato (above) had no capacity for growth, and it was not possible to even separate cells by mechanical means from several other plants.

Enzymatic separation. Cell separation can be assisted by treating the tissue with enzyme preparations such as crude pectinase or polygalacturonase which loosen the attachment between individual cells in a tissue. Zaitlin first used this technique in 1959 to separate viable cells from tobacco leaves. Methods of isolation have been described by Takebe *et al.* (1968); Servaites and Ogren (1977) and Dow and Callow (1979). Cells isolated in this way can be suspended in culture medium and remain metabolically active.

Separated cells from leaf tissue of tobacco pre-infected with Tobacco Mosaic Virus have been used to study the formation of viral RNA's in the infected cells, and for studies on the interaction between leaf tissue cells and elicitor chemicals produced by fungal pathogens (Dow and Callow, 1979). Button and Botha (1975) produced a suspension of single cells of *Citrus* by macerating callus with 2–3% Macerase enzyme: the degree of dispersion of cells from suspension cultures can also be improved by enzyme addition (Street, 1977d).

Protoplasts

A protoplast is the living part of a plant cell, consisting of the cytoplasm and nucleus with the cell wall removed. Protoplasts can be isolated from whole plant organs or tissue cultures. If they are then placed in a suitable nutrient medium, they can be induced to re-form a cell wall and divide. A small cluster of cells eventually arises from each cell and, providing the protoplasts were originally plated at a relatively low density, can be recognised as one of many discrete 'callus colonies'. Plants can often be regenerated from such callus. Protoplast culture therefore provides one route whereby plants can be multiplied, but it is not yet used for routine micropropagation work, although the number of species in which plant regeneration has been achieved is steadily increasing.

At present isolated protoplasts are used chiefly in research into plant virus infections, and for modifying the genetic information of the cell by inserting selected DNA fragments. Protoplasts may also be fused together to create plant cell hybrids. Genetically modified cells will be only of general practical value if whole plants having the new genetic constitution can be regenerated from them. The ability to recover plants from protoplast cultures is therefore of vital importance to the success of such genetic engineering projects in plant science.

Methods of protoplast preparation

There are several different methods by which protoplasts may be isolated:

- by mechanically cutting or breaking open the cell wall,

- by digesting away the cell wall with enzymes,

- by a combination of mechanical and enzymatic separation.

For successful isolation it has been found essential to cause the protoplast to contract away from the cell wall, to which, under normal circumstances, it is tightly adpressed. Contraction is achieved by plasmolysing cells with solutions of salts such as potassium chloride and magnesium sulphate, or with sugars or sugar alcohols (particularly mannitol) (see Chapter 9). These osmotica must be of sufficient concentration to cause shrinkage of the protoplasm, but of insufficient strength to cause cellular damage.

In the past, protoplasts have been mechanically isolated from pieces of sectioned plant material, but only very small numbers were obtained intact and undamaged. This method has therefore been almost completely replaced by enzymatic isolation techniques. Commercially available preparations used for protoplast isolation are often mixtures of enzymes from a fungal or bacterial source, and have pectinase, cellulase and/or hemicellulase activity: they derive part of their effectiveness from being of mixed composition (Evans and Cocking, 1977). Protoplasts are usually isolated using a combination of several different commercial products. Plasmolysis helps to protect the protoplast when the cell wall is ruptured during mechanical separation and also appears to make the cell more resistant to the toxic effects of the enzymes used for cell wall digestion. It also severs the plasmodesmata linking adjacent cells and so prevents the amalgamation of protoplasms when the cell walls are digested away.

Tissue from an entire plant to be used for protoplast separation, is first surface sterilised. Some further preparation to allow the penetration of osmotic solutions and the cell wall degrading enzymes, is often advantageous. For instance, when protoplasts are to be separated from leaf mesophyll, the epidermis of the leaf is first peeled away and the tissue segments are then plasmolysed. The next step is to incubate the tissue with pectinase and cellulase enzymes for up to 18 hours in the same osmoticum, during which time the cell walls are degraded. Agitation of the incubated medium after this interval causes protoplasts to be released. They are washed and separated in solutions of suitable osmotic potential before being transferred to a culture medium.

Less severe and prolonged enzymatic cell digestion is required if plant tissue is first treated to mild mechanical homogenisation before cellulase treatment. Another technique calls for the sequential use of enzymes; firstly pectinase to separate the cells, and then, when separation is complete, cellulase to digest the cell walls. The yield of viable protoplasts can sometimes be increased by pre-treatment of the chosen tissue with growth substances before separation is attempted (Kirby and Cheng, 1979). Protoplasts are also commonly isolated by enzymatic treatment of organs or tissues which have been cultured *in vitro*. Cells from suspension cultures which have been subcultured frequently, and are dividing rapidly, are one suitable source.

Mother plants. The successful isolation of viable protoplasts capable of cell division and growth, can depend on the manner in which the mother plant was grown. For example, Durand (1979) found that consistently successful protoplast isolation from haploid *Nicotiana sylvestris* plants depended on having reproducible batches of young plants *in vitro*. The composition of the medium on which these plants were cultured had a striking effect on protoplast yield and on their ability to divide. A low salt medium devoid of vitamins was particularly disadvantageous. The light intensity under which the plants were grown was also critical.

Protoplast culture

Isolated plant protoplasts are very fragile and particularly liable to either physical or chemical damage. Thus if they are suspended in a liquid medium, it must not be agitated, and the high osmotic potential of the medium in which isolation was carried out must be temporarily maintained. As growth depends on adequate aeration, protoplasts are usually cultured in very shallow containers of liquid or solid media; fairly high plating densities (5×10^4 to 10^5 protoplasts/ml) may be necessary, possibly because endogenous chemicals are liable to leak away from such unprotected cells. To promote growth, it may also be beneficial to add to the medium supplementary chemicals and growth factors not normally required for the culture of intact cells.

The capability of plant protoplasts to divide appears to be closely related to their ability to form a cell wall (Meyer and Abel, 1975a,b). The type of wall that is produced initially can be controlled to some extent by the nature of the culture medium. A non-rigid wall can be produced on tobacco mesophyll protoplasts, for example, by culture in a medium containing a relatively high concentration of salts; but although such cells will divide 2–3 times, further cell division does not occur unless a rigid wall is induced to be formed by a change in the culture medium (Meyer, 1974). Under favourable circumstances formation of a cell wall seems to occur as soon as protoplasts are removed from hydrolysing enzyme preparations, and the first signs of cellulose deposition can be detected after only about 16 hours in culture medium. Once wall formation is initiated, the concentration of osmoticum is reduced to favour cell growth. This is readily accomplished in a liquid medium, but where protoplasts have been plated onto a solidified medium it will be necessary to transfer the cells on blocks of agar, to another substrate.

When it has formed a cell wall, the regenerated plant cell generally increases in size and may divide in 3–5 days. If further cell divisions occur, each protoplast gives rise to a small group of intact cells and then a small callus colony. Green chloroplasts in cells derived from leaf mesophyll protoplasts, lose their integrity and disappear as callus formation proceeds. Protoplasts may originate from cells of the intact plant which are not all of the same genetic composition. If such cells are grown in liquid medium, they may stick together and form common cell walls. Colonies of mixed callus will result which could give rise to genetically different plants (see Chapter 3) or plant chimeras (D'Amato, 1978).

To avoid cell aggregation, protoplasts should be freely dispersed and cultured at as low a density as possible. This may mean that, as in the culture of intact cells at low density (page 18), nurse tissue, or a conditioned or specially supplemented medium, must be employed. A method of the latter kind was devised by Raveh *et al.* (1973). A fabric support has been used to suspend protoplasts in a liquid medium so that media changes can be made readily (Kirby and Cheng, 1979).

For further information, readers should consult one or other of the following references:

- Bajaj (1977a), Evans and Cocking (1977) and Evans and Bravo (1983), who provide good basic reviews of the subject;

- Gamborg *et al.* (1981), describe methods and protocols for protoplast isolation, culture (and fusion);

- Constabel (1982) and Fowke (1982a), chapters describing methods and equipment for protoplast isolation and culture.

Plant regeneration. An entire plant was first regenerated from callus originated from an isolated protoplast in 1971 (Takebe *et al.*, 1971). Since then plants have been produced from the protoplasts of a wide range of species, using indirect shoot morphogenesis or indirect embryogenesis (Davey and Power, 1988). The direct formation of somatic embryos (see below) from cultured protoplasts is also possible (Zapata and Sink, 1980).

Protoplast fusion

Although fusion of plant protoplasts was observed many years ago, it has become especially significant since methods have been developed for protoplast isolation and subsequent regeneration into intact plants. Isolated protoplasts do not normally fuse together because they carry a superficial negative charge causing them to repel one another. Various techniques have been discovered to induce fusion to take place. Two of the most successful techniques are the addition of polyethylene glycol (PEG) in the presence of a high concentration of calcium ions and a pH between 8–10, and the application of short pulses of direct electrical current (*electro-fusion*). By mixing protoplasts from plants of two different species or genera, fusions may be accomplished:

a). between protoplasts of the same plant where fusion of the nuclei of two cells would give rise to a *homokaryon* (synkaryon);

b). between protoplasts of the same plant species (intravarietal or intraspecific fusion);

c). between protoplasts of different plant species or genera (interspecific or intergeneric fusion).

Fusions of types (b) and (c) above can result in the formation of genetic hybrids (*heterokaryocytes*) which formally could only be obtained rarely through sexual crossings. By separating the fused hybrid cells from the mixed protoplast population before culture, or by devising a method whereby the cells arising from fused cells may be recognised once they have commenced growth, it has been possible to regenerate new somatic hybrid (as opposed to sexually hybrid) plants. Some novel interspecific and intergeneric hybrid plants have been obtained by this means. A fusion of the cytoplasm of one kind of plant with the nucleus of another is also possible. Such *cybrid* plants can be useful in plant breeding programmes for the transfer of cytoplasmic genes.

The following references give further details about this research topic and its implications for crop improvement:

- Schieder and Vasil (1980). A well-referenced review which lists somatic hybrid cell lines or plants obtained by protoplast fusion.

— Ferenczy and Farkas (1980) is a book on protoplast research in fungi, yeasts and plants. Several papers describe the results of fusions between protoplasts of different plant species or genera.

— Dodds and Roberts (1982), a short chapter describing methods and techniques.

— Keller *et al.* (1982), a useful review of the production and characterisation of somatic hybrids and the practical applications of protoplast fusion technology.

— Kao (1982) and Fowke (1982a,b) describe protocols for protoplast fusions in great detail.

— Mantell *et al.* (1985). An introduction to plant genetic engineering of various kinds.

— Glimelius (1988). Current uses of protoplast fusion for plant breeding objectives.

— Davey and Power (1988). Progress in protoplast culture, fusion and plant regeneration.

CYTODIFFERENTIATION

In an intact plant there are many kinds of cells all having different forms and functions. Meristematic cells, and soft thin-walled parenchymatous tissue, are said to be undifferentiated, while specialised cells are said to be *differentiated.* The cells of callus and suspension cultures are mainly undifferentiated, and it is not yet possible to induce them to become of just one differentiated type. This is partly because culture systems are usually designed to promote cell growth: differentiation frequently occurs as cells cease to divide actively and become quiescent. Furthermore, the formation of differentiated cells appears to be correlated with organ development, therefore the prior expression of genes governing organogenesis may often be required. The *in vitro* environment can also be very different to that in the whole plant where each cell is governed by the restraint and influence of other surrounding cells. In suspension cultures, for example, cells are largely deprived of directional signals, influences from neighbouring differentiated tissues, and correlative messages that may normally pass between adjacent cells by way of interconnecting strands of protoplasm (plasmodesmata).

The differentiated state is also difficult to preserve when cells are isolated from a plant. Askani and Beiderbeck (1988) tried to keep mesophyll cells in a differentiated state. The character of palisade parenchyma cells with regard to size, cell form, colour and size and distribution of chloroplasts could be preserved for 168 h, but after this the chloroplasts became light green, their distribution was no longer homogenous and some of the cells began to divide.

Differentiated cells are most effectively produced *in vitro* within organs such as shoots and roots; even here there may not be the full range of cell types found in intact plants *in vivo*.

THE CELL CYCLE

During division, a cell needs to pass through certain processes or phases which, because they are repeated sequentially from one division to the next, are jointly termed *the cell cycle*. Division of the nucleus (mitosis, *M*) is followed by the formation of two discrete cells (cytokinesis). Before a newly formed cell can divide again, there is always a time interval or *gap* (*G1* = Gap 1) during which most of the growth in organelles and cytoplasm takes place. This is followed by a period of time during which there is active DNA synthesis (*S* = synthesis phase) which results in an identical copy of each chromosome being produced. The copy and the original (which are then visibly indistinguishable) are known as *sister chromatids*. After the *S* phase there is another so- called gap, *G2*, following which the cell undergoes mitosis (Fig. 11). In a population of cells which is actively dividing, the time interval *S* + *G2* + *M* is normally very constant under a standard set of conditions: cells vary in the length of time which they spend in the *G1* phase.

According to the principal control point hypothesis (Van't Hof and Kovacs, 1972) the initiation (continuance), or the cessation, of plant cell division is primarily regulated by factors which operate during the *G1* and *G2* phases. Cells cease to divide and become arrested in either *G1* or *G2* when these factors are limiting. The compound trigonelline has been thought to determine whether cell division shall proceed (Van't Hof, 1985).

The differentiation of cells into defined types of tissue takes place in cells where division is arrested. In some texts on the cell cycle it has been proposed that differentiated cells have been arrested in a quiescent *G0* phase, from which they can only re-enter the cell cycle through a *L* (lag) phase which re-equipped them for passage into the *S* phase.

Many of the kinds of differentiation that a cell will ultimately show, appear to be decided during the processes which led to its formation (*i.e.* during the preceding cell cycle). Observations supporting this conclusion are that in cultures of some plants, the rate of xylem formation may exactly parallel the rate of cell proliferation (Fosket and Torry, 1969), and that preceding mitotic activity also seems to be a prerequisite (Phillips and Torry, 1973). However, some changes in cell structure and function such as cell expansion and the induction of flowering (Fosket, 1972) are not dependent on cell division, and there appear to be circumstances where differentiation may occur without mitotic division. For example, suberin is usually produced in the cells of potato tubers following wound-induced mitotic activity, but it can be formed in cells that have not undergone division immediately beforehand (Kahl *et al.*, 1969). Similarly, vascular elements have been noted to be formed without previous mitosis (Kohlenbach and Schmidt, 1975).

Cytodifferentiation appears always to require prior DNA synthesis, either within the nucleus or within other cell organelles. Where there is previous cell division this synthesis takes place during the *S* phase of the cell cycle. In non-dividing cells, DNA synthesis could occur by the amplification of those genes which are specific for the processes of differentiation that are to follow, or possibly by endopolyploidisation? Specific gene amplification has been shown to take place in animal cells (Brown and Dawid, 1968), but evidence for its operation in plant cells is less certain. The subject was reviewed by Buiatti (1977).

Endopolyploidy (or endomitosis, endoreduplication) is the duplication of the chromosome number (and DNA content) of cells, without the formation of a spindle and nuclear division. It seems to be associated with certain developmental processes in plants, and appears to occur frequently in cells forming tracheid elements (List, 1963). This could represent another kind of gene amplification (Fosket, 1972). The division of endopolyploid cells when differentiated tissue is transferred to culture, is thought to

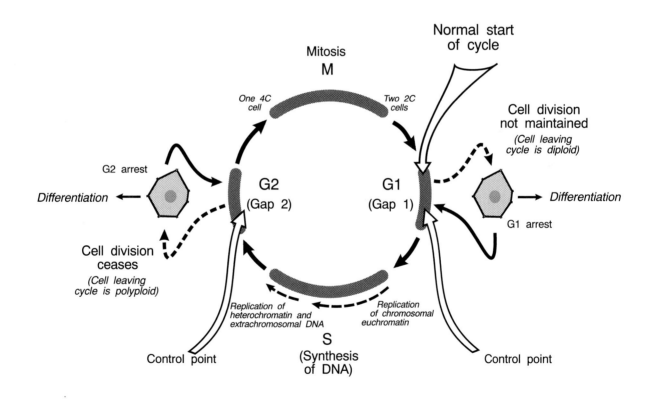

Fig. 11. A diagramatical representation of the cell cycle.

contribute to the irregular aneuploid chromosome numbers often found in callus tissues (Chapter 3). A cell would become polyploid if it left the cell cycle at the *G2* control point after the *S* phase, but before mitosis. The mitotic cell cycle in higher plants has been reviewed by Yeoman (1981) and by various authors in the book edited by Bryant and Francis (1985).

DIFFERENTIATED CELLS IN CALLUS AND CELL CULTURES

Three types of differentiated cells are commonly found in callus and cell cultures; these are vessels and tracheids (the cells from which the water-conducting vascular xylem is constructed), and cells containing chloroplasts (organelles carrying the green photosynthetic pigment, chlorophyll). Phloem seive tubes may be present but are difficult to distinguish from undifferentiated cells.

Tracheid formation

Callus cultures are more likely to contain tracheids than any other kind of differentiated cell. The proportion formed depends on the species from which the culture originated and especially upon the kind of sugar and growth regulators added to the medium. This is discussed further in Chapter 9. Tracheid formation may represent or be associated with an early stage in the development of shoot meristems. Nodules containing xylem elements in callus of *Pelargonium* have, for example, been observed to develop into shoots when moved to an auxin-free medium (Chen and Galston, 1967; Cassells, 1979).

The rapid cell division initiated when tissue is transferred to a nutrient medium usually occurs in meristems formed around the periphery of the explant. Cell differentiation does not take place in callus cultures during this phase but begins when peripheral meristematic activity is replaced or supplemented by the formation of centres of cell division deeper in the tissue. These internal centres generally take the form of meristematic nodules that may produce further expanded and undifferentiated cells (so contributing to callus growth) or cells which differentiate into xylem or phloem elements. Nodules can form primitive vascular bundles, with the xylem occurring centrally and the phloem peripherally, separated from the xylem by a meristematic region.

Chloroplast differentiation

The formation and maintenance of green chloroplasts in cultured plant cells represents another form of cellular differentiation which is easy to monitor, and which has been studied fairly extensively. When chloroplast-containing cells from an intact plant are transferred to a nutrient medium they begin to dedifferentiate. This process continues in the event of cell division and results in a loss of structure of the membranes containing chlorophyll (thylakoids) and the stacks (grana) into which they are arranged, and the accumulation of lipid-containing globules. The chloroplasts eventually change shape and degenerate.

Callus cells frequently do not contain chloroplasts but only plastids containing starch grains in which a slightly-developed lamellar system may be apparent. All the same, many calluses have been discovered that do turn green on continued exposure to light and are composed of a majority of chloroplast-containing cells. Chloroplast formation can also be connected with the capacity of callus to undergo morphogenesis. Green spots sometimes appear on some calluses and it is from these areas that new shoots arise. By subculturing areas with green spots, a highly morphogenic tissue can sometimes be obtained. The formation of chloroplasts and their continued integrity is also favoured by cell aggregation. When green callus tissue is used to initiate suspension cultures, the number of chloroplasts and their degree of differentiation is reduced. Nevertheless, there can be some increase in chlorophyll content during the stationary phase of batch cultures.

The level of chlorophyll so far obtained in tissue cultures is well below that found in mesophyll cells of whole plants of the same species, and the rate of chlorophyll formation on exposure of cultured cells to the light is extremely slow compared to the response of etiolated organised tissues. The greening of cultures also tends to be unpredictable and even within individual cells, a range in the degree of chloroplast development is often found. In the carbon dioxide concentrations found in culture vessels, green callus tissue is normally photomixotrophic (*i.e.* the chloroplasts are able to fix part of the carbon that the cells require) and growth is still partly dependent on the incorporation of sucrose into the medium (Vasil and Hildebrandt, 1966a). However, green photoautotrophic callus cultures have been obtained from several different kinds of plants. When grown at high carbon dioxide concentrations (1–5%), without a carbon source in the medium, they are capable of increasing in dry weight by photosynthetic carbon assimilation alone (see Street, 1977a).

Photoautotrophic cell suspensions have also been obtained. They too normally require high carbon dioxide levels, but cell lines of some species have been isolated capable of growing in ambient CO_2 concentration (Chunhe Xu *et al.*, 1988). Why cultured cells do not freely develop fully-functional chloroplasts is not fully known. Some hypotheses have been summarised by Dalton (1980). The cytology of chloroplast formation is described in Yeoman and Street (1977). Photoautotrophic growth of shoots is described in Chapter 7.

MORPHOGENESIS

NATURE AND INDUCTION

New organs such as shoots and roots can be induced to form on cultured plant tissues. Such freshly-originated organs are said to be *adventive* or *adventitious*. The creation of new form and organisation, where previously it was lacking, is termed *morphogenesis* or *organogenesis*. Tissues or organs which have the capacity for morphogenesis/organogenesis are said to be *morphogenic (morphogenetic)* or *organogenic (organogenetic)*. So far it has been possible to obtain the *de novo* (adventitious) formation of:

— shoots (*caulogenesis*) and roots (*rhizogenesis*) separately.

> The formation of leaves adventitiously *in vitro* usually denotes the presence of a shoot meristem. Sometimes leaves appear without apparent shoot formation: opinions are divided on whether such leaves can have arisen *de novo*, or whether a shoot meristem must have been present first of all and subsequently failed to develop.

— embryos that are structurally similar to the embryos found in true seeds.

> Such embryos often develop a region equivalent to the suspensor of zygotic embryos and, unlike shoot or root buds, come to have both a shoot and a root pole. To distiguish them from zygotic or seed embryos, embryos produced from cells or tissues of the plant body are called *somatic embryos* (or *embryoids*) and the process leading to their inception is termed *embryogenesis*. The word 'embryoid' has been especially used when it has been unclear whether the embryo-like structures seen in cultures were truly the somatic equivalent of zygotic embryos. Somatic embryogenesis is now such a widely observed and documented event that *somatic embryo* has become the preferred term.

— flowers, flower initials or perianth parts.

> The formation of flowers or floral parts is rare, occurring only under special circumstances and is not relevant to plant propagation.

Caulogenesis, rhizogenesis and embryogenesis are important for plant multiplication. New plants are seldom obtained in culture by the union of shoots and roots independently formed in callus; this is because vascular links between the two tend to be unreliable. Plantlet regeneration is therefore best achieved from adventitious shoots which are afterwards rooted, or from somatic embryos. Shoots, roots and somatic embryos arise from single cells, or groups of cells, which become induced by the cultural conditions to become centres of active cell division (morphogenetic meristems), each capable of producing an organ of the one kind.

Morphogenesis has now been observed *in vitro* in numerous plants of many genera, but it cannot yet be induced universally. Even within a single species, varieties can be found which are recalcitrant.

Direct and indirect morphogenesis

Morphogenetic meristems can theoretically occur in either of two distinct ways:

— from the differentiated cells of a newly-transferred piece of whole-plant tissue, without the proliferation of undifferentiated tissue;

— from the unspecialised, unorganised and dedifferentiated cells of callus tissues or suspension cultures.

Hicks (1980) described these two methods of morphogenesis as *direct* and *indirect* organogenesis respectively. In practice it is not always possible to distinguish between the two methods. Directly-formed meristems destined to become shoots or somatic embryos may proliferate to form a regenerative tissue similar in appearance to callus. Such meristems may also become surrounded by de-differentiated callus so that it is difficult to ascertain their origin. A type of callus bearing superficial shoot-forming meristems can often be separated from this kind of culture. Alternatively, shoot meristems may form within callus which is still attached to, or within the tissues of the primary explant, or may be produced simultaneously

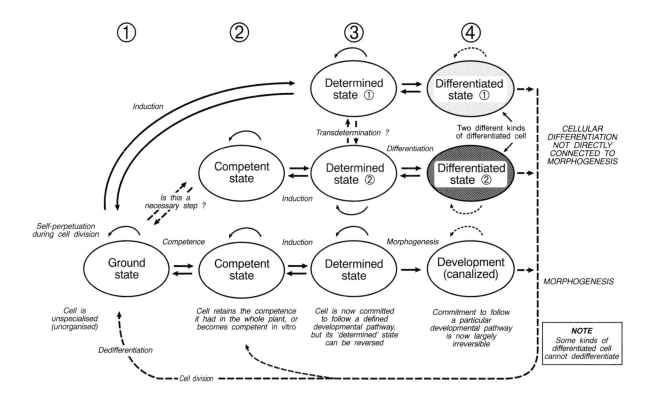

Fig. 12. Progressive steps in the capacity of a cell to become differentiated and/or morphogenic.
Competence can be one step on the pathway to determination; but it is not clear whether cells in the ground
state always have to pass through this stage as they are committed to development.

from such callus and from superficial cells of the explant (Bigot *et al.*, 1977).

Competence and determination

Highly specialised cells of the intact plant are never observed to change from their existing differentiated state. Similarly some cells do not become morphogenic and are supposed to have lost the capacity to form new plants. Cells which have retained the capacity for a particular kind of cellular differentiation or morphogenesis, or have acquired it in response to an appropriate stimulus, are said to be *competent*.

Some consider that morphogenic competence usually conveys an ability to proceed towards one particular developmental pathway; according to this hypothesis, a cell which is competent to undergo shoot morphogenesis may not be competent for root formation. It is also thought that if cells of an explant are not already competent at the time of excision, they may be induced to become so by *in vitro* culture on a medium with, or without, growth regulators. They are then enabled to

respond to the organogenic stimulus provided by a particular combination of growth regulators added to the medium.

Morphogenesis and cellular differentiation

Competence thus is the first step in the dedication of one or more undifferentiated cells (Stage 1 of Fig. 12) towards morphogenesis, or some other kind of specialised development (Stage 2). The second stage of dedication is then said to be the *induction* of determination in competent cells. Individual cells or groups of cells are said to be *determined* when they have become committed to follow a particular genetically-programmed developmental pathway, for example a particular kind of morphogenesis (Stage 3 in Fig. 12) and can continue towards that outcome without the further influence of growth regulants (Christianson, 1987). Determined cells differentiate to become the specialised component tissues of mature plants. In practice, the gaining of competence and determination are often hard to separate.

In both direct and indirect organogenesis, at some stage during the formation of new meristems from which organs will arise, the component cells adopt a different inherent programming (determination) which decides their subsequent pattern of development. In the case of unorganised tissue cultures, the programming is apparently induced by the effect of growth regulators (in combination with the presence of the correct nutritional factors). Although growth regulators may also help to induce direct morphogenesis, cells in some parts of a plant appear to be partially pre-determined to a particular morphogenetic pathway so that it takes only a slight change in environment to induce the tissues of some explants to form a morphogenetic meristem instead of progressing to become a differentiated cell within the intact plant. This is clearly seen in tissues which are already embryogenically committed. There is a high probability that somatic embryogenesis can be initiated from such tissues when they are explanted, either directly, or indirectly after some initial cell proliferation.

Morphogenesis from cells which are already committed to such development has been called *permissive*, while that from cells induced to become morphogenic by endogenous or exogenous growth regulators, *inductive* (Smith and Krikorian, 1988). Permissive and inductive morphogenesis are thus almost synonymous with direct and indirect morphogenesis.

Morphogenic centres arise from only a relatively small proportion of the total number of cells in a culture. It is not known why this should be. In many circumstances it would clearly be advantageous to be able to obtain increased numbers. The extent of pre-determination or commitment to morphogenesis varies between different tissues of the whole plant; that of any given tissue will differ according to the plant's genetic background. Some observers believe that the cells from which organ-producing meristems are formed, are the only ones in a cell population that are competent. An alternative hypothesis was put forward by Street (1977e), who suggested that although many cells may have the capacity to become competent, newly formed meristems may preferentially accept essential metabolites from surrounding cells which would then be less likely to follow the same developmental pathway.

There is, however, evidence (for example, Cassells, 1979) that additional meristems are primarily inhibited from developing by the growth substances produced by the first meristems to be initiated in the tissue. This would suggest that cells which preferentially give rise to meristems, do so because they become induced to differentiate slightly before their competitors. They may, for instance, be at an appropriate phase of the cell cycle at the time an inductive stimulus is applied.

Cellular differentiation. It is not clear to what extent competence is a pre-requisite of cellular differentiation. In some papers describing differentiation of a non-morphogenic kind (*e.g.* the capacity of cells to produce a pigment), the terms competence and determination are used synonymously. It has been suggested that plant cells determined for subsequent differentiation are able to switch, by *transdetermination*, from one determined state to another (Stage 3 of Fig. 12) in the same way as animal cells (Girod and Zyrd, 1987).

The epigenetic nature of commitment. A commitment to progress towards a defined developmental objective, means that a cell will follow a defined programme of development. Commitment is self-maintained in that it can be passed on to daughter cells and later cell generations. The message is not immutable though, and may be lost or changed by subsequent stimuli. Determination usually results in differentiated cells (Fig 12, Stage 4) which retain the developmental determination of their parents, so that their differentiated state is replicated during cell division. When morphogenic determination or cell differentiation becomes fixed, or irreversible, it is said to have become *canalized*.

Several kinds of morphogenetic determination are possible. For example, cells may become committed to produce root, shoot, leaf or floral meristems. Once canalization has occurred, progress through a single development pathway is then usually inevitable unless the cells are capable of being stimulated to divide under conditions which promote dedifferentiated growth. However, at an early stage of development, leaf and floral meristems can sometimes be induced to differentiate into shoots without dedifferentiation occurring. Some kinds of canalized development (*e.g.* the formation of tracheids) are irreversible.

Many interacting factors influence organogenesis *in vitro*. The most widely studied of these are discussed in the following sections or in later chapters, particularly Chapters 7 and 8 . Further aspects of competence and determination are discussed in Chapter 8.

DIRECT ORGANOGENESIS

When relatively large pieces of intact plants are transferred to nutrient media, new shoots, roots, somatic embryos and even flower initials are often formed without the prior growth of callus tissue. Small explants show organogenesis only rarely, although some exceptions have been reported. The part of the original plant from which the explant is taken is important in influencing its morphogenetic potential. Many species give rise to adventitious shoot buds on explants taken from a variety of organs including those derived from petioles, stems, roots, leaves and cotyledons. By contrast, adventitious embryos are directly formed much less commonly. They are produced on the leaves of a few plant species, and more frequently on nucellus tissue, or on pre-formed somatic embryos and on the seedlings derived from somatic embryos. Methods of inducing morphogenesis directly in explanted tissues are being discovered in an increasing number of plant species and direct shoot regeneration is an important means whereby several different kinds of plants may be propagated.

Direct root formation from non-root explants is relatively rare, but is possible; it has been observed in *Brassica* (Kartha *et al.*, 1974a); *Petunia* (Rao *et al.*, 1973a); *Capsicum* (Gunay and Rao, 1978) and *Abelmoschus esculentus* (Mangat and Roy, 1986).

Origin of adventitious buds

Shoot meristems formed directly on explanted tissues are often initiated by the commencement of cell divisions after about 48 hours in nutrient culture. Each preliminary mitosis is rapidly followed by further division, so that new meristematic primordia are formed, each comprised of a number of cells. These primordia appear to arise at random in morphogenetically competent explants or parts of explants, but finally tend to be spaced equidistantly. Sometimes each meristem clearly originates from

Table 2. Plants in which adventitious shoots may arise from single epidermal cells.

Achimenes	Broertjes (1972a)
Begonia	Doorbenbos & Karper (1975); Mikkelson & Sink (1978a)
Chrysanthemum	Roest & Bokelmann (1975); Roest (1977); Broertjes *et al.* (1976)
Linum	Murray et al. (1977)
Kalanchoe	Broertje & Leffring (1972)
Lilium	Broertjes *et al.* (1976)
Peperomia	Broertjes *et al.* (1976)
Saintpaulia	Arisumi & Frazier (1968); Broertjes (1972b)
	Grunewaldt (1977)
Streptocarpus	Broertjes (1969)
Nicotiana	De Nettancourt *et al.* (1971)

one cell, but whether this is always the case is the subject of controversy. There are many papers which describe how such meristems *can* arise from single epidermal cells (Table 2): in the cotyledons of conifers, meristems arise in subdermal mesophyll (Sommer *et al.*, 1975; Cheah and Cheng, 1978; Jansson and Bornman, 1981; Flinn *et al.*, 1988).

During direct organogenesis, adventitious buds may not all be immediately derived from cells of the explant. There is evidence that a single epidermal cell may sometimes give rise to meristematic centres, from one of which, up to 22 identical shoots may arise (Broertjes *et al.*, 1976).

The single cell origin of shoots can be confirmed by the high incidence of 'solid' mutant plants which occurs when suitable organs are subjected to mutagenic treatments. If meristems were initiated from several cells, a high proportion of chimeras would appear. Results such as these have led Broertjes and Van Harten (1978) and Broertjes and Keen (1980) to suggest that directly-regenerated adventitious shoot meristems may always be formed from one or a few daughter cells that originate from a single cell. This view is not shared by others.

Thomas *et al.* (1979) cautioned that extensive histological work is necessary to tell whether adventitious structures arise from single cells. From a study of shoot regeneration from the leaves of *Saintpaulia* chimeras, Norris and Smith (1981) concluded that the initiation of shoot meristems involves the association and the possible inclusion of cells beneath the epidermis. Adventitious bud meristems which formed between twin bulb scales of onion, arose from many cells in sub-epidermal layers (Falavigna *et al.*, 1980; Hussey and Falavigna, 1980). Similarly shoots on cultured explants of *Nicotiana tabacum* leaves were found to arise indirectly from nodules at the edges of the explant. The nodules were mainly formed by divisions of palisade mesophyll cells around the edge of the explant where wounding had occurred (Attfield and Evans, 1991a). By contrast, roots in this tissue were produced directly from the bundle sheath and vein parenchyma, but the number of cells which participated in their origin was not ascertained.

Meristemoids. Organs are frequently formed in explanted tissues, from single cells or from several cells which divide to give rise to a spherical mass of small meristematic cells filled with densely staining cytoplasm and containing large nuclei. Such specialised cell groups were called *meristemoids* by Torrey (1966). The term has been taken up by other workers, although the stage at which meristematic cells come to constitute a meristemoid, or the ultimate size of these structures, has not been precisely defined. The word *promeristemoid* has been used recently to indicate small organised groups of meristematic cells, less complicated than meristemoids, which are the sites from which organs, or meristemoids, are formed (Villalobos *et al.*, 1984; Flinn *et al.*, 1988).

Meristematic cell clusters consisting of 6–7 cells formed from pericycle cells adjacent to protoxylem within *Convolvulus* roots, and at this stage were considered by Bonnett and Torrey (1966) to be capable of developing into either roots or shoots. Lateral root initials of *Vicia faba* were found by Davidson (1972) to arise from 6 to 50 cells, the average being 24. Cells at the centre of the localized zones of cell division, eventually formed root or bud primordia. Meristemoids formed in other plants have also been considered to be undetermined and capable of developing into either roots or shoots (Thorpe, 1978a,1980; Hicks, 1980), but this interpretation may not be correct. Certainly in some plants, groups of 4–6 meristematic 'proembryoid' cells can become determined towards the formation of a shoot promordium after only 4–7 days of the explant being placed in culture (Flinn *et al.*, 1988).

Direct embryogenesis

Natural occurrence

Somatic embryogenesis does occur to a limited extent in nature, within ovules and more rarely on the leaves of a few plants (*e.g.* some in the genera *Asplenium, Cardamine, Kalanchoe, Ranunculus* and *Tolmiea*).

The seed embryos of plants are formed upon the fertilisation of an egg cell (or zygote) which has originated within nucellus tissue. Plants of some genera have a natural tendency to polyembryony and have more than one embryo in a seed. This sometimes occurs when a fertilised zygote or young embryo divides into one or more units (*cleavage polyembryony*). In many plants additional embryos are formed asexually from ovular tissues without the fusion of cells or nuclei. Such somatic embryos may also undergo cleavage. Their derivation is called *apomixis* and can result from a number of different processes. It is often due to embryos arising anew:

— from single diploid somatic cells in the embryo sac (apospory); or,

— from single cells of the nucellus (nucellar embryony).

Somatic embryos may completely replace zygotic embryos in the seeds of some plants. In other plants (*e.g.* polyembryonic varieties of *Citrus* and related genera) seeds may contain both sexual *and* asexual embryos.

As somatic embryos formed apomictically result in seedlings which are genetically identical to their mother plant, they can be used for vegetative propagation. The disadvantage of their formation is that the selection of new varieties from the progeny of sexual crosses is either not possible, or is considerably hampered.

Occurrence *in vitro*

Direct embryogenesis, that is to say, the formation of somatic embryos on explanted tissues without any intervening callus phase, is observed much more frequently *in vitro* than is the formation of adventitious embryos *in vivo*. Reports of direct embryogenesis *in vitro* have mainly described its occurrence on gametophyte (the gamete-producing generation) tissues, sporophytic (normal plant) tissues closely associated with the gametophyte, or tissues which have recently arisen in consequence of the fertilisation of gametes. Explants from which direct embryogenesis is most likely to occur include pollen microspores within the anther and tissues of all or part of the ovary [including the ovary wall (or carpels) Smith and Krikorian, 1988], ovule (especially the nucellus), zygotic embryo or young seedling. Physiologically, these explants are all very juvenile. Instances of direct embryo formation are discussed in Chapter 2.

Predetermination. According to one hypothesis advanced by Sharp *et al.* (1980); Evans *et al.* (1981a) and Sharp and Evans, (1982), direct embryogenesis occurs *in vitro* only from cells within the explant which are predisposed (predetermined) to become embryo-producing before their transfer to culture: nutrient media and other *in vitro* conditions serve only to enhance the process. Such cells are said to be pre-embryogenically determined (PEDCs). An explant will normally contain several types of tissue, not all of which may have this capacity. As an alternative hypothesis, Hepher *et al.* (1988) have suggested that the embryogenic potential of tissues, is related to their active role in nutrient transport: they say that many embryogenic tissues (*e.g.* nucellus, scutellum, synergids, the abaxial epidermis of soybean cotyledons) have this capacity.

The parts of a whole plant which are capable of supporting direct embryogenesis, can give rise, *in vitro*, to tissue of similar appearance to callus, but which has an immediate capacity for embryo regeneration. This tissue can sometimes also be used to initiate suspension cultures with a similar morphogenic potential (Smith and Krikorian, 1988, 1989). Although such cultures are described in the section on indirect embryogenesis which follows, they probably represent an extended form of direct embryogenesis.

INDIRECT ORGANOGENESIS

Separate root and shoot formation

Media and growth regulators which favour rapid cell proliferation and the formation of callus from an explant, are not usually conducive to the initiation of the morphogenetic meristems which give rise to roots or shoots. However, in cultures of some plants, organogenesis becomes inevitable when callus is maintained on a medium for a prolonged period, but may be prevented if the tissue is subcultured. In other cases unorganised callus initiated on one medium needs to be transferred to another of a different composition, with different combinations of growth regulators (a regeneration medium), for shoot initiation to occur (Fig. 13).

Organs are formed in callus tissues in a fashion comparable to that observed directly within explanted tissues. Cells from which organs are formed, have arisen from the reprogramming of dedifferentiated cells or, more commonly, have retained a commitment to morphogenesis which existed in the explanted tissues. This may explain why highly organogenic cultures are most frequently obtained from young actively dividing parts of plants. Sometimes it appears that meristemoids may have a different origin to other cells of the callus. Callus cultures derived from sections of sweet potato tubers developed meristematic centres of this kind from the cells of anomalous cambia within the tissue of the explant (Hwang *et al.*, 1981).

The position of meristematic centres may have some relation to the organization of the explant in newly-initiated callus; but after some while, although roots and shoots do develop within the interior of callus, they commonly occur superficially (exogenously). In some plants (*e.g. Convolvulus*) the two different kinds of organ have been shown to arise in different parts of the tissue, roots from cells in the upper part of the callus and shoots from those in contact with the medium (Christianson and Warnick, 1985). Again, it is not clear whether meristemoids are always formed with the capacity to give rise to one specific type of organ, *i.e.* whether the conditions which lead to their formation also decide the type of organ that will be produced, or whether meristemoid formation and organ development are separately and sequentially decided.

Sometimes adventitious shoots are thought to have arisen by caulogenesis, when in reality they have developed from somatic embryos. Pro-embryos cultured in a medium containing inappropriate growth regulators, produce shoots lacking roots (Sidavas *et al.*, 1990).

Fig. 13. Adventitious shoots arising on callus of Winged Bean.

Indirect somatic embryogenesis

Somatic embryos can also be produced indirectly in otherwise unorganised cell and tissue cultures. True indirect embryogenesis requires the differentiated cells of an explant to be induced to divide as undifferentiated callus and then for certain cells to be become committed or redetermined on an embryogenic pathway. In the terminology of Sharp *et al.* (1980), cells derived from previously differentiated tissue which have been newly induced to embryogenic determination are called IEDCs (*induced embryogenic determined cells*) (*c.f.* PEDCs on the previous page).

Cellular origin of somatic embryos

Because embryogenesis is often difficult to observe, there has been some controversy over its origin in unorganised cultures, but the developmental anatomy (ontogeny) of embryos has been studied in detail in several different species, *e.g.*:-

Daucus carota	McWilliam *et al.* (1974); Nomura and Komamine(1985)
Ranunculus scleratus	Konar *et al.* (1972a)
Pennisetum americanum	Vasil and Vasil (1982a)

Embryos can be distinguished from adventitious shoots because they are bipolar, having both a shoot and a root pole, a shoot axis and cotyledons (or a coleoptile and a scutellum in monocotyledons) of a similar venation to that in zygotic embryos. They also have no vascular connections with the underlying parental tissue. This is unlike axillary or adventitious buds which can induce the formation of procambial conducting strands in maternal tissue. In whole plants, these strands establish a connection between the young shoot and the vascular system of the mother plant.

Unlike the meristems which give rise to separate root or shoot initials (which may also be produced internally), somatic embryos nearly always arise superficially on callus and are detached easily from the surrounding cells. They may float free in suspension cultures from the globular stage onwards.

It is generally agreed that somatic embryos are formed from cells which are characteristically meristematic and therefore unlike the usual vacuolated parenchymatous cells found in callus and suspension cultures: they have dense cytoplasm and large nuclei and contain many starch grains. But do these cells, and hence somatic embryos, always originate from single determined cells?

Single cell origin. A plant embryo, whether it be zygotic, somatic, directly- or indirectly-initiated, has been defined as "a new individual arising from a single cell and having no vascular connection with the maternal tissues" (Haccius, 1978). It has been clearly shown that somatic embryos can arise from a single cell; directly upon ex-

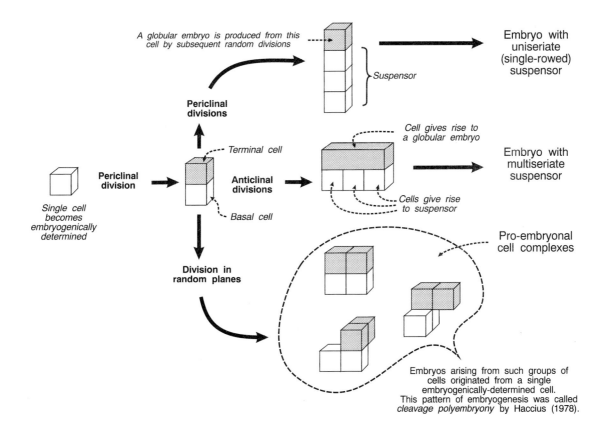

Fig. 14. Proembryonal cell complexes result from abnormal planes of cell division during embryo formation from single embryogenic cells [after Trigiano *et al.*, 1989].

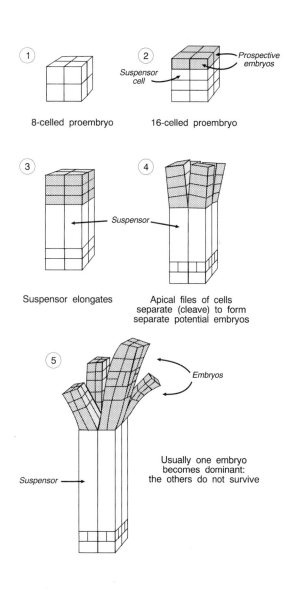

Fig. 15. A diagrammatic representation of zygotic cleavage embryogenesis in *Pinus*.

planted tissue; in both callus and suspension cultures (*e.g.* in carrot; Backs-Husemann and Reinert, 1970: Nomura and Komamine, 1986a: in pear; Mehra and Jaidka, 1985: in fennel; Miura and Tabata, 1986: and in rice; Jones and Rost, 1989); from protoplasts (Miura and Tabata, 1986); and from mechanically-isolated cells (Uragami *et al.*, 1990).

A change in the regular plane of cell division is one of the first indications of the formation of an embryogenetic tissue (Hepher *et al.*, 1988). Where embryos originate

from a single cell, an unequal periclinal division results in one small cytoplasmically-rich cell (the terminal cell) and another large vacuolated cell (the basal cell). In some cultures, the basal cell does not divide further, but in normal circumstances it can be seen to be the source of a suspensor (Fig. 14).

Polyembryony. Somatic embryos can often be seen to arise, not from single cells, but from globular clumps of tissue. Haccius (1978) suggested that such pro-embyonal cell complexes still have their origin in single embryogenically-dedicated cells and that formation of embryos from the globular tissue was the equivalent of the *cleavage polyembryony* which sometimes occurs *in vivo* (*i.e.* the division of the zygote or pro-embryo into two or more units). In *Dactylis glomerata* it has been proposed that pro-embryonal cell complexes or abnormal embryos are produced instead of normal somatic embryos, if the division of single embryogenically-determined cells proceeds in an anticlinal or random fashion (Trigiano *et al.*, 1989) (Fig 14). Somatic embryos with both uniseriate and multiseriate suspensors were produced later from proembryonal cell masses by cleavage polyembryony.

The emergence of embryos from a globular embryogenic tissue of *Picea* was called *polyembryogenesis* by Gupta and Durzan (1986a; 1987b: Durzan and Gupta, 1987) because of its analogy to the cleavage polyembryony which occurs during zygotic embryogenesis in the Pinaceae. In some genera of this family, a group of cells which would usually be expected to form a single embryo, divides (cleaves) into files of cells each of which begins to form an embryo. The genetically identical embryos compete and usually only one survives (see Fig 15). The very long suspensors produced during zygotic embryogenesis in the Pinaceae are also observed during somatic embryogenesis in this family, so that embryogenic tissue *in vitro* has been called *embryonal suspensor masses* (Gupta *et al.*,1988). A review of the terminolgy in zygotic and somatic embryogenesis in conifers is given by Tautorus *et al.* (1991).

Clumps of embryogenic tissue may arise in other ways. In rice it has been noted that many more embryos are initiated from single cells of the scutellum of zygotic embryo explants, than complete their development. Competition for resources (such as occurs during the maturation of one out of several embryos during cleavage polyembryony in gymnosperms) leads to many embryos proliferating, from the globular stage onwards, as parenchymatous 'callus' tissue. Clusters of embryos and related embryogenic callus tissue may form an epithelium similar to that of the scutellum, from which new somatic embryos may be originated (Jones and Rost, 1989). Globular cell clumps (pro-embryonal cell complexes) have also been observed to give rise to somatic embryos from single cells in both callus and suspension cultures of other species (*e.g.* by Button *et al.*, 1974; Kohlenbach, 1977)

Multicellular origin. Several authors have maintained that embryos may sometimes have a multicellular origin. Maheswaran and Williams (1985) concluded that the initiation of somatic embryos in *Trifolium repens* was predominantly multicellular. The first sign of embryogenesis in immature zygotic embryos was a change in the normal plane of cell division. This was followed by the formation of a file of cells which developed into a meristem. Somatic embryos could arise from single meristematic cells, but they were usually produced by multicellular budding. Proliferation of the meristem resulted in a distinctive globular tissue.

A multicellular origin for somatic embryos by folding or budding of embryogenic tissue has also been recognised in other plants (*e.g. Sorghum bicolor* — Wernicke *et al.*, 1982). Williams and Maheswaran (1986) suggested that it may occur when neighbouring cells are in the same stage of embryogenic induction: a group of adjacent cells may then associate and act conjointly in the process of embryo formation. The presence of broad suspensors on somatic embryos is thought to be indicative of a multicellular origin (Halperin, 1966; Armstrong and Phillips, 1988).

Rate of embryogenesis

Some callus cultures may produce somatic embryos slowly and so contain only a small number at any given time. The appearance of isolated somatic embryos in coffee calluses was called 'low frequency somatic embryogenesis' by Sondahl and Sharp (1977a,b,c, 1979) and Sondahl *et al.* (1979a,b). Embryogenic callus which comes to contain proliferating pro-embryonal tissue is usually different in appearance to non-embryogenic tissue: it can give rise to large numbers of somatic embryos. Such callus sometimes arises directly upon an explant, and on other occasions from non-embryogenic tissue, or tissue giving rise to a small number of embryos, after a period of culture. Appearance of a recognisably different globular embryogenic tissue from a high proportion of coffee calluses previously disposed to low frequency embryogenesis, was termed 'high frequency somatic embryogenesis' by Sondahl *et al.* (*loc. cit.*).

Pseudobulbils. Some calluses can be highly embryogenic and may consist entirely of globular cell masses from which new ones continually arise by budding. In other cultures, clumps of embryogenic meristematic cells form spherical nodules on the surface of callus, or cellular aggregates in suspension cultures. Globular bodies tend to reach a larger size under conditions that are not fully conducive to embryogenesis and are then sometimes called *pseudobulbils* (La Rue, 1954; Ranga Swamy, 1958; 1961).

Pseudobulbils are formed when conditions are not favourable for a completion of the process of embryogenesis. Button and Botha (1975) postulated that pseudobulbils seen within some embryogenic *Citrus* callus cultures are derived from globular proembryos in which polarity was not established by the 16–32 cell stage. In this tissue the pseudobulbils can enlarge into spherical bodies up to 4 mm in diameter. Small pseudobulbils are able to develop into heart-shaped, torpedo-shaped or cotyledonary embryos. Once they have attained a diameter of about 2 mm, pseudobulbils only produce occasional roots, although they do give rise to new proembryos from superficial cells (Button *et al.*, 1974).

Protocorms. Similar globular bodies, which frequently form on callus cultures of orchids, are not pseudobulbils, but *protocorm-like bodies*. These are the *in vitro* equivalent of the protocorms formed during the germination of orchid seeds (see page 55).

Proliferation of pre-embryogenically determined cells

As explained under **Direct Embryogenesis**, some explants (such as the nucellus of poly-embryonic *Citrus* species — see review by Rangaswamy, 1982), capable of direct embryogenesis, are invariably able to give rise to an embryogenic tissue or callus. Usually it occurs together with a simultaneous outgrowth of truly unorganised tissue. In grapevines, a white tissue (which the authors said did not look like callus because it consisted of a mass of tiny individually-organised units) appeared from the shoot apices and cotyledon regions of seed embryos and was accompanied by a creamy yellow unorganised friable callus. Immature polyembryonic zygotic embryos of conifers can be stimulated *in vitro* to proliferate a white embryonal tissue (an embryonal suspensor mass) from the suspensor region at the radical end, in conjuction with green non-embryogenic callus from other regions.

In cases such as those instanced above, indirect embryogenesis might be said to have occurred because somatic embryos did not appear on the primary explant. On the other hand, the embryogenic tissues appear to originate directly from pre-embryogenically determined cells and are not undifferentiated. The embryonal suspensor masses of *Picea* can be converted into somatic embryos through a change of medium and growth regulators (Krogstrup *et al.* 1988). The distinction between direct and indirect embryogenesis is clearly blurred, especially as in many reports of embryogenesis, it is not obvious whether the explant was embryogenically determined or not.

The embryogenic determination of tissues from different sites on a single plant, or from similar explants derived from different genotypes, clearly varies. Highly embryogenic callus is occasionally produced by culturing explants on a simple medium without growth regulators. However, the induction of embryogenesis usually requires explanted tissues to be placed on a medium containing an auxin. Growth regulators of this kind stimulate cell division and cause cells to become committed to embryo formation. In callus that has been grown for some while in an unorganised state without the induction of morphogenesis, the dedifferentiated cells require to be completely redetermined into an embryogenic condition before they can give rise to somatic embryos. Auxin growth regulators are once again primarily responsible for bringing about this altered commitment.

Stages of embryo development

The close structural similarity between somatic and zygotic embryos has naturally created much interest. Although within somatic embryos there is not an orderly pattern of cell division planes (once thought to be important for the eventual designation of cell function in zygotic embryos), variation in these segmentation patterns probably only reflects the different environment in which the cultured cells were contained and is, in any case, also known to occur sometimes during zygotic embryo growth (Street and Withers, 1974). As additionally, the later stages of development of zygotic and somatic embryos are very similar, it may be supposed that the processes of zygotic and somatic embryogenesis are essentially the same. The various stages in the development of somatic embryos in dicotyledons are shown diagramatically in Fig. 16. They are usually described as follows:

- pro-embryos: small clusters of meristematic cells from which somatic embryos will arise,

- globular stage: larger groups of cells not yet having a definite embryo-like shape,

- heart stage: a characteristic three-lobed stage where cotyledonary initials are separated from the root pole,

- torpedo stage: an elongated form of the heart-shaped embryo,

- plantlet: discernable small 'seedling' with primary root and shoot.

The stages in monocotyledons are somewhat different; at the globular stage, somatic embryos are easily confused with spherical shoot meristems and it can be difficult to

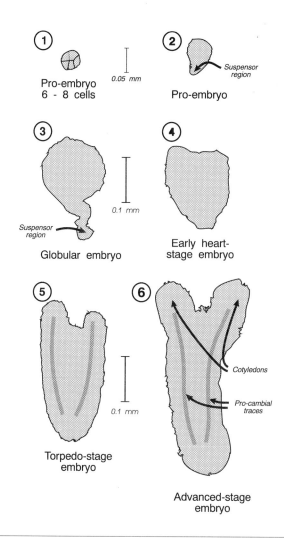

Fig. 16. Stages of somatic embryogenesis in a dicotyledon.

be sure that embryogenesis has taken place. However, the embryos of monocotyledons give rise to shoots from discrete globular bodies, which, as they grow, develop structures resembling a scutellum and coleoptile (Fig. 17); adventitious shoot buds form a clump of leaves. Somatic embryos also typically develop root and shoot poles and are discontinuous with the underlying callus.

Pro-embryos of both dicotyledons and monocotyledons typically have a number of cells at the root pole end which are equivalent to the suspensor of zygotic embryos; these cells may not be apparent in embryos which arise by multicellular budding, where the somatic embryo can be closely associated with the parent tissue.

Fujimura and Komamine (1980) found that in carrot, very different rates of cell division occur at different stages of somatic embryo formation. A marked increase in rate occurs after the pro-embryo stage and precedes the for-

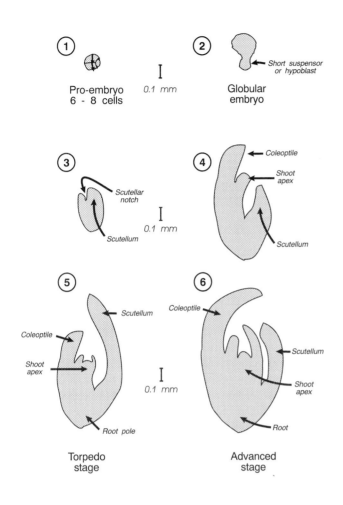

Fig. 17. Stages of somatic embryogenesis in monocotyledons.

1988), somatic embryos do contain some specific proteins not found in other tissues (Hahne *et al.*, 1988). The amounts and nature of these may change as growth proceeds (Zee and Wu, 1979): storage proteins accumulate which are not normally found in somatic tissues (Crouch, 1982; Stuart and Nelsen, 1988). Electrical currents have been found to move through globular bodies of embryogenic callus, pro-embryos and early stage embryos demonstrating that a distinctive polarity exists in these structures from a very early stage (Brawley *et al.*, 1984).

Germination. Somatic embryos which have been suitably matured can be germinated *in vitro* and sometimes *ex vivo* (see Chapter 14) to produce normal seedlings. Very large numbers of somatic embryos can be produced in some cultures, but normally only a small percentage of these ultimately gives rise to plants. The proportion which does, has been termed the *conversion* frequency by Redenbaugh *et al.* (1986, 1987b).

Occurrence of embryogenesis

In the past, somatic embryos have generally been obtained unreliably in tissue culture and their formation has been much less common than the separate formation of roots or shoots. Somatic embryo formation was at first induced in relatively few plant species (Tisserat *et al.*, 1979a), but its incidence is steadily being increased as controlling factors become better understood (Williams and Maheswaran, 1986 and the Tables in Chapter 17). In many species, indirect embryogenesis was originally noted only fortuitously, but may have occurred more frequently than was suspected. For example, when organogenesis occurred in clover callus cultures, Phillips and Collins (1980) were only able to deduce that somatic embryos had been formed. This was because the first and second leaves on shoots were cotyledon-like and unifoliate respectively: if separate adventitious shoot formation had taken place, all leaves would have been trifoliate. In other species a difference in leaf shape might be less easily detected.

mation of globular embryos. In maize, the start of both zygotic and somatic embryogenesis can be detected through changes in isoenzymes (Everett *et al.*, 1985). Although there may be only a small change in the total population of proteins during embryogenesis (Sung *et al.*,

HAPLOID PLANTS

ANTHER AND POLLEN CULTURE

In 1953 Tulecke discovered that haploid tissue (*i.e.* tissue composed of cells having half the chromosome number that is characteristic of a species), could be produced by the culture of *Ginkgo* pollen. Little notice was taken of

his work until Guha and Maheshwari (1964, 1967) managed to regenerate haploid plants from pollen of *Datura innoxia* by culturing intact anthers. Since then a great deal of research has been devoted to the subject.

The basis of pollen and anther culture is that on an appropriate medium the pollen microspores of some plant species can be induced to give rise to vegetative cells, instead of pollen grains. This change from a normal sexual gametophytic pattern of development into a vegetative (sporophytic) pattern, appears to be initiated in an early phase of the cell cycle when transcription of genes concerned with gametophytic development is blocked and genes concerned with sporophytic development are activated (Sunderland and Dunwell, 1977). The result is that in place of pollen with the capacity to produce gametes and a pollen tube, microspores are produced capable of forming haploid pro-embryos (somatic embryos formed directly from the microspores), or callus tissue. The formation of plants from pollen microspores in this way is sometimes called *androgenesis.*

Haploid plants are more readily regenerated by culturing microspores within anthers than by culturing isolated pollen. The presence of the anther wall provides a stimulus to sporophytic development. The nature of the stimulus is not known but it may be nutritional and/or hormonal. Embryogenesis has only been induced from *isolated* pollen of a very small number of plants.

The number of plants species from which anther culture has resulted in haploid plants is relatively few. It comprised about 70 species in 29 genera up to 1975 (Sunderland and Dunwell, 1977) and 121 species or hybrids in 20 families by 1981–1982 (Maheshwari *et al.*, 1982) and by now, very many more. The early stages of embryogenesis or callus formation without plant regeneration have been obtained in several other kinds of plants. Fifty- eight per cent of the reports of embryogenesis or plant regeneration in Maheshwari *et al.* (1982) were attributable to species within the family Solanaceae. Species in which haploid plants can be regenerated reliably and at high frequency remain a comparatively small part of the total. They again mainly comprise Solanaceous species such as *Datura, Nicotiana, Hyoscyamus, Solanum* and some brassicas.

For further information on pollen and anther culture which is outside the scope of the present book, the reader should consult the following books or review articles:

Clapham (1977); Collins (1978);Dunwell (1985); Foroughi-Wehr and Wenzel (1989); Giles and Prakash (1987); Heberle-Bors (1985); Hu and Yang (1986); Keller and Stringham (1978); Maheshwari *et al.* (1980, 1982); Morrison and Evans (1988); Nitsch (1977, 1981; 1983); Raghavan (1990); Reinert and Bajaj (1977); Sangwan and Sangwan-Norreel (1990); Sunderland and Dunwell (1977); Sunderland (1974, 1979); Vasil (1980c).

GYNOGENESIS

Another theoretical source of haploid plants in angiosperms is the female egg nucleus or ovum; this is contained within the nucellus of an ovule in a specialised cell (the *megaspore* or *embryo sac*). The ovum cannot be separated readily from other associated nuclei in the megaspore and so haploid plants can normally be produced from it, only by stimulating the development of unfertilised ovules into seedlings. In some species [*e.g. Gerbera jamesonii* (Sitbon, 1981; Meynet and Sibi, 1984); maize (Truong-Andre and Demarly, 1984); sugar beet (Hosemans and Bossoutrot, 1983); onion (Keller, 1990)], some haploid plants can be obtained by culturing unpollinated ovules, ovaries or flower buds. In some other plants (Pavlova, 1986), larger numbers of haploids are obtained if ovaries are pollinated by a distantly-related species (or genus) or with pollen which has been irradiated with X– or γ–rays. Successful pollination results in stimulation of endosperm growth by fusion of one of the generative nuclei of the pollen tube with central fusion nucleus of the megaspore, but fusion of the other generative nucleus with the egg cell does not occur and the egg cell is induced to grow into a seedling without being fertilised (*gynogenesis*). An alternative technique which has resulted in haploid *Petunia* seedlings (Raquin, 1986) is to treat ovaries with γ–rays and then pollinate them with normal pollen.

Gynogenesis has so far been employed much less frequently than androgenesis for the production of haploids. A review of progress in this area has been provided by Yang and Zhou (1990).

PRACTICAL USES

Haploid cells and haploid plants produced by androgenesis or gynogenesis have many uses in plant breeding and genetics (Vasil and Nitsch, 1975). Most recent research on anther culture has concentrated on trying to improve the efficiency of plantlet regeneration in economically important species. Haploid plants of cereals are particularly valuable in breeding programmes, but in the Gramineae, the frequency and reliability of recovery through anther culture is still too low for routine use.

2

Plant Propagation and Micropropagation

SEED *Versus* SOMA

Plants can be propagated through their two developmental life cycles; the sexual, or the asexual.

- In the sexual cycle new plants arise after fusion of the parental gametes, and develop from embryos contained within seeds or fruits. In most cases seedlings will be variable and each one will represent a new combination of genes, brought about during the formation of gametes (meiotic cell division) and their sexual fusion. By contrast,

- In the vegetative (asexual) cycle the unique characteristics of any individual plant selected for propagation (termed the *mother plant, stock plant* or *ortet*) are usually perpetuated because, during normal cell division (mitosis), genes are typically copied exactly at each (mitotic) division. In most cases, each new plant (or *ramet*) produced by this method may be considered to be an extension of the somatic cell line of one (sexually produced or mutant) individual. A group of such asexually reproduced plants (ramets) is termed a *clone*.

In the natural environment sexual and asexual reproduction have their appropriate selective advantages according to the stage of evolution of different kinds of plants. Plants selected and exploited by man also have different propensities for propagation by seed or by vegetative means.

Propagation using seeds

Seeds have several advantages as a means of propagation:

- they are often produced in large numbers so that the plants regenerated from them are individually inexpensive;

- they may usually be stored for long periods without loss of viability;

- they are easily distributed;

- plants grown from seed are without most of the pest and diseases which may have afflicted their parents.

For many agricultural and horticultural purposes it is desirable to cultivate clones or populations of plants which are practically identical. However, the seeds of many plants typically produce plants which differ genetically, and to obtain seeds which will give uniform offspring is either very difficult, or impossible in practical terms. Genetically uniform populations of plants can result from seeds in three ways:

1. **From inbred (homozygous) lines** which can be obtained in self-fertile (autogamous) species. Examples of autogamous crops are wheat, barley, rice and tobacco.

2. **From F$_1$ seeds** produced by crossing two homozygous parents. Besides being uniform, F$_1$ plants may also display hybrid vigour. F$_1$ seeds of many flowers and vegetables are now available, but due to high production costs, they are expensive.

3. **From apomictic seedlings.** In a few genera, plants which are genotypically identical to their parents are produced by apomixis. Seeds are formed without fertilization and their embryos develop by one of several asexual processes that ensure that the new plants are genetically identical to the female parent (*i.e.* they have been vegetatively reproduced).

Some plants do not produce viable seeds, or do so only after a long juvenile period. Alternatively, to grow plants from seed may not provide a practical method of making new field plantings. In such instances vegetative propagation is the only means of perpetuating and multiplying a unique individual with desirable characteristics.

Vegetative propagation

Many important crop plants are increased vegetatively and grown as clones. They include cassava, potato, sugar cane and many soft (small) fruits and tree fruits. A very large number of herbaceous and woody ornamental plants are also propagated by these means. Suitable methods for vegetative propagation have been developed over many centuries. These traditional '*macro*-propagation' techniques (or '*macro*-methods') which utilise relatively large pieces of plants, have been refined and improved by modern horticultural research. For instance, methods of applying fine water mists to prevent the desiccation of cuttings, better rooting composts and the control of temperature in the rooting zone, have considerably enhanced the rate at which many plants of horticultural or agricultural interest can be multiplied. Research to improve macropropagation methods continues, but has lost some impetus in recent years with the continued extension of tissue culture for plant multiplication.

Whether it will be most rewarding to propagate a plant by seed, by traditional vegetative techniques, or by tissue culture, will often not only depend on the plant species, but also on the development of proven techniques, relative costs and agronomic objectives. The extent to which tissue culture methods can be used for genetic manipulations and for propagation is changing continuously. Until recently, potato plants have been raised from seed during breeding programmes to select new varieties: tissue culture may have been employed to multiply certain lines and to propagate disease-free stocks of established cultivars, while macropropagation of field-grown tubers has been used to provide normal planting material. New research into genetic manipulations and methods of propagation using tissue culture techniques, can alter this situation: diversity can be introduced and controlled through genetic engineering while certified stock of new varieties can be produced on a large scale by micropropagation.

The selection of a propagation method for any given plant is constrained by its genetic potential. For example, some plants readily produce adventitious shoot buds on their roots, while others do not; trying to propagate a plant, which does not have this capability, from root cuttings or root explants, will be unsuccessful both *in vivo* and *in vitro*. Plant tissue culture does overcome some genetically imposed barriers, but a clear effect of genotype is still apparent. It is not yet possible to induce an apple tree to produce tubers!

PROPAGATION IN VITRO

Advantages

Methods available for propagating plants *in vitro* are largely an extension of those already developed for conventional propagation. *In vitro* techniques have the following advantages over traditional methods:

— Cultures are started with very small pieces of plants (explants), and thereafter small shoots or embryos are propagated (hence the term 'micro-propagation' to describe the *in vitro* methods). Only a small amount of space is required to maintain plants or to greatly increase their number.

— Propagation is ideally carried out in aseptic conditions, free from pathogens. Once cultures have been started there should be no loss through disease, and the plantlets finally produced should be free from bacteria, fungi and other micro-organ-

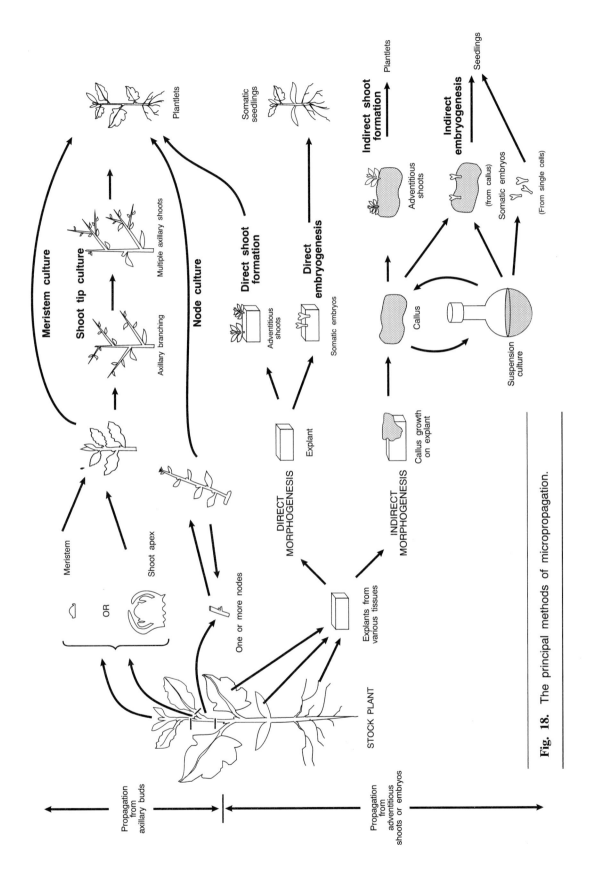

Fig. 18. The principal methods of micropropagation.

isms. (This may not always be the case, see Chapter 5).

— Methods are available to free plants from virus disease. Providing these techniques are employed, or virus-free material is used for initiating cultures, certified virus-free plants can be produced in large numbers.

— A more flexible adjustment of factors influencing vegetative regeneration is possible such as nutrient and growth regulator levels, light and temperature. The rate of propagation is therefore much greater than in macro-propagation and many more plants can be produced in a given time. This may enable newly selected varieties to be made available quickly and widely, and numerous plants to be produced in a short while. The technique is very suitable when high volume production is essential.

— It may be possible to produce clones of some kinds of plants that are otherwise slow and difficult (or even impossible) to propagate vegetatively.

— Plants may acquire a new temporary characteristic through micropropagation which makes them more desirable to the grower than conventionally-raised stock. A bushy habit (in ornamental pot plants) and increased runner formation (strawberries) are two examples.

— Production can be continued all the year round and is independent of seasonal changes.

— Vegetatively-reproduced material can often be stored over long periods.

— Less energy and space are required for propagation purposes and for the maintenance of stock plants (ortets).

— Plant material needs little attention between sub-cultures and there is no labour or materials requirement for watering, weeding, spraying etc. Micropropagtion is most advantageous when it costs less than traditional methods of multiplication; if this is not the case there must be some other important reason to make it worthwhile.

Disadvantages

The chief disadvantages of *in vitro* methods are that advanced skills are required for their successful operation; a specialised and expensive production facility is needed; fairly specific methods may be necessary to obtain optimum results from each species and variety;

and, because present methods are labour intensive, the cost of propagules is usually relatively high (Chapter 16). Further consequences of using *in vitro* adaptations are:

— Although they may be produced in large numbers, the plantlets obtained are initially small and sometimes have *undesirable* characteristics.

— In order to survive *in vitro*, explants and cultures have to be grown on a medium containing sucrose or some other carbon source. The plants derived from cultures are not initially able to produce their own requirement of organic matter by photosynthesis (*i.e.* they are not *autotrophic*) and have to undergo a transitional period before they are capable of independent growth.

— As they are raised within glass or plastic vessels in a high relative humidity, and are not usually photosynthetically self-sufficient, the young plantlets are more susceptible to water loss in an external environment. They may therfore have to be hardened in an atmosphere of slowly decreasing humidity and increased light.

— The chances of producing genetically aberrant plants may be increased.

A more extended discussion of all these points will be found in other sections.

TECHNIQUES

The methods that are theoretically available for the propagation of plants *in vitro* are illustrated in Fig. 18 and described in following sections of this chapter. They are essentially:

(i) by the multiplication of shoots from axillary buds:

(ii) by the formation of

adventitious shoots, and/or

adventitious somatic embryos,

either

a) directly

on pieces of tissue or organs (explants) removed from the mother plant;

or

b) indirectly

from unorganised cells (in suspension cultures) or tissues (in callus cultures) established by the proliferation of cells within explants;

on the semi-organised callus tissues or the propagation bodies (such as protocorms or pseudo-bulbils) that can be obtained from explants (particularly those from certain specialised whole plant organs).

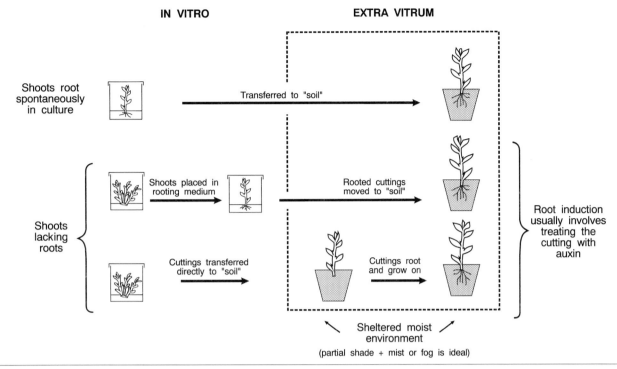

IN VITRO   **EXTRA VITRUM**

Shoots root
spontaneously
in culture

Transferred to "soil"

Shoots
lacking
roots

Shoots placed in
rooting medium

Rooted cuttings
moved to "soil"

Cuttings transferred
directly to "soil"

Cuttings root
and grow on

Root induction
usually involves
treating the
cutting with
auxin

Sheltered moist
environment
(partial shade + mist or fog is ideal)

Fig. 19. Alternative methods of rooting micropropagated shoots.

The techniques which have been developed for micropropagation are described in greater detail in the following sections of this chapter. In practice most micropropagated plants are produced at present by method (i), and those of only a few species (which will be instanced later) by method (ii). Shoots and/or plantlets do not always originate in a culture by a single method. For example, in shoot cultures, besides axillary shoots, there are sometimes adventitious shoots formed directly on existing leaves or stems, and/or shoots arising indirectly from callus at the base of the explant.

The most suitable and economic method for propagating plants of a particular species could well change with time. There are still severe limitations on the extent to which some methods can be used. Improvements will come from a better understanding of the factors controlling morphogenesis and genetic stability *in vitro*.

Rooting. Somatic embryos have both a root *and* a shoot meristem. Under ideal conditions they can grow into normal seedlings. The shoots procured from axillary or adventitious meristems are miniature cuttings. Sometimes these small cuttings form roots spontaneously, but usually they have to be assisted to do so (Fig. 19). The small rooted shoots produced by micropropagation are often called *plantlets*.

STAGES OF MICROPROPAGATION

Professor Murashige of the University of California (Riverside) defined three steps or stages (I–III) in the *in vitro* multiplication of plants (Murashige, 1974). These have been widely adopted by both research and commercial tissue culture laboratories because they not only describe procedural steps in the micropropagation process, but also usually represent points at which the cultural environment needs to be changed.

Some workers have suggested that the treatment and preparation of stock plants should be regarded as a separately numbered stage or stages. We have adopted the proposal of Debergh and Maene (1981) that such preparative procedures should be called Stage 0. A fourth stage (IV), at which plants are transferred to the external environment is now also commonly recognised. A general description of Stages 0—IV is therefore provided below, while the manner in which Stages I—III might be applied to different methods of micropropagation is given in Table 3.

Requirements for the completion of each stage of micropropagation vary according to the method being utilised; the progress of cultures will not always fit readily into neat compartments. Furthermore, it is not always neces-

Table 3. Stages in the available methods of micropropagation.

Method of Micropropagation	Stage of culture		
	I. Initiating a culture	**II.** Increasing propagules	**III.** Preparation for soil transfer
	Growth of excised tissues/organs in vitro free from algae, bacteria, fungi and other contaminants.	Inducing the cultures to produce numbers of shoots or somatic embryos	Separating and preparing propagules to have a high rate of survival as individual plants in the external environment
Shoot cultures	Transfer of disinfected shoot tips or lateral buds to solid or liquid media and the commencement of shoot growth to *ca*. 10 mm.	Induced multiple (axillary) shoot formation and growth of the shoots to a sufficient size for separation, either as new Stage II explants or for passage to III.	Elongation of buds formed at Stage II to uniform shoots. Rooting the shoots *in vitro* or outside the culture vessel.
Shoots from Floral Meristems	Aseptic isolation of pieces of compound floral meristems	Inducing the many meristems to produce vegetative shoots, then as shoot tip culture.	As for shoot tip culture.
Multiple Shoots from Seeds	Aseptic germination of seeds on a high cytokinin medium.	Inducing multiple shoot proliferation. Shoot subculture.	As for shoot tip culture.
Meristem culture	Transfer of very small shoot tips (length 0.2–0.5 mm) to culture. Longer shoot tips (1–2 mm) can be used as explants if obtained from heat treated plants.	Growth of shoots to *ca*. 10 mm, then as shoot tip culture, or shoot multiplication omitted and shoots transferred to Stage III.	As for shoot tip culture.
Node culture	As for shoot tip culture but shoots grown longer to show clear internodes.	Propagation by inducing the axillary bud at each node to grow into a single shoot. Subculturing can be repeated indefinitely.	As for shoot tip culture.
Direct Shoot regeneration from explants	Establishing suitable explants of mother plant tissue (e.g. leaf or stem segments) in culture without contamination.	The induction of shoots directly on the explant with no prior formation of callus. Shoots so formed can usually be divided and used as explants for new Stage II subcultures or shoot tip culture.	As for shoot tip culture
Direct Embryogenesis	Establishing suitable embryogenic tissue explants or previously-formed somatic embryos.	The direct induction of somatic embryos on the explants without prior formation of callus.	Growth of the embryos into plantlets which can be transferred to the outside environment.
Indirect Shoot regeneration from morphogenesic callus	Initiation and isolation of callus with superficial shoot meristems.	Repeated subculture of small callus pieces followed by transfer to a shoot-inducing medium. The growth of shoots *ca*. 10 mm. in length.	Individual shoots are grown and rooted.
Indirect Embryogenesis from embryogenetic callus or suspension cultures	Initiation and isolation of callus with the capacity to form somatic embryos, OR obtaining embryogenic suspension cultures from embryogenic callus or by *de novo* induction.	Subculture of the embryogenic callus or suspension culture followed by transfer to a medium favouring embryo development.	Growth of the somatic embryos into 'seedlings'.
Storage organ formation	Isolation and culture of tissue/organs capable of forming storage organs.	Inducing the formation of storage organs and sometimes dividing them to start new Stage II cultures.	Growing shoots/plantlets obtained from storage organs for transfer to soil: OR growing the storage organs themselves to a size suitable for soil planting.

sary to follow each of the prescribed steps. The stages are therefore described here for general guidance but should not be applied too rigidly.

Practices adopted at the various stages of micropropagation are discussed throughout the book, but are particularly mentioned in Chapters 12 and 14.

Stage 0: Mother plant selection and preparation

Before micropropagation commences, careful attention should be given to the selection of a stock plant or plants. They must be typical of the variety or species, and free from any symptoms of disease. It may be advantageous to treat the chosen plant (or parts of it) in some way to make *in vitro* culture successful. Steps to reduce the contamination level of explants (Chapter 4) were considered sufficiently important by Debergh and Maene (1981) to constitute a separate essential stage in a commercial micropropagation programme. Growth, morphogenesis and rates of propagation *in vitro* can be improved by appropriate environmental and chemical pre-treatment of stock plants: this subject is discussed in Chapter 8. Procedures to detect and reduce or eliminate systemic bacterial and virus diseases (see Chapter 5) may also be required. Disease indexing and disease elimination should be a definite part of all micropropagation work; but these precautions are unfortunately often omitted, sometimes with adverse consequencies. The difficulties which may be encountered in trying to propagate chimeras by tissue culture methods are discussed in Chapter 3.

It seems appropriate to include all procedures adopted in plant selection and pre-treatment within 'Stage 0'. The recognised numbering of Murashige's stages is then unaltered.

Stage I: Establishing an aseptic culture

The customary second step in the micropropagation process is to obtain an aseptic culture of the selected plant material. Success at this stage firstly requires that explants should be transferred to the cultural environment, free from obvious microbial contaminants; and that this should be followed by some kind of growth (*e.g.* growth of a shoot tip, or formation of callus on a stem piece). Usually a batch of explants is transferred to culture at the same time. After a short period of incubation, any containers found to have contaminated explants or medium are discarded. Stage I would be regarded as satisfactorily completed if an adequate number of explants had survived without contamination, and was growing on.

Stage I is unnecessary where micropropagation can be conducted under non-sterile conditions (see page 116).

Stage II: The production of suitable propagules

The object of Stage II is to bring about the production of new plant outgrowths or *propagules,* which, when separated from the culture are capable of giving rise to intact plants. According to the *in vitro* procedure that is being followed (Fig. 18), multiplication can be brought about from newly-derived axillary or adventitious shoots, somatics embryos, or miniature storage or propagative organs. In some micropropagation methods, Stage II will include the prior induction of meristematic centres from which adventitious organs may develop. Some of the propagules produced at Stage II (especially shoots) can also be used as the basis for further cycles of multiplication in that they can usually be cultured again (subcultured) to increase their number.

Stage III: Preparation for growth in the natural environment

Shoots or plantlets derived from Stage II are small, and not yet capable of self-supporting growth in soil or compost. At Stage III, steps are taken to grow individual plantlets, capable of carrying out photosynthesis, and survival without an artificial supply of carbohydrate. Some plantlets need to be specially treated at this stage so that they do not become stunted or dormant when taken out of the cultural environment. As originally proposed by Murashige, Stage III included the *in vitro* rooting of shoots prior to their transfer to soil.

Rooting shoots is a very important part of any *in vitro* propagation scheme. A few species form adventitious roots on shoots during the course of Stage III culture, but usually it is necessary to adopt a separate rooting procedure using special media, or methods, to induce roots to form. Sometimes shoots may need to be specially elongated before rooting is attempted. To reduce the costs of micropropagation, many laboratories now remove unrooted shoots from the *in vitro* environment and root them outside the culture vesssel (Fig. 19). Therefore, in cultures where micropropagation relies on adventitious or axillary shoots, Stage III is often conveniently divided, as Debergh and Maene (1981) suggested, into:

> **Stage IIIa,** the elongation of buds or shoots formed during Stage II, to provide shoots of a suitable size for Stage IIIb;

Stage IIIb, the rooting of Stage IIIa shoots *in vitro* or *extra vitrum*.

Procedures used to induce rooting are discussed in later chapters.

Stage IV: Transfer to the natural environment

Although not given a special numerical stage by Murashige, the methods whereby plantlets are transferred from the *in vitro* to the *ex vitro* external environment are extremely important. If not carried out carefully, transfer can result in significant loss of propagated material. There are two main reasons:

- Shoots developed in culture have often been produced in high humidity and a low light 'intensity'. This results in there being less leaf epicuticular wax than on plants raised in growth chambers or greenhouses. In some plants, the stomata of leaves produced *in vitro* may also be atypical and incapable of complete closure under conditions of low relative humidity. Tissue cultured plants therefore lose water rapidly when moved to external conditions (Sutter and Langhans, 1979, 1980).

- When supplied with sucrose (or some other carbohydrate) and kept in low light conditions, micropropagated plantlets are not fully dependent on their own photosynthesis (they are *mixotrophic* — Chapter 7). A stimulus which is not provided in the closed *in vitro* environment seems to be needed for them to change to being fully capable of producing their own requirements of carbon and reduced nitrogen (*i.e.* before they become capable of feeding themselves — *autotrophic)* (Marin and Gella, 1987). The change only occurs after the plants have spent a period of several days *ex vitro*.

In practice, plantlets are removed from their Stage III containers, and if they have been grown on agar, it is carefully washed from the roots. The application of an anti-transpirant film to the leaves has been recommended at this stage, but in practice, seems to be seldom used. Plantlets are then transplanted into a 'sterile' rooting medium (such as a peat:sand compost) and kept for several days in high humidity and reduced light 'intensity'. A fog of water vapour is very effective for maintaining humidity. Alternatively, intermittent water misting may be applied automatically, or the plants placed inside a clear plastic enclosure and misted by hand. With some plants, an *in vitro* Stage III can be omitted; shoots from Stage II are rooted directly in high humidity, and, at the same time, gradually hardened to the exterior environment.

The rooting of shoots using these methods is discussed fully in Chapter 14.

MICROPROPAGATION METHODS

THE PROPAGATION OF PLANTS FROM AXILLARY SHOOTS

The production of plants from axillary shoots has proved to be the most generally applicable and reliable method of *in vitro* propagation. Two methods are in use:

- Shoot culture

- Single, or multiple, node culture.

Both depend on stimulating precocious axillary shoot growth by overcoming the dominance of shoot apical meristems.

Shoot (or shoot tip) culture

The term *shoot culture* is now preferred for cultures started from explants bearing an intact shoot meristem, whose purpose is shoot multiplication by the repeated formation of axillary branches. In this technique, newly formed shoots (or shoot bases) serve as explants for repeated proliferation; severed shoots are finally rooted to form plantlets which can be grown *in vivo*. This the most widely used method of micropropagation.

Explant size. Shoot cultures are conventionally started from the apices of lateral or main shoots, up to 20 mm in length, dissected from actively-growing shoots or dormant buds. Larger explants are also sometimes used with advantage: they may consist of a larger part of the shoot apex or be stem segments bearing one or more lateral buds; sometimes shoots from other *in vitro* cultures are employed. When apical or lateral buds were used almost excusively as explants, the name 'shoot tip culture' came to be widely used for cultures of this kind. As the use of larger explants has become more common, the term *shoot culture* has become more appropriate .

Large explants have an advantage over smaller ones for initiating shoot tip cultures in that they:

— better survive the transfer to *in vitro* conditions,

— more rapidly commence growth, and

— contain more axillary buds.

However, the greater the size of the explant, the more difficult it may be to decontaminate from micro-organisms; in practice the size used will be the largest that can be gained in an aseptic condition. Shoot cultures are also frequently started directly from the shoots obtained from meristem tip cultures. Virus irradiation then precedes the shoot multiplication phase. Occasionally fragmented or macerated shoot tips are used (see elsewhere).

Meristem tip or *meristem* cultures are used for virus elimination (see Chapter 5). Meristem cultures are initiated from much smaller explants and a single plantlet is usually produced from each.

Regulating shoot proliferation

The growth and proliferation of axillary shoots in shoot cultures is usually promoted by incorporating growth regulators (usually cytokinins) into the growth medium. Treatment effectively removes the dominance of apical meristems so that axillary shoots are produced, often in large numbers. These shoots are used as miniature cuttings for plant multiplication.

Removing the apex. In some plants, pinching out the main shoot axis is used as an alternative, or an adjunct, to the use of growth regulators for decreasing apical dominance. Pinching was found to be effective for some kinds of rose (Bressan *et al.*, 1982) and for some apple cultivars (Yae *et al.*, 1987). Pinching or 'tipping' is usually done when plant material is removed for subculturing, for example removing the apical bud at the first subculture increased the branching of *Pistacia* shoot cultures (Barghchi, 1986b). An effective kind of shoot tipping occurs when shoots are cropped as microcuttings. Standardi (1982) and Shen and Mullins (1984) obtained effective shoot proliferation of *Rosa* varieties by transferring the basal shoot clump which is left at this stage, to fresh medium for further proliferation. (Note however that this practice can increase the likelihood of obtaining deviant plants — see below). In just a few plants neither cytokinins nor pinching effectively remove apical dominance. Geneve *et al.* (1990) reported that seedling shoots of *Gymnocladus dioicus* produced 1–5 shoots, but only one grew to any appreciable length. If this shoot was removed, another took over.

Placing explants horizontally. In pear, pinching out the tips of shoots resulted in the growth of larger axillary shoots than in the controls, but the number of shoots was less. The most effective physical check to apical dominance was achieved by pinching the tips, and/or placing shoot explants horizontally on the medium (Lane, 1979b; MacKay and Kitto, 1988). The treatment can be effective with many other woody plants: horizontal placement of shoot sections, consisting of 2–3 nodes, resulted in more axillary shoots being produced in cultures of *Acer rubrum*, *Amelanchier spicata*, *Betula nigra*, *Forsythia intermedia* and *Malus* × domestica, than when explants were upright (McClelland and Smith, 1990). Favourable results have also been reported with lilac (Hildebrandt and Harney, 1983) and other apple cultivars (Yae *et al.*, 1987).

The origin of shoots

Unfortunately not all the shoots arising in shoot cultures may originate from axillary buds. Frequently, adventitious shoots also arise, either directly from cultured shoot material, or indirectly from callus at the base of the subcultured shoot mass. For example, Nasir and Miles (1981) discovered that in subcultures of an apple rootstock, some new shoots arose from callus at the base of the shoot clump; both adventitious and axillary shoots were produced in *Hosta* cultures (Papachatzi *et al.*, 1981); and shoot proliferation from some kinds of potato shoot tips was exclusively from organogenic callus (Roca *et al.*, 1978).

The precise origin of shoots can sometimes only be determined from a careful anatomical examination. Hussey (1983) has termed cultures providing both adventitious and axillary shoots, 'mixed cultures'. Adventitious shoots, particularly those arising indirectly from callus, are not desirable. For reasons described in Chapter 3, shoots of axillary origin will normally be genetically identical to the parent plant, whereas there is a high probability that those regenerated from callus may differ in one or more characters. Genetically deviant plants may not occur with high frequency from newly initiated callus, but could begin to appear in significant number if shoot masses incorporating basal callus are simply chopped up to provide explants for subculture. The use of a strict protocol, using only axillary shoots, may present problems with some plants where the rate of shoot multiplication is comparatively slow. This has led to attempts by some workers to use a more relaxed regime and accept a proportion of adventitious shoots (*e.g.* with *Kalanchoe blossfeldiana* — Schwaiger and Horn, 1988). The usual consequence is a degree of variation amongst ramets which may, or may not, be acceptable. The formation of callus on shoot tip explants and the subsequent development of adventitious shoots can often be controlled by modifying the growth regulators in the medium.

Fragmentation of a meristem tip, or its culture in a certain way, can lead to the formation of multiple adventitious shoots which can be used for plant propagation. These modifications of conventional shoot culture are described on page 49 and in Chapter 5.

History

Although shoot culture has proved to be a widely applicable method of micropropagation, an appreciation of its potential value developed only slowly, and utilisation largely depended on improvements in tissue culture technology.

Robbins (1922a) seems to have been the first person to have successfully cultured excised shoot tips on a medium containing sugar. Tip explants of between 1.75 and 3.75 mm were taken from pea, corn and cotton, and placed in a liquid medium. For some reason the cultures were maintained in the dark where they only produced shoots with small chlorotic leaves and numerous roots. Although it is tempting to suppose that the potential of shoot culture for plant propagation might have been appreciated at a much earlier date had the cultures been transferred to the light, the rapid rate of shoot multiplication achieved in modern use of this technique depends on later developments in plant science.

Only very slow progress in shoot culture was made during the next 20 years. As part of his pioneering work on plant tissue culture, White (1933) experimented with small meristem tips (0.1 mm or less) of chickweed (*Stellaria media)*, but they were only maintained in hanging drops of nutrient solution. Leaf or flower primordia were observed to develop over a six week period. Shoot culture of a kind was also carried out by La Rue (1936). His explants largely consisted of the basal and upper halves of seed embryos. Nevertheless, the apical plumular meristems of several plants were grown to produce entire plants. Whole plants were also obtained from axillary buds of the aquatic plant *Radicula aquatica*.

Significant shoot growth from vegetative shoot tip explants was first achieved by Loo, and reported in 1945 and 1946. *Asparagus* shoot tips 5–10 mm in length were supported on glass wool over a liquid medium and later grown on a solidified substrate. Loo made several significant observations showing that:

— growth depended on sucrose concentration, higher levels being necessary in the dark than in the light;

— explants, instead of being supported, could be grown satisfactorily on 0.5% agar;

— *in vitro* shoot growth could apparently be continued indefinitely (35 transfers were made over 22 months);

— shoot tip culture afforded a way to propagate plant material (clones were established from several excised shoot apices).

This work failed to progress further because no roots were formed on the *Asparagus* shoots in culture. Honours for establishing the principles of modern shoot culture must therefore be shared between Loo and Ball. Ball (1946) was the first person to produce rooted shoots from cultured shoot apices. His explants consisted of an apical meristem and 2–3 leaf primordia. There was no shoot multiplication but plantlets of nasturtium (*Tropaelum majus)* and white lupin (*Lupinus alba*) were transferred to soil and grown successfully.

During several subsequent years, shoot apex (or meristem tip) culture was of interest only to plant pathologists who recognised its value for producing virus-free plants. It was during studies of this kind that Morel made the significant discovery of protocorm formation from *Cymbidium* orchid shoot tips. Although they may be started from the same explants, cultures giving rise to protocorms are not typical shoot cultures (see page 54).

The two major developments which made shoot culture feasible were the development of improved media for plant tissue culture (Murashige and Skoog, 1962) and the discovery of the cytokinins as a class of growth regulators (Miller, 1961b; Skoog *et al.*, 1965), with an ability to release lateral buds from dormancy (Wickson and Thimann, 1958; Sachs and Thimann, 1964). These developments were not immediately applied to shoot culture, and some years elapsed before it was appreciated that multiple shoots could be induced to form by appropriate growth regulator treatments.

Hackett and Anderson (1967) got either single shoots from carnation shoot apices, or else a proliferative tissue from which shoots were later regenerated. A similar kind of direct or indirect shoot proliferation was reported from *Nicotiana rustica* shoot tips by Walkey and Woolfitt (1968). Vine and Jones (1969) were able to transfer large shoot tips of hop (*Humulus*) to culture, but shoots were only rooted, and showed a high propensity for callus formation. Reports of plant multiplication using conventional shoot culture methods began to appear in the next decade.

Haramaki (1971) described the rapid multiplication of *Gloxinia* by shoot culture and by 1972 several reports of successful micropropagation by this method had appeared (Adams, 1972; Haramaki and Murashige, 1972). Since then the number of papers on shoot culture publish-

Fig. 20. Axillary shoots forming on a seedling explant of *Pinus*.

some species (*e.g. Eucalyptus*) it is an advantage to commence shoot cultures with a piece of the stem of the mother plant bearing one or more buds (stem nodes). Shoot growth from the bud, and treatment of the culture, is thereafter the same as in conventional shoot tip culture. The use of nodal explants should not be confused with *node culture* in which a method of shoot multiplication is used that is different to that in shoot culture (see later). Explants for shoot cultures are usually first placed on a semi-solid medium.

Shoot tips from trees, or other woody perennials, can be difficult to decontaminate. Because of this, Standardi and Catalano (1985) preferred to initiate shoot cultures of *Actinidia chinensis* from meristem tips which could be sterilised more easily. Shoot tips of woody plants are more liable than those of herbaceous species to release undesirable phenolic substances when first placed onto a growth medium. Buds taken from mature parts of the shrub or tree can also be reluctant to grow *in vitro* and seasonal factors may reinforce natural dormancy in buds from any source, so that cultures can only be readily initiated at certain times of the year (see Chapter 8). Shoot tip or lateral bud explants are usually most readily induced into growth if taken from juvenile shoots (see page 239) such as those of seedlings or young plants. The juvenile shoots which sometimes emerge from the base of mature plants or which arise form heavily pruned or coppiced bushes and trees, are alternative sources. However, developing techniques have made it possible to propagate some woody ornamentals, forest trees and fruit trees, using explants derived from mature shoots (see Chapter 17). De Fossard *et al.* (1977) could initiate cultures of *Eucalyptus ficifolia* with shoot tips from 36 year-old trees, but forest-gathered material was very difficult to decontaminate unless covered and protected for some period before excision.

Secondary explants. Stage II subcultures are initiated from axillary shoots separated from primary shoot clusters. Shoot tips may not be the best explants at this stage. A higher rate of shoot proliferation is often obtained from nodal explants or by subdivision of the basal shoot mass. Shoot tips were the best secondary explant for *Rosa* cv. 'Fraser McClay', but with cherry (cv. 'F12/1') nodal explants gave more than twice as many shoots, and basal masses, three times as many as shoot tips (Hutchinson, 1985).

To minimise the risk of genetic change in ramets, explants for subculture and shoots to be transferred to Stage III, should, as far as possible, be chosen from new shoots of axillary origin. It may be advisable to adjust the growth regulator content of the medium so that adventitious shoots are not formed, even though the rate of overall shoot multiplication is thereby reduced. In some circum-

ed annually has increased dramatically and the method has been utilised increasingly for commercial plant propagation. Factors which have influenced the choice of shoot culture for practical micropropagation have been:

— the way in which the method can be applied to a wide range of different plant species, using the same principles and basic methods;

— the possibility of obtaining simultaneous virus control;

— a general uniformity and 'trueness to type' of the regenerated plants;

— the relatively high rates of propagation which is possible in many species.

Methods

Primary explants. In most herbaceous plants, shoot tip explants may be derived from either apical or lateral buds of an intact plant, and consist of the meristematic stem apex with a subtended rudimentary stem bearing several leaf initials (Fig. 21). In the axils of the more developed leaf primordia there will be axillary bud meristems. In

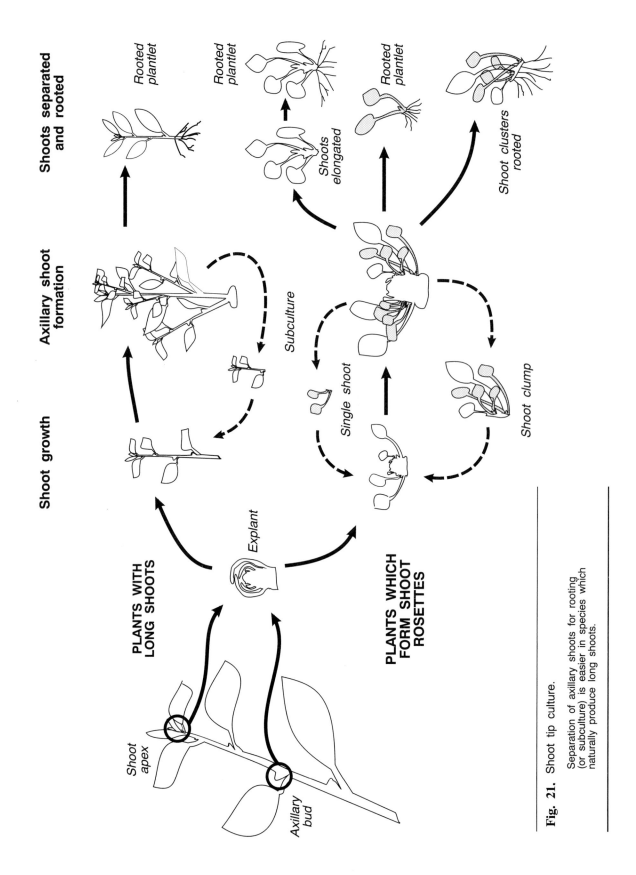

Fig. 21. Shoot tip culture.

Separation of axillary shoots for rooting (or subculture) is easier in species which naturally produce long shoots.

stances callus arising at the base of shoot tips may be semi-organised and therefore capable of producing genetically-stable plants (Chapter 3).

Stage II cultures are typically without roots, and shoots need to be detached and treated as miniature cuttings which, when rooted, will provide the new plants which are required.

Media and growth regulators. Advice on the selection of appropriate media for shoot cultures is given in Chapters 10 and 12. A notable feature of shoot culture is the need for high cytokinin levels at Stage II to promote the growth of multiple axillary shoots. A description of the compounds which can be employed and effective rates of treatment is given in Chapters 11 and 12.

Cytokinin growth regulators are usually extremely effective in removing the apical dominance of shoots. Their use can be combined with pinching the apex of shoots, or placing explants in an horizontal position (page 45). Cytokinin treatment can not only promote the formation of multiple shoots, but also (if the compound used is unsuitable, or the concentration used is too high), cause the shoots formed to be too short for rooting and transfer.

Because or their nature, or the absence of an adequate method of culture, plants of some kinds fail to produce multiple shoots at Stage II and retain their apical dominance. In shoot cultures of *Gymnocladus dioicus*, for example, despite the formation of several axillary shoots in the presence of BAP cytokinin, one shoot nearly always became dominant over the others (Geneve *et al.*, 1990). Most plants of this kind are best propagated by node culture (see below).

Elongation. The length of the axillary shoots produced in shoot cultures varies considerably from one kind of plant to another. Species which have an elongated shoot system *in vivo* will produce axillary shoots which can be easily separated as *microcuttings* and then individually rooted. Apically dominant shoots which have not branched can be treated in the same way.

At the other extreme are plants with a natural rosette habit of growth, which tend to produce shoot clusters in culture (Fig. 21). When these are micropropagated, it is difficult to separate individual shoots for use as secondary explants. It may then only be practical to divide the shoot mass into pieces and re-culture the fragments. Such shoot clusters can be induced to form roots when plants with a bushy habit are required (*e.g.* many species sold in pots for their attractive foliage). Otherwise it is necessary to specially elongate shoots before they are rooted (Stage IIIa). Shoot clusters are treated in such a way that axillary shoot formation is reduced, and shoot growth promoted. Individual shoots are then more readily handled and can

be rooted as microcuttings. Methods for elongating shoots are discussed in Chapters 11 and 12.

Rooting and transfer. The cytokinin growth regulators added to shoot culture media at Stage II to promote axillary shoot growth, usually inhibit root formation. Single shoots or shoot clusters must therefore be moved to a different medium for rooting *in vitro* before being transferred as plantlets to the external environment. An alternative strategy for some plants is to root the plant material *extra vitrum*. The methods employed are described in Chapter 14. Treatments need to be varied according to the type of growth; the nature of the shoot proliferation produced during Stage II culture; and the plant habit required by the customer.

To indicate how cultures having different branching capabilities need to be treated at Stage III, and whether Stage II cultures need to be passed to Stage IIIa before rooting, De Fossard (1986) found it useful, in his laboratory, to append suffixes to the conventional Stage II and Stage III labels, such as '–AD' (apically dominant), '–MS' (producing multiple shoots), and '–MC' (intended for microcuttings).

Current applications. Conventional shoot culture continues to be the most important method of micropropagation. It is very widely used by commercial tissue culture laboratories for the propagation of many herbaceous ornamental species and woody plants (see Chapters 16 and 17 for further details). The large numbers of manipulations required does, however, make the cost of each plantlet produced by this method comparatively expensive. Some success has been achieved in automating some stages of the process, in applying techniques for large-scale multiplication and in the use of robotics for plant separation and planting (Chapter 16).

Shoot proliferation from meristem tips

Barlass and Skene (1978; 1980a,b; 1982a,b) have shown that new shoots can be formed adventitiously when shoot tips of grapevine or *Citrus* are cut into several pieces before culture. Tideman and Hawker (1982) also had success using fragmented apices with *Asclepias rotundifolia* but not with *Euphorbia peplus*. Usually leaf-like structures first develop from the individual fragments, these enlarge and shoots form from basal swellings. Axillary shoots often arise from the initial adventitious shoots.

Shoot cultures transferred to agitated liquid culture may form a proliferating mass of shoots. Although high rates of multiplication are possible, leafy shoots usually become hyperhydric (see Chapter 13). However, in some species at least, shoots can be reduced in size to little more

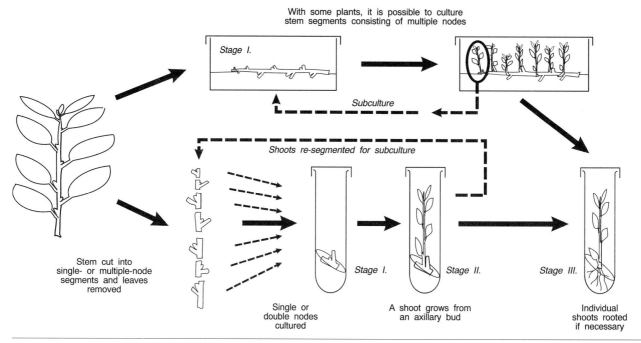

With some plants, it is possible to culture
stem segments consisting of multiple nodes

Stage I.

Subculture

Shoots re-segmented for subculture

Stem cut into
single- or multiple-node
segments and leaves
removed

Single or
double nodes
cultured

Stage I.

A shoot grows from
an axillary bud

Stage II.

Individual
shoots rooted
if necessary

Stage III.

Fig. 22. Single and multiple node culture.
Stage I cultures can be initiated also from meristem or shoot tips.

than proliferating shoot initials which are then suitable for large-scale multiplication (Chapters 12 and 16). A somewhat similar kind of culture consisting of superficial shoot meristems on a basal callus can sometimes be initiated from shoot tip explants or from the base of shoot cultures (page 54).

Single and multiple node culture (*in vitro* layering)

Single node culture is another *in vitro* technique which can be used for propagating some species of plants from axillary buds.

Primary explants

As with shoot culture, the primary explant for single node culture is a shoot apex, a lateral bud or a piece of shoot bearing one or more buds (*i.e.* having one or more nodes). When shoot apices are used, it can be advantageous to initiate cultures with large explants (up to 20 mm), unless virus-free cultures are required, when small meristem-tips will be employed.

Unbranched shoots are grown at Stage I until they are 5–10 cm in length and have several discrete and separated nodes. An environment which promotes etiolated shoot growth may be an advantage. Then at Stage II, instead of inducing axillary shoot growth with growth regulators (as in shoot culture), one of two manipulative methods is

used to overcome apical dominance and promote lateral bud break (Fig. 19):

- intact individual shoots may be placed on a fresh medium in an horizontal position. This method has been used by Wang (1977) to propagate potatoes, and has been termed '*in vitro* layering';

- each shoot may be cut into single- , or several-node pieces which are sub-cultured. Leaves are usually trimmed so that each second stage explant consists of a piece of stem bearing one or more lateral buds.

Unfortunately, *in vitro* layering seldom results in several axillary shoots of equal length, as shown in Fig. 22; apical dominance usually causes the leading shoot, or shoots, to grow more rapidly than the rest. El Hasan Anas and Debergh (1987) found that, even in potato, node culture was preferable. Note that 'node culture', is distinct from shoot cultures started from the nodes of seedlings or mature plants.

Secondary explants

The sprouted axillary buds obtained by either of the two methods above, are grown into single unbranched shoots. These are dissected and used to initiate new subcultures, or are rooted to produce plantlets. Node culture is therefore the simplest method of *in vitro* propagation, as it requires only that shoot growth should occur. Methods of rooting are the same as those employed for the microcut-

Table 4. Examples of the use of node culture in micropropagation.

Monocotyledons		*Solanum spp.*	Haberlach *et al.* (1985), Levy (1988), Sihachakr *et al.* (1988)
Alstroemeria	Hussey *et al.* (1980)		
Cymbopogon spp.	Jagadish Chandra and Sreenath (1982)	**Woody dicotyledons**	
Poa pratensis	Pieper and Smith (1988)	*Carpinus betulus*	Chalupa (1981a)
Asparagus officinalis	Yang and Clore (1973, 1974a)	*Castanea sativa*	Vieitez and Vieitez (1980b),
Dioscorea spp.	Ammirato (1976, 1982), Chaturvedi and Sinha (1979b)	*Castanea mollissima*	Yang *et al.* (1986)
		Eucalyptus grandis	Cresswell and Nitsch (1975)
Zea mays	King and Shimamoto (1984)	*Forsythia ovata*	Einset and Alexander (1985)
Orchid monocots.		*Fraxinus pennsylvanica*	Einset and Alexander (1985)
Dendrobium spp.	Ball and Arditti (1976)	*Juglans regia*	Dandekar *et al.* (1988)
Phalaenopsis spp.	Tanaka and Sakanishi (1978)	*Hevea brasiliensis*	Chen Z. (1984)
Thunia alba	Singh and Prakash (1984)	*Leucaena leucocephala*	Goyal *et al.* (1985)
Vanilla planifolia	Kononowicz and Janick (1984a)	*Ligustrum obtusifolium*	Einset and Alexander (1985)
Herbaceous dicotyledons		*Lonicera periclymenum*	Boonnour *et al.* (1988)
		Olea europea	Rugini and Fontenazza (1981)
Angelonia salicariaefolia	Datta and Datta (1984)	*Paulownia tomentosa*	Burger *et al.* (1985)
Cucumis sativus	Handley and Chambliss (1979)	*Poncirus trifoliata*	Barlass and Skene (1982b)
Glycyrrhiza glabra	Shah and Dalal (1980, 1982)	*Prosopis juliflora*	Wainwright and England (1987)
Rosmarinus officinalis	Misra and Chaturvedi (1984)	*Prunus armeniaca*	Snir (1984)
Rorippa nasturtium	Wainwright and Marsh (1986)	*Quercus robur*	Chalupa (1984a,b)
Solanum tuberosum	Hussey and Stacey (1981a), Kristensen (1984)	*Salix* spp.	Chalupa (1981a, 1983)
		Syringa spp.	Einset and Alexander (1985)
		Syringa × chinensis	Welander N.T.(1987)

tings derived from shoot culture, except that prior elongation of shoots is unnecessary.

Media and growth regulators. Media for single node culture are intrinsically the same as those suitable for shoot culture. As in shoot culture, optimum growth rate may depend on the selection of a medium particularly suited to the species being propagated, but adequate results can usually be produced from well-known formulations. It is often unnecessary to add growth regulators to the medium; for example, the shoots of some plants (*e.g. Chrysanthemum × morifolium*) elongate satisfactorily without any being provided. If they are required, regulants at both Stages I and II will usually comprise an auxin and a cytokinin at rates sufficient to support active shoot growth, but not tissue proliferation or lateral bud

growth. Sometimes gibberellic acid is advantageously added to the medium to make shoots longer and thus facilitate single node separation.

Current applications

Node culture is of value for propagating species that produce elongated shoots in culture (*e.g.* potato and *Alstroemeria*), especially if stimulation of lateral bud break is difficult to bring about with available cytokinins. The rate of multiplication is generally less than that which can be brought about through shoot culture, but there is less likelihood of associated callus formation and the formation of adventitious shoots, so that Stage II subculture carries very little risk of induced genetic irregularity. For this reason, node culture has been increasingly recommended by research workers as the micropropagation method least likely to induce mutation. In recent years, it has come to be used for a wide range of herbaceous and woody dicotyledons and several monocotyledons. Although it is not suited to all species and still not as widely used as shoot culture, there are some plants for which it is particularly useful. Some of the plants for which node culture has been described are listed in Table 4.

Multiple shoots from seeds (MSS)

During the early 1980's it was discovered that it was possible to initiate multiple shoot cultures directly from seeds. Seeds are sterilised and then placed onto a basal medium containing a cytokinin. As germination occurs, clusters of axillary and/or adventitious shoots ('multiple shoots') grow out, and may be split up and serially subcultured on the same medium. High rates of shoot multiplication are possible. For instance, Hisajima (1982a) estimates that 10 million shoots of almond could be derived theoretically from one seed in a year.

It is likely that multiple shoots can be initiated from the seeds of many species, particularly dicotyledons. The technique is effective in both herbaceous and woody species: soybean (Cheng *et al.*, 1980; Hisajima, 1981; Hisajima and Church, 1981): sugar beet (Powling and Hussey, 1981): almond (Hisajima, 1981; 1982a,b,c): walnut (Rodriguez, 1982b): pumpkin and melon (Hisajima, 1981): cucumber and pumpkin (Hisajima, 1981, 1982c): pea, peanut, mung bean, radish, *Zea mays* and rice (Hisajima, 1982c).

Shoots from floral meristems

Meristems that would normally produce flowers or floral parts can sometimes be induced to give vegetative shoots *in vitro*. Success depends on the use of young inflorescences where the determination of individual flower meristems is not canalized. Meristems in older inflorescences are likely to give rise to floral structures. Culture of immature inflorescence segments has, for example, resulted in shoot formation in :

Broccoli	Anderson and Carstens (1977)
Cauliflower	Pow (1969), Margara (1969a,b,c; 1977a), Crisp and Walkey (1974), Grout and Crisp (1977), Trimboli *et al.* (1977)
Coconut	Eeuwens and Blake (1977)
Chrysanthemum	Shu O Wang and Su Shien Ma (1978)
Date palm	Drira and Benbadis (1985)
Onion	Dunstan and Short (1977b; 1979a)

Sugar beet	Coumans-Gilles *et al.* (1981)

The exact origin of the shoots produced has not always been determined. In cauliflower and coconut they were thought to originate from actual flower meristems, but in sugar beet, from floral axillary buds. Some shoots formed from onion flower heads arose from various parts of the flower buds, but they were accompanied by other shoots which arose adventitiously over the entire receptacle surface. Shoots formed from young flower buds may therefore not always result from the reversion of floral meristems. In fact the direct formation of adventitious shoots is more widely reported.

PROPAGATION BY DIRECT ORGANOGENESIS

Direct adventitious shoot initiation

In certain species, adventitious shoots which arise directly from the tissues of the explant (and not within previously-formed callus) can provide a reliable method for micropropagation. However, the induction of direct shoot regeneration depends on the nature of the plant organ from which the explant was derived, and is highly dependent on plant genotype. In responsive plants, adventitious shoots can be formed *in vitro* on pieces of tissue derived from various organs (*e.g.* leaves, stems, flower petals or roots); in others species, they occur on only a limited range of tissues such as bulb scales, seed embryos or seedling tissues. Direct morphogenesis is observed rarely, or is unknown, in many plant genera.

Direct shoot formation is sometimes accompanied by proliferation of unorganised cells, and a regenerative tissue that could be classed as callus, may ultimately appear. Its formation can usually be reduced by adjustment of the growth regulators in the medium. Because there is a risk of regenerating plants with a different genetic identity (see Chapter 3), use of the callus for further propagation is not recommended unless it has a highly organised nature (see later). In some instances, the growth regulators used to initiate shoot buds directly on explants may not be conducive to continued bud growth. A closely packed mass of shoot primordia may then be mistaken for organised callus.

In those species where adult tissues have a high regenerative capacity, the main advantages of micropropagation by direct adventitious shoot regeneration are that:

— Initiation of Stage I cultures and Stage II shoot multiplication, are more easily achieved than by shoot culture. It is, for example, simpler to transfer aseptically several pieces of *Saintpaulia* leaf petiole to culture medium, than to isolate an equivalent number of shoot meristems.

— Rates of propagation can be high, particularly if numerous small shoots arise rapidly from each explant.

Stage I

Stage I consists of the establishment *in vitro* of suitable pieces of tissue, free from obvious contamination. As adventitious shoots are usually initiated on the tissue without transfer, Stages I and II are not generally discrete.

Stage II

Stage II of this micropropagation method is recognised by the formation, growth and proliferation of adventitious shoots from the primary explant. Stage II subcultures might, theoretically, then be established from individual shoots by the techniques familiar in shoot culture. In practice, in plants such as *Saintpaulia*, both further adventitious shoots and axillary shoots may develop in later stages of propagation. The result is a highly proliferative shoot mass and a very rapid rate of propagation. Subcultures are made by transferring shoot clumps (avoiding basal callus) to fresh media. Plants which form only a few adventitious shoots per explant, can sometimes be further multiplied by axillary shoot formation.

Adventitious shoots sometimes arise directly from the leaves of plants during shoot culture. This often happens when leaves bend down to touch the semi-solid medium. Adventitious shoot formation of certain plants will take place in large vessels of aerated liquid medium, allowing the scale of propagation to be much increased (see the discussion on liquid media in Chapter 7).

Stage III

This is similar to the Stage III of most propagation systems. Individual shoots or shoot clumps are transferred to a nutrient medium with added growth regulators that do not encourage further shoot proliferation and which promote rooting: alternatively shoots may be removed from culture and rooted *ex vitro*.

Some current applications

Several ornamental plants are at present propagated *in vitro* by direct shoot regeneration. Chief among these are plants of the family Gesneriaceae, (including *Achimenes, Saintpaulia, Sinningia* and *Streptocarpus*), where shoot buds can be freely regenerated directly on leaf explants without the formation of any intervening callus phase.

Many other ornamentals and crop plants either are (or could be) propagated efficiently by this means, for example, begonias, *Epiphyllum,* cacti, *Gerbera, Hosta* and *Lilium.* Further examples are quoted in the tables of Chapter 17.

Regeneration from root pieces. *In vitro* shoot regeneration from root pieces is mainly reported from plants which possess thick fleshy roots such as those of the genera *Cichorium, Armoracia, Convolvulus,* and *Taraxacum.* It is, however, a method of propagation that is potentially applicable to a wide range of species (Browse, 1980; Hodge, 1986).Shoots have, for instance, been induced to form directly on segments and apices of the roots of *Citrus* and *Poncirus* seedlings (Sauton *et al.,* 1982). Shoot regeneration from root pieces does not offer a continuous method of micropropagation unless there is a ready supply of aseptic root material (*e.g.* from isolated root cultures). Roots grown in soil *in vivo* are usually heavily contaminated and can be difficult to sterilize to provide an adequate number of uncontaminated cultures. They can however be used as an initial source of shoots which can be multiplied afterwards by shoot culture.

Tissue maceration

The capacity of young fern tissue to regenerate adventitious shoots can be very high. Fern prothallus tissue (the gametophyte generation produced from germinating spores) has a high capacity for regeneration; a new prothallus can usually be grown from small isolated pieces of tissue (Whittier and Steeves, 1962), or even from single cells produced by maceration (Miller J.H., 1968; De Fossard, 1976; Knauss, 1976b). Plants can also be regenerated from homogenised sporophyte tissue of some fern genera, and homogenisation has been incorporated into tissue culture, or partial tissue culture techniques for the propagation of plants of this class (see Chapter 17).

Because a high proportion of the direct cost of micropropagation is attributable to the manual separation and transfer of explants and cultured material between media (Chapter 16), the ability to regenerate plants from macerated tissue would be extremely advantageous. Unfortunately there there seem to be no publications describing the formation of shoots directly from machine-macerated tissue of higher plants apart from a patent of Lindemann (1984) (see the patents table in Chapter 16), the claims of which may have been somewhat optimistic. However, shoot regeneration from fragmented shoot tips (page 49), or micropropagation of some plants by culturing shoot material or tissue fragments in fermentors (Chapter 16), are somewhat comparable.

Organised calluses

In most callus cultures, shoots are produced from meristems which arise irregularly and so are very likely to be genetically altered. By contrast, so-called 'organised' or 'semi-organised' calluses are occasionally extracted in which there is is a superficial layer of proliferating shoot meristems, overlying an inner core of vacuolated cells acting as a mechanical and nutritional support. Calluses of this kind, which occasionally originated from monocotyledon explants, were termed *organoid colonies* by Hunault (1979).

The presence of the outer layer of shoot meristems seems to inhibit the unbridled proliferation of the unorganised central tissue (Hussey, 1983). Geier (1988) has suggested that the control mechanisms which ensure the genetic stability of shoot meristems are still fully, or partly, active. Maintenance of a semi-organised tissue system depends on a suitable method of subculture and upon the use of growth regulator levels which do not promote excessive unorganised cell growth. Repeated selective transfer of unorganised portions of an organised *Anthurium scherzerianum* callus eventually resulted in a loss of caulogenesis (Geier, 1986). Conversely, by consistently removing the unorganised tissue when subculturing took place, shoot formation from the callus was increased.

Cultures consisting of superficial shoot meristems above a basal callus, seem to occur with high frequency amongst those initiated from meristem tip, or shoot tip, explants. Hackett and Anderson (1967) induced the formation of tissue of this type from carnation shoot tips by mutilating them with a razor blade before culture. Similar cultures were also obtained from seedling plumular tip explants of two (out of five tested) varieties of *Pisum sativum* placed on an agar medium (Hussey and Gunn, 1983, 1984). The calli were highly regenerative over 2–3 years by regular subculture to agar or shaken liquid. Maintenance was best achieved with an inoculum prepared by removing larger shoots and chopping the remainder of the callus and small shoots into a slurry. A callus, formed at the base of *Solanum × curtilobum* meristem tips on filter paper bridges, gave rise to multiple adventitious shoots from its surface when transferred to shake culture in a liquid medium (Grout *et al.*, 1977).

Callus with superficial proliferative meristems has also been induced by culture of shoot or meristem tips on a rotated liquid medium, in:

Nicotiana rustica	Walkey and Woolfitt (1968)
Chrysanthemum morifolium	Earle and Langhans (1974c)
Stevia rebaudiana	Miyagawa *et al.* (1986)

In *Stevia rebaudiana* (above), a slow rotation speed (2 r.p.m.) was essential for initiation of an organised callus. A small callus formed upon the explant and in 2–3 weeks came to possess primary superficial shoot primordia which were globular and light green. Dark green aggregates of shoot primordia (termed 'secondary shoot primordia' by Miyagawa *et al.*) were developed within 6 weeks. If divided, the aggregations of shoot initials in both *Nicotiana* and *Stevia* could be increased by subculture or, if treated to a different cultural regime, could be made to develop into shoots with roots. Shoots were produced from the *Chrysanthemum* callus upon subculture to an agar medium. A spherical green dome-like structure was produced from meristem tips dissected from germinated *Eleusine coracana* (Gramineae) caryopses. When cut into four and subcultured, a green nodular structure was formed which grew to 5–10 mm in diameter. It was similar in appearance to a shoot dome, but much larger (a natural shoot dome is only 70–80 μm wide). The nodular structures were termed 'supradomes' by Wazizuka and Yamaguchi (1987) because, unlike normal callus, superficial cells were arranged in an anticlinal plane and those beneath had a periclinal arrangement. Numerous multiple buds could be induced to form when the organised tissue was subcultured to a less complex medium.

Although proliferative meristematic tissue formed from shoot tips always appears to be accompanied by a basal callus, the superficial meristematic cells may well be derived directly from the cells of the apical shoot meristem of the explant, for they preserve the same commitment to immediate shoot formation. The presence of the apical meristem in the explant seems to be essential and culture of tissue immediately beneath it does not produce a callus with the same characteristics (Hussey and Gunn, 1984). Similar semi-organised callus can appear at the base of conventional shoot cultures. In the green granular callus mass which formed at the base of *Rhododendron* shoot tips, each granule represented a potential shoot (Kyte and Briggs, 1979). Organised caulogenic callus is thus closely comparable to embryogenic callus formed from pre-embryogenically determined cells (see page 29).

Organised callus can be produced from explants other than shoot tips; in *Anthurium*, it has been derived from young leaf tissue (above, Geier, 1986) and from spadix pieces (Geier, 1987).

Organised callus has two characteristics which distinguish it from normal unorganised callus: the plants produced from it show very little genetic variation, and it can be subcultured for a very long period without losing its regenerative capacity. The callus of *Nicotiana* (above) was able to produce plantlets over a ten year period, while that of *Chrysanthemum* gave rise to plants continuously during four years.

The use of cultures with superficial proliferative meristems has not yet been widely used for micropropagation. There are three possible reasons:

- the genetic variation which is almost invariably induced by shoot regeneration from normal callus, has cautioned against the use of any sort of callus culture for this purpose;

- organised callus may not always be readily distinguished from its unorganised counterpart;

- methods of initiating organised callus in a predictable fashion have not yet been fully elucidated.

There are examples of the initiation of organised callus from a sufficiently wide range of plant species (particularly from meristem tip explants) to suggest that it could be a method of general applicability. Multiplication may well be amenable to large-scale culture in fermentors (Chapter 16).

Direct embryogenesis

Somatic embryos are often initiated directly upon explanted tissues. Of the occurrences mentioned in Chapter 1, one of the most common is during the *in vitro* culture of explants associated with, or immediately derived from, the female gametophyte. The tendency for these tissues to give rise to adventitious somatic embryos is especially high in plants where sporophytic polyembryony occurs naturally, for example, some varieties of *Citrus* and other closely related genera.

Ovules, nucellar embryos, nucellus tissues and other somatic embryos are particularly liable to display direct embryogenesis. In *Carica,* somatic embryos originated from the inner integument of ovules (Litz and Conover, 1981a,b) and in carrot, tissue of the mericarp seed coat can give rise to somatic embryos directly (Smith and Krikorian, 1988).

The nucellus tissue of many plants has the capacity for direct embryogenesis *in vitro* (Haccius and Hausner, 1976; Eichholtz *et al.*, 1979; Rangaswamy, 1982; Litz, 1987). As explained in Chapter 1, explants may also give rise to a proliferative tissue capable of embryogenesis. The high embryogenic competence of the nucellus is usually retained during subsequent cell generations *in vitro*, should the tissue be induced to form 'callus' (or cell suspensions). It is not clear whether all cells of the nucellus are embryogenically committed. In *Citrus*, somatic embryos are formed from the nucellus even in cultivars

that are normally monoembryonic (*i.e.* the seeds contain just one embryo derived from the zygote), whether the ovules have been fertilised or not. It has been suggested that only those cells destined to become zygotic proembryos can become somatic proembryos or give rise to embryogenic callus (Sabharwal, 1963); somatic embryos have been shown to arise particularly from the micropylar end of the *Citrus* nucellus.

Adventitious (adventive) embryos are commonly formed *in vitro* directly upon the zygotic embryos of monocotyledons, dicotyledons and gymnosperms, upon parts of young seedlings (especially hypocotyls and cotyledons) and upon somatic embryos at various stages of development (especially if their growth has been arrested). The stage of growth at which zygotic embryos may undergo adventive embryogenesis is species-dependent: in many plants it is only immature zygotic embryos which have this capacity.

Embryogenic determination can be retained through a phase of protoplast culture. Protoplasts isolated from embryogenic suspensions, may give rise to somatic embryos directly, without any intervening callus phase (Miura and Tabata, 1986; Sim *et al.*, 1988). Treating protoplasts derived from leaf tissue of *Medicago sativa* with an electric field, induced them to produce somatic embryos directly upon culture (Dijak *et al.*, 1986).

Adventive embryos arising on seedlings are sometimes produced from single epidermal cells (Konar *et al.*, 1972a; Thomas *et al.* 1976 — see Chapter 1). Zee and Wu (1979) described the formation of proembryoids within petiole tissue of Chinese celery seedlings, and Zee *et al.* (1979) showed that they arose from cortical cells adjacent to the vascular bundles which first became meristematic. Hypocotyl explants from seedlings of the leguminous tree *Albizia lebbek* showed signs of cracking after two weeks of culture and frequently young embryoids emerged (Gharyal and Maheshwari, 1981). Stamp and Henshaw (1982) found that primary and secondary embryogenesis occurred in morphogenically active ridges produced on the surface of cotyledon pieces taken from mature cassava seeds.

Somatic embryos have been observed on the roots and shoots of *Hosta* cultures (Zilis and Zwagerman, 1980) and on the needles and cultured shoots of various gymnosperm trees (Bonga, 1976; McCown and Amos, 1982).

Protocorm formation in orchids

The seeds of orchids (like those of some other saprophytic or semi-parasitic plants), contain a small embryo of only about 0.1 mm diameter, without any associated endosperm storage tissue. Upon germination, the embryo enlarges to form a small, corm-like structure, called a protocorm, which possesses a quiescent shoot and root meristem at opposite poles. In nature, a protocorm becomes green and accumulates carbohydrate reserves through photosynthesis. Only when it has grown and has sufficient stored organic matter does it give rise to a shoot and a root. Normal seedling growth then continues utilising the stored protocorm food reserves.

Bodies which, in their structure and growth into plantlets, appear to be identical with seedling protocorms (except that on synthetic media they may not be green), are formed during *in vitro* culture of orchids. These *somatic protocorms* can appear to be dissimilar to seedling protocorms, and many workers in the literature on orchid propagation, have used terms such as 'protocorm-like bodies' (PLBs) to describe them.

When a shoot tip of an orchid is transferred to culture on a suitable medium, it ceases to grow and develop as a mature shoot apex and instead behaves as though it were the apex of an embryo, *i.e.* it gives rise to a protocorm (Chapter 17). Protocorm-like bodies also arise directly on some other orchid explants and proliferate from other PLBs in a fashion which is exactly comparable to the direct formation of somatic embryos.

Champagnat and Morel (1972) and Norstog (1979) considered the appearance of protocorms to be a manifestation of embryogenesis because they represent a specialised stage in embryo development and are normally derived directly from zygotic embryos. We think that this is the correct interpretation: in a previous edition of this book, protocorms were described under 'storage organs'.

Other protocorm-like structures. *In vitro* culture of small immature proembryos from developing barley seeds (Norstog, 1961, 1965a, 1970) or from the fern *Todea barbara* (De Maggio and Wetmore, 1961) has been noted to result in the formation of protocorm-like tissue masses from which root and shoots are regenerated after a period of irregular growth. Mapes (1973) recorded the appearance of such protocorm-like structures on shoot tips of pineapple, and Abo El-Nil and Zettler (1976) describe their direct formation on shoot tip explants of the yam *Colocasia esculenta,* or indirectly in subsequent callus cultures. Norstog (1979) pointed out that during somatic embryogenesis *in vitro*, there is often the prior formation of groups of undifferentiated cells, comparable to protocorms, from which proembryonic buds arise: current opinions favour this view and would classify the protocorm-like tissues described above, as proliferations of pre-embryologically determined cells, or an example of *polyembryogenesis.*

Embryogenesis from pollen or anther culture

Somatic embryos can be initiated directly from pollen microspores. Usually it is necessary to culture the micropores within anthers, but occasionally it has been possible to induce embryogenesis from isolated pollen. Anther and pollen culture are described in Chapter 1, but because the plants produced by anther culture are likely to be dissimilar to their parents, we shall not consider the method in any detail in this book, and reports of anther culture have been largely omitted from the tables in Chapter 17.

Anther culture can result in callus formation; the callus may then give rise to plants through indirect embryogenesis or adventitious shoot formation.

Embryo proliferation

Accessory embryos on zygotic embryos. Occasionally new somatic embryos are formed directly on normal seed embryos that have been transferred to sterile culture. Such adventive embryos have been noted in:

> *Cuscuta reflexa* (Maheshwari and Baldev, 1961); barley (Norstog, 1970); *Ilex aquifolium* (Hu and Sussex, 1972; Hu, 1977; Hu *et al.*, 1978); *Thuja orientalis* (Konar and Oberoi, 1965); *Trifolium repens* (Maheswaran and Williams, 1985); *Zamia integrifolia* (Norstog, 1965b; Norstog and Rhamstine, 1967); cocoa (Pence *et al.*, 1980a,b); *Linum usitatissimum* (Pretova and Williams, 1986); *Vitis vinifera* (Stamp and Meredith (1988a).

When direct embryogenesis occurs on pre-formed embryonic tissue, the newly formed embryos are sometimes termed *direct secondary embryos* or *accessory embryos*.

Accessory embryos on somatic embryos. The *in vitro* induction of somatic embryogenesis starts a highly repetitive process, lacking some of the controls which must exist in nature during the formation of zygotic embryos. This results in the frequent development of small additional embryos on somatic embryos which have arisen directly on explants, or indirectly in callus and suspension cultures. Accessory embryos can occur along the whole axis of the original embryo, or grow preferentially from certain sites (*e.g.* the hypocotyl region or the scutellum of monocot. embryoids). In walnut, accessory embryos appear to arise from single cells of the epidermis of somatic embryos (McGranahan *et al.*, 1988b).

Sometimes the term *polyembryony* is used to describe the formation of accessory, or secondary, embryos (Radojević, 1988) (c.f. the term *polyembryogenesis* in Chapter 1). The process has also been called *repetitive embryo-*

genesis (Tulecke and McGranahan, 1985) or *recurrent somatic embryogenesis* (Lupotto, 1986). Such additional embryos are liable to be developed during all kinds of *in vitro* embryogenesis. They have been noted for example, on the somatic embryos formed in:

- **Anther cultures**: *Atropa belladonna* (Rashid and Street, 1973); *Brassica napus* (Thomas *et al.* 1976); *Carica papaya* (Tsay and Su, 1985); *Citrus aurantifolia* (Chaturvedi and Sharma, 1985); *Datura innoxia* (Geier and Kohlenbach, 1973); *Vitis* hybrids (Rajasekaran and Mullins, 1979).

- **Suspension cultures**: *Daucus carota* (Ammirato and Steward, 1971; McWilliam *et al.*, 1974); *Ranunculus scleratus* (Konar and Nataraja, 1965b; Konar *et al.*, 1972a).

- **Callus cultures**: *Aesculus hippocastanum* (Radojević, 1988); alfalfa (when individual embryoids were transferred to a fresh medium) (Saunders and Bingham, 1972); carrot (Petru, 1970); *Citrus* (Button and Kochba, 1977); parsley (Vasil and Hildebrandt, 1966b); *Pennisetum purpureum* (Wang and Vasil, 1982); *Ranunculus scleratus* (Konar and Nataraja, 1965a,b).

Protocorms arising directly on explanted shoot tips or leaf pieces of orchids, frequently produce other adventive 'daughter' protocorms in culture, in a fashion that is similar to the adventive formation of somatic embryos. Somatic embryos formed in callus of oil palm have been reported to give rise to protocorm-like bodies, which regenerated shoots repeatedly as subculture was continued (Paranjothy and Rohani, 1982).

Practical uses in propagation

Whereas indirect embryogenesis does provide an efficient method of micropropagation, the same is not true of direct embryogenesis when it is unaccompanied by the proliferation of the embryogenic tissue. Although plants can be regenerated from embryos directly initiated *in vitro*, and may be present in sufficient numbers for limited plant production in breeding programmes, the numbers of primary embryos per explant will usually be inadequate for large scale cloning. To increase the number of somatic embryos formed directly on immature zygotic embryos of sunflower, Freyssinet and Freyssinet (1988) cut larger zygotic embryos into 4 equal pieces.

Additional embryos are generally unwanted: they are frequently joined one to another as twins or larger groups so that abnormal seedlings with multiple shoots develop from them (see Fig. 24). The presence of accessory embryos can also impede the growth of the primary somatic embryo. Growth then becomes asynchronous and normal

seedlings may not be obtained unless the adventive embryos are removed.

However it has been suggested that accessory embryos might be used for micropropagating some species. Perhaps this is a method of micropropagation which will be developed more in the future? Examples of where it has been successful are:-

Helianthus annuus	Pélissier *et al..* (1990)
Juglans regia.	McGranahan *et al.* (1988b)
Medicago sativa	Lupotto (1986)

If the proliferation of PEDCs (polyembryogenesis) is included, then the potential of direct embryogenesis for plant propagation is considerable.

The propagation of orchids. During his work on the meristem culture of *Cymbidium* orchids for the removal of virus diseases, Morel (1960) noticed that structures resembling protocorms were formed on orchid shoot tips cultured on simple media without growth regulators, sometimes in great numbers. He then made the significant discovery that if these structures were divided, new 'protocorms' were formed from the pieces, whereas if they were not divided, original and regenerated 'protocorms' developed into new plantlets. Morel (1960, 1964) suggested that meristem or shoot tip explants could be used to establish cultures for the clonal propagation of orchids, providing thereby the basis of the method which is now used for many orchids genera. Rates of propagation are improved through the use of slightly more complex media than used by Morel, and by including growth regulators.

Some orchids not only form protocorms on apical meristems, but also directly on explants such as leaves (Churchill *et al.*, 1971; 1973; Tanaka *et al.*, 1975), or flower stalks (Flamée and Boesman, 1977; Arditti *et al.*, 1977), or they may be formed from callus or callus *via* suspension cultures (see the section on ORCHIDS in Chapter 17).

PROPAGATION BY INDIRECT ORGANOGENESIS

Propagation by all methods of indirect organogenesis carries a risk that the regenerated plants will differ genetically from each other and from the stock plant. The chances of this variability occurring are greatest in plants produced by indirect shoot formation and appear to be less (at least in some species) in those resulting from indirect embryogenesis. Propagation by indirect organogenesis is described here for the sake of completeness; because of its potential as a propagation method, if the

Indirect adventitious shoots from callus

Because they are not formed on tissues of the original mother plant, shoots (or other organs) are said to be regenerated *indirectly* when they are formed on previously unorganised callus, or in cell cultures. Separate root and shoot initials are characteristically formed in callus cultures and are only observed occasionally in suspensions where they are typically produced in large cell aggregates. Somatic embryogenesis occurs in both callus and suspension cultures. Adjustment of the growth regulators in the culture medium can bring about shoot or root formation in callus from a very large number of species. Inception of roots and shoots is most frequent in tissues that have been recently isolated, and morphogenic capacity generally declines with time as the tissues are subcultured. Nevertheless, some callus cultures maintain their regenerative ability over long periods.

As explained in Chapter 8, callus cultures vary in their morphogenic potential or *competence*. Because of this, the callus which originates from some plants, or from some kinds of explant, may not be responsive to techniques and media which frequently result in morphogenesis. The tissue may be non-morphogenic, or may only produce roots, from which plants cannot be regenerated. In some cases callus lines with different appearances and/or morphogenic capacities can be isolated from the *same* explant (Fig. 23). These differences may reflect the epigenetic potential of the cells, or be caused by the appearance of genetic variability amongst the cells of the culture (Chapter 3) and support Street's (1979) suggestion that primary explants may be composed of cells or tissues capable of morphogenesis (competent cells) and others that are incapable (non-competent cells).

Morphogenic and non-morphogeneic callus lines, selected from primary callus, can retain their characteristics over many years (Reuther, 1990). Special treatments, such as, a change of medium, an altered cultural environment, or an adjustment of the growth regulators added to the medium, may induce shoots or roots to form in some apparently non-morphogenic calluses; but generally, treatments to reverse a non-regenerative condition are unsuccessful.

In practice, the speed and efficiency with which plantlets can be regenerated from callus depends upon:

— the interval between culture initiation and the onset of morphogenesis;

— the frequency and rate of shoot bud initiation;

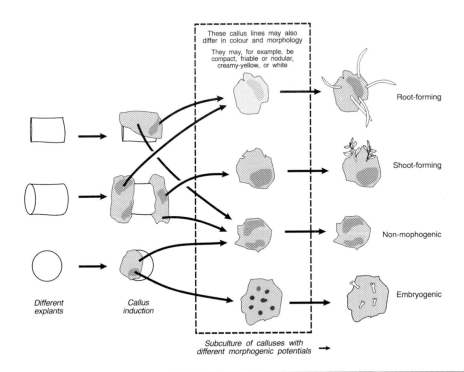

Fig. 23. Callus with different morphogenic potential is often isolated from a single explant.

— whether shoot regeneration can be readily re-induced when the callus is subcultured;

— the number of subcultures that are possible without loss of morphogenesis;

— whether newly-initiated buds can be grown into shoots capable of being isolated and subsequently rooted.

Normal callus cultures produce shoots relatively slowly, but from some plants, and certain explants, under conditions that are not yet fully understood, callus can be initiated which has an especially high ability to regenerate shoots or somatic embryos.

Stage I

In most herbaceous broadleafed plants, it is possible to initiate morphogenically competent callus cultures from explants derived from many different tissues. Leaf, stem or root segments, pieces of storage tissue (*e.g.* tubers), seed embryos, shoot tips and seedling tissues have been used at various times. In monocotyledons there is a narrower range of suitable organs; embryos, very young leaf tissue, stem nodes and immature inflorescences being the most common sources. Initiation of callus cultures of many tree species, including gymnosperms, is frequently limited to explants derived from tissues near the vascular bundles or the cambium of stem or root sections. Explants containing actively dividing cells may be necessary if callus possessing a high level of morphogenic competence is to be isolated.

Callus growth is usually initiated by placing the chosen explant on a semi-solid medium into which auxin has been incorporated at a relatively high level, with or without a cytokinin. Details of the compounds used are given in Chapter 11. One or more transfers on the same medium may be necessary before the callus is separated from the parental tissue for subculture. Because more than one kind of callus may arise from a single explant, successful propagation can depend on being able to recognise and subculture only the type (or types) which will eventually be able to give rise to shoots or somatic embryos. In the absence of previous experience, samples of each type of callus may have to be carried forward for testing on inductive media. Translucent, watery callus is seldom morphogenic, whereas nodular callus frequently is.

Organised adventitious shoots are usually induced to form in callus or suspension cultures by reducing the auxin level in the medium and/or increasing the concentration of cytokinin. To grow callus-derived shoots into plantlets capable of survival in the soil, they must be rooted as micro-cuttings. Root production by callus is of little consequence for micropropagation purposes; even if roots are formed concurrently with adventitious shoots, the vascular connections between roots and shoots, through the callus tissue, are almost invariably insufficient for the development of a functional plantlet.

Stage II

Once a morphogenic callus has been isolated, propagation is carried out either by callus subdivision, or by the preparation of cell suspensions. The success of each technique depends on the subcultured tissues or cells continuing to regenerate shoots.

Callus subdivision. Callus is cut into smaller pieces which increase in size when subcultured in a liquid or an agar-solidified medium. The callus can either be subdivided further, or shoot regeneration allowed to occur. This may take place on the same medium, or the callus may need to be transferred to another shoot-inducing medium. The organogenic capacity of callus is easily lost on repeated subculture. Use of high growth regulator levels can encourage the proliferation of non-regenerative callus which will displace tissues having the competence to form new shoots (*e.g.* in *Pelargonium;* Holdgate, 1977).

The preparation of cell suspensions. Compared to the relatively rapid rates of propagation that are possible with shoot culture of some kinds of plants, propagation from morphogenically competent callus can be slow initially. Krikorian and Kann (1979) quote a minimum of 135 days from the excision of daylily explants to the potting of plantlets. The rate at which propagation can proceed after that depends on the rate at which callus can be grown and subdivided. Providing a shoot-forming capacity is retained, a much faster rate of multiplication can be achieved by initiating a suspension culture from competent callus. After being increased by culture, the cells or cell aggregates can then be plated to produce new regenerative callus colonies. This is not an easy operation, as growth regulators favouring the formation of a dispersed cell suspension can cause the cells to lose their morphogenic capacity (see page 424). There is also the problem that, by prolonging the period before shoot regeneration, genetic variability within the cell line will be increased.

Genetic stability

In some crop plants, the genetic differences between the plants derived from callus and suspension cultures (discussed in Chapter 3) are considerable, and are sufficient to have attracted the interest of plant breeders as a new source of selectable variability. However, plants obtained from callus lines with a high degree of morphogenic competence, appear to be much more uniform genetically. Care must be taken though to see that primary explants are not taken from plant tissue likely to be endopolyploid. Subsequent exposure to high levels of growth substances such as 2,4-D should also be avoided as far as possible. Genetic stability of plants from highly competent callus cultures may be assisted by the continual presence of superficial meristems. These probably repress shoot formation from cells within the callus mass (Hussey, 1983).

Morphogenic cereal cultures

The shoot forming capacity of some callus cultures has been attributed to the proliferation of meristematic centres derived from the tissues of the explant. King *et al.* (1978) have suggested that the small number of shoots produced by certain cereal tissue cultures arises in this way (*e.g.* in wheat, rice, oat and maize). Cure and Mott (1978) noticed that aberrant root-like structures existed within cereal cultures from which shoots arose. Such primordia, whether of root or shoot origin, are thought to proliferate adventitiously *in vitro*, surrounded by less organised tissues. Regenerative capacity is usually lost rapidly when the shoot primordia are diluted during subculture. Cereal callus of this kind does not have the same kind of inherent morphogenic capacity found in other types of callus cultures. Despite these observations, experience shows that morphogenesis can occur from previously unorganised cereal callus. For a full description of plant regeneration from cereal cultures, see Chapter 17.

Current applications

In the past, several ornamental plants [*e.g. Freesia* (Hussey and Hargreaves, 1974) and *Pelargonium* (Holdgate, 1977)] have been micropropagated from adventitious shoots produced indirectly from callus. It had been hoped to extend the technique to other species possessing a strong natural tendency towards diploidy (*e.g.* some forest trees) where plantlets produced *in vitro* might have a normal karyotype (Mott, 1981), but it is now realised that the genetic changes which are almost universally induced in the genotype of cells during callus and cell culture make cloning by this technique inadvisable except where new genotypes are required for selection or further plant breeding.

Indirectly-initiated somatic embryos

Indirect formation of somatic embryos (or *adventitious somatic embryogenesis*) from callus or suspension cultures is observed more frequently than direct embryogenesis. Frequently callus which is wholly or partly embryogenic can be induced during the initial culture of explants derived from young meristematic tissues (see below), but induction is less common in cultures which have been kept and transferred for some period without organogenesis.

There are important requirements for the successful induction of embryogenic callus and suspension cultures:

— The plant genotype must be capable of embryogenesis on the chosen system of induction (medium plus added growth regulators). In some genera most genotypes are competent, but in others there may be a wide variation in competence even between different varieties or cultivars within a species (see Chapter 7).

— In most practical situations, cultures should be grown in the presence of an auxin for the initiation of embryogenesis (Stage I).

— The level of sugar (*e.g.* sucrose or glucose) in the medium may need to be within critical concentrations, and no embryos may be formed at all if the sugar concentration is too high (Lippman and Lippmann, 1984).

— After the beginning of embryogenesis, it is usually (but not invariably) necessary for Stage I tissues or cells to be subcultured to a medium containing a reduced auxin concentration, or containing no auxin at all (Stage II) (Chapter 12).

— There may be an optimum length of time during which the Stage I routine should be maintained. An extended period before subculture can result in the failure to obtain embryogenesis at Stage II (*e.g.* Dos Santos *et al.*1980). Maintenance of the cultures on high auxin usually causes embryo development to be arrested or a loss of embryogenic capability.

— A supply of reduced nitrogen is required. This may be supplied in the form of NH_4^+ ion and/or as an amino acid such as glutamine or alanine (see Chapter 9).

Embryogenesis in primary callus cultures

Callus capable of producing somatic embryos (embryogeneic callus) is most reliably obtained from an explant during the initial phase of culture, and is frequently produced in conjunction with non-morphogenic tissue.

Embryogenic callus can usually be distinguished by its nodular appearance, and is frequently produced preferentially from one part of an explant (*e.g.* the scutellum of a monocotyledon embryo), probably because only the cells of that part of the explant were embryogenically pre-determined. These may be the same tissues, which in another cultural environment are capable of producing embryos directly (Sharp *et al.*, 1980). According to this hypothesis, although competent and non-competent cells may produce callus, only that which grows from competent cells will give rise to somatic embryos.

The expression of competence depends on the use of a suitable medium for the culture, containing requisite growth regulators at the correct concentration. The formation of somatic embryos in *Lolium multiflorum,* for example, was medium dependent (Dale *et al.*, 1981). On the most suitable medium, immature inflorescence explants produced three types of callus, only one of which spontaneously formed embryo-like structures. Unless such different callus types are separated, cells of different regenerative capabilities may become mixed. Morphogenically competent cells could then be lost by competition in the combined callus tissue that results.

Stage I. Selection of an appropriate explant is most important. Embryogenic callus has been commonly gained from seed embryos, nucelli or other highly meristematic tissues such as parts of seedlings, the youngest parts of newly initiated leaves and inflorescence primordia. The initiation of embryogenic callus from root tissue is rare but has been reported in some monocotyledons *e.g.* rice (Inoue and Maeda, 1982; Toshinari and Futsuhara, 1985); oil palm (Paranjothy and Rohani, 1982), Italian ryegrass (Jackson and Dale, 1988) and *Allium carinatum* (Havel and Novak, 1988). Callus is usually commenced on a semi-solid medium incorporating a relatively high level of an auxin; compounds commonly used for this purpose are described in Chapters 11 and 12. Only a few tissues with a high natural embryogenic capacity do not require the addition of endogenous auxin for the development of embryogenic callus. Occasionally, primary callus arising from an explant may show no morphogenic capacity, but can be induced to give rise to new embryogenic tissue during later (secondary) subcultures by transfer to an inductive medium. Ahee *et al.* (1981) have used this method to propagate oil palms. On the medium used, calluses arising on the veins of young leaf fragments had no morphogenic capability. However, when primary calluses were subcultured onto appropriate media (unspecified), some of them gave rise to tissue that was different in structure and form, and grew at a much faster rate. These 'fast-growing calluses' could be induced to produce structures resembling embryoids, and afterwards plantlets, upon further subculture to other media.

One highly embryogenic tissue that has been extensively studied is that of the nucellus of the polyembryonic 'Shamouti' orange (Spiegel-Roy and Kochba, 1980). Here it seems that cells at just one end of the embryo sac (the micropylar end) are embryogenically predetermined and retain this capacity in subsequent cell generations. On subculture, proliferation of the nucellus cells proceeds without the addition of growth regulators to the medium, and results in the formation of an *habituated* callus. A tissue is said to have become habituated when it will grow without a growth regulator or some other organic substance, which is normally necessary, being added to the medium (see Chapter 11). Addition of auxins to the growth medium is inhibitory to the growth of auxin-habituated 'Shamouti' orange tissue, which has been thought to be composed (at least initially) of numerous pro-embryos and not of undifferentiated cells (Button *et al.*, 1974). Embryogenic callus has also been obtained from the nucellus tissue of other plants.

Stage II. As a general rule, somatic embryos formed on a medium containing a relatively high concentration of an auxin, will only develop further if the callus culture is transferred to a second medium from which auxin has been omitted, another 'less active' auxin has been substituted, or the level of the original auxin much reduced. This treatment is occasionally ineffective (Handley and Sink, 1985a) and sometimes adding a cytokinin helps to ensure embryo growth. A further essential requirement is for there to be a supply of reduced nitrogen in the form of an ammonium salt or amino acid. No change of nitrogen source is required if **MS** medium was used for Stage I, but if, for example, White's medium were used for Stage I, it would need to be supplemented with reduced nitrogen, or the culture transferred to **MS**.

Callus subculture. Once obtained, embryogenic callus can continue to give rise to somatic embryos during many subcultures over long periods. The continued production of somatic embryos in these circumstances depends either on the continued proliferation of pro-embryogenic nodules, and/or the *de novo* formation of embryogenic tissue from young somatic embryos during each subculture. Inocula for subcultures must be carefully selected. In wheat, callus with continued embryogenesis was only re-initiated from inocula taken close to somatic embryos; tissue from the same culture which did not contain embryos was not embryogenic in the next passage (Chu *et al.*, 1987).

Sometimes the number of embryos produced per unit weight of callus rises during a few passages and then slowly falls, the capacity to form somatic embryos eventually being irrevocably lost. Callus derived from the nucellus of Shamouti oranges increased in its capacity to form somatic embryos when subcultured at 10–15 week intervals, while transfer at 4–5 week intervals, reduced embryogenesis (Kochba and Button, 1974).

Somatic embryos can be formed relatively freely in callus tissue, but where they are to be used for large scale propagation, their numbers can often be increased more rapidly and conveniently by initiating an embryogenic suspension culture from the primary callus (see below).

Embryogenesis in suspension cultures

Cultures from embryogenic callus (Stage I). Suspension cultures can sometimes be initiated from embryogenic callus tissue, and the cells still retain the capacity to regenerate somatic embryos freely. Obtaining such cultures is not always a simple matter, for the auxin levels that are often used to promote cell dispersion may result in the loss of morphogenic capability. Embryogenic cell suspensions are most commonly initiated from embryogenic callus that is placed in liquid medium on a shaker. Vasil and Vasil (1981a,b) and Lu and Vasil (1981a,b) have reported producing cultures of this type from pearl millet and guinea grass respectively. Suspensions were initiated and subcultured in **MS** medium containing 1–2.5 mg/l 2.4-D and 2.5–5% coconut milk, and came to be composed of a mixture of embryogenic cells (small, highly cytoplasmic and often containing starch) and non-embryogenic cells (large and vacuolated). Embryoids were induced to develop into somatic seedlings when plated onto an agar medium without growth regulators, or with lower levels of auxin than used at the previous stage.

Cultures from non-embryogenic sources. Embryogenesis can be induced in cell suspensions of some plants when the cultures are produced from non- morphogenic callus and have been maintained without morphogenesis for one or more transfers. Induction occurs most readily in recently isolated suspensions and usually becomes much less probable with increasing culture age. Loss of regenerative ability is often associated with the appearance of some cells with abnormal chromosome numbers, but it can also be due to culture on an inappropriate medium.

Embryogenesis in suspension cultures seems to require media at Stage I and Stage II with similar compositions to those necessary for somatic embryo formation in callus cultures. Somatic embryos can be formed in suspension cultures in very large numbers. Reinert *et al.* (1971) demonstrated that the continued capacity of carrot cell suspensions to form embryos depended on an adequate supply of nitrogen. Embryogenesis ceased on a medium containing little nitrogen, but it was reinduced for several transfers after the culture was returned to a high-nitrogen medium.

In a few kinds of plants it is possible to induce embryogenesis in previously unorganised suspension cultures. Success is so far recorded only in members of the families Apiaceae (Umbelliferae), Cruciferae and Scrophulariaceae. This is not therefore a method of propagation

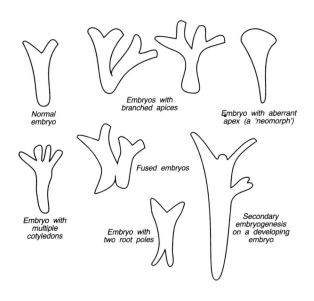

Fig. 24. Some of the abnormalities which can occur amongst somatic embryos.

which can be readily utilised. There is a greater chance of obtaining an embryogenic suspension culture from embryogenic callus.

Abnormal embryos and plantlets

Unfortunately embryogenesis in both callus and suspension cultures is seldom synchronous so that embryoids at different stages of development are usually present in a Stage II culture from the onset. This presents a major drawback for plant propagation which could otherwise be very rapid, especially from suspensions. A proportion of the seedlings developing from somatic embryos can also be atypical: abnormalities include the possession of multiple or malformed cotyledons, more than one shoot or root axis, and and the presence of secondary adventive embryos (Fig. 24). Embryos with three cotyledons have been observed to give rise to well-formed plantlets (Smith and Krikorian, 1990b), but those with grossly malformed apices do not. Abnormal somatic embryos do however produce secondary embryos, which are usually of normal morphology.

Pretova and Williams (1986) suggested that embryo proliferation (page 56), or 'cleavage' (page 29), and the formation of accessory cotyledons and root poles, to be homologous with the production of discrete complete embryoids. They suggested that production of accessory cotyledons and somatic embryos on the hypocotyl, and additional root poles near the base of existing embryos, may represent either a gradient along these organs in the early stages of determination, or, be caused by a factor affecting cell to cell coordination.

The uniformity of embryo populations in suspension cultures can be improved by differential filtering and sedimentation to separate embryos at different stages of development (Giuliano *et al.*, 1983). In addition cultures can be maintained on media containing high levels of sucrose (Ammirato and Steward, 1971), and/or low levels of abscisic acid (Ammirato, 1973; 1974). High levels of sucrose and abscisic acid induce reversible dormancy in somatic embryos and thus might be used to temporarily suspend growth should this be advantageous in a planned micropropagation programme.

Genetic stability

Plants regenerated through somatic embryogenesis are usually morphologically and cytologically normal, but sometimes a proportion of aberrant plants is obtained. Genetically abnormal plants are more likely to occur where embryogenesis is initiated in callus or suspension cultures after a period of unorganised growth or when embryogenic cultures are maintained for several months (Orton, 1985) [see Chapter 3].

A proportion of albino plants lacking chlorophyll is characteristically produced in anther culture of cereals and grasses (Sunderland and Dunwell, 1977) and during embryogenesis from other monocot. explants. Dale *et al.(loc.cit.)* found that plants produced from embryogenic callus cultures of Italian ryegrass were more likely to be devoid of chlorophyll the longer the cultures were maintained. After one year, some cultures produced only albinos. Embryo- like structures (although still present on the surface of the callus) tended to be distorted.

Current applications

Few plant species are at present propagated on a large scale *via* embryogenesis *in vitro*. This method of morphogenesis does however offer advantages which suggest that it will be used increasingly for plant cloning in the future:

- in some monocotyledons (*e.g.* cereals, date palm and oil palm) it provides a method of micropropagation where shoot culture and separate shoot regeneration have not been successful;

- providing embryogenic cell suspensions can be established, plantlets can theoretically be produced in large numbers and at much lower cost because plantlets do not have to be handled and subcultured individually;

- somatic embryos probably provide the only way for tissue culture methods of plant propagation to be economically deployed on extensively planted field crops and forest trees.

Techniques for the germination and field planting of somatic embryos are discussed in Chapter 14.

STORAGE ORGAN FORMATION

Many ornamental and crop species are normally propagated, stored and planted in the form of vegetative storage organs. It is therefore not surprising that, where such organs are produced *in vitro*, they often provide a convenient means of micropropagation and/or genotype storage. Characteristic, though small, storage structures can be induced to form in cultures of several plant species, for example:

Bulbils	*Amaryllis,* hyacinth, lily, onion, narcissus
Cormlets	*Gladiolus*
Protocorms	Orchids
Miniature tubers	Potato, yams

Protocorm formation as a method of propagation has been considered under Direct Embryogenesis.

Methods of obtaining storage organs vary according to the kind of tissue being cultured. Some storage organs formed *in vitro* can be planted *extra vitrum* directly into the soil (Chapter 14).

The production of bulbils and cormlets

Species that naturally produce bulbs can be induced to form small bulbs (bulbils or bulblets) in culture. Bulbils can be produced from axillary buds, but frequently they are formed from adventitious buds developed on pieces of leaf, on inflorescence stalks, or on ovaries, and particularly on detached pieces of bulb scale.

Both axillary and adventitious shoots and bulbils are formed on bulb scale pieces *in vitro*. Strong dominance of the main shoot apex often prevents the formation of axillary buds at the bases of bulb scales *in vivo*, but buds capable of giving rise to bulblets (or to shoots upon which bulbs will be formed later) are freely produced when bulb scales or bulb sections are cultured. In some species it is important to include part of the basal plate in the explant. Depending on the kind of bulb being cultured, explants for continued Stage II propagation may consist of scales taken from bulblets, swollen shoot bases, or bulblets which have been trimmed and split. Propagules for transfer from Stage III to the external environment can be plantlets, plantlets with a bulblet at the base, or dormant bulblets.

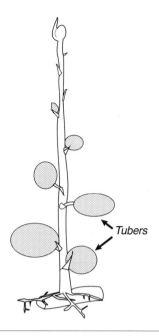

Tubers

Fig. 25. Miniature tubers formed on an *in vitro* shoot of potato.

Instead of producing storage organs composed of swollen leaf bases (bulbs), some monocotyledons store food reserves in swollen stem bases (corms). Small corms (cormlets) of *Gladiolus* may be formed directly on explanted tissue or on callus in culture (Ziv *et al.*, 1970; Ziv and Halevy, 1972), or they are produced on rooted plantlets grown in culture jars until the leaves senesce. Cormlets formed *in vitro* can be planted in soil or used to start new *in vitro* cultures (Hussey, 1978a,b).

The production of plantlets from genera producing bulbs and corms is discussed more fully in Chapter 17.

Miniature tubers

Under appropriate environmental conditions, plants that naturally produce tubers can be induced to produce miniature versions of these storage organs, in a medium containing high cytokinin levels (Chapter 17). Tubers normally formed on underground stolons are produced *in vitro* in axillary positions along *in vitro* shoots (Fig. 25). Two crops where miniature tubers have been utilised for propagation are potato and yams. Methods for inducing the *in vitro* tuberization of potatoes were first described by Lin *et al.* (1978, *in* Wang and Hu, 1980) and Hussey and Stacey (1981a,b), and since by several other workers. Potato tubers form best in darkness, but those of *Dioscorea* mainly appear at the base of stem node cuttings in the light (Ng, 1988).

Miniature tubers have the great advantage that they can be readily removed from culture flasks in a dormant condition and stored *ex vitro* without precautions against sepsis. When planted in soil they behave as normal tubers and produce plants from axillary shoots. If they are produced *in vitro* from virus-free shoots, miniature tubers provide an ideal method of propagating and distributing virus-free stock to growers.

MICROGRAFTING

The transfer of small shoot apices onto rootstocks (termed *micrografting*), can be carried out *in vivo* or *in vitro*. Navarro (1988) lists four uses which have been found for the technique:

1. Obtaining plants free from virus and virus-like diseases (see Chapter 5);

2. A method for separating virus and virus-like organisms in mixed infections;

3. For studying graft incompatibility between scions and rootstocks, and the histological and physiological aspects of grafting;

4. A minimum risk method for importing plant material through quarantine (see Chapter 6).

Micrografting is thus indirectly useful in micropropagation: the necessary techniques are usually too time consuming and the proportion of successful takes is generally too low, for it to be of direct application.

The rootstocks used for micrografting are commonly newly-germinated seedlings, but it is also possible to use rooted cuttings or micropropagated shoots. Before micrografting can be carried out, it is necessary to prepare suitable rootstock material. When seedling rootstocks are used, and all stages of grafting are conducted *in vitro*, seeds are surface sterilised and germinated axenically in vessels containing nutrient salts (*e.g.* those of **MS** medium). The seedlings may be supported on agar or on a porous substrate, such as sterile vermiculite, which allows the growth of a branched root system. Micrografting is then effected by cutting off the tops of the seedling rootstocks and placing small shoot apices onto the exposed surface. When grafts are successful, rootstock and scion grow together to produce a plant. It is usually necessary to examine freshly grafted seedlings on a regular basis and remove any adventitious shoots arising on or below the graft union.

Shoot tips to be grafted onto seedling rootstocks (*i.e.* the scions) are carefully excised from preferred plant material. In *Citrus* there has been most success when scions have been placed directly in one of two positions:

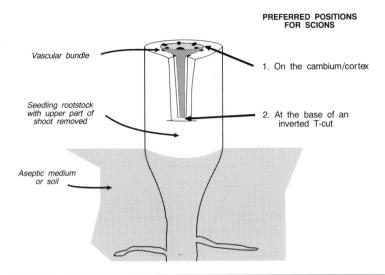

Fig. 26. Preferred positions for placing a shoot tip scion in the micrografting of *Citrus*
[after Navarro *et al.*, 1975).

— into inverted T-shaped incisions immediately below the cut surface of a decapitated 'rootstock',
or,

— onto the cambium layer or vascular ring of the cut
surface (Fig. 26).

Shoot or meristem tips intended for grafting can be taken
from apical or axillary buds of actively growing shoots in
the greenhouse or field, or may be removed from shoots
growing *in vitro*. Once transferred, the survival of micro-
grafted apices is partly dependent on their size. Very
small apices must be used for virus elimination, making
the technique difficult and unreliable. Tips 0.1–0.2 mm
in length have been grafted for virus elimination from
vines; with peach, slightly larger apices (0.5–1 mm) have
been employed. The excision and tranfer of very small
shoot apices requires precise micro-manipulation under
a binocular microscope.

If large shoot apices are to be grafted, their bases are often
cut into a wedge which is then inserted into a vertical cut
on the rootstock (Fig. 27).

Several techniques have been found to increase the proportion of successful graft unions:

Tissue blackening (see Chapter 13), which commonly
results in the death of very small scions, can be reduced
by soaking explants in an anti-oxidant solution, and/or
placing a drop of solution onto the severed rootstock
immediately before inserting the scion. A solution of 2
g/l sodium diethyldithiocarbamate (DIECA) has been
used for this purpose. Navarro (1988) advocates rapid
manipulations to prevent phenolic oxidation and says that
it is more effective than anti-oxidants.

Apices to be grafted may be placed either directly onto a
decapitated rootstock, or cultured for a short period before being transferred. There is often a better 'take' and
and more rapid growth if they are pre-cultured for a short
while supported on paper above an **MS** mineral salt
medium containing growth regulators. Jonard *et al.*
(1983) found that adding a cytokinin to the medium (*e.g.*
0.1 mg/l zeatin if the apex is cultured for 48 h; 0.01 mg/l
zeatin if the culture is continued for 48–240 h) was
particulary effective in encouraging the rapid formation
of leafy shoots once the graft has been made. An alternative is to place scion shoot tips into a growth regulator
solution for a short period before grafting: a 5–10 minute
immersion in either 10 mg/l 2,4-D or 1 mg/l BAP, doubled the number of successful micrografts of *Citrus*
(Edriss and Burger, 1984b). Starrantino and Caruso
(1988) got a greater percentage of viable grafts when they
dipped both shoot tips and the cut apex of young rootstocks in 0.5 mg/l BAP for 20 min before the two were
united. Yet another method is to place cytokinin (*e.g.*
2mg/l BAP or, for peach, 10 mg/l zeatin) in a drop of
water or agar between the scion and the rootstock.

A greater proportion of graft unions may result from
growing isolated meristem tips to a larger size before they
are implanted. Isolated scion tips of peach have been
cultured *in vitro* by the initial stages of meristem tip
culture for a period of about two weeks until they have
grown from 0.5–1 mm to ca. 10 mm.

Desiccation is a major cause of the failure of graft unions.
To prevent drying, Pliego-Alfaro and Murashige (1987)
applied a layer of moist nutrient agar to connect the graft
area with the medium. The agar had to be progressively

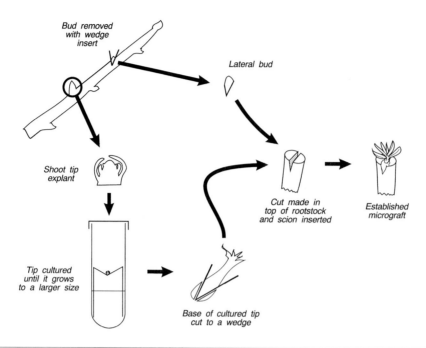

Bud removed
with wedge
insert

Lateral bud

Shoot tip
explant

Cut made in
top of rootstock
and scion inserted

Established
micrograft

Tip cultured
until it grows
to a larger size

Base of cultured tip
cut to a wedge

Fig. 27. Two alternative methods of micrografting with large scions [after Pliego-Alfaro and Murashige, 1987; Navarro, 1988].

area with the medium. The agar had to be progressively removed from the top downwards during weeks 1–3 after grafting, or poor unions resulted.

When, as has been most common, micrografting has been carried out *in vitro*, considerable care needs to be taken over transferring grafted plants to the external environment. However, several authors have found that sterility is not necessary and that shoot apices can be united onto rootstocks grown *in vivo*. The proportion of completed grafts may be less than under aseptic conditions, but problems with eventual transfer are eliminated. A variety of scion material has been utilised for *in vivo* grafting, including directly-excised 0.1–0.2 mm tips of *Citrus limon,* and meristem-cultured scion tips of peach. One again, graft unions may be improved if cut surfaces are anointed with a DIECA (1g/l) plus cytokinin (10 g/l) solution (Jonard *et al.*, 1983). Plants are probably best kept in a growth room for a period after grafting, and desiccation of the graft union prevented by enclosing

each plant in a plastic bag or by placing an elastic strip around the graft.

Grafting mature shoots of woody perennials onto juvenile rootstocks is known to induce juvenile characteristics in the resulting shoots, particularly if it is repeated successively (Chapter 8). Half of the plants resulting from micrografting adult lateral buds of avocado onto seedling rootstock were found to have some juvenile symptoms (Pliego-Alfaro and Murashige, 1987). But in *Citrus* micrografting does not seem to induce juvenile characteristics, providing shoot tips are taken from an adult source: plants are thornless and come into flower rapidly (Navarro, 1988).

From having been developed as a method of producing virus-free *Citrus,* micrografting is now widely used for the improvement of plants of this and related genera. It has also been practised on a wide range of other plants, primarily for virus-elimination (see reviews by Jonard *et al.*, 1983; Burger, 1985 and Navarro, 1988).

REVIEWS OF MICROPROPAGATION METHODS

General reviews of micropropagation methods have been written by Harney (1982); Holdgate (1977); Hussey (1978a, 1983); Lane (1982); Murashige (1974) and Vasil and Vasil (1980a).

Books devoted specifically to *in vitro* propagation are Conger (1981), Debergh and Zimmerman (1990), de Fossard (1981), Kyte (1983), Pennell (1987) and Wetherell (1982).

3

Variation in Cultures and Regenerated Plants

The *in vitro* culture of plant material can induce or reveal differences between cells, tissues and organs; thereby creating variation within cultures, or between the plants derived from them. Some, or all, of the regenerated plants may be physically different from the stock plant from which the culture was derived. Variability of this kind, which usually occurs spontaneously and is largely unable to be controlled or directed, can be of two different kinds:

- that caused by cells having undergone a persistent genetic change;

- that caused by temporary changes to cells or tissues which is either genetically or environmentally induced.

Genetic variability can also be deliberately created in cultured cells using genetic engineering techniques. A detailed description of this subject is beyond the scope of this book, but a summary of the techniques is given at the end of this chapter, because, after cells have been modified, *in vitro* propagation techniques are required for plant regeneration and multiplication.

Uncontrolled variation. The frequency of persistent and temporary change differs, but both are unusually high amongst the cells in some kinds of tissue cultures. It is

therefore most important to use only the most reliable tissue culture methods for micropropagation; when this is done, variation between ramets is usually no more than would occur in conventional macropropagation.

Even so, there is an ever-present risk of generating permanent genetic change during micropropagation. A population of plants possessing a significant degree of genetic variation can easily be produced by the use of inappropriate techniques. High rates of plant multiplication *in vitro* can also cause problems. If, for example, a variant shoot should arise (or be placed) in shoot culture and go undetected through several subcultures, large numbers of off-type plantlets will be produced in a very short time. It is therefore wise to re-initiate cultures from genetically typical stock plants (ortets) at regular intervals.

PHENOTYPE AND GENOTYPE

The physical make-up and appearance of a plant (its *phenotype)* is conditioned by its genetic constitution (*genotype)*, by the environment in which it is grown, and by the particular way the genotype may react to environmental factors. There is obviously a complex series of

67

developmental processes by which a genotype results in a phenotype, and this has been termed the *epigenotype* (Waddington, 1942). Differences between plants can result both from their having different genotypes (*genotypic variation*), and from environmental effects (*environmental* or *phenotypic variation*).

Each living plant cell typically contains a complete set of the genetic information (the *genome*) which determines the characteristics of the whole organism. The genome is encoded on molecules of de-oxyribonucleic acid (DNA) in discrete units of heredity called *genes*. The total collection of genes in a plant is divided between distinct DNA molecules, called chromosomes, mainly contained within the cell nucleus. Some genes are also located on simple chromosomes within the cytoplasm, in chloroplasts and mitochondria : the DNA in these organelles is called cytoplasmic DNA. The cytoplasmic genome is normally transmitted to sexual progeny via the female parent (*i.e.* it is maternally inherited).

Species are distinguished by having a characteristic basic number of nuclear chromosomes. During the vegetative phase of growth, plant cells normally have a *diploid* (from the Greek, meaning two-fold) chromosome complement that is twice the basic number: each cell then possesses pairs of *homologous* chromosomes carrying the same kinds of genes. Other whole multiples, such as haploid (*Gr.* single), triploid and tetraploid are commonly encountered. Organisms whose somatic nuclei contain more than two haploid sets of chromosomes are said to be *polyploid.*

At each locus on a chromosome of a diploid plant, genes of similar function are paired. Where the paired genes are identical, the locus is said to be *homozygous*, and where they are not, *heterozygous*. The function of one of a pair of genes may be expressed in preference to that of its partner. The gene is then said to be *dominant* and the other *recessive*. A recessive gene will only be expressed when the locus at which it occurs is homozygous.

The chromosome complement that is characteristic of a plant, or of a cell population, is called its *karyotype*. Chromosome number is determined by counting the chromosomes in cells that have been fixed and stained while at a particular stage of division. The relative ploidy level of non-dividing cells in a cell population can be estimated by DNA staining or radio-active labelling even when it is not possible to count actual chromosome numbers. This is because when it is not in the process of dividing, a cell has a DNA content that is proportional to the number of chromosomes it contains. Flow cytometry can facilitate the analysis of large cell populations by this method.

SPONTANEOUS VARIATION *IN VITRO*

Phenotypic changes

The phenotype of cells, tissues, or plants can be altered by both temporary environmental and genetic changes, and by permanent changes to the genotype; therefore when variation is detected in cultures, or in populations of plants regenerated from tissue cultures, it is often difficult to ascertain its nature. Temporary variation often results from the expression of genes in some cells, tissues or organs which are not normally active. It may also be due to the carry-over of plant growth regulatory substances from one subculture to another, or from plant material in culture to plants established in greenhouse or field.

Persistent variation is usually caused by changes to the genome, but to be sure that any new characteristic is due to genetic change it is necessary to observe that it is heritable in sexually-produced offspring.

Temporary variation

Cells do not utilise their complete store of genetic information at any one time. Some genes may function (become expressed) continuously, but others only on specific occasions. Gene expression is regulated by the environment in which a cell finds itself, including its interactions with neighbouring cells. Many changes in gene expression occur only temporarily in response to a stimulus and disappear when it is removed. The phenotypic abnormalities which result give rise to *physiological variation* (Chaleff, 1981). Sometimes a particular pattern of gene expression can be induced which persists over a long period, well after the removal of the inductive conditions, and may be passed on from one generation of cells to another. If such a change occurs during *in vitro* culture, the phenotype of the cells, tissues or organs may then be altered or atypical. Phenotypic variation of this kind, which is also ultimately reversible and is not sexually transmitted, is called *epigenetic variation.*

Temporary changes are often noted in cultured plant cells and tissues, and also in plants regenerated from and propagated by tissue culture. For example, during successive subcultures it is sometimes possible to isolate strains of callus which differ in such characteristics as colour, shape, growth rate and greening. Changes of this kind are often reversible (Ogihara and Tsunewaki, 1979). Non-persistent variation is sometimes observed amongst micropropagated plants which might display a change in growth habit, a more rapid development to flowering and the production of more axillary shoots. In some circumstances such phenotypes are advantageous, in other cases they are deleterious.

The causes of temporary changes in phenotypic expression are not fully understood. They may result, in part, from unstable changes in the genotype due to mutation, gene amplification (Latunde-Dada and Lucas, 1988), or the induction of unstable genes (Groose and Bingham, 1986a,b) possibly caused by the activity of transposable elements (see page 73) (Lee and Phillips, 1988).

Cells also respond to the environment through epigenetic changes in the genes which are expressed through transcription or translation. Regulation of this kind can be brought about by plant growth regulators and Quemada *et al.* (1987) and Meins (1987) suggested that it could occur during *in vitro* culture through the loss of

DNA-methylation. This would result in genes becoming activated: re-methylation occurring in regenerated plant tissues would inactivate the genes involved.

It can be difficult to separate true epigenetic changes, resulting from differences in gene regulation and expression, from the other kinds of impermanent phenotypes which result from a genuinely altered genotype (Meins, 1987). Some unstable changes in genetic material can be transferred in sexual crosses, whereas epigenetic changes are not. Effects of epigenetic expression are discussed in Chapter 8, and habituation, an impermanent abnormality having a physiological or epigenetic basis, is described in Chapter 11. Abnormalities which have been found im micropropagated plants are discussed in Chapter 15.

SPONTANEOUS GENETIC VARIATION

MUTATION

A cell is said to have undergone a mutation when its genetic makeup is suddenly and unexpectedly changed without the formation and sexual fusion of gametes. Mutations can occur through alterations in karyotype, involving one or more chromosomes, or through small changes in the structure or position of one or more genes. A low rate of 'spontaneous' mutation occurs continously in all living organisms and so a small proportion of variants will always occur during plant propagation even though their occurrence is generally undesirable.

Many of the mutations produced during *in vitro* culture are deleterious and their expression results in plant phenotypes of reduced vigour or abnormal appearance. However some can be useful for plant improvement, either immediately, or after inclusion in a plant breeding programme which will combine the new character or characters with other desirable attributes. Alternatively, new genotypes may be of value in the selection of cell lines required for the production of secondary products or the transformation of chemicals.

Phenotypic variability is a very common consequence of the culture of unorganised callus and suspension cultures of plants of all genera (including those initiated from protoplasts). Most of the observed changes are due to alterations in cell genotypes and can occur at high frequency (*e.g.* 0.03–0.07 mutations per cell per cell division). Mutations are much less common in organ cultures or in tissue cultures in which shoots or somatic embryos are induced to form directly on explants. A first sign of

induced variation in unorganised cultures can be the appearance of callus sectors or cell types having an unusual colour, morphology, physiology, or an altered morphogenic potential (Fig. 23). Subsequently, a high proportion of regenerated plants may differ from the the stock plant. However, many mutations remain undetected *in vitro* and may only become apparent upon careful genetic analysis of regenerated ramets.

Plants derived from tissue cultures can have a wide range of altered characteristics, from temporary changes in phenotype, to sexually transmitted genetic changes involving both dominant and recessive single gene factors or characters controlled by many genes. Genetic changes persist throughout the life of the plants and are potentially heritable. Some mutations are similar to those induced by chemical mutagens or ionising radiation, while others are unique. In tomato, mutations induced by *in vitro* culture were found to be different in effect from those which were produced by exposure to chemical mutagens and sometimes resulted in a different pattern of subsequent segregation: homozygous 'solid' mutants were frequently recovered in plants regenerated from tissue culture (Gavazzi *et al.*, 1987).

Although *in vitro* culture induces the most obvious mutations in the nuclear genomes of plants, the chromosomes of cytoplasmic organelles can also be altered by *in vitro* culture (Sibi, 1976; Pring *et al.*, 1981; Day and Ellis, 1984; Wilson *et al.*, 1985; De Buyser *et al.*, 1988). Genetic changes are usually random in nature, but sometimes there has been a pronounced tendency for a high proportion of mutations to have influenced the phenotype in a similar direction. It is common for the majority of

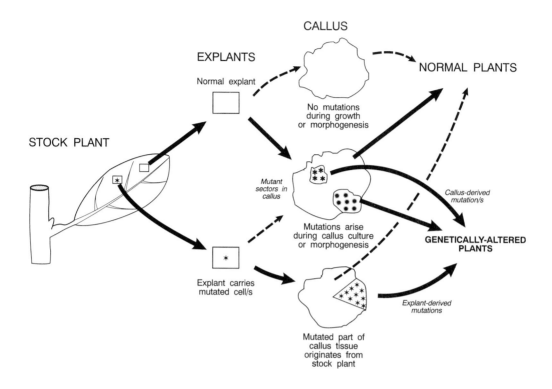

Fig. 28. Sources of genetic variation in plants obtained through organogenesis in callus cultures.
Events shown by broken lines occur less frequently.

changes to have an adverse effect on the phenotype (*e.g.* a decrease in plant height and low seed fertility — Oono, 1982), but sometimes the opposite effect has been noted (*e.g.* an increased resistance of sugar canes to Fiji disease — Krishnamurthy and Tlaskal, 1974; or eyespot toxin — Larkin and Scowcroft, 1983: tolerance of *Medicago* to wilt caused by *Verticillium albo- atrum* — Latunde-Dada and Lucas, 1983).

Many genetic traits are likely to be altered during tissue culture but less variation occurs in qualitative, highly conserved characteristics than in those which are strongly influenced by the environment. Changes in characters which are critical to normal cellular function (i.e the formation of *lethal mutants*) either do not occur, or are eliminated if they interfere with cell survival (Wang and Holl, 1988). Genes which, when functional, have such a markedly deleterious effect that the organism carrying them is unable to survive, are known as *lethal factors*. They are usually recessive and their effect is only manifested in the homozygous state.

Loss of regenerative ability

A gradual increase in the proportion of cells with atypical chromosome complement is believed to be one of the main reasons why tissue cultures of many plant species lose the ability to regenerate shoots with progressive subculturing (see Chapter 8) (Torrey, 1958a, 1967; Murashige and Nakano, 1965).

THE BASIS OF GENETIC CHANGE

It is thought that the occurrence of genetic variability within tissue cultures may partly originate from cellular changes in the mother plant and partly (and more frequently) from changes in the normal karyotype that are induced during culture (Fig. 28): it is often impossible to determine which has been the main contributory factor. Karyotypic changes of stock plant origin are suspected when polyploid shoots arise almost simultaneously with callus initiation from explants taken from a diploid plant (Horák *et al.*, 1975a). It has been said that variability associated with *in vitro* growth is particularly liable to occur, or be amplified, at three different stages of cell or callus culture (D'Amato, 1978):

— during the induction of a culture;

— during the growth of a culture;

— during plant regeneration.

Changes of mother plant origin

Vegetative parts of plants are typically composed of cells that all have the same genetic potential (genotype), but it is possible for cells with different genetic constitutions to exist and co-operate in the growth and functioning of a whole plant. Experience with grafting shows that compatibility between diverse cell types may even extend to those from plants in different genera. Plants composed of cells of different genetic or physiolgical potential are called chimeras (or chimaeras) (see the following section), but the description is not usually applied unless the whole plant or a major portion of it can be so described and until a mixture of distinct cell types has been demonstrated experimentally.

As tissue cultures are liable to be genetically variable if they are started from tissues of a stock plant comprised of genetically different cells, those initiated from known chimeras are very likely to become composed of a mixture of cell types. Cell variation in cultures can also be induced if callus is initiated from explants containing differentiated and mature tissues which have a specialised function; this is because plant cells can undergo karyological change during differentiation. In many species (but not all), the chromosomes of such cells become duplicated without the nucleus dividing in the usual way (mitosis) and without the division of the cytoplasm (cytokinesis) and the formation of a cell wall: the process is termed endo-reduplication and leads to endo-polyploidy, or may result in nuclear fragmentation (Cionini et al., 1978). Differentiation is also sometimes accompanied by other mistakes in cell division such as the failure of the cytoplasm to divide, more than one nuclear division in a single cell, and the replication of chromatids during the S phase of the cell cycle without their separation polyteny. These conditions do not occur in meristems and in tissues closely associated with sporophytic reproduction, where cells usually retain a constant ploidy.

The existence of cells having different multiples of the normal somatic chromosome number within the somatic tissues of a whole plant is called polysomaty or polysomatism. It seems to be particularly prevalent in polyploid species, where cells may also contain less than the characteristic number of chromosomes without serious consequences. Cells with an exact (euploid), or an inexact (aneuploid) multiple of the normal haploid chromosome complement of the species, can be intermingled (mixoploidy): this condition apppears be tolerated in polyploids because of 'genetic buffering' between the multiple chromosome sets. Such mosaicism can exist in some commercial sugar cane clones which are complex polyploids derived from interspecific hybridisation (Maretzki, 1987).

If tissues which have unusual karyotypes are artificially stimulated to divide in tissue culture, they are liable to give rise to cells having greater than normal ploidy levels. Callus initiated from mixoploid tissue is also likely to become composed of cells with abnormal chromosome numbers.

Explant-derived variation

Because some parts of a mature plant are more liable to be polysomatic than others, the extent of variation in cultured cells (particularly ploidy levels) can differ according to the nature of the explant chosen for culture initiation. The most stable callus cultures are likely to be obtained from meristematic tissue of a mature plant or from tissues of a very young organ still of a meristematic nature. Very young pea leaves are thought to consist of cells still functioning as a plate meristem (Rubluo et al., 1984).

All the plants obtained by Wakasa (1979) from syncarp (compound ovary) or slip (small shoots which appear just below the fruit) callus of pineapple were variants while only 7% of those obtained from crown (the shoot axis at the top of a fruit) callus were variable. Many of the plants regenerated from callus derived from the seeds of four Cymbopogon species were atypical, but those obtained from inflorescence calluses closely resembled the parents, with only a negligable number of variations (Jagadish Chandra and Sreenath, 1982). Plantlets obtained indirectly from spadix explants of Anthurium scherzerianum were less variable than those produced from leaf segments. Geier (1987) suggested that this was because callus produced from spadix segments was more organised than that from leaves.

Polytene cells and a high proportion of polyploid cells can occur in the cotyledon tissue of some plants: plants regenerated from cotyledon-derived callus or protoplast cultures can be more variable than those obtained from leaf callus (Colijn- Hooymans et al., 1988a; Osifo et al., 1989a). Stem tissue of diploid potato varieties is mainly diploid and therefore has a 2C amount of DNA in the G1 phase of the cell cycle (page 22), and a 4C amount in G2 phase (C is defined as the DNA content of a monohaploid cell in G1 phase). Mature tobacco pith tissue is primarily polyploid (i.e. 4C or greater) and gives rise to very variable callus cultures (Murashige and Nakano, 1967). Similarly, pith cells of soil-grown tubers of monoploid, diploid and tetraploid potato varieties can have 8C or 16C amounts of DNA (Hovenkamp-Hermelink et al., 1988). By contrast, root tissues of monohaploid, diploid and tetraploid potato genotypes have been found to vary less in ploidy level than stem internode tissues (Sree Ramulu and Dijkhuis, 1986).

Genetic changes arising in culture

Actively dividing 'meristematic' cells in callus and in cell clusters of suspension cultures, frequently remain genetically homogenous and stable, while variable DNA levels occur in the large vacuolated cells and in the free-floating cells and cell groups of suspensions cultures (Kibler and Neumann, 1980). Cells in these 'parenchymatous tissues' often come to have unusual ploidy levels and some are thought to become endopolyploid in the same way as certain differentiated cells in intact plants. Endopolyploid cells do not normally divide again, but if they *are* stimulated to do so *in vitro*, tetraploid or octaploid chromosome complements could result. Endo-reduplication is more prevalent in cultures that have been maintained for a long period.

If for any reason a cell with an altered genetic composition should appear, its survival will depend on how well it can grow and divide in the particular cultural environment provided. Although some genetic changes may reduce the chances of a cell dividing *in vitro*, it is clear that many abnormalites do not impose this restraint. It is, for instance, well known that aneuploid cells can continue to divide *in vitro* (Murashige and Nakano, 1967), while the widespread occurrence of genetic abnormalities amongst plants regenerated from callus cultures shows that aberrant cells can participate in meristem formation and subsequent plant growth. However, cells which have undergone major changes in genotype do lose the capacity to undergo morphogenesis.

Polyploidy and aneuploidy. The proportion of polyploid or aneuploid cells arising during *in vitro* culture can vary in similar experiments. In some cases, polyploidy has been accompanied by very few other changes in the genotype (Jagadish Chandra and Sreenath, 1982). Some authors have pointed out that even if there is some associated variability, tissue culture can be a useful method for producing polyploid plants required in breeding programmes. An interesting example is the regeneration of fertile amphidiploid (2n = XXYY = 32) shallot plants by Seo and Kim (1988). The chromosome number of callus derived from bulb scales became amphidiploid during the third and fourth subcultures. The normal plant, which is vegetatively multiplied from bulbs, is amphihaploid (2n = XY = 16) and sterile.

One reason for the generation of polyploid cells in cultures, is the failure of spindle formation during mitosis (Bayliss, 1973) or the occurrence of abnormal multipolar, instead of the usual bipolar, spindles. Where a spindle

fails to form properly, two chromosome complements may combine resulting in a cell with a doubled chromosome complement. Multipolar spindle formation or nuclear fusion may be the cause of the occasional appearance of cell lines with uneven ploidy (*e.g.* haploids or triploids) (D'Amato, 1977; Bennici and D'Amato, 1978). Another possible reason is that cells may become temporarily arrested in *G2* but then be stimulated to re-enter the cell cycle at *G1* without have completed normal mitosis.

Aneuploid cells result from other mistakes during nuclear division. For example, chromosomes may break into two or more fragments and chromosome lag at the anaphase stage of mitosis (mitotic non-disjunction) can lead to the formation of daughter cells, one with a lower, and the other with a higher than normal chromosome number.

Structural changes. Although in some species much of the genetic variation between cells can be explained by changes in chromosome number (Groose and Bingham, 1984), in others most altered karyotypes are caused by the breakage and structural alteration of chromosomes or chromatids (half chromosomes during the early stages of mitosis). Chromosome breakage often occurs during the division of unorganised cells *in vitro* and can result in many different rearrangements of the karyotype. For instance:

- segments may be being rearranged in another part of the same chromosome or reattached to another non-homologous chromosome (*translocation*);

- segments may be lost, resulting in the appearance of chromosomes with missing genetic sequences (*deletions*);

- breakage at a centromere can lead to the formation of two chromosomes in place of one;

- breakage during mitosis followed by healing of the chomatid ends can lead to the formation of ring chromosomes or chromosomes having two or three centromeres (*dicentric* or *tricentric* chromosomes).

Some researchers think that an exchange of segments between homologous chromosomes may occur at mitosis (*somatic* or *mitotic crossing over*) causing the recombination of genetic material (Evans *et al.*, 1984).

Review articles. The character and causes of chromosomal variation in tissue cultures have been reviewed by D'Amato (1975), Skirvin (1977), Sunderland (1977), Bayliss (1980), Constantin (1981), Murata and Orton (1983) and Lee and Phillips (1988).

Cryptic modifications

Many of the genetic changes described above can be detected by cytological examination. Other modifications of the genome may not be immediately obvious. The translocation of chromosome segments to other positions in the same chromosome or their attachment to another, the exchange of segments between sister chromatids (Dolezel and Novák, 1986) and with non-homologous chromosomes, or the deletion or turning around (inversion) of chromosome segments (McCoy et al., 1982), would require careful genetic analysis. Other hidden changes may also occur during culture such as the activation, repositioning and possible duplication of *transposable elements* and the mutation of single genes or of loci affecting quantitative traits.

Translocations. A reliable method of transferring genes from one species to another which would result in their integration into a new environment (*introgression*) would be of great significance to plant breeding. Interspecific crosses can result in hybrids carrying some or all of the chromosomes of two species, but chromosomes of different origin are usually non-homologous and translocations between them are rare in nature and usually require some degree of *homoeology* (*i.e.* the two chromosomes are homologous for part of their length). Translocations can sometimes be induced between resident and alien chromosomes in plants containing one or more foreign chromosomes (*addition lines*), by introducing a mutant gene which partially relaxes the normal resistance to pairing, but this process is laborious and only rarely successful.

Translocations occasioned by *in vitro* culture do not appear to be restricted by homoeology. Larkin *et al.* (1990) report that tissue culture can result in the transfer of small interstitial fragments from alien chromosomes into the basic chromosome set of a crop species. Through culture of immature embryos or young inflorescence tissue of addition lines, it has been possible to introduce into wheat, resistance to cereal cyst nematode from rye, and resistance to barley dwarf yellow virus from *Thinopyrum* (*Agropyrum*) *intermedium*.

Transposable elements. A transposable element (or a transposable controlling element, now usually called a *transposon*) is a genetic sequence which, under certain circumstances, is capable of moving from one position in the genome to another, including movement between chromosomes. Such elements are of more than one kind. When a transposon becomes positioned at a new locus, a *mutator* (*dissociator*) element causes an unstable suppression or modification of adjacent genes. The effect of a mutator element depends upon the presence in the genome of one or more migratory *activator* loci (Goodenough, 1978; Larkin and Scowcroft, 1981; Chourey and

Kemble, 1982). Besides temporarily suppressing gene action, transposons can induce the duplication of DNA segments and rearrangements of the genome, such as the fusion or inversion of chromosome segments, or the deletion or alteration of DNA sequences. Transposable elements may become especially active *in vitro* (Groose and Bingham, 1986a; Peschke *et al.*, 1987; Lee and Phillips, 1988; Phillips *et al.*, 1990). As they respond to signals in a programmed way, it is thought that they have the capacity to be involved in differentiation (Shepherd *et al.*, 1982).

As the changes in genetic potential resulting from 'cryptic' changes to the genome are probably more likely than aneuploidy or polyploidy to be responsible for the variation sometimes found in regenerants (see later), chromosome number can be a poor guide to the genetic stability of tissue cultures (Ashmore and Gould, 1981; Gould, 1982). The kinds of chromosome breakages induced by tissue culture may be different from those occurring in nature (Ogihara, 1982).

Detecting genetic change

Without detailed analysis, minor cryptic changes in the genome brought about by tissue culture can be difficult to identify and quantify. Analysis of the lengths of DNA fragments produced by DNA digestion with restriction endonuclease enzymes (restriction fragment length polymorphisms) (Beckmann and Soller, 1986) has been suggested as one method which might provide sufficient accuracy (Jarret and Florkowski, 1990).

WHAT INDUCES GENETIC VARIATION IN VITRO?

DNA-methylation

Until recently the causes of genetic change during tissue culture have been obscure. Phillips *et al.* (1990) have now advanced the hypothesis that most, if not all, the mutational events occasioned by tissue culture are directly or indirectly related to alterations in the state of DNA methylation. When DNA is highly methylated (*hyper-* methylated), gene activity is suppressed. A decrease in methylation (*hypo*-methylation) correlates with increased gene activity.

According to this hypothesis, an increase, or decrease in DNA-methylation might account for qualitative mutations, such as those controlled by single recessive genes; for increased transposable element activity, for simultaneous changes in quantitative characters, and for the mutations occasioned by chromosome breakage. It is thought that activation of a previously dormant and stable transposable element sequence through chromosome breakage or DNA-hypomethylation, can affect the methylation and genetic activity of other similar sequences. There is some evidence that DNA-methylation and the methylation of activated transposable elements, may decrease the longer plant tissues are maintained in culture (Kunze *et al.*, 1988): if this is found to be generally valid, increased transposable element activity could be responsible for the genetic changes in callus and cell culture which occur during prolonged incubation.

Chromosomal DNA is replicated during the *S* phase of the cell cycle preceding mitosis. Double-stranded DNA unwinds to allow each single strand to serve as a template for the growth of new complementary partner. Replication is not instantaneous, so that some regions of a chromosome, particularly the *heterochromatin*, will persistently replicate after others (Fig. 10). Heterochromatin, unlike the *euchromatin*, seems to be genetically inert, but involved in 'chromosome mechanics' and breaks in chromosomes or chromatids are particularly likely to occur in the regions where it occurs. Sacristan (1971) and McCoy *et al.* (1982) suggested that in tissue cultured plants cells, DNA replication may be delayed, so the heterochomatic parts of chromosomal DNA strands may fail to replicate before mitosis. This would lead such anomalies as aneuploidy and the breakage and sectorial rearrangment of chromosomes, all of which are frequently observed in callus and cell cultures. DNA methylation has been found to be correlated with late replication in mammals, leading Phillips *et al.* (1990) to propose that it could also be the primary causative factor in the tissue culture situation.

If an altered methylation state induces genetic change, what is responsible for this condition? It could be that the unnatural conditions *in vitro* impose a stress or a shock which disturbs the physiology of the cell. This seems unlikely as culture under very similar conditions does not occasion genetic change in cells of organised meristems and organs. Lo Schiavo *et al.* (1989) have shown that there is more 5-methyl cytosine in the DNA of cultured carrot cells in the presence of a natural or synthetic auxin. Auxin-induced methylation, which was thought to occur in a random fashion, decreased when 2,4-D was removed from the medium and embryogenesis initiated, but embryogenesis was blocked by hypomethylating drugs.

The occurrence of genetic change is very much influenced by the method of culture that is employed for any particular species. In appropriate conditions, genetic variation produced by tissue culture can be much greater than that induced by well-known mutagenic agents.

A lack of nucleic acid precursors

Swartz (1991) suggests that shortage of the precursors necessary for the rapid nucleic acid biosyntheis which occurs in many tissue cultures, may be responsible for some of the mutations observed. Adenine is sometimes added to plant culture media, but the use of other DNA bases is very rare. Whether supplying these compounds to plant cells would help to stabilize mitoses and reduce mutagenesis, is unknown.

Growth regulators

Unorganised *in vitro* growth is an unusual plant condition and, unfortunately, high levels of exogenous plant growth regulating compounds have to be used to obtain the relatively rapid cell division necessary to induce and sustain it. Several workers have found that the plant growth regulators added to a medium are instrumental in inducing genetic changes in tissue cultures. However, it is unclear how changes are effected. Can regulants directly induce mutations, or is it only the high rate of cell division which induces them? In some instances growth regulators may preferentially increase the rate of division in those cells already genetically abnormal (Bayliss, 1980). Regulants may alter the state of DNA-methylation.

The genetic composition of a cell population can be influenced by the relative levels of both cytokinin and auxin growth regulators (D'Amato, 1975) and cells of normal ploidy are often seen to be at a selective advantage in media where these chemicals are present in low concentrations or entirely absent. A mutagenic effect has been associated with both classes of compound used alone, or in combination.

Auxins

An auxin is almost invariably added to a culture medium to induce the formation, and maintain the growth, of unorganised calli and cell suspensions. Genetic changes are highly likely to be initiated in cultures of this kind. Perhaps it is no coincidence that auxins have been found greatly to increase the rate of DNA-methylation (Lo Schiavo *et al.*, 1989)

The auxin 2,4-D which is frequently employed for the initiation and maintenance of callus and cell cultures, has often been associated with genetic abnormalities such as aneuploidy (D'Amato, 1978), polyploidy, and the stimulation of DNA synthesis which may result in endoreduplication (Swartz, 1991). Often a greater proportion of polyploid cells is produced by using 2,4-D in media, than when NAA is supplied instead (*e.g.* in *Haplopappus* cell suspensions — Sunderland, 1977). Using *Vigna sinensis*, Jha and Roy (1982) obtained similar results to those of Sunderland, and found that the maximum chromosome number in cultures grown with NAA was hexaploid, while octaploid cells were discovered in cultures on a medium with 2,4-D.

Chromosome abnormalities in *Nigella sativa* tissues occurred at maximum frequency when 2,4-D, rather than one of the alternative auxins, IAA or NAA, was present in the medium, together with kinetin (Chand and Roy, 1980). By contrast, in the experiments of Singh and co-workers (Singh and Harvey, 1975; Singh *et al.*, 1975), cell cultures of *Vicia* and *Happlopappus* remained diploid in high levels of 2,4-D but became polyploid on lower levels. Bayliss (1980) concluded that there was no evidence to implicate 2,4-D as the direct causal agent of mitotic aberrations leading to changes in the chromosome number of plant cells; the auxin only affected mitosis because it stimulated disorganised growth.

A high concentration of 2,4-D was found by Creemers-Molenaar *et al.* (1988) to be partly responsible for the formation of albino plants from indirectly-formed somatic embryos of *Lolium*, particularly *Lolium perenne*. It was thought that both nuclear and chloroplast genes had been altered or deleted during the cultural process. Albinism is very liable to occur in cereal plants regenerated from pollen *via* anther culture. Day and Ellis (1984, 1985) found that in wheat this was associated with large deletions in the chloroplast genome.

Cytokinins

Cytokinins increase the rate of cell division in cultured tissues, and in low concentrations they may decrease the range of ploidies in cell suspensions by stimulating the division of cytologically-stable meristematic cells (Kibler and Neumann, 1980). By contrast, high concentrations of many compounds with cytokinin activity, can increase the frequency of polyploid cells (Zakhlenyuk and Kunakh, 1987). Oono (1982) reported that a high level of benzyladenine (30 mg/l) greatly increased the genetic variability of rice callus cultures compared to that found in cultures incubated with 2 mg/l.

Auxins and cytokinins in combination

Sacristan (1967) showed that the proportion of tobacco cells with different levels of ploidy could be changed by varying the ratio of auxin to cytokinin in the medium. In this study each of four callus strains responded in a different manner. Swartz (1991) suggests that unbalanced concentrations of cytokinins and auxins are most likely to induce polyploidy.

Both the cytokinins BAP and kinetin, and the auxins IAA and 2,4-D, induced abnormal anaphase stages during mitosis in *Vicia faba* root tips immersed for 6 h in concentrations of 0.1 mg/l or more (1 mg/l for kinetin). In callus cultures of this species, the frequency of abnormal anaphase cells closely parallels the frequency of aneuploid or polyploid cells (Ogura, 1982).

Composition of the culture medium

The composition of the medium on which cultures are grown is also able to influence the ploidy level of cultures and the relative proportions of cells with different chromosome numbers. Mitotic cells in root segments of *Pisum* were all diploid when the tissue was cultured on a simple medium. The addition of yeast extract, coconut milk or kinetin increased the rate of cell division and resulted in a tissue where dividing cells were diploid, tetraploid and octaploid. Torrey (1961) supposed that kinetin, and the alternative media ingredients, had caused the division of normally-dormant endopolyploid cells.

The selective effect of media constituents on cell karyotypes has been well demonstrated by using artificial mixtures of cells having different chromosome numbers. An abnormal line of carrot cells became predominant over those of a normal diploid line in a mixed culture on standard **MS** medium or **MS** medium containing half the normal phosphate level. By contrast, the proportion of diploid cells increased when frequent subcultures were made to **MS** medium with only one quarter the normal nitrogen level (Bayliss, 1977). Most haploid cell lines of *Datura innoxia* retained their normal ploidy (with *ca.* 30% diploid, tetraploid or aneuploid cells) in a standard medium, but became composed of diploid and tetraploid cells on a medium containing only organic nitrogen (Furner *et al.*, 1978).

The level of potassium nitrate in the culture medium has been shown to influence the number of albino plants regenerated from wheat anther callus cultures (Feng and Ouyang, 1988). Albinism is probably caused by deletions in the DNA of cytoplasmic genomes (see above).

Chelating agents and some micronutrient metals have been noted to induce chromosome breakage. The effectiveness of metal ions in inducing mutation is in proportion to their electronegativity; thus in plant culture media the mutagenic effect of nutrient ions would be expected to be:

$$Zn^{2+} > Cu^{2+} > Ni^{2+} > Co^{2+} > Fe^{3+} > Mn^{2+} > Mg^{2+} > Ca^{2+},$$

and related to the ability of the metal to form stable complexes with cell constituents (Steffensen, 1961). Eichhorn (1980) records that in bacteria, low concentrations of some micronutrient metals favour complemen   -

tary DNA-base pairing whereas high levels (*e.g.* of Mg ions) produce indiscriminate pairing: Mn ions cause a decrease in the fidelity of viral DNA synthesis and also induce errors in bacterial RNA synthesis. Could supra-optimal micronutrient levels in culture media have the same effects on plant tissues?

Cultural conditions

Pro-oxidant states

In animal cells, conditions which lead to abnormally high cellular concentrations of the activated forms of oxygen (caused by overproduction, or cells lacking the means to destroy these species) lead to mutations, such as sister chromatid exchanges and chromosome aberrations. Cytotoxicity, carcinogenesis and cellular degeneration related to aging may result (Cerutti, 1985). Antioxidant enzymes and chemicals usually provide a natural defence.

Highly oxidising conditions occur during the isolation of protoplasts, cells and explants for tissue culture and, by analogy, it is tempting to speculate that cellular mutation experienced in tissue cultures could be generated at this time. Effects of antioxidants are discussed in Chapter 7 and treatments to minimise the effect of oxidising conditions during explant excision and culture are discussed in Chapter 13.

Temperature

The temperature at which cultures are incubated can influence the rate of mutation. Tobacco callus incubated at 35°C remained predominantly diploid, while the same tissue cultured at 25°C showed marked karyological instability and became mainly tetraploid (Binns and Meins, 1980). In *Lolium multiflorum*, the occurrence of albino seedlings from somatic embryos depended mainly on genotype, but was also strongly influenced by temperature: the percentage of aberrant plants increased as the incubation temperature was raised above 10–15°C (Jackson and Dale, 1988).

Method of culture

Where plant tissues without reduplicated cells are used as explants, callus or suspension cultures are initially produced with the same ploidy level as the stock plant from which they were derived. In diploid species, particularly those with a small number of chromosomes, it may be possible to retain the original ploidy level over many subcultures, although less obvious karyotypic changes are still likely to occur. Frequent subcultures and/or the isolation and subculture of meristematic nodules, appear

to offer the best means of preserving an unchanged chromosome number. Evans and Gamborg (1980) reported that they had been able to maintain stable euploid (chromosomally normal) lines of some plant species by subculturing cell suspensions twice a week to maintain a rapid rate of cell division. Polyploidy increased when *Hevea* cells were cultured in suspension, but decreased when they were recultured as callus on a solid medium (Wilson *et al.*, 1976). A population of genetically homogenous cells can often be isolated from cell suspensions by filtering off clusters of actively-dividing cells. Compact cell masses in daylily suspensions (referred to as 'nubbins' by Krikorian *et al.*, 1982a) gave rise to plants which were cytologically homogenous and identical in ploidy and chromosome morphology to the parents.

VARIATIONS OBSERVED IN CELL POPULATIONS

The effect of genotype

Genetic disturbance has been found in cell and callus cultures of a very wide range of plant species, but its extent and occurrence depends on the genetic constitution of the cells being cultured. The callus of some species (see later) is not especially prone to genetic disturbance. Roy (1980) found that the callus of two species of *Allium* responded differently to the selective pressure of similar cultural conditions. Callus of *A. tuberosum* came to contain cells that were mainly aneuploid or had chromosomes with structural abnormalities, while in *A. cepa*, aberrant cells had mainly 2 or 4 times the normal number of chromosomes.

Susceptibility to genetic variation may even differ between different varieties or cultivars within a species. In open pollinated celery varieties, for example, the proportion of diploid, aneuploid and polyploid cells in callus cultures, varied between those originated from different mother plants (Browers and Orton, 1982a,b). As plants regenerated from genetically variable callus are more liable to be variable than those derived from a stable strain, the proportion of genetically-altered plants obtained *via* indirect morphogenesis is very genotype-dependent (see later).

The extent of mutation in culture can also depend on the strain of callus which is cultured (Oono, 1982), showing that some primary genetic changes are more likely than others to engender further modification.

Sensitivity to mutation in culture accompanied by changes in ploidy (particularly aneuploidy), is often particularly marked in species that are naturally polyploid or amphiploid (*e.g.* potato, sugar cane and tobacco). There are exceptions: diploid races of *Cymbopogon* (aromatic grasses) were more likely to experience ploidy changes after a long period of culture than polyploid ones (Jagadish Chandra and Sreenath, 1982).

Haploid cultures have been said to be less stable than those of diploids (Novák, 1980a), and plants with polyploid and sometimes aneuploid chromosome complements may be regenerated from anther cultures (McCoy and Bingham, 1979; Han *et al.*, 1982), particularly where regeneration is from anther-derived callus.

Period of occurrence

The proportion of mutated cells generally increases when cultures are maintained for a protracted period. It is therefore wise to subculture unorganised callus only 2–3 times if true-to-type plants are required to be regenerated from it. Constantin *et al.* (1978), for instance, found that a greater proportion of plants with aberrant morphology, or which did not set seed, were regenerated from long-term tobacco callus cultures than from those which had been subcultured only twice. Contrary to this advice, there is evidence that in some cultures (*e.g.* those derived from protoplasts) the bulk of new genetic variation arises very soon after culture initiation.

Genetic change is also often accentuated by prolonged intervals between subcultures. The proportion of cells with an above average ploidy in a highly embryogenic suspension culture of alfalfa, was greatly increased if a long subculture interval was used; the culture also lost its embryogenic capacity when treated in this way. Ploidy was stable when subcultures were carried out at 7 day intervals (Binarová and Dolezel, 1988).

Direct selection

Apart from governing which cells survive in culture, genetic changes amongst the cells in callus and suspensions are often sufficient to enable cell types to be selected which are either different morphologically or physiologically from the parental cell line, show resistance or preference for particular chemical or physical factors, or produce abnormal levels of certain secondary products. Unfortunately genetic instability in such lines may make them unsuitable for long-term use (Deus-Neumann and Zenk, 1984).

GENETICALLY ABNORMAL PLANTS

Somaclonal variation

Occurrence

Clones of plants regenerated from callus are sometimes called *calliclones* and those originating from protoplasts, *protoclones*. Larkin and Scowcroft (1981) proposed the term *somaclone* to describe the plants originating from any type of tissue culture: genetic variation found to occur between somaclones was then called *somaclonal variation.*

A lack of uniformity amongst the plants regenerated from callus has been described in a wide range of plant species. However, many authors have not analysed the cause of the phenotypic variation: it could sometimes have had a physiological origin, but in the majority of cases, it will have resulted from morphogenesis having been initiated in the kinds of genetically altered cells described in the sections above. Possible sources of genetic variability amongst plants produced from callus are shown in Fig. 28 (page 70) and Fig. 29. Some regenerated plants may be grossly abnormal. Others may show useful changes in general plant morphology, yield attributes, flower colour or disease resistance. Mutations can affect both qualitative and quantitative characters (Fig. 30), and can prove to be stable, and transmissible to subsequent seed-derived generations (Ahloowalia and Sherington, 1985).

As the range of genetic variability in callus cultures depends on the genotype of the parent plant, it is not unexpected that both the frequency and type of variabililty occurring in regenerated plants should be genotype specific as well. Flashman (1982) found that genetically characterised lines of tobacco differed markedly in all these respects.

Even though cultures may contain cells having different chromosome numbers, abnormal cells are not necessarily included in the meristems from which plants are regenerated. Selective pressures can operate within mixed cell populations to preserve genetic normality: in diploid species, diploid cells often participate preferentially (*diplontic* selection) in the formation of root and shoot meristems. A high proportion of euploid shoots may then be regenerated from predominantly aneuploid callus (Flashman, 1981; Traynor and Flashman, 1981; Ogihara, 1982; Murashige and Nakano, 1965; Novák and Vyskot, 1975; Mok *et al.*, 1976; Wenzel *et al.*, 1979).

Shoots and plants with aneuploid chromosome numbers are sometimes produced from callus cultures. They have been found, for example, in:

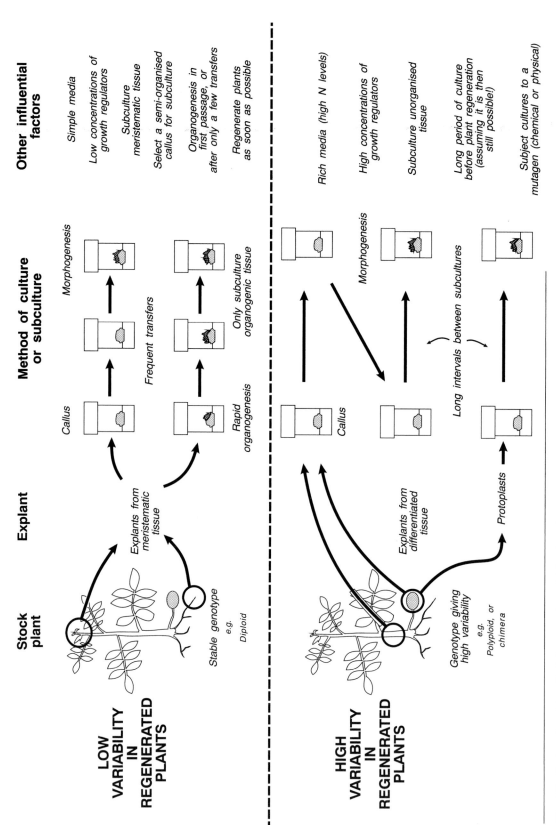

Fig. 29. Factors found to affect the genetic variability in callus cultures and in plants regenerated from them.

Tobacco	Sacristan and Melchers (1969); Sacristan and Lutz (*1970*); Zagorska *et al.*(1974); Ogura (1976); Nuti Ronchi *et al.*(1981)
Sugar Cane	Heinz and Mee (1971); Nickell (1977); Liu *et al.* (1977) ; Krishnamurthi (1982)
Potato	Thomas *et al.*(1982); Bright *et al.*(1982)
Rice	Oono (1978)
Strawberry	Fukui and Niizeki (1982)

It is probably no coincidence that most of the above species are naturally polyploid. Possibly the presence in polyploids of identical genes at loci on different chromosomes, helps to buffer the normally disadvantageous effect of aneuploidy and other genetic disorders.

A summary of the most commonly accepted ways of decreasing or increasing the genetic variation in callus cultures and in the plants regenerated from them, is shown in Fig. 29. For plant breeding purposes, variability can be further increased by mutagenic treatments (*e.g.* deliberately adding chemical mutagens to the culture medium, or subjecting the culture to ionising radiation).

Further information can be obtained from the following papers and review articles

General reviews covering several crops

— Skirvin (1977); O'Neill (1981); Larkin and Scowcroft (1981); Evans *et al.* (1984); Semal (1985).

A new *Pelargonium* variety from calliclones

— Skirvin and Janick (1976a); Janick *et al.* (1977)

Results obtained with sugar cane

— Liu and Chen (1976, 1978); Heinz *et al.*(1977); Krishnamurthi (1982); Maretzki (1987); Larkin and Scowcroft (1983) — and see Chapter 17.

Useful somatic mutations in tobacco

— Kasperbauer *et al.* (1981).

Formation of chimeras. If several cells of different genotypes participate in the formation of an adventitious shoot meristem, a plant can be formed in which the cell layers are cytologically distinct. Plants of this kind are called chimeras (see later in this chapter).

Variable plants from protoplasts

Although plants regenerated from protoplast calluses of dihaploid potatoes (having half the number of chromosomes found in the naturally tetraploid, cultivated potato, *Solanum tuberosum*) were found to be all true-to-type (Binding *et al.*, 1978), those obtained from protoplasts of

normal potato cultivars have been discovered to be very variable (Butenko and Kuchko, 1978; Shepard, 1980b; Thomas *et al.*, 1982). The wide range of potentially exploitable somaclonal variation in potato first attracted attention through the work of Shepard and his colleagues (1980). Protoclones derived from the cultivar 'Russet Burbank' differed from the parent plant in characteristics such as habit of growth, tuber size and shape, date of tuber initiation, fruit production, leaf variegation and resistance to potato early and late blight (Shepard, 1980b). 'Russet Burbank' is an American cultivar which has been cultivated over many years. At first it was thought that the new variation might have resulted from the exposure of mutations that had accumulated in the cultivar during numerous vegetative generations, but a high variability has since been detected in plants from protoplasts of modern potato varieties and many other species.

The kinds of cell mutation observed in protoplast-derived callus are the same as those occurring in callus originating from multi-celled explants. The causes of variation have thus been attributed to endopolyploidy in parental material and to aberrant mitoses during callus formation. However, some authors have proposed that genetically aberrant cells arise mainly during the cell divisions which immediately follow isolation (Barbier and Dulieu, 1983; Sree Ramulu *et al.*, 1984), and this seems to be borne out by the finding that variation can also occur amongst plants regenerated from protoplasts by direct embryogenesis (Eapen *et al.*, 1989). In callus arising from protoplasts, polyploidy, aneuploidy, and small structural changes in the chromosomes, are most common (Gill *et al.*, 1982; Sree Ramulu *et al.*, 1984)). The degree of aneuploidy in potato protoclones was found to depend more on the method of protoplast isolation and culture than on the variety of potato (Bright *et al.*, 1982).

The chloroplast and mitochondrial DNA of protoclones can also be mutated through protoplast isolation and culture (Rose *et al.*, 1986a).

SCREENING FOR BENEFICIAL VARIANTS

The existence of genetic variation in cell cultures makes it possible to screen for resistance to a selection pressure. Sometimes selection can be effective *in vivo* after a population of variable plants has been obtained. Pathogen resistance has been found by testing plants regenerated from cultures in the glasshouse or field (*e.g.* Krishnamurthi and Tlaskal, 1974; Heath-Pagliuso and Rappaport, 1988). Griesbach (1989) reported isolating an interesting

Fig. 30. Variation in *Petunia* plants which were all regenerated from callus, derived from a single plant.

dwarf form of *Hemerocallis* which occurred through somaclonal variation.

A more efficient selection system can often result from the application of an appropriate stress *in vitro*. Cell lines tolerant to abnormal temperatures, drugs, herbicides, fungal toxins and high levels of salt, can be obtained by adding an appropriate compound to callus or cell cultures. In some cases plants resistant to the normally-damaging principle have been regenerated: if its cells are undamaged by a fungal toxin, a plant may have field resistance to the disease organism (Earle, 1983; Elshennawy and Blackmon, 1988; Masirevec *et al.*, 1988).

Some obligate fungal pathogens can be grown *in vitro* by inoculating shoot cultures with fungal spores. Providing there is a correlation with results *in vivo*, shoot cultures may be screened for immunity to these organisms. The technique has been used successfully for screening peaches for resistance to *Xanthomonas campestris*, *Malus* to the rust fungus *Gynosporangium juniperi- virginianae* (Joung *et al.*, 1987), vines to *Plasmopara viticola* (Barlass *et al.*, 1986) and *Oidium tuckeri* (Reustle *et al.*, 1988). Resistant plant genotypes can be selected by this method from a variable plant population. In *Pinus taeda* there is a strong correlation between *in vitro* and field performance to fusiform rust (Mott *et al.*, 1986).

VARIATION INDUCED BY DIFFERENT MICROPROPAGATION METHODS

The probability that plants obtained from tissue cultures will be phenotypically and genetically changed, depends on the nature of the stock plant, the method by which its tissues are cultured, and method by which plantlets are produced. Each of these factors must be taken into account when devising a micropropagation scheme with the aim of producing plants which are genetically and phenotypically identical to each other and to the norm. By contrast, plant breeders might look for ways to maximise the variation which may be obtained.

Cell and callus cultures

Although there is a high risk of generating somaclonal variation in unorganised cultures, it is unusual for *all* the plants regenerated from a callus or suspension culture to be genetically different to the original stock plant. As shown in Fig. 28, on some occasions a culture may retain genetic integrity, while at other times only part may be composed of genetically altered cells. The proportion of genetically-normal plants regenerated from the culture may reflect this situation, or may be increased because cells possessing unmodified karyotypes are more liable to become committed to organogenesis, than those which are mutated. Such a selection pressure is likely to be most effective in eliminating polyploid and aneuploid regenerants from diploid species: it may not prevent morphogenesis from cells which have experienced subtle changes in their nuclear chromosomes, or those possessing altered cytoplasmic genotypes. The disadvantage of aneuploidy and hyperploidy is less apparent in naturally polyploid species.

The genetic background of a plant has a strong influence on the degree of somaclonal variation resulting from its tissue culture (and conversely, the degree with which the genotype is conserved, unaltered). Even closely related plants may differ in this respect. For instance, some varieties of *Anthurium scherzerianum* (Geier, 1987), and *Kalanchoe blossfeldiana* (Schwaiger and Horn, 1988), are more likely to give rise to variable plants from callus, than others.

There are many reports of phenotypically normal plants having been produced from indirectly formed adventitious shoots, and even a few in which plants were superior to the original mother plant. In *Gynura aurantiaca*, for example, plants regenerated from leaf callus had a different leaf shape than normal plants, but grew larger, were more uniform in growth and time of flowering, and had more flowers per plant (Myerson and Krul, 1982). In such cases changes could be due to genetic change, chimeral segregation or, if the effects are not persistent, epigenetic factors.

Usually when normal plants are produced, shoot regeneration has taken place after only a short period of callus culture, and a steadily increasing proportion of deviant plants is obtained during successive callus passages (Hussey, 1976b; Westerhof *et al.*, 1984). In other cases the proportion of abnormal plants regenerated from callus has remained fairly constant during consecutive multiplication cycles (Geier, 1987). Zimmerman (1982) reported that *Alocasia* had been regularly micropropagated from shoots derived from callus cultures without phenotypic variation.

Callus of diploid plants has frequently been noted to retain its euploidy during culture (*e.g.* that of *Lilium longiflorum* — Sheridan 1975; Simmonds and Cumming, 1976b; *Brachycome dichromosomatica* — Gould, 1979; *Hemerocallis* — Chen and Goeden- Kallemeyn, 1979; *Freesia* — Stimart and Ascher, 1982; *Asparagus* — Reuther and Becker, 1987) and a capacity to regenerate plants after many subcultures. *Lilium* callus is not always genetically stable; some chromosomal alterations were detected by Sheridan (1974) and atypical plants have been obtained from other cultures of this species (Bennici, 1979). In addition, even plants regenerated with euploid chromosome numbers are liable to display somaclonal variation (Eapen and Rao, 1985).

Plants derived from the callus produced by a single plant of alfalfa were all phenotypically indistinguishable. When, however, plants were grown to maturity and selfed, the seedlings showed greater numbers of variants than were found among the selfed seedlings of the parent plant (Johnson *et al.*, 1980). Genetic mutations had apparently occurred in culture which were not immediately obvious.

From semi-organised cultures

The cell of callus and suspension cultures are not always dedifferentiated. Embryogenetically determined calluses sometimes comprise a mass of self- replicating meristematic centres which generate somatic embryos from superficial cells. Semi-organised shoot forming calluses are also occasionally discovered and in these, shoot-producing meristems continuously proliferate. Examples are:

- the granular callus fragments or 'nubbins' of *Hemerocallis* maintained in liquid media (Krikorian and Kann, 1979; 1981; Krikorian *et al.* 1982a):

- callus with superficial meristems produced from shoot tip explants (see page 54)

The callus which forms in shoot cultures at the base of shoot clumps is often semi-organised. In the green granular callus mass which formed at the base of *Rhododendron* shoot tips, each granule represented a potential shoot (Kyte and Briggs, 1979).

Cultures containing organised meristematic centres are found to give rise to genetically normal plants over a long period, for the morphogenic centres proliferate as the 'callus' is subcultured. The capacity of this tissue to produce shoots does not decline, as it does in calluses where organogenetic meristems have to arise *de novo* on each occasion.

Treating suspension cultures with an auxin often results in a mixture of highly vacuolated cells and others with dense and highly granular cytoplasm. The latter divide to form clusters of 10–20 cells. A highly embryogenic and stable cell line can sometimes be obtained by several cycles of filtration which allows the retention of the dense cells and small cell clusters. Somatic embryos formed from such tissue usually give rise to plants which are genetically normal (Kumar *et al.*, 1988).

The method of regeneration

The degree of genetic variation amongst regenerated plants can depend on the method by which they have been produced from callus or suspension cultures. Plants obtained by indirect shoot organogenesis are liable to be most variable, while those derived through indirect somatic embryogenesis are more stable.

Indirect embryogenesis

Monocotyledons. No evidence of cytological abnormality or phenotypic variability has been found by Vasil and co-workers amongst several species of cereals and grasses (*Pennisetum, Panicum, Saccharum, Sorghum, Triticum* and *Zea)* regenerated through somatic embryogenesis (Vasil, 1983). Although other workers have also obtained plants which are all normal phenotypically and cytologically (Swedlund and Locy, 1988), some experimentalists have found plants derived from somatic embryos of Graminaceous species to possess somaclonal variation.

Green (1977) found that most of the plants regenerated from embryogenic maize callus were normal, but some were composed of a mosaic of normal and abnormal (aneuploid or polyploid) cells. In this study, morphological irregularities such an abnormal ear and leaf arrangement also appeared in a proportion of the embryo-derived plants and, at maturity, the entire population had fewer nodes on average and were shorter than plants grown from seed. These characteristics were not apparently genetically based because F_1 plants from selfing were normal in height and node number. By contrast, many of the maize plants regenerated from embryogenic callus cultures were found by Armstrong and Phillips (1988) to have at least one abnormality in cytology, pollen sterility, or other phenotypic characters.

A high degree of cytological variation was reported by Maddock *et al.* (1983, 1985) in plants regenerated from embryogenic cultures of wheat. Chromosome loss was discovered in tetraploid genotypes of *Lolium multiflorum* propagated through somatic embryogenesis, although diploid genotypes retained their normal chromosome number (apart from a low frequency of tetraploidy) (Jackson and Dale, 1988).

Oil palms regenerated from embryogenic callus of high yielding female plants at first appeared to be phenotypically uniform (Wooi *et al.*, 1982a,b), but as new plantations have matured, a high proportion of plants has been found to have abnormal flowers. It is not clear whether the cause is somaclonal variation or an epigenetic phenomenon (Chapter 8).

Dicotyledons. Variable and non-variable populations of plants regenerated from somatic embryos have also been reported in dicotyledonous species. Embryogenic *Citrus* callus has remained diploid during prolonged subculture (Spiegel-Roy and Kochba, 1980) and regenerated plants have been normal. Seedlings with abnormal phenotypic characters (thought to have a genetic origin) were obtained by embryogenesis in nucellus callus of *Citrus* by Navarro *et al.* (1985). The abnormalities persisted for 7 years in the greenhouse and were reproduced through budwood cuttings.

Williams and Collin (1976) found that seedlings of celery produced through embryogenesis were normal, but Orton (1985) obtained some genetic variability in plants of this species regenerated by embryogenesis from callus which had been maintained in culture for 6 months. Many had an accessory chromosome and approximately 2% of selfed progeny showed a recessive mutation, causing abnormal leaf morphology. *Trifolium pratense* plants produced by Wang and Holl (1988) from embryogenic calli after one year of culture, were polyploid or diploid/polyploid mosaics.

In *Coptis japonica* and *Angelica acutiloba*, plantlets obtained from somatic embryos in suspension cultures have been found to show a high degree of genetic uniformity: occasional aneuploid plants appeared when suspensions had been subcultured over 2 years (Nakagawa *et al.*, 1982).

Plants of the grapevine 'Cabernet Sauvignon' raised from somatic embryos produced on nucellus callus (Mullins and Srinivasan, 1976) were found to exhibit considerable variation when grown in the field (Mullins, 1982), whereas those of the variety 'Seyval' regenerated by embryogenesis were said to be phenotypically identical (Krul and Myerson, 1977).

Conflicting results. The reason for these conflicting results is not clear. Probably there has been a difference in the type of embryogenic tissue isolated. Vasil (1983) suggested that callus cultures composed of enlarged and vacuolated parenchymatous cells were most prone to karyological change. Embryogenic cultures which consist exclusively of small, non-vacuolated, richly cytoplasmic cells, similar to those found in the shoot meristems

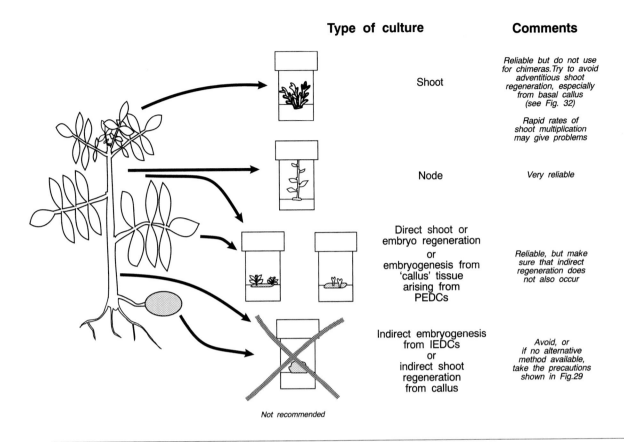

	Type of culture	Comments
	Shoot	*Reliable but do not use for chimeras.Try to avoid adventitious shoot regeneration, especially from basal callus (see Fig. 32)*
		Rapid rates of shoot multiplication may give problems
	Node	*Very reliable*
	Direct shoot or embryo regeneration or embryogenesis from 'callus' tissue arising from PEDCs	*Reliable, but make sure that indirect regeneration does not also occur*
	Indirect embryogenesis from IEDCs or indirect shoot regeneration from callus	*Avoid, or if no alternative method available, take the precautions shown in Fig.29*

Not recommended

Fig. 31. The methods of micropropagtion least liable to produce plants with genetic variation.

of intact plants, seem to be cytologically stable. Any abnormalities which these cells develop could result in the loss of meristematic activity.

Is the explanation that embryogenic tissue formed directly on explants is frequently a proliferation of semi-organised pre- embryogenically determined cells (PEDCs), and that cells of this kind, and the embryos to which they give rise, have the ability to remain cytologically stable? Somatic embryos which are formed within previously unorganised callus or suspensions, from IEDCs (page 30), are more likely to be genetically variable. Directly-formed somatic embryos also arise from PEDCs, and the plants to which they give rise also seem to be strictly normal (see below).

Another hypothesis which has been advanced to explain an apparent uniformity in the plants obtained through embryogenesis, is that only normal cells have the ability to develop as somatic embryos, whereas atypical cells may participate in the formation of adventitious buds. In view of the variation detected by other workers, this idea does not appear to be credible.

RELIABILITY OF OTHER METHODS OF PROPAGATION

The risk of obtaining variable plants, has deterred most laboratories from using the regeneration of plants from unorganised callus and cell cultures, including indirect embryogenesis, as a common method of *in vitro* plant propagation. Providing correct precautions are taken, genetically abnormal plants are only rarely produced by most other methods of micropropagation, unless adventitious organs are indirectly initiated, or mother plants are chimeras. The most generally reliable methods of avoiding the occurrence of genetic variation during micropropagation are therfore as summarized in Fig. 31, and as discussed below.

Direct shoot formation

Plants produced from directly formed shoots and somatic embryos appear to have a high chance of being phenotypically normal. Direct shoot formation is used as a method for the micropropagation of certain plants, par-

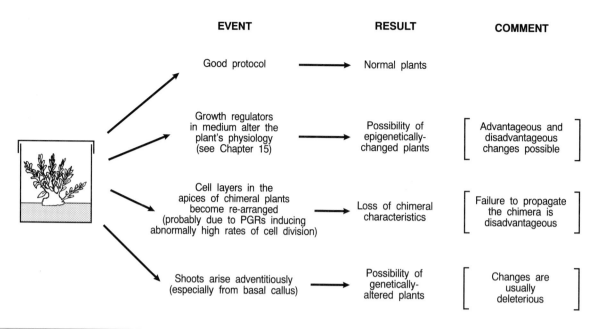

Fig. 32. Sources of variation in shoot tip cultures.

ticularly ornamental plants in the family Gesneriaceae which are produced annually in large numbers using leaf and petiole pieces as explants. With most varieties, very few abnormal plants are obtained. In some plant species, directly-formed adventitious shoots arise only from epidermal cells and in others more than one cell layer may be involved. In either case particular care needs to be taken to see that the stock plants to be propagated are not periclinal chimeras (see below) or separation of the cell types may occur, resulting in off-type plants.

Onion plants regenerated from adventitious shoots on bulb scales, were nearly all diploid and phenotypically normal. Hussey and Falavigna (1980) suggested that this was because the shoot meristems originated from many cells. Even so, they obtained two chimeral plants and one tetraploid.

Variant plants can be produced by direct shoot formation in some species and particularly using certain explants. They have been discovered amongst *Begonia × hiemalis* plants propagated from shoots formed on leaf, stem and petiole explants (Bigot, 1982). Variability depended to a large extent on the variety of begonia cultured: many more of the plants produced from double flowered Rieger begonias had abnormalities than those from single flowered Schwabenland types. Directly-formed shoots were initiated in the epidermal layer of explants, but if the epidermis was separated and used as an explant without underlying tissues, the proportion of abnormal plants was increased.

Root cultures maintain a high degree of genetic stability (Zelcer *et al.*, 1983) and in some plants isolated roots can

be used as a source of adventitious shoots which are genetically uniform. However, it cannot be assumed that shoots arising adventitiously from roots will always be genetically similar to the parental material. Those with a direct origin arise normally from the L3 layer of the plant and so will have a different genotype if the parent was a *periclinal chimera* (see later, Fig. 34).

Plants produced *in vivo* from adventitious shoots on cauliflower roots were frequently abnormal. Two deviant plants had unusual chromosome numbers but the rest possessed the normal diploid number, yet showed such characters as multiple branching, precocious flower formation, abnormal leaf structure, sterility and a slow growth rate (Grout and Crisp, 1980).

Direct embryogenesis

Plants derived from somatic embryos produced directly on zygotic embryos of *Trifolium pratense* were tested extensively by Maheswaran and Williams (1987) and found to be uniform in all characteristics. There were also no differences between primary and secondary regenerants from the same embryo. The authors concluded that "direct embryogenesis on immature zygotic embryos is a conservative, clonal regeneration process".

Albino plants often result from barley anther culture when regeneration occurs by indirect embryogenesis from micropore-derived callus. As explained previously, albinism is thought to result from genetic changes in the chloroplast genome. A significant increase in the proportion of green haploid plants, most with a normal karyotype, was obtained by Powell *et al.* (1988) from the direct regeneration of somatic embryos from barley microspores. Direct, instead of indirect embryogenesis, was encouraged by placing only one lobe of the anthers in contact with an agarose medium, instead of both lobes, as has been customary.

Orchid protocorms. Variable plants were reported to arise from mericlones of triploid *Vanda* orchids, but not from *Cymbidium* and *Dendrobium* varieties (Teo and Teo, 1974). However, some variation in *Dendrobium* was reported by Vajrabhaya (1977). A superior variety was obtained as a mutant from mericloning *Brassolaeliocattleya* 'Cover Girl' and named as a new variety (Mullins, 1982).

Node and shoot culture

Single node culture is the most reliable method of micropropagation: production of aberrant plants is practically unknown and those which do occur probably arise by spontaneous mutation. Widespread adoption of the method is limited by plant growth habit, and by a slow rate of multiplication.

Shoot culture nearly always results in plants which are true-to-type, but changes in phenotype are sometimes found (Fig. 32). Most of the changes observed are of a temporary nature: without careful analysis it is often not possible to know whether these are due to an altered genotype or epigenotype. Changes in flower colour occur in some varieties of *Gerbera* with a frequency which varies with genotype are sometimes permanent and sometimes lost upon further micropropagation (Törmälä, 1990).

Genetically altered plants are occasionally obtained from shoot cultures. This is sometimes associated with the formation of shoots from adventitious buds on basal callus rather than from axillary buds. Boston fern (*Nephrolepis exaltata bostoniensis*) tends to be unstable in micropropagation and may yield up to 25% aberrant plants. Possibly this is due to the large number of adventitious shoots which may arise in fern shoot cultures. Zimmerman (1982) recommended that only a small number of subcultures should be conducted before new cultures are initiated.

Shoot tips from buds or suckers of plantain *(Musa* sp.) proliferated to form a small clump of bulbous structures, covered with minute meristems. Although 'semi-organised' cultures such as these often maintain genetic uniformity, Vuylsteke *et al.* (1988) found that about 6% of plants obtained from such cultures displayed phenotypic variation in inflorescence structure or in the shape, varie-

gation or habit of leaves. The foliage malformations re-appeared when the plants were ratooned, suggesting that they had a genetic basis. The occurrence of a significant proportion of deviant plants during *Musa* (banana) micropropagation is very common and has also been reported by Reuveni *et al.* (1984), Hwang and Ko (1984), Drew (1986), Hwang (1986), Reuveni and Israeli (1990) and Sandoval *et al.* (1991, reported in Villalobos *et al.*, 1991).

In *Pelargonium,* it is almost impossible to prevent shoot tips producing a small callus from which shoots are regenerated (Bigot, 1983). The proliferating shoot tip can be divided to a limited extent, or shoots can be removed and grown *in vitro* to a stage where they can be cut into single node pieces for further multiplication: plants are then obtained directly from axillary buds, directly from the shoot tissue, or indirectly from a small primary callus at the cut ends. Bigot (1983) and Reuther (1988c) report that variability is commonly found amongst the plants obtained by this method of propagation. Its extent and nature depends on the stock plants being propagated. The types of variants obtained include total chlorophyll loss or sectorial deficiencies, leaf deformations, dwarfism and giant forms. Variability in these cultures seems to arise mainly from the proliferating shoot tips, for it is high in plants obtained from initial subcultures but tends to decline with further propagation, when the lower multiplication rate of aberrant plants favours the selection of true-to-type progenies. Initial variants can be aneuploid or chimeral. Sometimes triploids are formed which have high vigour.

Jones and Murashige (1974) reported obtaining genetically aberrant plants from *Aechmea fasciata* through shoot culture. Two per cent of ramets were atypical when only 3 subcultures had been carried out in 6 months, but from cultures which had been maintained for one year by subculturing every 6 weeks, 20 per cent of the plantlets obtained were abnormal. Similar results were reported by Zimmer and Pieper (1976). It is possible that once deviant shoots occurred in these cultures, their proportion was increased through subclturing.

PLANT CHIMERAS

Their nature

Cellular basis

A chimera is a plant composed of tissues of two or more types (usually genetically different) that are capable of a congruent and integrated existence. Usually a substantial part of a plant must be formed from a distinctly different

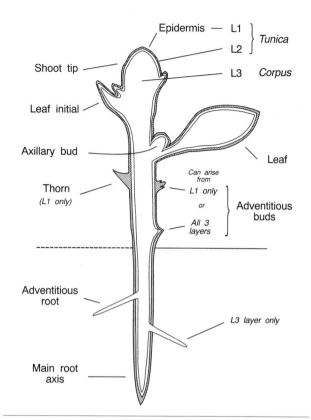

Fig. 33. Cell layers in a typical dicotyledonous plant and some organs derived from them.

kind of cell type before a chimera can be recognised. Obvious chimeras occur either because a mutation has occurrred in one or more cells, or because tissues of different kinds have been combined together by an unusual event. A chimera in which an unusual cell type was arranged in a mosaic throughout the plant would be difficult to detect, and is only likely to occur when the basic cell karyotype is inherently unstable so that cells of a different genotype are regularly formed.

Mutations usually occur at low frequencies and cells with changed genotypes will probably not be noticed unless they become part of meristems which give rise to new vegetative tissue, seeds or pollen. If a mutation occurs in an apical meristem, just one of the layers, or a solitary segment of the plant, may become composed of genetically altered cells.

The rapidly dividing cells in plant apical meristems are found to be composed of three or more layers (or *histogens*) (L1, L2 and L3) (see Fig. 33) that lie one over the other (like the layers of a Russian doll). Each layer is destined to give rise to whole plant tissues of separate types. Cells of the L1 layer produce the epidermis, those of the L2 and L3 the internal cortex and vascular system. Adventitious shoots can arise from the L1 layer only, from

the L2 or L3 layers or from a combination of all three. Adventitious roots only arise from the L3 layer. The L1 layer is only initiated during the early stages of shoot formation and is thought not to be equivalent to the wound periderm which grows on callus and other tissues isolated *in vitro* (Bruck and Walker, 1985).

Plant chimeras are classified according to the manner in which the distinctly different tissues are located. Shoot apex mutations often result in all the cells of one layer becoming changed, producing a *periclinal* chimera (Fig. 34). Sometimes genetically changed cells do not take over the whole of a cell layer and then *mericlinal* (incomplete periclinal) chimeras are formed. Truly sectorial ('slice of cake') chimeras in which all the cell layers in one sector of the stem are of a different genotype, are probably very rare but may result from some graft unions.

Horticultural value

The characteristics of many plants are enhanced by their being chimeral (chimeric). Many attractively variegated leaf patterns and flower petal colours are due to dissimilar pigments being produced by cells of the epidermis and underlying cell layers. Sports of some varieties of fruit trees bearing fruits of an atypical colour have been found to be chimeras. Chimeras can be produced from the amalgamation of cells from different species or genera; they may then have the appearance of hybrids. Some of these are of value as ornamentals. +*Cytisus adami*, which arose at the graft union between *Laburnum anagyroides* and *Cytisus purpureus*, was shown to be a periclinal chimera with an inner core of laburnum surrounded by an epidermal layer of *C. purpureus* (Crane and Lawrence, 1956). +*Crataegomespilus (Crataemespilus) dardarii* and +*C. asnieresii* are graft chimeras between hawthorn and medlar. The former has a central core of hawthorn and an outer sheath of medlar tissue (and bears medlar-like fruits) and in the latter (which has fruits similar to hawthorn), hawthorn forms the outer envelope.

The differences between the constituent layers of a chimera may not always be large and then the chimeral nature of the plant may not be suspected from its external appearance. Not all leaf variegation is due to the chimeral composition of tissues. The leaf colours of *Coleus blumei* and some kinds of *Episcia* may be due to complex factors which nevertheless can still result in the regeneration of plants with uncharacteristic foliage markings from tissue culture (Hervey and Robbins, 1978; Sunblade and Meyer, 1982). Certain *Pelargonium* varieties derive their variegated leaf patterns from the presence of virus-like infections (Cassells *et al.*, 1980; Cassells and Minas, 1983). In some plants leaf variegation is not apparent during the juvenile phase of growth.

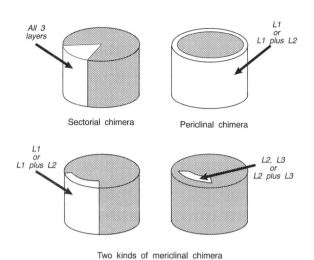

Fig. 34. Sections of plant stems showing different kinds of plant chimeras.

Chimeral separation

In vitro propagation of chimeras, frequently results in the loss or rearrangement of one or more or the cell layers, especially if plants are regenerated indirectly; ramets are then produced which have different characteristics to those of the original mother plant. Once formed, the new phenotypes may be stable over subsequent vegetative (or even sexual) generations. Many reports of unusual phenotypes emerging after a short period of shoot or meristem culture (*e.g.* in *Chrysanthemum*, Machin, 1978), direct or indirect shoot regeneration, may have been due to chimeral rearrangement of unsuspected chimeras. When Sutter and Langhans (1981) regenerated plants from leaf callus of *Chrysanthemum × morifolium*, they found that there were many plants with aberrant form. The remaining 85% of ramets with an apparently normal morphology, had excessive lateral shoot growth: flowers were small and irregularly formed, flowering was considerably delayed and a longer short day treatment than normal was needed to promote it. In this case it is unclear whether the observed effects were due to somaclonal variation, chimeral rearrangement or the epigenetic consequences of *in vitro* culture.

Reviews of the nature of chimeras, their importance in horticulture, and problems experienced in their propagation, have been provided by Vaughn (1983) and Tilney-Bassett (1986).

The micropropagation of obvious chimeras

Shoot culture

Chimeras are usually maintained by conventional vegetative propagation, although periclinal chimeras are not very stable and rearrangement of cell layers frequently occurs during the formation of axillary buds (Broertjes and Van Harten, 1985). Micropropagation techniques are much more likely to cause desirable chimeral characteristics to be lost or to disappear. The chances of obtaining unaltered chimeral plants from *in vitro* multiplication are greatest when shoots are only produced from apices or axillary shoots. Shoot culture should therefore be suitable, but in practice it cannot always be relied upon to propagate chimeras that are true-to-type. Some possible explanations for this observation are that:

— it is often very difficult to control the origin of shoots from shoot cultures and many shoots may arise adventitiously, either directly from organs or indirectly from basal callus;

— conditions *in vitro* may favour the more rapid division of one type of cell, leading to the elimination of a disadvantaged cell type from meristems;

— the swift rate of growth *in vitro* may result in the perforation or re-arrangement of the L1, L2 and L3 histogens within apical meristems and a consequent alteration in chimeral characteristics;

— chimeral phenotypes may sometimes be due to epigenetically determined differences between the cells of different histogenic cell layers, the programming of which is disturbed by *in vitro* culture.

Murashige (1974) cautioned against the micropropagation of chimeras because their component tissues were easily separated and the desired traits of a cultivar were consequently lost. There have been many subsequent reports to show that his advice is correct, but providing a slow multiplication rate can be coupled with visual screening, *in vitro* propagation is possible.

Loss of phenotype. Murashige failed to maintain the leaf variegations of *Cryptanthus,* variegated pineapple and bromeliads (Jones and Murashige, 1974) through shoot culture. Similar difficulties were experienced in a commercial laboratory with *Dracaena marginata* var. tricolor, and variegated pineapple, *Schefflera,* and *Dracaena warneckeii* (Oglesby, 1978). Shoot culture of chimeric thornless blackberries usually results in a proportion of the offspring having rearranged cell layers.

Only half of the plants obtained from shoot culture of the blackberry 'Thornless Evergreen', had a normal rambling phenotype while the remainder were dwarfed (but still without thorns) (McPheeters and Skirvin, 1981, 1982, 1983). 'Thornless Evergreen' is a periclinal chimera and the abnormal plants were thought to be derived, not from axillary shoots, but from adventitious shoots arising from the epidermis; this is the only cell layer in the chimera having the thornless phenotype.

Attempts to propagate *Cordyline terminalis* cv. 'Celestine Queen' (a chimera with green, red and yellow leaf variegation) failed, even though tissue culture provides a good method for propagating non-chimeral types. Plantlets obtained from 'Celestine Queen' cultures did not have the characteristic leaf colours, the yellow marking being especially liable to be lost (Maene and Debergh, 1982). Shoot culture of the chimeric 'White Sim' carnation (Hackett and Anderson, 1967; Dommergues and Gillot, 1973) and two Indianapolis bronze varieties of chrysanthemum (Bush *et al.*, 1976) resulted in a proportion of the regenerated plants having atypically pigmented flowers.

Phase of growth. Prolonged periods of shoot culture of *Hosta decorata* (where shoots had both an axillary and an adventitious origin), generally resulted in the loss of a characteristic leaf margin variegation. The variegation could be partly restored by placing potted plants obtained by *in vitro* multiplication in a cold room. After 4 weeks a thin white margin appeared in 30% of the plants; 50% of the plants had variegated leaves after 12 weeks, and 80% after 20 weeks storage (Papachatzi *et al.*, 1981). This observation could have been due to the plants slowly returning to the adult phase. The multicoloured foliage of *Episcia* is not apparent after propagation by shoot culture because the plantlets produced are temporarily juvenile (page 240) (Bilkey and McCown, 1979).

Successful micropropagation. There are several reports to show that chimeric characteristics can be preserved during micropropagation provided that only low rates of cytokinins are added to the medium, giving a slow rate of shoot multiplication from only lateral or apical meristems.

Debergh (1975, 1976) and Debergh and Maene (1990) *were* able to propagate *Dracaena deremensis* and *Cordyline terminalis* chimeras with only a small proportion of the resulting plants having a modified chimeral leaf pattern, by culturing stem sections bearing a dormant bud, and by shoot culture using the cytokinin kinetin, instead of BAP, to ensure that only axillary shoots were produced. Similarly the chimeral plant *Yucca elephantipes* 'Regal' was multiplied sucessfully by Pierik and Steegmans (1983): non-chimeral shoots only occurred

when an abnormally high level of the cytokinin BAP was added to the medium. This induced the production of adventitious shoots from callus. Some *Pelargonium* varieties which owe leaf or petal variegation to their chimeral nature can be multiplied faithfully through shoot culture, while others are liable to a chimeral rearrangement (Cassells and Minas, 1983). Shoot culture of the pear chimera 'Louise Bonne Panachée' using 1 µM TDZ resulted in 61% of shoots remaining as chimeras (true-to-type), but 75% were chimeras if only 0.5 µM TDZ was used (Abu-Qaoud *et al.*, 1990). Clearly even less of this compound (or another cytokinin) would need to be employed if routine micropropagation were to be contemplated.

Slow and cautious shoot culture of runner tips of the chimeral strawberry *Fragaria vesca* cv. 'Albo Marginata', using a minimum of cytokinin, resulted in single plantlets which were true-to-type (Marcotrigiano *et al.*, 1987). This plant is stable when propagated from runners *in vivo*, but if subcultured *in vitro* with as little as 1.3 µM BAP in the medium, 87% of the ramets differed histogenically from the parent plant. The proportion of variants was even greater if the concentration of BAP was increased.

Several possible explanations were advanced by Marcotrigiano *et al.* (*loc. cit.*) to explain the high numbers of variant plants:

1). Some of the shoots obtained could have originated adventitiously from basal callus, or from hyperhydric (see Chapter 13) leaf and petiole tissue. These shoots would not be chimeral if they arose from single cells or groups of similar cells;

2). A displacement of some of the cells in individual cell layers of the apex could occur during the high rates of cell division experienced *in vitro*. Clustered apical meristems have been noted to occur in strawberry under these conditions: their appearance is likely to disrupt the normal anticlinal planes of cell division in the outer layers of the apical meristem.

Variegated foliage chimeras of *Rhododendron, Cornus kousa* and a miniature rose have been propagated by Pogany and Lineberger (1991) by using low multiplication rates. Success with *Rhododendron* depended on using only a low level of 2-iP cytokinin, and by taking great care only to subculture variegated shoots. The presence of hyperhydricity had to be especially avoided, because the waterlogged appearance of shoots masked foliage characteristics.

Callus derived from small stem tips or leaf sections of the chimeras *Episcia* × *wilsonii* 'Ember Lace' and *E. cupreata* 'Cleopatra' and 'Pink Brocade', gave rise to green or albino shoots (Bilkey and McCown, 1979; Chin, 1979;

1980), but plants of the first two varieties could be obtained with characteristic leaf markings, by culturing shoot tips larger than 5 mm. Probably this was because, despite a high cytokinin level in the medium, these explants only produced axillary shoots at a slow rate (Bilkey and McCown, 1979).

A proportion of true-to-type plants has been regenerated from inflorescences of *Hosta sieboldiana* (Meyer, 1980) and *Saintpaulia* (Lineburger and Druckenbrod, 1985) chimeras, probably because shoots were derived from dormant lateral meristems, or because floral meristems reverted to vegetative ones.

Using adventitious shoots

Plants from directly-formed shoots. Shoot buds arising directly on the leaves of plants are often assumed to be derived from single cells (see Chapter 1). If that were the case it would be expected that the shoots obtained would not perpetuate chimeral leaf variegation patterns.

Leaf variegation of chimeral African violets *is* maintained however when the plants are propagated from leaves *in vitro*. Norris and Smith (1981) thought this suggested that the meristem had a multicellular origin. A similar perpetuation of variegated foliage was obtained on shoots regenerated both from *Saintpaulia* leaves and from leaf and petal tissues of *Episcia*. Meyer (Meyer, 1982; Sunblade and Meyer, 1982) conjectured that in these plants, chimeral patterns may be due to epigenetic changes in one of the layers of the meristem rather than completely different genetic layers.

When adventitious shoots were produced from flowers of a chimeral cultivar of *Hosta sieboldiana*, only 45% of the regenerated plants retained the chimeral characteristic; in the remainder the histogenic layers had separated to give shoots with either green or gold foliage. All of the adventitious shoots regenerated from the leaves of the pear chimeras 'Louise Bonne Panachée' and 'Red Hardy' were non-chimeral (Abu-Qaoud *et al.*, 1990) (*c.f* the results described above for plants multiplied by shoot culture). Three new kinds of variegation patterns (which may have been chimeras) were obtained when shoots were produced directly from petioles and leaves of *Liquidambar styraciflua 'Variegata' (Brand and Lineberger, 1988)*.

Plants from indirectly-formed shoots. Plants which are true-to-type are extremely unlikely to be regenerated from callus cultures of tissue taken from chimeral plants (Debergh, 1976), because the distinctive arrangement of the cell layers of the parent plant becomes disorganised. Even though cells of each different genotype may proliferate to form a 'mixed callus', adventitious shoots are usually composed entirely of cells of only one kind.

Ben-Jaacov and Langhans (1972b) obtained some plants with yellow flowers from callus cultures of the chimeric chrysanthemum 'Giant Indianapolis White', and when Chua *et al.* (1981) propagated *Dracaena marginata* 'Tricolor' by callus culture, the regenerated plants no longer showed the 'Tricolor' markings.

Often direct or indirect adventitious shoot initiation has been employed deliberately to separate the component tissues of chimeras and so regenerate previously unavailable plants having a single 'pure' genotype (Stewart *et al.*, 1974; Kasperbauer *et al.*, 1981; McPheeters and Skirvin, 1981; 1982; Preil and Engelhardt, 1982). Sectorial chimeras are more readily separated than periclinal ones.

However new chimeras can be produced from callus cultures. When Marcotrigiano (1986) initiated callus cultures from leaf disc explants of a periclinal tobacco chimera, 51 out of the 658 shoots which were regenerated were chimeras. Not all of these were periclinal, as was the original plant. Sahavacharin (1982) has reported propagating *Caladium bicolor* satisfactorily from adventitious shoots regenerated from callus. Although some of the plants obtained were of the parental type, many showed a variety of new variegation patterns, but this was said to be advantageous.

Further causes of failure

Success in propagating chimeral plants may depend on the precise method of culture used. Whereas some atypical plants were obtained from callus cultures derived from shoot tips of the chrysanthemum 'Giant Indianapolis White' by Ben-Jaacov and Langhans (1972b), all the plants obtained by Earle and Langhans (1974a,b,c) from callus (with organised meristematic centres) which arose at the base of shoot cultures of this variety, were normal.

Lane (1982) has pointed out that chimeras can break down under conditions where the growth of one of the cell types is selectively favoured, and suggests that media may need to be modified to prevent this happening with chimeric tissues *in vitro*. Interestingly, in a chimeric *Cordyline*, which could be propagated true-to-type from conventional cuttings, only half the plants were typical when produced in the greenhouse from axillary shoots that had been stimulated to grow on mother plants by weekly 500 mg/l BAP sprays (Maene and Debergh, 1982). This may have been because cytokinin increased the rate of division of cells in one meristematic layer more than in others, as has been observed in other plants (Mauseth, 1979).

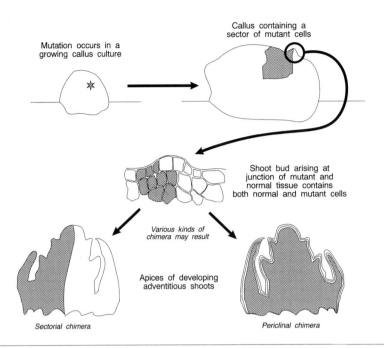

Fig. 35. How chimeral plants may arise if a mutation occurs in a callus culture.

The generation of chimeras

Using callus cultures

Natural chimeras have arisen most frequently as adventitious shoots at the point of a graft union. As mentioned earlier in this chapter, chimeric shoots can be regenerated *in vitro* from callus that is composed of cells of different genetic composition. One method by which this could occur is illustrated in Fig.35. Cells of different genotypes can arise in callus through induced genetic variabilty, or because callus derived from two genetically different plants has been deliberately mixed. Stable periclinal and mericlinal chimeras have been regenerated from callus of *Lycopersicon peruvianum* (Sree Ramulu *et al.,* 1976a,b) and that of other species (Horak, 1972; Bennici, 1979; Bennici and D'Amato, 1978). The possible horticultural value of chimeral plants has led to several experiments to see whether tissue culture could be used to produce them in large numbers. At first sight it might appear that the induction of adventitious shoots from mixed callus cultures could be used to produce chimeras deliberately (Fig 36). However, Marcotrigiano (1986) says that results have been disappointing: "mere adjacency of cells of two different kinds may not be sufficient" (Ball, 1969).

To be chimeral, an adventitious shoot must have a multi-celled origin, but in practice it is difficult to induce cells of widely different genotypes to co-operate in its formation. In mixed callus cultures, cells of markedly different kinds (*e.g.* those of two different species) frequently have a different organogenic capacity, or each may require a different medium, or a medium with different levels of growth regulating compounds for optimum growth or shoot regeneration. Marcotrigiano and Gouin (1984a,b) managed to obtain some chimeral shoots from mixed callus cultures of tobacco *Su/Su* and *su/su* genotypes (*Su* is a semi-dominant sulfur-leaf marker), but were unable to do so when callus tissues of *Nicotiana glauca* and *N. tabacum Su/su* were grown together. Adventitious shoots were produced from the *Su/su* tissue when 3mg/l kinetin and 0.3 mg/l IAA was added to **MS** medium, but *N. glauca* tissue did not respond to this treatment: interspecific chimeras were only obtained by treating graft unions with auxin-lanolin pastes. Shoots composed of the cells of two genotypes have been regenerated from mixed callus cultures by Carlson and Chaleff, 1974; and Zatyko *et al.* 1982.

From apical buds

The occasional production of new chimeric plants has been reported to occur during the shoot culture of some strawberry varieties (*e.g.* cv. 'Aliso'; Schaeffer *et al.*, 1980).

McPheeters and Skirvin (1983) found that they could obtain some plants with a new chimeral rearrangement by culturing physically wounded axillary buds of 'Thornless Evergreen' trailing blackberry. One new chimera of

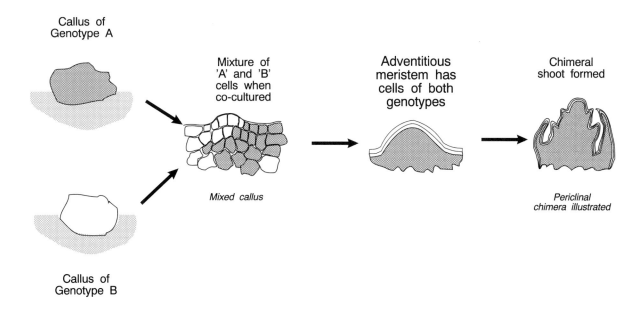

Fig. 36. The formation of new chimeras from adventitious shoots arising in mixed callus cultures.

'Louise Bonne Panachée' pear was obtained by Abu-Qaoud *et al.* (1990) using this technique: axillary buds were cultured after they had been wounded with a scalpel. The three histogenic layers of the original variety are 'Green – Green – Albino' ((L1, L2 and L3): those of the new form were 'Green (?) – Albino – Green'.

Regeneration from protoplasts

A successful method of producing chimeras from protoplast cultures has been described by Binding and Kollman (1985). Protoplasts isolated from genetically different plants are embedded together at a local high density in droplets or 'lenses' of an agarose medium: the droplets are afterwards streaked onto plates and covered with liquid medium. Compaction of the protoplasts results in a high rate of shoot regeneration and adjacent groups of cells becoming grafted together as they divide. These two factors favour the formation of chimeras. The use of this technique to obtain a sectorial chimera having *Solanum nigrum* tissues within *N. tabacum*, is described by Binding *et al.* (1988). They also produced a periclinal chimera where the L1 layer of *N. tabacum* was associated with an inner core of *S. nigrum*.

INDUCED GENETIC VARIATION

DIRECTED GENETIC CHANGE

Most of the variation described in the preceeding sections of this chapter occurs spontaneously *in vitro* and, with present knowledge, is largely random and beyond the control of the operator. Although the new genotypes which can appear as a result of tissue culture are largely unwanted, there are occasional beneficial variants amongst cell lines or regenerated plants which can be isolated by selection (page 79). The extent of undirected genetic change, can be increased by appropriate cultural techniques, or by the administration of chemical or physical mutagenic agents.

In contrast to the largely uncontrolled variation in tissue cultures, genetic manipulation (*genetic engineering*) techniques, developed over recent years, have begun to

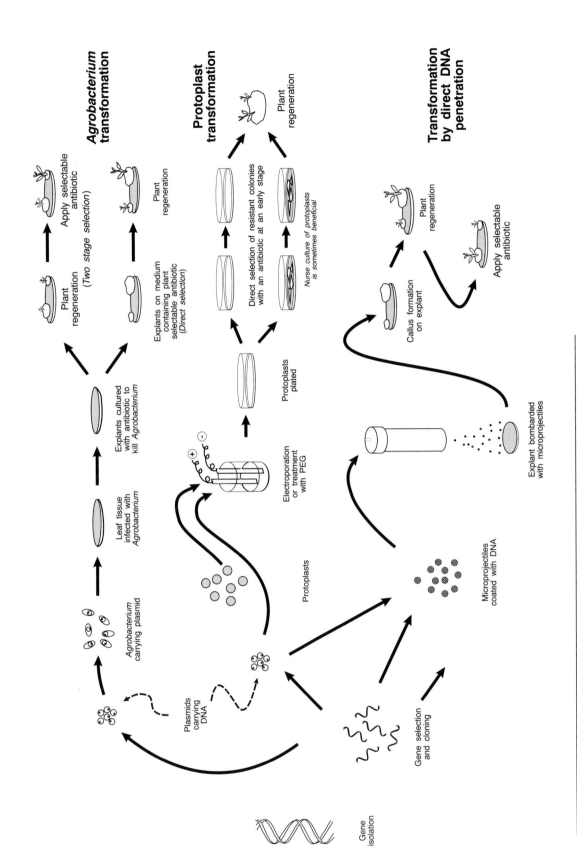

Fig. 37. Three methods of transformation which rely on tissue culture and micropropagation.

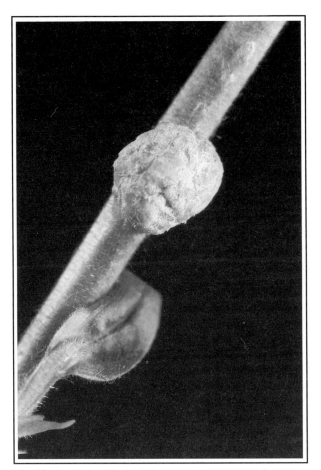

Fig. 38. A crown gall induced by *Agrobacterium tumefaciens* on the stem of a plant of *Helianthus annuus*.

allow directed and desired changes to plant genotypes. At the simplest level these permit alteration of the ploidy level (page 35), or the amalgamation of the nuclear or cytoplasmic DNA of genetically different plants through protoplast fusion (page 21).

Gene isolation and plant transformation

Gene isolation and cloning

Many genes of known function have been isolated from different life forms (plant, animal or prokaryotic origin). These segments of DNA are annealed into the DNA of a plasmid (or a phage) so that the plasmid DNA is now *recombined*. Plasmids are circular strands of autonomously replicating DNA found in almost every bacterium; some kinds are infectious and can transfer themselves to other bacteria. Plasmids multiply as bacterial numbers increase, so that if recombinant plasmids can be used as cloning vehicles or *vectors*; if they are induced to be taken up by *E. coli* bacteria, they can be cloned through

bacterial culture. Many different kinds of plasmids exist, many of which carry resistance factors. Bacteria carrying the recombinant plasmid are therefore selected through the pattern of protein or drug resistance which the selected vector displays.

Vectors for plant transformation

Various vectors which have been constructed from plant viruses, or plasmids, are able to enter plant cells and transfer all or part of their DNA (transfer or T-DNA), to the DNA within the plant nucleus (*transformation*)). By inserting selected genes within the T-DNA, foreign genes can be tranferred to plant cells, where they may become incorporated into the genome. In this way, plants may be obtained possessing characteristics which have been difficult, or impossible, to introduce by conventional breeding methods.

Transient gene expression. Introduced genes which become integrated into the DNA of the plant, can become permanetly established and sexually transmitted. Some foreign genes are active soon after they have been inserted into plant cells, but not on a long-term basis. It is presumed that, in these cases, transient expression results from DNA which has not been fully integrated and which is eventually broken down.

Transformation with *Agrobacterium*

The crown gall bacterium, *Agrobacterium tumefaciens,* has been widely used for plant transformations. This bacterium naturally harbours a (Ti) plasmid, the unaltered T-DNA of which causes a tumour to form on the stems of infected plants (usually at the crown — hence the name 'crown gall') (Fig. 38). The bacterium can be used experimentally to introduce into plants, novel plasmid vectors in which some of the original DNA sequences have been replaced with a chosen gene, or genes. The technique can only be used with dicotyledons, as monocotyledons are generally not susceptible to *Agrobacterium* infection. In dicotyledons, pieces of tissue, such as aseptic leaf, stem or cotyledon explants are usually cultured for a short while before being dipped in, or covered with, an *Agrobacterium tumefaciens* culture.

Once *Agrobacterium* has transferred the plasmid to plant cells, the infection is removed after 1–2 days of incubation; for this purpose the explants are transferred to a medium containing one or more antibiotics.

Successful transformation occurs in only a proportion of the cells in a tissue, so that it is desirable to select those plant cells into which the foreign DNA has been transferred. Sometimes the gene to be transferred has selectable properties. If it does not, plasmid genes are available which convey resistance to kanamycin or hygromycin, antibiotics to which plant cells are susceptible (page 140). One of these genes is therefore often also introduced into the plasmid so that by now growing the plant tissue in the antibiotic (Fig. 37), transformed plant cells can be selected. Construction of a plasmid containing both a non-selectable gene and a selectable marker can sometimes be avoided by co–transformation; this involves infecting cells with a mixture of plasmids, some containing a non-selectable gene, others a selectable one. Callus which forms on the explant in the presence of the antibiotic should carry the resistance gene and may also express the other chosen genes.

Callus colonies which appear on the explants are transferred to a shoot regeneration medium without the selection agent. Adventitious shoots are rooted as cuttings. As shoots are regerated from callus by this technique, some unwanted somaclonal variation may appear in the regenerated plants. This can be minimised by ensuring rapid adventitious shoot formation.

Sometimes selection of antibiotic-resistant callus is not particularly effective; but can be accomplished in a two stage process, in which antibiotic treatment is delayed until the shoot regeneration, or rooted plantlet stage.

Direct transformation of protoplasts

Plant protoplasts can be directly transformed by being chemically or electrically treated in the presence of plasmid DNA. Once again plasmids are constructed which carry genes foreign to the plant, and in many cases, a gene conveying antibiotic resistance as a separate selectable marker. The plasmids are introduced into a suspension of plant protoplasts and their uptake into the plant cells is facilitated by electrical treatment in a special apparatus (electroporation), or by treatment with polyethylene glycol (Fig. 37).

The protoplasts are then plated on a culture medium. After a short interval, selection of transformed cells is usually carried out by introducing an antibiotic to which the tissues are susceptible, and against which plasmid DNA conveys resistance. Plant regeneration is required from callus colonies which develop with resistance to the antibiotic.

Delivery of DNA on microprojectiles

Klein *et al.* (1987, 1988) devised a method of inserting foreign DNA into plant cells, or plant tissues, on high velocity microprojectiles, such as tungsten powder with a particle diameter of 1–4 µm. Such particles, coated with plant virus or bacterial plasmids, were placed at the front of a large projectile and fired towards the target. The large projectile was arrested, leaving the smaller particles to hit the plant cells (Fig. 37).

Methods of selecting cells transformed in this way, and subsequent plant regeneration, are similar to those used with protoplasts or following *Agrobacterium* transformation.

4

Equipment and Procedures

LABORATORY ACCOMMODATION

The nature and size of the accommodation required for micropropagation will vary widely according to the interests of the propagator. Amateurs and small nurseries can, and do, propagate plants using equipment contained in little more than one room, whereas many commercial firms operate from a suite of laboratories, growth rooms and offices. The accommodation required for academic research into tissue culture propagation differs from that which is necessary for large-scale plant production. Descriptions of the facilities and procedures required for experimental plant tissue culture work have been given by Butenko (1964), and by Street (1977b), although the standards exemplified by Street are unnecessarily elaborate for commercial micropropagation.

This chapter describes, in the main, the kind of facilities needed by a moderately-sized commercial laboratory: the reader may scale these requirements either up or down according to the kind of facility envisaged. Comments have been added to indicate how micropropagation can be conducted on a small scale without the purchase of expensive equipment. Some excellent ideas for economy in small laboratories have been put forward by De Fossard and Bourne (1977) and Stoltz (1979b). Other useful information can be found in Holdgate (1977) and Holdgate and Aynsley (1977). Accounts of the apparatus

and equipment which is ideal for a tissue culture unit have been written by Biondi and Thorpe (1981). Descriptions of the facilities at some established commercial laboratories have been given by Briggs (1975); Oglesby and Strode (1978); Oki (1978); Zilis *et al.* (1979); Zimmerman (1979); De Wald (1982) (a small laboratory); Hartney and Kabay (1985); Kee (1983); Broome (1986); Bridgen and Bartok (1988) and Hill (1988).

Siting a new laboratory

Before beginning to build a new facility, check that you have the necessary permits from your local planning authority. Buildings should not be located in places liable to be dusty or exposed to draughts or wind. Proximity to potential sources of microbial or chemical contamination is also undesirable. In a horticultural nursery, this may mean siting a laboratory away from the pesticide store, the car park, the potting shed, and the waste tip!

DESIGN

Where only a small number of propagules is to be produced, the various operations required to propagate plants

95

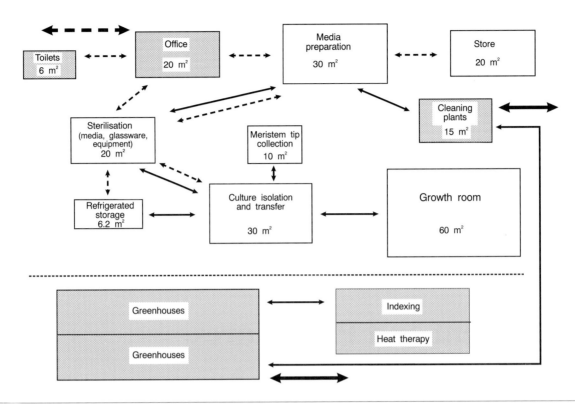

Fig. 39. Suggested room sizes for a medium-sized micropropagtion laboratory dealing mainly with woody plants (after Damiano, 1980b). In this figure (and also in Figs. 40–42 which follow), the movement of plant material is indicated by solid arrows; the movement of people alone, by broken ones. Clean area are unshaded; 'dirty' areas, shaded.

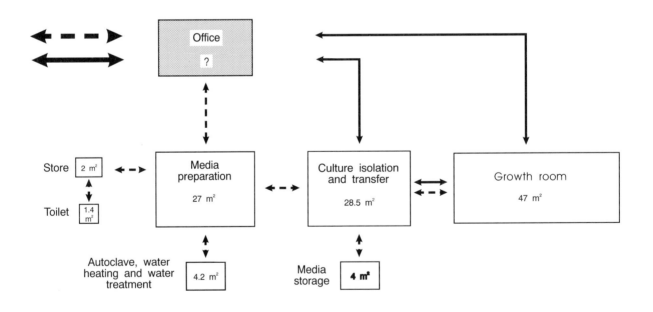

Fig. 40. Room sizes and interconnections for a moderately-sized general purpose micropropagation laboratory [after Kyte, 1983].

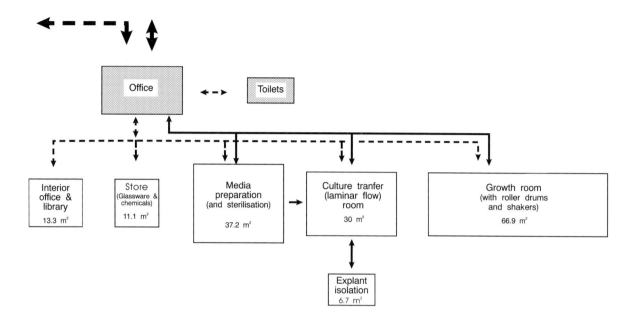

Fig. 41. Suggested room sizes for a moderately-sized micropropagation laboratory dealing with orchids and tropical ornamentals [after Kee, 1983].

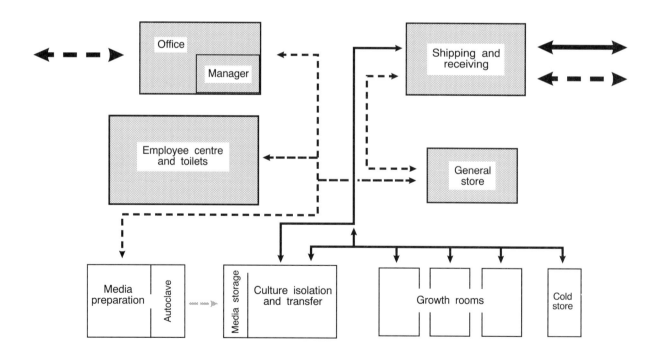

Fig. 42. A laboratory layout suggested by Broome (1986). Room sizes were not given.

by tissue culture could be handled from one general purpose office/laboratory with an incubator or an attached growth room. However, no-one concerned with serious micropropagation would consider such an arrangement to be adequate. Commercial firms and major academic institutions always conduct operations such as the isolation of explants, the transfer of cultures between flasks, and culture maintenance, in separate rooms isolated from other activities. This ensures that there is the minimum contamination of cultures.

Indications of the room sizes recommended by three different authors for a moderately-sized commercial micropropagation business are given in Figs. 39, 40 and 41. Such a unit would have about 5 laminar-flow hoods and a potential annual output (depending on the species propagated) of 1–2 million propagules per year. The total floor area required to produce such a large number of plants annually, is surprisingly low; but despite being of comparatively small size, the laboratory needs a considerable capital investment in equipment and materials. Before building commences, thought needs to be given to the movement of people and plant material between different areas, so that doors are correctly positioned. To keep contamination to a minimum, separate rooms ('clean areas') should be used for explant isolation, culture transfer and the growth of cultures.

Access to, and movement of plant material between rooms were not indicated by Kee; those in Fig. 41 are suggestions for a suitable arrangement. It has been assumed that access to clean areas in the laboratory described by Kyte (1983) was through an outer office. None of the arrangements shown in Figs. 39–41 have a definite provision of rooms for the receipt and shipping of plant material, or for employee relaxation. These were included in the designs given by Broome (1986) (Fig. 42). Strode and Abner (1986) recommend some free space in the laboratory design which can be brought into use in emergencies.

Buildings to accommodate a micropropagation laboratory can be constructed from many different materials. The cheapest and most versatile are probably those in which the various work areas are assembled within a single large outer warehouse or barn (Burr, 1984). If the laboratory complex is also built from movable panels, the size and arrangement of rooms can be changed relatively easily: the positioning of internal partitions is simplified if the outer building has a clear floor area, unobstructed by roof supports. A gap of 0.3–1.5 m between the walls and ceiling of the laboratory complex, and the walls and roof of the outer building, helps to insulate the laboratory from extremes of temperature in the exterior environment (Broome *et al.*, 1986).

Pre-fabricated buildings can also be used to house micropropagation laboratories; they are relatively cheap and flexible, although seldom so pleasant in appearance and to work within as a purpose- built laboratory. However as the rooms in a permanent building are in fixed positions, changes when an expansion becomes necessary may be expensive and disruptive to work.

In all buildings, the allocation of rooms and the space available will be subject to the nature of the work undertaken and to personal preference. The actual design of a laboratory, the kinds of rooms which it has and their sizes, will depend not only on the scale of the operation, but also on the kinds of plants to be propagated and the way in which propagules are to be sold. No greenhouse, but an elaborate shipping area is needed if Stage II or Stage III plantlets are always to be sold directly to growers; a greenhouse, but less growth room space, will be needed if many plantlets are to be rooted *ex vitro*.

General requirements

The building in which a plant culture laboratory is to be housed should have a strong concrete floor, capable of taking the weight of equipment without cracking. The final surface should be covered to prevent dust. A cheap method is to paint the surface with a floor finish, but a PVC or linoleum covering is preferable. Walls, ceilings (and if possible floors) of the building, should be well insulated.

Services which will be required for a micropropagation laboratory include: mains water (a 22 mm supply pipe may be necessary), connection to a main sewer or a septic tank, and an electricity supply. Before arranging for the electrical service to be connected, add up the wattages of all the equipment and lighting you will want to employ (including an allowance for future expansion) and divide by the voltage of your supply to calculate how many amperes you will be consuming at peak load. A back up generator should ideally be available to maintain lighting and temperature control in the event of a general power failure.

A gas supply from mains or bottled gas is an optional extra. The laboratory will require heating and/or cooling equipment to maintain a temperature of *ca.* 21°C (70°F) in both summer and winter. Growth rooms may need to be operated at higher temperatures. In cool climates it is possible to recirculate the heat generated by equipment and growth room lighting. Laboratories situated in warmer climatic zones will need to give greater emphasis to cooling. The use of heat pumps for heating and cooling has been recommended (Broome *et al.*, 1986).

Worktops in all laboratory areas should be covered with materials which are easily cleaned and which will withstand disinfectant solutions. Laminated plastic finishes are suitable for bench tops. Wall surfaces and bench fronts should also be smooth and made from material which will not accumulated dust and is able to be easily and regularly cleaned. Laminated plastic is again ideal, but hard-wearing paints can be applied to normal wall plaster. Drainage pipes made from plastic materials are resistant to acids and alkalis. General purpose equipment should include first aid supplies, fire blankets and extinguishers.

Laboratories differ in whether or not incoming air is filtered. The entire suite of rooms in some laboratories is supplied with air filtered through HEPA (high efficiency particle-removal air) filters which are capable of trapping particles greater than 0.3 µm in section, particularly fungal spores and bacteria (Burr, 1984). It can be very advantageous to supply at least the 'clean' rooms of the laboratory with HEPA-filtered air. The risk of contamination is then reduced and it may be possible to avoid the purchase of laminar air- flow cabinets for culture isolation and transfer (see below). A system can be designed to introduce cool air in summer and re-cycle warm air during the winter. Providing the system is adequately maintained, even general air filtration through filters of less than HEPA standard can reduce the ingress of contaminants.

Although it is noticeable that most university departments have less rigorous standards, it is wise for commercial micropropagation laboratories to restrict entry to clean rooms to persons who have gone through proper preparative procedures and have put on special laboratory coats and footwear. The number of comings and goings should be reduced to a minimum. Traffic in and out of an inoculation room can sometimes be reduced by passing materials through a service window. The entrance to the entire laboratory area should be screened: many managers insist that persons change their shoes upon entry. Ideally, clean areas should be maintained at a slightly higher air pressure than other rooms and be entered through two separate sets of doors, between which there is a space. The first doors are then always closed before the second are opened, so restricting the passage of contaminants between the different environments.

All doorways, air-locks, and aisles between benches, should be wide enough to permit the free passage of trolleys. Small trolleys, or carts, are useful for transporting media and glassware. Shelving fitted with castors can facilitate the movement of cultures between the transfer room and growth room/s.

1. Office accommodation

In a moderately-sized micropropagation unit, an outer office can serve as a combined reception area, working office and as a staff entry point. Larger laboratories will advantageously designate special areas to each of these functions and will allocate a separate room to management activities.

> **Equipment** . The manager will require a room with a desk or desks, chairs and shelving, which will probably need to be equipped with a filing cabinet, a calculator, reference books and catalogues from suppliers of chemicals and equipment. Records of plant cultures, past and present, will probably be kept here together with details of customers and their requirements and materials ordered. Such details may be recorded in files or books, or on a personal computer (see below).
>
> Other office equipment which should be considered includes: card files, filing cabinet, typewriter, bookshelves, reference books, a black (or white) board.

2. Media preparation room.

Some laboratories purchase ready-dissolved and pre-sterilised media and so do not need elaborate preparation facilities. Others choose to use commercially formulated media supplied as ready-mixed powders which need only to be dissolved and sterilised. However, many working in this field, for reasons of cost or preference, prepare media from constituent chemicals, something which every laboratory will need to do from time to time for experimental purposes. A preparation room will therefore usually contain shelves or cupboards for stocks of chemicals and perhaps a separate store room for the same purpose. The equipment required for the preparation of media is discussed more fully in Chapter 10.

Glassware should be stored in the preparation room or near the washing area, so that it can be accessed and replaced easily from both.

Sterilisation of media and equipment

There are several methods by which the containers, apparatus and media used for plant tissue culture may be sterilised: three are commonly used for plant tissue culture:

- — dry heat;

- — autoclaving (steam heating under pressure);

- — ionising radiation. Gamma (γ)-irradiation is most common, utilising the services of a commercial irradiation plant.

Some laboratories conduct sterilisation by autoclaving or oven heating within a general purpose preparation room. Others have a special room reserved for it.

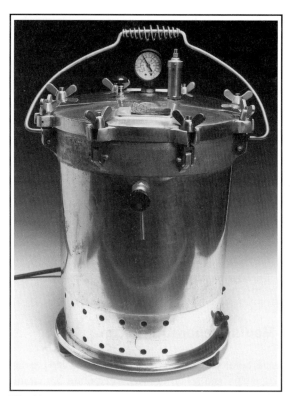

Fig. 43. A small portable electrically-heated autoclave suitable for small laboratories, or as standby.

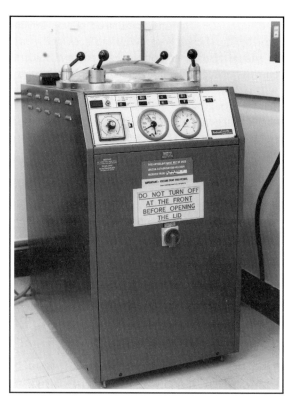

Fig. 44 A top-loading automatic electrically-heated autoclave.

Glassware and most dissecting tools can be sterilised by dry heat in an oven maintained at 150–160°C for 1½–2 hours. Dry heat is not suitable for plastics, paper or other organic materials. Items to be sterilised are wrapped in heavy duty aluminium foil, or placed in unpainted metal containers such as biscuit tins. Before being used for the first time, such tins should be heated in the oven with their lids off for several hours to drive off volatile materials. Sharp cutting blades are liable to loose their temper by being heated in an oven, and so should be autoclaved instead.

Autoclaves. For autoclaving, upright front-loading pressure vessels are the most convenient, but may be more expensive than the older-style top-loading variety. A very small laboratory will be able to manage by using only large domestic pressure cookers and these can be useful, even in larger laboratories for small-scale preparations, for various cleaning tasks and as an emergency back-up facility. It is advisable to fill autoclaves with distilled or de-ionised water to prevent the formation of scale deposits. Autoclaves should be sited with free space around them so that they can be easily serviced.

Broome (1986) and Strode and Abner (1986) have pointed out the merits of large double-door autoclaves which can be opened from two opposite sides. If these autoclaves are situated between the medium preparation room and the transfer room, they can be loaded with vessels containing media through one door, and after the autoclaving process, unloaded in a reserved area of the transfer room, where the vessels are cooled and stored before use.

Items to be autoclaved are pre-wrapped in heavy grade paper: if glassware is to be sterilised by autoclaving, all openings should be covered with aluminium foil. If glassware is tightly wrapped in foil, steam may not penetrate: it should therefore be loosely covered, or if tightly wrapped, partly-filled with water first of all. As paper is dampened by autoclaving, it should be dried afterwards by placing the wrapped packages into a warm oven for a brief period.

Glassware and equipment. Solutions are sterilised in bottles or flasks plugged with gauze-wrapped cotton or stoppered with loose fitting caps which are tightened after removal. A special metal container for sharp instruments (a 'SIN' bin) is recommended, so that sharp surfaces do not cause injury.

It is easy to mistake autoclaved equipment for that which is still non-sterile, causing serious contamination at a later stage. The problem is easily solved by marking items placed in the autoclave with commercially-available tape which changes colour during the sterilisation process.

Glassware and equipment should be autoclaved at 120°C, 15 p.s.i. (103kPa), for 15–20 min. The length of exposure is measured from the time when the autoclave has reached the correct temperature and all air remaining in the autoclave has been replaced by steam. Tablets which change colour can provide a useful check that the correct combination of temperature and time has been achieved.

Empty containers and apparatus should not be autoclaved together with plant culture media. Glass containers which are to be used for plant cultures can be autoclaved *after* the medium has been added and the top capped, but when heat-susceptible plastic containers are to be used for cultures, media are bulk-sterilised and dispensed afterwards in an aseptic area. The larger volumes of medium required for this purpose will need to be autoclaved for longer periods (see Chapter 10). If autoclaving is used to destroy contaminated cultures, take precautions never to place the affected vessels in the vicinity of clean ones.

Equipment required for the preparation and sterilisation of equipment and media:-

Refrigerator; deepfreeze; autoclave/s; large domestic pressure cooker/s; steamer for the preparation of media containing agar; water distillation still and/or a de-ionising unit to produce purified water complete with one or more large storage tanks; a coarse balance for weighing large quantities and another capable of weighing small amounts to and accuracy of 1–2 mg; hot plate/s with a combined magnetic stirrer; equipment for filter sterilising (see Chapter 10), including a vacuum pump; a microwave oven (optional); an oven for dry sterilising equipment and drying glassware, a pH meter; a timer; an automatic medium-dispensing machine; wire baskets, racks and trays, to hold glassware and culture vessels which is to be autoclaved; a sterile area (box or cupboard) for the short-term storage of sterilised equipment and media; trolley for transporting apparatus, cultures and media; shelves for chemicals; fireproof solvents cupboard; lockable cupboard for poisons; waste bins; labels and/or a labelling machine.

Glassware etc.: glass and/or plastic beakers, flasks, measuring cylinders, jugs, storage bottles, and volumentric flasks; graduated pipettes and Pasteur pipettes (with plastic or rubber teats); a variety of glass and/or plastic containers for plant culture; pipette fillers; burettes, membrane filters with holders and hypodermic syringes to cold-sterilise media components; filter flasks and funnels; filter pump; wash bottles.

Consumable items: chemicals, filter papers, towels, cleaning cloths, paper towels, aluminium foil, autoclave film, indicator tape, adhesive tapes, labels.

3. Dish-washing room

Some laboratories amalgamate the washing of glassware and the preparation of media, into a single working area or room. Withers (1984a) cautions against this practice to avoid contaminating media with detergents. If the use of a combined room is unavoidable, balances for weighing should be placed in a separate small room and Bhojwani and Razdan (1983) suggest that a partition should be erected to screen off the washing area. At least one large sink is required for washing; hot and cold watershould be provided, and also a supply of purified water (double distilled and/or de-ionised). One large sink is better than several small ones, as large objects can then be handled easily: when it is necessary to wash small objects, the sink can be subdivided, or washing bowls can be inserted within it.

It is convenient to locate the washing area close to the sterilisation room, so that culture vessels containing contaminants can be autoclaved before being discarded.

It is advisable to place glassware in water immediately after use to prevent deposits from drying. That which is not obviously soiled can be soaked in a mild detergent solution (*e.g.* one tablespoonful Teepol™ per 5 litres of tap water) for 2–3 hours and then rinsed in tap water for 2–3 hours and finally rinsed in de-ionised water. Items which are more soiled may need to be cleaned by soaking in a more powerful detergent, scrubbed in hot detergent solution, or soaked in an acid/chromate bath. All such items must be carefully rinsed before use. The sodium metasilicate solution described on page 112 is an effective cleaning agent, which both cleans and coats soda glass culture vessels for re-use.

An automatic dish-washing machine can help considerably with routine washing. Items within the washer are subjected to jets of hot cleaning solutions at high pressure: rinsing in tap water is normally followed by further rinsing with distilled or demineralised water. Dish-washers are able to use corrosive cleaning agents at temperatures which would be damaging to the hands if used during manual cleaning. Small laboratories will probably use washers designed for domestic or laboratory use. These machines will not eliminate the need for some containers and equipment to be cleaned by hand (*e.g.* the initial disposal of cultured plant material and the removal of agar). Large laboratories are well advised to invest in the type of washer used by large restaurants. The latter have traps for the removal of debris which are large enough to allow vessels conating agar and plant material to be processed without prior handling.

Washed glassware is drained, oven dried and, if necessary, sterilised, before use.

The equipment required for cleaning and dish-washing is all fairly obvious. The list might include the items listed below:

Equipment required. Large double sink; a laboratory or industrial dish-washing machine, waste bins for broken glass and plant material, buckets or bins to soak equipment, drying ovens or cabinets, and dust-free storage. Detergents and reagents for cleaning.

4. Rooms for culture isolation and transfer.

Explant isolation and the re-flasking of cultures must be conducted on a sterile surface and within an environment which will ensure that there is a very low risk of explants becoming re-infected and contaminants entering the culture vessel.

A small number of manipulations (*e.g.* those which might be carried out by students conducting practical experiments) can be made in still air in an ordinary room. A proportion of the vessels which are inoculated can be expected to become contaminated by microbes. The risk of contamination can be reduced by covering the inoculation area with sterile paper or better still, a glass or Perspex® tunnel. Providing surfaces are wiped with a sterilant solution (see later), dissections and transfers carried out in tunnels can result in low rates of contamination. For example, students often only have 10% or less contaminated cultures in classwork.

Glove boxes. Small numbers of inoculations and transfers can be made with very little risk of contamination inside isolation boxes fitted with gloves. Commercial versions of such 'glove boxes' are available, including miniaturized ones made largely from transparent plastic. Stoltz (1979b) described the construction and use of a cheap home made isolation chamber from plywood painted with epoxy paint. The box has a glass front, sealed to the plywood with a silicon cement, and contains a fluorescent light and a germicidal U.V. lamp which is switched on 30–40 minutes before work and switched off while the box is being used. Holes are cut in the front of the box to allow the operator's arms to enter: the holes should be fitted with sleeves or arm-length rubber gloves. The presence of ozone is not a problem with this type of chamber.

Sterile rooms. The use of such equipment is not adequate for large-scale micropropagation where one or more special rooms need to be dedicated to the purpose. One method could be to use a sterile room of the kind used in the past for bacteriological research. Such rooms are usually small, have no windows, and should preferably be supplied with air which has been filtered to remove dust and fungal spores. The walls are covered with smooth washable material (*e.g.* glazed tiles) so that they can be rinsed frequently with a sterilant solution, and the room is equipped with ultraviolet lights (one of which can be lowered over the bench) which are turned on when the room is not in use, to kill micro-organisms. Only those surfaces receiving the radiation will be sterilised and shaded areas are unaffected. Ultra violet light is damaging to the eyes and causes skin burning and must be turned off before the room is used. As light of this wavelength also converts oxygen to ozone, it can be hazardous to enter a room until the concentration of the gas has decreased (usually about 20 minutes).

In the past, some research laboratories used to inject steam into their isolation room shortly before use to cause fungal spores to settle out. Although the treatment was effective, the high humidity made operating conditions unpleasant. Because it is depressing to work inside rooms of these types for long periods, laboratories nowadays use isolation chambers or hoods instead.

Laminar flow hoods

The most effective and convenient way to prevent contaminants from settling on an inoculation bench is to pass bacteriologically-clean air across it. Factory-made benches which utilise this principal have come to be very widely used for aseptic work over recent years. Two kinds are available, with either vertical or horizontal air flow. The former kind is used in some bacteriological and medical work, where operators can be at risk from infectious organisms on the working surface. Benches with horizontal or laminar air-flow are used for plant culture work. In these, a continuous flow of air which has been blown through a HEPA filter passes horizontally across the working surface. The bench is provided with a covered top and sides; the enclosed volume is then kept at positive pressure, compared to the air in the surrounding room. As clean air is continually passing out of the chamber, the entry of micro-organisms is unlikely. Benches of this kind are comfortable to work at because they afford a large working area and allow the operator room for free movement. Models with slight variations are now available from many different manufacturers, in sizes suitable for single operators, or for two or more persons working side by side. A drawing of a typical unit is shown in Fig. 45.

Details of how a laminar air flow cabinet can be constructed in-house, were given by Meyer (1986). In this design, the bench area was made suitable for use with a microscope by minimising vibration. This was achieved by situating the electric fan in a separate module or even outside the transfer area. There are two advantages in positioning the fan outside the transfer room: firstly noise is reduced, and secondly the inward flow of air creates a positive static pressure which helps to prevent the entry of dust and spores into the entire room (see above).

Laminar flow cabinets characteristically contain filters of two kinds: an outer one which can be washed in warm water, and an inner HEPA one which must be replaced when clogged. Dirty filters will cause the flow of air to be diminished: periodic checks of the rate of air move-

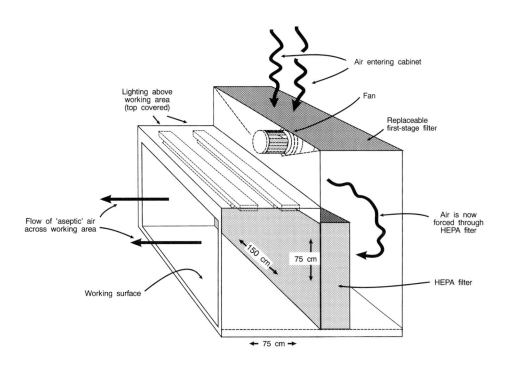

Air entering cabinet

Fan

Replaceable
first-stage filter

Lighting above
working area
(top covered)

Air is now
forced through
HEPA filter

Flow of 'aseptic' air
across working area

150 cm

75 cm

75 cm

HEPA filter

Working surface

Fig. 45. The principle of the laminar air-flow cabinet used for aseptic transfers.
Cabinets such as this one, are usually free-standing, with knee-space under the bench.

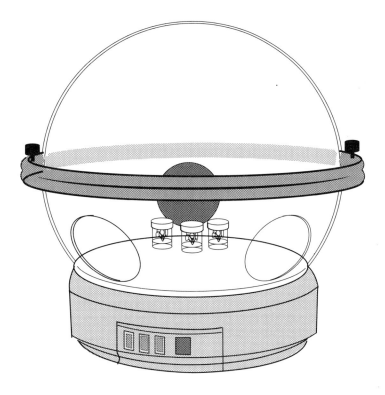

Fig. 46. A portable benchtop cleanroom which provides an alternative to a laminar flow cabinet
(made by Safetech Ltd., Limerick, Ireland).

ment across the working area, using a small portable anemometer, are therefore recommended. Meyer suggested that a four speed motor be used to draw air over the filters. The speed of the motor can then be increased as particles accumulate and the air flow decreases: the effective life of the HEPA filter is thus considerably increased. The cost saving through having to replace the filter less frequently must be weighed against an increased electricity demand.

If the whole laboratory is receiving filtered air, it is possible to use more cheaply constructed cabinets with filters which are easily maintained (see Burr, 1984). A small portable plastic bench-top isolation chamber, developed out of ideas from Prof. Cassells team in Cork, has recently been placed on the market (Fig. 46). This also uses the filtered air-flow principle, but within a closed dome. As the ports are relatively small, the unit it only suitable for use with small culture vessels.

Room design

The transfer room is the one room which it is *essential* to keep especially clean and most commercial laboratories have strict rules governing access. It says much for the efficiency of modern laminar air flow cabinets to find that even where they are situated in areas of common access (as in many university departments), only very low levels of contamination are experienced in newly initiated cultures. Some commercial laboratories lay specially impregnated sticky mats on the floor to reduce dust.

In many climates, tranfer rooms are likely to become hot and airless when in continuous use due, to the heat generated from the laminar flow hoods and the associated sterilising equipment. If the room is not served by central air conditioning, it may therefore need a ventilation system and air conditioner. Rooms which have floor space designated to receive vessels from a double sided autoclave (see page 100), will need an exhaust fan in the immediate vicinity to expel steam and heat, and an associated filtered air inlet.

Because continuous work at the laminar flow bench can be monotonous, in a dedicated micropropagation laboratory, it is advisable to make the transfer room a bright and attractive area. It should not be small and likely to induce a feeling of claustrophobia and, where possible, it should possess non- opening windows providing a view on the outside world. Operators should be provided with comfortable chairs fitted with a foot rest, on which the height and back rest can be adjusted. Broome (1986) suggests that the waste bins necessary at each hood position, are placed at a height which makes it easy to discard refuse and De Fossard and Bourne (1977), advocate that 'piped' music should be provided (occasionally?).

Binocular microscopes. The isolation of explants such as meristems and shoot tips requires a binocular microscope providing a range of magnifications between 8 and 50 times. The purchase of a cheap instrument will prove to be a false economy. The dissecting microscope should have an adequate 'working distance' (*e.g.* a 7.5 cm focal distance) and should preferably have a zoom lens. A conventional compound microscope may be required during problem solving for the more detailed examination of tissues and cells.

> **Equipment required.** Laminar flow isolation cabinet and/or isolation chambers; anemometer to monitor the air flow on laminar flow benches (to check when filters or motor speeds need to be changed); instruments for dissecting explants and manipulating cultures (scalpels, spatulas, needles, forceps — both fine tipped and blunt; cork borer; racks for instruments; gas or electric bunsen for sterilising instruments; film for sealing vessels; paper towels and wipes; waste bins; hand lens; dissecting microscope; microscope for examining tissues and cells; pens and markers for labelling; gowns, face masks and hair covers with lockers for their storage; sink.

5. Growth (Culture) Rooms

The incubation area required for plant cultures will depend very much on the kind of work to be undertaken. Experimental work on plants of many kinds might be best accommodated in several small rooms and/or cabinets in which temperature can be strictly controlled and lighting adjusted to a range of irradiances. A small number of cultures could be accommodated in a standard microbiological incubator: many callus cultures will grow in the dark, but light will be required by most organ cultures required for plant propagation. Although controlled lighting and heating can be provided in small cabinets, they are really only suitable for experimental work: all commercial propagation establishments possess controlled environment rooms. Some laboratories have only a single growth room with multiple racks of shelving. In a single room, the radiant flux density of lighting can easily be varied on different shelves, but controlled variation of temperature is more difficult. Dark incubation or regulation of daylength can be conducted within a partitioned area, or culture vessels can be placed in boxes or covered with dark cloth. Such arrangements are clearly less convenient than having several smaller growth rooms, each devoted to different incubation conditions. A laboratory propagating widely different kinds of plants might designate separate growth rooms for:

- the provision of different photoperiods,

- a warm lighted area for foliage plant culture,

- a cooler lighted area for the growth of woody plants,

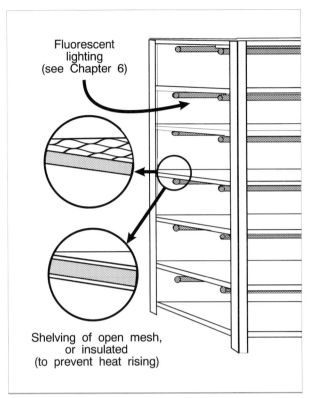

Fluorescent lighting (see Chapter 6)

Shelving of open mesh, or insulated (to prevent heat rising)

Fig. 47. The type of shelving used in culture rooms. It is advantageous to keep vessels on trays, for ease of handling (see text).

— cultures not requiring light,

— high light intensity (possibly with bottom-cooled shelving) for conditioning cultures before rooting and transfer to soil.

Although satisfactory rooms can be constructed on-site, in many countries purpose-built growth rooms can be purchased from several different local suppliers. Where economy is important, readers may care to investigate the availability and pricing of the cold rooms used in butchers' premises. Because of their widespread use, the price of these standardised rooms can be highly competitive with that of other constant environment rooms, but their built-in cooling facilities will, of course, need to be modified to cover the range of temperatures required for plant growth, and lighting will need to be installed.

The walls of the growth room should be painted white to reflect light and those used for culture isolation should preferably be fitted with sliding doors to minimise the introduction of dust and contaminants by air movement (Chandler and Haque, 1984). It is probably unwise to clean growth rooms frequently while cultures are in place, as this raises dust and increases the chances of contaminants entering vessels. Care should therefore be taken to minimise the entry of dust and dirt. A positive air pressure within the room and tacky mats inside the doorways are typical precautionary measures.

The use of trays

Many commercial micropropagation laboratories now convey culture vessels throughout the laboratory on trays, a practice which is found to decrease handling and improve efficiency. Once vessels are placed on trays, they are kept thereon without disturbance for storage, filling with medium, autoclaving and storage until being inoculated. Removal from the trays is necessary only at the tranfer bench, but then the vessels are replaced and kept upon the same trays within the growth room. In some laboratories, used vessels are even placed in a washer without removal from the tray. It is therefore important to choose a tray size which is suitable for the autoclave, washer and racks used in the growth room. A typical tray would hold 30–35 vessels. It must be made of heat-durable material and contain holes which will allow free dainage and air circulation in the growth room. A metal mesh is probably most suitable.

Hartney and Kabay (1985) described a stacking system for culture vessels. The stacks were used in the same way as trays for batch-processing cultures through media preparation, autoclaving, culture growth and dispatch, but had the advantage that they saved space in the growth room.

Racks for cultures

Within a growth room, static cultures are usually placed on racks. To make maximum use of the controlled environment, there can be up to eight shelves per rack, although access to upper and lower shelves is then difficult. Access is better if there are only 5–6 shelves each about 40–45 cm apart, with the lowest about 10 cm from the floor (Figs. 47, 48 and 49). Fluorescent lighting tubes (see Chapter 7 for a discussion on the most suitable types) are installed beneath the shelves, with reflectors to direct the light onto the shelf beneath. The number of tubes per shelf is varied according to the illuminance (or irradiance) required for a particular plant species or variety, and its cultural stage.

As lighting tubes become warm during operation, shelves should be made of wood, or some other insulating material which can prevent containers on the shelf above becoming overheated. The preferred alternative is to have shelving made from open metal mesh through which air can circulate freely. This kind of shelving has the advantage that light tends to be shared between different levels on the rack.

De Fossard and Bourne (1977) have described putting some inoculated vessels into perforated polythene

Fig. 48. A view of shelving within a growth room used for micropropagation.
Lighting is provided by fluorescent tubes.

Fig. 49. A view of one shelf in a growth room.
The shelving here is of open mesh.

sleeves. These can be hung in a greenhouse or in a growth room from a ceiling-mounted grid.

Bottom cooling

Even with the use of insulated shelving on the type of rack illustrated in Fig 47, the base of containers is liable to be warmer than the top. This contributes to high humidity within the culture vessel which can lead to hyperhydricity (see page 116). Racks within some part of a common growth room, or those in a specially dedicated room, might therefore be equipped with a cooling system for the bases of shelves. This facility would be particularly useful on shelving to accommodate plant material which is shortly to be rooted and weaned.

The growth room environment

Lighting. Lighted culture rooms are generally used for most plant propagation purposes. Cultures can be incubated in rooms receiving natural daylight, or even in greenhouses; but although there is a saving in cost, light levels and temperatures will not be constant and reproducible. Fluctuating temperatures can result in variable growth rates and, in the case of cultures used for plant propagation, variable plant quality (Holdgate and Aynsley, 1977). Many callus cultures can be grown in the dark or in a low level of artificial lighting from fluorecent lamps. An illuminance of *ca.* 100–1000 lux is usually adequate. An irradiance of about 12 μmol m^{-2} s^{-2} (approximately equivalent to an illuminance of 1000 lux) is suitable for the initial establishment and early growth of shoot and meristem cultures of many plants, but shoots and plantlets generally need to be maintained in stronger light (*ca.* 3000 lux) prior to being transferred to soil, and growth under greenhouse conditions. The effects of temperature and lighting conditions on culture growth and morphogenesis are discussed more fully in Chapter 7.

Daylength is regulated by time clocks (time switches). It is clearly difficult to operate different daylength regimes within a single room. If each growth room has at least two lighting circuits there is less likelihood of there being no light in the case of a breakdown.

Temperature. Growth rooms used for plant tissue cultures are kept at thermostatically regulated temperature levels. A variation or ±1 to 2°C is normally accepted. Both heating and cooling facilities will usually be required, the extent and pre-dominance of each depending on the climate of the area in which the laboratory is located. Heating is more simply achieved than cooling. The latter requires the use of air conditioners, heat pumps and fans, all of which tend to be noisy and liable to mechanical breakdown.

Heat generated by lighting can be used advantageously in well-insulated rooms. Air circulation may be necessary within lighted rooms to achieve even heat distribution and to prevent local hot spots adjacent to light sources. However some smaller laboratories have been known to take advantage of temperature variations within a single growth area, placing cultures requiring an elevated temperature in an appropriate place. The ballasts required to operate fluorescent lights produce a great deal of heat. It is suggested that they should be situated outside growth rooms: the heat they generate can be used to provide warmth to other parts of the building when it is needed. In hot climates it may be advantageous to locate lighting ballasts outside the building on an external wall.

Most plants will grow satisfactorily at a lower temperature during the night than during the day, although for others a constant temperature may be more satisfactory. Temperate species will generally grow well with the day temperature set to 21–25°C and the night temperature to 18–21°C although there are some which prefer temperatures lower than this. Tropical species often grow well in a day temperature of *ca.* 30°C.

Even if ballasts are located externally, the heat generated by the lighting tubes in a well insulated growth room can be sufficient to overheat the room if the cooling system fails. A trip switch should therefore be installed in each culture chamber so that the lighting is automatically turned off in these circumstances. Plant cultures will survive for one or more days in the dark, but they are easily killed by an excessive temperature. Fot monitoring purposes, the room should be fitted with a maximum/minimum thermometer or a thermograph.

Relative humidity. Air within culture rooms must not be allowed to become too dry or cultures will tend to desiccate, but if the air becomes too moist, closures will become wetted and this could lead to contamination. An ideal relative humidity is close to 70 percent; in many climates a humidifier may be required to bring the growth room environment up to this level, but in the tropics de-humidifiers may be essential. Unfortunately, undesirable contaminating organisms can build up inside some humidifiers: their use must be balanced against the risk of increasing the proportion of infected cultures.

Some part of the growth room will be reserved for one or more orbital shakers or rotating drums used with liquid cultures and suspensions.

Equipment required: Temperature and humidity controls, shelving and lighting as described; equipment to monitor the environment (*e.g.* thermometers, thermohygrograph, light meters etc.); shakers for liquid cultures; apparatus for rotating cultures.

Glassware etc.: Flasks and containers for culturing plants, trays for holding vessels.

6. Staff areas

It is important to provide a room in which staff can relax for breaks during the working day. This area usually doubles as as a conference room. It should be provided with tables and chairs. Facilities for making hot drinks, a refrigerator for storing food and a microwave oven will be welcome adjuncts. Toilets (rest rooms) should be of a sufficient size and so equipped that staff can use them to change into protective laboratory clothing. Lockers will be needed to hold outdoor garments and personal possessions.

7. Store

A stock of glassware, disposable containers, chemicals and equipment will need to be maintained both for constant availability and to take advantage of the cost savings obtainable from purchasing in bulk. However there are disadvantages in purchasing large bottles of chemicals for which there is only a low demand: samples may become cross-contaminated with materials from other containers, pick up moisture, or otherwise deteriorate with the passage of time. The purchase of small lots on a regular basis can overcome these problems. For stocks which are essential, a secure room fitted with shelving and some cupboard space is required. Glassware may need to be kept under cover to protect it from dust. The internal environment of the storeroom should be such that chemicals, especially organic compounds, do not deteriorate. A refrigerator may therefore be required for the storage of heat-labile chemicals. Prepared media should only be stored for a limited time.

A room with a floor area of 10–20 m^2 has been suggested for a store room in Figs. 39 and 41. Kyte (1983) recommended two small stores, one attached to the medium preparation room, the other within the culture transfer room.

Hazardous chemicals

Poisonous and environmentally-sensitive chemicals should be kept in a lockable cupboard: bottles of solvents in use in a flame-proof box. The main solvent store should be located outside the main building.

Under United Kingdom legislation, a Control of Substances Hazardous to Health (COSSHH) assessment form must be prepared for each chemical carrying a risk label, which is used by a laboratory. The form details how the chemical should be used, and for what purposes, and what should be done if there is a spillage or an accident. All persons using that compound must be aware of the entries on the form, which must be kept in a readily accessible place. The regulations not only cover poisons such as mercuric chloride, but also growth regulators such as 2,4-D and picloram.

8. Propagating house

Laboratories do not need a greenhouse facility if they only produce rooted plantlets which are to be weaned into acclimatised plants by other growers or plant nurseries. Nowadays however, very many micropropagation laboratories sell some, or all of their output, as plants already accustomed to growing *in vivo*: a greenhouse is then essential. Plantlets need a sheltered environment during the acclimatisation process. Plantlets or micro-cuttings taken *extra vitrum* need to be kept in partial shade and high humidity until they are properly acclimatised, rooted and autotrophic (see Chapter 14). These conditions can be achieved in part or all of a greenhouse, depending on the scale of the micropropagation work undertaken. A mist-propagator or water fogging apparatus is of great advantage.

A description of a complex modern greenhouse facility for micropropagation work has been provided by M. Hill (1988). The facilities included the computerised control of supplementary lighting under controlled daylengths, shading, humidity control by fogging, cooling and ventilation. The design incorporated the provision of double glazing and adequate access. Greenhouses used in warm climates need fan- assisted drip-pad cooling, especially during the summer period (Broome, 1986).

METHODS OF WORKING

EMPLOYMENT

The number of inoculations or transfers which can be made by a single operator in a day, will clearly vary according to working practices and the kind of plant material being handled. A good technician was said to be able to initiate cultures with 600 fern stolon tips in a day (Burr, 1975), whereas Hartney and Kabay (1985) calculated that each operator (presumably in an 8-hour shift) could place about 1000 *Eucalyptus* shoots of a single clone onto an agar-based medium each day, as well as maintain the clone on a shoot multiplication medium. Others (*e.g.* McKenzie, 1983) have reported that tissue culture laboratories expect to make about 5000–6000 transfers per week within a laminar flow cabinet.

Although it is possible to work for much longer at a laminar air-flow bench than in U.V.-sterilised rooms or cabinets, the work is painstaking and trying and a 4 hour day is generally sufficient for maximum efficiency. Aseptic isolation and transfer is therefore an ideal part-time employment, except that operators need to be carefully trained. A few laboratories make maximum use of their capital investment in equipment by employing several shifts of workers during the day, even to the extent of keeping the laboratory open for 24 hours.

The skill of an operator can influence the number of cultures established in a given time, the proportion of cultures which are successfully established, and the rate at which contaminants are introduced. The recording system used (see below) by well-run laboratories will therefore allow the management to monitor the performance of each bench operative so that the origin of unsatisfactory cultures can be discovered quickly and faulty techniques corrected by re- training. Because high standards must be maintained, payment on a purely piece-work basis is not to be recommended. Some laboratories do however run an incentive bonus scheme, whereby operators are awarded production points for transfers completed above a certain target level. A good system of recording can ensure that points are only translated into cash in the absence of long-term problems with the cultures initiated.

WORKING PRACTICES

Movement within the laboratory

To reduce the entry of bacterial and fungal spores, the passage of persons and equipment into transfer and culture rooms should be restricted to that which is strictly necessary. Casual entry should therefore be forbidden. Do not make two journeys when one will do! Doors leading into clean rooms should always be kept closed and so arranged that it is impossible for draughts of air to carry micro-organisms inside. It may be advantageous to fit automatic closing devices. The door or doors into the tranfer room should not be opened at all while inoculations or transfers are taking place.

Clothing

Standards of laboratory hygiene vary widely. They depend on the size of the laboratory, whether it is producing material for sale, the size of the tissue culture containers which are being inoculated, and the proportion of contaminated cultures which can be accepted.

Normal clothing can carry germ-laden particles, the release of which is contained by wearing a clean overgarment. Strict establishments, therefore require technicians working in 'clean areas' to wear laboratory coats or gowns, and hair coverings. Entry into transfer rooms is forbidden to people wearing outdoor shoes: special footwear or overshoes are provided.

Operatives should always wash their hands before carrying out transfer work; hands should then be wiped with 70% ethanol, or wiped with a skin cleansing fluid. An alternative is to wear sterilised rubber gloves. According to O'Ríordáin (1988), washing should be done gently, as scrubbing the hands loosens particles of skin which may then fall into cultures and increase contamination. If operators do not wear laboratory coats they should roll up the sleeves of outdoor clothes and wash both their hands and arms.

Some laboratories advocate the use of facial masks, while others think they are unnecessary. According to Paul (1959), very few bacteria are exhaled during normal breathing, but the number increases greatly during speech or coughing. Face masks can be filled with bacteria during these events and then even normal breathing can cause the micro-organisms to be expelled. The best advice is to keep the face well away from cultures, do not to lean over work unless it is absolutely necessary, and refrain from talking while manipulating cultures.

Face masks, gowns and hair covers may be kept within the culture isolation room in suitable lockers, but are probably better kept outside so that operatives are suitably clothed before entering the clean work area.

PRODUCTION PLANNING

Labelling and record keeping

Plant tissue culture laboratories conducting micropropagation on a commercial basis, need a method for recording data pertaining to their work. An efficient system should be capable of providing the information necessary for the smooth operation of all stages of the micropropagation process, linking production schedules to orders in a way that assists planning and helps to minimise costs.

It is not necessary to have all the information in one centralised system. Indeed some records, such as the precise methods for propagating any one plant or cultivar, accountancy books, costs, salaries and personnel records will need to be kept confidentially. Many records are suitable for storing on cards, or on a microcomputer. The latter has the advantage that data can be sorted and processed into reports, but the disadvantage that, unless a there are a series of terminals in a networked system (an expensive solution), it is not available at most points where information needs to be gathered. The list below gives some suggestions for the records which might be profitably generated. The list may look formidable, but it can be simplified to several forms, or computer screens into which data can be quickly entered.

Cultural methods

A record of the cultural procedure, media and PGRs for each plant.

Recipes for media and methods of preparation.

Experimental work

Plants giving difficulty, problem to be solved.

Details of experiments in progress.

Orders

Customer details.

Plants required, type of plant (*e.g.* Stage II, III), when wanted.

An ability to tell customer when order can be delivered according to current commitment of lab.

Price of each product.

Details of despatch.

Accountancy

Invoices

Credit control

Purchases

Salaries and wages.

Routine checks on cleanliness and safety

Filter changes, checks on water quality, periodic cleaning schedules, safety checks, statutory safety records.

Major items of equipment

Dates of purchase, details of maintenance contracts, when maintenance due.

Stock plants and stock cultures.

Availability.

Number of explants which could be obtained.

Transfer room records

Plants and vessels handled, vessels handled by each employee.

Growth room assessments

Contaminated cultures discarded.

Progress of each culture, checks on expected dates of transfer, notes on best conditions for growth. Space available at present and expected to be available in the future.

Storage

Details of cultures placed in store, treatments given, when attention needed.

Culture records

For each batch of cultures, the following should be recorded:

Plant being cultured.

Type of culture and current stage.

The medium (and batch) on which the culture has been grown at each stage.

The growth regulators used.

Dates of each operation.

The date on which it next needs attention; type and number of vessels, explants/shoots/plantlets per vessel, which employee carried out the work.

The environmental conditions to which the culture was subjected.

The location of the culture.

Numbers contaminated and discarded, employees associated with contaminations.

The above records should provide the progressive history of the cultured material.

Greenhouse records

Plants in stock.

Losses during acclimatisation.

Growth records.

Consumables

Current supplies of vessels, closures, chemicals for sterilisation, media preparation.

Costs.

Employee records

Daily working hours.

Hours actually worked.

Hourly rate.

Cultures worked on.

Productivity (number of transfers, or production points awarded per unit time (page 105).

Contamination record.

Bonus.

Pay, tax.

Attendance, Sickness.

Holidays.

Training given, training needs.

Planning

The manager should be able to know instantly about the progress of cultures, their location, their current stage, and when they will be moved or despatched off site. He will need to use the records to plan what needs to be done next, and what will be required during the next weeks and months.

Staff hours expected to be available.

Cultures which need to be initiated, transferred: source and numbers.

Forward planning

From the above records, there should be a method of extracting daily and forward plans for:

Media preparation: number of vessels needed to be filled with media/autoclaved each day, vessels to be disposed of, washed and recycled.

Transfer room: cultures to be worked on, vessels, medium, hours of work expected.

Packaging, greenhouse: plants expected, destinations, procedures, despatches.

Costings of product lines

The recorded information should provide information for product costing. Necessary imputs will be:

Plant numbers, length of time at each production stage, fixed costs, consumables and labour can be used to determine actual production costs for comparison against prices to the customer (see Chapter 15).

The use of a computerised database in micropropagation laboratory has been discussed by Clark and Casiero (1979). Interactive programs of this type have been found to be very useful in practice (Hartney and Kabay, 1985). Hempel (1988) described a computer program written specifically for a commercial micropropagation laboratory to assist all stages of production and sales. Although the entry of information into a computer is time consuming, the extra cost is probably worthwhile. Remember that staff need to be trained to use computerised systems, and that data stored on computers can easily be corrupted or lost, unless routine back-up procedures are adopted. Will the laboratory come to a halt if there is a machine breakdown, and how soon can a repair be effected?

Efficient labelling is just as important as record keeping. Labels need to stay attached to culture vessels and carry an easily-understood code. Vessels can be quickly labelled with the type of machine used for the pricing of goods in supermarkets (Fig. 50). Alternatively bar-coded or printed labels can be generated on a computer. Bar codes can be directly read back into a computer, but need special equipment for interpretation, so that the nature of a culture may not be readily apparent.

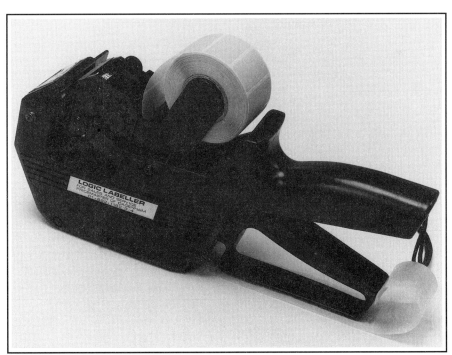

Fig. 50. A labelling machine which can be used for marking culture vessels.

CONTAINERS FOR PLANT CULTURES

Containers used for plant tissue cultures need to be translucent so that cultures may be illuminated and/or inspected easily. Both plastic and glass vessels are suitable, but plastic containers vary considerably in their durability. Many plastics are degraded by autoclaving: those which can withstand repeated autoclaving and washing are the most expensive.

Choice of vessel

The usual practice is to use progressively larger vessels at each stage of micropropagation, for example 30 ml, 60 ml and 120 ml jars. However, the size of the vessel needed at Stages II and III depends on the nature of the plant being cultured, and the number of pieces of tissue or organs which are to be accommodated together. Placing individual explants into separate containers is the best way to minimize the spread of infection, but opening and closing numerous jars is very time consuming. It is likely to be more cost effective to insist on a higher standard of hygiene in the transfer area. This will reduce the risk of contamination, allowing larger containers to be employed into which many explants can be placed comparatively quickly.

Vessel size and shape may influence growth directly (see page 207); the optimum size to use will depend on the type of plant material being multiplied and may have to be determined by experiment. A minimum size for Stage II cultures will usually be 60–100 ml (*e.g.* 4 × 4.5 cm or 5 × 5 cm jars) but better results may be obtained in vessels of at least 200 ml capacity. For apple shoot cultures, Snir and Erez (1980) used:

For Stage I and early Stage II cultures	2.5 × 10 cm (45 ml) test tubes. Agar medium.
For later Stage II cultures	6.5 × 15 cm (500 ml) jars Agar medium.
For repeated Stage II multiplication	100 ml flasks with 10 ml liquid medium, shaken.

The amount of medium placed in a container varies from about 20–30% of the total volume for small tubes, to about 20% in larger jars (*e.g.* those of 250 ml total capacity).

Standardising on a single size. Many practical laboratory procedures are simplified if only one type of vessel is used, at least for routine Stage II cultures. In the opinion of Strode and Abner (1986), such a decision is "the most important decision which the laboratory will make". A disadvantage is that that not all cultures will then be grown in the most efficient manner.

Glass containers

Glass vessels have the advantage that they can be repeatedly washed, sterilised and re-used. Unfortunately cheaper glass containers made of soft soda glass are liable to influence the composition of the medium after a period of time, causing cultures to grow less well. Bonner and Axtman (1937) found, for example, that pea embryos made some growth in liquid medium in borosilicate glass vessels, but none at all within vessels made from soft glass. Thus ideally glass containers should be made from borosilicate, but although laboratory glassware of this nature is essential for research work, many laboratories use ordinary soda glass vessels for practical micropropagation.

According to de Fossard (1976), soda glass vessels do not inhibit plant cultures until they have been used for 12–18 months. He therefore suggested that they should be used for this length of time and then either discarded, or treated with a Hopkins and Williams product, 'Repelcoat'® which restores their original condition. An alternative method which has been used for many years at the University of Southampton, is that described by Paul (1959) [*ex* Harding and Trebler, 1947] which not only acts as an alkali treatment for cleaning glassware, but deposits a monolayer of glass on the washed surfaces. It is as follows:

> Prepare a stock solution (×100) by dissolving 80g sodium meta-silicate and 9 g Calgon [sodium hexametaphosphate — $Na(PO_3)_n$) per litre of tap water, and filtering. Calgon is a water softening chemical.
>
> Soda glassware is first scrubbed in water to remove débris. The vessels are then transferred to a boiler (an electrically-heated domestic wash boiler is very suitable) and immersed in 1 part of the stock solution to 100 parts tap water. The solution is brought to the boil, maintained at this temperature for about 20 minutes. Cool and discard the solution and then rinse the glassware, two to three times in tap water. It is then placed in 0.001–0.01 N HCl, rinsed in tap water, and finally in distilled water and allowed to drain. This process should be repeated prior to each occasion on which the glassware is to be re-used.

Batch suspension cultures are commonly contained in 1.5 or 2.5 litre round borosilicate flasks, and shaken cultures are conveniently placed in Erlenmeyer flasks. For most kinds of micropropagation it is possible to employ a variety of cheaper alternatives.

Types of container. Glass test tubes are commonly used for the initiation of cultures from explants: sizes commonly used range from 1.2 × 7.5 cm (8 ml) to 2.5 × 15 cm (70 ml). Flat-bottomed tubes have an advantage over

Fig. 51. Glass vessels of various sizes with aluminium lids, which are suitable for micropropagation.

Fig. 52. A 10cm plastic culture vessel containing *Chrysanthemum* shoots.

conventional test tubes in that they can be stood upright, but narrow ones are very easily knocked over and so still need to be supported in a sandwich box or wire basket. Glass, or pre-sterilised disposable plastic Petri dishes can be used for the initial culture of explants (McKenzie, 1983).

Initial explants are best placed each in a single container because there is the danger that when several are placed together in a single dish, infection from contaminated tissue can easily spread throughout (Welander, 1979).

Test tubes may not be satisfactory for the later stages of micropropagation when growth and morphogenesis is likely to be impeded unless the cultures are transferred to larger vessels. For instance, strawberry meristem tip cultures initiated in 1.5 cm diameter test tubes became restricted by the walls of the tube and only transfer to 2.5 cm diameter tubes allowed normal development and rooting (Adams, 1972). Test tubes cannot be used for the later stages of micropropagation if several clumps of multiple

Fig. 53. Glass vessel containing a culture of pineapple.

shoots are to be grown together. The use of glass or plastic vessels with wide mouths will then facilitate manipulations. Plant material growing on semi-solid media in Erlenmeyer flasks is difficult to reach through the narrow neck.

A variety of cheap soda glass jars is available; a selection of some suitable ones is pictured in Figs. 51 and 53. Honey jars, preserving jars, and baby food jars are widely used: they can often be obtained with clip-on aluminium caps which make convenient closures (the cardboard inner insert should be removed before use). Some laboratories have successfully used 0.5–1 litre glass preserving jars (Burr, 1976; Boxus *et al.*, 1977; Harris and Mason, 1983), while others have turned to plastic ware.

Plastic and metal containers

Glassware has the advantage that it is long-lasting, but plant cultures can be grown in a variety of other translucent materials providing they are sterile on arrival or can be sterilised afterwards.

Disposable vessels. The use of disposable culture vessels considerably reduces the cost of washing. Disposable plastic vessels sold by laboratory suppliers have been pre-sterilised; they will usually be too expensive for most commercial tissue culture operations, and it is usually possible to find cheaper alternatives. PVC pots and jars manufactured for the food industry are particularly useful. Fortunately the heat used in their manufacture ensures a relatively high degree of sterility and many kinds can be used directly without further treatment. Plastic vessels of this kind are unable to withstand autoclaving, and so to be absolutely sure that they are sterile, they would require to be treated with γ-rays at an industrial irradiation plant. This kind of sterilisation would be necessary if it was desired to employ the vessels on a second occasion: normally they are thrown away after use.

Clear PVC containers with snap-on clear plastic lids (internal volume 300–500 ml) such as those used on delicatessen counters are suitable for micopropagation work (Fig. 53). Fast food containers have been used in a tissue culture laboratory in New Zealand (McKenzie, 1983) and autoclavable polypropylene food containers were employed as disposable vessels for the culture of *Eucalyptus* by Hartney and Kabay (1985).

Plastic ware which can be autoclaved. Several laboratory equipment suppliers now sell specially designed plastic containers with closures suitable for plant micropropagation. These are often made from polypropylene or polycarbonate which is resistant to autoclaving and washing. Polypropylene and polycarbonate tubes, jars and boxes designed for other purposes (*e.g.* food containers and sandwich boxes) may prove to be cheaper alternatives. They often turn cloudy after repeated autoclaving which is a disadvantage, because the passage of light is reduced.

Some commercial laboratories have used aluminium foil food trays for the final stage of micropropagation, fixing or crimping clear plastic covers on the top to make a sealed container.

Disposable culture vessels made from fluorocarbon plastic films which are transparent, impervious to water but fairly permeable to gases, were described by Tanaka *et al.* (1988b; 1991). 'Neoflon'® polymer film (Daikin Industries Ltd., Osaka, Japan) of 25–100 μm thickness was shaped into 8 cm × 15 cm culture bags (Fig. 54) or a box-shaped container (7.5 × 7.5 × 10.5 cm), around a stainless steel wire cage. Film which was 12.5 μm was too thin to properly support the cultures. Neoflon film is capable of being autoclaved, and boxes were pre-filled with medium before autoclaving, while culture bags were sterilised and then filled with autoclaved medium. After explants had been transferred, the containers were heat-sealed and so became completely enclosed. At the end of the culture period the plastic was cut open with a knife.

A bag made from a plastic material with similar properties to 'Neoflon' (the Falcon® 'Cultusak'™, Agristar Inc.) [†], is useful for making a light-weight container for despatching cultured material from one location to another. The bag can be heat sealed in a variety of ways to make one large container or several smaller ones.

Closures

Tubes and other vessels used for tissue culture need to be closed to prevent the entry of micro-organisms and pests, but should *not* be sealed in such a way that there is little or no gaseous exchange between the *in vitro* and *in vivo* environment (see Chapter 7). If the closure makes a tight seal, it should have some degree of gas permeability. Non-permeable closures should be left sufficiently loose for gases to enter and leave the container. Few closure systems have ideal characteristics. Tubes and flasks are often sealed with non-absorbent cotton wool (sometimes wrapped in gauze), polyurethane foam plugs, aluminium or stainless steel caps, aluminium foil or specially-made plastic plugs. Larger containers, especially unconventional jars and boxes, may sometimes be purchased with suitable screw-top lids, but may be covered in other ways. For instance, round glass jars are often conveniently covered with the lids or bases of glass or plastic Petri

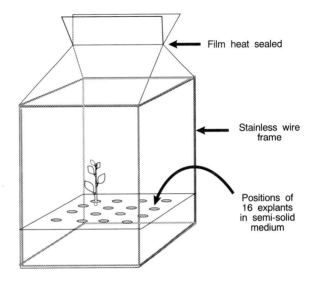

Fig. 54. A container made out of 'Neoflon' ® film used by Tanaka *et al.* (1988b).

dishes. The Petri dish lid is sealed and held in place by being covered with film. Parafilm® or Nescofilm® are often used for this purpose. Ventilation can be increased by making several 0.5 cm slits in the film at the junction of lid and jar.

Sondahl (1982) described sealing bottles used for coffee callus culture with only PVC film of 16.5 μm thickness. PVC film is not heat stable and must be sterilised by some other method than autoclaving. Polypropylene film is heat-resistant and several workers describe using it as the only closure for culture vessels (*e.g.* Walkey and Woolfitt, 1970; Crisp and Walkey, 1974; and Blake, 1966). Mahlberg *et al.* (1980) recommended using polypropylene film which was 25 μm or less in thickness. The film is transparent and non-greasy, and can be used to seal large containers such as beakers. It is cut to size and autoclaved in envelopes. A piece is then placed over the orifice of a container and attached with a rubber band. Unfortunately normal polypropylene film does not allow as much gas exchange as is desirable. A microporous

†   Marketed in the U.K.by Becton Dickinson U.K. Ltd., Cowley, Oxford.

polypropylene film (Celgard 4410, Hoechst Celanese Co.) on the other hand has excellent gas exchange properties (Kozai *et al.*, 1988) and should be valuable for closing vessels if it can be obtained sufficiently cheaply. A gas permeable 'micropore tape' is also available (3M) which can be used to seal around the edge of vessels covered with a loose fitting lid (Topping and Lindsey, 1991).

Polythene has better gas exchange characteristics than normal polypropylene, but cannot be autoclaved. It could be used if a laboratory has cheap access to sterilisation by U.V. or gamma-irradiation. Silicone rubber is suitable, but too expensive for common use.

Oki (1981) cultured Boston ferns in an aluminium meat loaf pan enclosed within in a clear Mylar® plastic oven bag: both the pan and the bag can be autoclaved. The culture vessels made of 'Neoflon' film designed by Tanaka *et al.* (1988b) described above, were either sealed with clips or closed by heat welding.

The looser the closure on a culture vessel, the lower will be the relative humidity inside (Short *et al.*, 1987) and the greater the likelihood that contaminants and pests will enter (see Chapter 5). A low relative humidity is advantageous during Stage II of the micropropagation of many plants, as it helps to prevent *hyperhydricity* (page 212, and Chapter 13). However the medium in vessels with cotton plugs or loose fitting lids, dries out during the incubation period, adversely affecting growth of the cultured tissues. Desiccation can be greatly reduced by wrapping a film around the cap. 'Parafilm'® (a paraffin-impregnated paper which is supplied in pre-sterilised rolls), or aluminium foil, are widely used for this purpose. Polythene and PVC cling films are also employed.

After a period of culture, vessels with close fitting or firmly screwed- down caps, or those sealed with film may come to contain less oxygen than air and increased concentrations of carbon dioxide (Chapter 7) and ethylene (Chapter 11). There are many reports of tightly closed vessels inhibiting growth: we may cite:

- the failure of *Ginkgo* embryos to germinate if cotton-plugged tubes were covered with 'Parafilm', callus formation occurred instead (Webb *et al.*,1986);

- the failure of *Phalaenopsis* flower stalk cuttings to produce shoots in vessels plugged with rubber stoppers (Tanaka *et al.*, 1988c);

- a decrease in shoot regeneration from potato callus and no regeneration of shoot primordia into whole shoots if dishes were sealed with 'Parafilm' (Hovenkamp-Hermelink *et al.*, 1988).

Jars with loose-fitting closures (*e.g.* the lids or bases of Petri dishes) which need to be covered with plastic film to prevent contamination, can be given adequate ventilation by making small slits (*ca.* 5 mm) in the film (Fish and Jones, 1988; Topping and Lindsey, 1991). Alternatively the lid can be surrounded with gas-permeable tape of the type mentioned above. To prevent abnormal growth of orchid plantlets, Tanaka *et al.* (1988a) had to make small holes in their fluorocarbon film vessels: the holes were afterwards covered with 4 mm diameter 'Millipore'® discs (0.45 μm pore size).

PREPARING PLANT MATERIAL FOR CULTURE

This section describes the decontamination of plant material intended for culture. Environmental and physical parameters which may need to be adjusted so that plants will provide explants, or explants of the requisite quality, are described in Chapters 7 and 8.

The occurrence of contaminants

Plants are invariably infested externally with fungi, bacteria, yeasts, and animal pests. These organisms may be present on all external surfaces and are also likely to find their way into small crevices, such as those between bud scales and under ligules or stipules. It is always very important to ensure that explants are only taken from vigorous plants with no disease symptoms and no history of disease. Even if these precautions are taken, there may also be concealed pests or systemic pathogens, and microbial contaminants which can only be detected and eliminated later in culture by elaborate procedures descibed in Chapter 5.

Is decontamination necessary?

For most kinds of tissue culture it *is* necessary to remove external micro-orgnisms from plant tissues with chemical disinfectants, or sterilants before cultures are commenced. This is because bacteria and fungi are able to grow readily on plant culture media which contain organic compounds such as sugars, amino acids and vitamins. However Bowes (1990) and Bowes and Curtis (1991) have shown that plants such as *Begonia, Saintpaulia ionantha, Peperomia residifolia* and *Stepto-*

carpus hybrida, which readily regenerate adventitious shoots from leaf cuttings, can be micropropagated *in vitro without* prior surface sterilisation. Explants are placed into covered containers onto a dilute mineral salts medium such as ½**Knop (1865)**, solidified with with agar, but containing no sugar or growth regulators (although it was thought that these might be advantageous for some genotypes). Little contamination is observed and the explants produce rooted shoots.

For the great majority of plant cultures, superficial contamination needs to be controlled before the explants are introduced to the medium. The facility with which this can be done depends on the plant species and the environment in which the mother plant has been grown.

DECONTAMINATION

In temperate climates, contamination varies according to the time of year, often becoming worse in late spring and

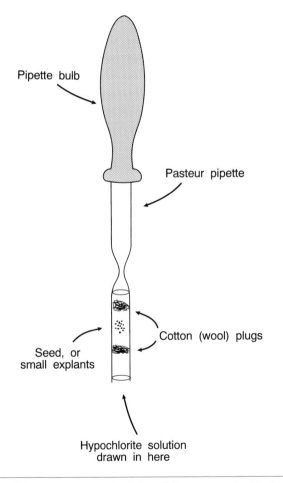

Pipette bulb

Pasteur pipette

Cotton (wool) plugs

Seed, or small explants

Hypochlorite solution drawn in here

Fig. 55. A convenient method of sterilising very small subjects such as mature orchid seeds.

summer: in the tropics it can be troublesome at all times. There is also considerable variation between the different kinds of explants which can be obtained from a single plant.

As a general rule large, hard explants such as seeds, fruits, or sections of stems, may be sterilised directly without being harmed by the sterilisation procedure, whereas soft, delicate tissues are likely to be damaged. But delicate explants, such as small shoot tips or immature ovules, within protective outer coverings, are often free from superficial microbial contaminants. Once the structure containing them has been sterilised, they can be dissected out under sterile conditions and placed directly into culture. For starting callus cultures, internal plant tissues, especially those of large organs such as tubers or storage roots, are a convenient source of explant tissue as they are usually free from natural contamination. But most tissue cultures, especially those to be used in practical micropropagation, have to be initiated from a less easily sterilised part of a whole plant where pests and microbes have penetrated inside coverings such as bud scales. It may then be necessary to use disinfectants on both the outer surfaces of the plant material and again on the parts selected for explants when they have been dissected or prepared. If sterilants have to be re-used on delicate material, they should be applied only for a short duration, followed by careful washing (see below).

Parts of the plant which grow in or near the soil are difficult to sterilise. The structure of other explants may lead to problems. For example it is not easy to disinfest *Rhododendron* shoots tips because the hairy and sticky nature of young leaves prevents the penetration of germicidal solutions.

Seeds are usually relatively easy to disinfect and are therefore a convenient starting point for experimental tissue culture work. After surface sterilisation, they may be grown on a nutrient medium to give rise to a callus culture directly, or if germinated on a simpler medium without growth regulators, can produce contaminant-free seedlings which may then be cut up under aseptic conditions to be used as explant material. However seeds have the disadvantage that, as they are the result of sexual reproduction, their tissues are frequently genetically-different from those of their parent.

General procedures

The steps which are necessary for effective decontamination will depend on the nature of the plant material and the kind of explant which is to be taken from it. In general, the part of the plant from which the explant is to be dissected is first cleaned. Underground structures such as roots, tubers, corms and bulbs may have to be scrubbed in water with a brush to remove any soil which is present. Any dead or superfluous tissue is removed and the material is then usually washed under running tap water or soaked for several hours in water containing a wetting agent. This can help to reduce the level of superficial contaminants and make the organisms more liable to be killed by subsequent treatments with disinfectants. Finally the chosen part of the plant is placed into a flask or screw top vial, disinfecting chemical treatments are applied, and the container covered or sealed.

After exposure to sterilant solutions, explants are washed and/or soaked in several changes of sterile water to remove all traces of the sterilising agent before being prepared and transferred to culture. Some authors advocate briefly re-exposing the explant to a chlorine-based sterilant immediately before it is placed *in vitro* (see below). All, or at least the last, steps in any sterilisation procedure should be conducted in a sterile inoculation area (*e.g.* on the work surface of a laminar air-flow hood).

Orchid seeds, which are very small, are often placed inside a Pasteur pipette plugged with cotton (cotton wool). Another piece of cotton is inserted to prevent the seeds from coming out (Fig. 55). A sterilant solution is then sucked into the pipette with a rubber bulb or teat and expelled after an appropriate period. It is replaced on several occasions by sterile distilled water and finally the outer cotton plug is removed so that the seeds can be expelled into a container of medium.

SURFACE STERILANTS

Surface sterilisation may be carried out with several different germicidal reagents. Clearly the best products are those which are cheap, non-toxic to both plants and people, and effective on a wide range of plant material. The most commonly used materials are:

- the hypochlorite ion (hypochlorous acid),

- simple alcohols, particularly ethanol.

As the germicide should make the best possible contact with the plant material, it is advisable to add a few drops of wetting agent to aqueous sterilant solutions (see below).

Hypochlorite solutions

The hypochlorite ion is usually obtained from sodium hypochlorite (NaOCl) or calcium hypochlorite. Sodium hypochlorite is soluble in water and although aqueous solutions can be obtained from laboratory suppliers, most laboratories use household or industrial bleach solutions as a convenient source. The final concentration required may vary from 0.25–2% w/v according to the plant material and the period to which it is exposed to the compound. This may equate to 5–20 per cent v/v of a domestic bleach solution, depending on the commercial product employed.

The bactericidal action of hypochlorite solutions is due to both hypochlorous acid (HOCl) and the OCl^- ion. The former is probably much more active than the latter because the disinfecting efficiency of chlorine is best in slightly acid hypochlorite solutions and decreases with an increase in the pH, corresponding to conversion of hypochlorous acid to OCl^- (Dychdala, 1977). For the most effective disinfection of plant material, hypochlorite solutions should therefore be used at pH 6–7.

The potential germicidal activity of sodium hypochlorite and calcium hypochlorite is related to their oxidising capacity. This is assayed chemically by the available chlorine content of the preparation. That in NaOCl solutions can be found by multiplying the w/v concentration by 0.9523. Commercial bleach solutions vary in strength. Clorox®, Javex ® and Purex® contain 5.25 per cent w/v NaOCl (5% available chlorine) (Smith and Thorpe, 1975a; Dodds and Roberts, 1982), but some other brands of bleach solution contain less active ingredient. Domestos® has 4% available chlorine (4.2% w/v NaOCl) (Alderson and Barghchi, 1982). It will be seen from Table 5 that plant material is usually sterilised in solutions of between 0.25–1.5% available chlorine, longer exposure times tending to be required if more dilute solutions are employed.

Calcium hypochlorite is sold in powder form and so is less conveniently handled than sodium hypochlorite, but frequently it is cheaper. High purity calcium hypochlorite [$Ca(OCl)_2$] theoretically contains 99.2% available chlorine, but economically it is not practical to manufacture a product for general sale with more than 65–70% purity. 'Bleaching powders' therefore usually contain 50–70% calcium hypochlorite together with calcium chloride and unreacted calcium hydroxide; the label should declare the available chlorine content of the product. Providing the powder has not deteriorated, dissolving 50 grams of a product with 65% available chlorine in 1 litre of water should give an aqueous solution containing 3.25% available chlorine.

Calcium hypochlorite solutions are prepared by stirring bleaching powder into distilled water. The sediment is allowed to settle and the solution is then filtered and used immediately. Some workers have thought calcium hypochlorite to be less effective than NaOCl in removing contaminants (Gorter, 1965), but others have found it equal in activity and less liable to induce tissue browning or injury (Sweet and Bolton, 1979), possibly due to the high concentration of calcium ions in solution. Reporting the w/v concentration of a calcium hypochlorite sterilant solution is meaningless unless the available chlorine content of the powder from which it was made is also given.

Calcium hypochlorite liberates chlorine as it dissolves in water: this implies that chlorine will be lost from bleaching powders if they become damp. As sodium hypochlorite solutions may also deteriorate with time, especially if exposed to strong light, it is advisable to renew stocks of all hypochlorite preparations regularly and to carry out periodic tests on the available chlorine content of the solutions prepared from them. This can be done by titration, or alternatively by using the tablets sold for chlorine estimation in swimming pools (O'Ríordáin, 1988).

Tablets sold for sterilising drinking water can provide a convenient source of hypochlorite solution for use in small scale experiments or on field excursions.

Other halogens and chlorine compounds.

Chlorine water is another source of hypochlorous acid and has been employed occasionally on plant material. It may be prepared conveniently by adding 50 ml of 38% HCl to 15 g potassium permanganate and bubbling the chlorine evolved into 500 ml distilled water (Tyagi et al, 1985).

Two other halogens, bromine and iodine, are effective germicides. The use of bromine water is occasionally reported (e.g. Bogorad, 1950), but although it is effective, it is not readily available like sodium and calcium hypochlorite, and has to be freshly prepared on each occasion. McCulloch and Briggs (1983) said that they had found elemental iodine to be an extremely effective plant sterilant. They used 0.005% of a decolourised tincture of iodine for 15–20 minutes (this gave less staining than a brown iodine formulation).

Organic chloramine disinfectants have been used by some workers in part of their surface decontamination procedures. These compounds probably hydrolyse to release hypochlorous acid but they are slower in action than inorganic hypochlorites. Some example of their reported use are:

- Stems: 'Chloramine B' (3% soln. 5 mins) (Kolar et al.1976);

- Leaves: 'Chloramine T' (5%, 30 mins) (Cellarova et al.1982)

- Seeds of *Cinchona* (saturated solution of Chloramine, 20 min) (Koblitz et al, 1983a).

Chloramine T has also been used by Jelaska et al. (1984; 1985) under the trade name 'Halamid'.

Alcohols

Amongst the alcohols, ethanol is most widely used for sterilisation, but only rarely can explant material be disinfested in ethanol alone. However, Higuchi and Amaki (1989) found that a 4 min dip in 70% ethanol was more effective than 10–15 min in 1% NaOCl for removing contaminants from *Asplenium* rhizome segments.

Alcohols are not only germicidal, but also remove surface waxes from plant tissue. Dips in a 70–95% aqueous solution are frequently combined with soaks in other sterilants. Thus a preliminary dip in ethanol permits plant tissues to be more effectively wetted and penetrated by another germicide. The duration of such a pre-treatment needs to be varied according to the type of tissue or organ (30 sec – 1 min is often recommended for soft material, 1–2 min for seeds). The proportion of contaminant-free cultures can sometimes be increased by dipping tissue in 45–80% ethanol for a short period (e.g. 3–5 mins.) *after* soaking in hypochlorite. In the latter case it is necessary to rinse again with sterile water.

Methanol is less germicidal than ethanol, isopropanol more so, but it brings an increased risk of phytotoxicity. However, some workers dip selected plant material briefly in isopropanol before beginning dissection or other decontamination procedures. Snir (1982a) disinfested short segments of sour cherry twigs in 80% isopropanol for 30 mins before dissecting buds to remove shoot tips; Valle and Boxus (1987a,b) used 0.5–1 min dips in 100% isopropanol between soaks in other disinfectants to decontaminate single node shoot cuttings of rose.

Heavy metal ions

The next most common sterilant is mercuric chloride. In view of the high mammalian toxicity of this compound and the environmental hazard of mercury products, it should be used with caution. Waste solution should not be rinsed down the sink. Organomercurial compounds can also be used for sterilisation purposes, but they are environmentally unacceptable, and so not recommended. Powling and Hussey (1981) placed sugar beet seeds for 20 min in a 40 g/l solution of ethyl mercuric phosphate to decontaminate them before aseptic germination. Silver ions have also occasionally been employed as an antimicrobial treatment on plant material.

Heavy metal ions would be toxic if introduced into a culture medium and so special care should be taken to remove all traces after they have been used as a sterilant. Lakshmi Sita and Shoha Rani (1985) washed shoot material exposed to mercuric choride in eight changes of sterile water, while Van Geyt and Jacobs (1985) immersed *Beta* seeds which had been sterilied with $HgCl_2$ in a solution of EDTA chelating agent for 5 min.

Alternative sterilants

Two other oxidising agents, hydrogen peroxide and potassium permanganate, have been reported to be suitable antimicrobial agents for explants: neither is very widely used. Chalupa (1979) immersed the lateral buds of various broad leafed trees in 5% hydrogen peroxide for 5 minutes after first treating them with calcium hypochlorite solution; while Gupta and Durzan (1985) used a 15 min immersion in 30% hydrogen peroxide as part of a complex sterilisation procedure for field-gathered stem segments of *Pseudotsuga* and *Pinus*. Hydrogen peroxide solutions are unstable and even concentrates have a limited life. McCulloch and Briggs (1983) found that potassium permanganate (a 0.01% solution for 4–32 min) was a much better sterilant than hydrogen peroxide.

Drinking water tablets which contain halozone *(p-* carboxybenzenesulphodichloramide) as the active ingredient have been found to be an effective surface sterilant for use on field expeditions to collect germplasm (Yidana *et al.*, 1987). Ten 4 mg tablets (*i.e.* 40 mg active ingredient) were dissolved in 100 ml of boiled water. Plant material was immersed for 30 min.

General antiseptics

Several antiseptic preparations can apparently be employed on plant tissues to good effect.

Desogerme (a quaternary alkyl chloride plus poly-iminobiguanide salts) with fungicidal and bactericidal properties was used by Enjalric *et al.* (1988) for a preliminary wash of *Hevea* buds before alchol and NaOCl treatments.

Diamantoglou and Mitrakos (1979) report that 10 minutes immersion (concentration not specified) in Sevezan® bactericide (Bayer) was more effective than NaOCl or $Ca(OCl)_2$ for sterilising olive seeds prior to embryo culture. Bhojwani and Hayward (1977) placed wheat seeds in a 1% v/v solution of Cetrimide® (ICI p.l.c) before sodium hypochlorite treatment. The same compound (2% w/v) was used as a first antiseptic treatment for young *Ephedra* ovules (Singh *et al.*, 1981).

Biedermann (1987) employed 5% Zephiram® (benzalkonium chloride) for 30 min with slow agitation, after a NaOCl wash, for the sterilisation of *Magnolia* shoot tips.

However, this germicide was found by McCulloch and Briggs (1983) to be generally ineffective.

Plant tissues are sensitive to many of the phenol-type disinfectants which are commonly used as household germicides. McCulloch and Briggs (1983) found that tissues became necrotic after exposure and stained the medium dark brown. However Valles and Boxus (1987a,b) used a 10 min dip in 5% Dettol® (contains 4.8% chloroxylenol) as part of their sterilisation procedure for rose shoot cuttings. Chloroxylenol is said in pharmacopoeias to have both germicidal and fungicidal properties.

Fungicides

Plant tissue is sometimes immersed in fungicides as part of a sterilisation procedure. Chemicals active against plant fungi are also added to plant tissue culture media when it is necessary to control systemic contaminants. The most suitable compounds for both purposes are described on page 143.

Antibiotics

Antibiotics are sometimes used to remove or control contaminants which may occur in cultures once they are established (see page 134), and have been employed occasionally for the removal of superficial contaminants from explants. They can also be effective, sprayed onto stock plants, in bringing down the level of contamination (see page 135). Some examples of antibiotics being utilised for the direct elimination of microbes from explant material are:

- 0.15% streptomycin + 0.01% merthiolate added to a 4% solution of NaOCl for the surface sterilisation of *Euterpe* fruits (12 h exposure) (Guerra and Handro, 1988)

- 100 μg/l of a penicillin/streptomycin mixture for 15 min brought contamination on shoot tips from actively-growing peach trees to a lower level than that achieved with NaOCl. Shoot tips taken early in the growing season were damaged by the antibiotics (Hammerschlag, 1980, 1982a).

- 17% Alcide for 1 hour followed by the antibiotic rifampicin (50 μg/ml) was the best treatment to remove superficial contaminants from stem and nodal explants of the tropical hardwood, *Nauclea* (Mathias *et al.*, 1987).

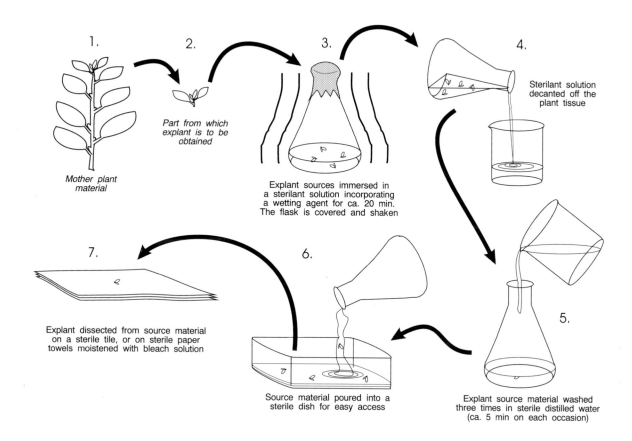

Fig. 56. One method of sterilising explants.
Steps 4 through 7 should be carried out in a sterile environment, such as the bench of a laminar flow cabinet.

THE MOST EFFECTIVE USE OF STERILANTS

Methods of treatment

It is important that a sterilant makes good contact with all surfaces of the plant tissue. Penetration is considerably assisted by a short prior immersion in 70% ethanol or by adding a non-phytotoxic wetting agent to the sterilant solution. Many detergents are suitable: among those often employed are Teepol® or Lissapol F® (0.05–0.1%), Tween 20® or Tween 80® (0.01–0.05%), 7X® (0.1%), and Alconox® (0.2%). It may be nessary to withdraw air trapped within the explant. This may be done by applying a partial vacuum to the sterilant. The container can be placed in a desiccator attached to a vacuum pump, or the explant and solution can be put into a hypodermic syringe: having expelled any air, the needle end is blocked and the plunger pulled back. Exposure of all external surfaces to sterilants is assisted by agitating the sterilant solution, either by hand, or on a shaking machine. A typical routine is illustrated in Fig. 56

. Instead of decanting used sterilant and rinsing water from the explant sources (Stages 4–6 in the diagram), thus risking the loss of small pieces of plant material from the container, a water pump can be employed to suck solution into a flask *via* a sterile pipette (dipped into the solution). The pipette is inserted into a length of flexible tubing (King and Shimamoto, 1984).

To prevent uptake of sterilants, the cut surface of plant pieces is sometimes dipped into molten paraffin wax. By sealing the cut ends in this way, it was possible to treat rice stem sections with 1.75% NaOCl for 30 minutes. Nodal segments were then excised and successfully cultured after a further 3 minutes in 0.2% mercuric chloride (Yao and Krikorian, 1981).

A typical procedure. To extract the florets from buds of *Rhododendron,* Dai *et al.* (1987) placed flower buds in 70% ethanol for 3 min and then absorbed the excess alcohol on a paper towel, on which the outer resinous bud scales were removed. The buds were then placed in 0.5% NaOCl (plus one drop of Tween 80 per 10 ml solution) and shaken on an orbital shaker at 100 r.p.m. for 20 min,

Table 5. Examples of sterilant solutions used in the preparation of explants.

Concentration	Available Cl	Exposure	Material	Part of a sequence of treatments ?	Reference
%	%	min			
NaOCl					
0.26	0.25	45	*Anthurium* buds	No	Kunisaki (1980)
0.50	0.48	10	*Typha* - young inflorescence	No	Zimmermann & Read (1986)
0.53	0.50	15	*Populus* buds	No	Garton & Moses (1986)
0.53	0.50	15	*Trillium* buds	No	Pence & Soukup (1986)
0.53	0.50	30	*Sophora* shoot tips & nodes	No *	Froberg (1986)
0.8	0.76	10	*Elaeagnus* flushed shoots	No *	Economou & Spanoudaki (1988)
0.53	0.50	15–20	*Quercus* nodal sections	Yes	Bennett (1987)
0.5	0.48	30	*Persea* nodes with buds	Yes	Cooper P.A.(1987)
1.6	1.52	30	Subterranean tissues	No	Duncan & Lineberger (1981)
0.5	0.48	30	Conifer buds	Yes	Kurz (1986)
1.05	1.0	30	*Corylus* seeds (without testa)	Yes	Perez *et al.* (1985)
Ca(OCl)$_2$					
2.75	—	5	*Armoracia* leaves	Yes	Gorecka (1987)
6	—	15	*Quercus* seeds (no pericarp)	Yes	Bellarosa (1988)
5	—	0.16–14h	Orchid seeds	No	Van Waes & Debergh (1986)
—	4	10	Buds of forest trees	Yes	Chalupa (1979)
HgCl$_2$					
1	—	30	*Stangeria* roots	Yes	Osborne & Van Staden (1987)
0.05	—	10	Apple dormant buds	Yes	Hennerty *et al.* (1988)
1	—	10	*Simmondsia* single nodes	—	Jacoboni & Standardi (1987)
0.1	—	3	*Crocus* corms	—	Homes *et al.* (1987)
0.05	—	10	Pinaceae shoot segments	Yes	Gupta & Durzan (1985)
0.1	—	4	*Echinochloa* flower buds	—	Wang & Yan (1984)
0.1	—	15	Field-grown *Eucalyptus* shoots	—	Lakshmi Sita & Shoba Rani (1985)
0.2	—	?	Alfalfa seeds	No	Brown (1988)

* = Mother plant treated with antimicrobials

following which they were washed four times in sterile distilled water and the explants excised.

Exposure times

Both the concentration and the duration of exposure to disinfectants are important. If they are repectively too high or too long, the plant tissues will be damaged, but too mild an exposure will not destroy the micro-organisms. In between lies the point of most effective germicidal treatment. A low concentration for a long period may not be as effective as a higher concentration for a shorter interval: five minutes in 1% NaOCl was more effective in decontaminating *Epiphyllum* stem cuttings than 10 minutes in 0.1% (Gaiser *et al.*, 1981).

Typical exposure times, depending on the material to be treated, are given in Table 5. Although these times can be used as a guide, explants from different species and different parts of a plant vary considerably in their sensitivity to bleach solutions. Khosh-Khui and Sink (1982a) found that rose shoot tips were more sensitive to excess NaOCl than lateral buds, and slightly excessive treatment or incomplete rinsing, resulted in explants being severely injured. As hypochlorite treatment can have a deleterious effect on *Vitis* shoot apices, Martinez and Tizio (1989) initiated shoot cultures from the fifth node below the apex. *Cordyline* spp. could only be propagated from an apical bud because sterilant solutions entered the stem through the cut surfaces of leaf bases and so killed axillary buds (Debergh and Maene, 1981).

Buds from field-grown *Syringa* and some other woody ornamental shrubs were found by Einset and Alexander (1985) to be very susceptible to hypochlorite in early spring, when an exposure of one minute in a dilute solution caused up to 98% to die. Explants taken later in the year were more resistant, but then the tissues were highly contaminated. The best source of explants was rooted cuttings in the greenhouse (see later).

Fruits and seeds are usually resistant to sterilants and, providing the pericarp or testa is not porous, can be immersed in bleach solutions for relatively long periods (*e.g.* fruits of *Euterope* shaken in 4% NaOCl for 12 h before the excision of embryos — Guerra and Handro, 1988). The optimum period for immersing the seeds of orchids of different species and genera in 5% calcium hypochlorite, varied from 0.16 hr to 14 hr (Van Waes and Debergh, 1986). Duncan and Lineberger (1981) advocated the use of 1.6% NaOCl for 30 minutes to decontaminate subterranean tissues that are otherwise difficult to clean. Fobert and Webb (1988) immersed seeds of *Solanum melongena* in 95% ethanol for 1 minute, then in 1.2% NaOCl for 30 minutes. After washing in water, the seeds were hydrated in sterile water overnight, and then

again disinfected in bleach before being placed onto water agar for germination.

Examples of combined treatments

Many authors now describe placing plant material successively in one sterilant and then another, or placing it in hypochlorite on two occasions with an ethanol dip in between (or *vice versa*). Here are some examples of combined treatments:

— Oak shoot tips placed in: 1% Liquinox wetter, 20 min; 70% ethanol, 2 min; 10% Chlorox, 15–20 min; 70% ethanol 1–2 min; and then 3 washes in sterile water (Bennett, 1987).

— Shoot segments from mature *Pinus* trees dipped in: 2.625% NaOCl, 15 min; 70% ethanol, 2 min; 2.625% NaOCl, 15 min again: before washing in sterile water (Kaul, 1985).

— Stem segments from field-grown *Pseudotsuga* and *Pinus* trees (Gupta and Durzan, 1985) treated with:

   i). running water, 3–4 min;

   ii). detergent (0.1% Linbro®) 5–10 min;

   iii). 30% v/v hydrogen peroxide 15 min;

   iv). 0.53% w/v sodium hypochlorite, 10 min;

   v). 0.05% w/v mercuric chloride 10 min. [3–4 sterile water washes were used after steps 2–4 above; 6–8 washes after step 5] .

— Stem sections, 4–6 cm in length, cut from field-grown Douglas fir and White spruce trees just before the spring lush when bud size was 1–2 cm (Kurz, 1986). Needles were removed and the exposed buds treated with:

   i). a quick dip in isopropyl alcohol;

   ii). 4 h in a solution of Tween 20 wetter (changed every 30 min);

   iii). bud scales removed and buds then treated with benomyl solution for 2h;

   iv). 10% NaOCl (presumably 10% of a commercial solution), 30 min;

   v). 4–5 washes in sterile water. The small portion of brown basal tissue removed before inoculation.

The most effective combined treatment for controlling contamination of a particular plant may only be found by experiment. A good example is provided in the paper of Hennerty *et al.* (1988). Meristems taken from growing shoots of apple could be effectively decontaminated if they were placed for 2 min in 95% ethanol followed by a brief dip in 9% calcium hypochlorite before washing. If dormant buds were treated in the same way, the cultures which were obtained from dissected shoot tips were almost all contaminated with bacteria. Increasing the duration of the calcium hypochlorite treatment to 120 min or combining this with an immersion of the dissected meristems in 1% calcium hypochlorite, did not overcome the problem. It was only solved by the following set of treatments:

- 95% ethanol, 2 min;
- 0.05% $HgCl_2$ plus 3 drops Tween 20 wetter per 100 ml, 10 min;
- sterile distilled water wash 10 min;
- NaOCl (1% w/v available chlorine), 20 min;
- four washes in sterile distilled water.

Tissues of a semi-aquatic plant, *Chrysosplenium*, were difficult to sterilise without causing senescence. The best compromise was a 5–7 min soak in 5% NaOCl , then a 1 min dip in 80% ethanol before sterile distilled water rinses. Even though there was subsequently a rapid loss of chlorophyll, adventitious buds began to form after 3 weeks (Brisson *et al.*, 1988)

REDUCING SURFACE CONTAMINATION

Not all plant material is of a suitable quality for initiating tissue cultures. That which is heavily infested will be difficult to decontaminate properly and the stringent sterilisation necessary for any chance of success will increase the likelihood of damage, and decrease the probability of survival. For these reasons it is sensible, wherever possible, to treat stock plants, or stock plant material, in ways which will minimise the level of contamination, and to select as explants those tissues in which contamination is likely to be at the lowest level.

Selection of explants

Unless presented with the last remaining shoot tip of a species hitherto thought to be extinct, no tissue culturalist would attempt to initiate cultures from a single explant, because the risk of failure is too high. Several different explants are always selected, each being placed into a separate tube: any cultures which are found to be contaminated or which fail to become established are then discarded, together with any which are surplus to requirement, after a period of incubation.

The proportion of contaminated cultures will depend on the type of explant selected. For example, Enjalric *et al.* (1988) obtained 21% aseptic cultures from 3 mm axillary bud explants of *Hevea*, 42% from 6 mm shoot tips, but 74% from 1 mm shoot apices. Although lateral buds on horseradish roots can be difficult to sterilise, Gorecka (1987) obtained almost no contaminated cultures from leaf segments.

Roots and other underground organs of soil grown plants are not the best material for initiating cultures as they are invariably highly contaminated. However the level of contamination may be less if plants from which explants are to be taken, have been grown in containers of sterilised soil. Hussey (1975b,c) found bulb explants of *Hyacinthus* were much more difficult to free from contaminants than explants from other organs, and bulb explants more difficult to decontaminate than those from corms. If an underground organ is the only material available, consider whether adventitious or axillary shoots can be sprouted as a source of explants. If these shoots are not forced in soil, but in some other sterile material, they are less likely to be heavily contaminated, particularly if they are also etiolated by being grown in the dark.

Etiolation. Explants obtained from etiolated shoots tend to give rise to cultures with less contamination than normal. This may be because contaminants do not have suitable conditions in which to multiply rapidly when shoots are elongated, particularly if this is done under relatively dry conditions. The rudimentary leaves and and reduced surface structures on etiolated shoots also offer a smaller number of sites in which micro-organisms can flourish. O'Ríordáin (1988) suggested that micro-organisms on the original plant material were spread over a larger surface area during etiolation. By etiolating shoots of *Persea americana* (avocado) in a darkroom in low relative humidity, the proportion of contaminated cultures originated from shoot tips could be reduced from 55% (initially), to zero after the fourth harvest of explants, two months later (Cooper, 1987). Murasaki and Tsurushima (1988) found that etiolation eliminated internal microbial contamination of *Cyclamen persicum* petioles.

Explants from field-grown plants

Bacterial and fungal contamination may vary between plants from different ecological sites. It is especially high on the shoots of plants growing in hot, humid areas. Superficial organisms are often very prevalent on tree species and are usually more abundant on older tissues or on those with a rough surface.

The level of contamination can change on plants at different seasons of the year. Shoot explants from papaya trees were seriously contaminated during the Florida winter (Litz and Conover, 1977). In temperate climates contamination almost invariably increases as the growing season progresses. Apple shoot tip explants were less contaminated if obtained from trees in mid-spring or summer, rather than autumn or winter (Hutchinson, 1982a), and contamination became a major problem on *Pinus strobus* shoots collected in late spring or early summer (Kaul, 1985).

Shoots of many plants are less contaminated when they are in active growth than at other times. Thus, although the basal parts of *Pinus sylvestris* buds were readily contaminated, shoot tip explants were rarely infected during May to October: the proportion of contaminated shoot tips was greater when they were excised at other periods of the year (Hohtola, 1988). Survival of apical meristems of *Vitis rotundifolia* was high if they were excised from actively growing shoots of about 10 cm length, but poor if they were taken from shorter or longer shoots which were not growing rapidly (Gray and Benton, 1991),

Surface contamination of plant material can be reduced if some thought is given to growing or sampling plants. Precultural treatment can be so essential that Debergh and Maene (1981) think that it should be considered as a routine stage (Stage 0 — see Chapter 2) of the micropropagation process. Choice of explant material is as important. Parts of plants can also be kept dry and shielded from micro-organisms by splash barriers or by being covered with cellophane, or glacine sleeves, for a period before explants are taken. Some workers have used polyethylene bags, but as they are not porous to water vapour, internal humidity is liable to be very high, leading to the development of moulds and rotting. Infection of *Rosa hybrida* shoot tips was increased by keeping shoots in hermetically sealed plastic bags for one week before sampling (Valles and Boxus, 1987a). De Fossard *et al.* (1977), who used a glacine bagging technique on greenhouse and field grown *Eucalyptus* trees, point out that it is important to spray selected branches with fungicide and/or insecticide beforehand to prevent subsequent fungal or insect infestations from undetected spores or eggs.

Le Roux and Van Staden (1991) sprayed *Eucalyptus* stock plants with benomyl (1 g/l) twice a week for 2 weeks before explants were removed. This procedure was an essential part of effective decontamination.

Care of stock plants

Compared to that on field grown material, the degree of superficial microbial contamination is usually much less on stock plants reared in a greenhouse, laboratory or growth room, particularly if plants are grown under controlled conditions. Plants should be potted in clean,

bleach-sterilised containers using a clean, (and preferably) pasteurised, potting mix and kept *completely free* of arthropods such as insects, arachnids and myriapods by suitable sprays. Contamination will be reduced if plants are not grown in soil or potting compost. Hydroponic culture is an alternative. Read (1988) found that ornamentals from the families Bromeliaceae and Marantaceae were best grown in expanded clay particles.

Low humidity is an important factor in lowering microbial growth: some researchers also advocate cool temperatures (Knauss and Knauss, 1980). If shoot or leaf material is to be used for explants it is essential to avoid wetting the upper part of the stock plant (or splashing it with soil) (Romberger *et al.* 1970; Evert and Holt, 1975; Knauss, 1976a; Cooper, 1987). Debergh and Maene (1981) grew plants for up to 3 months in a greenhouse at 25°C in a relatively low humidity (70%). During this period, water was only supplied to the pots through plastic irrigation tubes or from a capillary bed. Even though stock plants treated this way showed some signs of stress, the number of uncontaminated cultures obtained from explants was consistently greater than that derived from unprepared plants. Furthermore, decontamination of explants from Stage 0 plants could be effected with less rigorous defoliation of stems, so that axillary bud meristems were less liable to be killed by the sterilising solutions.

Some plants do not grow well under low relative humidity or it may be difficult to bring down the humidity in some greenhouses, particularly in tropical areas. Under these circumstances there are likely to be far fewer superficial contaminants if stock plants are moved to a growth room; or to a dry, clean and well ventilated indoor area, some 4–6 weeks before explants are required.

If buds need to be taken from near the base of a plant, Debergh (1987) recommended that the 'soil' substrate should be removed from their vicinity a few months before excision, so that they are in a cleaner and drier environment. The runners required to start cultures for fern propagation, can be obtained in a relatively clean state if they are taken from plants growing in hanging baskets rather than in pots.

A difficult case. Garton and Moses (1986) found that field gathered shoots from a select *Populus* tree gave 100% contaminated cultures and so did shoots taken from a greenhouse-grown cutting of the same clone. Uncontaminated cultures were finally obtained by rooting shoots grown in a contaminated *in vitro* culture and establishing them in the greenhouse. When the resulting vigorous soft growth was re-explanted, it gave contaminant-free cultures.

Fungicide and antibiotic sprays. Where the level of contaminants is expected to be high, it can be advisable to spray or drench stock plants with fungicides and antibiotics on several occasions before tissue is removed for explanting. For example Starrantino and Caruso (1987) first sprayed plants of *Citrus sinensis* × *Poncirus* with 0.5% copper oxychloride and then, after 2 days, applied a solution of 10 mg/l rifampicin plus 500 mg/l ampicillin. The second treatment was repeated twice per week. Oliphant (1988) sprayed *Lavendula* mother plants with a benlate-thiram mixture.

The use of forced shoots

Shoot cultures of woody plants are less contaminated if they are initiated from the apices of shoots which have been forced into bud break, rather than dormant buds which have met their chilling requirement (Hammerschlag, 1981a). Shoots to be forced can be stored in a refrigerator until required; they are then stood in a laboratory or growth room (at *ca*. 20–25°C) with their cut ends in water or in a solution similar to that used for the preservation of cut flowers. Read and Yang (1987) used a 2% sucrose solution containing 200 mg/l 8- hydroxyquinoline (8-HQ) citrate (or sulphate). To this was added 100 mg/l GA₃. Marks *et al.* (1987) who have used this solution successfully, have expressed some concern about the possible mutagenic effect of 8-HQ.

Skirvin and Chu (1978b in Skirvin, 1981) obtained uncontaminated explants of peach by gathering shoots in early spring and keeping them until explants were required. The degree of contamination in the field rose in parallel with the increase in outside temperatures. It can be advisable to treat field-gathered shoots with fungicides (*e.g.* 0.05% Benlate + 0.05% Captan, Economou and Spanoudaki, 1988) before buds are forced open. Shoot apices still need to be surface sterilised before explants are dissected from them.

Hammerschlag (1980) found that only 3.6% of field gathered shoots of *Prunus persica* were free from contamination, but that completely contaminant-free cultures could be obtained from forced shoots. Having forced buds into growth, leaves were removed from the shoots which were then trimmed to 5 mm and surface sterilised with 0.5% sodium hypochlorite in a solution of 0.01% Tween 20 wetter. Following this, the shoots were transferred to a 100–500 p.p.m. solution of commercial penicillin and streptomycin mixture for 15 minutes before washing and *in vitro* culture.

Seedlings as explants

As mentioned on page 117, although there can be disadvantages in using seedlings, their tissues often provide suitable explants. Adventitious shoots can often be induced to form directly on cotyledons, hypocotyls or young leaves, or these explants may be used to initiate callus growth. Seedling shoot apices can also be used to start shoot cultures.

Where seedling-derived explants are required, seeds are germinated in aseptic conditions. Seeds are first sterilised. Those with hard seed coats can be subjected to quite rigorous treatments without damage: concentrations of sterilants can be higher than those used on soft tissues, and the period of contact longer. Sterilised seeds may be placed onto a simple solidified medium containing only nutrient salts, or they may be sown in a sterile container on a sterilised substrate such as vermiculite (which advantageously may be wetted with a nutrient salt solution). The seedlings which emerge *in vitro* are usually free from contaminants and explants can be removed from them without further treatment with sterilants.

Occasionally, seed coats prove difficult to decontaminte fully, causing bacteria to be carried onto some seedlings. A plant where this has been found to occur frequently is sugarbeet. To ensure that seedling material *was* contaminant-free, Konwar and Coutts (1990) removed the shoot tips of supposedly aseptic seedlings, and transferred them twice to **MS** medium without growth regulators for 8 day periods. Only if there was no sign of the medium having been contaminated (see Chapter 5) were petiole and leaf sections removed as explants.

ASEPTIC TECHNIQUES FOR ISOLATION AND TRANSFER

AT THE LAMINAR FLOW BENCH

Cleaning bench tops and other equipment

The air flow through the transfer cabinet or chamber should be turned on at least 20 minutes before the bench is to be used. The working surface of the bench should be disinfected with 70% v/v isopropanol, 70% v/v ethanol (industrial spirits), hypochlorite solution or a solution of hibitane in ethanol. Some laboratories have used 20% phenol, but this is not recommended as the solution is corrosive and phenol vapour has both acute and chronic toxicity. Commercially-available 'disinfestation towels' impregnated with iso-propanol can be useful during a

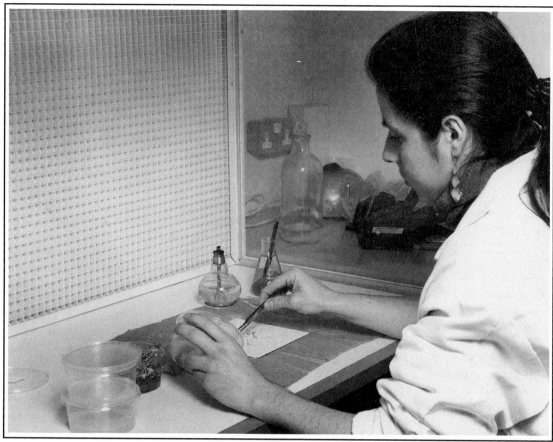

Fig. 57. A laminar flow bench in use in a university department.

Note that an alcohol burner, such as that shown in this photograph, is not recommended for resterilising instruments when critical work is to be undertaken (see text).

Dissection is carried out here on a sterile ceramic tile with scalpel and forceps. The tile is surrounded by the greaseproof paper in which it was wrapped during autoclaving. Instruments are stored in 70% aqeous alcohol contained in the conical flask, and re-sterilised by flaming between transfers.

working session for wiping hands and the surface of the inoculation bench.

A dissecting microscope will need to be kept permanently in a laminar air flow cabinet for the isolation of very small explants. It should be wiped over with a sterile paper towel moistened with 70% ethanol before use. The stage and control knobs should be given particular attention and should be re-cleaned after each dissection. Do not allow the ethanol to come in contact with the lenses of the instrument as they may be damaged.

Instruments and glassware

Dissecting instruments

Stainless steel scalpels and forceps (including some with long handles to reach into deep containers) are normally used for handling plant tissue cultures. Fine dissections are carried out with needles. These can be sewing needles or ones made from tungsten wire. Either kind is mounted in a stainless needle holder. Knives suitable for dissecting very small objects such as meristem tips, can be conveniently made from broken pieces of a brittle kind of razor blade, glued or mounted on a handle. Robust instruments can be pre-sterilised in a hot oven. At the bench they are normally sterilised by prolonged flaming or by heating in an electric furnace, and are then cooled and stored in 70% aqueous ethanol or methylated spirits until required. [Do not plunge hot instruments into flammable spirits!]. A further flaming burns the spirit off. The instruments need to be cooled before they touch plant material: this can be done in sterile water. A working area would normally be provided with more than one set of forceps and scalpels. Flaming will be repeated on frequent occasions during the processes of explant isolation and culture transfer.

De Fossard (1976) warned that 70% ethanol should be utilised for storing and dipping instruments, as bacterial spores are not killed in 95–100% alcohol. Kunneman and Faaij-Groenen (1988) have found that bacteria can survive immersion in 96% ethanol for at least 40 minutes and agree that it is not a suitable antiseptic for tools, even if other sterilants are added to it. Hypochlorite solutions have been used by some laboratories for sterilising instruments but are liable to cause their detioration by corrosion.

Singha *et al.* (1987a) also discovered that an alcohol dip was inadequate to remove micro-organisms and that it was essential to heat instruments in the hot flame of a bunsen burner for about 12 seconds or even longer in an electric 'bunsen' before all contaminants are killed. Electrically operated sterilisers are safer than naked flames and are convenient for sterilising instruments. One type, often used for sterilising bacteriological instruments, comprises a heated ceramic tube; another is a tub-like heater containing glass beads. The latter is satisfactory but must be regularly cleaned to ensure that plant material does not accumulate. As an individual instrument needs to be left in the hot glass beads for at least one minute before becoming sterile, each bench needs to be equipped with several sets of dissecting tools. A further kind of steriliser uses ultrasonics and a bactericidal cleaning solution.

The spores of some bacteria, particularly *Bacillus* spp., are heat-resistant. It is therefore important to use the hottest part of a high gas bunsen flame and, with electric furnaces, to take account of the time necessary to fully heat the element when it is first turned on. The time needed for adequate sterilisation is longer if instruments are heavily loaded with organic matter. The low flames of gas-burning bunsens and the flames of alcohol burners are not sufficiently hot. Boxus and Terzi (1988) have suspected that a heat resistant bacterium might be able to survive in the alcohol within alcohol burners. Inadequate sterilisation of instruments can lead to a worker picking up a contaminant and spreading it to many subsequent cultures until the end of the working day (Boxus and Terzi, 1987).

Ceramic heating tubes are particularly liable to damage knives and forceps, and flaming destroys the temper of metal and removes the plating from cheaper instruments such as sewing needles. The latter should therefore be changed regularly before they become rusted. It is advisable not to sterilise miniature dissecting knives by flaming. They should be autoclaved wrapped in metal foil which is opened at the working surface. Between use they should be placed in a sterile beaker of 70% ethanol, washed in sterile water and stored on the bench within folded sterile paper.

Handling plant material

Plant organs and tissue are moved into culture or subcultured on an aseptic bench. A typical laminar air flow bench with a set of simple dissecting tools is shown in Figs. 57.

Following a final thorough washing in sterile water to remove all traces of the sterilants which have been employed, tissue is removed from the water with sterile instruments; it is then placed on a sterile surface of the inoculating area for trimming or final dissection, should this be necessary. A sterilised ceramic tile, a sterilised Petri dish, or a pad of sterile paper towels is convenient for this purpose. De Fossard and Bourne (1977) recommended an autoclaved Petri dish containing *ca.* 10 filter papers. The uppermost paper is discarded after each dissection. Many laboratories moisten paper towels with an hypochlorite solution, but for plants such as ferns which are sensitive to bleach, only sufficient solution should be used to cause the paper to be slightly dampened. If paper has been used as a platform, waste material can be wrapped in it at the end of dissection and thrown into a waste bin.

It is often advisable to cut away tissues which have been bleached by sterilant solutions. Dissected explants are then normally placed directly in, or on, a sterile nutrient medium in suitable containers, but de Fossard and de Fossard (1988a) dip the prepared explant into a sodium hypochorite solution before placing it on the medium: the dipping solution contains either 1%, 0.1% or 0.01% available chlorine, depending on the sensitivity of the plant material. The same practice is used during subculture (see below).

As fungal spores, bacteria and mites are carried on the person, operators working in sterile rooms or at laminar air-flow hoods, should not bend over plant material or unsealed sterilised containers. Sometimes disease organisms can be trapped on the outer parts of a large organ (*e.g.* the scales surrounding a bud). It is therefore important that as dissection proceeds, the eventual explant (*e.g.* the interior of a bud) should only be placed onto a fresh sterile surface and *not* put onto the same part of a tile or paper on which previously dissected material was deposited some moments before (Kurz, 1986).

The carry-over of superficial contaminants into a newly established culture (or the introduction of new microbes through careless technique), may only become apparent after 10–14 days (Sweet and Bolton, 1979). Many workers therefore advocate placing explants initially on a simple minerals-sucrose-agar medium lacking expensive growth substances. Non-contaminated cultures are then transferred to the requisite complex medium (de Fossard and Bourne, 1977; Gorst *et al.*, 1978; Perinet and Lalonde, 1983). Others favour culturing explants on a microbiological medium for a short period to encourage the growth of any micro-organisms that may be present (see Chapter 5).

Initial isolations

The precise method which is appropriate for making inititial isolations, will vary from plant to plant. The smaller the initial explant is to be, the greater the requisite expertise, time and patience. Explants such as stem or root segments, leaf segments or leaf discs (which can be cut with a sterile cork borer), and single node pieces can be separated with the naked eye. Shoot tip explants, and particularly meristem tip explants, require to be isolated under a dissecting microscope.

Meristem isolation. A general method of dissection is as follows:

- See that the bench to be used for isolation is properly equipped with all the necessary instruments, equipment and solutions.

- Select a suitable magnification (*e.g.* 10× or 15×) on the microscope.

- Pick up a previously decontaminated bud with sterile tweezers and hold it on the microscope stage with one hand. Bring the bud into focus and then with the aid of a needle or fine cutting blade held in the other hand; carefully remove the outer leaves from the bud, one by one, until several leaf initials remain below the the meristematic dome.

- A shoot tip explant can now be obtained by making a horizontal or V-shaped cut below the top of the meristem. If you know by experience that an apex of this size will not be contaminated, no further dissection is necessary.

- To be more sure of obtaining an aseptic explant, further young leaves are removed from the apex

until the dome is only accompanied by 2–3 leaf primordia and some stem tissue containing pro-cambial strands. The dome is usually recognised by having a translucent or glossy appearance. A 'meristem tip' apex of this size, 0.4–0.5 mm in length from the tip, is suitable for virus elimination in many plants, especially if the stock plant has been heat-treated. For very critical virus elimination work, only the meristematic dome (*ca.* 0.1–0.2 mm) is excised.

- Explants are transferred to a container which has been previously filled with a suitable medium.

Subculturing

The external surfaces of previously sterilised vessels are liable to be re-contaminated. It is therefore good practice to rotate the top of all glass containers in a flame. This should ideally be done before caps or plugs have been taken off and before plant material is removed or inserted. The tops of plastic vessels cannot be treated in the same way for fear of melting or deforming them. The risk of contaminating cultures from dust on the lips of vessels is minimised by covering the stoppers and necks with aluminium foil, parafilm or clingfilm plastic. As this has the effect of tightly sealing the containers it may not always be advisable.

Before containers of established cultures are opened for subculturing, it can be advisable to wipe the exterior with an antiseptic towel of the type mentioned previously (O'Ríordáin, 1988). The culture vessel is then opened, the plant material withdrawn using long-handled forceps and once again dissected on a sterile platform. The selected pieces of tissue or organ are transferred to new medium in fresh containers which are then sealed. Divided pieces of cultures should be returned to containers of fresh medium as soon as possible. Those of some plants (*e.g. Rosa hybrida*, Stimart, 1986) are especially liable to be damaged by drying out at this time.

5

Controlling Persistent Contaminants and Plant Diseases

THE PROBLEM TO BE SOLVED

Plants growing *in vivo* may become systemically infected with fungal, bacterial and virus diseases, and attacked by insect pests and nematodes. They also invariably carry the superficial contaminants described in Chapter 1. To survive and grow properly, *in vitro* plant cultures need to be largely free of pests, fungi and most bacterial infections. Contaminants can cause large losses during micropropagation and their control is usually the most frequent and difficult problem encountered by micropropagation laboratories. If contamination is to be avoided, it is important to detect and eliminate contaminating organisms before they are transferred to many culture vessels during routine subcultures.

Simple surface sterilisation does not always remove contamination or infection by bacteria, yeasts, viruses, viroids, mycoplasmas and rickettsias. Plant material can be cultured and multiplied without the presence of a microorganism being recognised. The infection is then said to be *latent* or *hidden*. It may become troublesome later in the life of the culture, or may be transferred to the plantlets which are produced.

Micropropagated plants are therefore not disease-free *ipso facto*. The belief that virus diseases and other micro-

organisms were automatically removed during meristem tip culture has led in the past, to the spread of virus in *Cattleya* and other orchid genera (Lawson and Hearon, 1973; 1974a,b; Lawson, 1974) and the distribution of bacterially- and virus-infected plants of other kinds.

Neverthless because customers purchasing newly propagated plant material do expect it to be pest and disease-free, the detection and elimination of disease organisms should be high on the list of priorities of any modern tissue culture laboratory. At the very least the management should be fully aware of the disease status of the material they are offering for sale and should make this information freely available to prospective purchasers.

Beneficial infections

In the vast majority of cases it is very advantageous to propagate clean and disease free plants, because they are usually more vigorous and have a faster growth rate than infected stock. Occasionally, the presence of viruses, mycoplasmas or rickettsia-like organisms can produce horticulturally-valuable changes to plants: irradication of the organism may then be undesirable. In these cases special precautions may need to be taken during tissue culture of the plant to ensure that the systemic infection is *not* irradiated.

A good example of a beneficial effect produced by a systemic infection is the valuable variegation in flower or leaf colour produced in some tulips and pelargoniums by rickettsia-like organisms. A graft-transmissible agent causes poinsettias to branch freely (Dole and Wilkins, 1988), but plants of 3 freely-branching cultivars, regenerated from suspension cultures *via* somatic embryogenesis, had completely lost this trait (Preil, 1991). Plants infected with some viruses show a greater resistance (cross protection) to infection by other more damaging viruses and fungi. Potato clones from which infections of Potato Virus X were removed, were found to be severely susceptible to mosaic diseases (Wang and Hu, 1980). In such cases the re-infection of plants with mild strains of protective viruses could be beneficial, and might be possible *in vitro* before plantlets are transferred to the external environment. Some varieties of virus-infected rhubarb can be forced in the early spring after a cold treatment: virus-free stock may not respond in the same way (Case, 1973).

Mycorrhizal fungi. Many fungi grow in a symbiotic, or weakly parasitic, association with the roots of the terrestrial plants; the association is called a *mycorrhiza*. Some such fungi grow within plant roots while others are ectotrophic. Those of one important genus of the former kind, *Glomus*, are called *vesicular-arbuscular* (VA) fungi because, within the root cortex, they usually produce structures resembling haustoria (arbuscules) and sacs (vesicles). Ectotrophic fungi which live mainly on the external surfaces of roots, form an enveloping mantle of hyphae around rootlets but eventually produce typical fungal fruiting bodies such as cups, toadstools, or truffles. VA fungi do not form fruiting bodies of this kind, but produce large resting spores within the soil. Mycelia of both kinds of fungi grow outwards from plant roots into the soil nearby. The hyphae then act as an extension of the plant root system and supply it with inorganic ions, while the fungus obtains organic nutrients from the plant.

Mycorrhizal fungi are eliminated during micropropagation and so, as most plants benefit from their presence (and some grow very poorly in their absence), it can be advantageous to re- introduce this kind of fungal infection before plants are put into containers or transferred to the field. Introduction can be effective when micro-cuttings

are rooted or transferred to the external environment (Chapter 14).

Orchids generally require to have a mycorrhizal association. Species of terrestrial orchids whose seeds can be germinated on aseptic culture media, are sometimes difficult to establish *in vivo*, because no symbiont has been introduced to the roots. More success may be obtained by germinating seeds in the presence of a suitable fungus.

A review of the use of mycorrhizal fungi in horticultural crops has been provided by Maronek *et al.* (1981) and in woody species by Dixon and Marx (1987).

Disease resistance

Disease resistance of plants can usually be attributed to a specialised morphology, the ubiquitous presence of inhibitory chemicals or response to various triggers (*elicitors*) (notably infection, but also mechanical damage, and artificial stimuli, such as fungal preparations) which cause a plant to initiate defence mechanisms against attack by a pathogen. These may include the local production of an inhibitory substance (a *phytoalexin*), the increased production of enzymes or the deposition of lignin. Partial resistance *caused* by *in vitro* culture has been described by Msikita *et al.* (1990a). Cucumber plants grown from cultured embryonic axes (*i.e.* embryos dissected from seeds, free of the cotyledons) were less susceptible to certain isolates of the fungus *Pythium aphanidermatum* than normal seedlings, particularly where callus had developed on the crowns. It was suggested that this might have been due to morphological changes in the outer cells of primary roots or to physiological mechanisms.

In appropriate environmental conditions, cultured plant tissues usually react typically to plant pathogens, so that they can be used to study disease resistance (Helgeson and Haberlach, 1980) and to screen for resistant plant genotypes (Brettell *et al.*., 1980a). Plants derived from tissue cultures can be more susceptible to disease than conventionally propagated material. This is thought to be associated with their juvenile condition (Chapter 8).

Plant tissue culture can be used to generate somaclonal genetic resistance to plant diseases, to select for resistance or to facilitate the introduction of genes responsible for resistance (Day, 1980) (Chapter 3).

FUNGAL AND BACTERIAL DISEASES, AND CONTAMINANTS

Plant tissue cultures have been said to be liable to three kinds of contamination (Constantine, 1986; Long *et al.*, 1988):

1. The sudden and severe kind (*acute* contamination) which occurs during the establishment of a culture. This is nearly always caused by ineffective surface sterilisation.

2. Contamination that occurs after establishment, caused by:

   — micro-organisms that were concealed within the explant (endogenous micro-organisms); or,

   — micro-organisms that have been introduced during subculturing.

3. Contamination which is of a deap seated and long lived nature (*chronic* contamination) which occurs simultaneously in a batch of cultures after a long period of apparent sterility.

Problems of these kinds are produced by bacteria, yeasts or fungi. The first kind can obviously be cured by more effective sterilisation procedures. Organisms responsible for the last two types of contamination are more difficult to detect. Sometimes infection does not become apparent until the culture has been maintained for a considerable period, but may then become so severe that cultures are lost. Contaminated cultures will often be revealed by the presence of a cloudy medium. Shoots of some plants develop brown spots on their leaves or brown patches at the base which, when examined under a microscope are found to contain bacteria.

TYPES OF CONTAMINANTS

Bacteria and yeasts

Bacteria constitute the most common and troublesome kind of contaminating micro-organism in plant cultures. Numerous genera have been found associated with the shoot or root environment of plants *in vivo*, including those listed below. Those shown in bold type have frequently been found in plant cultures:

Acinebacter, Acetobacter, Aerococcus, Aeromonas, Alcaligenes, **Agrobacterium***, Agromyces, Alcaligenes, Arthrobacter, Azotomonas ,* **Bacillus***, Bordetella, Cellulomonas, Chromobacterium, Citrobacter, Clavibacter, Clostridium,* **Corynebacterium***, Curtobacterium,*

Erwinia, Enterobacter, Flavobacterium, Hyphomicrobium*, Klebsiella, Kurthia,* **Lactobacillus, Micrococcus***, Oerskovia, Propionobacterium,* **Pseudomonas***, Rhizobium, Rhodococcus, Sarcina, Serratia,* **Staphylococcus, Xanthomonas***.

Yeasts also inhabit the external surfaces of plants, and although one would suspect that they would contaminate plant cultures, their existence *in vitro* has seldom been admitted. A smell of fermentation when the culture is opened is a reliable guide to their presence. *Torulopsis* was isolated by Boxus and Terzi (1987) during mass propagation schedules; six unnamed yeasts were obtained from shoot cultures of ornamental plants (Leggatt *et al.*, 1988), and two kinds from apple meristem cultures (Poulsen, 1988). Where identificaton of yeast contaminants is desirable, a method published by Leifert *et al.* (1990) may be useful.

Although bacteria in some of the above genera can be pathogenic, most are found in soil as saprophytes, and on plants as epiphytic flora. But even normally-harmless species can interfere with growth *in vitro* and lead to the death of plant cultures. Sterilisation routines should control all superficial contaminants, and are usually relied upon to set up 'aseptic' (axenic) cultures. Unfortunately there are no tests accurate enough to detect the presence of micro-organisms within plant tissue without first increasing their numbers. Therefore to be sure that no superficial contaminants remain, or to detect bacteria concealed within plant tissues, it is necessary to culture explants on one or more media which favour the rapid growth of micro-organisms. This can quickly reveal the *presence* of contaminants but accurate identification of the organism/s involved may prove too specialised a task for most micropropagation laboratories.

The identification of bacteria has traditionally relied on a series of morphological, physiological and biochemical tests (Schaad, 1980; Bradbury, 1988) which may nowadays be supplemented with chemical analyses such as serology and fatty acid profiling using gas chromatography (Stead, 1988). Tests for specific bacteria (*e.g.* those known to cause a particular plant disease) can be carried out using ELISA (page 153), immunofluorescent staining, immunobinding, monoclonal antibodies, or DNA hybridisation techniques, but test kits and computer software are now commercially available† to simplify characterisation of many contaminants to the species level (Leifert *et al.*, 1989a). Specialist laboratories will also undertake the identification of contaminants, and other plant health tests, under contract (Prakesh, 1988).

---

† API- bioMérieux, Basingstoke, England.

Latent infections

As experience with micropropagation has progressed, it has become increasingly evident that plants can harbour some kinds of bacterial contaminants interstitially between cells, or within their vascular system. Some bacteria of this kind are pathogens. The xylem-limited bacterium *Clavibacter xyli* causes Bermuda Grass stunt, and sugarcane ratoon stunting disease (*C. xyli* ssp. *xyli*). Other organisms found inside plants may not be known pathogens, and can be present without causing obvious symptoms of disease, or without apparent hindrance to the growth of a culture: these are called *endophytes*. A persistent *Pseudomonas* bacterium prevented the survival of *Carica papaya* shoot tip explants during the winter months, but not during the summer where it contaminated cultures without apparent adverse effects until after the 13th subculture. Then the cultures began to decline (Part 2, Chapter 13) and the bacterium gradually became dominant. It was not known whether contamination was instrumental in causing the decline (Litz and Conover, 1981c).

Endophytic contaminants will not be eliminated by surface treatments. Fortunately they seem to be relatively uncommon *in vitro* and only associated with certain categories of plant material (Debergh and Maene, 1984). Nevertheless, some kinds of bacterium tend to be particularly troublesome. Pierik (1988) instanced *Bacillus licheniformis* or *B. subtilis* as frequent cause of hidden infections.

Latent contaminants do not immediately reveal their presence by visible growth on the plant material or culture medium. The bacterium may need to adapt to conditions *in vitro*, or may not be able to multiply until the culture is transferred to a medium more favourable to its growth. Often a latent organism will be detected only after a culture has been maintained for several months, but during this time it may have been transferred to many vessels during subcultures. It is therefore important to eliminate contaminated plant material as quickly as possible. For instance, a contaminant may not show up on the media used for proliferation or elongation of shoot cultures, but become virulent in the rooting medium (Boxus and Terzi, 1987). Microbial contamination of *Catharanthus roseus* was more serious in suspension cultures than in static callus culture (Carew and Patterson, 1970). A covert contaminant present in Reiger begonia cultures was able to survive *in vitro* for up to 7 months before suddenly becoming apparent (Hannings and Langhans, 1974). This serves to emphasise the need for careful adherence to aseptic techniques during transfers. Careless technique can easily result in a single worker spreading a hidden contaminant from one container to many, during a working session.

The effect of contaminants. Malignant infections can cause the death of cultures, and even the presence of more benign organisms may result in growth retardation; necrosis (Knauss and Miller, 1978; Long *et al.,* 1988); an altered morphogenetic potential (de Fossard, 1977), including a reduced rate of rooting (Hanus and Rohr, 1987); or a reduction of axillary shoot proliferation. Such effects may not be immediately discernable but become more prominent the longer the culture is continued. Shoot cultures of plants which are specially liable have to hidden contaminants may need to be re-initiated frequently (Stimart, 1986).

There are some bacterial contaminants which seem to have little apparent effect: a benign latent contaminant was, for instance, found by Monette (1986a) in all shoot cultures initiated from kiwifruit vines. The infection was not seen on agar media, but consistently appeared on a liquid medium. Although the cultures were always nonaxenic, successful micropropagation could be carried out. Leggatt *et al.* (1988) obtained evidence of there being several internal micro-organisms in some apparently disease-free *Fremontodendron* and *Geranium* cultures.

Even if contaminants do not cause serious problems in micropropagation, their presence in plant cultures is not desirable. Some bacteria of this kind can supply plant cultures with utilisable organic substrates and so lead to anomalous results between batches of cultures, or in critical physiological experiments. For example, *Hyphomicrobium* contamination is not readily detectable in suspension cultures of *Datura innoxia*, because neither growth rate of the culture, nor the turbidity of the culture medium noticeably altered. The bacterium does however have the capacity to supply plant cells with small amounts of adenine, sufficient to maintain slow growth of an adenine-requiring autotrophic cell line of *Datura* (Hirsch and Conti, 1964).

Fungi

Fungi are common plant pathogens and saprophytic soil inhabitants. Very many fungal genera are therefore associated with plants, but those especially noted as contaminants in tissue cultures include species of *Aspergillus, Candida, Cladosporium, Microsprium* and *Phialophora.*

In vitro culture of the small explants used to initiate cultures will usually result in fungal contaminants soon becoming apparent. Fungal infections generally result in the death of the explant, but sometimes a dual culture can be obtained (see Ingram and Helgeson, 1980), where growth of the cultured plant material can continue. The fungus *Acremonium coenophialum* does not kill callus cultures of the grass Festuca arundinacea but causes them to have a characteristic habit of growth (Conger and McDaniell, 1983). Once this habit was recognised to be due to the fungal infection, callus culture proved to be a rapid method of screening for infection, which is symptomless in the mature plant and can otherwise only be detected by microscopy or ELISA tests. Fungi can grow as saprophytes on plant tissue culture media and so hyphal growth may appear on the medium or on the explanted tissue, or both. The plant pathogen *Alternaria brassicae* will grow on callus cultures of *Brassica* as a dual culture, but the fungus also grows on the culture medium as a saprophyte. Although fungicides can be used to eliminate fungal contaminants (see below), it is usually sufficient to examine cultures regularly and discard any which are infected.

Mollicutes and rickettsias

Rickettsias are small prokaryotic bacteria-like parasites with a well-defined cell wall. The mollicutes (a grouping which includes mycoplasmas and spiroplasmas) are prokaryotic organisms lacking a true cell wall and surrounded only by an external membrane (Holliday, P., 1989). They are frequently submicroscopic, much smaller than rickettsias, and assume a variety of shapes. It is not possible to culture them on standard bacteriological media, and although some can be grown on media containing serum, they may lose their pathogenicity thereby. They can however be troublesome contaminants of animal cell cultures.

Both mollicutes and rickettsias are surface contaminants of plants *in vivo* and may occur within the vascular tissues (rickettsias in xylem amd phloem, mollicutes in the phloem), to which they are transmitted by aphids or other insect vectors. They are responsible for some leaf yellowing, wilt-inducing and stunting diseases of major economic importance.

Control measures

Plant mollicutes and rickettsias within plant tissues can be killed, or inhibited, by the heat therapy normally employed against virus infections. Mollicutes are said to be sensitive to tetracycline antibiotics (Holliday, P., 1989), and rickettsias to penicillins.

Diseases of this kind, and some systemic bacterial infections, can be eliminated by shoot or meristem culture if the original explants do not yet possess xylem and phloem vascular elements. Control appears to depend on the rate of plant vegetative growth exceeding that of the microorganism, or upon there being disorganised growth. A mycoplasma causing Aster Yellows seemed to degenerate in the phloem of carrot root segments when they were cultured. Mycoplasma-like bodies did not appear to infect the callus formed from these explants, neither were they detected in the phloem of plants regenerated indirectly from the callus (Bové, 1988) . Ulrychova and Petru (1975) discovered that the mycoplasma causing potato witches broom disease was eliminated from tobacco plants regenerated from callus cultures. The auxin 2,4-D was here suspected of eliminating the rickettsia because infectivity was lost from tissues *in vitro* after 4 weeks culture with the regulant.

DETECTING INFECTION

Indexing stock plants

The first step in obtaining clean cultures is to ensure that plants from which explants are to be taken, originate from a healthy batch, and do not possess obvious disease symptoms. Stock plants should then be maintained under conditions which limit the spread of infection. Surface sterilisation of the explant (described in Chapter 4) then destroys most epiphytic organisms and superficial spores, but may not eliminate infections within the tissue. Besides visually inspecting stock plants, it can be advisable to test (or *index*) them for the presence of systemic infections before they are used as a source of explants. Similar precautions have been used in conjunction with large scale macropropagation. In the 'cultured cutting' method, cuttings from a stock plant are divided into two halves. The upper half of the shoot is rooted while the lower section is placed on nutrient agar which is incubated. Propagation is only continued from the rooted cutting if no disease organisms develop in the cultures. The presence of *Verticillium* and bacterial blight *(Erwinia chrysanthemi)* in chrysanthemums and of *Fusarium oxysporum, Pseudomonas caryophylli* and *Phialophera cinerescencs* (causing wilt) in carnations, has been revealed by these techniques (Dimock, 1962).

In pelargoniums, leaf spot and stem rot caused by the bacterium *Xanthomonas pelargonii* can exist within plants without displaying visible external symptoms. This and other pathogens must be eliminated in order to micropropagate healthy plantlets and to obtain elite stock plants for macropropagation. Cassells *et al.* (1980) devised the system of indexing stock plants shown in Fig. 58. Transversally-split explants from mother plants or sap from surface- sterilised stem cores, were inoculated onto common bacteriological media. ELISA and DNA-hybridisation tests were used to detect the presence of the *Xanthomonas* pathogen. It was found to be ubiquitous: other bacteria occurred only at random, suggesting that

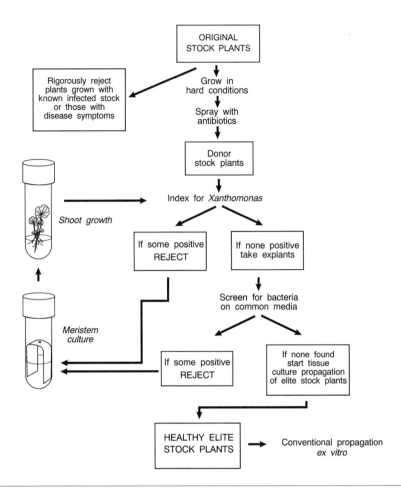

Fig. 58. The scheme used by Cassells *et al.* (1980) to index stock plants of *Pelargonium* for *Xanthomonas* infection.

their presence was dependent on the presence of the main pathogen. Micropropagation was only practised if the donor plant/s were bacteria-free. If some contamination was present, meristem culture was used (see below).

Escapes from initial decontamination

A mathmatical model for minimising the cost of contamination constructed by Korhonen *et al.* (1988), showed that the optimum time to test for its presence was during the first two cycles of micropropagation. To reveal the presence of micro-organisms which might have escaped the decontamination procedure at Stage I, many laboratories place initial explants on a simple minerals plus sucrose medium for one to two weeks. Only those cultures which appear to be aseptic are transferred to the next stage. Micro-organisms may be more likely to be discovered if the Stage I medium is supplemented with organic compounds: yeast extract (250–500 mg/l) and/or peptone are often added. To detect the presence of *Xanthomonas* and *Corynebacterium,* Beauchesne *et al.* (1977) added

250 mg/l peptone of casein and 250 mg/l yeast extract to the medium (containing 30 g/l glucose) on which they isolated *Pelargonium* meristems, while Boxus and Terzi (1987) routinely add 265 mg/l Bacto Difco peptone and 88 mg/l Bacto yeast extract to their Stage II proliferation medium; this enables contaminated jars to be detected and removed. The special organic additions were not toxic at these levels.

Fisse *et al.* (1987) noted that many bacteria require a sugar other than sucrose. Bacterial growth is therefore more likely to occur if, at Stage I, explants are placed on a medium containing glucose. To discern the presence of bacterial infections, they initially put shoot tips of *Syngonium, Philodendron* and *Ficus elastica* on the following '**NB**' medium:

$$1200 \text{ mg/l } NH_4NO_3;$$
$$1200 \text{ mg/l } K_2HPO_4;$$
$$480 \text{ mg/l } MgSO_4.7H_2O;$$
$$1200 \text{ mg/l } NaCl;$$
$$2400 \text{ mg/l yeast extract;}$$
$$24 \text{ g/l glucose.}$$

Remember that contaminants may not necessarily originate from the initial explant: media and containers can be improperly sterilised, or the medium contaminated while it is being dispensed; and micro-organisms are easily introduced into containers when cultures are being manipulated or subcultured. In studying the types of bacteria which appeared in subcultured plant material of two micropropagation laboratories, Leifert *et al.* (1989a) thought that 50–70% of infections were likely to have arisen from the original explant, the rest through reinfection during handling. In this study, *Bacillus circulans* was isolated only from cultures contained in autoclaved glass vessels and not from those in irradiated plastic. This bacterium is known to be able to survive autoclaving at 121°C for 20 min. As *Bacillus pumilis* could be isolated from insufficiently sterilized media, the occurrence of *Bacillus* in cultures of many different plant species suggested that another likely cause of contamination was insufficient sterilisation of media. The natural habitat of *Staphilococcus epidermidis*, *Micrococcus kristinae*, and *Lactobacillus acidophilus* is the skin and tissues of animals, including humans. Discovery of these bacteria only in cultures which had been subcultured many times indicated that they had been introduced during handling.

Contamination in growth rooms. Cultures within culture rooms should be examined with a hand lens or binocular microscope on a regular basis for signs of contamination or pest infestation. De Fossard (1985) advised that the microbial status of shoot cultures that are being used for the production of plantlets, should be monitored after every 3–6 passages. Under normal circumstances, contaminated cultures should be destroyed by autoclaving. Never open the culture vessels before placing them in the autoclave, and keep contaminated and clean equipment apart.

Cryptic contaminants

As mentioned above, sometimes signs of contamination only appear after cultures have been through several passages. This may be because an infectious bacterium has only been able to grow extremely slowly in a plant culture medium, or because it has hitherto been latent. One method of detecting the presence of internal bacteria at later stages, is to touch the cut surface of shoot pieces onto a nutrient agar slope as cultures are being subdivided (de Fossard and de Fossard, 1988a). A large supply of slopes and systematic labelling is clearly required. Where this method is not entirely effective, it will be necessary to remove samples of the growing culture on several occasions and to plate the tissues onto media known to support bacterial growth. Explants should be cut open to

expose the vascular tissues and then placed, cut surface downward, on the medium. To ensure that there is the maximum chance of exposing hidden contaminants, some workers have recommended that the tissue should first be macerated under sterile conditions. Deimling and Mollers (1988) suggested that enzymatic maceration should be used, as in the preparation of protoplasts. Sap which has been induced to exude under pressure is a good source of inoculum but its extraction without introducing stray contamination may be difficult.

Media containing yeast and meat extracts are usually employed to discover hidden contaminants: for example, a yeast, glucose and calcium carbonate (**YGC**); or a peptone, yeast, agar (**PYA**) medium was best for indicating the presence of hidden bacterial contaminants of potato (Long *et al.*, 1988), while Cornu and Michel (1987) used a 'PYGA' medium to indicate the presence of bacteria in *Prunus avium* shoot cultures. It was composed of:

Difco peptone (P)	5 g/l
Difco yeast extract (Y)	5 g/l
Glucose (G)	5 g/l
Agar (A)	15 g/l

If plant tissue gave rise to no visible bacterial growth on an **NBY** medium:

K_2HPO_4	2 g/l
KH_2PO_4	0.5 g/l
$MgSO_4.7H_2O^*$	24.65 g/l
Nutrient broth (Oxoid No. 2)	2g/l
Yeast extract (Difco)	2 g/l
Beef extract (Difco)	3 g/l
Glucose*	5 g/l
Agar	15 g/l

* = Autoclaved separately

Leifert *et al.* (1989a) moved the tissue, with some of the medium, to:

½**MS** medium (no PGRs), plus:

Nutrient broth No. 2 (Oxoid)	10 g/l
Yeast extract (Difco)	10 g/l
Beef extract (Difco)	3 g/l
Glucose	5 g/l

The presence of turbidity in the liquid after 3 weeks incubation at 30°C indicated the presence of a contaminant. A sample of the turbid medium was then plated to other media for isolation of the causal agent/s.

Unfortunately bacteria can be highly selective over the substrates on which they will grow and it cannot be expected that the presence of all possible contaminants will be revealed by culture on a single mixture of nutri-

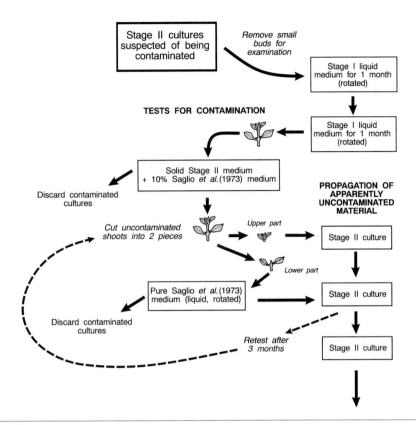

Fig. 59. A method used by Debergh and Vanderschaeghe (1988) to detect and eliminate hidden contaminants.

ents. Several tests must be conducted using different microbial media. Some bacterial contaminants can only be cultured satisfactorily on specialised media (Horsch and King, 1983; Leifert *et al.*, 1989b). Eleven different nutrient compositions were used by Cassells *et al.* (1988).

Table 6. The medium of Saglio et al. (1973) as used by Debergh and Vandershaeghe (1988) to detect hidden bacterial infections.

	Quantities per 100 ml
PPLO broth base (Difco)	2.1 g
Tryptone (Difco)	1.0 g
Glucose	0.1 g
Fructose	0.1 g
Sucrose	1.0 g
Sorbitol	7.0 g
Fresh yeast extract	25% solution
Horse serum	20 ml
Phenol red	2.5 g

Recipes for suitable preparations can be found in Bradbury (1970), Schaad (1980), Krieg and Holt (1984), Sneath *et al.* (1986) and Lelliott and Stead (1987). A bacterium of the genus *Hyphomicrobium* which was found growing as a covert contaminant in suspension cultures of *Datura innoxia,* could be grown on:

Nutrient broth (Becton Dickinson) 5 g/l,   or

Beef peptone (Difco)   10 g/l

but grew much better on the defined medium '**337**' of **Hirsch and Conti (1964)** (Horsch and King, 1983). Using the medium of **Saglio *et al.* (1973)** (Table 6), Debergh and Vanderschaeghe (1988) used the procedure shown in Fig. 59 to reveal the presence of microbial organisms in *Morantha rosea picta* but could not demonstrate those in *Calathea crocata* although plants being cultured were obviously contaminated.

Review articles

The nature and problem of contaminating organisms in plant cultures is presented in detail in a series of papers in Acta Horticulturae, Volume 225, and in a review article by Leifert and Waites (1990).

REMOVING PERSISTENT CONTAMINANTS

Initial treatments

Sterilants, such as hypochlorite, which destroy superficial contaminants, are not usually effective in eliminating those hidden within plant tissues. However, there are several reports that another sterilant, Alcide® (a chlorine-dioxide complex, Alcide Co., U.S.A.), *can* eliminate cryptic contaminants. Soaking *Magnolia × soulangeana* meristems for 3–5 minutes in a 1% filter sterilised solution gave cultures which were apparently free of infection (when tested on the medium of Saglio *et al.*, 1973), whereas control cultures had a systemic bacterium (Debergh and Vanderschaeghe (1988).

Re-treating explants with sterilants

As a preventative measure against the spread of contaminants, de Fossard and de Fossard (1988) say that in shoot cultures of many kinds of plants, they routinely run a layer of hypochorite over the medium and leave it there for 20 minutes before removing and dissecting plant material for subculture. Ferns cannot be treated in this way as cultures are particularly sensitive to bleach: with *Begonia* the sterilant solution must be introduced extremely carefully down the side of the wall of the culture vessel and only those shoots remaining above the bleach solution taken for subculture. Dissected plant pieces are given a final dip in hypochlorite and are also rinsed before being placed onto fresh medium: this treatment helps to further safeguard against the development of contamination.

Although De Fossard and De Fossard (*loc.cit.*) recommend that cultures which are obviously contaminated should be destroyed, they have found that those of particular value for commercial propagation can sometimes be subcultured by the careful removal of plant material growing well away from the surface of the medium. On obviously contaminated cultures of some genera (*Aglaonema, Anthurium, Alocasia, Dieffenbachia, Monstera* and *Syngonium* were mentioned), hypochlorite re-treatment has been possible. Shoot clusters of these plants were completely immersed in hypochlorite for periods from 10 minutes to 1 hour, dissected on hypochlorite-soaked paper towelling and the divided material returned to hypochlorite for a further short period before subcultures were initiated. Even though the tissue was bleached and growth was at first retarded, some explants survived, apparently contaminant-free.

Meristem culture

In *Pelargonium* and some other plants, internal contaminants tend to be concentrated in the lower parts of the stem. Apical shoot tips up to 1 mm length (but not those from lateral buds), are practically free from contaminants. After one or more cycles of meristem/shoot culture, shoots can be obtained free from micro-organisms (Fig. 58). Reuther (1988a) also used meristem culture to free *Pelargonium* from *Xanthomonas* bacteria during micropropagation (Fig. 60). Leaflets and basal segments of *in vitro* plantlets were indexed for the disease. Bacterial growth was encouraged by soaking the explants in liquid **Bouillon** medium, and any bacteria which were present identified by streaking the medium onto a yeast, dextrose, carbonate, agar.

Centrifuging

As protoplasts are generally discrete, they can sometimes be separated from bacteria by repeated centrifugation. Several washes followed by Percoll density gradient centrifugation reduced the concentration of bacteria associated with potato protoplasts to zero (Deimling and Mollers, 1988). The fungal and bacterial contamination of protoplasts can also be reduced by Ficoll density cetrifugation. In practice these techniques have been found to be not always effective. Where they have been tried, centrifuging and density separation have usually been accompanied by antibiotic treatment.

The use of antibiotics and selective biocides

Properties of an antibiotic

An antibiotic is, by definition, a substance produced by one micro-organism which is able to control, or prevent the growth of, another. However, synthetic drugs having the same kind of selective anti-microbial activity are often grouped under the same heading: the use of the word *antibiotic* in this book includes compounds of both origins.

Theoretically it might seem that all persistent contaminants could be removed from plant tissue cultures by adding one or more antibiotic to the culture medium, but this is seldom possible or desirable for routine work. Antibiotics are no substitute for careful aseptic techniques and should only be employed where conventional techniques are inadequate. Falkiner (1990) recommends that they should be used for the prevention of disease (prophylaxis), rather than for the treatment of infection.

Falkiner (1988; 1990) gives 11 desirable features for an antimicrobial chemical in plant tissue cultures. It should:

1). be soluble,

2). be stable,

3). be unaffected by pH,

4). be unaffected by culture media,

5). have minimum side effects (*i.e.* no phytotoxicity),

6). possess a broad spectrum of activity,

7). be bactericidal (and not simply prevent bacterial growth),

8). be systemic within plant tissues,

9). be suitable for use in combination with other antimicrobial agents,

10). have a mode of action such that there is the minimum chance of bacterial resistance developing,

11). be inexpensive and preferably not used in clinical medicine.

Few, if any, compounds meet all of these criteria and many compounds do not eliminate a micro-organism but are only bacteriostatic or fungistatic (*i.e.* they arrest growth of the contaminant without killing it). To be effectively controlled by antibiotics, micro-organisms should be growing actively: in many plant tissue cultures this is not the case.

Choice of compound for *in vitro* use

Antibiotics are frequently tested for their effect in controlling microbial growth by placing small (5 mm diameter) impregnated filter paper discs onto a microbial medium inoculated with a pure culture of a contaminant. Discs already impregnated with antibiotics can be purchased from several suppliers (*e.g.* Oxoid, 'Multodisks'®). Sometimes plates are inoculated with a control organism on one side and a test organism on the other. Antibiotic discs are then placed along the line between the two organisms. In both types of test, plates are incubated and the sensitivity of the cultured microbes to an antibiotic is shown by the size of the zone around the disc in which microbial growth is inhibited. After choosing a suitable antibiotic by this method, be sure that it will not prove to be phytotoxic before introducing it into a valuable culture.

The effectiveness of antibiotics can be greatly influenced by the characteristics of the medium in which they are

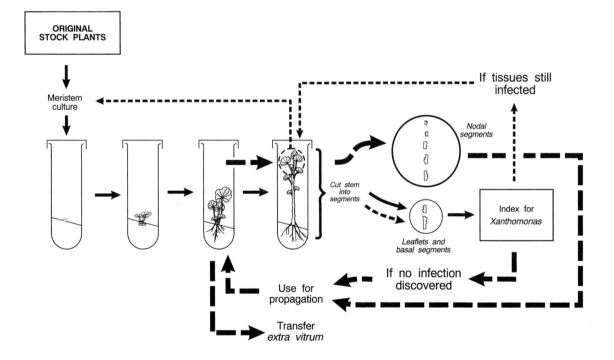

Fig. 60. The method of propagating *Pelargonium* free from *Xanthomonas* used by Reuther (based on 1988 paper and personal commmunication).

tested. For example, aminoglycosides such as neomycin, kanamycin, gentamycin and, particularly, streptomycin, are more effective at a slightly alkaline pH than they are at an acid pH. High levels of metallic ions can reduce the effectiveness of gentamycin against *Pseudomonas*. Antibiotics effective against a known contaminant in a bacterial medium may therefore be much less effective when added to plant culture media. Tests against micro-organisms should be conducted on media which are as similar as possible to the plant medium in which the biocide is eventually to be introduced. Unfortunatly the composition and characteristics of media change rapidly during the culture of plant material.

Falkiner (1988) suggested that two further steps are necessary after a disc diffusion assay, when trying to determine which antibiotics are likely to be effective in plant cultures:

1.   **The minimum concentration of antibiotic necessary to inhibit bacterial growth**. An equal inoculum of each isolated contaminant is cultured in tubes of agar-solidified or liquid plant culture medium, containing increasing concentrations of a chosen antibiotic. The lowest concentration of antibiotic to prevent bacterial growth was termed the *minimum inhibition concentration* (MIC).

2.   **The minimum concentration of antibiotic necessary to have a bactericidal effect**. This was determined by subculturing from apparently bacteria-free tubes (at and above the MIC antibiotic concentration) from the MIC test, onto a bacterially-nutritious recovery medium. The lowest concentration of antibiotic in the MIC test at which no bacterial recovery occurred was termed the *minimum bactericidal concentration* (MBC).

Stability. Antibiotics are normally sterilised by ultrafiltration before use, even though they are antimicrobial. Some compounds may not be substantially degraded by autoclaving [(*e.g.* griseofulvin (Carew and Patterson, 1970); bacitracin (Rier and Henderson, 1956); chloramphenicol, cycloheximide, kanamycin, neomycin and streptomycin]. The fungicide benomyl can be autoclaved: it is denatured in the process, but the breakdown product, 2-benzimidazole, is the antifungal principle of benomyl (Haldeman *et al.*, 1987). Most antibiotics will be slowly degraded in the medium during incubation.

Phytotoxicity. The use of antibiotics for controlling plant contaminants is limited by the fact that many such compounds injure or modify the growth and development of plant tissues. The tolerance of animal tissues seems to be no guide to the effect on plants. Phytotoxicity can vary markedly between plant species and closely related genotypes, and also depends on the way that an antibiotic is

administered. Mathews (1988) noted that whereas cotyledon and shoot tips of *Brassica juncea* were completely inhibited by 20–50 µg/ml kanamycin, seedlings could be raised in a concentration of 2000 µg/l: this presumably indicates markedly different levels of uptake into excised and intact organs. Seedlings of *Vigna radiata*, and shoots regenerated from cotyledons of this species, were unaffected by 4000 mg/l.

The toxicity of antibiotics is frequently due to their damaging effect on plastids and mitochondria (Zamski and Umiel, 1978); chlorophyll formation is impaired. The incorporation of amino acids into plant cells has also been said to be inhibited by antibiotics (Watts and King, 1973a). Prolonged exposure of cells or tissues to antibiotics can result in the development of a resistant cell population either through mutation or by selection in the cytoplasmic genes within these organelles (Maliga *et al.*, 1973, 1975; Umiel and Goldner, 1976; Hamill *et al.*, 1986). A list of some of the antibiotics which have been tried on plant cell cultures and a summary of the results obtained is provided in Table 8 (page 158).

Falkiner (1990) regarded the aminoglycoside antibiotics and chloramphenicol as phytotoxic and recommended that they should not be used for the removal of contaminants. The antibiotic chloramphenicol (Shah, 1976) and the fungicide griseofulvin can induce chromosome instability (Griesbach and Sink, 1982).

Antibiotic toxicity in genetic manipulation. The toxic effect of antibiotics on plant cells is used to advantage in genetic manipulation experiments (page 93). Some bacterial plasmids carry antibiotic resistance genes resistance; if one of these genes is inserted into a vector, together with a non-selectable gene, it can be used as a marker during subsequent tissue culture. Some common plasmid genes convey resistance to ampicillin, chloramphenicol, kanamycin, streptomycin, sulphonamide drugs, and tetracycline. Antibiotics which have been used in plant cell selection, include:

Compound	Gene/s conveying resistance
Hygromycin Geneticin Paromomycin	Hygromycin phosphotransferase (HPT)
Kanamycin	neomycin phosphotransferase (NPT II) kanamycin phosphotransferase [APH(3′)II]
Neomycin	neomycin phosphotransferase
Phosphinothricin	Phosphinothricin acetyltransferase (PAT)
Chloramphenicol	Chloramphenicol acetyltransferase (CAT)

Kanamycin and hygromycin resistance has been most widely employed.

Effects on growth and morphogenesis. Some antibiotics have been noted to modify the growth rate or the morphogenetic response of cultured tissues (Table 8). The mechanisms by which such changes are effected have not yet been elucidated. The penicillins carbenicillin and penicillin G, which promote the growth of *Bouvardia ternifolia* cells, possess a lateral chain; this is capable of forming the auxin phenylacetic acid, if split off from the entire molecule by hydrolysis. However, Robert *et al.* (1986) found that phenylacetic acid did not reproduce the same effect. Enhanced morphogenesis is often associated with some inhibition of callus growth, but Owens (1979b) thought the two phenomena unrelated.

Some examples of the stimulatory effect of antibiotics on plant cultures are:

50–100 µg/ml bacitracin stimulated the growth of *Catharanthus roseus* callus cultures; low doses of kanamycin enhanced morphogenesis in protoplast-derived calli of carrot and tobacco (Owens, 1979a); filter sterilised carbenicillin (60 µg/l) and cefotaxime (100 µg/l) stimulated growth and increased the number of embryogenic calli formed from immature zygotic embryos (Mathias and Boyd, 1986); 0.8 µg/l hygromycin and 64 µg/l cefotaxime stimulated plant regeneration from sugar beet callus (although at higher concentrations plant morphogenesis was inhibited by cefotaxime, especially where callus had a low capacity for regeneration) (Okkels and Pedersen, 1988); the rooting of aspen shoots was promoted by dipping the cut ends in a weak solution of penicillin and streptomycin (Ahuja and Muhs, 1982).

A virus-induced tumour tissue of *Rumex acetosa*, which normally required thiamine for growth, was found by Nickell (1952) to grow without thiamine in the presence of *ca.* 5 ppm of either penicillin, terramycin, streptomycin, thiolutin or bacitracin.

The choice of antibiotic for controlling contaminants in plant cultures must be influenced by the ratio of the concentrations inducing plant and bacterial toxicity. A factor of two is generally satisfactory: thus a compound which kills bacteria at a concentration of 50 µg/ml, but does not cause phytotoxicity until the concentration is increased to 100 µg/ml, should be safe to use. Reports on how well antibiotics controlled contaminating bacteria grown on bacterial media, are not particularly informative unless they are also accompanied by results of tests for phytotoxicity. Even when there is a good margin between the concentrations required for these two purposes, incompatibility with plant culture media may result in microbial control being less good than expected.

Mixtures of antibiotics. Table 8 instances the use of single antibiotics, but many compounds have a narrow bactericidal spectrum: they often control either Gram positive or Gram negative bacteria, while some have antifungal properties. As plant cultures can contain more than one contaminant, mixtures of antimicrobial agents may be the most reliable prophylactic method.

Horsch and King (1983) found that neither 500 µg/l streptomycin nor 500 µg/l carbenicillin would eliminate a *Hyphomicrobium* contaminant of *Datura* cell suspension, but control was obtained if 100 µg/l of both compounds was used in combination. Shoot cultures of apple, rhododendron and Douglas fir were said to be decontaminated if the plant material was first incubated in liquid **Schenk and Hildebrandt (1972)** medium containing several antibiotics and then cultured upright on a solid medium containing the same mixture (see below) (Young *et al.*, 1984). If any phytotoxicity was noticed, polymixin B was omitted.

Bacteria of the genus *Agrobacterium* harbouring a plasmid are frequently added to pieces of plant tissue to cause a genetic transformation (see page 93). They need to be removed after co-culture to transfer the plasmid to plant cells, because continued presence can interfer with plant growth, or cause the death of the culture. Eradication is usually accomplished by adding one or more antibiotic to the culture medium. Cefotaxime or carbenicillin, or a mixture of the two are often employed. In transformation experiments an antibiotic is often employed as a selection agent for cells carrying foreign genes. The addition of one of these compounds (page 140), together with cefotaxime or carbenicillin, helps to control the bacterium. *Agrobacterium* was removed from transformed potato discs with 50–100 µg/ml (depending on cultivar) kanamycin plus 200 µg/ml cefotaxime (Stiekema *et al.*, 1988).

Mixtures of antibiotics often show synergistic effects, not only in the control of micro-organisms, but also in the induction of plant damage. As in the case of antibiotics used singly, combinations which are effective in one situation may be harmful in another. A mixture of 10 µg/ml rifampicin plus 1 g/l benomyl was an effective combination to control fungal and bacterial contaiminants in *Camellia* cultures (Haldeman *et al.*, 1987), but the rifampicin and trimethoprim mixture recommended by Pollock *et al.* (1983), increased the phenolic oxidation of coffee explants (Duhem *et al.*, 1988). Careful testing of combinations of antibiotics is therefore advised before they are introduced into valuable cultures.

Some further examples of the use of antibiotic mixtures for the removal of contaminants, are as follows:-

1. 250 µg/ml carbenicillin + 25 units/ml nystatin for 1 week. Protoplasts several spp. (Watts and King, 1973a)

2. 250 µg/ml carbenicillin + 2.5 µg/l amphotericin B for 1 week. Protoplasts several spp. (Watts and King, 1973a)

3. 15 µg/ml Rifamycin + 15 µg/ml trimethoprim + 0.1% fungicide Tilt MBC (Yidana *et al.*, 1987)

4. 25 μg/ml cefotaxime, 25 μg/ml tetracycline, 6 μg/ml rifampicin and 6 μg/ml polymixin B (Young *et al.,* 1984)

5. 10 μg/ml rifampicin plus 1 g/l benomyl (Haldeman *et al.,* 1987)

6. 50–100 μg/ml (depending on cultivar) kanamycin plus 200 μg/ml cefotaxime (Stiekema *et al.,* 1988)

7. Complex mixture (Enjalric *et al.,* 1988) 20 μg/ml gentamycin + 20 μg/ml kanamycin + 30 μg/ml chlortetracycline + 60 μg/ml chloramphenicol + 75 μg/ml rifampicin + 750 μg/ml benomyl.

8. Vancomycin-HCl + mycostatin (Johnson *et al.,* 1974)

9. 20 μg/ml rifampicin + 20 μg/ml trimethoprim (Pollock *et al.,* 1983)

Spencer *et al.* (1980) described a medium for the culture of *Phalaenopsis* flower stalk nodes which, they claimed, did not need to be pre-sterilised. A precise procedure for making up the medium is given in the paper: the antibiotics given in Table 7 were added once the agar had dissolved and cooled. Explants still required sterilisation in the usual way, and care had to be taken to avoid any unnecessary exposure to prospective contaminants.

Table 7. Anticontaminants used by Spencer *et al.* (1980) in their 'sterile' medium.

Compounds	Concentration mg/l
Benomyl	50
Nystatin	25
Penicillin G	100
Gentamycin	50

Other methods of using antibiotics

Treating explants. Antibiotics need not necessarily be added to plant culture media. Explants can be dipped or soaked in a solution of the antibiotic before culture, or mother plants can be sprayed with antibiotics before explants are removed. Tubers of *Cyclamen persicum* suffer from a high level of internal contamination, but Geier (1977) found that a satisfactory proportion of uncontaminated cultures could be obtained if tuber explants were kept for 1–4 days in 50 μg/l achromycin before transfer to the culture medium. When present in the medium continuously, antimicrobial concentrations of the drug were phytotoxic. In experiments of Scortichini and Chariotti (1988), dipping *Prunus* shoot tip explants

into 75 μg/ml rifampicin for one minute before inoculation, gave better control of bacterial contaminants than when the same concentration of antibiotic was added to the culture medium: however, the most effective control was achieved when explants were both dipped in the antibiotic and it was also added to the culture medium. Similar results were obtained with piperacillin and streptomycin sulphate.

Treating mother plants with antimicrobial compounds. The bacteristatic effect of a complex mixture of antimicrobial compounds on *Hevea* shoot tips and axillary buds was greatest when it was added to the culture medium. Soaking the explants was not so effective (Enjalric *et al.,* 1988). Impaired shoot growth resulted from adding the antimicrobials to the culture medium, but did not occur if the mixture was sprayed onto mother plants every two days beginning 15 days before excision, when contamination was very effectively reduced. There are other encouraging reports of treating stock plants with antibiotics. By spraying geranium plants to run off with 200 μg/ml oxytetracyline at weekly intervals from March to August, Kim *et al.* (1984) reduced the incidence of galls caused by the systemic bacterium *Corynebacterium fascians*. Treated plants eventually became stunted and chlorotic, but such adverse effects could be overcome by discontinuing the antibiotic treatments and applying fertilizer. Cassells *et al.* (1988) sprayed stock plants three times at two week intervals with Mycoshield® (Pfizer Chemical Corp.) (200 μg/ml a.i., oxytetracyline). This resulted in systemic bacterial contaminants spreading less far into the apex of the treated plants; and the concentration of bacteria lower down the stems, being much reduced. Shoot tip explants from mother plants treated in this way would have been less likely to have been contaminated than if they had been taken from untreated controls.

Practical applications

Opinions still vary amongst research workers as to whether antibiotics do provide an effective means of controlling contamination. Although there are now many published reports of successful use in plant tissue cultures, Debergh and Vanderschaeghe (1988) were sceptical about many of the results, because usually no evidence is provided that the treatment has eliminated the contaminant. If antibiotics have a bacteristatic or fungistatic action, bacterial growth can re-occur once the compound is removed (Fisse *et al.,* 1987). Debergh (1987) and co-workers reported that, in their laboratory, the addition of antibiotics to the medium had seldom eliminated established bacterial infections, although contaminated shoot cultures were sometimes rescued by incorporating antibiotics into an elongation medium. Duhem *et al.* (1988) could not control bacterial infection of coffee cultures with antibiotics. The best compound tested (500 µg/ml cefotaxime) only hindered bacterial proliferation but did not kill the contaminant.

Antibiotics are not suitable for the routine removal of superficial contaminants: compounds are expensive, some may only be available on medical prescription, and most are able to restrain only a narrow spectrum of micro-organisms. As the ineffective use of antibiotics is liable to create resistant strains of micro-organisms, there are also ethical and medical reasons for not using them at all, or for using them only with extreme caution. Control of contamination is therefore much better left to simple sterilants, combined with good isolation practices, leaving antibiotics to be employed only where explanted material contains concealed micro-organisms or superficial contaminants that prove impossible to eliminate by other means. It is then usual to incorporate the chosen antibiotic/s into the medium for just the initial stage of culture. The use of antibiotics in plant tissue culture and in micropropagation has been reviewed by Waldenmaier *et al.* (1986) and Pollock *et al.* (1983). A list of available compounds, and some guidance in the selection of the most suitable kinds, is given by Falkiner (1990).

Fungicides

Many antibiotics (*e.g.* Amphotericin B and Nystatin in Table 8, page 158) have an anti-fungal activity. Several workers have also used known synthetic fungicides for the control of fungi on explanted material and in established cultures, but phytotoxicity is very genotype dependent. Shields *et al.* (1984) looked at the effect of several fungicides against *in vitro* fungal contaminants and their toxicity to different kinds of tobacco cultures. Two benzimidazole fungicides, carbendazim and fenbendazole (30 µg/ml), were recommended by this study.

Benomyl (100 µg/ml) reduced the contamination of cherry fruits without affecting fruit growth (Wittenbach and Bukovac, 1980) and was used as part of the decontamination routine for conifer buds by Kurz (1986). When 5–50 µg/ml was dissolved in dimethylsulphoxide and added to the medium supporting callus derived from *Cymbidium* shoot tips, it inhibited plantlet formation. Similarly 50 µg/ml (but not lower rates) prevented *in vitro* seed germination of three different genera of orchids (Brown *et al.*, 1982). However, benomyl, dissolved in dimethylsulphoxide is toxic to suspension cultures (Hauptmann *et al.*, 1985) and protoplasts in tightly closed Petri dishes. It is broken down in solution and within plants to carbendazim (above) and a volatile compound, butylisocyanate. The latter seems to be damaging to plant tissues in sealed containers. Boiling or autoclaving benomyl solutions also degrades the compound to carbendazim (Thurston *et al.*, 1979) and presumably drives off butylisocyanate. If dissolved by either of these methods, benomyl is non-toxic and can be used at rates up to 50 µg/ml to remove fungal contaminants from plant cell cultures without visibly retarding growth (Hauptmann *et al.*, 1985; Haldemann *et al.*, 1987).

Alternative fungicides are imazalil (20 µg/ml) (Shields *et al.*, 1984) and captafol (100 µg/ml), which checked fungal contamination and saprophytic growth of the fungus *Alternaria brassicae* on callus cultures of *Brassica juncea* without toxicity (Joshi *et al.*, 1988). A mixture of propiconazole plus carbendazim [Tilt® MBC (Ciba Geigy) 0.1%] was non-toxic to cocoa and apparently controlled fungal contaminants (Yidana *et al.*, 1987).

Control of yeasts

Chlotrimazole was recommended for elimination of yeasts from tissue cultures by Shields *et al.* (1984). It was only effective against one of the two yeasts identified by Poulsen (1988) as contaminants of apple meristem cultures: (10 µg/ml) iminooctadine controlled both organisms but even 0.1 µg/ml was phytotoxic. Ampfotericin B and nystatin which are used to eliminate yeasts from mammalian tissue cultures, were ineffective (Poulsen, 1988).

PESTS

Various arthropods can be troublesome in plant culture laboratories. Very small insects and arachnids (particularly thrips and spider mites) can contaminate tissue cultures: their small size makes it possible for them to enter culture vessels where they can multiply rapidly without being readily detected. Ants can enter culture culture flasks, particularly very small species. The tiny Pharoah's ant (*Monomorium pharaonis*), which is found nearly all over the world, can be a serious invader. Ants and cockroaches can be difficult to exclude from the laboratory. Although cockroaches do not enter culture flasks, their presence in clean rooms will lead to the introduction and spread of other contaminating organisms. In temperate climates, arthropod pests are only likely to present a problem during the summer months; but in the tropics and subtropics, pests of all kinds constantly cause difficulties.

Mites and thrips

Mites

Mites are the most frequent and inconvenient pest within culture vessels. They are very small (less than 1 mm in size), occur ubiquitously in the environment and can be carried on dust particles, insects and animals (including humans). Only scrupulous attention to laboratory hygiene will prevent them being transmitted into transfer and growth rooms.

Some species of mites are found in a variety of human foodstuffs, while others are parasitic or saprophytic on animals. They occur widely on human skin, hair and clothing. Many mites can feed on dead plant material, and the high humidity within vessels is ideal for their growth and reproduction. They usually cause little damage to living plant tissues, but because they carry fungal and bacterial spores on their bodies, their entry into plant cultures is a source of multiple contamination. Often the first noticeable indication of their presence is the occurrence of fungal growth in cultures. The occurrence, within a flask, of a line of fungal colonies, is a tell-tale sign of mite infection. As mites need only about two weeks to complete their life cycle, their numbers can be substantial by the time fungal contamination is detected. In addition, if the containers used for culture are incompletely sealed (as is frequently the case, page 115), both mites and thrips can move easily from one vessel to another, rapidly creating a serious contamination problem. Mites which do not introduce fungi, but only bacte-

rial contaminants, can be very difficult to spot; so too are cultures containing mites which are apparently contaminant-free. In both cases, mites may be transferred from flask to flask during subcultures, along with plant material. Most mites are recognised by having a rounded singly-segmented body (there is no demarcation between the prosoma and the opisthosoma), and (usually) four pairs of legs. Gall mites have two pairs. Larval and adult stages differ in size but are otherwise often very similar.

If mite infection is found, all cultures in the contaminated batch, and those in the growth room in the immediate vicinity, should be destroyed by autoclaving. The outsides of all other culture vessels in the room, should be wiped with a disinfectant or with 70% ethanol and then sealed with film. Remaining cultures should be removed, and all the surfaces of the room sprayed with an acaricide before they are returned. Actellic D® was recommended by Blake (1988): she also suggested that as a long-term preventative measure, the walls and ceilings of clean areas might be painted with an acaricidal paint. Ali (1988) reported that fenbutatin-oxide (Vendex™) has been used successfully for mite control when painted onto shelving of the growth room at 6-monthly inervals.

Thrips

Thrip insects are common on glasshouse-grown plants; they often inhabit the shoot apices of plants where they damage the soft tissue and feed on sap which is exuded. Thrips lay their eggs just below the epidermis of plants and one cause of contamination will be the establishment of cultures with infected explants. Careful attention to the pest-free status of stock plants is therefore necessary. However, entry into cultures usually seems to occur through the arrival of airbourne thrips into growth rooms. Thrips are very small and slender insects (Fig. 61), and cultures contaminated with them can be difficult to detect; but Reustle *et al.* (1988) found that, in infected cultures, the leaves of vine plants had a shiny metallic leaf surface. Species of thrips which have been reported as contaminants in the literature, have been of the genera *Thrips, Allothrips* and *Frankliniella*. Like mites, these insects have a very short life, and in some species it can be completed in 3 weeks: the adult form is preceded by two nymphal and two pupal stages.

Cultures contaminated with thrips should also be discarded; those heavily infested will die. Occasionally, very valuable cultures may be included in a contaminated batch: any which appear not to be infected could be kept under strict isolation and daily observation. It is probably safe to consider them free from mites if no infection appears after a period of three weeks. It may also be possible to save valuable material by adding a non-phy-

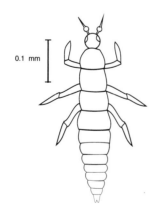

0.1 mm

Fig. 61. The nymphal stage of a thrips species which can infect tissue cultures.

totoxic insecticide to existing cultures or by transferring them to fresh medium into which an insecticide has been incorporated. Klocke and Myers (1984) reported that acephate (10 and 100 mg/l technical grade Orthene™, Chevron Chemical Co., Richmond, Ca.) gave complete control of *Allothrips*. This insecticide could be added to **MS** medium and autoclaved at 1.1 kg/cm^2 and 121°C for 15 min without any breakdown products being detected.

General control measures

Insect pest problems can be reduced to the minimum through careful hygiene and the routine examination of cultures. Old cultures have a greater chance of containing dead plant material (a source of food for mites), and so they should not be kept unless absolutely necessary: wherever possible, transfer plant material to fresh media on a regular and frequent basis. Some laboratories have used vapourising strip insecticides, but continuous use is probably inadvisable as eventually resistant strains of insect are likely to occur.

Ants and cockroaches

These insects are best excluded by physical means. Applications of insecticide around the outside walls of the laboratory can effectively repel ants. Cockroaches inside the laboratory must be trapped with baits or killed with recommended poisons.

VIRUS DISEASES

OCCURRENCE OF VIRUS *IN VITRO*

There is a variable concentration of virus in the cells of an intact plant. Many viruses are not seed-transmitted and do not infect the reproductive organs of plants. In particular, apical shoot and root meristems are liable to contain very little, or may even be virus-free. This is thought to be the main reason why plants obtained from cultured meristem tips are disease-free. Meristems may not always be free of virus: in a very early report, White (1934b) noted that Aucuba mosaic and tobacco mosaic virus occurred in the root tips of infected plants of tomato and persisted in the root cultures which were established from them. He suggested this could be a convenient way to multiply and maintain viruses for experimental purposes.

Even when explants are not free from virus at the time of excision, the infection may disappear from some or all cells as the tissues are being cultured. Why this should happen is not clear. It has been proposed that eradication could be:

- associated with cell injury caused by excising the explant (Mellor and Stace-Smith, 1977). The smaller the initial explant, the greater would be the metabolic changes in proportion to cell volume. This would explain why virus-free cultures are more likely to result from the use of small meristem tips.

- due to components of the culture medium inhibiting virus replication. Certain amino acids (Segretain and Hirth, 1953), and growth substances (Quak, 1961), particularly auxins (Hollings and Stone, 1965) and cytokinins (Milo and Srivastava, 1969a,b) have at various times been thought to be responsible.

> Evidence in favour of the latter explanation has come from the work of Antoniw *et al.* (1981). Proteins PR-1a and PR-1b, associated with the natural resistance of plant cells to virus, were found to occur in large amounts in cultured plant tissues in the absence of virus. That production of these resistance factors might be induced by auxins and cytokinins in the growth medium, was suggested by the discovery that injections of IAA, 2,4-D and BAP into tobacco leaves also stimulated the formation of PR-1a and possibly a small amount of PR-1b. Whatever the cause, virus eradication *in vitro*, when it occurs, can be rapid. Carnation meristems which appeared to carry carnation mottle viruses were noted to lose their infectivity after only 30 hours in culture (Hollings and Stone, 1964).

For whatever reason elimination occurs, tissue culture has become an important means of freeing plants from virus diseases. Possibly the significance of tissue culture methods will diminish as virus resistance becomes incorporated into plants by genetic engineering (Grumet, 1990).

Virus in callus tissues

Callus tissues established from virus-infected explants are usually infected and plants regenerated from such short-term cultures are unlikely to be virus-free (Langhans *et al.,* 1977). Healthy callus cultures can also be directly infected with virus if the tissue is slightly abraded and inoculated with a concentrated preparation. Continued replication of tobacco mosaic virus in the same tobacco callus over a ten year period has been recorded (Hildebrandt, 1977), but this situation is unusual. Most frequently the level of virus infection diminishes markedly as the tissue proliferates. Cells often become free from virus after only a short period in culture, or else the callus comes to be composed of a mosaic of healthy and virus-containing cells, even though uninfected cells are apparently susceptible to infection. How this situation arises is uncertain. Besides the reasons for virus elimination proposed above, it has been suggested that:

— cell growth proceeds more rapidly in callus cultures than viral replication. This could be because cultured cells have relatively low rates of amino acid and protein biosynthesis upon which the formation of virus particles depends (Kassanis, 1957).

— virus replication is inhibited by the meristematic nature of callus tissue. Virus is very often absent from whole plant meristems and young cells in actively-growing tissue cultures are more resistant to virus infection and multiplication than cells in older cultures (Hildebrandt, 1977). The biosynthesis of proteins and nucleic acids required for cell division might therefore be competitive with that necessary for virus formation (Wu *et al.*, 1960).

— cytoplasmic connections between cells (plasmodesmata) may not be universal in callus cultures, even though they are known to occur (Spencer and Kimmins, 1969). If cell to cell virus transfer occurs *via* plasmodesmata, then unlinked cells could be protected.

— there is an above average level of synthesis of resistance factors in some cells, associated with their state of cyto-differentiation.

METHODS OF ELIMINATION

Adventitious shoot initiation

Given that cultures may readily lose an initial virus infection, or become composed of some healthy and some infected cells, it is not surprising that the regeneration of virus-free plants has been reported from callus (Abo El-Nil and Hildebrandt, 1971b; Simonson and Hildebrandt, 1971), including that established from protoplasts (Shepard, 1975). However, callus-derived plants are not invariably virus-free (*e.g.* Davies and Allen, 1973) and furthermore they may frequently be genetically dissimilar to the original parental plant (Chapter 3). This has

mitigated against the use of callus cultures for practical virus eradication.

Regeneration from reproductive tissues. Viruses are often excluded from the nucellus or its adjacent tissues due to the absence of vascular connections with the rest of the plant, and in consequence are not seed-borne. There would therefore appear to be a fairly high probability of virus-free plantlets being regenerated from nucellus-derived callus *via* adventitious buds, or somatic embryos. Seedlings of *Citrus* and mango produced apomictically from the nucellus *in vivo* are often without virus infection (Maheshwari, 1950). Moreover Esan (1973) noted the absence of virus infection in seedlings of *Citrus* and *Citrus*-related species which were derived from somatic embryos arising directly on explanted nucellus tissue *in vitro*. Cultures derived from *Citrus* ovules can also be virus-free (Starrantino and Russo, 1983; Geraci and Tusa, 1988), but somatic embryogenesis in this genus would not be a practical way of obtaining virus-free clones because the plants so derived retain a juvenile and non-fruiting form for many years. A similar objection does not apply to grapevines (Mullins and Srinivasan, 1976).

Meristem-tip or shoot-tip grafting

The possible culture of isolated shoot tips for virus elimination was investigated by Morel and Martin (1952); but although they obtained shoots from shoot tip explants, they were unable to obtain rooted plantlets *in vitro*, and so grafted the shoots onto virus-free seedlings. This kind of micro-grafting has since been used by several workers to produce virus-free stocks in species where meristem tip culture has not been successful. Techniques are described in Chapter 2. For virus elimination, seeds that are not virus-infected are decapitated and used as the 'rootstocks' for graft unions. The scion can consist either of a meristem tip removed with aseptic precautions directly from a virus-infected mother plant, or of a small shoot that has resulted from *in vitro* culture of a meristem tip.

Micro-grafting has only been used in recent years where meristem culture has not proved possible, for instance in woody species. The direct transfer of shoot apices is difficult and demands particular dexterity. Survival rates of between 5 and 40 per cent are common (Murashige and Jones, 1974), and although this may be improved upon by utilising larger stem apices, virus elimination is then less likely.

Meristem-tip grafting was used by Murashige *et al.* (1972a) to produce and propagate virus-free *Citrus*. A mycoplasmal infection was eliminated from all the regenerated plants and in just over half of them, the exocortis viroid was also removed. Navarro *et al.* (1975) developed several methods of inserting shoot tips; by using *Poncirus trifoliata* seedlings as rootstocks, it was possible, because of their leaf shape, to detect adventitious shoots which did not originate from the scion. Virus-free clones of sweet oranges, mandarins and lemons have been obtained by these techniques (Navarro and Juarez, 1977). Unlike *Citrus* plants produced from somatic embryos, those obtained from shoot tip grafts do not have a protracted juvenility (Spiegel-Roy and Kochba, 1980). Shoot tip grafting methods have also been used to obtain virus-free apples (Alskief and Villemur, 1978; Huang and Millikan, 1979, 1980).

Meristem tip culture

Holmes (1948, 1955) found that he could eradicate spotted wilt disease from dahlia plants by rooting tip cuttings in soil, and success in obtaining virus-free plants of dahlia by shoot apex culture followed by grafting, led Morel and Martin (1955) to experiment again with shoot apex culture using six virus-infected varieties of potato. This time rooted shoots were produced that could be grown directly

into plants in which viruses originally present in the mother plant, were no longer detectable. This work, and Morel's success with shoot apex culture of different plant species, led other plant virologists to employ similar techniques. It was discovered that, providing small apical meristems were used, a high proportion of virus-free plants could often be procured. The range of plants which can be treated in this way has gradually increased as tissue culture procedures and media have been improved. The culture of very small shoot tips is now the most common method for obtaining virus-free plant material (Fig. 62). It is often combined with heat treatment of the mother plants (see later).

Cultures intiated with small shoot apices and carried out with the intention of virus eradication, have been variously termed in the literature. Names now frequently used are *meristem culture* (Wang and Hu, 1980) or *meristem tip culture*. The latter term was suggested by Hollings (1965) to distinguish between the culture of true meristematic domes and the actual tip cuttings usually removed from heat treated plants (see below) which include the meristem, together with one or more primordial leaves and adjacent stem tissue. Meristem tip is thus the

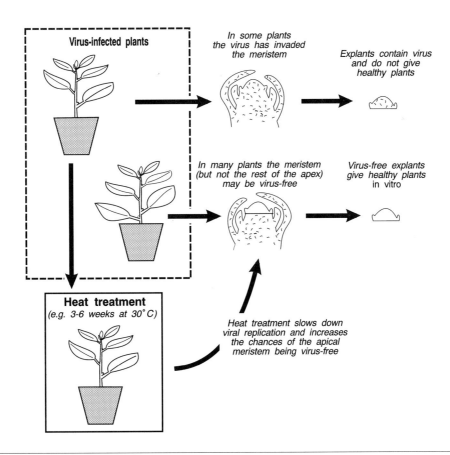

Fig. 62. Strategies for obtaining virus-free plants by meristem culture.

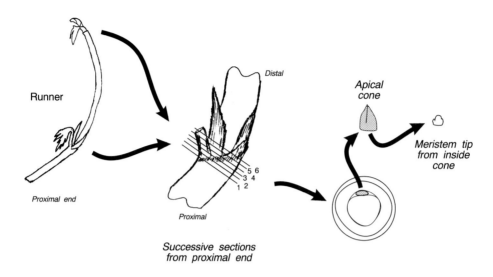

Fig. 63. A rapid method of isolating strawberry meristems (after McGrew, 1980).

more accurate term to describe the explants used in most cultures for virus elimination, but abbreviating 'meristem tip culture' to 'meristem culture' is without serious consequence. Either term conveniently distinguishes cultures commenced with the purpose of virus-removal, from those started for micropropagation. Unfortunately the terms 'meristemming' and 'mericloning' are widely accepted in the micropropagation of orchids (Chapter 17). Confusion may also arise when commercial tissue culture propagation is begun using fresh plant material and meristem tip explants are used in the first instance to obtain virus-free cultures. Shoots so obtained can then (after virus indexing — see later), serve as the starting point for propagation by shoot culture.

Once a virus-free culture is established, new cycles of propagation are best started with large shoot pieces because they adapt and grow much more rapidly in culture than small meristem explants. For the same reason, where freedom from virus is not essential, cultures intended to be used for plant propagation are commenced by using shoot tip explants. However, meristem tip explants are sometimes preferred for this purpose because, unlike the shoot tips of some plants, they can be obtained from stored dormant buds and are readily sterilised (Standardi and Catalano, 1985).

Explants. The growing point of a shoot consists of a dome of cells capable of cell division (the apical meristem). Beneath the meristem there are ridges of progressively increasing size, which represent newly formed leaf initials. Some workers have been able to initiate cultures

from just the apical meristematic dome (Smith and Murashige, 1970), but this is extremely difficult and rarely attempted. Growth of an isolated apical meristem is initially very slow. Normal practice is to excise an apical meristematic shoot dome plus one, two or three rudimentary leaf initials. As explained in the previous chapter, explants of this size are small and need to be removed under a dissecting microscope. As this is a slow and laborious task, it can be advantageous to explore different methods of dissection. For example, McGrew (1980) found that isolation of *Fragaria* meristems was very slow if they were exposed by progressively removing each layer of clasping stipules. It was possible to work much more rapidly and obtain 20 meristem tips per hour by approaching the meristematic area from the proximal side. The distal end of a runner shoot is held with fine watchmaker's tweezers and progressive transverse slices are then removed from the base of the shoot apex (the proximal end) working towards the apex, until the cone, which includes the apical dome and one or two embryonic leaves, can be teased out (Fig. 63). The same technique can be used to remove the meristem tips from lateral buds, further down strawberry runners (Kyte, 1983), and might be applied to the soft extension shoots of other plants.

Because the chance of survival is low, several meristem tips are usually transferred to culture at the same time, and placed on slopes of agar medium or on filter paper bridges above a liquid medium (Figs. 58 and 66). Appropriate media are discussed in Chapter 12.

The survival of meristem tip explants is usually greater when they have been taken from the growing points of plants, rather than from lateral buds. This may be because apical meristems are naturally in active growth, while meristems in lateral buds are dormant. The optimal length of meristem tip explants is usually between 0.2–1.0 mm, but the size actually used is dependent on plant species and the skill of the operator. The proportion of plants free from virus infection may be greater if small explants (*e.g.* 0.1 mm) are used, but survival *in vitro* and the number of rooted plantlets subsequently obtained is often better if larger (1 mm) shoot tips are cultured. In strawberry, nearly all plants obtained from 0.1 mm tips were free from pallidosis virus disease, but very few rooted plantlets were obtained. By contrast all the shoots produced from 2.5 mm tips formed roots, but only about 20% were virus-free. Combining the results of rooting with freedom with pallidosis, showed that the optimum length of tips for meristem culture was 0.5–0.9 mm (McGrew, 1980). Difficulties in inducing the shoots obtained from meristem culture to form roots, have now been largely overcome in many species by appropriate growth regulator treatments.

The concentration of virus in free-living plants, and the presence of virus in their shoot apices, is often reduced during summer months. This may be because high temperatures are less favourable for viral replication and actively growing shoot tips are more likely be free from virus than those that are dormant. Unfortunately the optimum time for minimal virus infection may not always coincide with the period when shoot apex culture is most readily initiated.

Fragmented shoot apices

If shoot tips (*ca.* 1 mm in length) of grapevines are cut into small pieces *in vitro*, new shoots are formed adventitiously from fragments of leaf primordia rather than by growth of the apical dome (Barlass and Skene, 1978, 1980a,b; Barlass *et al.*, 1981). This interesting variation of shoot tip culture (see Chapter 2) has been used instead of meristem tip culture by Barlass *et al.* (1982) for virus control. Plants regenerated from buds formed adventitiously on shoot apex tissue were found to be free from many economically significant virus infections.

Other virus-free explants

Leaves of virus-infected plants often have islands of dark green tissue where the pathogen has not penetrated. Using explants from such areas, Murakishi and Carlson (1979) cultured *Brassica*, *Petunia* and tobacco genotypes initially infected with, respectively, Turnip Yellow Mosaic virus, Tobacco Mosaic virus and Tobacco Etch virus.

Half of the tobacco, 16% of *Petunia* and 20% (visual assay) of *Brassica* regenerants were virus-free. Mori *et al.* (1982) found that they could also obtain some apparently virus-free callus colonies from protoplasts isolated from dark green areas of tobacco plants infected with Tobacco Mosaic virus. Most protoplasts from yellow-green areas of leaf were infected with virus, and many grew abnormally and did not form callus. Plants regenerated from the protoclones derived from dark green leaf areas were all virus-free, but only very few of those from virus-infected callus.

Heat therapy

Elevated temperatures have been found to be effective for the inactivation and eventual elimination of many (but not all) viruses and some systemic bacterial diseases (Sivanesan and Waller, 1986). For this purpose it is necessary to select a temperature regime which is above the optimum for growth but not lethal to the plant or the plant material. Parts of plants, such as cuttings (of sugar cane) or bulbs and tubers, are often placed in hot water or hot air at 50–52°C for periods of between 10 and 30 minutes. Although initial bud growth may be somewhat impaired by such treatment, shoots and hence plants can be obtained which are virus-free. Unfortunately heat treatment does not eliminate viruses from dormant seeds: it is most effective on actively-growing vegetative material.

Heat treatment may help to eliminate systemic bacteria (Damann, 1983) but has been ineffective for the removal of some plant viroids. These diseases may be eliminated if plants are kept at an abnormally low temperature (*e.g.* 1–5°C) (Purcell, 1977), especially if plants are treated simultaneously to low irradiance lighting and these treatments are followed by meristem tip culture (Paludan, 1980; Paduch-Chical and Kryczynski, 1987). Cold treatment may also eliminate virus infections but is less efficient than heat therapy (Barnett et al. 1975).

Treating whole plants

When whole plants are heat-treated, they are subjected to less extreme temperatures than those indicated above (between 32°C and 40°C for longer intervals of 4–30 weeks, according to the species). Some daily alternation of temperature is often employed (*e.g.* 36°C day/33°C night — Mellor and Stace-Smith, 1977). For species which are not heat-tolerant (*e.g.* hydrangeas, pelargoniums), high temperatures can often be alternated with more normal temperatures to minimise damage (*e.g.* 4 hrs at 40°C and 20 hrs at 16–20°C daily for 6 weeks — Hamid and Locke, 1961; 8 hrs at 40°C plus 8 hrs at 22°C/day, 8 hrs at 22°C/night — Walkey, 1976; 5 hr at 35°C in the light then 3 hr at 28°C in the dark alternating three times a day for at least 3 weeks — Appelgren, 1984). As exposure to high temperatures is debilitating, only sturdy plants with adequate carbohydrate reserves should be employed. Heat therapy alone can effectively eliminate about half the viruses known to infect vegetatively propagated plant species: rod and filamentous viruses tend to be heat resistant (Wang and Hu, 1980). Whole plants are usually treated with the object of obtaining virus-free cuttings, or scions, rather than freeing the entire plant from infection.

Heat treatment inhibits viral replication and simultaneously induces viral degradation, although the processes through which these results are achieved are not yet fully known. The reasons for describing heat treatment in this chapter are, firstly to show that there is often a simple alternative to *in vitro* culture for virus inactivation, and secondly because heat treatment is now often used in conjunction with meristem tip culture for virus eradication.

Heat treatment combined with meristem culture

Heat treatment is now very commonly combined with meristem culture for virus removal (Fig. 62). Whole plants are grown at elevated temperatures before meristem tips are excised for *in vitro* culture. Small explants from heat-treated plants may not survive well in culture, but às virus is less likely to be found in the apex, longer explants than normal can be taken safely and the chances of *in vitro* growth thereby increased. The combination of mother plant heat treatment plus meristem culture, is more effective for virus removal than either alone. It was first used by Thomson (1956a) to free potatoes from Virus Y.

Culturing meristems at elevated temperatures

Rather than subjecting mother plants to elevated temperatures, some workers have cultured *excised meristems* in an abnormally warm environment. As this can decrease the rate of explant survival, the method is not commonly used. Walkey and Cooper (1975) were able to free *Nicotiana rustica* from cucumber mosaic and alfalfa mosaic viruses (but not tobacco mosaic virus) by culturing meristems for 45 days at 32°C rather than at 22°C (at which temperature infection was not removed). Nine days at 40°C was an equally effective treatment, but if the tissues were returned to normal conditions before the virus was completely inactivated, an even greater level of infection than was present originally, could result (Walkey, 1976). A rapid replication of virus particles was probably made possible by the loss of a resistance factor from the plant

cells during their high temperature incubation (Walkey, 1980). Virus-free plants have also been regenerated from the organised callus cultures of *N. rustica* which resulted from treating germinating seeds to heat treatments *in vitro* (Cooper and Walkey, 1978). Yoshino and Hashimoto (1975) produced a high proportion of virus-free strawberry plants by culturing apical meristems of virus-infected cultivars at 25–28°C and then afterwards maintaining the plantlets produced at 38°C for 15 days.

In grapevine, the most effective temperature regime for eradication, varied from one virus to another (Barlass *et al.*, 1982). Cultures of fragmented shoot tips at 27°C day/20°C night, caused four viruses to be eliminated but not grape fan-leaf virus. This disease and three others were eradicated by culture at 35°C, but not grape yellow speckle virus (eliminated at 27/20°C). If grapevine plants were kept at 32/28°C before culture at 27/20°C, summer mottle virus was not eliminated, although it was removed by either of the direct culture systems.

Chemotherapy

The eradication of virus from cultured tissues and organs would obviously be greatly simplified if there were a chemical compound which could limit virus replication or movement in a wide range of plant species. It would simply be necessary to add the anti-viral agent to ordinary shoot cultures, or cultures of directly regenerating shoots. Time-consuming heat treatment of mother plants and difficult meristem cultures would then not be needed. However, although screening has been carried out in both public sector and industrial research establishments (Fraser and Whenham, 1978; Cassells and Long, 1980b; Simpkins *et al.*, 1981), only a few suitable compounds have been discovered.

The prevention of virus infection and spread in whole plants is influenced by 2-thiouracil. It may inhibit viral RNA synthesis, or, by becoming incorporated into the RNA, cause a virus to be non-infective (Barta *et al.*, 1981). Kassanis (Bawden, 1958) found that 2-thiouracil added to the culture medium helped to eliminate Potato Virus Y from tobacco callus. Similarly Norris (1953) and later Oshima and Livingstone (1961) reported that low concentrations of malachite green (diaminotri-phenyl-methane) seemed to assist in the removal of virus from potato shoot tips. But neither 2-thiouracil nor malachite green were reliable therapeutic agents *in vitro* (Thomson, 1956b; Oshima and Livingstone, 1961). Chrysanthemum plants free from chrysanthemum stunt viroid have been obtained by adding amantadine to a tissue culture medium (Horst and Cohen, 1980).

Ribavirin

The chemical ribavirin (Virazole®) (1-β-D–ribofuranos-yl-1,2,4- triazole-3-carboxamide) is the most successful antiviral agent to be used in tissue cultures, but it is not universally or sufficiently effective to be used in place of other techniques for virus elimination. Nevertheless, plants free from virus have been obtained from several different kinds of *in vitro* cultures to which ribavirin has been added. Cassells and Long (1980a,b) suggested that ribavirin might prevent virus infection moving from an explant into newly formed bud meristems and plantlets. The compound prevents virus replication in both plant and animal cells. Without the synthesis of new virus particles (Simpkins *et al.*, 1981) cells can become virus-free; pre-existing virus particles are naturally degraded, but a long period of culture may be necessary before the virus is eradicated.

Early successful results were reported by Lerch (1977) who found that tobacco plants infected with potato virus X, remained symptomless when grown *in vivo* in a nutrient solution containing 5 mg/l ribavirin, and Shepard (1977a). Shepard obtained virus-free plants from potato protoplast-derived callus cultures, infected with the same virus, when he added 100 mg/l ribavirin to the shoot regeneration medium. The compound was not effective when added to the medium in which the protoplasts were originally plated.

Ribavirin (1mM) combined with 0.1 mM adenine arabinoside (see below) eliminated tobacco mosaic virus from *Nicotiana tabacum* tissue cultures (Lozoya-Saldana *et al.,* 1984) and Walkey and Neely (1980) and Simpkins *et al.* (1981) found that 50 and 100 mg/l ribavirin added to the growth medium, could decrease the concentration or eliminate cucumber mosaic virus and alfalfa mosaic virus in callus cultures or in directly regenerated shoots of *Nicotiana rustica.*

Cassells and Long (1980a,b) were able to regenerate plantlets directly (or with minimum callus formation) from petioles of *Nicotiana tabacum* plants infected with potato virus Y and cucumber mosaic virus if they incorporated 50 mg/l ribavirin into the **MS** medium on which shoot formation was induced. A long period of exposure to the drug was required. Early withdrawal resulted in apparently-healthy shoots becoming reinfected.

Adding 35 mg/l ribavirin to the culture medium during protocorm proliferation of a *Cymbidium* orchid, caused a rapid and significant decrease in virus levels and a high proportion of virus-free protocorms (Albouy *et al.,* 1988). The compound was most effective during the first two protocorm subcultures and could not be left in the medium continuously because at 25–35 p.p.m., it inhibited long term protocorm formation. Ribavirin did not, however, eliminate leaf-roll virus from *Vitis vinifera* cultures, but only delayed the onset of symptom expression by about 50 days (Stevenson and Monette, 1983).

Cytokinins. Some authors have suggested that cytokinins may be responsible for the eradication of virus during meristem tip culture, but this is not a view which is widely supported. Ribavirin was noted by Simpkins *et al.* (*loc. cit.*) to have a cytokinin-like effect in their cultures. Shepard (1977a) reported that some plantlets regenerated from callus in the presence of the compound had a temporarily abnormal leaf structure. The symptoms he describes are similar to those noted on some ornamental species when plantlets are produced from shoot cultures in the presence of high cytokinin levels (see Chapter 15). Another antiviral agent vidarabine (adenine arabinoside), which was used by Stone *et al.* (1979) to produce virus-free sweet potato plants from tissue cultures, might also be expected from its structure to have cytokinin-like activity. Stone (1982) found that 1 mg/l vidarabine increased the survival in culture of meristem tips of a Peruvian vegetable, *Ullucus tuberosus*, and also seemed to increase the chances of producing plantlets free from several viruses.

Review articles

Reviews of the production of virus-free plants through tissue culture have been written by Walkey (1980, 1985) and Horst (1988).

VIRUS INDEXING

Meristem tip culture, even if combined with thermo- or chemo-therapy, is no guarantee that any particular plant obtained through *in vitro* culture will no longer carry virus infection. Heat treatment or meristem culture may reduce virus to a very low level in the tissues but the remaining inoculum may still be capable of fully infecting a plant. Frequently some plantlets are virus-free while a proportion is still infected. It is therefore necessary to test all regenerated plants to see that they do not harbour an infection. Testing for the presence of virus is known as virus indexing. Usually tests are delayed until plantlets have been transferred to the external *ex vitro* environment and grown for several weeks in pots. "Plants can only be said to be free of those viruses for which tests have been made and negative results obtained" (Hollings, 1965). For this reason plants which have been indexed and afterwards propagated by tissue culture, are sold as 'virus-tested' and are not described as being 'virus-free'.

Several techniques are now employed in virus indexing which vary somewhat in their applicability, according to the nature of the virus diseases being studied. They may be grouped under the following headings:

- tests using indicator plants;

- searching for the presence of virus particles by electron microscopy;

- serological tests;

- analysis of nucleic acids.

Indicator plants

Inoculation

Tests are usually carried out by inoculating plants which are known from experience to react to infection by the production of leaf lesions. These may be plants of the species being worked with, or plants of species such as *Chenopodium quinoa, Chenopodium amaranticola, Gomphena globosa* and *Nicotiana* spp. which react to a wide range of plant virus diseases. Certain other plants may be especially reactive to particular diseases. During the summer months, mistletoe shows distinct symptoms of chrysanthemum stunt virus: the chrysanthemum cultivar 'Carte Blanche' is a reliable year-round indicator (Raju and Trolinger, 1986).

So that they will show the maximum sensitivity to inoculation, test plants need to be grown rapidly without a check, in conditions where they are not exposed to virus infection. They are generally kept in the dark for 12–24 hours before being used. Inoculation consists of rubbing extracts of the plants suspected of being infected, together with an abrasive powder, onto leaves of indicator plants. Extracts are usually prepared in a phosphate buffer, to which is added an antioxidant, or a chelating agent, to enhance infectivity and overcome viral inactivators in the host. Bentonite clay powder is also often added to an inoculum to negate the effect of viral transmission inhibitors found in some donor plants.

The presence of virus in treated host plants is indicated by the development of lesions in 4–7 days. A longer interval may occur if meristem tip culture has resulted in the survival of an attenuated form of a virus. Stone (1978) therefore emphasizes that indicator plants should be kept for a sufficiently long period. A single test may not be sufficient to indicate the absence of virus. Appelgren repeated a test with *Chenopodium quinoa* at least two further times if no symptoms developed on the first occasion. While waiting for the development of viral symptoms, indicator plants must be isolated in insect-proof growth rooms or greenhouses, so the space occu-

pied by replicated tests can be considerable and costly. If plants are grown in greenhouses, sensitivity to virus can vary according to the time of year.

Indicator plants are widely used for routine virus indexing because the presence of many viruses can be assessed with 10–100 times greater sensitivity than simple serological tests or electron microscopic examination. However, some modified serological tests are now even more sensitive and have the advantage of giving more rapid results.

Grafting

Virus-infection is not always detected by inoculation onto indicator plants and may only be revealed when the plants to be tested (or parts of them) are grafted as either scions or rootstocks:

- to virus-free seedlings, or

- to plantlets of the same or similar species, known to indicate the presence of the disease.

Symptoms may only appear after a long interval; for example, those of sunblotch viroid can take up to 2 years to develop in grafted avocado indicator seedlings (Palukaitis *et al.*, 1981).

Damiano (1980a) used leaf grafting to virus-index strawberry plants resulting from meristem culture, before proceeding with large-scale micropropagation. The middle leaflet of a leaf was grafted onto a *Fragaria vesca* indicator plant in place of a similar one (Harris and King, 1942; Bringhurst and Voth, 1965; McGrew, 1967).

Electron microscopy

Examination of sap preparations or of sectioned plant material under an electron microscope, can reveal the presence of virus particles. Rod or filamentous forms are more readily distinguished than spherical ones, and observations are only reliable when relatively high concentrations of virus are present. A much more accurate assessment of infection can be obtained when electron microscopy is combined with serology.

Serological tests

Viral proteins act as antigens, *i.e.* substances capable of inducing an immune response in an animal by provoking the production of antibodies. Antibodies can be used in many ways to detect viruses in plant material.

The production of antibodies

Antisera containing globulin antibody proteins are obtained from the blood of animals (usually rabbits) which have been previously injected with small amounts of specific viral preparations. Once obtained, sera can be stored for long periods and used for repeated testing. Serological tests provide quick results and also have the advantage that viral antigens in suitably stored plant extracts, remain detectable for several days, whereas the infectivity required for tests with indicator plants is rapidly lost.

Antibodies against a particular virus, can also be prepared as monoclonal antibodies (MCA); some which are specific to certain plant viruses are available commercially. Monoclonal antibodies are prepared by immunising mice with an antigen, extracting lymphocyte spleen cells from the killed animal and fusing them with mice myeloma cells. The resulting somatic hybrid cells are cloned and screened for the production of antibody in the medium. Large scale production of MCA from a selected cell line can be obtained by injecting the hybridoma (antibody-secreting cell type) back into mice, subcutaneously or intraperitoneally, to induce a tumour or ascites. The antibody is contained in the animal's blood or abdominal fluid.

Tests using antibodies

Many different procedures have been devised to use antibodies for the detection of plant viruses. Wang and Hu (1980) describe seven methods commonly used: chloroplast agglutination, tube precipitation, quantitative precipitation, ring interface, gel-diffusion, immuno- osmophoresis and antibody tracer tests. Others are the passive haemagglutination (PHA) and latex flocculation tests.

> In the latter methods, red blood corpuscles which have been exposed to tannic acid (*i.e.* tanned), bentonite or polystyrene latex particles as carriers, are sensitized with antigens or serum globulin antibody preparations. This results in the ability to detect virus at lower concentrations than would be possible in normal precipitation tests (Abu Salih *et al.*, 1968a,b). PHA can be several hundred times more sensitive than tube precipitation tests but red blood cells have a short storage life, and a high concentration of antiserum globulin is required for initial preparation of the conjugates. The latex test can be advantageously used instead of PHA, although with slight loss of sensitivity. Nevertheless the test is simple and non-specific, can be performed in the field with a portable kit, and will detect the presence of more than one strain of virus. It can be 100–200 times more sensitive than gel immuno-diffusion assay, and the sensitivity has also been shown to be improved if the latex is coated with protein A (a protein obtained from the cell walls of *Staphylococcus* bacteria) before being linked to serum antibodies (Querfurth and Paul, 1979; Torrance, 1980a).

Two further kinds of serological technique have equal or greater, sensitivity than tests with indicator plants.

Enzyme-linked immunosorbent assay (ELISA)

ELISA was adapted from medical research for the study of plant viruses (Clark and Adams, 1977). ELISA tests are very sensitive and their introduction has made a major contribution to the diagnosis and measurement of virus infection in perennial and vegetatively propagated plants. They can be automated and provide rapid, simple, reliable and economical methods for the commercial virus indexing of ornamental horticultural plants (Newhart *et al.*, 1980).

For the detection of virus, ELISA is several thousand times more sensitive than immunodiffusion tests and has the advantage that concentrated plant extracts are not required. ELISA tests are also several hundred times more sensitive than flocculation tests and often more sensitive than infectivity tests (*e.g.* by a factor of about 600 times for lettuce necrotic yellows virus — Chu and Francki, 1982). Perhaps the greatest advantage over using indicator plants, is that ELISA results can be available in 24 hours, compared to 1–3 weeks.

Several different kinds of ELISA test have been developed. They all involve the use of an anti-virus antibody obtained from antisera, or as a monoclonal antibody. Two procedures are outlined below, one direct and the other indirect. In direct procedures an enzyme is directly attached to the antibody, while in indirect methods it is attached to an antiglobulin.

Double antibody sandwich method. The double antibody sandwich (DAS) form of ELISA is a direct method which uses the basic steps shown in Fig. 64. The technique is highly specific to just the strain of virus against which an antiserum was raised: different strains of the same virus are at best only weakly detected. It can be advantageous to distinguish between individual virus strains for research purposes and high specificity can prevent misidentification. However, in work aimed at producing healthy plants for vegetative propagation, it is important not to overlook the presence of any viral species. Here *indirect* ELISA tests are most suitable, as strains of virus similar to the one for which the antiserum or antisera were produced, are also detected.

The antiserum specificity of DAS can be overcome using a variation of the technique in which antibody is labelled with biotin instead of an enzyme. This avoids the need to prepare two viral antibodies and an anti-antibody. Biotin-labelled antibodies which become bound to virus are detected by using enzyme-labelled avidin and then a colorimetric or fluorimetric test for the enzyme (Zrein *et al.*, 1986).

Indirect ELISA. The indirect ELISA method follows the basic procedures shown in Fig. 65 (Van Regenmortel and Burckard, 1980; Koenig, 1981).

Simplified versions of indirect ELISA were described by Torrance (1980b, 1981) and Barbara and Clark (1982), but several variations have since been developed. Indirect ELISA is as sensitive as the double antibody sandwich method for the detection of virus, but yet also able to pick out heterologous viral strains. Its main advantages are that enzyme-labelled globulins are commercially available and a single one of these reagents can be used for the detection of different viruses. It is unecessary to prepare individual virus-specific immunoglobulin-enzyme conjugates for each virus or anti-serum to be tested.

Using ELISA with monoclonal antibodies

Monoclonal antibodies (MCAs) are selected to recognize specific conformational features of an antigen. In some cases an MCA raised against a particular virus may react with the protein shell of the virus, but not with the protein subunits of the coat if it is not dissociated. For this reason, many MCAs specific to plant viruses may only react with the antigen when used in a particular kind of ELISA test (Van Regenmortel *et al.*, 1988).

Serologically specific electron microscopy (SSEM)

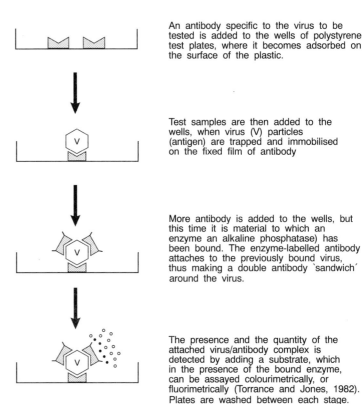

An antibody specific to the virus to be tested is added to the wells of polystyrene test plates, where it becomes adsorbed on the surface of the plastic.

Test samples are then added to the wells, when virus (V) particles (antigen) are trapped and immobilised on the fixed film of antibody

More antibody is added to the wells, but this time it is material to which an enzyme an alkaline phosphatase) has been bound. The enzyme-labelled antibody attaches to the previously bound virus, thus making a double antibody 'sandwich' around the virus.

The presence and the quantity of the attached virus/antibody complex is detected by adding a substrate, which in the presence of the bound enzyme, can be assayed colourimetrically, or fluorimetrically (Torrance and Jones, 1982). Plates are washed between each stage.

Fig. 64. The double antibody sandwich ELISA test for viruses.

In early attempts to combine electron microscopy (EM) with serology, virus/antiserum precipitates were dried on grids for examination. Viewing was difficult and the limit of detection no greater than where virus preparations were applied to grids without antiserum (Derrick, 1973). The analytical advantage of combined EM-serology was realised by simply pre-coating EM grids with an adsorbed film of antiserum specific for a particular virus (or by coating first with Protein A and then with specific antiserum — Gough and Shukla, 1980). When such grids are floated on extracts from virus-infected tissue, virus particles are specifically attached and concentrated *(trapped)* on the grid surface. In other techniques virus particles attached to a grid are coated with antibody and said to be *decorated* when viewed under the microscope, or antiserum is mixed with virus particles before placement on the grid, causing them to appear in clumps.

SSEM (or immunoelectron microscopy) techniques are probably the most sensitive methods yet available for detecting the presence of virus, and often have about twice the sensitivity of ELISA. SSEM is a quick and reliable test and the presence of several different viruses can be detected simultaneously. According to Thomas (1980), it is simpler than ELISA because less preparation is required and there are fewer steps in sample analysis. It also uses less antiserum and can be completed in one day. The obvious disadvantage is that an expensive electron microscope is required.

Immunoelectron microscopy techniques have been improved by adding gold labelling, Protein A, or antiglubulin antibody to antisera. This enables virus particles to be visualised under the electron microscope: it is even possible to determine the exact position of antigenic sites on viruses.

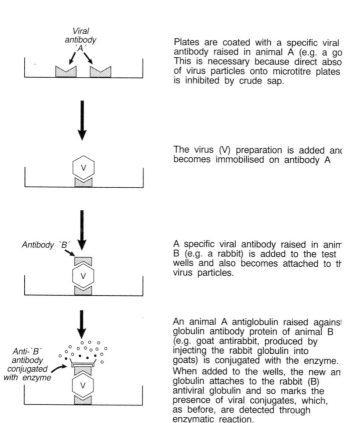

Plates are coated with a specific viral antibody raised in animal A (e.g. a go This is necessary because direct abso of virus particles onto microtitre plates is inhibited by crude sap.

The virus (V) preparation is added anc becomes immobilised on antibody A

A specific viral antibody raised in anim B (e.g. a rabbit) is added to the test wells and also becomes attached to th virus particles.

An animal A antiglobulin raised agains' globulin antibody protein of animal B (e.g. goat antirabbit, produced by injecting the rabbit globulin into goats) is conjugated with the enzyme. When added to the wells, the new an' globulin attaches to the rabbit (B) antiviral globulin and so marks the presence of viral conjugates, which, as before, are detected through enzymatic reaction.

Fig. 65. One method of indirect ELISA.

The serological diagnosis of plant viruses is reviewed by Van Regenmortel *et al.* (1988).

Nucleic acid analysis

Animal antibodies are only created against foreign proteins. Thus although antisera can be produced against viruses for later serological tests, they cannot be obtained for viroids, which consist only of RNA and have no associated protein molecules. The presence of viroids can be ascertained by extraction of leaf nucleic acids or double stranded RNA (dsRNA) (Morris and Dodds, 1979; Hicks *et al.*, 1988), followed by separation by polyacryamide gel electrophoresis ('PAGE'), and staining to identify the bands produced. Disease diagnosis by dsRNA analysis is based on the premise that high molecular weight (0.1×10^6) dsRNA is only found in plants infected with RNA viruses or virus-like agents (Jordan, 1986). A more sensitive method has been used to index

the viroids causing chrysanthemum stunt (Palukaitis and Symons, 1979) and sunblotch disease of avocados (ASBV) (Palukaitis *et al.* 1981; Allen and Dale, 1981). It consists of preparing a ^{32}P-labelled complementary DNA (c-DNA) from the viroid RNA template by using a reverse transcriptase enzyme (which makes DNA copies of RNA chains). Once prepared, the ^{32}P-cDNA could be used to assay the concentration of viroid RNA in partially purified nucleic acid extracts of avocado leaves. Viroid specific DNA/RNA hybridisation occurred, the extent of which was measured by resistance to nuclease enzyme digestion. Hybridisation analysis was found to be a rapid and reliable procedure for detection of ASBV which could indicate the presence of the viroid in seven days, compared to the two years required for indexing by graft-transmission tests.

Similar nucleic acid hybridisation techniques (often called *spot* or *blot* hybridization) have been developed for plant viruses. Samples of sap from an infected plant are spotted (or dotted) onto a nitrocellulose plate which is afterwards baked. A complementary DNA 'probe' labelled with ^{32}P or ^{3}H is then introduced and hybridization to viral RNA assessed by autoradiography. Spot hybridisation is usually more sensitive than ELISA for the detection of virus: the limit can be as low as 5–10 pg in a single spot (Wang *et al.*, 1988). Although it is useful where conventional tests do not detect viroids, it is more complicated and time cosuming than ELISA (Lawson, 1986).

PRACTICAL ACHIEVEMENTS

Lists of some of the plants freed from known virus diseases by meristem culture or by meristem culture combined with heat therapy, were given by Quak (1977), Walkey (1980,1985), Kartha (1981a) and Villalobos Arámbula (1984) . They include many important ornamental plants, and food and fruit crops. Methods of freeing vegetatively-propagated plants from viruses have since become standardised and used as a matter of routine by larger plant tissue culture laboratories and organisations supplying planting material to the horticultural trade. The number of different kinds of plants from which viruses have been eliminated using tissue culture techniques is now very high.

Most virus diseases are not transmitted through the seeds of plants. Plants subjected to meristem culture are therefore mainly those which are normally vegetatively propagated, where the problems of virus eradication are greatest. It may, however, be advantageous to eliminate viruses from some seed-propagated crops (*e.g.* cauliflowers) where clones are maintained for breeding purposes. The improved ability to propagate woody plants *in vitro* has caused increased interest in producing virus-tested stock plants of woody ornamentals for distribution to nurserymen.

Ornamentals. Chrysanthemum and carnation, ornamentals which are intensively grown in greenhouses in Europe and North America, are now almost invariably grown from cuttings derived from virus-tested stock plants. Large distributors carry out their own meristem cultures and virus testing programmes. Growers either purchase directly from them or, in some instances, may procure virus-tested material from tissue culture laboratories to propagate in a limited way themselves.

Field crops. Besides being used for ornamentals, meristem culture techniques are being used routinely to ob-

tain virus-tested planting material of several major field crops. Virus diseases of potatoes, even those which produce no symptoms, are recognised to be capable of causing losses of yield in all varieties. For many years steps have been taken to propagate potatoes needed for 'seed' purposes in environments where aphids capable of distributing virus infection are uncommon. *In vitro* techniques now not only provide an effective means of removing virus infections, but can also be used to maintain virus tested stocks. Micropropagation is being used for this purpose on commercial varieties and on potatoes collected as a source of germplasm for breeding programmes. Many of the latter have been in danger of being lost as a result of disease (Westcott *et al.*, 1977a,b). Potatoes freed from virus diseases may become more prone to fungi, so that, even though their yielding potential is increased, crops may need to be grown with greater attention to other cultural practices such as fungicidal sprays. Some of the common potato viruses have been easy to eliminate, others have proved more obstinate. In order of increasing difficulty of elimination they are:

> potato leaf roll (PLRV), potato virus A (PVA), PVY, aucuba mosaic, PVM, PVX, PVS, spindle tuber virus (PSTV) (Mellor and Stace-Smith, 1977).

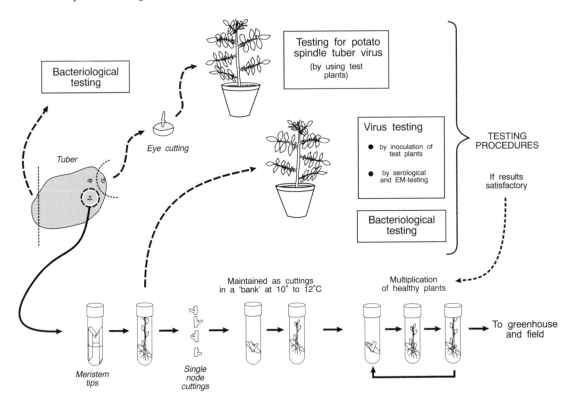

Fig. 66. Virus and bacteriological testing of potato stocks followed by *in vitro* multiplication [after Kristensen, 1984].

Virus elimination by meristem culture followed by rapid clonal propagation by tissue culture techniques is now commonly used for the multiplication of strawberries intended for field planting. The importance of virus free-dom in cassava is realised and new varieties distributed to growers in the tropics can be virus-tested by meristem culture (Kartha and Gamborg, 1975b; Nestel and Cock, 1976; Bozzini, 1980), before being multiplied rapidly from small stem cuttings (Howland, 1976).

Combined testing

Plant pathologist responsible for the phytosanitary status of a crop will often combine virus testing with a more general programme for investigating the health of plant-ing stocks. Methods employed by Kristensen (1984) pro-vide a good example of how in vitro culture may need to be integrated with both bacteriological and viral testing to ensure that only disease-free plantlets are used for eventual micropropagation. Indexing may have to be carried out at more than one stage to ensure that diseased stocks are detected (Fig. 66).

REVIEW ARTICLES

One or more of the following reviews of virus elimination through plant tissue culture, should be consulted by those seeking further information:

- Hollings (1965). An excellent review of methods of virus elimination and control, much of which is still relevant.

- Murashige and Jones (1974). Cell and organ cul-ture methods in virus desease therapy.

- Ingram (1977). A good review of the applications of tissue culture in plant pathology.

- Quak (1977). Meristem culture and virus-free plants.

- Ingram and Helgeson (eds.) 1980. A book on tissue culture methods for plant pathologists, and particularly chapters by:

• Walkey (1980). Production of virus-free plants by tissue culture;

• Dale et al. (1980). Pathogen elimination and in vitro plant storage in forage grasses and legumes.

- Torrance and Jones (1981). Developments in se-rological methods suited for use in routine testing for plant viruses.

- Clark (1981). Daie and Wyse (1982). Reviews of immunoassay (ELISA) techniques.

- Walkey (1985). Chapters on virus detection and virus elimination.

MAINTENANCE OF VIRUS-FREE PLANTS

Plants from which viruses or virus-like organisms have been eliminated can easily become re-infected. Any plant material discovered to harbour virus should therefore be burnt or carefully transported well away from the site. Virus-indexed plants which are to be used as stocks for future micropropagation must be kept in scrupulously clean conditions. They should be grown in sterilised soil in screened greenhouses or growth rooms, and subjected to regular pesticide sprays to prevent attack by insect or nematode vectors. Although regular observations should be made for symptoms of pests and disease, plants must be handled as little as possible to reduce the chances of the mechanical transmission of virus.

It is usually recommended that in vitro cultures and stock plants which are to serve as the stocks for continued micropropagation should be re-indexed for virus at least every twelve months, even though measures to prevent infection may have been taken.

Table 8. Some reports on the phytotoxicity of antibiotics, and their use against contaminants of plant tissue cultures.

Compound	Safety or phytotoxicity reported				Success in removing microbial contaminants				
	Effect	Rate μg/ml	Plant/Result	Reference	Rate μg/ml	Plant	Organism	Results	Reference
Amphotericin B	Safe	—	Plant cell culture	Duchefa catalogue					
	Inhibited seed germin.	1	Vanda tricolour orchid	Brown et al. (1982)					
	Normal growth after delay	10	Cymbidium shoot tips						
Ampicillin (sodium)	Safe	—	Plant cell culture	Duchefa catalogue	400	Petunia protoplasts	Contaminants	Bactericidal (with other compounds)	Davey et al. (1976)
	Safe	—	N. plumbaginifolia	Pollock et al. (1983)					
Augmentine	Safe	—	Plant cell culture	Duchefa catalogue					
Bacitracin	Growth inhibited	100	Sunflower	Rier & Henderson (1956)	100	Helianthus annuus	Contaminants	Bactericidal	Rier & Henderson (1956)
	Growth stimulation	5	Rumex acetosa callus	Nickell (1952)					
Carbenicillin (sodium)	Stimulated plant growth	50–100	Catharanthus roseus	Carew & Patterson (1970)	50–200	Catharanthus roseus	Bacteria	Bactericidal	Carew & Patterson (1970)
					500–1000	Nicotiana protoplasts	Agrobacterium	Bactericidal	Davey et al. (1980)
	Toxic	>1000	Beta vulgaris	Okkels & Pederson (1988)	500	Beta vulgaris	Agrobacterium	50% inhibition	Okkels & Pederson (1988)
	Toxic	1500	Daucus carota	Okkels & Pederson (1988)	—	Triticum aestivum	Agrobacterium	Bacteristatic	Mathias & Boyd (1986)
	Growth promotion	216 mM	Bouvardia ternifolia,	Robert et al. (1986)	—	Solanum nigrum	Agrobacterium	Bactericidal	Wei et al. (1986)
	Safe	—	N. plumbaginifolia	Pollock et al. (1983)	400	Solanum tuberosum	Agrobacterium	Bactericidal	Visser (1991)
					500	Solanum tuberosum	Agrobacterium	Bactericidal	McCormick (1991)
Cefalexin monohydrate	Safe	—	Plant cell culture	Duchefa catalogue					
Cefotaxime (sodium) (only suitable if filter sterilised)	Safe	<500	Malus (M.26)	Poulsen (1988)	75–100	Malus (M.26)	Two bacteria	Bactericidal	Poulsen (1988)
	Stimulated growth	60–100	Triticum aestivum callus	Mathias & Boyd (1986)	200	Solanum tuberosum	Agrobacterium	Bactericidal	Stiekema et al. (1988)
	Increased morphogenesis	500	Linum usitatissimum	Xiang-can et al. (1989)	200	Solanum tuberosum	Agrobacterium	Bactericidal	Visser (1991)
		—	Tissue culture tested	Sigma catalogue	—	Syngonium, Ficus	Several	Bacteristatic	Fisse et al. (1987)
	Toxic	>1000	Beta vulgaris	Okkels & Pederson (1988)	—	Triticum aestivum	Agrobacterium	Bacteristatic	Mathias & Boyd (1986)
	Toxic	300	Daucus carota		90	Beta vulgaris	Agrobacterium	50% inhibition	Okkels & Pederson (1988)
					200	Beta vulgaris	Agrobacterium	Bactericidal	Lindsey et al. (1991)
					200	Malus × domestica	Agrobacterium	Bactericidal	James & Dandekar (1991)
Cefoxitin	Safe	100	N. plumbaginifolia	Pollock et al. (1983)	500	Cacao	Several	Bacteristatic	Duhem et al. (1988)
Cefsulodine	Safe	100	N. plumbaginifolia	Pollock et al. (1983)					
Cephaloridine	Safe	—	Plant cell culture	Duchefa catalogue	—	Syngonium, Ficus	Several	Bacteristatic	Fisse et al. (1987)

Compound	Safety or phytotoxicity reported				Success in removing microbial contaminants				
	Effect	Rate μg/ml	Plant/Result	Reference	Rate μg/ml	Plant	Organism	Results	Reference
Cephaloridine (cont.)						*Philodendron*	Several	Bacteristatic	
Cephalosporin C	Safe	<500	*Malus* (M.26)	Poulsen (1988)	150	*Malus* (M.26)	Two bacteria	Bactericidal	Poulsen (1988)
Chloramphenicol	Safe	—	Plant cell culture	Duchefa catalogue					
	Toxic	5–10	*N. plumbaginifolia*	Pollock *et al.* (1983)					
	Toxic	8	*Beta vulgaris*	Okkels & Pederson (1988)					
	Toxic	25	*Daucus carota*						
	Toxic	50	*Helianthus annuus*	Phillips *et al.* (1981)					
Chlortetracycline		—				*Malus*	*Acinetobacter*	Bacteristatic	Zimmerman (1984)
Clindamycine HCl	Safe	—	Plant cell culture	Duchefa catalogue					
Doxycycline HCl						*Gerbera*	—	Bacteristatic	Podwyszynska & Hempel (1987)
Erythromycin	Toxic	80	*N. plumbaginifolia*	Pollock et al. (1983)	—	*N. plumbaginifolia*	Gram +ve bacteria	Bactericidal	Pollock *et al.* (1983)
Gentamycin (sulphate)	Safe	—	Tissue culture tested	Sigma catalogue					
	Toxic	>10	*Datura innoxia*	Horsch & King (1983)					
	Inhibited seed germination	50	*Vanda* tricolor orchid	Brown *et al.* (1982)					
	Toxic to shoot tips	5–50	*Cymbidium* orchid						
	Unacceptable results	—	Shoot tip cultures	Knauss & Knauss (1980)					
Griseofulvin	Safe	2–5	*Catharanthus roseus*	Carew & Patterson (1970)	2.5	*Catharanthus roseus*	—	Not phytotoxic	Carew & Patterson (1970)
Hygromycine B	Inhibited callus formation	15–30	*Arabidopsis thaliana*	Patton & Meinke (1988)					
	Toxic	5	*Beta vulgaris*	Okkels & Pederson (1988)					
	Toxic	9	*Daucus carota*						
	Inhibited callus formation	<10	*Solanum tuberosum*	Visser (1991)					
	Inhibited callus formation	20	*Brassica napus*	Rouan & Guerche (1991)					
	Inhibited embryogenic callus growth	20	*Dactylis glomerata*	Horn (1991)					
	Inhibit. protocallus growth	30	*Oryza sativa*	Kyozuki & Sihimamoto (1991)					
	Inhibit. protocallus growth	20	*Arabidopsis thaliana*	Damm & Willmitzer (1991)					

Table 8. (continued) Antibitics in tissue culture.

Compound	Safety or phytotoxicity reported				Success in removing microbial contaminants				
	Effect	Rate µg/ml	Plant/Result	Reference	Rate µg/ml	Plant	Organism	Results	Reference
Kanamycin (sulphate)	Safe	—	Tissue culture tested	Sigma catalogue					
	Toxic	—	Datura innoxia	Horsch & King (1983)					
	Inhibited morphogenesis	50–200	Arabidopsis thaliana	Patton & Meinke (1988)					
	Stimulated caulogenesis / Stimulated morphogenesis	1.43 / 4.3–7.2	N. tabacum microcalli / N. tabacum callus / D. carota callus	Owens (1979a,b)					
	Toxic	150	Beta vulgaris	Okkels & Pederson (1988)					
	Toxic	1	Daucus catota						
	Safe	4	Vigna radiata seedlings	Mathews (1988)					
	Toxic / Safe	10–50 / 2000	Brassica juncea explants / B. juncea seedlings						
	Toxic	8	N. plumbaginifolia	Pollock et al. (1983)					
	Inhibited callus growth	20–60	Malus × domestica	James & Dandekar (1991)					
	Inhibited callus growth	100	Beta vulgaris	Lindsey et al. (1991)					
	Inhibited callus growth	100	Lycopersicon esculentum	McCormick (1991)					
	Inhibited callus growth	<50	Solanum tuberosum	Visser (1991)					
	Safe	200	Dactylis glomerata	Horn (1991)					
Lincomycin HCl	Safe	—	Plant cell culture	Duchefa catalogue					
Oligomycine	Safe	—	Plant cell culture	Duchefa catalogue					
Oxytetracycline	Safe	2.5–5	Catharanthus roseus	Carew & Patterson (1970)	2.5–5	Catharanthus roseus	—	Slight phytotoxicity	Carew & Patterson (1970)
					—	Prunus avium	Several	—	Cornu & Michel (1987)
Neomycin (sulphate)	Toxic	50	Prunus avium	Cornu & Michel (1987)					
	Safe	—	Plant cell culture	Duchefa catalogue					
	Toxic	2	N. plumbaginifolia	Pollock et al. (1983)					
Nystatin	Safe	—	Plant cell culture	Duchefa catalogue					
	Prevented seed germin.	25	Cattleya elongata	Brown et al. (1982)					
Paromomycin (sulphate)	Safe	—	Plant cell culture	Duchefa catalogue					
	Inhibited callus growth	20	Brassica napus	Rouan & Guerche (1991)					

Compound	Safety or phytotoxicity reported				Success in removing microbial contaminants				
	Effect	Rate µg/ml	Plant/Result	Reference	Rate µg/ml	Plant	Organism	Results	Reference
Penicillin	Growth stimulation	10	Rumex acetosa	Nickell (1952)					
	Stimulated plant growth	10	Helianthus tuberosus	Phillips et al. (1981)					
	Inhibited tumour tissue	500	Helianthus annuus	De Ropp (1949)					
	Stimulated normal tissue	500	Vinca rosea						
Penicillin G (Na salt)	Safe	—	Cell culture tested	Duchefa catalogue					
	Safe	100	N. plumbaginifolia	Pollock et al. (1983)					
	Prevented seed germin.	100	Cattleya elongata	Brown et al. (1982)					
	Inhibited organogenesis	100	Cymbidium callus						
	Growth promotion	—	Bouvardia ternifolia,	Robert et al. (1986)					
	Promoted N reductase	100	Sedum telephinum callus	Santos & Salema (1989)					
Phosphomycin	Stimulated plant growth	—	Helianthus tuberosus	Phillips et al. (1981)					
Piperacillin					100–200	Prunus persica	—	—	Scortichini & Chiariotti (1988)
Polymixin B (sulphate)	Safe	—	Cell culture tested	Duchefa catalogue	25–50	Nauclea diderrichii	Bacteria	Control	Mathias et al. (1987)
Polymixin E	Toxic	10	N. plumbaginifolia	Pollock et al. (1983)	5	N. plumbaginifolia	Gram +ve bacteria	Control	Pollock et al. (1983)
Rifampicin	Increased tissue browning	25–50	Nauclea diderrichii	Mathias et al. (1987)	25	Nauclea diderrichii	Bacteria	Effect. control	Mathias et al. (1987)
	Toxic	0.7	N. plumbaginifolia	Pollock et al. (1983)	50	Helianthus tuberosus	—	Bactericidal	Phillips et al. (1981)
	Toxic	10	N. plumbaginifolia	Pollock et al. (1983)	20	Helianthus tuberosus	—	Bacteristatic	Phillips (1987)
	Safe	—	Tissue culture tested	Sigma catalogue		Gerbera	—	Bacteristatic	Podwyszynska & Hempel (1987)
	Safe	—	Plant cell culture	Duchefa catalogue	50	Prunus avium	Several	Bacteristatic	Cornu & Michel (1987)
	Toxic	50	Prunus avium (2 clones)	Cornu & Michel (1987)	250–400	Malus (M.26)	Two bacteria	Bactericidal	Poulsen (1988)
	Toxic	>20	N. plumbaginifolia	Pollock et al. (1983)	50	Aconitum noveboraceae	Contaminants	Effect. control	Cervelli (1987)
					10–50	Camellia japonica	Bacteria	Bactericidal	Haldeman et al. (1987)
Spectinomycin sulphate	Toxic	100–500	Cattleya seedlings	Thurston et al. (1979)					
	Safe	—	Cell culture tested	Duchefa catalogue					

Table 8. (continued)   Antibitics in tissue culture.

Compound	Safety or phytotoxicity reported				Success in removing microbial contaminants				
	Effect	Rate µg/ml	Plant/Result	Reference	Rate µg/ml	Plant	Organism	Results	Reference
Streptomycin (sulphate)	Toxic	>2.5	*Catharanthus roseus*	Carew & Patterson (1970)	100	*Syngonium, Ficus*	Several	Bactericidal	Fisse *et al.* (1987)
	Growth stimulation	5	*Rumex acetosa* callus	Nickell (1952)	200	*Philodendron*	Several	Bactericidal	Fisse *et al.* (1987)
	Toxic	>0.5	*N. tabacum* callus	Umiel & Goldner (1976) Zomski & Umiel (1978)	<2.5	*Catharanthus roseus*	Bacteria	Bactericidal	Carew & Patterson (1970)
	Damage to plastids	>1.75	*N. tabacum* callus						
	Toxic	>10	*Helianthus tuberosus*	Phillips *et al.* (1981)					
	Toxic	25	*Prunus avium*	Cornu & Michel (1987)					
	Safe	<2.5	*Catharanthus roseus*	Carew & Patterson (1970)					
	Slight growth inhibition	500	*Datura innoxia*						
	Toxic	10–20	*Catharanthus roseus*						
	Safe	—	Plant cell culture	Duchefa catalogue					
	Toxic	24	*Beat vulgaris*	Okkels & Pederson (1988)					
	Toxic	45	*Daucus carota*						
	Stimulated caulogenesis	50 µM	Tobacco leaf sections	Owens (1979b)					
	Toxic (explant dip + incorporation in medium)	100–200	*Prunus persica*	Scortichini & Chiariotti (1988)					
Terramycin	Growth stimulation	5	*Rumex acetosa* callus	Nickell (1952)					
Tetracycline HCl	Toxic	—	Several genera	Bastiaens *et al.* (1983)	50–200	*Prunus avium*	Several	Little phytotoxicy	Cornu & Michel (1987)
	Safe	—	Cell culture tested	Duchefa catalogue					
	Toxic	32	*Beta vulgaris*	Okkels & Pederson (1988)					
	Toxic	45	*Daucus carota*						
	Toxic	50–200	*Prunus avium*	Cornu & Michel (1987)					
	Toxic	5	*N. plumbaginifolia*	Pollock *et al.* (1983)					
Trimethoprim	Toxic	90	*N. plumbaginifolia*	Pollock et al. (1983)	30	*N. plumbaginifolia*	Bacteria	Also used in mixtures	Pollock *et al.* (1983)
	Toxic	435	*N. debneyi* protoplasts	Scowcroft & Larkin (1980)					
Vancomycin HCl	Toxic to shoot tips	50	*Cymbidium* orchid	Brown *et al.* (1982)	500	*Arabidopsis thaliana*	*Agrobacterium*	Slight phytotoxicity	Patton & Meinke (1988)
	Safe	—	Plant cell culture	Duchefa catalogue					
	Toxic	>100	*N. plumbaginifolia*	Pollock *et al.* (1983)					

6

Storing and Distributing Clonal Material

Plant material is stored as both produce intended for future consumption, and as a resource for further propagation. Reserves are necessary for the latter purpose:

1. To allow planting to be delayed until climatic conditions are again favourable, or until there is a renewed demand for the plant, or crop. Seed or vegetative planting material usually only needs to be stored for a short while for this purpose.

2. To conserve stocks of horticulturally and agriculturally interesting species or varieties. Seed or vegetative material needs to be multiplied and maintained while interest in the species or variety continues.

3. To retain genotypes for as long as they are needed in immediate plant breeding programmes.

4. To preserve the widest possible range of genes (*germplasm*) for possible use in the future. Individual species, varieties, cultivars or ecotypes may need to be preserved continuously.

Tissue culture provides new methods of storing the plant material needed for many purposes connected with propagation: the 'produce' of a tissue culture laboratory (*i.e.* the plantlets intended for sale), can also be stored for a short period.

SHORT-TERM STORAGE

Desiccation of seed embryos

Since 1982, much research has been devoted to methods by which somatic embryos might be sown directly into soil, and there has been limited success in sowing dried naked embryos, or embryos surrounded by a protective capsule (see Chapter 14). For the ultimate commerciali-sation of these techniques, it will be essential to be able to store somatic embryos reliably. Ideally they should be able to survive as long as true seeds, but even if this were not possible, short term storage would be necessary to accumulate sufficient stocks, and to allow for delays

163

between production and sowing. A short period of dormancy has been induced in some somatic embryos by desiccation, but periods of successful storage so far come nowhere near the intervals over which the embryos in dried seeds maintain their viability.

Attempts to induce dormancy in encapsulated somatic embryos have included the use of abscisic acid (ABA) (Chapter 11), and drying. Non-desiccated embryos have been stored for short periods, but desiccated embryos of several plants have been found to have relatively short shelf lives. Gray (1987b), for example, found that when

orchardgrass embryos were dried to 13% water content, 18% germinated after 7 days, but only 4% after 14 days. However, *Medicago sativa* embryos matured in the presence of abscisic acid and dried to a moisture content of 8–15%, have remained fully viable at room temperature and humidity for 12 months (Redenbaugh *et al.*, 1991). Dried embryos may survive for longer periods if they are encapsulated in a polymer coating (Kitto and Janick, 1985a,b). Embryo desiccation in discussed further in Chapter 14 in relation to somatic embryos being sown directly into soil.

SHORT TO MEDIUM-TERM STORAGE

Providing due precautions are taken, the genotype of plants propagated by node or shoot culture can be preserved without change. This kind of *in vitro* culture can therefore be used to maintain genotypes over long periods. However, it would be costly to use normal methods of shoot culture, involving frequent subcultures, for preserving many different kinds of plants. There would also be a high risk of losing material through equipment failures, the contamination of cultures, or through mistakes in labelling. Fortunately several ways have been found to reduce the rate of growth of cultured material so that it can be kept unattended for moderate lengths of time.

Species vary in the length of time during which their cultures can be stored: periods of between 6 and 24 months are frequently described. Single shoots, unrooted shoot clusters, somatic embryos or rooted plantlets are suitable for storage. The storage of plantlets is frequently most satisfactory.

MINIMAL GROWTH TECHNIQUES

There are various ways in which the life of cultured tissues or organs can be extended.

1. Laissez-faire

At the very simplest, cultures can be left untouched on the shelf of the growth room. Their growth slows as the medium is depleted: shoots or tissues stay alive until they become desiccated; or until the medium is exhausted or becomes toxic. Drying can be prevented or minimised by using appropriate closures. Loose fitting lids are inappropriate; instead, tubes should be sealed with caps, or film,

which allow gaseous exchange but prevent the escape of water vapour. Gunning and Lagerstedt (1986) record the following storage times:

Mentha spp.	6–13 months
Rubus spectabilis	12–15 months
'Merton' thornless blackberry	13–16 months
Vaccinium ovatum	17 months

Rooted plantlets of various *Pistacia* species could be stored for one year under normal culture conditions (Barghchi, 1986b), while those of *Coffea arabica*, not exceeding 3–4 cm in height, were maintained at 26°C under 16 h 7500 lux lighting, for more than 2 years with only one transfer on the root-inducing medium (Kartha *et al.*, 1981). Culture tubes were fitted with screw caps.

2. Control of temperature and lighting

Intervals between transfers can often be greatly reduced by keeping cultures in weak light (or in the dark) and at a temperature which is less than that which is optimal for active growth. Whether dark or light storage is preferable, and the most suitable temperature for storage, depends on genotype.

Walk-in insulated storage rooms are recommended for tissue culture laboratories handling large numbers of plants. A cold room should be equipped with racks like a growth room, but only low wattage lighting (a flux density of *ca.* 10–35 $\mu mol\ m^{-2}\ s^{-1}$; daylength 12–16 h, or possibly shorter) needs be provided, and some plants can be stored in the dark (see below). Chilled air should be circulated with a fan. One or two rooms may be required, depending on the species which are being grown, and whether they all store best at a temperature close to 0°C, or whether some require a more elevated temperature.

Expense must also be weighed against the risk of loss: it is clearly better to safeguard against equipment failure by apportioning similar cultures between two rooms with a similar environment, if that is possible. In practice however, warming of a cold room to ambient temperature will not harm the cultures and they can usually be returned to cold storage after transfer to fresh medium. Alarms can be fitted to the room to warn against overheating and overcooling.

Shoots, plantlets and shoot-bearing cultures (including those of directly-regenerated adventitious shoots) have been most frequently stored in this way. Plantlets produced from somatic embryos can be treated similarly.

Cool temperature storage

Shoots and plantlets. Shoots and plantlets of many species have been reported to have been stored successfully at temperatures close to freezing. Optimal conditions vary from one genus to another. The tips of apple shoots grown *in vitro* were remained viable at 1°C and 4°C for one year in the dark and gave good rates of shoot proliferation when returned to 26°C (Mullin and Schlegel, 1976). Temperatures from 0–5°C have since been found by others to be suitable for conserving shoot-cultured material of other temperate woody species (Lundergan and Janick, 1979; Chun and Hall, 1986; Aitken-Christie and Singh, 1987).

D.R. Smith *et al.* (1982) found that cultures containing directly initiated shoots of *Pinus radiata* could be stored for at least 8 months at 2°C and they then resumed normal growth when returned to 23–27°C. In this species, clumps of 3–6 proliferating shoots, 20 mm high have been kept satisfactorily at 4°C in low light (Aitken-Christie and Singh, 1987). In other species, rooted plantlets may survive rather better.

Material to be stored should be in a good physiological condition. The most suitable kind and size of plant material for storage may vary between species. Small 5 mm shoots or shoot clumps generally survive less well than ones which are 2–4 times this size. In some species small shoots are prone to become hyperhydric (this is an condition in which shoots have an abnormal glassy or water-soaked appearance — see Chapter 13); the ability to survive is similarly low in shoots which are unhealthy or hyperhydric before storage. Precautions need to be taken to prevent moisture loss. This can be done by sealing the tops of vessels with plastic film or 'Parafilm', and/or placing vessels in plastic bags. The high humidity in vessels is not generally a problem except to shoots with a 'wet' appearance which become translucent and hyperhydric, especially if they touch the side of the jar (Aitken-Christie and Singh, 1987).

Cultures may be stored in vessels of many kinds and sizes; although contamination losses are minimised without any extra spacial requirement, if there are many replicates of single shoots, or shoot clumps, each in a single small tube, rather than if the total number is contained in one or two large vessels. No special media are required for long-term storage, although it is generally agreed that cultures are best moved to the cold 1–2 weeks after a transfer, before the medium is spent. Freshly-transferred material generally survives less satisfactorily.

Somatic embryos. Somatic embryos can be stored for at temperatures just above freezing. The period of successful storage is variously described as from several weeks to 'extended periods'. A temperature of *ca*. 4°C has been recommended (Durzan, 1988), although Lutz *et al.* (1985) could keep somatic embryos of carrot for at least 120 days at 10°C without deleterious effects.

Bapat and Rao (1988) managed to germinate a few seedlings from encapsulated *Santalum album* embryos stored for 45 days at 4°C on moist **MS** medium and abscisic acid-matured embryos of *Medicago sativa* have been kept at this temperature for 2 months without loss of viability (Redenbaugh *et al.*, 1991). 'Matured' (see Chapter 14) somatic embryos of conifers can be stored at 4°C for extended periods while on the embryo development medium (Pullman and Gupta, 1991).

Grout (1990) has suggested that somatic embryos might be stored in the cold at –20°C, after being treated with growth retardants and then dried (page 164).

Storage in the dark. Dark storage is satisfactory for some species. Vigorous *Prunus* shoot cultures were best kept in the dark at –3°C, where they remained viable for up to 10 months (Marino *et al.*, 1985) and *Kalmia* and *Populus* cultures can be kept in the dark at 3–4°C for 1–2 years (Chun and Hall, 1986; McCulloch, 1988). Pedicel explants of *Chrysanthemum*, once they had formed shoots of transferable size, could be stored for at least 6 months at 2°C in continuous darkness (Roest and Bokelmann, 1975). Individual shoots rooted readily afterwards at 20°C. Proliferating shoot cultures of *Fuchsia hybrida* and *Trifolium repens* could be stored for 10 months at 5°C in darkness without losing their potential for rapid multiplication (Stevenson and Harris, 1980; Bhojwani, 1981).

The cold storage of herbaceous species has been reviewed by Bhojwani and Razdan (1983), and that of woody plants by Aitken–Christie and Singh (1987).

Successful long–term storage.

Some plants have been stored for considerable periods without attention, but subculturing at yearly intervals is probably a wise precaution. Nozeran *et al.* (1977) found that they could keep potato shoot cultures at 3°C (in the light) for long periods, and Marinus (1983) stored cultures at 5°C and 5 h light (1000 lux) for 33(196)52 weeks. Most seemed dead after this period but 38–80% (depending on genotype) regrew when moved to 20°C and 16 h light. Four varieties recovered best under 4000 lux, two others under 22 000 lux.

Drosera plantlets can be kept for up to 18 months at 1–8°C (Kukulczanka and Czastka, 1988) and Aitken-Christie and Singh (1987) reported having kept *Pinus radiata* cultures for 5.5 years with only one subculture, made necessary by an equipment malfunction. Plantlets of seven different grass species regenerated from apical or tiller buds, were stored under minimum growth conditions for three or more years at the Welsh Plant Breeding Station. Cultures were maintained *in vitro* at 2–4°C in 300 lux of white fluorescent light for 8 h photoperiods. After 10–11 months, further nutrients were supplied by subculturing the plantlets to a fresh medium (Dale *et al.*, 1980). Under the same conditions, the forage legumes white and red clover and alfalfa were stored for 15–18 months. One red clover variety, 'Norseman', was best kept in darkness (Cheyne and Dale, 1980).

An alternative to subculturing can be to supply fresh liquid medium to a culture without removing the plant material. Mullin and Schlegel (1976) were able to maintain meristem tip plantlets (about 6 mm high with roots 13 mm long) for 6 years at 4°C. The plants were on filter paper bridges in small glass tubes containing 2.5 ml medium. The tubes were checked every 3 months and 1–2 drops of fresh medium was added to any showing signs of desiccation.

Promotion of flowering. *In vitro* storage at low temperature may induce flowering of some species. Storage of *Senecio × hybridus* plantlets was unsuccessful in an illuminace of 100–200 lux, because shoots turned brown and died after 3 months; but plantlets could be kept for 25 weeks at 10°C under cool white lamps (20 h, 400 lux) (Gertsson, 1988a). However, when finally transferred to soil, plants which had earlier been maintained at 10°C, flowered earlier, and had shorter foliage and taller inflorescences, than those derived from plantlets which had been grown at 21°C (Gertsson, 1988b).

Storage at higher temperatures

Plantlets and shoot cultures of some temperate-zone plants, and many tropical and sub-tropical species, lose their viability if stored at low temperature; for many of these species minimal growth is best achieved at 14–20°C (Henshaw *et al.*, 1980).

Cassava shoot cultures deteriorated if stored at temperatures lower than 20°C (Roca *et al.*, 1982) and benefited from being illuminated at 500–1000 lux. An international

germplasm collection of *Musa* spp. is kept as shoot cultures stored at 15°C under an illuminance of 1000–2000 lux. *Musa* cultures die within 6 weeks if kept at 5°C, and within 3 months at 10°C; but at 15°C, they can be kept for 13–17 months, according to their genotype (Banerjee and De Langhe, 1985).

Some woody plants which are cold-tolerant in the resting stage, require relatively high temperatures for storage of vegetative shoots. Shoot cultures of *Actinidia chinensis* could be stored in the dark for one year at 8°C: storage at 4°C was less successful (Monette, 1986c). *Vitis* shoots have been found to maintain their viability for at least 11 months at 9–12°C on a dilute media: survival was not satisfactory at 2 or 7°C (Galzy, 1969). It may be necessary to adjust both the amount of sugar and the light supplied to cultures of different *Vitis* genotypes so that each kind maintains just a slow rate of growth. A photon flux density of 12 μmol m^{-2} s^{-1} was suitable for both *Vitis rupestris* and *Vitis vinifera*, but differing capacities for photosynthesis *in vitro* caused cultures of the former to require only 3 g/l sucrose, while the latter needed 15 g/l (Galzy and Compan, 1988).

Sugar beet and potato are examples of temperate zone plants which are best stored at intermediate temperatures. Plantlets of the former only required subculturing at 18 week intervals if kept at 12°C (Hussey and Hephar, 1978a). Shoot cultures of potato and related species have been kept at 6–10°C for up to one year (Henshaw, 1982a; Henshaw *et al.*, 1980; Roca *et al.*, 1982; Westcott *et al.*, 1977a,b; Westcott, 1981a). The minimum temperature is critical and varies according to genotype: at 2°C there is very poor survival. The viability of cultures after low temperature storage was often found to be increased when they contained multiple (rather than single) shoots. Westcott (1981a) found that temperature cycling (12°C during a 16 h photoperiod and 6°C in the dark phase) prolonged the interval possible between transfers of potato shoot cultures from 4 weeks (Westcott *et al.* 1977a,b), to one year or more.

Decline and contamination

Once a suitable temperature for storage has been discovered, it is usual for a high proportion of cultures to remain viable for an extended period. After one year, 95–100% survival is quite common. Only after prolonged storage is the proportion of viable shoots decreased. Where poor survival is experienced, storage conditions need to be changed. Eight woody native plants of Australia were best stored at 10°C in the light. Darkness increased the extent of hyperhydricity and lower temperatures reduced survival. After storage, some species could be returned to room temperature immediately; while to minimise losses, others (*e.g. Cheirantha volubilis*) needed to be kept for some while at an intermediate temperature of 15°C (Williams and Taji, 1987).

Storage at 5°C has given some problems at the U.S. National Clonal Germplasm Repository. Plants kept at 5°C in the dark had reduced growth, but this was accompanied by a gradual decline of the culture and browning of the medium. Cultures of *Fragaria*, *Mentha*, Rubus, and *Vaccinium* were kept for one year but the growth of bacteria from internal contaminants or surface spores became noticable. Better results were obtained with cold tolerant species such as *Mentha* (300 clones) and *Fragaria chiloensis*, if they were kept at –1°C. Because plant growth is severely reduced or eliminated at the lower temperature, media do not become depleted nor shoots etiolated. The problem of delayed contamination is also lessened (Gunning and Langerstedt, 1986). *Prunus* was stored at –3°C for six months by Marino *et al.* (1985).

Musa cultures in the INIBAP germplasm collection (see above) are checked monthly and those which are necrotic or contaminated are immediately discarded. Twenty cultures of each accession are started and when only 12 healthy ones remain, the entire accession is returned to the normal cultural environment and subcultured to restore 20 healthy cultures once more (De Smet and Van den Houwen, 1991).

Cold temperature storage of callus cultures

The maintenance of healthy callus cultures normally requires frequent subdivision of the tissue and transfer onto fresh medium. Failure to do so, leads first to partial necrosis of the callus, and then to ultimate death. Necrotic tissue does not grow readily upon subculture, possibly due to the accumulation of toxic materials. The morphogenetic capacity of unorganised callus from the majority of species is diminished with successive passages (page 261). Intervals between normal transfers of healthy tissue can be extended by growing cultures at less than optimum temperatures. There have been attempts to extend subculturing frequencies even further by using temperatures close to 0°C, but in comparison the storage of shoot cultures by this technique, they have not met with much success.

The ability of callus to withstand low temperatures is genotype-dependent; Hiraoka and Kodama (1982) could store callus of *Lithospermum erythrorhizon*, *Phytolacca americana* and *Bupleurum falcatum* for 6 months at around 4°C without there being any significant growth retardation upon subsequent re-culture at 25°C. The same was true for tobacco, but only for storage periods of up to 2 months: callus of *Dioscorea tokoro* and *Mallotus japonicus* was incapable of withstanding even the 2 months treatment. Bannier and Steponkus (1972, 1976)

managed to store callus cultures of *Chrysanthemum × morifolium* in a viable condition for up to one month at –3.5°C after a preliminary period at 4–5°C. Withers (1978) reported that callus of *Capsicum annuum* remained alive for 25 days at 4°C. The storage period could be almost tripled if the tissue was first treated with ethanolamine.

Desiccation combined with cold treatment

Nitzsche (1978, 1980, 1983) has shown that carrot callus can survive storage for up to 2 years, if it is pretreated and dried. Pretreatment involved growing calluses on a basal medium [**Gamborg and Eveleigh (1968) PRL-4**] supplemented with 10 mg/l of the growth regulator abscisic acid (ABA) and 50 g/l (instead of 20 g/l) of sucrose for 16 days. The optimum pretreatment period was 12–20 days (Nitzsche, 1983). Callus tissues were then dried overnight on sterile filter paper in the air stream of a laminar flow cabinet. In sealed Petri dishes, two out of three carrot varieties were best stored at –80°C (which gave survival rates of 90 and 100%). The third variety showed greatest survival after storage at - 20°C (75%). In other experiments carrot dried carrot callus has been stored at 25% relative humidity and 15°C for over two years (Nitzsche, 1983). Regrowth occurred after four weeks when the callus was returned to the original medium at normal temperatures and plants could be subsequently be regenerated.

New growth has also been obtained from dried and cold-stored calluses of plants in the family Gramineae, but subsequent morphogenesis was limited. Experiments with red clover were completely unsuccessful and in only one experiment with potatoes was regrowth achieved after drying (Nitzsche, 1980).

Prospects for callus storage. There are several reasons why long-term storage of callus cultures has not been the subject of vigorous research:

- The regeneration of plants from cultures maintained or sub-cultured over long periods can be problematical;

- Such callus can become composed of genetically variable cells (Chapter 3). If this occurs it can result in:

  regenerated plants that may be dissimilar to the parent,

  the preferential survival of cold tolerant cells during cool temperature storage. Cell lines obtained upon eventual sub-culture will then have a genotype different to that of the parent plant (Dix and Street, 1976).

Both the problem of loss of morphogenetic capacity and the risk of genetic change during low temperature storage might be reduced by committing to storage only highly regenerative cultures, or semi–organised callus. For example, *Bupleurum falcatum* first passage callus retains its rhizogenetic capacity after one year at 4°C. It would normally become non-organogenetic after a few passages at customary growth room temperatures (Hiraoka and Kodama, 1982).

3. Reduced oxygen tension

Placing cultures in an environment with a low partial pressure of oxygen appears to have potential for limiting their *in vitro* growth, and reduction in oxygen tension undoubtedly has a part to play in the successful storage of cultures in tightly sealed vessels.

Caplin (1959) used a mineral oil overlay to conserve callus cultures. He attributed a decrease in growth rates to oxygen being prevented from reaching the plant tissues. The contaminating and toxic effects of oils are disadvantageous, and Moriguchi *et al.* (1988) have suggested that autoclaved silicone (100 centistokes, Wako Pure Chemical Industries Ltd.), which dissolves 10 times the amount of oxygen that is solubilised in water, may be more effective in regulating oxygen supply. They found that plants could be obtained from embryogenic *Vitis vinifera* callus cultures which had been stored at 10 or 15°C for one year covered with silicone to a depth of 90 mm., provided the callus was then moved to a fresh regeneration medium. Storage at 1 or 5°C was not effective. Somatic embryos of *Selinum candolii* formed under a later of liquid paraffin oil remained viable for at least 240 days, although when they were removed there was a lag period of 20–25 days before they resumed growth (Mathur, 1991).

A slight doubt has been cast over the wisdom of using overlays by the results of Mannonen *et al.* (1990). After six months storage, callus of *Panax ginseng* and *Catharanthus roseus*, while still viable, seemed to have lost the ability to produce, respectively, ginsenosides and indole alkaloids. Cells of both species which had been cryopreserved at –196 °C for the same period, had retained their biosynthetic capacity.

Bridgen and Staby (1981, 1983) experimented with a direct reduction in oxygen supply. They subjected *Nicotiana tabacum* and *Chrysanthemum* × *morifolium* shoot and callus cultures to a reduced partial pressure of oxygen for six weeks by either decreasing the atmospheric pressure (thereby reducing the partial pressure of all the gases surrounding the tissue), or by replacing some of the oxygen in air at normal atmospheric pressure with an inert gas. Both treatments reduced the growth rates of the cultures. Oxygen availability, and not some other atmos-

pheric factor (such as humidity or ethylene level), was thought to be the cause. Partial pressures of oxygen lower than 0.066 atm (50 mm Hg), were necessary to slow growth: progressive decreases in partial pressure below this figure caused further growth reduction in both species. No deleterious effects on the phenotypes of regenerated plants were noted on returning to normal cultural conditions, but reducing oxygen tension by lowering the atmospheric pressure, caused the medium to become desiccated and the plant material dehydrated.

Shoot proliferation in cultures of *Spiraea nipponica* is reduced by storage at 4°C and reduced still further when containers are flushed with nitrogen once per week during the storage period (Norton and Norton, 1988b).

One very simple way to reduce the supply of oxygen reaching tissues and organs is to place them in a long narrow vessel in which the distance between the culture and the point of gas exchange with the external atmosphere is at a maximum. As the diffusion distance is increased, the rate of tissue growth decreases and this allows the frequency of subculturing to be reduced (Bateson *et al.*, 1987; Grout, 1990) (page 194).

4. Altering the constituents of the culture medium

Decreasing the carbohydrate/nutrient supply. Growth of a culture slows as the constituents of the medium are used up, but a spent medium which may contain toxic products and have an unfavourable pH, may not be an ideal substrate on which to store shoots or plantlets for a considerable period. There may be merit in transferring material to a fresh, but less concentrated, medium. One containing a comparatively low level of sugar could result in a reduced growth rate (Gunning and Lagerstedt, 1986). Coffee shoot cultures can be stored effectively for 2 years at 26°C in a 16 h day (7500 lux) providing they were kept on a half strength modified **MS** medium medium without sucrose (Kartha *et al.*, 1981), but those of cassava were best maintained at 20–22°C on a medium containing 20–40 mM nitrogen (nitrate and ammonium ions) and 4% sucrose (Roca *et al.*, 1982). The growth of somatic embryos is inhibited by the absence of sugar (see Chapter 12).

Decreasing the supply of inorganic nutrients. The restricted growth of coffee plantlets achieved by Kartha *et al.* (1981) (above), may have been partly due to the reduced supply of inorganic salts. This can be seen from the experiments of Schnapp and Preece (1986), who showed that subcultured tomato shoots formed roots, but shoot growth was considerably reduced, if they were placed on ¾**MS** medium containing 5% sucrose. The reduction in growth was caused by the low salt concentration, because shoots on full strength MS medium were four times the height. A significant reduction in the growth of carnation plantlets required a reduction in the MS salt level to 25 or 50% of normal. On the basis of these results Moriguchi and Yamaki (1989) have experimented with the storage of *Vitis* shoot cultures on MS medium, modified to contain a reduced concentration of ammonium nitrate: in standard culture conditions (28°C, 35–40 mol m^{-2} s^{-1}), subcultured nodes of three species survived best when the quantity of NH$_4$NO$_3$ added to MS medium was 6–25% of normal. Cultures were supplied with 3% sucrose and 1 μM BAP. Reduction of macronutrient availability (especially reduction of nitrate and ammonium ions) could therefore provide an alternative way to facilitate the storage of vines.

Changing the osmotic potential. As its concentration in a high salt medium is increased above 4–5 per cent, sucrose begins to have an inhibitory but non-toxic effect on plant cell growth. High sucrose levels can therefore be used to maintain cultures in a dormant condition for long periods (Schenk and Hildebrandt, 1972). This appears to be an osmotic effect (see Chapter 9), because Codron *et al.* (1979) showed that mannitol (200–385 mM) added to the culture medium to create a hypertonic solution can also prevent the rapid cell death that otherwise occurs when auxin-requiring cells are grown on a medium without auxin. These authors suggested that mannitol was able to preserve membrane integrity and prevent solute leakage. Adding 1–4% mannitol to the medium enhanced the viability of *Cinchona ledgeriana* shoots stored at 12°C, although at 26–28°C it was inhibitory (Hunter *et al.*, 1986). Henshaw *et al.* (1980) have found that media containing 8% sucrose can assist in restricting the growth of potato shoot cultures kept in cool temperatures: combinations of sucrose and mannitol were also effective.

Mannitol does not retard the growth of all species. Although in a medium containing 0.11 M glucose, the addition of 0.025–0.11 M mannitol progressively reduced the length of shoots produced in cultures of two *Mentha* species, lateral branching was stimulated. Sorbitol (with glucose omitted) seemed to be more valuable for suppressing the growth of these plants (Gunning and Lagerstedt, 1986). In combination with glucose, 0.22 M mannitol is toxic to *Mentha*: mannitol was also toxic to cassava cultures if the storage temperature was lower than 20°C (Roca *et al.*, 1982). Sugar in high concentration prevents the growth of somatic embryos.

The nature of the medium. Cultures of some woody plants have been reported to store more satisfactorily on liquid than on solid media (Williams and Dodds, 1983). By contrast, shoot cultures of 'Merton Thornless' blackberry, *Mentha* × *dunetorum*, *Vaccinium ovatum*, and *V.*

uliginosum were found to retain their viability better on a medium containing 8 or 10 g/l agar, than on one with 6 g/l (Gunning and Lagerstedt, 1986). Williams and Taji (1987) found that several Australian woody plants survived best on a medium gelled with Gelrite, rather than agar, particularly when cultures were kept at 22°C: the pH of the medium was noted to decrease progressively the longer the cultures were maintained.

5. The use of growth regulators

Growth regulators are normally added to culture media to promote and regulate plant growth *in vitro*. Withdrawal of these chemicals can assist in the storage of certain plants. Two strawberry cultivars continued to proliferate when kept at normal temperatures unless cultures were transferred to a medium without growth regulants, when thick shoots with long petioles were produced and cultures remained viable for over 5 months (Gunning and Langerstedt, 1986).

Some chemical treatments may help to slow down the growth of *in vitro* cultures by, for example:

- acting directly to induce organ dormancy, to reduce cellular metabolism, or to prevent cell or nuclear division;

- making cells less susceptible to cold. This may enable cultures to be stored for longer periods at low temperatures (possibly by permitting the storage temperature to be reduced).

The growth regulator abscisic acid (ABA) (and some other compounds with related structures), is able to induce dormancy in plant meristems. In caraway (*Carum*), 0.1 mM ABA was found by Ammirato (1974) to arrest the growth of late stage somatic embryos. Embryos formed in suspension cultures remained dormant for as long as the ABA was present, but continued to grow and develop once it was removed. Storage of embryogenic cultures in a state of induced dormancy therefore provides another method by which plant genotypes can be preserved *in vitro*. Somatic embryos can be stored for many weeks on ABA-containing media without germinating or detiorating (Gupta *et al.*, 1991).

Additions of low concentrations of ABA to the medium increased the viablity of single node cuttings of potato stored at 8–10°C, but the regulant had a detrimental effect on viability when combined with high sucrose concentrations and low temperature (Roca *et al.*, 1982). At a concentration of 10 mM, the growth retardant chormequat (CCC) can prolong the life of some shoot cultures. Tolerance to the chemical is very specific (Gunning and Landerstedt, 1986). Shoot cultures of *Prunus avium* which were kept in the dark at 0.5°C, recovered more effectively if 0.2 mg/l paclobutrazol had been added to the medium used during storage (Snir, 1988). Mix (1981) added 50 mg/l daminozide to shoot cultures of potato which were successfully stored for two years at 10°C on salts of a similar concentration to those of **MS** medium.

6. Treatments in combination.

Minimal growth may be effectively induced by a combination of treatments. For example, shoot cultures of *Pelargonium* stock plants were maintained at 12°C on a medium without growth regulators (Horn, 1988). Henshaw *et al.* (1980) and Westcott (1981b) have discovered that the survival of potato shoot cultures at cool temperatures is enhanced by additions of ABA (5–10 mg/l), high sucrose (up to 8%) and/or mannitol (3–6%), to the medium, and that the period of storage can be extended thereby to at least 57 months. There may often be alternative ways of storing cultures of any particular plant which are equally effective. The precise combination of treatments preferred will therefore vary from one laboratory to another. Schilde-Rentschler *et al.* (1982) stored potato shoot tips satisfactorily on **MS** medium with 0.5% sucrose and 220 mM mannitol.

Increasing the volume of medium can result in increased survival of plant material after long storage periods. With *Solanum* organ cultures, the success of this method was genotype-dependent, being partly related to the ability of varieties to form tubers *in vitro* (Westcott, 1981a).

7. Storage of autotrophic plantlets.

It has been suggested that by using gas permeable vessels, it might be possible to grow plants *in vitro* that are capable of photosynthesis (Tanaka *et al.*, 1988a,b). This might be a convenient method for storing genotypes, providing the plants could be miniaturised and their growth slowed: the use of simple media containing only inorganic salts should allow a less stringent requirement for aseptic conditions.

Applications

Minimal growth storage is clearly useful for the preservation of clones which are required as stocks for continued propagation *in vivo* or *in vitro*, or as parents in plant breeding programmes. The technique is not ideal for the long term storage of genotypes, because the periods during which cultures can be left unattended are only relatively short. Nevertheless, in the absence of a reliable alternative method, minimal growth storage is being used in conjunction with shoot or node culture, to maintain genotypes in botanic gardens and germplasm banks.

Advantages for the tissue culture laboratory

To obtain sufficient cuttings or divisions for traditional macropropagation methods, nurserymen usually keep large numbers of stock plants. The space needed can be considerable, and the material must be continually safeguarded against pests and diseases. Stock plants are also often kept in heated greenhouses or covered areas, and so occupy costly bench or bed space that could be more profitably used for other purposes. One advantage of micropropagation is that the necessity of maintaining large numbers of stock plants is removed. Only a few plants typical of each variety need to be kept, as a source of fresh explant material for the re-initiation of cultures.

Minimal growth storage techniques enable tissue culture laboratories to carry out year-round production of some kinds of plants required for seasonal planting, or those for which customer demand occurs only at sporadic intervals. When an order for several different clones is received, those which produce a large number of shoots can be held in storage until an adequate number of shoots is available from plants having slower multiplication rates, thus enabling simultaneous delivery.

Cool temperature storage particularly, is useful to give increased flexibility in micropropagation and to overcome temporary difficulties in normal production, which can arise from a variety of circumstances (*e.g.* staff holidays, absenteeism, shortage of growth room space and customer difficulties). Shoots and plantlets can also be held over until there is space in the greenhouse, or kept during the winter months before transfer *extra vitrum* so that costly winter heating of a greenhouse is avoided (Aitken- Christie and Singh, 1987).

Advantages in plant breeding

Short-term storage of genotypes. Micropropagation techniques can be of value in the breeding of a perennial crops as a back-up to breeders' collections, providing security against the loss of valuable material (Jarret and Florkowski, 1990). Tissue culture can also be employed usefully for the short-term storage of parental material. During breeding programmes for annual crops, it is sometimes only possible to select the best parents for further crossing by testing their progeny. In the interval (of up to one year) while the necessary crosses are made and seedlings grown and evaluated, all the potential parents need to be maintained vegetatively. It may then be desirable to propagate the chosen parent/s so that sufficient plants are available to produce a large amount of seed. Vegetative micropropagation may also be valuable to store the parents of commercial seed lines so that multiplier populations can be available during several generations to produce basic seed lots. D.R. Smith *et al.* (1982) and Aitken-Christie and Singh (1987) mention that it is advantageous in tree breeding programmes to be able to store some ramets from a clone while others are field tested or progeny tested. Cultures need to be maintained for several years for this purpose but are then be available to propagate the promising genotypes on a large scale.

Some plants have low seed viability so that germplasm can only be stored conveniently in the vegetative phase. Coffee is a good example, where seed no longer germinates if it is stored for a period greater than 4 months. Consequently Kartha *et al.* (1981) have developed a technique which permits shoot cultures to be maintained for up to 2 years without transfer, and they suggest that it could enable valuable genetic material to be stored *in vitro*.

The maintenance of parental lines. Plant breeders have produced F_1 hybrid varieties of many flowers and vegetables during recent years, which are more vigorous and more uniform than conventional crossbred varieties. The production of F_1 varieties often entails the use of cytoplasmically inherited male sterility (CMS). This assists the production of pure hybrid seed, but makes the maintenance of breeding lines rather complicated and time-consuming. The necessary breeding programme has to incorporate CMS genes into a line that is to serve as the seed-producing parent (the restorer line). To preserve the female line it is additionally necessary to produce, and have available, a third maintainer line with the same nuclear genes. If, however, the parents are propagated vegetatively (rather than by seed), a maintainer line is no longer needed, and both its initial production and its annual propagation can be avoided. Using micropropagation methods, sufficient plants of just the female parent and the restorer line are produced vegetatively each year to permit the required quantity of hybrid seed to be obtained. If necessary, the parental genotype can also be stored *in vitro* until plants are needed as seed parents.

GERMPLASM STORAGE

Interest in plant collecting and an expectation of bringing new species and varieties into horticultural cultivation, led to the founding of botanic gardens, some of the most famous of which have been in existence for over 200 years. More recently, germplasm repositories and international collections of varieties and species related to important field crops have been established with the specific aim of conserving diverse gene pools. There are now many such plant collections, each a source of genes relevant to crop improvement and the maintenance of variety within the plant kingdom (for a review see Sneep and Hendriksen, 1979). Both the crop- and botanically-related plant collections have begun to assume a new importance as many native plant habitats have been destroyed or disturbed by agricultural activity, and pressure has intensified from a rapidly–expanding world population. Furthermore, as new high yielding cultivars have been introduced, many genetically diverse, but low yielding traditional ('land-race') varieties of crop, especially cereals, have gone out of production and have tended to be lost.

Collections of plant germplasm need to be maintained under conditions in which individual genotypes can be preserved unchanged at minimal cost. Frequent propagation is to be avoided as far as possible because of the expense entailed. Where crop species can be sexually propagated, collections of representative genotypes can usually be kept as seed. Collections of the seeds of rare and unusual plants (including many that are not usually cultivated) have also been established in recent years. They are stored in the cold at low humidity (page 173). Unfortunately the seeds of many plants, particulary those of the humid tropics, will not tolerate drying and remain viable for only very short periods. Germplasm of these species, and clones of crops that are normally propagated vegetatively (such as potato cultivars, cassava and sugar cane), can only be stored conveniently as living collections. This is costly, and problems are experienced in live field collections with disease and pest control.

The use of micropropagation techniques

The possible use of plant tissue culture techniques in maintaining some of the large world collections of vegetatively reproduced plants has long been in the minds of research workers. Some of the advantages that have been envisaged are:

— a saving in field space (see below);

— plants are withdrawn into a protected environment where they are less likely to be damaged or killed by pathogens and predators;

— Plants or tissues in culture could be made disease free and then maintained in a healthy state;

— Genetic stocks would be constantly in a suitable condition for international exchange;

— Individual genotypes could be multiplied rapidly when required;

— The cost of maintaining collections might be reduced.

The success of a germplasm collection can be measured by the extent to which it is able to make the material in its care available for research and crop improvement. Here tissue cultured collections have a big advantage for the preservation of vegetatively propagated plants, because distribution is readily accomplished.

Tissue culture methods have indeed begun to be used for the preservation of valuable plant material, but it is necessary to use the techniques cautiously with due regard to possible disadvantages:

— There is no universally-applicable routine, and it may even be necessary to employ different protocols for the species and varieties in a single collection;

— Some *in vitro* methods can cause the loss of the genetic integrity of cultured material so that regenerated or propagated plants will be genetically dissimilar to the plant from which they were originally derived;

For these reasons, callus cultures are generally considered to be unsuitable for germplasm storage (page 167). The risk of genetic change should be much less using node or shoot culture, which are now employed, together with techniques to minimize growth, for some major germplasm collections.

A valuable comparison of the merits and costs of the maintenance of a gene bank of a vegetatively propagated crop using '*in vitro*- active' techniques or field plot methods, has been provided by Jarret and Florkowski (1990). The costs of both methods were roughly comparable. Field gene banks provide a continuous opportunity to evaluate and compare the characteristics of different genotypes. This may not be so important for crops which quickly grow to maturity, but is likely of greater significance in tree crops which have a long juvenile period. Against this, there are considerable risks that virus infection will mask the true phenotypic potential of genotypes. Although living collections must be located in areas climatically suited to crop growth, tissue culture storage can be conducted in a completely different geographical area, where there may be better technical facilities or expertise. There must though, be facilities for shipments from that site to all plant breeding centres. The techniques needed for the maintenance of a tissue cultured collection are much less crop-specific than those necessary for field culture, so that a laboratory could handle the storage of several crops simultaneously.

Root cultures for germplasm storage

The direct regeneration of adventitious shoots from root pieces is only commonly reported *in vitro* from plants which possess thick fleshy roots such as those of the genera *Cichorium*, *Armoracia*, *Convolvulus*, and *Taraxacum*. It is, however, a method of propagation that is potentially applicable to a wide range of species (Browse, 1980; Hodge, 1986), and can be used as a basis for micropropagation. Shoots have, for instance, been induced to form directly on segments and apices of the roots of species as diverse as *Citrus* (Sauton *et al.*, 1982) and *Vanilla* (Philip and Nainar, 1988) and upon roots which have been grown in isolated culture, such as those of *Populus* (Zeldin and McCown, 1986a). Cells appear to maintain genetic stability in root cultures, and several authors have suggested that it should be possible to store plant material in this form, regenerating plants as they are required.

Danckwardt-Lillieström (1957) was able to regenerate shoots from isolated roots of *Isatis tinctoria* which were in their sixteenth passage. Chaturvedi *et al.* (1982b) record the successful maintenance of *Atropa belladonna*, *Solanum khasianum* (and to some extent *Rauwolfia serpentiana*) for 6–10 years as isolated root cultures. Shoots were then regenerated from segments of root from the root cultures, and grown into plants which appeared normal under field conditions.

Root cultures are easily maintained but normally need frequent attention. Several methods have been investigated to reduce the intervals at which root cultures intended for germplasm storage need to be handled, but no storage protocols appear to have been proposed.

Saving field space

The field space saved by utilising *in vitro* methods for germplasm storage can be considerable. Morel (1975) described how nodal cuttings of grapevines could be multiplied and cultured at a reduced temperature so that six plants of each of 800 varieties were preserved on $2\,m^2$ of controlled environment room space. If the plants had been grown in the field, about 1 ha of suitable land would be required with much higher labour and management costs. Lundergan and Janick (1979) stored a collection of *Malus* cultivars in $0.28\,m^3$ of cold room, whereas to establish a germ bank in the field would have taken 5.7 ha. *Pinus radiata* shoot cultures stored in 2000 culture tubes which occupy $3.83\,m^3$ of cold room, would require 4 ha of field space if planted as hedged ramets (Aitken-Christie and Singh, 1987).

Nodal cultures of *Lotus corniculatus* used in a breeding programme at the University of Guelph were stored for four weeks at -2 to $-4°C$ under continuous low light (1

W/m^2) without losing their viability or propagation potential (Tomes, 1979). One hundred genotypes with four replicates each occupied just 0.24 m^2 of shelf space in an incubator, whereas they would have taken up 18 m^2 in a growth room or 400 m^2 in the field. Also thirty-four of one hundred genotypes were lost one winter from the field, but all incubator-stored accessions were maintained.

Review articles

In vitro methods for germplasm storage and their applications, have been reviewed by Bajaj (1979c), Bajaj and Reinert (1977), Brooks and Barton (1983), de Langhe (1984), Henshaw (1982), Jarret and Florkowski (1990); Kartha (1981a; 1982c; 1985a,b), Nitzsche (1983), Towill (1988) and Withers (1980a,b,c,d; 1984b, 1987a,b).

LONG-TERM STORAGE

Although minimal growth storage can be used to maintain collections of clonal plant material, it is clearly not an ideal technique for long-term storage of genetically valuable plants because collections need frequent attention. A method which requires the same degree of attention and is as reliable as seed storage would be ideal.

Dry seeds remain dormant because living cells become metabolically inert when deprived of water in the liquid phase. Biochemical reactions which are dependent on the presence of water are then suspended, especially if the seeds are also stored at low temperature. The embryos of seeds stored at low humidity (*ca.* 5%) retain their viability for long periods, the period of effective storage being extended if they are also kept at a low temperature (*e.g.* −20°C).

Dry seed storage is now widely used in germplasm repositories as an effective means of storing very many plant genotypes. However, for plants which have seeds which do not tolerate desiccation, and for plants which are normally vegetatively propagated, it would clearly be desirable to have a reliable alternative method of storing important genotypes.

In theory, the withdrawal of water should permit plant tissues other than seeds and zygotic embryos, to be stored. Vegetative tissues can remain viable after water has been removed by evaporation (page 167) and drying seems to be eminently suited to preserving somatic embryos. Its value for preserving vegetative tissues is less certain.

Freezing offers an alternative method of making water unavailable to metabolic processes. By converting water into the solid or vitrified phase, at temperatures which are sufficiently low for there to be no free energy available for molecular movement, biochemical reactions and diffusion are arrested. Therefore, in theory, living cells kept at ultra-low temperatures should remain indefinitely in suspended animation, without losing viability. Certain animal tissues (animal sperm in particular) can be kept safely for long periods, deep frozen in liquid nitrogen and and similar techniques of freeze-storage (cryopreservation) hold promise for storing vegetative plant material and embryos of plants whose seeds are difficult in a desiccated state. Undifferentiated tissues, somatic embryos, and organised meristems are suitable subjects.

CRYOPRESERVATION

Conventional deep freezers are insufficiently cold to be suitable for long term storage. In experimental cryogenics, biological specimens are usually stored in liquid nitrogen at minus 196°C or, less frequently, in the vapour above liquid nitrogen (*ca.* 150°C). Even at −196°C some biochemical activity has been thought to occur in animal cell cultures, leading to water migration (Peterson and Stulberg, 1964).

Attempts to store plant tissues at very low temperatures have met with difficulties. Some seeds can be cryopreserved successfully, but it is more difficult to freeze and later retrieve without harm, the hydrated plant cells found in somatic tissues. As success only results from freezing and thawing specimens evenly and rapidly, storage must be limited to cell samples, small pieces of tissue, or small organs. Aseptic techniques and sterile containers must be used in all procedures.

Compact and densely cytoplasmic cells with a low water content (such as actively growing meristematic cells), have a better survival potential than large, thick-walled, highly vacuolated ones, which are more prone to ice damage. This has been demonstrated in several species, *e.g.*

Carrot	Nag and Street (1975a,b)
Sycamore	Sugawara and Sakai (1974)

| Carnation | Seibert (1976);
Seibert and Wetherbee (1977) |
| Andean potato | Grout and Henshaw (1980) |

Genetic stability

Cells taken from suspension cultures are suitable subjects for cryopreservation, but as has been explained in Chapter 3, they are prone to genetic change. The freeze storage of most cultures of this kind does not, therefore, provide a suitable method for germplasm preservation and needs to be treated with caution when the ultimate objective is to regenerate plants that are genetically identical to the plant from which the tissues or cells were originally derived. There is little point in perfecting a storage method for a population of cells that is intrinsically variable. Suspensions of embryogenically-determined cells are a possible exception; problems with intrinsic genetic variability should be avoided by preserving shoot tip explants.

Genetic variation arising from aberrant divisions of cell nuclei could occur during tissue culture before or after cryopreservation, or during eventual plant regeneration. During the storage phase, some genetic variation could be induced by the accumulation of mutations caused by background ionising radiation, even in explants which were previously genetically stable. Variability of this kind is only likely to be significant after decades in storage (Whittingham et al., 1977). If dimethyl sulphoxide (DMSO) is incorporated as a cryoprotectant (see below), the chance of radiation damage may be reduced, since the compound also has radio-protectant properties. Storing deep-frozen cultures in glass containers can also reduce the exposure of tissues to ionising radiation, but glass vessels have a tendency to explode on thawing due to the penetration of liquid nitrogen.

Freezing and thawing protocols do not appear to cause mutation in bacteria or animal tissues (Towill, 1988), but some of the compounds used as cryoprotectants (including DMSO) may well do so (Vannini and Poli, 1983; Ashwood-Smith, 1985) and their affects have not yet been fully elucidated.

Factors affecting survival

Cold conditioning

When plants are subjected to low temperatures, compounds can accumulate, and changes in membrane structure occur, that enable constituent cells to withstand subsequent freeze injury. Plants vary considerably in their liability to frost injury, so that it is not surprising that the tolerance of cells or tissues to low temperature storage is also variable. In many species, conditioning mother plants by keeping them in the cold (e.g. 1–4°C) for several days, is found to increase the probability of successful cryopreservation of shoot apical meristems (Seibert and Wetherbee, 1977; Kartha et al., 1979, 1980). Cold hardening procedures have also been beneficially applied to callus cultures prior to freeze storage, but seem not to be necessary for suspension cultured cells. The protection provided by initial cold conditioning can be sufficient to enable tissues to be stored at ultra low temperatures and to be viably retrieved without the use of cryoprotectant chemicals (see below), but these cryoprotectants are usually applied to experimental material as an extra precaution (Table 9, page 179).

Preventing injury during freezing

Nearly all the damage that may result to cells during transfer to very low temperatures or subsequent thawing, is a consequence of their water content. A possible exception is the damage caused by interference with biochemical or biophysical pathways during temperature reduction. Living cells are seriously harmed by the internal formation of ice crystals. Thus the main object of cryopreservation protocols must be to change the physical state of the water within cells to a frozen glass-like condition without crystallisation. The transformation of water from a liquid to a solid (glass-like) phase is called *vitrification* (Luyet, 1937; Fahy et al., 1984). Various precautions must therefore be taken during freezing and thawing to prevent the appearance of intra-cellular ice crystals.

Slow freezing. One effective method of cryopreservation is to cool material to be frozen at ultra-low temperature at a slow and controlled rate to between –30°C and –60°C, before plunging it into liquid nitrogen. Slow cooling gives rise to cellular dehydration which progressively concentrates the cellular constituents and depresses their freezing point (Fig. 67). Thus at a low initial freezing rate, 'ice damage' is prevented (although there is the danger that excessive concentration of solutes will cause toxicity — see Henshaw, 1975; Withers, 1980b).

Intracellular ice will begin to grow during the slow cooling phase if the preliminary rate of cooling is too fast to allow vapour pressure equilibration. The resulting ice crystals rupture cell membranes, notably the plasmalemma and tonoplast. Since these membranes are composed of a water-lipid-protein complex, most of the damage is probably caused during the freezing of bound (as opposed to free) water. Once cell solutions have been concentrated by slow cooling, remaining water can usually be vitrified by freezing the plant material as rapidly as possible, thus avoiding further damage (Luyet, 1937).

In slow cooling protocols, material is cooled and frozen in a solution consisting of the medium plus cryoprotectants, or, after the application of cryoprotectants, it is sometimes blotted dry and processed while enclosed in a foil envelope.

Stepwise cooling. As an alternative to gradual slow pre-cooling, specimens which have been treated with cryoprotectant chemicals are subjected to a series of sub-zero temperatures (each one progressively lower than the last), before being plunged into liquid nitrogen. For example, suspension cultured cells of *Acer pseudoplatanus* in 5% glucose and 12% DMSO were held for 3 minutes at each of –10, –15, –20, –30 and –40°C, before being placed in liquid nitrogen (Sugawara and Sakai, 1974). Such stepwise freezing has been found to be unsuccessful for some organised plant structures (Nitzsche, 1983), although in other experiments it has been employed satisfactorily. A protocol for the cryopreservation of *Trifolium repens* apical meristems involved freezing to –7°C at 0.5°C per minute, then to –40°C at 0.3°C per minute, before the specimens were plunged into liquid nitrogen (Yamada *et al.*, 1991).

Rapid freezing. The high cost of the apparatus needed to achieve various experimental rates of controlled slow cooling, has limited the application of cryopreservation research to a few specialised laboratories. However, cells which have dense cytoplasm and a relatively low water content, can be preserved if they are cooled sufficiently rapidly for internal water to become directly vitrified without prior slow cooling. Thus, small plant meristems have sometimes been stored in a viable condition when they have been cooled in the vapour above liquid nitrogen (cooling rate 10°C per minute) and then plunged into the liquid, or by being placed into directly into liquid nitrogen (cooling rate 300–1000 °C per minute). The rate of cooling which can be achieved by such methods, when large samples are enclosed within a thick-walled container, is insufficient to prevent cell damage. Tissues with a high water content are also injured by such treatment.

Recent experiments have shown that small plant samples can be transferred immediately to minus 196°C without

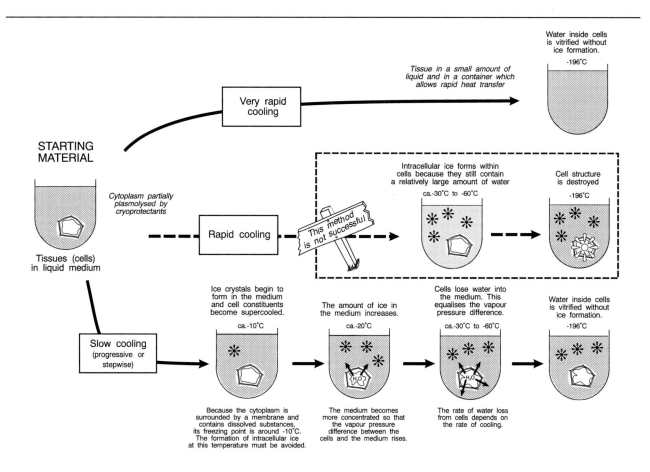

Fig. 67. Physico-chemical events during three methods of cryogenic cooling.
For successful cryopreservation, material must either be cooled slowly to ca. -30°C to -60°C before trannsfer to liquid nitrogen, or else be cooled very quickly in a small volume of liquid (see text).

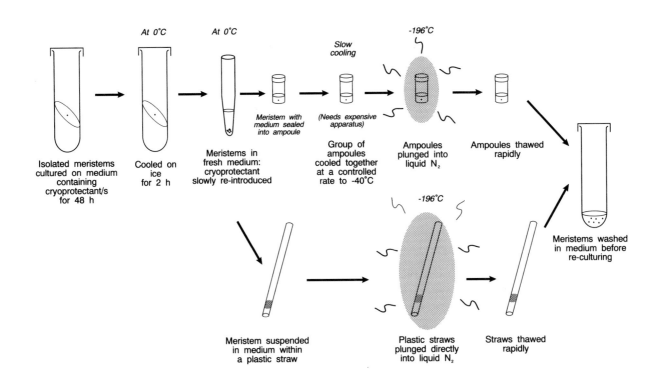

Fig. 68. Alternative methods for the cryopreservation of plant meristems.

damage, providing their tissues have been induced to take up cryoprotectant chemicals, and they have been placed in a container, such as a plastic straw, which presents a minimum interference to heat transfer (Grout, 1990) (Fig. 68).

Injury during thawing

Reversal of the freezing process also has attendant hazards:

- At around −130°C ice structure can change from vitreous to crystalline. If ice crystals should result, they will be as damaging as if they had appeared during freezing;

- At about −70°C and above, ice crystals may form and grow on the surface of smaller pre-existing crystals by a process of re-crystallization.

For these reasons very rapid thawing of frozen specimens is usually most successful in preserving viability, for then the amount of ice crystal formation which occurs before the water in the cells melts, is reduced to a minimum. Ampoules are usually placed in water at 35–40°C until

thawed and thereafter transferred to room temperature. Some specimens frozen without cryoprotectants, have been thawed in a liquid medium at 25–30°C (Reed, 1989). The subsequent viability of *Coleus blumei* suspensions or callus was improved if cryopreserved material was thawed in a water bath at 60°C (rather than 45°C) or thawed in a microwave oven (Reuff *et al.*, 1988).

The use of cryoprotectants

Various chemicals exhibit protective properties when biological samples are chilled to extreme temperatures. Such 'cryoprotectants' have little in common except a high solubility in water. Their mode of action is not entirely clear; it may depend on an ability both to reduce the concentration of salts within the cell, and restrict the growth of damaging ice crystals. Some long-chain alcohols withdraw water from cells, leaving them partly plasmolysed. Usually one or more cryoprotectant is advantageously incorporated into a cryopreservation protocol. Bajaj and Reinert (1977) suggested that an efficient cryoprotectant should have the following properties:

- no toxicity;

- a low molecular weight;

- be readily miscible with water;

- an ability to permeate cells rapidly;

- an ability to be easily washed away from cells.

Commonly used protectants are dimethylsulphoxide (DMSO), glycerol, mannitol, sorbitol, and (poly)ethylene glycol, either alone or in combination. Withers and King (1979) reported that proline (which accumulates naturally in the cells of many plants under stress), can give tissues a greater tolerance of poor thaw recovery conditions than DMSO or glycerol. Sugars, amino acids and methanol are also sometimes employed, particularly in conjuction with another compound. The most appropriate cryoprotectant depends on the kind of plant being treated. So far, DMSO is the most popular, but it can be toxic at high concentrations. Concentrations of between 5–15% are commonly used for the slow freezing of shoot apical meristems. Mixtures of cryoprotectants have often been more successful than single compounds (Finkle and Ulrick, 1979; Nag and Street, 1973; Maddox *et al.*, 1983) especially in conjunction with DMSO, which may enhance uptake of the other components (Morris, 1980). Mixtures of chemicals are frequently used for suspension cultures. The total concentration of the protectants is usually 1–2 M. Although they are only likely to be acting as osmotica, all extracellular and some intracellular solutes will contribute to the overall cryoprotective effect.

Storage

Successful cryopreservation should enable valuable germplasm to be preserved for long periods. In an ideal protocol, frozen tissues should retain their viability during many years and be capable of regenerating plants after thawing. Many reports describe the regeneration of plants from a proportion of explants after a brief period at −196°C, but few describe successful storage for longer intervals.

In theory, once the water in plant tissues has been inactivated by non-disruptive freezing, the period of storage should make little difference to viability. This has been the case in some experiments, for example there was little difference in the proportion of *Pisum sativum* meristems which survived in liquid nitrogen for 1 (68%) and 26 weeks (61%) (Kartha *et al.*, 1979), and storage up to 10 months had no effect on plant regeneration from *Trifolium repens* meristems (Yamada *et al.*, 1991). Some material has been kept successfully in liquid nitrogen for long periods. Bajaj (1981b) was able to grow potato plants from meristems stored for 2 years. Loss of viability has been recorded in some instances: 95% of *Fragaria* meristems survived for one week in liquid nitrogen to produce plants after thawing, whereas only over 55% produced plants when the storage interval was extended to 8 weeks (Kartha *et al.*, 1980).

Viability testing

In developing cryopreservation techniques, the ability to assess the condition of specimens at various stages is very beneficial. A qualitative assessment of structural damage can be made by direct microscopic examination. Ultrastructural examination with electron microscopes has also provided information on cellular damage and the pattern of recovery growth. Loss of osmotic property can be detected by treatment with hypertonic or hypotonic solutions. Histological viability tests are also available which can be quick and objective and can provide information (sometimes of a quantitative nature) about the specific physiological condition of frozen and thawed cells. These tests have, however, been criticised on the grounds that:

- they give information about organelles as opposed to cells;

- their use may contribute to a loss of viability that is not noticed at the time of testing.

True physiological condition is probably best assessed with the combined results from a wide range of tests and, ultimately, the ability of the cells or organ to grow and regenerate.

Progress and prospects

Although a considerable amount of experimental work has been put into cryopreservation techniques, methods are not yet sufficiently reliable to be used for storing the germplasm of major plant collections. Experimental work is aimed at remedying this situation. The need to conserve plant cells that are genetically true-to-type limits the range of plant material that can be considered suitable for storage.

Suspension cultures

Highly cytoplasmic cells are most likely to be found in suspension cultures at the end of lag phase or during the period of exponential growth. Samples of cells withdrawn at these times generally have high recovery rates after freeze preservation and provide a very suitable material for the cryopreservation of many different kinds of plants (see reviews by Withers, 1980a,c). The best results are often obtained with dense suspensions (Brown *et al.*, 1974; Bajaj, 1976).

Unfortunately, cells in suspension cultures are very likely to undergo genetic change. There is also the added difficulty that many suspension cultures are not morphogenic. The use of suspensions for reliable germplasm storage therefore depends on being able to select, with confidence, genetically stable and morphogenically competent cell lines. Genetically stable ones have been isolated in only a very limited range of species; some embryogenic suspensions may be an exception.

Techniques. Maddox *et al.* (1983) developed a simple method, requiring very little customised equipment, to freeze cell suspensions of tobacco species. The suspensions, initially with a packed cell volume of 60%, were recovered on Caboche (1980) medium (designed to support the growth of cells at low density) with only a low level of auxin. Haploid *Nicotiana plumbaginifolia* cells, stored in this way, were recovered after more than one year in liquid nitrogen, and had retained their original ploidy.

In experiments of Weber *et al.* (1983), fast growing cell suspensions of soybean, Downy Thornapple and carrot were pretreated by partial plasmolysis using 1.0 M sorbitol in the medium. Temperature was decreased from 0°C to –35°C at 1°C per minute. The cultures were then kept for up to six months at –80° or –196°C, and eventually thawed rapidly to 22°C in the presence of 1.0 M sorbitol. At least 19% of the colony-forming capacity of the cells was retained after storage at the lower temperature. Carrot plantlets were retrieved at high frequency from the colonies and were apparently true-to-type. Soybean protoplast cultures subjected to the same protocol but with 0.7 M sorbitol, produced cell clones from individual protoplasts with only one-thousandth the efficiency of unfrozen control.

Watanabe *et al.* (1983) obtained suspensions from lavender callus pieces. These were subjected to storage in liquid nitrogen for 6–21 days using a cryoprotection protocol involving stepwise freezing, followed by rapid thawing. The cells which were recovered formed colonies, and eventually normal-looking calluses, on solid **Linsmaier and Skoog (1965)** medium. Morphogenic potential (*i.e.* spontaneous root and shoot production) and bio-synthetic capacity were unaltered from the pre-storage state.

Before freezing is commenced, it can be beneficial to apply a short period of osmotic stress to cell suspensions by adding mannitol or sorbitol to the medium for a single passage (Pritchard *et al.*, 1986). An embryogenic cell suspension of *Picea glauca* was pre-cultured for 24 h in a medium containing 0.4 M sorbitol. Cells were then treated with a cryoprotectant combination of 0.4 M sorbitol and 5% (0.64 M) DMSO. The process of freezing

was then begun: firstly to –35°C at a controlled rate of 0.3°C per minute, and then to liquid nitrogen. Callus capable of giving rise to plantlets could be obtained from the stored cells after one year of storage: its embryogenic capacity was the same as that of an unfrozen control (Kartha *et al.*, 1988).

Callus cultures

Some success has been reported with the freeze preservation of callus, for example that of cherry, *Prunus cerasus* (Tumanov *et al.*, 1968), *Atropa belladonna* (Nag and Street, 1975a,b), and tobacco (Michler and Lineberger, 1981). Sakai and Sugawara (1973) achieved survival of hybrid Black Poplar *(Populus euramericana)* calli in liquid nitrogen by cold hardening the tissue initially and then freezing in a stepwise manner. Cryoprotectants were not employed. Tisserat *et al.* (1981) revived embryogenic callus cultures and regenerated plantlets of date palms after three months in freeze storage. Protocols for the freeze preservation of callus, in which rice callus is used as a model, have been given by Finkle and Ulrich (1983).

The storage of buds and meristems

Many plant organs have proved to be difficult or impossible to store at low temperatures. This has probably been on account of their size and the fact that they are generally composed of cells which are structurally and functionally different. Each cell type may require a specific freeze-thaw protocol to avoid damage. Differential cell sensitivity can even be detected in structures of a relatively low level of organisation as illustrated by the work of Grout and Henshaw (1980) and of Towill (1981). Shoot tip explants consisting of the apical dome and two or three leaf primordia, were stored at –196°C. On revival, it was noted that many of the primordial cells had been irreversibly damaged, but a much lower percentage of meristematic cells had lost their viability.

Because of their genetic stability and the uniformity of the progeny to which they are able to give rise, the most suitable explants for the long term storage of germplasm would be apical meristems or meristems within larger buds, and possibly somatic embryos from a genetically stable regeneration system. These organs are also suitable subjects for cryopreservation on account of their small size, high density, and low water content. Research effort has been especially devoted to finding suitable methods for the storage of meristems. Usually they are dissected from buds before cryopreservation, but in some plants it has been possible to freeze intact buds in liquid nitrogen and dissect out the meristems for culture after the buds have been thawed (Yakuwa and Oka, 1988).

Table 9. Examples of the successful cryopreservation of meristem tips in five different plant genera.

SPECIES/ REFERENCE	CRYOPROTECTION	COLD CONDITIONING	FREEZING RATE	THAWING RATE	RECOVERY	SURVIVAL	COMMENTS
Carnation (*Dianthus caryophyllus*) Seibert & Wetherbee (1977)	5% DMSO for 80–100min in rinsing solution	Yes - parent plants grown at 4°C for at least 3 days	Rapid. Best at greater than 50°C/min. Vial immersed in liquid N_2	Rapid. Explant immersed in water at 37°C	At room temperature. Washed twice with rinsing solution	Plantlets from about 60% of cultures after 6 months storage	Apices with 2–3 leaf primordia gave the best results. Those with 4 primordia also produced callus. Rinsing solution based on **MS** medium.
Carnation (*Dianthus caryophyllus*) Dereuddre et al. (1988)	Pre-culture on 0.75M sucrose & treated with 5% (or more) DMSO	No	Slow. 0.5°C/min to −40°C then to liquid N_2 for storage	2 min in water bath at 40°C	To culture medium with 0.75M sucrose. Subcultured daily on decreasing sucrose until standard 0.1M reached	100% regrowth from tips of shoots precultured for 2 months *in vitro*	Apices fom shoots cultured *in vitro* survived best; progressive improvements to 3 weeks culture. Resistance to freezing decreased as distance of bud from apex increased.
Andean potato (*Solanum goniocalyx*) Grout & Henshaw (1978, 1980)	5% DMSO for 1 h while explant held on paper bridge in liquid medium	No - plants grown at a minimum of 10°C in a greenhouse	Rapid. Explant removed on a needle and plunged into liquid N_2	Rapid. Explant immersed in liquid medium at 35°C for one minute	Explant kept on filter paper bridge at room temperature before culture	20% survival after 3 weeks cryopreservation (assessed as production of shoots or green callus)	Much of the primordial tissue & some apical dome was damaged. When apices could regenerate, they gave 50% plants & 50% callus formation. All shoots produced plantlets within 6 weeks
Pea (*Pisum sativum*) Kartha et al., (1979); Kartha (1981b)	Precultured with 5% DMSO on solid **B5** medium, then moved to liquid **B5** & DMSO added to 5% over 30 min. Further 10 minutes equilibration	Yes - seeds germinated at 4°C in dark	Slow. Machine controlled at 0.6°C/min until −40°C then put into liquid N_2	Rapid. Tubes containing explants plunged into water at 37°C for 90 sec then placed in ice bath	Medium containing specimens diluted by stepwise addition of **B5** over 30 min. Then washed with **B5** medium	% explants that regenerated into plants as follows: 1 hour - 73% 26 weeks - 60% 52 weeks - 60%	Well developed shoots formed 21 days after thawing were rooted and grown normally. Cryopreservation better than seed storage because of possibility of eliminating Pea Seed-borne Mosaic Virus.
Rubus spp. (5 accessions) Reed & Lagerstedt (1987)	Combination of 10% PEG + 10% glucose + 10% DSMO best cryoprotectant mixture	No	Slow. 0.8°C/min to −40°C then rapidly to −196°C in presence of cryoprotectants	Warmed at 40°C/sec	Water bath at room temperature. Drained then to culture medium with 1 μM BAP	50–90% recovery according to spp. & cv.	Another cryoprotectant mixture (10%PEG + 10% trehalose + 10% DMSO) was very good with *R. ideaus* cvs.
Strawberry (*Fragaria × ananassa*) *Kartha et al.* (1980); Kartha (1981b)	Precultured on mass propagation medium (**MS**+2.25g/l BAP) + 5% DMSO for 2 days. Moved to liquid **MS** & 5% DMSO added over 30 min equilibration	As Kartha et al. (1979) above	Slow. Controlled by machine 0.5–1%/min until −40°C then plunged into liquid N_2	As Kartha et al. (1979) above except **MS** medium was used	As Kartha et al. (1979) above except **MS** medium was used	After storage for : 1 week - 95% 80 weeks - 75% (Kartha, 1981b)	Growth on the initiation medium was resumed within 7–10 days after thawing. Shoots developed following meristem swelling. Transferred to a mass propagation medium where many shoots were produced.

Unfortunately, present techniques seldom ensure that all the cells within a shoot tip or bud are able to preserve their viability during the process of freezing and thawing. The eventual survival of only a proportion of the cells in the tissue can result in the loss of organ integrity. In only some instances have shoots been grown directly from frozen buds as would be expected. Frequently the capacity for normal co- ordinated growth has been disrupted by cryogenic storage, resulting in surviving cells giving rise to adventitious shoots, or somatic embryos. In other instances a primary callus has grown from the tissues of thawed buds, requiring the production of adventitious shoots before plants could be regenerated. Indirect shoot formation is undesirable because genetic variation may result during the callus phase.

Embryos and pseudobulbils formed from cultured ovules of *Citrus sinensis* were frozen in liquid nitrogen for 5 minutes by Marin and Duran-Vila (1988). The embryos turned brown when they were returned to culture medium after slow thawing, but after 34–65 days some developed green patches from which grew new embryos, pseudobulbils and callus. Somatic embryos of *Picea abies* have been stored in liquid nitrogen (Boulay *et al.*, 1988).

Techniques. Table 9 illustrates protocols for the storage of meristem tips of five different species. Similar methods have been employed to preserve and recover viable meristems, shoot tips or buds of other plants, including: apple, asparagus, carnation, cassava, chickpea, gooseberry, peanut, pear, potato and wild *Solanum*, strawberry, and tomato. Steps which are typically adopted are shown in Fig. 68.

Kartha *et al.* (1982) described a *droplet freezing* technique. The actual freeze/thaw routine was fairly similar to that described by Kartha and co-workers for different species (Table 9), but the freezing vehicle was unique. According to this method a 'freezing solution' is prepared (cryoprotectant and medium) in which meristems are equilibrated. Freezing takes place in droplets created by an 18 μm gauge sterile aluminium foil mesh placed within Petri dishes. Meristems are evenly distributed over the foil along with 2–3 μl of freezing solution for each organ. A high proportion of cassava meristems survived and produced callus, callus and leaves, or plantlets, after they had been stored frozen for 1 hour.

Protocols need to be improved before the cryopreservation of meristems can be used for the storage of genetically valuable material. Methods are far from standardized and those recommended for different kinds of plants still vary quite widely. The proportion of explants which recover and grow after freeze storage also varies from one experiment to another and is often unacceptably low. Towill (1988) suggested that a cryopreservation method was insufficiently reliable for germplasm storage until predictably, at least 80% of stored meristems can be induced into regrowth after thawing.

Embryos

Somatic embryos, or immature zygotic embryos, have been successfully cryopreserved. Desiccation or plasmolysis before freezing seems to be essential. *Capsella bursa-pastoris* embryos were successfully cryopreserved after they had been pre-cultured for several days on a medium containing 0.8 M sucrose (Monnier and Leddet, 1978, 1980). Increasing the concentration of sucrose in the culture medium from 0.1 M to 0.3 M for a period before cryopreservation, increased the number of somatic embryos of oil palm which survived freezing Engelmann *et al.* 1985). In 1986, Engelmann and Baubault listed 12 species in which somatic embryos had been cryopreserved, and 10 species in which success had been achieved with zygotic embryos.

Other organs

Anthers (*e.g.* Bajaj, 1981a) and isolated pollen have also been sucessfully cryopreserved so that direct embryogenesis, or callus followed by plant regeneration, could be induced upon thawing. After freezing, isolated microspores of *Brassica napus* produced only 10% of the number of somatic embryos that could be obtained from unfrozen pollen. However, 88 % of the resulting plantlets were diploid and 12% haploid. Only 7% of the plantlets obtained from unfrozen microspores were diploid (Charne *et al*, 1988). These workers suggested that if microspore survival could be improved, low temperature freezing could proved a valuable method of producing homozygous diploid plants from pollen.

Review articles

The freeze preservation of plant material has been extensively reviewed, for example by Sakai (1984, 1985); Steponkus (1985), various authors in the book edited by Kartha (1985b); Chen and Kartha (1987); Dereuddre and Engelmann (1987); Withers (1985, 1987a,b, 1988); and Villalobos *et al.* (1991).

SHIPMENT AND DISTRIBUTION

Germplasm exchange

Plant material *in vitro*, that can be certified free from pests and diseases, is obviously suitable for the exchange of genetic resources between countries, particularly those of vegetatively propagated species. In fact there are many theoretical advantages to the importer and exporter from using *in vitro* material for international exchange; some of those listed by Parliman (1986) are:

— the small size of the shipments;

— that shipments are buffered against the external environment while being despatched;

— the absence of contamination of the culture shows that many obvious pests are absent;

— meristem tip cultures are likely to be virus-free, but if virus-infected material is imported there is little risk of cross contamination;

— virus- or pest-indexed tissues can be shipped, stored and maintained, with little opportunity for re-infection;

— tissue can be held *in vitro* during greenhouse or field testing, and when released some can be kept *in vitro* to safeguard against reinfestation;

— multiplication of released material can be rapid;

— as all imported plantlets can be derived from a single meristem, the importer does not have to identify subclones.

Contamination and disease

The risk of importing pests and diseases in cultures is clearly far less than than from the import of whole plants or plant parts. The possible contamination of material upon transfer from a collection to suitable containers for shipment, can be guarded against by allowing a delay of 7–10 days defore shipment, so that any fresh containation can be detected before the consignment is despatched.

Nevertheless, tissue cultures can carry hidden contaminants and obligate pathogens and parasites, so that officials at the point of origin cannot always be sure of their absence. For this reason, plants cultured *in vitro* may be still subject to import restrictions and may need to be re-established as intact plants in quarantine greenhouses for further examination. This applies particularly to all prohibited species. Most countries have a list of such plants for which virulent pests and diseases are known, whose import would consid-erably endanger native species or crops. The import of material of prohibited species is only licensed under special circumstances. Plants imported as tissue cultures will invariably still be tested for pathogens before release.

Shipments

It will be obvious from the above, that shoot material (meristem tip, shoot cultures, or rooted plantlets) is usually the best material for despatch abroad, although, where they can be produced, storage organs such as microtubers, or bulblets, may be more appropriate. Sprouted mini-tubers of potato packed in damp cotton wool can be stored on arrival or immediately planted into pots where they will give rise to plants without a period of dormancy (Estrada *et al.*, 1986).

Entry for any particular consignment of plant material will depend on the genotype of the plant and the purpose of the importation. It may be easier to gain entry for a few cultures intended for research within a recognised laboratory, than for larger shipments intended to provide stock for *in vivo* cultivation. Shipments of prohibited species will clearly present the most problems. Tissue cultured material is convenient for despatch, but can be disturbed and damaged during transit unless handled carefully. Packages of tissue cultures should be despatched by air, and carried on the person, or sent as freight. Their small size and lightness, and the fact that they are probably better able to withstand transit conditions than intact plants, make them especially suitable for this purpose. Special precautions are only necessary to ensure against breakage and extremes of temperature; flexible plastic containers are to be preferred.

Cultures grown in a sealed sleeves are particularly suitable for transit. An effective method of shipping sweet potato is to culture single-node cuttings in 10 mm × 35 mm plastic Petri dishes containing 5 ml of an **MS** salt medium (3% sucrose, 1% agar), and to seal the dishes in sterile plastic sleeves (Jarret and Florkowski, 1990). *Musa* germplasm is shipped as rooted plantlets in Cultu- Saks (see page 115), if plantlets are required by the recipient which can be transferred directly to soil. It is sent as proliferating shoot cultures, in transparent plastic vials with screwcaps, if tissue culture facilities are available, and the recipient wishes to multiply the material (De Smet and Van den Houwen, 1991).

Documentation

When plant cultures are to be sent to a remote location, it is important to send adequate documentation with the shipment. The recipient needs to know in detail, the source of the culture; its age; its history (including details of subculturing procedures); the medium on which it has been grown; and the media and conditions recommended for continued culture, plant regeneration and acclimatization. The material must be accompanied by an invoice (which will usually state that the material is intended only for scientific purposes); a packing list; an import permit supplied by the consignee (if this is required by the country of destination); and a phytosanitary certificate, issued within two weeks of shipment by the Ministry of Agriculture of the donor country, describing the disease status of the original stock plant, therapeutic measures which have been employed during *in vitro* culture,and the results of subsequent diagnostic tests to detect the presence of pathogens. Obtaining a phytosanitary certificate entails an inspection by officials of an appropriate government department. In the United Kingdom and the U.S.A. there is a rigorous checking procedure of the entire laboratory, and an export licence may be denied if disease or contamination is discovered in cultures, even if they are not the ones intended for export. An importing country may require a declaration in addition to the phytosanitary certificate, stating for example, that certain treatments have been administered to the imported material, or that a particular pest of that plant is not known to occur in the country of origin. It may be stipulated that tissue cultures must have originated from virus indexed mother plants.

The provision of an added declaration can considerably improve the perceived health status of the consignment, although the best guarantee of health is where there is co-operation between importing and exporting countries, and a certification of health status is accepted as valid (Kahn, 1986).

Procedures on import.

Cultures will be examined at the point of entry, together with the accompanying phytosanitary certificate. The inspector will be especially vigilant for signs of contamination and pest infestation. The medium must be therefore be clear and should not contain additives which will make it cloudy or opaque (*i.e.* charcoal) (Kahn, 1986). Contaminated cultures, or possibly a whole consignment containing just one or two contaminated vessels, will be rejected.

Tissue culture techniques can be used beneficially as part of quarantine procedures. After a preliminary inspection, budwood of *Citrus* imported into Spain, is disinfested and transferred to a simple medium *in vitro* until bud flushing occurs. The flushed shoots are then disinfected and their tips micrografted onto seedling rootstocks for precaution-

ary virus elimination (Chapter 5). Micro-grafted plants are then transferred to a quarantine glasshouse where they are studied and indexed over a two-year period. Virus- infected material is destroyed unless the accession is rare and important, when micrografting would be employed again in a further attempt to eliminate the pathogen (Navarro, 1984).

Present practice

There are several improvements in tissue culture techniques which would make the exchange of plant material more simple. It would, for example, be an advantage if tissue culture methods could be used on all plant genotypes with equal success; if the risk of genetic variants could be reduced; if tissue cultures could be started with equal facility at all times of the year; and if there were an *in vitro* method of virus indexing (Parliman, 1986).

The widespread use of *in vitro* cultures, or plantlets, for the international shipment of clonally propagated germplasm has been slow to develop. *In vitro* shipment has been accepted by various countries as a safe means of receiving clonal *Solanum and Manihot* (cassava) (Roca *et al.*, 1979; 1982: Kartha, 1984). According to Parliman and Daubeny (1988), the exchange of *in vitro* cultures of *Ipomoea* and *Fragaria* is now also relatively common, but the general transfer of plants in this way is not yet practical, nor justifiable. Early optimism that tissue cultured plants could readily be grown free of all pests and diseases has not been fulfilled. Common cultural practices do not eliminate obligate parasites from plant material and even when special procedures are followed, it is still difficult to ensure that all fungal, bacterial, viral and virus-like parasites and contaminants have been removed. As practices for the shipment and receipt of plant material grown by standard horticultural methods are often adequate, quarantine authorities in many parts of the world have not seen the need to set up special tissue culture facilities or to retrain staff in appropriate techniques.

Future prospects

Despite these cautionary remarks, there is no doubt that the shipment of plants *in vitro* will increase as the micropropagation of rare and unusual plants continues to develop. Kahn (1978; 1986) has reviewed the use of tissue cultures for the exchange of genetic stocks; discusses the problems associated with importation; and cites several examples of how they have been used to import and export plants into and out of the U.S.A.

7

Factors affecting Growth and Morphogenesis

I. Genotype and the Physical Environment

Factors influencing the growth and morphogenesis of tissue cultures can be grouped under three main headings:

- **Genotype** (*i.e.* the genetic constitution) of the plant material cultured. In the present context, the terms genotype and variety are interchangeable since it is by virtue of genotype that plant varieties differ:

- **Environment**. The conditions under which the culture is grown:

- **Tissue dependent factors**, described in the following Chapter.

Many features of the environment have an effect on plant tissue cultures. Those discussed in this chapter are those of the physical environment (factors such as temperature and light).

The effect of the substrate on which the culture is grown is discussed in Chapter 9, while growth regulator additions are described in Chapters 11 and 12.

Under each of the headings above, there are numerous factors capable of modifying the behaviour of plant tissue cultures; many are capable of interacting one with another, sometimes making the task of optimising growth and/or morphogenesis *in vitro* extremely difficult. The most successful protocols for plant propagation are those in which conditions have been defined to enable a large number of plants to be produced reliably from a wide range of genetic material.

THE EFFECTS OF GENOTYPE

The growth of cultured tissues of organs, and morphogenesis *in vitro*, are more influenced by genotype than by any other factor. There are numerous examples in the literature in which the results obtained during tissue culture have varied from one variety of plant to another, and it is probably true to say that effects of genotype impose one of the greatest constraints to the tissue culture and micropropagation of plants. In some instances, observed responses have been related by identifiable genetic factors, *e.g.*:

Nuclear genes	Bullock *et al.* (1982)
	Foroughi-Wehr *et al.* (1982)
	Lazar *et al.* (1984)
	Rhodes *et al.* (1986a)
	Szakács *et al.* (1988)
	Mathias and Fukui (1986)
Cytoplasmic genes	Matthias *et al.* (1986)
	Narasimhulu *et al.* (1988)
	Wan *et al.* (1988a)
Gene interactions	Keyes and Bingham (1979)
	Wan *et al.* (1988a)

Nuclear genes governing morphogenesis have been thought to have a high general combining ability (tomato — Frankenberger and Tigchelaar, 1980); to be recessive (tomato — Frankenberger *et al.*, 1981); to be dominant, or partially dominant (alfalfa — Reisch and Bingham, 1980: *Zea mays* — Rhodes *et al.*, 1986a); or to be additive (*Brassica* — Buiatti *et al.*, 1974a,b). Ploidy is found to have an effect in some genera: dihaploid lines of *Solanum tuberosum* are more likely to produce adventitious shoots from callus than are their tetraploid parents (Fish and Jones, 1988).

Many genotype-dependent effects are caused by interactions between the plant's genotype and the cultural environment. Variety *A* may undergo morphogenesis in response to growth regulators of one kind, while variety *B* is unresponsive until the concentration of the regulants is changed and/or different regulatory compounds are used. Other differential responses can be due to plants of varying genotypes requiring specific media or environmental conditions.

Because of genotypic specificity, media and the cultural environment often need to be varied from one genus or species of plant to another. Although general methodologies can be established for plant tissue culture, even closely related varieties of plants can differ in their cultural requirements. The best method of micro-propagating a new plant must usually be determined by experiment. It has been particularly difficult to obtain regulate

morphogenesis of many plants within the families Leguminosae and Gramineae.

PREDOMINANTLY GENOTYPIC EFFECTS

If interaction with the environment were the only cause of genotype specificity, it should be possible to culture all plants of a similar kind with equal success once the specific conditions for each had been ascertained. Unfortunately, the behaviour of plant tissues *in vitro* in processes such as callus formation and growth and morphogenesis often seem to be under an over-riding genetic control, with other factors exerting only a minor effect. Thus in wheat, some genotypes give rise to plants from tissues cultured on several different media, while little success is obtained with other varieties on any of these choices (Lazar *et al.*, 1983). Similarly in *Medicago* more plants were produced from somatic embryos in highly regenerative cultivars than from those with a low capacity for regeneration, regardless of the media employed (Brown and Atanassov, 1985). It is still not possible to say whether the inability to induce morphogenesis in some genotypes is due only to our incomplete knowledge, or to an over-riding genetic constraint.

Plant genotype has a sufficiently marked effect on the behaviour of cultured plant tissues for it to be possible to breed plants for improvements in all aspects of *in vitro* performance (see below). Some of the more obvious ways in which growth and morphogenesis have been found to be influenced by genotype are discussed below.

Culture initiation

Surprisingly, in some genera, the rate at which explants survive in culture can depend on apparently minor differences in the genotype of mother plants. For example, there were large differences in the capacity of shoot tip explants from different mature *Eucalyptus marginata* trees to grow *in vitro* after the necessary sterilisation procedures (McComb and Bennett, 1982) and the survival of *Dahlia* meristem tips in culture varied even between closely related plant varieties (Wang *et al.*, 1988). Hammerschlag (1982a) found a big difference in the viability of newly explanted shoot tips derived from different peach cultivars, and Roca *et al.* (1978) recorded that varieties of potato and their hybrids differed more in their behaviour to shoot tip initiation than in shoot proliferation at Stage II.

Callus

Initiation and growth

Many reports illustrate how the capacity of explanted tissues to form callus and the subsequent growth rate of callus cultures, can both be variety-dependent. Results from the following plants provide some examples:

Brassica	Baroncelli *et al.* (1974)
Helianthus	Espinasse and Lay (1989)
Maize	Shannon and Batey (1973) Green and Phillips (1975)
Oats	Cummings *et al.* (1976)
Pelargonium	Jelaska and Jelencic (1980)
Petunia	Izhar and Power (1977)
Potato	Simon and Peloquin (1977)
Rice	Abe and Sasahara (1982)
Sainfoin	Arcioni and Mariotti (1983)
Tobacco	Venketeswaran and Mahlberg(1962) Cheng and Smith (1973) Keyes *et al.* (1981)
Wheat	Shimada and Makino (1975) Sears and Deckard (1982)

The effect of genotype is also seen in differences in the texture and colour (Taira *et al.*, 1977), and morphogenic capacity, of callus from closely related varieties of plants.

The results obtained in any particular test depend on the medium, the growth regulators used, and other environmental factors. Under the conditions employed by Gresshoff and Doy (1972a), callus cultures could be established from only three out of eighteen *Arabidopsis thaliana* genotypes, and one out of forty-three barley lines. Bayliss and Dunn (1979), however, could plot a normal distribution of the amount of callus produced from the seed embryos of each of 45 randomly chosen barley varieties on **MS** medium containing 1 mg/l 2,4-D.

Baroncelli *et al.* (1978) found that the genetic control of wheat callus growth was different in root and nodal explants, and a somewhat similar result was obtained in rice by Mikami and Kinoshita (1988). Although vigorously-growing callus was formed on the tissues of only some varieties, the growth response of seed, coleoptile and radicle explants was broadly related. However, the ability of the varieties to form callus from anthers was not correlated with the results obtained from the other explants. The authors suggested that their results might have been due to there being different genetic determinants of callus formation according to the physiological condition of the explants or according to their ploidy.

Direct morphogenesis

Adventitious shoots

Plants vary considerably in their ability to produce adventitious shoots directly on tissue explants. In general, success *in vitro* closely parallels the ease with which adventitious shoots may be regenerated without resort to aseptic culture, except that under controlled and disease-free conditions, the morphogenic potential of the species is magnified, and shoots are produced more freely than they otherwise would be. Thus those genera which produce plantlets readily from severed leaves placed in soil or compost in a greenhouse (*e.g. Begonia, Peperomia, Saintpaulia*, and *Streptocarpus*) also give rise to large numbers of adventitious shoots directly from leaf or petiole segments when these are cultured on an appropriate medium. In some other kinds of plants, aseptic culture can be used to induce direct shoot regeneration that otherwise is seldom observed. *Chrysanthemum × morifolium*, for instance, can give rise to adventitious shoots *in vitro* from explants of small leaves, petioles, stems, flower pedicels or young flower buds. Direct shoot regeneration commonly occurs on the explanted tissues of dicotyledonous species, but in monocotyledons is only normally observed in species which produced fleshy storage leaves.

Species which produce bulbs seem to be universally capable of producing adventitious shoots from the basal part of explanted bulb scale leaves. According to Broertjes *et al.* (1968), only monocotyledons of the families Amaryllidaceae, Araceae, Liliaceae and Taccaceae are capable of forming adventitious shoots on leaf tissue. Many of these plants can also produce buds on floral stems (scapes).

Despite these very broad differences between species and genera, the capacity for direct morphogenesis on any given medium can also be found to vary between closely related plant varieties. Mutant lines of the weed *Arabidopsis thaliana* had a lower shoot- and root-forming capacity than the normal (parent) line, but morphogenic ability was fully restored in their hybrids (Nobuharu, 1980; Goto, 1981). This is an illustration of complementation, each of the pair of genomes present in the hybrid supplying one or more products absent or impaired by the mutation in the other. Sometimes the hybrids would show *heterosis* (hybrid vigour) by exceeding the organogenic capability of the normal lines.

The shoot forming capacities of two pure lines of tomato ('Apedice' and 'Porphyre') and their reciprocal hybrids, were found by Bigot *et al.* (1977) to vary according to the derivation of explants and the growth regulators used. Shoots were initiated directly on the explanted tissue and/or on callus produced from superficial tissues. 'Porphyre' always produced more shoots from hypocotyl explants than 'Apedice'. This ability was maternally transmitted to one of the hybrids and, with one particular combination of auxin and cytokinin, hybrids produced significantly more shoots than the parents (a further example of heterosis). The relative regenerative capacity of the genotypes studied was not the same when cotyledon or leaf explants were cultured.

Root formation

Whether roots or shoots can be induced to form in callus cultures can frequently be controlled by addition of growth regulators, but in some cultures even closely related genotypes may have different propensities (Kim *et al.*, 1988). Similarly, the facility with which adventitious roots can be induced to form directly on shoots grown *in vitro*, varies widely, sometimes even amongst varieties of the same species (Chapter 14).

Embryogenesis

The ability of closely related plants to produce somatic embryos directly on explants is also under genetic control and differences between varieties are often found. Stamp and Meredith (1988a) obtained somatic embryos on the zygotic embryos of four cultivars of *Vitis vinifera*, but could not induce them to form on the cultivar 'Pinot Noir'. The direct formation of somatic embryos on apple leaf segments was genotype-dependent (Welander, 1988).

Axillary shoot formation and proliferation

In shoot cultures, whether axillary shoots can be induced to grow and proliferate, and the rate of shoot multiplication on any given medium, is genotype dependent. The following are two examples from many in the literature:

The number of transferable shoots produced in 22 days of shoot culture of *Antirrhinum* varied between 2.14 in the variety with the slowest rate of multiplication of the nine tested, to 5.91 in the variety with the highest rate (Newbury, 1986).

DeWald *et al.* (1988) found that, on a single medium with the same growth regulators, the number of pineapple plantlets produced in 13 months from a single bud, varied from 210–380 for the variety 'Prolera'; to 300–350 for 'PR–1–

67'; and 40–85 for 'Smooth Cayenne'. In this case, although multiplication was mainly from axillary shoots, some adventitious shoots arose from basal callus.

Occasionally, genotypic factors may prevent a variety from producing any shoots on a selected medium. Shoots of one variety of *Liquidambar styraciflua* remained stunted, whereas three others could be multiplied satisfactorily by shoot culture (Sutter and Barker, 1984). In using a single medium to propagate several plum (*Prunus domestica*) cultivars, Jona and Vigliocco (1987) found that cv. 'Bluefire' formed hardly any multiple-shooted rosettes and so could not be multiplied. The cultivar 'Stanley' initially formed rosettes better than 'President', but the latter cultivar eventually proliferated most rapidly.

Indirect morphogenesis

Genotypic effects are influential in the regulation of adventitious organ formation from callus tissues. Separate root and shoot formation, or embryogenesis, is readily induced in plants of certain families or genera, and is obtained with difficulty in others. Differences in the morphogenic capacity of callus from different species or even varieties of plant are also commonly found. Examples will be seen in the work of:

Klimaszewska (1979)	*Peperomia*
Bourgin *et al.* (1979)	*Nicotiana*
Gosch-Wackerle *et al.* (1979)	*Triticum.*

To the extent that indirect morphogenesis is impossible without prior callus formation, callus growth and morphogenesis are connected. The rate of callus proliferation from genetically similar plants may not, however, always be a guide to the morphogenic capacity of the callus. In other cases morphogenic competence and callus production seem to be influenced by the same genes. In cauliflower, the weight of callus produced on leaf explants of inbred lines was related to the number of shoots formed directly on petal explants of the same varieties (Baroncelli *et al.*, 1973).

Intervarietal differences in the morphogenic capacities of callus tissues are also commonly found. The rate of adventitious shoot formation can vary between lines within a species [*e.g.* in *Glycine canescens*; Hammatt *et al.* (1987)], and the facility with which embryogenesis can be induced may vary between cultivars [*e.g.* in *Solanum melongena*; Matsuoka and Hinata (1979); alfalfa; Brown and Atanassov, (1985)]. In many experiments to study plant regeneration, callus of different plant varieties is induced to form on a single medium, but frequently when the calluses are plated onto a common regeneration medium, each has a different organogenic potential (*e.g.*

Barg and Umiel, 1977a; Margara, 1977b; Ohki *et al.*, 1978). Cummings *et al.* (1976) obtained plantlet formation from callus of 16 out of 23 varieties of oats, and Wehner and Locy (1981), shoot regeneration from only 28 out of 85 cucumber lines, although callus cultures were produced from explants in every case.

GENETIC CONTROL

The genetic control of growth and morphogenesis *in vitro* can result from either the primary or secondary effect of genes. Thus certain kinds of morphogenic responses in tissue cultures are seen to be directly related to the behaviour exhibited by whole plants or parts of plants *in vivo*, whereas features of the whole plant which influence other characteristics of *in vitro* culture, such as the rate of callus growth, are more difficult to determine. Genetically determined characteristics of the latter kind probably result from only the secondary effect of normal gene function. This represents a *spurious pleiotropy* in which the main effect of a gene or genes causes other unrelated things to happen.

By correlating both the rate of callus growth and the ability to form adventitious buds with characters of the mature plant, Baroncelli *et al.* (1974) suggested that in inbred lines of cauliflower there might be groups of genes capable of shifting plant development in different directions, their effect in culture being to influence the competing processes of cell proliferation and morphogenesis. Such genes have been thought most likely to exert their influence by regulating the effective levels of growth substances (Bayliss and Dunn, 1979). Endogenous growth substance levels may vary in different genotypes.

Inbred varieties of several plants have been found to produce callus less well than their hybrid progeny, in which heterosis seems to be manifest (*e.g.* from explants of maize endosperm — Tabata and Motoyoshi, 1965; alfalfa — Keyes and Bingham, 1979; tobacco cotyledons — Keyes *et al.* 1981). Heterosis may also be seen in the ability of anthers to form callus (Bullock *et al.*, 1982) or produce haploid embryos. Keyes *et al.* (1981) noted how in several plants, correlations were found between the rate of growth of tissues *in vitro*, and vigour in other agronomic traits. They suggested that characteristics of *in vitro* cultures might be of value for the rapid identification of hybrid combinations which could produce superior plants in the field. In *Petunia hybrida* however, Hanson and Read (1981) found that although F_1 hybrids

generally gave more vigorous plants and callus cultures than their inbred parents, there was no consistent correlation between tissue culture and field performance. Callus from the shoot meristems of the interspecific hybrid between *Trifolium hybridum* and *T. ambiguum* grew more slowly than that of either of the parental species (Rupert *et al.*, 1976).

Some of the characteristics of *in vitro* cultures of closely related genotypes have been subjected to biometrical analyses and in *Brassica oleracea* have been shown to be correlated in a complex fashion with apparently unrelated features of whole plants *in vivo* (Baroncelli *et al.*, 1973, 1974; Buiatti *et al.*, 1974a,b).

Genes governing the capacity for *in vitro* callus growth have been shown to be located in particular portions of wheat chromosomes (Shimada and Makino, 1975; Baroncelli *et al.*, 1978), and genes situated on *Nicotiana glauca* chromosomes were thought to be responsible for the relative rates of callus proliferation of triploid hybrid plants resulting from a *N. glauca* and *N. langsdorffii* cross (Cheng and Smith, 1973). Genetic factors governing callus formation and shoot regeneration in *N. tabacum* were deduced to reside chiefly in the part of its genome derived from *N. sylvestris* (Ogura and Tsuji, 1977).

Embryogenic callus resulted from culturing immature embryos of a *Vigna glabrescens* × *V. radiata* hybrid, but only non-morphogenic callus could be obtained from embryos of the reciprocal cross (Chen *et al.*, 1990).

Selection. Some *in vitro* characters can have high heritabilities†. In inbred cauliflower lines, Baroncelli and co-workers (1973) found values of 0.42 for the number of roots formed per callus, 0.39 for the proportion of petals which gave rise to callus, and 0.47 for the relative rates of callus growth. Selection amongst progeny segregating for these characteristics would clearly have resulted in improvement. Since then it has been clearly established that it is possible to improve upon the results obtained from plant tissues and organs *in vitro* by conventional plant breeding techniques.

Recurrent selection within a species has been effective in increasing the proportion of genotypes capable of regeneration from callus (*e.g.* from tetraploid alfalfa callus — Bingham *et al.*, 1975; Reisch and Bingham, 1980), and has enabled the selection and release of tetraploid alfalfa cultivars ('Regen S', 'Regen Y' and 'RA-3') having a high capacity for regeneration from tissue cultures. Selection of a diploid clone having this attribute has also been possible (McCoy and Bingham, 1977, 1979). Lines capa-

---

†   Heritability is that part of the variation in a character due to heritable differences

ble of improved morphogenesis could be selected from the progeny of crosses between *Trifolium* genotypes capable of producing adventitious buds directly from explants (Webb *et al.*, 1987).

Somaclonal variation. The degree of somaclonal variation engendered during *in vitro* culture is influenced by plant genotype to a marked extent (see Chapter 3).

THE SEX OF PLANTS

The sex of dioecious plant species appears to be genetically determined. The genes which are responsible for the sex of individual plants frequently give rise to a spurious pleiotropism *in vitro* in that they also modify the response of cultured tissues and organs.

Gui (1979) reported that more plantlets were generated from stem callus of female plants of *Actinidia chinensis* than from males. Even greater differences were discov-

ered by Mehra and Cheema (1980b) in *Populus ciliata*. In the presence of BAP, adventitious shoots were formed directly on immature leaf discs taken from female plants, whereas under identical conditions, none were produced on explants from males. Variation which also occurred using other explants in the growth of axillary shoots, callusing and adventitious root formation, led the authors to believe that in the tissues of the two sexes there were intrinsically dissimilar growth substance levels.

Carica papaya is dioecious. Litz and Conover (1981c) found that shoot tips of staminate plants of this species (which they say usually grow rapidly in the field and are not especially subject to adverse environments), became established more rapidly and proliferated more rapidly in shoot cultures, than those of pistillate ones. De Winnaar (1988) had the opposite experience. Only a small proportion of explants from staminate plants survived in a medium in which all the ones from pistillate or bisexual plants could be established satisfactorily.

THE ENVIRONMENT — SUBSTRATE EFFECTS

COMPOSITION OF THE MEDIUM

Media often need to be varied for different plant genera and according to the kind of culture to be undertaken. Frequently it is advantageous to move a culture from one kind of medium to another when the pattern of growth needs to be modified, or morphogenesis induced. However, many different kinds of plant cultures can be grown on one kind of medium. That of **Murashige and Skoog (1962)** (MS medium) has proved to be suitable for callus growth, direct and indirect morphogenesis, and shoot culture of many plant species.

Direct shoot formation can occur on the explants of some species in water alone. A very simple medium containing sucrose and a relatively low concentration of mineral salts is generally all that is required for root cultures and the micropropagation of most orchids, but both direct and indirect morphogenesis is very dependent on the medium used for *in vitro* culture, and a correct balance of inorganic, organic, and growth regulator constituents is essential.

Various compositions have been developed to improve the growth of one or more particular tissues in culture. Some of the features of these formulations which can influence growth and morphogenesis, are discussed in Chapter 9. However, as mentioned previously, most workers have found a distinct difference between charac-

ters such as growth, shoot proliferation and morphogenesis in tissue cultures from the best and the worst of a series of cultivars, behaviour which is only modified to a small extent by changing the composition of the medium on which they are cultured (*e.g.* in wheat — Lazar *et al.*, 1983; in *Brassica* — Narasimhulu and Chopra, 1988; and in alfalfa — Brown, 1988). Mathias and Simpson (1986) found that shoot regeneration in *Triticum* was more dependent on genotype than on the presence of complex organic additives in the medium.

Growth regulators

Growth and organogenesis *in vitro* are highly dependent on the interaction between naturally occurring endogenous growth substances and the analagous synthetic growth regulators which may be added to the medium. Growth regulators can bring about *de novo* morphogenesis on media containing suboptimal salt concentrations, and considerably enhance morphogenesis on an otherwise optimal medium (Margara, 1969b). The most effective growth regulator or combination of regulators, may depend upon other medium constituents. Marked differences between the regenerative abilities of plants, apparent on simple media, are likely to be produced by the use of appropriate growth regulants. Cotyledons originating from separate clones of Douglas fir, exhibit clear differences in their capacity to produce adventitious buds on a medium without growth regulators; but with the addition of a suitable auxin and a cytokinin, this variation diminishes considerably (Cheng, 1976a). The effects of regulants on morphogenesis are discussed extensively in Chapter 11.

Growth regulator × genotype interactions

It is often necessary to alter the growth regulator composition and/or concentration for *in vitro* culture according to the species or variety of plant being grown, and so it is wise to test any new genotype on media containing several different combinations of regulants. There are many examples of this genotype-induced specificity in the literature. The following illustrate the types of interactions commonly experienced.

The concentration of 2,4-D required for the development and further growth of callus tissue from *Phaseolus* hypocotyl tissue was shown by Mok and Mok (1977) to depend upon the species and variety of plant from which the explants were taken. The growth regulator was inhibitory to *P. lunatus* genotypes at 0.55 mg/l but 2.2 mg/l was required to arrest callus growth of the *P. vulgaris* varieties examined. Callus of *P. lunatus* cv. 'Kingston' showed near optimum growth at 4.4 mg/l 2,4-D, whereas that of cv. 'PI 194314' was inhibited at this concentration. There was also an eight-fold difference in the auxin requirement of 'Romana' and two other *P. vulgaris* genotypes. Mok *et al.* (1982b) have reported similar differences between *Phaseolus* genotypes in respect of their response to cytokinins. The activity of thidiazuron was approximately equal to that of zeatin in promoting the growth of callus of *P. lunatus* cv. 'Jackson Wonder', but in cv. 'PI 260415' it was at least ten times higher than that of zeatin. 'Jackson Wonder' callus showed cytokinin autonomy after treatment with either substance, whereas 'PI 260415' remained cytokinin-dependent under all conditions tested.

No cotyledon explants of *Brassica campestris* produced adventitious buds when placed on a medium containing 11.4 μM IAA plus 8.8 μM BAP, but 43% of those of *B. nigra* did so. *B. campestris* cotyledons required a mixture of 5.3μM NAA plus 4.4 μM BAP to promote shoot formation, but this combination of regulants was completely ineffective on *B. nigra* (Narasimhulu and Chopra, 1988).

Varieties of beet grown on **N30K** medium each needed different combinations of cytokinin and auxin to induce shoot formation from callus derived from flower bud explants (Margara, 1977b). The number of shoots formed from hyocotyl callus of two inbred tomato varieties depended on the quantity of auxin (IAA) and cytokinin (2-iP) in the growth medium. One of the reciprocal hybrids between them produced an intermediate number of shoots with 2-iP alone, but it gave rise to significantly more shoots than either parent when IAA and 2-iP were present together (Ohki *et al.*, 1978).

CONSISTENCY OF THE MEDIUM

Using solid or liquid media

Semi-solid media

The rate at which cultures grow and produce shoots during micropropagation can be influenced by the physical nature of the medium. For many purposes it is convenient to make media semi-solid by incorporating a gel such as agar (see page 338). The chief advantages of using a solidified medium are that:

- small explants are easily seen and recovered

- explants retain the same orientation throughout culture

- plant material is held above the medium so that no special means of aerating the culture is required

- shoots and roots grow in a more orderly fashion because the medium is stationary. In a moving liquid medium growth can be disorientated, shoot buds may be initiated but fail to grow into shoots; and in shoot cultures, separation of shoots for micropropagation can be difficult

- in an agitated liquid medium, callus may break up and/or shed cells to form a suspension culture. This does not occur on a solid medium.

Disadvantages of solidified media. There are disadvantages with the use of semi-solid media. Some agars contain inhibitory substances which may prevent morphogenesis in certain cultures (Powell and Uhrig, 1987), rates of growth can be slow (see below), toxic exudates from explants do not diffuse away quickly; and gel adhering to rooted plantlets may have to be washed off before they are transferred to soil. A further disadvantage is that the use of semi-solid media increases the time taken to clean containers and glassware for re-use. Vessels may need to be be autoclaved to re-melt the agar, scrubbed and hand rinsed before being placed in a dishwasher (although this will probably not be necessary if a heavy duty machine is used). Tubes which have been used with liquid medium can be placed directly into a washer.

Liquid media

As explained in Chapter 1, liquid media are necessary for suspension cultures but can also be used advantageously for the culture of callus and organs. Their use often results in faster rates of growth than are possible on semi-solid media (Table 10). This is because a greater surface area of the explant is in contact with a liquid, and, providing the medium is agitated, the diffusion gradients between it and the explant are reduced. These two factors combined enable a more efficient uptake of nutrients and growth regulators. In addition, toxic metabolites which may accumulate in the vicinity of the tissue are effectively dispersed.

There is a stationary film of water immediately adjacent to cultured plant tissue (the so-called *'Nernst' layer* — Nernst, 1904) which can reduce diffusion and be particularly rate-limiting to ion uptake from dilute solutions (Jenny, 1966; Polle and Jenny, 1971) where the concentration gradient across the film is low. The thickness of the film in liquid media will depend on the amount of agitation applied: in semi-solid media where there is little water movement, the layer may well impede micronutrient uptake.

Because plant material must normally be supplied with adequate oxygen, the uses to which a static liquid medium can be put are limited. Aeration is not a problem in cultures contained in very small volumes of liquid (*e.g.*

hanging drops), or in those submersed in shallow layers of liquid medium. Where a static liquid is to be used for the culture of large pieces of tissue or organs, explants must either be placed in a very shallow layer, so that some of the tissue protrudes above the surface; must float upon its surface; or be supported above the medium (see Chapter 9). A supply of oxygen for submerged cells, tissues or organs in large volumes of liquid media is normally obtained by shaking (Fig. 69), rotating the containers, stirring the medium, or by introducing a flow of sterile air (or a controlled mixture of gases) into the culture vessel. These measures also have the effect of suspending and moving the cultured cells or tissues in the medium, making the uptake of nutrients more effective. Special apparatus and/or special culture vessels are necessary for some of these techniques.

Anthers float on a liquid medium, but microspore-derived embryos or calluses are more dense and will sink if the dish is disturbed or moved: they may then die from lack of aeration. Small organs or small pieces of tissue can be made to float more effectively on liquid media if its density is increased by the addition of Ficoll. Anther-derived callus of barley (Kao, 1981) and embryos of *Triticum* could be made to float on the surface of a liquid medium, where they received improved aeration, when 100 g/l Ficoll (Type 400) was incorporated in the medium. In wheat, this treatment resulted in a high proportion of embryos developing into plants: growth in a

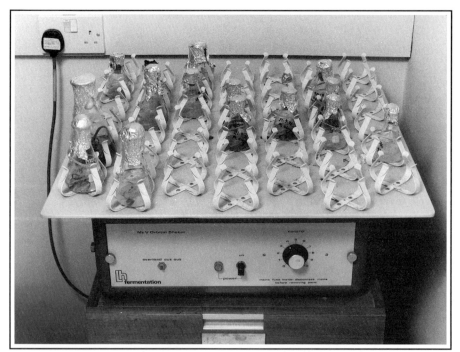

Fig. 69. A small rotary shaker of the type commonly used to agitate cell suspensions, or organ cultures, grown on a liquid medium.

Table 10. Examples of faster rates of growth using liquid, rather than solid media.

Plant	Method of culture	Results	Author/s,
Cattleya orchid	Tubes on roller drum	Explants reached 2 mm in 2 months *cf.* 4–6 months on agar medium	Lindemann *et al.*(1970)
Begonia × *hiemalis*	Shaken liquid	Increased rate of shoot growth	Simmonds and Werry (1987)
Boston fern stolon tips	Shaken in flasks	More rapid rate of shoot development	De Donato (1979)
Apple shoot tips	Shaken liquid	Faster growth rate	Snir and Erez (1980),
Peach shoot tips	Tubes on roller drum	20–30 fold increase in dry wt. on liquid *cf.* 8 fold increase on 0.6% agar	Hammerschlag (1982a)
Scutellaria shoot tips	Shaken liquid	30% more shoots than on 0.6% agar	Uhring (1982)

standard liquid medium was less effective (Jones and Petolino, 1988).

Disadvantages of liquid media. Just occasionally a liquid medium is disadvantageous. For instance, although it was hoped that liquid culture would produce faster *in vitro* growth of *Cypripedium reginae* orchids, all attempts to grow seeds, protocorms or young green plantlets in liquid culture failed. Seeds would not germinate, and protocorms and plantlets rapidly became brown and died (Harvais, 1982). Maize cells in suspension culture produce a mucilage which interferes with cell growth: the formation of a very large amount of mucilage similarly hampered the culture of *Phragmites australis* embryogenic callus (Straub *et al.*, 1988).

Delicate tissue may be damaged by the motion within liquid cultures. The growth of 'meristemoid-like' green globular bodies (produced from *Asplenium nidus* rhizome segments) was unsuccessful on rotated or shaken liquid medium. Higuchi and Amaki (1989) suggested that this might have been due to the meristems on the surface of the globular bodies suffering from collision damage.

One serious disadvantage of using liquid media for shoot growth and multiplication is that shoots which are perpetually submerged in liquid cultures may have a water-soaked appearance (*i.e.* they are 'hyperhydric' — see below and Chapter 13) and will then be useless for micro propagation.

Porous support systems. For certain kinds of culture, the disadvantages of a semi-solid or liquid medium can be overcome by growing cells, tissues or organs on a porous material irrigated with a liquid medium (see Chapters 9 and 14).

Liquid media for shoot culture. A liquid medium can be used successfully for shoot cultures. It is usual at Stage I to establish explants on an agar medium, and afterwards transfer them to a rotated or shaken liquid medium to promote rapid shoot growth at Stage II. This method was used for instance with carnation (Earle and Langhans, 1974b; Takayama and Misawa, 1982c), *Colocasia esculenta* (Jackson *et al.* 1977b), *Eucalyptus* (Mascarenhas *et al.* 1982b), chrysanthemum and periwinkle (Takayama and Misawa, 1982c). Axillary shoots are separated and rooted on an agar medium at Stage III or else are rooted *extra vitrum.* Jackson *et al.* (1977b) reported that *Colocasia* shoot tip or axillary bud explants grew well when placed on liquid medium at Stage I. There was no lag period as on agar medium.

Differential effects

Miller and Murashige (1976) demonstrated that selection between agar-gelled and liquid media (whether shaken or stationary) should not be undertaken arbitrarily. Shoot cultures of four kinds of tropical foliage plants responded differently to liquid or solid media during explant initiation (Stage I) and shoot multiplication (Stage II). The best results were obtained with the following substrates:

Species	Stage I	Stage II	Stage IIIb
Cordyline terminalis	Liquid (*S* or *R*)	Solid	Solid
Dracaena godseffiana	Liquid (*SF*)	Liquid (*S*)	Solid
Scindapsus aureus	Solid	Solid	Solid
Syngonium podophyllum	Liquid (*R*)	Liquid (*S*)	Solid

(*S*) = Stationary liquid; (*R*) = Rotated liquid;
(*SF*) = Filter paper support over *S*.

In these experiments, *Cordyline* explants at Stage I survived equally well on solid or liquid medium, but the latter was preferred because it induced greater shoot elongation. None of the *Scindapsus* explants stayed alive on a rotated liquid medium, only a small proportion survived on a static liquid medium, but nearly all grew satisfactorily on a filter paper support or on an agar medium (the solidified medium giving the better shoot growth). The fastest rate of *Dracaena* shoot multiplication at Stage II was obtained from explants grown on filter paper supports at Stage I. Culture of *Cordyline* or *Scindapsus* on static liquid medium at Stage II caused shoots to elongate rather than proliferate.

The advantage of using a liquid medium for the micropropagation of *Cymbidium* orchids was shown by Wimber (1965). On a solid medium there was only a small amount of protocorm multiplication and protocorms tended to differentiate into shoots. On a shaken liquid medium, protocorms of most clones continued proliferation. A rapid rate of micropropagation was achieved by transferring protocorms produced in shake culture back to an agar-solidified medium, where, left undisturbed, they gave rise to plantlets. Similar results were obtained on *Cattleya* and *Dendrobium* orchids by Scully (1967) and Sagawa and Shoji (1967) (see the section on ORCHIDS in Chapter 17). Liquid medium has since often been found to enhance morphogenesis or the rate of shoot multiplication in other kinds of plant.

Single shoots of *Stellaria media* did not form multiple shoots on a static medium, but gave rise to a mass of proliferating shoots in moving liquid culture (Walkey and Cooper, 1976). The leaves and stems of cocoa shoot tips elongated on liquid medium, but on agar, growth was restricted to bud swelling. Orchard *et al.* (1979) thought this was because on agar the cut surfaces of the explant became covered with a viscous exudate which restricted the movement of nutrients. There was a higher frequency of adventitious leaf (shoot) regeneration from *Arabidopsis* callus on liquid than on agar-solidified medium (Negrutiu and Jacobs, 1978a) and in experiments of Grewal *et al.* (1979), callus of *Hyoscyamus muticus* produced some complete plantlets on liquid medium, whereas on a solid medium the callus only proliferated. Callus of *Tylophora indica* formed somatic embryos in liquid medium, but they did not develop further unless the callus was transferred to a supplemented agar medium (Rao and Narayanaswami, 1972). When zygotic embryos of cocoa were grown in liquid culture, their development was more typical of that *in vivo*. Compared to embryos cultured on a semi-solid medium, there was additionally a higher incidence of asexual embryogenesis (Pence *et al.* 1980a).

Propagation rates

Shoot cultures of several different kinds of plants can be multiplied satisfactorily *in vitro* at Stages II and III, when partly submerged in shallow layers of liquid medium without any agitation. Some micropropagation laboratories favour this technique for shoot cultures as it avoids the addition of expensive agar to the medium. Plantlets are also finally obtained without having to wash agar from their roots. Davis *et al.* (1977) were able to grow Stage II carnation shoot cultures in 50 ml liquid medium in 1000 ml flasks (*i.e.* a shallow layer) with only gentle agitation (one horizontal revolution per minute). Hussey and Stacey (1981b) grew single nodes of potato in liquid culture within Petri dishes. The shoots which were produced, developed roots naturally and so there was no need for a separate rooting stage.

Mass propagation using liquid media

Most attempts at producing very high numbers of plants by *in vitro* methods rely upon the use of liquid media for shoot or shoot meristem multiplication (see Chapter 16). Attempts to scale-up shoot culture in very large vessels of liquid medium have in the past been largely frustrated by the problem of hyperhydricity.

The differential results obtained on liquid and solid media can often be effectively combined to obtain the most efficient micropropagation system, *e.g.* shoot initials formed on an agar solidified medium can be transferred to a liquid medium to produce rapid shoot growth. Simmonds and Cumming (1976b) found that callus of *Lilium* hybrids could be multiplied most rapidly on a liquid medium, but that for the maximum rate of plantlet production it was necessary to transfer the tissue to solid medium. By successive use of liquid and then agar media, it was possible, theoretically, to produce 6×10^{12} plantlets per year. A very similar method of propagating daylilies was described by Krikorian and Kann (1979).

Although bulblets multiplied in liquid culture can be normal phenotypically, the multiplication of leafy shoots submerged in a liquid culture medium can be more problematical. A high rate of multiplication may occur, but as mentioned above, shoots frequently become hyperhydric. This was experienced, for example, with chrysanthemum (Earle and Langhans (1974c), carnation (Earle and Langhans, 1975; Davis *et al.* 1977), peach (Hammerschlag, 1982a) and *Alstroemeria* (Pierik *et al.*, 1988b). When removed from the flasks, shoots were turgid, water-soaked and brittle. The leaves of hyperhydric shoots are often abnormally broad and thick, and lack superficial wax (see Chapter 13). Shoots of this kind are easily damaged by desiccation or excessive sunlight and survive very poorly when subcultured or transferred to the external environment.

Double-phase media

Several workers have experimented with adding a layer of static liquid medium to the top of a semi-solid medium. Johansson *et al.* (1982) found that somatic embryogenesis could be induced more effectively from anthers if they were cultured upon a liquid medium over a layer of agar-solidified medium containing activated charcoal. Maene and Debergh (1985) tried a two-layered medium as a possible method of minimising the cost of elongating and rooting shoots from cultures of ornamental plants (see Chapter 14). The technique was effective on *Begonia* × *tuberhybrida* shoot clumps. Shoot elongation could either be brought about by moving the clumps from the initial medium to an agar-solidified elongation medium, or a liquid elongation medium could be poured onto the surface of the initial agar medium without transferring the cultures (Viseur and Lievens, 1987).

The combined use of both solid and liquid medium has been patented in Hungary as an improved method of *in vitro* mass propagation (Molnár, 1987). In his paper Molnár says that shoot cultures of a wide range of plants including dicotyledons, monocotyledons and ferns, have been found to produce more axillary buds and shoots in a 2-phase system than on a comparable semi-solid medium. The micro-cuttings obtained were also more vigorous and formed strong roots more rapidly. The best results were obtained when both auxin and cytokinin growth regulators were put into the solid phase, but only cytokinins into the upper liquid medium. Explants seemed to take up nutrients and growth regulators from both the lower and upper layers: presence of the basal solid medium ensured that explants were suitably anchored.

Viseur (1987) discovered that while *Pyrus communis* shoot tips produced a high number of axillary shoots on liquid medium, the shoots soon became hyperhydric and unsuitable for propagation. There was no hyperhydricity on a medium solidified with 5–8 g/l agar, but the number of axillary shoots per explant was then low. The rate of shoot multiplication could be increased however, by adding a layer of liquid medium above the agar medium. Varieties very prone to hyperhydricity required 8 g/l agar in the solid phase: otherwise the best rate of shoot multiplication occurred with 5 g/l. A culture medium had to be present in both the solid and the liquid phase. The use of water-agar or water in the liquid phase, led to hyperhydricity and a decrease in both shoot quality and yield. Molnár emphasised that the upper layer of liquid medium must coat the explants, while Viseur says that the best results are obtained when the tops of shoots are not quite covered with liquid.

The suitability of 2-phase shoot culture for pear, has been confirmed by Rodríguez *et al.* (1991). Chauvin and Salesses (1988) have reported that the use of a double phase medium improved both the number and the length of axillary shoots in shoot cultures of *Castanea sativa* and *C. crenata*.

Others have found that nutrients can be replenished by adding a layer of liquid medium above a semi-solid medium once it has become exhausted. Shoot cultures which would otherwise need to be subcultured can be maintained in this way, thereby reducing labour costs and the stress which is imposed on explants during subculture (Aitken-Christie and Jones,1987; Vermeer and Evers, 1987a,b).

THE GASEOUS ENVIRONMENT

OXYGEN TENSION AND REDOX POTENTIAL

Control of oxygen supply

Although a small flow of gas into and out of cultured plant tissues will be caused by fluctuations in the temperature and atmospheric pressure of the growth room, most of the exchange of oxygen and other gases, is due to diffusion (Jackson *et al.*, 1987b). The available oxygen within cultured plant tissues is therefore influenced by:

— The concentration of the gas in the ambient atmosphere;

— its rate of diffusion into the culture vessel; and

— its rate of diffusion into the cultured cells or tissues.

The concentration will be closest to that in the ambient atmosphere when the tissue stands free of the medium and is surrounded by a minimum film of moisture or medium. Submerged tissues or organs in a static medium are very poorly aerated. The situation in a typical culture vessel is illustrated in Fig. 70.

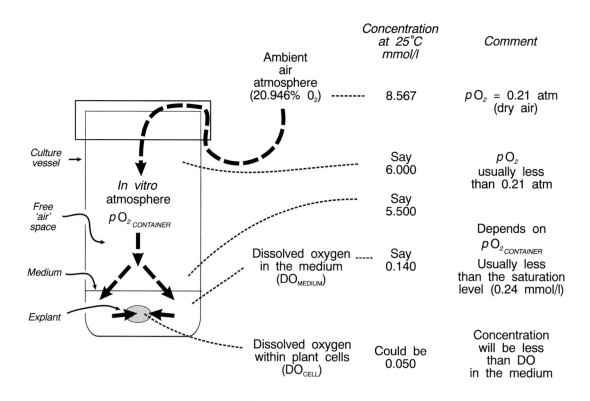

Fig. 70. How the concentration of oxygen can decrease between the ambient air and the cells within a typical explant

The ambient atmosphere

The simplest way to influence the oxygen supplied to tissue cultures is to alter the concentration in the external atmosphere. The concentration of oxygen in air is normally 20.946% by volume; thus, in the absence of water vapour, its partial pressure (pO_2), when the atmospheric pressure is 760 mm Hg, equals 0.20946×760 mm Hg (159.19 mm Hg; 0.21 atm; 21 kPa). In an incubator or growth chamber, oxygen can be maintained at a concentration which is above or below that in ambient air. Reductions are achieved by introducing nitrogen gas, and monitoring equipment is commercially available (*e.g.* the Oxyreducer™, Reming Bioinstruments, Redfield, N.Y., U.S.A.) which controls the rate of nitrogen injection, so that the ambient oxygen level remains very close to a predetermined level.

As will be apparent from the paragraphs which follow, the partial pressure of oxygen, is only a general guide to the amount of oxygen available to cultured tissues. An experiment on the effect of oxygen on cultures is generally not repeatable unless, besides pO_2, the experimental procedure is described in detail. Greater accuracy can be obtained by measuring dissolved oxygen instrumentally.

Gaseous environment in the container

If sterilised air, or a gas mixture, is introduced directly into the culture vessel, problems of gas diffusion clearly do not exist. However with unventilated cultures growing in sealed vessels, oxygen concentration at the level of the medium or the tissues can be considerably less than that found externally. This is because use of oxygen by the culture creates a local deficit which may not be immediately compensated because of the impedance to diffusion created by closures, especially if they are tightly fitting and impermeable. Kozai *et al.* (1988) found that there were 0.1 air changes per hour inside 47 ml tubes if they were covered with aluminium caps, 1.0 change when they were plugged with formed plastic caps, but 6.2 changes per hour if the tubes were covered with microporous polypropylene.

The shape of the culture vessel will influence gaseous diffusion. Bateson *et al.* (1987) have shown that in vessels of equal volume, growth is rapid where the diffusion distance is small, but is diminished as the length of the container is increased relative to its diameter.

The concentration of oxygen within the tissues of cultures grown predominantly above the surface of the medium is largely influenced by the partial pressure of the gas within

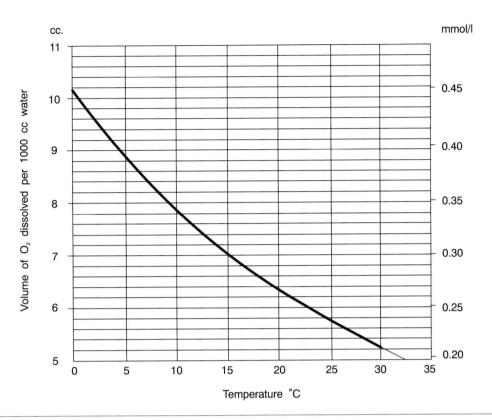

Fig. 71. The effect of temperature on the volume of oxygen which can be dissolved in water from air (pO_2 = 0.20 atm.)

the vessel. The leaves of shoot cultures can therefore absorb oxygen from the surrounding atmosphere as they would *in vivo*. Meristem tips on a filter paper supported above a liquid medium are probably better aerated than if they were placed on an agar medium.

Diffusion into the medium

Oxygen is only sparingly soluble in water. At 0°C, a solution oxygenated to saturation point from air contains only 10.2 cc oxygen per 1000 cc, and the amount which can be dissolved decreases as the temperature rises (Fig. 71). Thus, increasing the incubation temperature of a culture from 21°C to 25°C will decrease the maximum amount of oxygen which can be dissolved in the medium by approximately 9%. Because air is a mixture of gases, more oxygen can be dissolved if water, or an aqueous solution of compounds, is flushed with pure oxygen gas at barometric pressure.

At 25°C and 760 mm Hg, the weight of oxygen in 1 litre of air is 274 mg. The concentration of oxygen in air at this temperature and pressure is therefore sometimes said to be 8.57 mM. At 25°C the maximum weight of oxygen which can be dissolved in one litre of a fully aerated plant culture medium is *ca.* 7.68 mg/l, which corresponds to a concentration of *ca.* 0.24 mM [total pressure 760 mm; pO_2 = 159.2 minus 4.98 mm Hg (the proportional effect of water vapour pressure†) = 154.2 mm Hg; 0.20 atm]. In a medium exposed to pure oxygen at this temperature [total pressure = 760 mm, pO_2 = 760 – 23.76 mm (the vapour pressure of water) = 736.24 mm], the concentration would be *ca.* 1.15 mM (36.6 mg/l).

Slightly less oxygen can be dissolved in a plant culture medium than is indicated for water by Fig. 71, because of a phenomenon called the 'salting out effect'. Dissolved salts and non-electrolytes such as sucrose, diminish the solubility of gases. In addition, the concentration of oxygen in plant culture media will usually not reach the saturation level. That actually found will depend on the surface to volume ratio of the medium in the vessel and the concentration (partial pressure) in the immediate gas phase. The former will be smaller when an identical

†   The vapour pressure of water at 25°C is 23.756 mm Hg: the proportional water vapour pressure is therefore 23.756 × 0.20946 = 4.98 mm Hg

volume of medium is placed in a test tube rather than a Petri dish. Surface to volume ratio is increased when liquid media are agitated or when gaseous mixtures are injected into them. The rate of oxygen uptake from air then depends on the rate of agitation or the rate of gas input into the medium. In a 30 ml flask it was found to be 700 µl/hr at a shaking rate of 100 cycles/min and 1500 µl/hr at 140 cycles/min (Long, 1961).

Oxygen diffuses considerably more slowly through water than through air (respective coefficients of diffusion at 25°C, 2.4×10^{-5} cm^2/s and 0.205 cm^2/s: Jackson *et al.*, 1987b). Unless a medium is agitated, oxygen will only be supplied very slowly to tissues submerged at any depth. The oxygen uptake of tissues on semi-solid medium is therefore predominantly through those parts which are exposed above the surface.

Diffusion into plant tissues

The passage of oxygen into plant tissues from a gas phase does not seem to present much of a restraint to normal Krebs' cycle respiration, diffusion into the tissue apparently being much more rapid than from an aqueous medium. For example, the rate of diffusion of oxygen through potato tuber tissue is said to be at least 400 times more rapid than through water (Davies D.D., 1980). Nevertheless, the rate of growth of potato callus growing in air on an agar medium can be increased slightly if a large piece of callus is cut into small pieces (Van der Plas and Wagner, 1986).

Diffusion of oxygen into tissues from water is slow. The partial pressure of oxygen for half-maximum respiration (pO_{50}) of slices of an aroid spadix in moist air was only 0.002 atm, but this increased to 0.16 atm when the tissue was immersed in phosphate buffer shaken at 120 cycles/min (Yocum and Hackett, 1957).

Soffer and Burger (1988) have obtained evidence that diffusion of oxygen from stationary water into plant tissues is impeded at the water/tissue interface, suggesting that the Nernst layer effect (see above) is operative. This resistance to diffusion is diminished or eliminated if the water, or medium, is stirred or agitated. Even a film of liquid over an otherwise exposed explant will reduce the rate of oxygen uptake into the tissues: the thicker the covering, the greater will be the barrier to the passage of the gas (Konings and Jackson, 1979).

Oxygen requirements of cultures

The most effective level of oxygen for growth and development in plant tissue cultures is not often described in scientific papers. There is some evidence that the optimum level, or the lowest tolerable level, may vary accord-ing to plant species and the type of culture being grown. Much of the differential behaviour of plant cultures on liquid and solid media described in the preceding part of this chapter may have been related to preferences for oxygen availability.

Respiration. Plant growth and development is dependent on respiration. This may take place through several biochemical pathways. The most common and efficient method *via* the Krebs' cycle, takes place in both light and dark, although it is often called 'dark' respiration to distinguish it from photorespiration (see below). Krebs' cycle respiration requires oxygen: its rate usually decreases immediately the concentration of oxygen falls below that in air. Kozai (1991) suggests that pO_2 needs to be *ca*. 0.5 atm in the gas phase (*ca*. 10% O_2) to maintain the normal rate of 'dark' respiration in cultured plant shoots.

The respiration of some plant tissues may even increase as oxygen level is increased above the normal atmospheric concentration (Forward, 1965). The growth of potato callus can be doubled if the tissue is moved from air to an atmosphere containing 70% oxygen. Van der Plas and Wagner (1986) showed that this was because respiration was not at a maximum when the cultures were maintained in air. They suggested that oxygen supplementation could be generally employed to increase the rate of growth of callus cultures without inducing injury. It is not clear to what extent this result is due to poor oxygen diffusion through the medium into the tissue. Respiration of potato tuber tissue has been said to be at a maximum when oxygen in the intercellular spaces of the tissue reaches a partial pressure of 0.2 atm, *i.e.* at the concentration of oxygen in air (Mapson and Burton, 1962).

The half saturation point for overall oxygen uptake (*i.e.* respiration) in potato tuber tissue seems to be *ca*. 0.01 atm *in the intercellular spaces of the tissue*. Reduction in oxygen partial pressure up to this point leads to a slow decline in respiration: between 0.01 atm and complete absence of oxygen (*anoxia*), respiration declines linearly (Forward, 1965).

Growth. The rate of plant growth can be diminished by limiting oxygen supply (*hypoxia, hypo-oxia*). It can be seen to slow down at significantly higher oxygen partial pressures than those that markedly restrict respiration.

In a natural environment, roots frequently have to grow in low oxygen tensions: root cultures have been said to tolerate relatively low levels of oxygen availability (Street, 1957, 1969). However, the growth of roots in hydroponic solutions is increased by aeration, and cultured tomato roots have also been found to grow more rapidly if a liquid medium is subjected to a continuous gentle agitation (Said and Murashige, 1979). Roots initiated on the shoots of some plants can be seen to grow on the surface of agar, rather than down into it, suggesting that oxygenation of the medium is limiting. The rate of growth of plant roots grown on media solidified with 1% agar can be almost doubled if the plants are placed instead onto 3.5% nutrient agar which has been crumbled to make it porous (Barrett-Lennard and Dracup, 1988). However diffusion of oxygen into a normal agar medium does take place, for root growth of cultured potato plants is reduced if a 2-3 mm layer of paraffin is placed on the surface of the agar medium (Crane and Hughes, 1990).

The rate of elongation of maize roots in a humid atmosphere, is reduced to only 50–60% of the maximum, when the partial pressure of oxygen falls to 0.1 atm (10 kPa, 75.2 mm Hg), or in a liquid medium, to ca 0.3 atm. Saglio et al. (1984) attributed the reduction in growth to the effect of oxygen on non-respiratory processes with a low affinity for oxygen. They found that cell division (the number of cells produced or the number of mitotic divisions) was not affected until the partial pressure of oxygen in the gaseous environment was reduced to 1 kPa (0.01 atm). The formation and growth of adventitious roots on microcuttings is oxygen-dependent (see Chapter 14).

The rate of uptake of sucrose, nitrate and other nutrient ions by roots or unorganised tissues is reduced in conditions of hypoxia, although nitrogen supply does not limit growth even when the oxygen in solution is as low as 0.003 mmol l^{-1}, for some uptake still occurs (Kessel and Carr, 1972; Buwalda and Greenway, 1989). Cells die when oxygen levels fall below a critical level (anoxia).

Growth of non-photosynthetic tissues in vitro can be slowed considerably, apparently without damage, if the oxygen tension of the medium is appreciably reduced, either by supplying a controlled gaseous mixture to the culture or by preventing the diffusion of air by applying mineral oil or silicone overlays (see Chapter 6). Growth inhibition in these circumstances is due partly to a lack of oxygen, and partly to an accumulation of carbon dioxide in the tissue. The growth of N. tabacum and Chrysanthemum × morifolium callus and shoots was arrested when the partial pressure of oxygen was reduced below 0.066 atm (50 mm Hg; 6.6 kPa). The maximum volume of dissolved oxygen in the medium would then have been only 31% of that normally available, and the actual dissolved oxygen concentration ca. 0.05 mmol l^{-1} (Bridgen and Staby, 1981). The level of oxygen below which no aerobic respiration is detectable in cultured Solanum nigrum cells is approximately 0.06 mmol l^{-1} medium (Lindsey and Yeoman, 1983).

Cultures needing good aeration

Adequate gaseous exchange is essential to ensure a fast rate of multiplication in most tissue cultures, but a satisfactory rate of growth can usually be obtained when the dissolved oxygen concentration is below the aerobic saturation point. The best cell doubling time in suspension cultures of Euphorbia pulcherrima in one and two litre flasks, was achieved when the partial pressure of oxygen, pO_2 was 60% (0.12 atm) (Preil et al., 1988). Similarly the best relative growth rate of embryogenic alfalfa suspensions seemed to occur when the medium was aerated so that it was 70% saturated with dissolved oxygen (pO_2 0.14 atm) (Stuart et al., 1987). The rate of growth of the Euphorbia culture (above) declined very rapidly if pO_2 dropped below 10% (pO_2 0.02 atm).

A relatively high level of dissolved oxygen appears to be necessary for the formation of adventitious bulblets in vitro. Only a very small number of bulblets was formed from Lilium speciosum bulb scales in 100 ml of static liquid medium contained in 300 ml flasks (Takayama and Misawa, 1983b). By contrast, the number and dry weight of bulblets produced in 50 ml of the same medium unshaken in 90 × 20 mm Petri dishes were high, and the rate of proliferation even slightly exceeded that obtained when liquid medium in the 300 ml flasks was shaken at 180 r.p.m. Poor aeration in a column bio-reactor reduced the rate of bulblet proliferation (Takayama and Misawa, 1981). By contrast, although shoot growth of potatoes in large fermentors was found by Akita and Takayama (1988) to require conditions of high aeration [(2 litres of medium in an 8 litre bio-reactor supplied with air at 0.1 v.v.m. (vessel volumes per minute)], once shoots of an adequate length had been obtained, they could be induced to produce miniature tubers in a larger volume of medium (6 litres in an 8 litre bio-reactor) where the aeration was less good. Tubers were not formed if shoots were cultured in the larger volume of medium from the start.

Beneficial effects of a diminished oxygen tension

There are several reports which indicate that a reduction in the partial pressure of oxygen can be used to regulate growth and development in plant tissue cultures.

Photorespiration

Although the growth of non-photosynthetic tissue is decreased when oxygen is limiting, that of green shoots or plants in the light may be increased. Intact plants with the C_3 method of photosynthesis (most plants) increase in mass about twice as fast as those grown in air when grown in 2–5% oxygen. This is because in such plants as much as 50% of carbon fixed by photosynthesis in normal air is wasted by so-called *photorespiration*. This is a rapid form of respiration specifically associated with substrates produced during photosynthesis (particularly glycollic acid) through the activity of the enzymes glycollate oxidase and ribulose-P_2 carboxylase/oxygenase. These enzymes have a high affinity for oxygen and their activity is inhibited by O_2 concentrations below those in air, and almost completely repressed when the atmospheric oxygen level is about 1–2% (Zelitch, 1978). Krebs' cycle respiration utilising electron transfer from cytochrome oxidase to oxygen can take place at much lower oxygen concentrations. In high light, shoots grown at low oxygen tensions can therefore accumulate dry matter quicker than they can in air, but to achieve the most rapid gain, it may be necessary to supply rather more oxygen during the night to permit Krebs' cycle reactions to proceed efficiently.

Shimada *et al.* (1988) have shown that the net photosynthetic rate of green shoot cultures of *Primula malacoides* and *Chrysanthemum × morifolium* increases by about 1.5 times when they are grown in an atmosphere containing 10% oxygen instead of normal air. The net photosynthetic rate in 1% oxygen was about 3 times that in air, and was comparable to that of plants growing *in vivo*: plants were autotrophic (see below) and grew using only carbon derived from carbon dioxide, without sugar being added to the medium.

Differentiation

The nature of cell differentiation in culture may be regulated by the available oxygen concentration. Dalton and Street (1976) have found chloroplast development in suspension cultures to be favoured by low partial pressures of oxygen and high CO_2 concentrations (5–10%). Ethylene, naturally produced by the cultured cells, was antagonistic. Friable callus strains (which may admit more oxygen or may have insufficient internal thickness for full respiratory inhibition) are less liable to develop chlorophyll than compact calluses from the same plant tissue (Street, 1977b). The effect of oxygen on chloroplast formation may be unusual, because other kinds of development in plant cells and tissues appear to be promoted in oxidative conditions (see below). Lignin synthesis has been noticed to be inhibited by antioxidants (Siegel and Porto, 1961).

Organogenesis and embryogenesis

Embryogenesis. If, in the medium used for suspension cultures of carrot cells, the dissolved oxygen concentration was reduced below a critical level of 1.3 mg/l (41

μmol l^{-1} or approx. 16% of the saturation level), small 'meristematic' cells were produced which resembled those formed under the influence of high auxin concentrations. These cells differentiated into embryoids, whereas the larger cells produced at higher oxygen concentrations only gave rise to roots (Kessel and Carr, 1972).

Carman (1988) found that wheat somatic embryos, incubated in an atmosphere containing 3.2 mmol l^{-1} oxygen (7.8% oxygen at a total pressure of 760 mm and 25 °C which could produce a maximum of *ca.* 90 μmol l^{-1} dissolved oxygen), formed less callus than in ambient air, but the proportion of embryogenic scutellar callus to non-embryogenic embryo axis callus was increased. The embryoids formed in low oxygen had fewer abnormalities, secondary embryos, or precocious germination than normal, and a high proportion of them germinated to give seedlings. Abnormal *in vitro* growth and precocious germination of immature zygotic embryos of barley was prevented by culture in an atmosphere containing less than 9% oxygen (*i.e.* less than *ca.* 3.7 mmol l^{-1}) (Norstog and Klein, 1972).

As pollen microspores confined within an anther are more easily induced to produce sporophytic embryoids than if they are isolated on culture media, Sopory and Maheshwari (1976a) suggested that reduced oxygen tension is also necessary for androgenesis. This hypothesis seems to be confirmed by the results of Harada and Imamura (1983). Culturing *Nicotiana tabacum* anthers at reduced atmospheric pressure, in an anaerobic environment, or in a nitrogen atmosphere containing less oxygen than is found in air, increased the proportion of microspores undergoing direct embryogenesis: this resulted in more anthers producing plantlets and a greater number of plantlets per anther. When incubation was carried out at 28°C and 1 bar, the most stimulatory oxygen concentration was 5% (giving *ca.* 56 μmol l^{-1} dissolved oxygen).

Suspension cultured cells of *Selinum candolii* produced 4–5 times more somatic embryos per fresh weight of inoculum if, after they were plated on a medium lacking an auxin, they were covered with a layer of liquid paraffin oil. Mathur (1991) supposed that this was due to the reduced concentration of oxygen in the medium.

As a reduction in the partial pressure of oxygen would be expected to reduce the exposure of cells to oxidative conditions, the above findings are in contrast to the reports of Earnshaw and Johnson (1986) (see page 200), which suggest that oxidative conditions are required for embryogenesis. Jullien (1974) also thought that a relatively high oxygen tension was necessary.

Orchid protocorms. Many seeds with a hard seed coat are able to begin germination under anoxic conditions until the seed coat is ruptured, when normal aerobic respiration takes over. Henrich *et al.* (1981) noted that seeds of some orchids would germinate with very little oxygen, submerged at the bottom of 15 ml static liquid medium. The protocorms passed through their early developmental stages as if they had been on the surface of an agar medium. Other workers have found that in general, callus growth and somatic protocorm proliferation in orchids is promoted in liquid media where there is a good supply of air, while shoot growth is favoured on static liquid media (Alpi and Garibaldi, 1969; Cheng and Chua, 1982).

Shoot proliferation. The oxygen tension of a medium may be one factor determining organogenesis and subsequent bud growth. Proliferation of *Spiraea* shoots was increased (apparently by more adventitious shoots being formed) after shoot cultures were subjected to a period of anoxia by flushing with nitrogen gas (Norton, 1988; Norton and Norton, 1988b).

It is possible that there is an optimum oxygen concentration for the formation of multiple shoot primordia from cultured meristems. In *Stevia rebaudiana*, Miyagawa *et al.* (1986) found that explants only produced multiple shoot primordia when rotated in a liquid medium at 2 r.p.m.

An unshaken liquid medium was better than a shaken one (or agar) for inducing coconut flower meristems to grow into 'shootlets' (Blake and Eeuwens, 1982).

Physiological effects of oxygen availability

Redox potential

The redox potential (E_h) of an aqueous solution is a measure of its tendency to take, or give up electrons (*i.e.* to become reduced or oxidized). Redox potential is measured in units of electrical potential difference (volts). The more positive the value of E_h becomes, the greater is the proportion of oxidant to reductant in solution. As E_h becomes more negative, the relative proportion of reductants increases. The resistance which a solution shows to a change in its E_h is known as its *poise*. This is analogous to the buffering of solutions against changes in pH.

The redox potential of a solution is altered by pH (increasing as pH is reduced); temperature; and in the case of a gas, pressure. *Standard redox potentials* (E'_0) are therefore defined at a given pH, pressure and temperature (usually pH7, 25°C and 1 atmosphere, unless otherwise stated) when the concentrations of reductant and oxidant are equal (*i.e.* when the compound in solution is 50% oxidized or reduced).

The redox potential of a plant culture medium varies according to the concentration of dissolved oxygen and the respiratory activity of the cells or tissues growing in it. Anaerobic bacteria cannot be cultured until there is very little oxygen in the medium and bacteriologists often estimate the oxygen tension of a medium or culture by using redox-sensitive dyes which are coloured when oxidized and colourless when reduced. The E_h values at which colour changes occur, vary according to the dye chosen and the pH of the solution.

Oxygen in respiration. In the first stage of normal respiration, *glycolysis* (which does not require oxygen), glucose is converted to pyruvic acid. Pyruvate is normally passed to the Krebs' or tri-carboxylic acid (TCA) cycle, which is the most energy-efficient of the respiratory processes and requires oxygen for the oxidation of carbon compounds to carbon dioxide. In the process of being oxidized, substrates donate electrons which are passed on through a series of carriers of increasingly positive redox potential to oxygen, which is thereby reduced to water. The redox reactions involved are indicated below.

$$\tfrac{1}{2}O_2 \xrightarrow{e^-} \tfrac{1}{2}O_2^{\bullet -} \xrightarrow[H^+]{e^-} \tfrac{1}{2}H_2O_2 \xrightarrow{e^-} OH^\bullet \xrightarrow[H^+]{e^-} H_2O$$

| di–oxygen | superoxide | hydrogen peroxide | hydroxyl radical | water |

When oxygen is deficient, so that the TCA cycle cannot operate, plants can obtain some further energy (but with much less efficiency) by the decarboxylation of pyruvate to acetaldehyde and the reduction of this compound to ethanol (fermentation). The presence of these two last compounds in tissue culture vessels indicates that glycolysis has been followed by fermentation in some parts of the cultured tissues (Jackson *et al.*, 1987b): both chemicals have been commonly detected where the presence of volatiles has been examined [*e.g.* in flasks containing callus cultures — Thomas and Murashige (1979a,b); or in *Prunus* shoot cultures — Righetti *et al.* (1988)].

Plants are also capable of respiration in the presence of oxygen by another route, the 'hexose monophosphate shunt' or the 'pentose phosphate pathway'. In tobacco callus this method becomes much more dominant during adventitious shoot formation (Thorpe and Laishley, 1973; Brown and Thorpe, 1980b). Although the pentose phosphate pathway is slightly less energy-efficient than glycolysis linked to the oxidative-TCA cycle, it allows for the formation of higher concentrations of reduced nucleotides and 5-carbon intermediates, important for the synthesis of nucleic acids.

Redox status in development. Some workers have suggested that development is associated with hypoxia (page

198 and below): others have thought it to be an oxidative process. Publications describing the addition of oxidising or reducing agents to plant tissue cultures, have provided evidence supporting both views.

1). The frequent addition of hydrogen peroxide (a strong oxidising agent) has been shown to increase the yield of somatic embryos and bring about a decrease in the concentration of glutathione (Kapik *et al.*, 1986). But on the other hand, Harada and Imamura (1983) were able to increase embryogenesis from pollen within *Nicotiana tabacum* anthers by incorporating the reductants ascorbic acid (0.6–568 μM), mercaptoethanol (1–1000 μM) or dithiothreitol (0.6–648 μM), and Joy *et al.* (1988) found that the addition of 40–80 mM ascorbic acid to a shoot-forming medium, enhanced adventitious shoots in both young and old *Nicotiana tabacum* callus.

2). The concentration of reduced glutathione (GSH, Fig. 58), another reducing agent, has been noted to be higher in proliferating callus than in embryogenic callus of wild carrot (Earnshaw and Johnson, 1985), suggesting that oxidative conditions were required for embryogenesis. This result is supported by the later finding that adding reduced glutathione to the growth medium prevents embryogenesis in carrot tissue cultures: the addition of other antioxidants (ascorbic acid and vitamin E), can have a similar effect (Earnshaw and Johnson, 1986). By contrast 10 mg/l glutathione (presumably GSH) has been added to media for the induction of embryogenesis in *Medicago sativa*, apparently without inhibitory effects (Senaratna *et al.*, 1989a).

3). Tissues often become brown and necrotic after excision due to the presence of activated oxygen and other oxidising substances. Several authors have noticed that tissue browning and necrosis is not necessarily detrimental to morphogenesis, and Krul and Worley (1977a) found that somatic embryos of *Vitis* all arose adjacent to areas of necrotic cells. In *Paulownia tomentosa*, the presence of necrotic tissue was apparently essential for the initiation of embryogenesis (Radojević, 1979).

Reducing agents

It is sensible to include a discussion of the effects of reducing agents on *in vitro* cultures at this point, even though they are not factors of the external environment.

Ascorbic acid. L-ascorbic acid (ascorbate, Vitamin C) is synthesized by plants and occurs naturally in cells in relatively high concentrations [*e.g.* 13 mg/100 g fresh weight of suspensions of *Rosa rugosa* cultured in the dark (and even more in the light) (Wegg and Townsley, 1983);

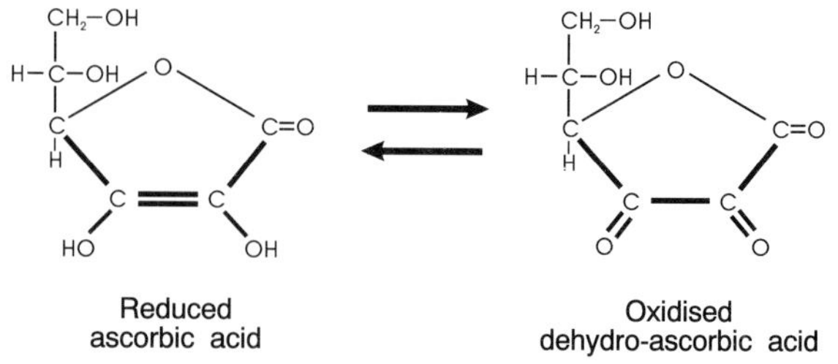

Fig. 72. Reduced and oxidised forms of L-ascorbic acid.

23.4 g/100 g chlorophyll in protoplasts (Foyer *et al.*, 1983)]. Ascorbate acts as a reductant, being converted by oxidation to dehydro-ascorbic acid (Fig. 72). Reconversion of dehydroascorbic acid to ascorbic acid, by the enzyme dehydroascorbate reductase, brings about the oxidation of glutathione (Fig. 73).

Ascorbic acid, which is water soluble, and Vitamin E which is hydrophobic and associated with membranes (see below), provide cells with a defence against oxidative injury. Vitamin C can scavenge injurious hydrogen peroxide (Foyer *et al.*, 1983; Thompson *et al.*, 1987) and some other activated oxygen radicals. It is responsible for reducing the oxidised form of Vitamin E.

Ascorbic acid has been added to few published media for plant tissue culture (*ca.* 16%) and so it is not an essential ingredient. Several researchers have included small quantities (*i.e.* 0.1–1.0 mg/l) without evidence of a clearly beneficial effect. Definite responses have, however, been measured in the presence of 0.06–0.8 mM (10–141 mg/l). Bonner and Axtman (1937) reported that the growth of isolated *Pisum sativum* roots was increased by adding 50 mg/l (but not 25 or 100 mg/l) to the culture medium. The validity of this finding has been confirmed by Liso *et al.* (1988) who found that root growth of *Allium cepa* roots was increased over periods of several weeks by moderate concentrations of ascorbic acid (or its precursor, L-galactose-γ-lactone). It was noted that 0.1 mM ascorbic acid stimulated DNA synthesis in root meristems and appeared to shorten the cell cycle, especially the *G1* phase. Chlorophyll formation in callus cultures of several plants

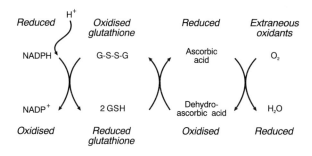

Fig. 73. Ascorbic acid controls the oxidation and reduction of glutathione.

was assisted by the presence of 10 mg/l ascorbic acid or ascorbate (Fukami and Hildebrandt, 1967).

The addition of exogenous ascorbic acid to plant tissues has been said to increase their metabolic acitivity and accelerate the release of sugars. There was a greater concentration of free soluble sugars in old *Nicotiana* callus during the early stages of culture when ascorbate was present (Joy *et al.*, 1988) and the addition of 0.4–0.8 mM ascorbate to a shoot-forming medium, increased the numbers of shoots produced from both young and old *Nicotiana tabacum* callus. The rate at which the shoots were were formed was also increased. Ascorbic acid (together with two other reductants) has been found to improve embryogenesis in tobacco anther cultures, but to inhibit carrot embryogenesis (page 200).

Thiourea (thiocarbamide). The reducing agent, thiourea is routinely incorporated into media by some workers (Pua *et al.*, 1983) and is said to have an envigorating effect. It has been reported to enhance the growth of *Lactuca sativa* and *Cichorium endiva* callus (Fukami and Hildebrandt, 1967) and to promote the growth of uniform cell suspensions (Nitsch *et al.*, 1970). Its antioxidant effect has been noted to produce a growth regulatory effect *in vivo*; dormant peach buds, which can be stimulated to grow in partially anaerobic conditions (Erez *et al.*, 1980), can also be forced into growth by sprays of thiourea.

Together with other thiocarbamides, the compound has three notable biological properties: it complexes with metal ions, particularly with those of copper and Fe(III);

together with other carbamides, it is (like ascorbic acid) an effective scavenger for hydrogen peroxide (being readily oxidised to a disulphide); and is able to inactivate peroxidase enzymes (Skellern, 1989).

Glutathione. Fuchigami and Nee (1987) have suggested that glutathione has a role in overcoming rest or dormancy in plants. Reduced glutathione is thought to maintain protein thiols in a reduced state, thereby inducing polysome (the association of one m-RNA molecule with several ribosomes) activation and protein synthesis. Like pentose phosphate respiration, high levels of reduced glutathione ensure an above-normal availability of NADPH. It has been proposed that the balance of reduced glutathione (GSH) to oxidised glutathione (GSSH) influences cell extension, growth and cell division (Standardi and Micheli, 1988). The addition of 2 mM glutathione to **Gamborg *et al.* (1968) B5** medium, promoted cell division of *Brassica* callus (Sethi *et al.*, 1988). As with embryogenesis (see above), indirect adventitious shoot formation in *Malus* was prevented by 100 mg/l GSH (James *et al.*, 1984).

Vitamin E. Vitamin E (α-tocopherol) is an antioxidant which promotes 'juvenile' characteristics of human lung fibroblasts and is used to reduce blindness and intraventricular bleeding in premature babies reared in hyperbaric oxygen incubators. Oswald and co-workers (1977a) found that 0.95 mM Vitamin E acetate promoted the formation of undifferentiated friable callus from germinating embryos of several maize cultivars. In the suspension cultures which were then initiated, the compound enhanced individual cell viability and the formation of large lipid bodies in young cells. When Vitamin E was added to suspension cultures of ladino clover and soybean (Oswald *et al.* 1977b), it promoted cell dispersion. Cell organelles and lipid bodies also retained their structural integrity and were even released intact into the medium during cell turnover. These effects were thought to be due to the ability of the vitamin to prevent lipid breakdown. Its withdrawl from suspension cultures resulted in greater cell aggregation. In another paper, Oswald *et al.* (1977c) reported that Vitamin E increased the sensitivity of white clover cells to auxins.

Vitamin E has not been widely used in other research work. Sroga (1983) found it assisted callus formation from *Lupinus angustifolius* hypocotyl explants, and Viseur (1987) added 1 mg/l to the medium used for the initial culture of *Pyrus communis* shoot tips. Like ascorbic acid (page 200), Vitamin E can prevent carrot embryogenesis.

Phenolic compounds. Several phenolic compounds which occur in plants, such as catechol, resorcinol, quinol and phloroglucinol, are strong reducing agents. The use of some of these chemicals as plant growth regulants is discussed in Chapter 11.

Growth regulators

Auxins have been found to activate enzymes regulating respiration *via* the pentose phosphate pathway, while enzymes concerned with glycolytic respiration are reduced in activity (Black and Humphreys, 1962). Kinetin too has been thought to have the same effect (MacLeod, 1968) and carrot cells prompted to divide by kinetin were noted to consume less oxygen than when this cytokinin was absent (Neumann, 1968). Some cytokinins are capable of acting as reducing agents in photochemical reactions and Rothwell and Wright (1967) proposed that this might account for part of their biological activity.

Active cell division is promoted by high levels of the naturally-occurring auxin, IAA. This phytohormone is readily denatured by enzymes in oxidative conditions, but breakdown can be prevented by anti-oxidants of various kinds (Stonier *et al.*, 1970). The synthetic auxin 2,4-D, which is frequently used to control the continuation of proliferative growth or the onset of embryogenesis, has been said to elevate cellular antioxidant (GSH) concentrations (Earnshaw and Johnson, 1986), while the addition of ascorbate to culture media decreases it in favour

of oxidised glutathione (GSSH) (Standardi and Micheli, 1988). This suggests that it may be important to correlate redox potential with stages of morphogenesis.

The effect of oxygen tension and antioxidants (reducing agents) on the blackening of explants is discussed in Chapter 13.

CARBON DIOXIDE

All cultured plant tissues produce carbon dioxide during the respiration on which their metabolism and growth depend: the gas is only taken up in significant quantities by photosynthetically active cells or tissues.

The primary substrate for the respiration of most cultured plant tissues is the carbohydrate (usually sucrose) added to the medium. Tissues which are completely dependent on this as an energy source are described as being *heterotrophic*. Cells, tissues, or organs which contain chlorophyll may be capable of synthesizing from carbon dioxide some, or all, of the carbon compounds they require for respiration. Those which rely partly on sucrose in the medium and partly on compounds produced through photosynthesis, are called *mixotrophic*; those which can fully sustain respiration through photosynthe-

Table 11. The effect of light and carbon dioxide on photosynthesis.

Controlling factors		Photosynthesis		
		At compensation point	For autotrophic cultures	Near saturation level ? *
	Photosynthetic photon flux	20 μmol m^{-2} s^{-1} (*ca.* 1.5 klx)	65-250 μmol m^{-2} s^{-1} (*ca.* 4.9-18.8 klx)	100-2000 μmol m^{-2} s^{-1} (*ca.* 7.5-150 klx)
	Carbon dioxide concentration within the tissue culture container	30-80 v.p.m.	350 v.p.m.	500-1000 v.p.m.

* Typical irradiation on leaf surfaces from daylight on a sunny day can be 1000–3000 μmol m^{-2} s^{-1} (*ca.* 9-27 MJ m^{-2} per day).

sis alone are termed *autotrophic*. The amount of photosynthesis carried out by a culture determines whether it is mixotrophic or autotrophic. It depends particularly on the intensity of available light, the concentration of carbon dioxide in the culture vessel, temperature, and the nature of the culture medium.

Besides its importance for photosynthesis, carbon dioxide appears to be required for non-photosynthetic assimilation and may also have one or more growth regulatory roles.

Observed concentrations

The concentration of carbon dioxide in air is *ca.* 0.035% [350 v.p.m. (volumes per million)]; that within growth rooms is usually somewhat higher (*ca.* 400–800 v.p.m., Kozai *et al.*, 1988). The level within culture vessels will not necessarily be the same as that in the external atmosphere because diffusion of carbon dioxide, and other physiologically active gases, into and out of the tissues of plant tissue cultures will be dependent on the same factors that control oxygen availability (Fig. 70). Respiration of non–photosynthetic plant tissues (or tissues capable of

photosynthesis maintained in the dark), can cause carbon dioxide in the gas phase of culture vessels to reach abnormally high levels. There may be as much as 30% CO_2 by volume in tightly sealed containers (Righetti *et al.*, 1988). The respiration of green shoots or plantlets may also cause CO_2 concentrations in containers to reach 3000–50,000 v.p.m. during the night when photosynthesis is inoperative (De Proft *et al.*, 1985; Fujiwara *et al.*, 1987; Kozai, 1989).

Photosynthesis

Lighting and carbon dioxide concentration

Providing they receive sufficient carbon dioxide and light energy, leafy shoots or plantlets *in vitro* are theoretically capable of assimilating enough carbon by photosynthesis to remain autotrophic. If either CO_2 or lighting is below a certain threshold, photosynthesis reaches its *compensation point* where the rate of dry matter accumulation is inadequate to support respiration. Where this occurs persistently *in vivo*, parts of plants (*e.g.* shaded leaves), or the whole plant, will die. Inadequate rates of photosyn-

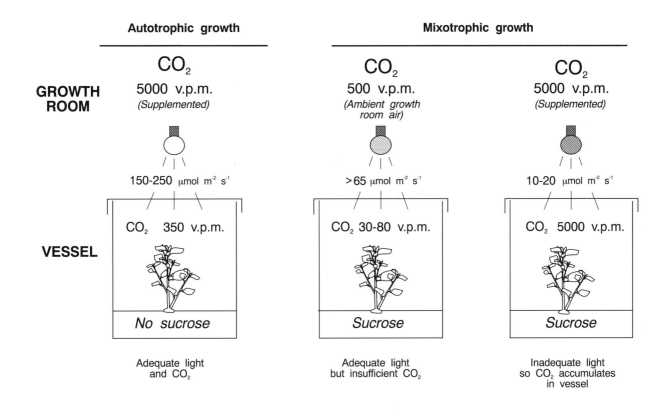

Fig. 74. How light and carbon dioxide concentrations affect the growth of cultured plant tissues.

thesis *in vitro* and the presence of a sugar, cause green tissues or organs to become mixotrophic. Some reports have indicated that shoots and plantlets grown on a sugar-based medium are capable of only very low rates of photosynthesis *in vitro* or when first moved to the *ex vitro* situation (Grout and Aston, 1978; Donnelly and Vidaver, 1984). However, Kozai (1991) thinks that the measurement of photosynthesis with an infra-red gas analyzer can give misleading results: experiments with several different kinds of plants have led him to conclude that cultured green shoots have a high capacity for photosynthesis, but achieving a rate adequate to support autotrophic growth requires higher light levels than those normally supplied to cultures, and a level of CO_2 which is at least close to that normally present in air. A maximum rate of photosynthesis occurs when the requirement for both CO_2 and light is saturated (Table 11).

Inadequate carbon dioxide. Unless the CO_2 in sealed or partly-sealed containers can be readily replenished, photosynthesis conducted by cultured shoots in adequate light (greater than 65 $\mu mol\ m^{-2}\ s^{-1}$), quickly reduces the intra-vessel CO_2 to a level where the rate of photosynthesis is depressed. In such lighting, with 500 v.p.m. CO_2 in the growth room and restricted diffusion, the level of CO_2 within a vessel would typically drop to 30–100 v.p.m. (Fig 59). Even 9000 v.p.m CO_2 accumulated in a flask during a dark period is soon reduced to a concentration insufficient for plants to retain their full photosynthetic capacity (Fujiwara *et al.*, 1987). For much of the light period such cultures are therefore likely to become mixotrophic, relying upon sugar in the medium to maintain their growth.

The level of carbon dioxide inside tubes and jars with loosely fitting or gas-permeable caps is somewhat improved, but in high lighting it may still fall to 100–200 v.p.m. so that photosynthesis is restricted (Kozai and Sekimoto, 1988).

Inadequate light. A different situation occurs when light levels are insufficient to bring photosynthesis above the compensation point: high levels of carbon dioxide may then accumulate in the culture vessel, because the rate of respiration exceeds that of photosynthesis (Fig. 74). In hermetically sealed flasks, *Cinchona ledgeriana* shoot cultures grown under a photon flux density of 119 μmol $m^{-2}\ s^{-1}$ (photosynthetically active radiation, PAR) accumulated up to 15% CO_2 in both continuous light or continuous darkness. If the flasks were capped with aluminium foil, itself covered with cling-film plastic, the CO_2 concentration was lower (7000 v.p.m.) (Hunter *et al.*, 1986).

Heterotrophic growth

Heterotrophic growth is common in conventional shoot cultures. The leaves thereof become modified for this manner of growth, and may not be photosynthetically competent when transferred to a sugar-free medium or moved into the *ex vitro* environment. Although they have chloroplasts with a light-stimulated electron transport system comparable to the leaves of plants grown *in vivo*, the activity of the photosynthetic enzyme, ribulose biphosphate carboxylase, and chlorophyll levels, are much lower than normal (Grout and Donkin, 1987). Plantlets therefore have to be carefully weaned after *extra vitrum* transfer until photosynthetic competence is restored (see Chapter 14).

Effect of sugars. The rate of photosynthesis of shoots grown on media containing sucrose varies between different genera. Some (e.g *Dieffenbachia*) are capable of efficient photosynthesis from which they derive a positive carbon balance (Grout and Price, 1987). In many other plants, photosynthesis is very much reduced *in vitro* and cultured tissues appear to be 'lazy' for they utilise sugar in the medium even when conditions are favourable for autotrophic growth; in these cases carbon dioxide utilisation is depressed by the presence of externally-available sucrose (Langford and Wainwright, 1988). Grout and Donkin (1987) suggested that this might be occur through sucrose inhibiting the ribulose biphosphate carboxylase (RubPcase) enzyme. The depression of RubPcase activity usually continues after transfer to a sucrose-free medium. Grout and Price (1987) showed that leaves of strawberry produced on a medium containing 2.5% sucrose had a low rate of photosynthesis and were unable to become autotrophic when plantlets were tranferred to a medium without sucrose: the leaves became necrotic and the plantlets died. If however the plantlets were defoliated before transfer, new shoots arose on the sucrose-free medium which had a much higher photosynthetic rate, and high RubPcase. The plants were then autotrophic and capable of survival.

The significance of this finding is that once a culture has been initiated on a sugar-based medium, autotrophic growth may be difficult to re-establish. Photosynthetic activity of cultured cells can sometimes be triggered by sequentially reducing the supply of sugar (*e.g.* Dalton, 1980).

Autotrophic growth

Shoots and plantlets. Autotrophic growth of rooted seedlings and plantlets *in vitro* is definitely possible, although the rate of photosynthesis may be less than that of comparable plants grown *in vivo* (Aoki and Oda, 1988; Pospisilova *et al.*, 1987). Opinions vary on whether autotrophic growth is worthwhile, and whether cultures at earlier stages can also be grown economically in this way. Heterotrophic or mixotrophic growth is clearly still going to be necessary for the early stages of cultures initiated from very small explants: autotrophic growth might be suitable for later cultural stages. Plants with a low surface to volume ratio (*e.g.* cacti) are likely always to grow more rapidly on a sucrose-supplemented medium than in autotrophic conditions or *in vivo*.

There are several reports (Kozai *et al.*, 1987a,b; 1988; Kozai and Iwanami, 1988; Arai *et al.*, 1989; Kozai, 1991) of shoot or node cultures, or plantlets grown under high light and carbon dioxide enrichment, growing more rapidly and surviving better than those grown under mixotrophic conditions. Plants are said to be less liable to fungal and bacterial contamination and so can be grown in larger vessels without exaggerating the losses due to contamination. Whether these findings can be translated into practical and cost-efficient methods of micropropagation has yet to be proved. The high light conditions required for autotrophy are expensive both in terms of equipment and running costs.

To achieve autotrophic growth, CO_2 must be supplied to culture vessels at an adequate rate (Fujiwara *et al.*, 1987) either by deliberate introduction, or through diffusion. The former method can be employed in large suspension cultures and might be used for the other kinds of culture used in micropropagation, if it were possible to employ large containers, with an internal volume of one or more litres. A suitable chamber was described by Fujiwara *et al.* (1988): maintaining a slight positive pressure inside the container helps to prevent the ingress of air.

It would not be practical to link together many small containers for direct CO_2 supply. The supply of carbon dioxide into small vessels currently used for shoot and node cultures is best improved by increased diffusion. Closures on small vessels usually restrict diffusion to a significant extent: if autotrophic growth is to be achieved in closed containers, it is therefore important to have adequate gas entry. This can present difficulties, allowing water to move out of the container, causing media to dry out.

Diffusion of carbon dioxide to cultured tissues is also enhanced if the carbon dioxide in the atmosphere of the growth room is supplemented (using the same kind of equipment that is commonly used in greenhouses). Usually the level within containers can be maintained at *ca.* 350 v.p.m. during photosynthesis, if the concentration in the growth room is kept at 500 v.p.m. at the beginning of the multiplication stage, and then increased by 500 v.p.m. every 7 days (Kozai, 1991).

Situations which, according to Kozai (1989), allow or disallow autotrophic growth are summarised in Fig. 76. He recommended that normal rigid containers should be loosely capped, or covered with a gas-permeable plastic film, or that cultures should be grown in the type of containers made entirely of gas-permeable film, described in Chapter 4. Plastic film covers have the added advantage that light is not obstructed.

Optimum cultural environment. The cultural environment for autotrophic growth may not be the same as that required for heterotrophic cultures. Kozai *et al.*. (1988) found that carnation shoots grew better under conditions of high light and adequate CO_2, if they were placed on a medium containing only a simple salt solution normally used for hydroponics rather than ½**Murashige and Skoog (1962)**. The optimum temperature for autotrophic photosynthesis may also be less than that used for normal cultures (Grout and Price, 1987).

Hayashi and Kozai (1987) found that the growth of plantlets in an automated acclimatization chamber, was improved if CO_2 concentrations were supplemented when solar radiation was greater than 58 W m^{-2}. Fujiwara *et al.* (1988) obtained similar results in an apparatus for culturing shoots and plantlets at the stage where they need to be rooted and acclimatized. They describe much more rapid growth of strawberry shoots to rooted plantlets, than is possible in conventional tubes on an agar medium. Shoots were supported in a large plastic container above a recirculated ½**MS** liquid medium with no sucrose. The container was fed with CO_2 so that the level under an irradiance of 96 μmol m^{-2} s^{-1} PAR (photosynthetically active radiation — see later in this Chapter), did not drop below 300–330 v.p.m.

Autotrophy in cell and callus cultures. Photoautotrophic growth has also been achieved in callus or suspension cultures of many different plant species (Hüsemann *et al.*, 1990). Most of these cultures require the presence of high CO_2 concentrations (*ca.* 1–5%), but a few cell lines have been selected which are capable of autotrophic growth in the CO_2 concentration of air (330 v.p.m.), although in these examples a low growth rate and photosynthetic capacity has been obtained. At 25°C, growth rates of autotrophic *Marchantia polymorpha* suspension cultures have been found to be at a maximum when they are supplied with 1% CO_2 and a photon flux density of 165 μmol m^{-2} s^{-1}. Specific growth rate in this liverwort declined exponentially as the CO_2 concentration increased above an optimum (*e.g.* in *Marchantia polymorpha* cells grown at 25°C and a photon flux density of 90 μmol m^{-2} s^{-1}, it was 0.42/d in 1% CO_2 but only 0.16/d in 10% CO_2) (Katoh and Hirose, 1982).

Supplementary CO₂ and rooting. The effect of supplementary carbon dioxide on the rooting and hardening of shoots propagated *in vitro* is described in Chapter 14.

Growth improvement in mixotrophic conditions.

Although the plants grown autotrophically by Kozai and co-workers (*loc. cit.*) were of an equivalent size and weight to those grown heterotrophically, Desjardins *et al.* (1988) did not obtain such unequivocal results. Their plants were grown under high light conditions (80, 150 or 250 $\mu mol\ m^{-2}\ s^{-1}$) in chambers supplemented with CO_2, but were contained in test tubes sealed with Magenta® caps. Under these conditions plants of strawberry, raspberry and asparagus had a significant carbon metabolism, but grew relatively slowly unless 3% sucrose was present in the medium. When the CO_2 level was 330 v.p.m., photosynthesis reduced the concentration inside the tubes to 100 v.p.m. (limiting to further photosynthesis); 1650 v.p.m. CO_2 was reduced to 1000 v.p.m.; 3000 v.p.m. to 1800–2000 v.p.m.

Predieri *et al.* (1991) have also recorded increased fresh and dry weight and better shoot proliferation of *Actinidia* and *Malus* shoot cultures given CO_2 enrichment in the presence of sucrose. A photon flux density of 30–70 $\mu mol\ m^{-2}\ s^{-1}$ was required, together with only 1% sucrose in the medium.

Growth regulation

Non-autotrophic requirement

Animal cells are unable to survive without carbon dioxide. Plants may also have a non-photosynthetic requirement. The presence of carbon dioxide (optimum partial pressure 0.1 atm) has been shown to be essential for the initiation of new growth in low density cultures of sycamore cells in suspensions, or on agar plates. The gas had a conditioning effect: non-photosynthetic fixation resulted in the cells producing organic acids and amino acids which were essential for growth. Attempts to replace these naturally-produced compounds with synthetic alternatives were unsuccessful (Stuart and Street, 1971: Gathercole *et al.*, 1976). These results have been confirmed in other plants. Besides leading to the biosynthesis of organic and amino acids, non-autotrophic fixation has also been found to result in the production of lipids (Nesius and Fletcher, 1975; Obata-Sasamoto *et al.*, 1984; Plumb-Dhindsa *et al.*, 1979; Vanderhoven and Zyrd, 1978). It has also been thought that plant cells have a requirement for CO_2 during division (Nesius and Fletcher, 1973).

Effect on organogenesis

Ethylene gas is an endogenous plant hormone (see Chapter 11). Low concentrations of carbon dioxide can stimulate ethylene biosynthesis: at higher concentrations (1–10% CO_2) it competitively inhibits ethylene action.

Shoot formation from tobacco cotyledons was inhibited if the gas phase contained 1% CO_2 rather than ambient levels during the first 7 days of incubation. A similar effect was produced by 5 μM aminoethoxyvinylglycine, an inhibitor of ethylene biosynthesis, which led Everett (1982) to suggest that carbon dioxide was antagonising the action of ethylene. By contrast, Cornejo-Martin *et al.* (1979) reported that ethylene (5 v.p.m.) combined with 2% CO_2 was more effective than ethylene alone for promoting shoot formation in rice callus in the presence of BAP. Similarly Kumar *et al.* (1986) found that the ethylene *and* the carbon dioxide which built up in sealed containers after inoculation of *Pinus radiata* cotyledons, were responsible for promoting shoot morphogenesis on a medium containing BAP.

CONTAINER SIZE

Types of containers used for micropropagation work have been described in Chapter 4. Container volume can sometimes affect growth and morphogenesis *in vitro*. These effects are probably due to different concentrations of oxygen, carbon dioxide (this Chapter), ethylene and other volatiles (Chapter 11) in the air space within the container. Vessels of different size usually differ in the ratio of explant to medium, explant to air, and medium to air: the shape of the vessel can also influence the growth rate of cultures by modifying the rate of gaseous diffusion (Bateson *et al.* 1987) (page 194).

There are many examples in the literature of vessel size having an effect on the rate of culture growth or the rate of shoot proliferation. They usually show that growth is not at an optimum in very small containers: sometimes an optimum size of container has been demonstrated. Fresh weight increase, morphogenesis or the rate of axillary shoot proliferation are frequently affected in different ways. Growth of *Saintpaulia* shoots was greater in 120 ml jars than in 60 ml ones (Start and Cumming, 1976) and shoot proliferation in shoot cultures of several woody plants better in 200 ml or 350 ml vessels than in 60 ml tubes (McClelland and Smith, 1990).

Saintpaulia cultures initiated from petiole sections produced twice as many plantlets in 125 ml Erlenmeyer flasks as in 30 ml glass jars. Plantlet development in the small jars was however more rapid, and the total weight of tissue produced per explant was twice as great as in the flasks (Bilkey and McCown, 1978). A similar result was obtained by Monette (1983) with proliferating grapevine shoot cultures, but not by Chun *et al.* (1986) with *Populus*. The grapevine shoot cultures produced a significantly greater number of shoots 3mm or longer in 473 ml jars than in 125 or 250 ml flasks, but in those of *Populus alba × P. grandidentata* an initial difference in shoot number between 74, 135 and 233 ml vessels had disappeared after 4 weeks of culture. In both *Saintpaulia* and grapevine, jars and flasks contained the same volume (10 and 7.5 ml respectively) of medium. In the first experiment the vessels had the same size of opening, so that only air volume; diffusion distance; and medium depth, and surface area, varied.

The quantity and quality of shoots obtained from *Gerbera* shoot cultures was better in 125 ml jars than in 25 x 150 mm test tubes (Wozniak *et al.*, 1982) and de Fossard and de Fossard (1988b) reported better rooting and shoot growth of many plant species in 250 ml vessels than in 40 ml ones. Survival and eventual rooting of *Narcissus* meristem tips was much better in 35 ml tubes than in 8 ml ones (Stone, 1973).

An optimum size of flask

Shoot tips of *Actinidia chinensis* produced more shoots in 125 ml flasks than in 50, 250 or 500 ml flasks. Although flask size had no effect on the relative gain in fresh weight, cultures in 50 ml flasks had a higher dry weight relative to their size (Monette, 1986a). The number of shoots obtained from *Artemisia dracunculus* cultures was greater in 55 × 70 mm jars than in 90 × 95 mm ones (although this might not been entirely an effect of size, as the tops of the larger jars were wrappped with film and the smaller ones were not). The length of shoots was greater in the 55 × 70 mm jars than in 25 × 150 mm tubes or 90 × 95 mm jars (Mackay and Kitto, 1988).

The percentage of tobacco anthers forming pollen embryos and the number of plantlets formed from these somatic embryos, was found to depend on the size of culture vessel used. Best results were obtained when the volume of air above 2 ml of medium, was either 5.6 or 15 ml (Dunwell and Roberts, 1975). Poor response in the lowest air volume was thought to have been due to a high concentration of either CO_2 or ethylene, or to an interaction between the two gases. Dunwell (1981a) later compared the growth and morphogenesis of leaf discs of three brassicas, in glass containers of 8, 16 and 29 ml capacity. The same volume of medium (2 ml), and the same number of discs (15) was placed in each size. Final disc diameter and weight, and the number of roots formed per disc, increased as the volume of the culture flask was increased. Dalton and Dale (1981) found that after 3 months, tiller explants of *Lolium multiflorum* in 250 ml flasks (50 ml medium) produced 3 times the number of shoots that were obtained in 30 ml (10 ml medium) or 60 ml (15 ml medium) containers. But a higher rate of tiller production was finally obtained by subculturing every 4–5 weeks from 30 ml tubes rather than subculturing less frequently from larger vessels.

Practical recommendations

The results above show that it is impossible to recommend vessel sizes for any particular type of micropropagation proceedure without prior experimentation. The best size and shape of vessel will vary from one species to another, and will depend on factors such as the material from which the vessel is made (*e.g.* glass or gas-permeable plastic), the type of closures used, the volume of medium and the density of inoculation.

Takayama and Misawa have attempted to scale-up the propagation of various kinds of ornamental plants (Chapter 16) using liquid culture in large vessels. Leaf segments of *Begonia × hiemalis* undergoing direct shoot regeneration cultured in jar or bubble column fermentors had a lower growth rate than those in shaken 150 ml Erlenmeyer flasks. This was thought to be due to the relative rates of aeration (Takayama and Misawa, 1981).

THE PHYSICAL ENVIRONMENT

TEMPERATURE

In their natural environment, plants usually experience temperatures which fluctuate widely, especially between day and night. It is advantageous to mimic such a diurnal variation wherever possible. The growth of many plant cultures is improved by these conditions and where growth rooms have to be heated, there is a saving in fuel costs by reducing the night temperature. A further advantage of alternating temperatures is that they assist the exchange of gases in culture vessels (Chalupa, 1987). However, such variation is not essential and, in many laboratories, tissue cultures are maintained in growth rooms at the same temperature by night and day.

To speed growth and morphogenesis *in vitro*, cultures are generally maintained at mean temperatures which are higher than those which would be experienced by the same plants growing *in vivo*. The average constant growth room temperature employed in a large sample of experimental reports was found to be 25°C (with a range between 17° and 32°C). Tropical and subtropical plants such as cotton, rice, *Citrus* and *Bougainvillea* tend to be cultured at slightly higher temperatures than temperate species (average 27.7°C, range 24–32°C). Where a diurnal fluctuation is preferred, a somewhat higher-than-average day temperature is usually coupled with a dark-period value that is *ca.* 4–8°C lower than the daytime figure: typical variations adopted are 25°C day: 20°C night, or 28°C/24°C.

There is not a single defined temperature for the tissue culture of any one species and that employed in published reports will often be found to vary according to the experimenter and the kind of organ or tissue being cultured. Such differences usually have only minor effects on the rate growth or propagation.

Many small micropropagation laboratories have only a single growth room in which temperature is fairly uniform. Different kinds of plant can be successful multiplied under such conditions, but there are frequent examples in the literature to prove that different plant species can have distinct temperature optima. *Dicentra spectabilis* shoot cultures proliferate most rapidly at 22°C and explant growth and shoot proliferation are both poor at 27°C. Commercial laboratories in the U.S.A. tend to maintain shoot cultures of temperate plants at 22°C and tropical species at 28°C (Stimart, 1986).

Note that in lighted rooms, the temperature inside culture vessels is usually several degrees higher than room temperature, due to the greenhouse effect (Debergh, 1988). In addition, the base of the vessels is frequently warmer than the top (see page 212).

The following discussion shows how explant establishment, culture growth, plantlet development, and morphogenesis can be temperature-dependent.

Culture establishment and growth

The rate at which plant material grows *in vitro*, usually declines slowly as temperatures are reduced below the optimum, while above the optimum, the rate of growth falls off more rapidly, and cultures also frequently appear to be unhealthy. Although shoot cultures of *Artocarpus heterophyllus* (Jackfruit) produced more axillary shoots at 25 or 30°C than at 20°C, hardly any were obtained at 35°C. Rahman and Blake (1988a) supposed that at the higher temperature, respiration exceeded photosynthesis.

A clear temperature optimum was discovered for the growth of olive embryos by Diamantoglou and Mitrakos (1979). Although growth was slow initially at 25°C, 70% of the embryos developed into plantlets at this temperature while at 15, 20 or 30°C, the success rate was more than halved. Leaf blade explants of *Vitis* survived in culture at 20° and 25°C, but did not grow. Growth was only satisfactory at 29°C; at 32° and 34°C the explants survived for only a short while (Favre, 1977).

Culturing explanted peach shoot tips at 21–24°C ensured 80–90 per cent survival, but only 7 per cent survived at 28°C (Hammerschlag, 1981a, 1982a). Callus cultures too, show large differences in growth rate depending on temperature. Tumour callus of sorrel grew rapidly at 21° and 25°C and only poorly at 5, 15 or 30°C. At 36° and 45°C there was little growth and the callus turned brown (Nickell and Burkholder, 1950).

Temperature preferences can sometimes vary between quite closely related genotypes. Having established cultures from stem nodes of 14 different *Rosa* hybrids at 24°C, Horn *et al.* (1988b) looked at the effect of a range of temperatures on the rate of shoot multiplication. The best overall results were obtained at 18°C, but certain 'thermonegative' hybrids gave the best results at 12°C while in other 'thermopositive' ones, shoot proliferation was at an optimum at 18 or 24°C.

There are many other examples where the cultures of certain plants require below-average temperatures. For example, the best plantlet growth from the floral meristems in cauliflower curd tissue occurred at 18°C: growth was less at 22°C (Walkey and Woolfitt, 1970). Single node cultures of *Syringa vulgaris* grew satisfactorily at 21°C in a 16 h day under an irradiance of 5 W m^{-2}, but if the cultures were kept at 25 or 27°C, growth was abnormal and there was leaf yellowing and curling (Pierik *et al.*, 1988c).

Root cultures. Root cultures of most plants can be grown at 20–25°C. The optimum temperature for the culture of isolated roots of most varieties of tomato is 27°C (Street (1957) or 28°C (Janes *et al.*, 1988), although in one variety, White (1937a) apparently found the most rapid growth occurred at 37°C.

Morphogenesis

Shoot bud formation

Organogenesis frequently reaches an optimum within a narrow range of temperatures, which varies between species.

Induction at relatively low temperatures. Adventitious shoot initiation on *Begonia × cheimantha* leaf explants has been observed to be at an optimum in leaf cuttings at 15°C (Heide, 1965) and in petiole segments at 15–20°C (Fonnesbech, 1974a). Further shoot development was, however, enhanced at 24°C (Fonnesbech, 1974c). The initiation process is promoted by cytokinins, and in both series of experiments, incubation at 25–27°C inhibited kinetin-induced bud formation. Similarly in *Streptocarpus × hybridus*, direct shoot formation on leaf discs (which were not maintained aseptically) was best at an incubation temperature of 12°C, and less buds were formed per disc as the temperature was increased up to 30°C (Appelgren and Heide, 1972). Shoot induction on peduncle explants of *Anemone coronaria* took place only at 15–19°C, and above 26°C most explants died (Sutter and Langhans, 1978a).

Induction at high temperatures. In some plants the temperature for the best induction of adventitious organs is somewhat higher than that required for growth. In *Pinus radiata* for example, adventitious buds formed most readily on juvenile explants when they were cultured in a 28°C (day), 24°C (night) regime, whereas the shoots which were formed grew best at 24°/20°C (Aitken *et al.*, 1981). A very different temperature optimum was found for shoot formation for fragmented shoot apices of *Vitis vinifera*. Here the rate of initiation and multiplication of adventitious shoot buds was much greater at 35°C than at 27°, although explants were killed at 38°C (Barlass and Skene, 1982a).

Induction at normal temperatures. In other plants, shoot regeneration seems to be most effectively induced at temperatures closer to those used for normal tissue culture. On rapeseed (Colza) flower stalk segments, where adventitious shoots were readily formed at 24°C, low temperatures (13°C for 16 h day, 6°C at night) inhibited subsequent morphogenesis, especially when applied during the first 1–2 weeks of culture (Margara and Leydecker, 1978). Although in *Brassica campestris*, adventitious shoot formation from leaf discs was better at 20°C than at 25°C, it occurred satisfactorily at several temperatures in *B. napus* and *B. oleracea* (Dunwell, 1981a; Johnson and Mitchell, 1978c). Very similar results were obtained by Kato and Ozawa (1979) with leaf fragments of *Heloniopsis*. Shoot bud formation (here largely independent of the addition of benzyl adenine) was at an optimum at 21–25°C. Pre-treatment at 30°C for 7 days or more, reduced the number of buds eventually formed in segments of both young etiolated, and mature green leaves, but not in segments of young green leaves unless they were kept in the dark at the same time.

Pretreatments. Morphogenesis is often influenced by the temperature at which mother plants or cultures have been maintained previously. Kato and Ozawa (1979) reported that *Heloniopsis* shoot initiation was inhanced if explants were maintained at 16°C for 7–21 days before culture at a higher temperature and Von Arnold and Eriksson (1979b) found that to induce a high proportion of *Picea abies* needles to form adventious buds, they should be kept at 10–16°C before incubation at 20°C. Even lower temperatures are inductive in other plants (see below). Maintaining tomato stem explants for an unspecified time at a 'low' temperature of 19°C was described as enhancing their regenerative potential (Reynolds J. F. *et al.*, 1982).

Selection for a low temperature response. Heating costs involved in the greenhouse culture of ornamentals make it desirable to obtain varieties with an ability to grow and flower in reduced temperatures. Grunewaldt (1988a) has reported the selection of clones with an ability to grow at 16°C (instead of the normal 20°C) by low temperature induction of direct shoot regeneration in leaf explants, some of which were from mutagen-treated plants. The earliest clones to flower at 16° were amongst the plants regenerated by a 7 d incubation at 26°C followed by 12 weeks at 15°C.

Direct adventitious root formation

The formation of adventitious roots on shoots is temperature dependent. For example no callus or roots formed on young shoot tips of *Asparagus* at 0, 10 or 15°C, but 20 per cent of cuttings rooted at 20°C, and 45 per cent at 25°C (Gorter, 1965). In many plants, root induction on the shoot micro-cuttings produced *in vitro* seems to require a slightly lower temperature than is necessary for shoot multiplication and growth.

Conifers seem to root most effectively at a temperature of *ca.* 20°C (Chalupa, 1987). Shoots derived from Douglas fir shoot cultures grown at 24°C, yielded only a few plantlets if root induction was carried out at this temperature. The plantlets also showed a discontinuity in their anatomy due to the formation of callus at the shoot-root transition zone. On the other hand, many plantlets of normal appearance were produced at 19°C (Cheng, 1978a). *Digitalis lanata* shoots from cultures grown at 24°C were best rooted at 19°C/14°C (day/night) (Schöner and Reinhard, 1982, 1986) and shoots obtained from *Aconitum carmichaeli* shoot cultures multiplied at 25°C produced more roots at 20° than at 25°C (Hatano et al., 1988).

Not all plants respond in this way: shoots of some may root better at a higher temperature. Microcuttings of two apple varieties produced at 25°C, rooted well at 24–26°C but rooting was partially suppressed at 20–22°C or 28°C (Kataeva and Butenko, 1987). Zimmerman (1984b) obtained similar results with shoots of different apple cultivars from shoot cultures maintained at 25°C. A very high

Table 12. Cold treatment used to overcome bulb dormancy in monocotyledonous species.

Species	Treatment	Authors
Gladiolus	3–4 weeks at 5°C	Hussey (1976c, 1977a)
Hyacinthus	3–4 weeks at 5°C	Hussey (1977a)
	4–8 weeks at 4°C (longer tmt. for larger bulbs)	Paek (1982)
Iris hollandica	3–4 weeks at 5°C	Hussey (1977a)
	4 weeks at 5°C	Anderson *et al.* (1990)
Lilium longiflorum	3–4 weeks at 5°C	Hussey (1977a)
Lilium pyrenaicum	3–4 weeks at 5°C	Hussey (1977a)
Lilium speciosum	6 weeks at 2°C	Van Aartrijk and Blom-Barnhoorn (1979)
		Paffen *et al.* (1990)
Narcissus	3–4 weeks at 5°C	Hussey (1977a)
	6–8 weeks at 5°C	Hussey and Hilton (1978a, 1980a)
	10 weeks at 5°C	Hussey (1982)
Tulipa gesneriana	3 months at 4°C	Hussey (1976c, 1977a)
	8 weeks at 4°C	Rice *et al.* (1983)
	3 months at 4°C	Rivière and Müller (1976)
	11–14 weeks at 5°C	Nishiuchi (1980)

proportion of shoots rooted when placed on a rooting medium in the dark at 30°C for one week, followed by a 16/8 h regime at 25°C. The rooting of 'Delicious' and 'Vermont Spur Delicious' was improved by incubation at 30°C, while that of 'Royal Red Delicious' was best at 35°C.

The effect of temperature on *in vitro* rooting is discussed further in Chapter 14.

Tuber and bulblet production

Incubation temperature is reported to have a marked effect on the rate of *in vitro* tuber formation in potato. At least 10 times more tubers were formed at a constant 20°C than at 28°C, or at a day temperature of 27°C and cooler nights (Wang and Hu, 1982). In bulbous species, culture at certain temperatures can cause the cessation of shoot growth, a type of dormancy which often requires a cold treatment to reverse it (see below).

Culturing *Lilium longiflorum* bulbscales *in vitro* at 30°C resulted in the formation of bulblets which produced leaves when transplanted, either without further treatment or after the bulblets had been immersed in water at 45°C for one hour. All the bulblets regenerated at 25°C

were fully dormant however, and did not produce leaf axes when transplanted (Stimart and Ascher, 1978a; Stimart *et al.* 1983). Scale sections of *Lilium speciosum* cultured at 20 or 25°C, produced bulblets which were dormant when planted *ex vitro*; but bulblets produced from section grown at 15°C began growth straight away (Paffen *et al.*, 1990).

Low temperature treatments

Callus

The proportion of *Arabidopsis* callus cultures forming shoots and roots was increased when 9 month old callus was kept for 3–6 days at 4°C before transfer to regeneration medium at the normal culture temperature of 25°C. The weight of roots per callus was also increased by this treatment (Negrutiu and Jacobs, 1978a).

Cold treatments to reverse dormancy

The value of cold treatments to overcome the natural resting state of buds from which explants are required, is discussed in Chapter 8. A similar cold-sensitive dormancy occurs occasionally during *in vitro* culture, or immediately after plantlets have been transferred to the external environment. It has been most frequently reported in bulbous species where plants often become gradually dormant (particularly if they are not subcultured).

Bulbs. Plants which produce a bulb *in vitro* often become dormant; this is sometimes manifested by senescence of the shoot above the bulb (*e.g.* in onion — Hussey and Falavigna, 1980). Dormant plants or bulbils can often be induced to resume growth or to germinate, either *in vitro* or in an external environment, if they are kept for a few weeks at a low temperature (1–10°C has been found to be appropriate). Effective treatments for some commonly propagated species are shown in Table 12.

Graves *et al.* (1978) administered cold to plantlets of *Lilium, Hemerocallis* and *Hippeastrum* at Stage III before they were potted into soil, similarly finding that it reduced the risk of injury and allowed the young plants to initiate rapid growth. Bulblets of *Lilium auratum* and other *Lilium* species produced on **MS** + 90 g/l sucrose, required 100–140 days at 5°C before dormancy was broken, but those formed on the same medium containing 30 g/l sucrose required only about 50–70 days of cold (Takayama and Misawa, 1980; Takayama *et al.*, 1982).

Where continued subculture is desired, treatments other than cold can sometimes be used to encourage plants to resume active growth. Splitting crowns into two after 12–14 weeks of culture was effective in *Freesia,* but in some other members of the Iridaceae, this treatment resulted in very weak plants (Hussey, 1976c). Mahotiere *et al.* (1976a,b) found that onion shoot dormancy could be avoided by transferring cultures from 20°C to 10°C for 96 h. Continued growth could alternatively be promoted by the addition of 100 mg/l kinetin and/or 100 mg/l sucrose to the medium. Dormancy of *Gladiolus, Iris, Sparaxis* and *Schizostylis* plants *in vitro* was prevented by 0.03 mg/l BAP (Hussey, 1976c, 1977b).

Woody plants. Shoots in cultures of woody plants can become dormant *in vitro*, although this is rare. One reported example is in *Clematis*, where dormancy in many cultivated varieties is triggered by short days and cool temperatures. Shoots derived from shoot cultures of var. 'Elsa Spath' became dormant *in vitro* in short days, especially if this treatment was accompanied by cool temperatures. The dormancy could be broken by 100 mg/l GA₃, or chilling in short days. Placing shoot cultures in long days during the chilling period resulted in the incomplete elimination of dormancy, and subsequent rosetted growth (Kratz and Langhans, 1978).

Dormancy in plantlets of woody species is more common when rooted plantlets are transferred *extra vitrum*. They may then fail to grow vigorously or may form an obvious resting terminal bud and cease growth altogether. Dormancy of this kind can usually be overcome by cold, or gibberellic acid, treatments. Plantlets of *Prunus institia* (plum rootstock) remained small with weak growth unless kept for two months at 0°C or given a spray of 200 mg/l GA₃ after potting (Howard and Oehl, 1981). Gibberellic acid is often added to media used for propagating fruit and nut species to promote shoot elongation (Lane, 1982). Significantly greater growth and clonal uniformity of some *Prunus* and *Malus* species was achieved when plantlets which had been rooted *in vitro*, were kept for at least 42 days at 2–4°C in the dark before they were planted in the greenhouse [Suttle (Driver and Suttle, 1987)].

Dormancy, similar to that occurring in some shoot cultures, may result from embryo culture of species in which seeds require to be subjected to a period of cold moist conditions (stratification) before normal growth. Then embryos dissected out from unchilled seeds may germinate *in vitro* but produce dwarfed plants, typically having a rosette of leaves and virtually no internode growth. Plants may remain in this condition for many years (Flemion, 1959) unless chilled or treated with a gibberellin (Barton, 1956). If kept in constant temperatures, pine callus cultures occasionally cease growing, but will resume active growth at normal temperatures if stored in the cold for about 6 weeks (Bonga, 1977b).

The induction of flowering

Cold treatments promote the flowering of certain plants *in vivo*, particularly biennials. The work of Gertsson (1988b) has suggested that *in vitro* culture at cool temperatures may have a similar effect. Plants of *Senecio* × *hybridus* obtained from shoot cultures maintained at 10°C, flowered earlier, had a greater foliage height, and taller inflorescences, than those from cultures grown at 21°C.

HUMIDITY

Relative humidity (R.H.) is a measure of the amount of water vapour contained in a gaseous atmosphere. It is expressed as the ratio of the quantity of water an atmosphere actually contains, to that which it could contain when saturated. Relative humidity within culture flasks has not often been discussed in papers on tissue culture, and had not been thought to be an important environmental factor until its effect on the hyperhydricity of cultured shoots and plantlets became apparent.

The R.H. of the gaseous mixture ('air') above the medium within a culture vessel depends on its temperature and that of the medium. Where the temperature of the air equals that of the medium, and the vessel is effectively sealed, the relative humidity should theoretically be in the range 98–99.5% (see page 336). The air may become almost fully saturated if the temperature of the medium exceeds that of the air, but relative humidity will decrease if there is an exchange of water vapour from the vessel to the growth room. Short *et al.* (1987) recorded the following effect of type of closure on intra-vessel relative humidity:

Closed screw-top lid	100%
Partly-closed screw-top lid	80%
Cotton wool plug	70%
Cling-film wrap	60%
Filter paper	50%

A relative humidity of *ca.* 70% is usually recommended for growth rooms. Humidities lower than this can occur in rooms fitted with cooling units, causing media within partly sealed vessels to dry out rapidly. An humidifier should be placed within growth rooms to rectify this situation.

The optimum humidity for cultures

Because cultures grown in high humidities are liable to become hyperhydric, it would be ideal to surround shoot and organ cultures with air which is not fully saturated. Unfortunately a reduction in humidity below 75–80% R.H. is disadvantageous for many kinds of tissue culture. Jones (1974b) found that carrot embryoids would not stand desiccation and were best kept at a relative humidity of 80–90%. They all died if it was less than 60%. The rate of shoot proliferation of *Pelargonium* shoot cultures was poor when the relative humidity was below 75% (Cassells and Minas, 1983), and cauliflower plantlets exposed to 30% and 15% R.H. *in vitro* experienced high mortality. Such low humidities can be produced experimentally by covering the medium with molten lanolin (33% R.H.) and placing silica gel in the vessel (10–20% R.H.) (Wardle *et al.*, 1983a) (Fig. 75).

The humidity in vessels containing cultured shoots also depends on their total leaf area (*i.e.* upon the number and size of shoots per vessel). R.H. may fall below the optimum for growth when there is only a small number of shoots in a large culture container. Evert and Holt (1975) found it advantageous to place small beakers of water inside plastic boxes used for chrysanthemum shoot tips cultured on a semi-solid medium. Normally growth in large vessels is improved by the presence of several shoots, which together help to maintain an adequate relative humidity. Lane (1982) noticed that growing 3 or 4 pear shoots per tube (instead of one), was effective in

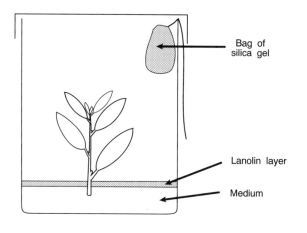

Fig. 75. The experimental method used by Wardle *et al.* (1983a) to lower humidity in culture vessels.

preventing shoot necrosis. Injury occurred when humidity in the culture tubes dropped below 95%; this also resulted in shoots forming roots less readily.

Cooling the base of vessels

A common situation in growth rooms is for the bases of vessels, resting above a warm light source, to be at a higher temperature than their tops. In these circumstances, if the air in the vessel has a high relative humidity, the top of the vessel may then reach the dew point and water will condense on the sides, or upon the lid, at the coolest point. Table 13 shows the humidities at which this may happen.

The relative humidity inside culture flasks will be less than 100% if the air temperature is higher than the temperature of the medium, for then water in the atmosphere condenses into the medium (Vanderschaeghe and Debergh, 1987). Thus the most effective method of reducing R.H. in culture vessels is to stand them on a cooled platform so that the medium is cooler than the air above it. In high relative humidities, the temperature of the medium then becomes the potential dew point (Debergh, 1986a,b; 1988; Vanderschaeghe and Debergh, 1987; 1988). Reductions in relative humidity which can be achieved *in vitro* by this method, can be deduced from Table 13.

In the experiments of Vanderschaeghe and Deberghe (1987), the most cost efficient method of cooling the shelving of growth rooms was found to be the circulation of a mixture of antigel fluid and water (previously cooled by a cryostat) within metal pipes. Flasks were placed on a metal shelf over the pipes.

Table 13. Relative humidities (%) within culture vessels at which condensation will occur .

Temperature difference between top and bottom of vessel °C	Temperature at top or bottom of vessel		
	20°C	25°C	30°C
0.5	97	97	97
1.0	94	94	94
2.0	88	88	88
3.0	83	83	84
4.0	78	79	80
5.0	74	75	75

Note that condensation will occur either when the top of the vessel is cooler than the bottom or *vice versa*. Thus, if the bottom of a culture vessel is at 25°C and the top at 21°C, there will be internal condensation at the top when the relative humidity inside the vessel is 79% or above.
Similarly, if the base of a vessel is held at 20°C while the top is at 24 °C, there will be condensation at the base (into the medium) at 78% R.H. and above.

Survival *ex vitro*.

Frequently there are high losses when shoots or plantlets which have been grown in enclosed containers under high humidity, are transferred to an external environment. This is partly because they may have become hyperhydric, and partly because they are not adapted to a dry environment (see Chapter 14). The degree of adaptation can be increased by growing shoots in a reduced humidity before transfer, but shoot growth and rooting capacity decline progressively as humidity is lowered (Short *et al.*, 1987). This means that such treatments are only practical for a short period before transfer. Normally cultures are grown in high humidity until they are removed from the culture vessel and only then are shoots gradually hardened to the harsher external environment.

THE EFFECTS OF LIGHT

Physical properties

The nature of light

Light is radiant energy of those wavelengths which produce visual sensations to the eye. The visible radiant energy spectrum encompasses wavelengths from about 390 nm (violet), to around 700 nm (red region), which have the average relative visibilities (or efficiencies of providing visible light — *illumination*), shown in Fig. 62. [The wavelength of light (λ) used to be expressed in Ångström units (Å), but is now given in *nano*-metres (1 nm = 10 Å)].

A range of units has been devised to compare the luminous qualities (illuminating capabilities) provided by light sources. These units are not ideal for describing the effects of light on plants because plant pigments do not have the same relative sensitivities as the human eye to radiant energy of different wavelengths, and so it is better to define the light regimes experienced by plants in physical (energy) terms. Nevertheless illumination units have been widely used in early botanical literature (that on plant tissue culture being no exception). The following section therefore gives a brief description of the derivation of both illumination and energy units and how they may be approximately interconverted for comparative purposes.

Units of light measurement

Energy units. Standard units (*e.g. erg* and *joule*) are used to quantify light energy. The amount of radiant energy emitted (or received) from a light source, per unit time, is termed the *radiant flux*. Radiant flux per unit area is known as the *radiant flux density*, and that intercepted per unit area, as *irradiance* (or the radiant flux density at a surface). These concepts are illustrated diagrammatically in Fig. 76. *Intensity* refers to the energy output of a point source of radiation (or of a point on a radiation source). As energy from such a point source radiates outwards in all directions, its intensity is measured, independently of distance, as the energy emitted per unit time (radiant flux) per solid angle (steradian). There are 4π (12.57) steradians per sphere and so the radiant flux from a point source of 1 W sr^{-1} (W/sr) intensity is 12.57 W. The term 'intensity' is incorrectly used in many publications on plant tissue culture (see page 226).

Quantum units. Radiant energy in wave form (including light), is emitted in discrete indivisible quantities called 'quanta' or 'photons'. The very small amount of energy in each quantum is inversely proportional to the wavelength of the radiation. Quantum units are particularly suited to the measurement of light where its energy may be utilised for photochemical reactions, especially photosynthesis. Quanta are measured in moles (the preferred SI unit), or Einsteins, one Einstein (E) being defined as the energy of 6.023×10^{23} (*i.e.* the number of molecules per gram molecule, Avogadro's number) photons. A substance must absorb one Einstein of radiant energy per mole to take part in a photochemical reaction. The energy of an Einstein varies inversely with the wavelength of light (Fig. 77) and is greatest in the blue and ultra-violet

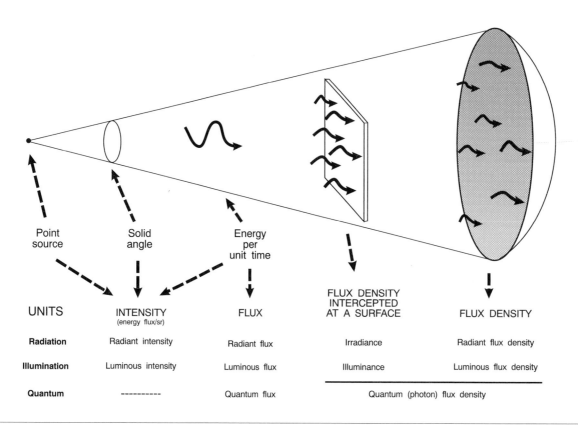

UNITS	INTENSITY (energy flux/sr)	FLUX	FLUX DENSITY INTERCEPTED AT A SURFACE	FLUX DENSITY
Radiation	Radiant intensity	Radiant flux	Irradiance	Radiant flux density
Illumination	Luminous intensity	Luminous flux	Illuminance	Luminous flux density
Quantum	----------	Quantum flux	Quantum (photon) flux density	

Fig. 76. A representation of the terms used to describe transmitted and incident light.

part of the spectrum. The *quantum* (or *photon*) *flux density at a surface* is equivalent to irradiance measured in standard energy units. The size of a photon flux is sometimes referred to as the *rate of photon fluence*.

Units relating to illumination. The luminous qualities of light are defined in a similar fashion to its radiant energy attributes. *Luminous flux* (the passage of light per unit time) is measured in *lumens* and luminous intensity (luminous energy flux per solid angle), in lumens per steradian, or by the equivalent term *candela*. The candela now replaces the formerly accepted unit of visible light intensity, the *candle*. Intercepted visible light per unit area is termed *illuminance* (or illumination), corresponding to irradiance in energy terms. Illuminance (measured in lumens m^{-2} or lux) is thus luminous flux density at a surface. Under older terminology, illuminance was measured in foot candles. One foot candle was equivalent to one lumen per square foot.

Table 14 summarises these different categories of light units. It is only possible to convert between irradiance [or photon (quantum) flux density] and illuminance for any given wavelength of light. Exact factors for light sources

emitting over many wavelengths are therefore impossible, and even average conversion factors will depend on the precise spectral emission. The interconversions between illuminance and energy units presented in Table 15 should therefore only be used to make approximate comparisons between dissimilar units reported in different scientific papers.

The light requirements of plants

The growth and development of plants is dependent on light for:

- **Photosynthesis**, the process whereby light energy is converted to chemical energy in the biosynthesis of chemicals from carbon dioxide and water.

- **Photomorphogenesis**, the light-induced development of structure or form. Photomorphogenesis does not necessarily involve the absorption of large amounts of light energy, and uses receptor systems which act as switching devices setting in motion the morphogenetic processes characteristic of light-grown plants. There are however some photomorphogenetic systems which require prolonged exposure to high irradiance (HI) before they will occur. The mechanisms involved in HI responses are not fully understood.

- **Phototropism**, the growth response of plants which is induced by unilateral light.

Photosynthesis, photomorphogenesis and phototropism are all facilitated by pigments in the tissues which absorb radiation of particular wave-lengths.

As explained in the section above on carbon dioxide, the photosynthesis carried out by most cultured plant material is relatively low, and cultures are mainly dependent on an external supply of sucrose. In these circumstances, light is most important for its effect on photomorphogenesis. Phototropism is not of great relevance in plant tissue cultures.

Photosynthesis

Photosynthesis is energised by light of wavelengths between 400 and 700 nm, and light in this waveband is termed *photosynthetically active radiation* (PAR). The terms *photosynthetic photon flux density* (PPFD) or *photosynthetic photon flux* (PPF) are therefore often used to describe the photon flux density of 400–700 nm light.

Photomorphogenesis

Plants can follow two alternative developmental strategies depending on whether they are grown in the dark (*skotomorphogenesis*) or in the light (*photomorphogenesis*). In the dark, plants become etiolated, *i.e.* they invest their energy in rapid stem elongation; there is no leaf expansion, and a functional photosynthetic apparatus is not formed. Exposure to light induces a rapid change in gene expression leading to the normal pattern of development.

The signals which lead to the photomorphogenic reactions of plants are subdivided according to the part of the

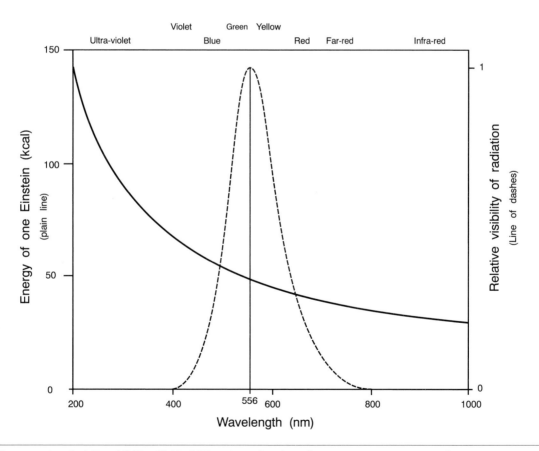

Fig. 77. The energy* and relative visibility of light of different wavelengths   [* after Goodwin and Mercer, 1972].

Table 14. Units and symbols used in the measurement of various light characteristics

CHARACTERISTIC	UNIT	SYMBOL
Wavelength	Nanometer (1 nanometer = 10^{-9} metres)	nm
Energy	Joule Erg Einstein Calorie	J erg E Cal
Energy flux	Watt	W
Luminous flux	{ Lumen Candela steradians	lu cd.st
Radiant intensity	Watts per steradian	W/st
Luminous intensity	Candela (replaces candle) Lumens per steradian	Cd (Candle = c) lu/st
Illuminance (Illumination) (Luminous flux density at a surface)	Lumen per square foot [or Foot candle] { Lux Lumen per square metre	(lu ft^{-2}) lu/ft^2 [ft.c.] lx lu m^{-2} (lu/m^2)

Incident radiant flux
    Irradiance
      (Radiant flux density at a surface)
 	
    Quantum (Photon) flux density
	{ Watts per square metre
	Joules per square metre per second
	Ergs per square metre per second
	
	{ Einsteins per square metre per second, or
	Moles (photons) per square metre per second
		W m^{-2} (W/m^2)
		J m^{-2} s^{-1} (J/m^2/s)
		erg m^{-2} s^{-1} (erg/m^2/s)
		
		E m^{-2} s^{-1} (E/m^2/s)
		mol m^{-2} s^{-1} (mol/m^2/s)

N.B.   Terms which are bracketted are equivalent

Table 15. Factors for converting between light units commonly found in the plant tissue culture literature.

Units of Energy	1 erg = 1 x 10^{-7} joules
	1 cal = 4.185 joules
	Energy of 1 E = 1.2 x $10^{8}/\lambda$ joules
	   An Einstein (E) is 1 mole of photons, and the energy it
	   provides therefore varies with the wavelength (λ) of light in nm.

Units of Illuminance	1 foot candle = 10.764 lux or lumen m^{-2} 1 candle (standard) = 0.02 Watts.
Units of Luminous flux	1 candlepower = 4π lumens
Units of Irradiance	1 erg cm^{-2} s^{-1} = 1 $\times$ 10^{-3} W m^{-2} 1 μmol m^{-2} s^{-1} = 1 μE m^{-2} s^{-1} = 0.215 W m^{-2} = 0.215 J m^{-2} s^{-1}

N.B.   Take reciprocals to convert in the opposite direction, e.g.

$$1 \text{ erg} = 10^{-7} \text{ J}$$

$$1 \text{ J} \;\; = \;\; \frac{1}{10^{-7}} \text{ erg} \;\; = \;\; 10^{7} \text{ erg}$$

Table 16. A comparison between units of Incident Radiant Flux.

Approximate conversion factors are given below for three fluorescent light sources that are commonly used in plant tissue culture growth rooms [after McCree, 1972b]

To convert from lux (units of illuminance) into Irradiance or Quantum Flux Density units, divide lux by the following figures, depending on the type of fluorescent lighting tube.

Units		Warm white	Cool white	Grolux
W m^{-2} = J m^{-2} s^{-1}	W/m^2 = J/m^2/s	390	370	280
mW cm^{-2}	mW/cm^2	3900	3700	2800
μW cm^{-2}	μW/cm^2	3.9	3.7	2.8
mW cm^{-2}	mW/dm^2	39	37	28
erg mm^{-2} s^{-1}	erg/mm^2/s	39	37	25
erg cm^{-2} s^{-1}	erg/cm^2/s	0.39	0.37	0.25
μmol m^{-2} s^{-1} (μE m^{-2} s^{-1})	μmol/m^2/s (μE/m^2/s)	83	80	59
μmol cm^{-2} s^{-1} or (μE cm^{-2} s^{-1})	μmol/cm^2/s (μE/cm^2/s)	8.3 $\times10^{5}$	8.0 $\times 10^{5}$	5.9 $\times 10^{5}$

N.B.   These figures are approximate and should only be used for rough comparisons. Exact conversions vary according to wavelength, and so cannot be given for multiple band light sources. The spectral emission of different makes of tube is also variable.

spectrum which produces the response. The majority of responses are induced by either red or blue wavelengths. Red light-mediated systems have been extensively studied in plant material, and at least three photochromic pigments called phytochromes are now thought to act as receptors (Sharrock and Quail, 1989). Phytochromes not only absorb red light but also low wavelength ultra-violet light. Blue light receptors are less well understood and a positive identification of the pigments concerned has not been made. One pigment, primarily absorbing light of 450–480 nm wavelengths (the blue/UV–A part of the spectrum), has been termed *cryptochrome*; the other absorbs irradiation of wavelengths around 290–300 nm (the UV–B spectrum). Plant responses to light of the blue–UV regions of the spectrum can therefore be due to the effect of one receptor, or of two (*e.g.* a phytochrome and cryptochrome) or more, interacting together (Schäfer *et al.*, 1990). Sometimes the blue–UV sensory pigments need to be activated before a phytochrome response can be triggered (Mohr, 1987).

Photosynthetic pigments act as a light trap and pass on the energy they absorb to other molecules which then facilitate the oxidation-reduction reactions leading to carbohydrate synthesis. A photochromic pigment like phytochrome, on the other hand, is one whose absorption properties change after exposure to light of a specific wavelength and threshold. In one form, Type II phytochrome has its absorption maximum in the red light region; upon exposure to red light the absorption maximum changes to the far-red region. Exposure of the pigment to far-red light while it is in this state, reverts a high proportion of it to the original form. This property of Type II phytochrome, which gives it a 'switching' capability, is often represented by the equation in Fig. 78.

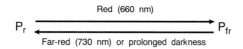

$$P_r \xrightleftharpoons[\text{Far-red (730 nm) or prolonged darkness}]{\text{Red (660 nm)}} P_{fr}$$

P_r = Red receptive form of phytochrome
    (has an absorption maximum in the red region of the spectrum)

P_{fr} = Far-red receptive form of phytochrome
    (has an absorption maximum in the far-red region of the spectrum)

Fig. 78. The conversion of phytochrome into an active form (P_{fr}) by red light, and reversal by far-red light.

Action peak spectra for phytochrome *in vitro* have been found to be 10 nm lower than the above values (Smith and Kendrick, 1976).

The manner in which phytochrome pigments in their alternative forms regulate specific biochemical reactions, is not yet known. Photomorphogenic responses that are only fully expressed under prolonged exposure to high incident flux densities, are also thought to partly involve the phytochrome system. For example, some of the physiological responses initiated in plant material by brief periods of red irradiation, and prevented by subsequent far red (FR) light, are also effectively promoted by prolonged far red irradiation (action peak *ca.* 720 nm) (Satter and Galston, 1976). Even though far red light is only 15% as effective as red light in converting P_r phytochrome to P_{fr}, it is widely believed that phytochrome is the receptive pigment for such duration-dependent (*photoperiodic*) responses to light. The P_{fr} pigment form is probably maintained for a longer period in light of 720 nm because it is only degraded slowly at this wavelength. Other investigators have thought that an excited state of P_{fr} could be created by high levels of irradiance or that phytochrome and chlorophyll *a* are jointly involved. The response of plants to high irradiance is sometimes under the control of another 'Type I' phytochrome, which is less stable than the 'Type II' pigment.

THE INFLUENCE OF LIGHT ON TISSUE CULTURES

The three qualities of light which most clearly influence *in vitro* growth and morphogenesis, are:

- wavelength;

- flux density; and

- the duration of light exposure or *photoperiod*. Each of these attributes has an effect on both photomorphogenesis and photosynthesis. The influence can be direct, through an action on tissue already growing *in vitro*, or indirect through the influence of light on stock plants. In the latter case, the growth or morphogenesis displayed *in vitro* is modified by the light treatments applied to the stock plant before explants are removed (see Chapter 8). The effects of light on photosynthesis are not of great importance in tissue cultures, unless photoautotrophic growth is required.

The growth of organised plant tissues *in vitro* is not generally inhibited by light, which is often required for optimal results. On the other hand, initial cell divisions of explants and the growth of callus tissues are sometimes prevented by light.

Forms of lighting for growth rooms

Most micropropagation work is carried out under artificial lighting in temperature-controlled growth rooms.

Seibert *et al.* (1975) found that although growth and morphogenesis of tobacco callus was only influenced by low irradiance blue or near-U.V. monochromatic light, when tubes emitting white light (composed of many wavelengths) were compared, the best growth and shoot formation was obtained with tubes emitting a fair proportion of total light energy in the red region (600–700 nm). Similarly Fridborg and Eriksson (1975a) discovered much lower hormone levels to be necessary under light from white tubes (supplying 8 W m^{-2}). These results suggest that red light can reinforce the stimulatory effect of blue and near-U.V. light when it is supplied simultaneously. Various seedling explants of *Brassica* produced more adventitious shoots in Grolux light of 32 μmol m^{-2} s^{-1} than under 30 μmol m^{-2} s^{-1} from white fluorescent tubes (Lazzeri and Dunwell, 1986b).

Fluorescent tubes. Fluorescent tubes are used almost universally to provide light for cultures. They have the advantage that shelves within a room can be conveniently illuminated without the creation of too great an amount of heat. Fluorescent lighting is sometimes supplemented with incandescent bulbs to ensure an adequate supply of wavelengths in the red end of the spectrum, but this is not always desirable. Micropropagation growth rooms are usually equipped with cool white (warm white), or Grolux tubes, or mixtures thereof (Seabrook, 1987). A mixture of cool-white and Agrolite™ (F40/AGO Westinghouse) gave plants from single node cuttings of potato which had the maximum leaf area, number of leaves, stem length and fresh and dry weight. Phillips TL-84 fluorescent lights produced plants with short internodes.

A mixture of Grolux and cool white tubes gave satisfactory rates of shoot proliferation of fruit tree cultures (Fiorino and Loreti, 1987): leaves of cultured shoots were said to be greener than under normal fluorescent lights (Rugini *et al.*, 1987), but Hasegawa *et al.* (1973) found no difference between the effectiveness of cool white or Grolux fluorescent lamps in promoting the formation of shoots from shoot cultures of *Asparagus*.

Other lighting sources. Bulblet formation on *Achimenes longifera* leaf and stem cuttings was promoted by high illuminance (15 000–20 000 lux) light from a mixture of Grolux and cool white tubes, but was strongly inhibited in light of the same luminous flux density from mercury vapour tungsten filament lamps (Deutch, 1974). A disproportionately high emission of far red and infra-

red light from the mercury vapour lamps seemed to be responsible for the inhibition. Incandescent lamps can also be a source of far-red irradiation. The profuse branching of *Xanthium strumarium* plants kept under fluorescent lights for 16 h each day, was prevented if the plants were given an additional 30 minutes illumination from tungsten filament bulbs. The inhibition was thought to have been caused by the far red light content of the incandescent lighting (Tucker and Mansfield, 1972). Murashige and Nakano discovered incandescent lamps to be unsatisfactory for promoting organogenesis in tobacco (Hasegawa *et al.*, 1973).

To supply light at sufficiently high photon flux densities to support active photosynthesis of cultured shoots and plantlets, several research establishments (*e.g.* Kozai and co–workers, 1987b; Lee N. *et al.*, 1988) have installed metal–halide or sodium vapour lamps, or have used them in conjunction with fluorescent lighting, in growth rooms. Norton *et al.* (1988a; Norton and Norton, 1986) found that shoot proliferation in shoot cultures of woody plants was almost twice as great in the light from high pressure sodium discharge lamps as in that supplied by fluorescent tubes. Plant growth under light from metal halide lamps was also greater than under fluorescent tubes, but less than under the sodium sources. Unfortunately, lamps supplying high energy light also emit considerable amounts of heat, and their use within growth rooms can necessitate considerable additional cooling costs unless the heat is channelled away by some means. Two suggested means of doing this are:

i)   placing a water-cooled filter between the lamps and the plant containers;

ii) situating the lamps and their starters outside the growth room and channelling the light into the near vicinity of cultured tissues through prism light guides or optical fibres (Norton *et al.*, 1988a) after focussing it through a lens and extracting radiant heat (Kozai, 1991).

Wavelength

Blue and near-U.V. light

Callus growth and morphogenesis. Callus of some species can be initiated and grown in the dark, while tissues of other plants grow better in continuous light or in a regular photoperiod (*e.g.* that of potato — Helgeson, 1980; tomato fruits — Mukund *et al.*, 1988).

By using sources emitting light over narrow bandwidths, it has been shown that near U.V. and blue light can have a controlling influence on the rate of growth and morphogenesis of some callus cultures. Callus initiated in the dark is often moved into the light when indirect morphogenesis is desired.

In a detailed study, Seibert *et al.* (1975) demonstrated that the combined effect of both wavelength and flux density can be important for callus growth and morphogenesis. Using tobacco callus, they showed that although the tissue would grow in the dark, its growth was stimulated, and shoot formation was promoted to the greatest extent by near-U.V. light (371 nm) at the very low irradiance of 0.24 W m^{-2} (an illuminance of *ca.* 90 lux), but was inhibited when the incident flux density was more than 1.5 W m^{-2} (*ca.* 540 lux); blue light of 420 or 467 nm wavelengths caused growth stimulation which was maximal at 3 and 6 W m^{-2} (*ca.* 1080 and 2160 lux) respectively.

Other experiments have given conflicting results. Bergmann and Balz (1966) obtained stimulation of tobacco callus growth with blue light (435 nm) at an irradiance of 2.4 W m^{-2} (*ca.* 860 lux) and Weis and Jaffe (1969) found that blue light of mixed spectral composition (15.5 W m^{-2} or *ca.* 5600 lux), or white light, was essential for shoot bud development from tobacco callus. Red and green light were without effect. By contrast, in experiments of Ward and Vance (1968), even though callus growth of *Pelargonium* was particularly enhanced when cultures were kept in white and blue (450 nm) light, a stimulatory effect was also caused by light of other colours. *Crepis capillaris* callus increased in fresh weight more quickly in blue light than in darkness, but the greatest rate of growth occurred in red light (Hüsemann and Reinert, 1976). Red light has been noted to promote growth and organogenesis in cultures of some other species (see later).

Hedtrich (1977) obtained no root formation from leaf discs of *Prunus mahaleb* in darkness, a small number of roots in light from white fluorescent lamps (3000 lux), but more where some of the light was provided by lamps giving near-U.V. light.

As mentioned on page 218, blue and near-U.V. responses are thought to be regulated by one or more pigments which are particularly sensitive to light of these wavelengths. The situation is complicated, because phytochrome P$_r$ and P$_{fr}$ have minor absorption peaks at 365 nm (near-U.V.) and 495 nm (blue) respectively, and in some circumstances blue and near-U.V. light is capable of converting P$_r$ into P$_{fr}$, but much less effectively than red light (Smith and Kendrick, 1976). Phytochrome also has strong absorbance at 280 nm (U.V.). This has been attributed to absorbtion by the inactive protein part of the molecule, energy then being transferred from the protein to the chromophore moiety.

Inhibition of callus growth. Inhibition of callus growth or cell division by blue light of higher incident flux densities than used by Seibert *et al.* (*loc. cit.*) has been reported on several other occasions, for example, in *Parthenocissus* (Klein, 1964), tobacco (Beauchesne and Poulain, 1966a,b), carrot (Polevaja, 1967), Jerusalem artichoke (Fraser *et al.*, 1967), *Pseudotsuga menziesii* (Kadkade and Jopson, 1978) and *Actinidia deliciosa* (Loreti *et al.*, 1991). The growth of *Haplopappus gracilis* callus was suppressed when cultures were moved from the dark to the light (Stickland and Sunderland, 1972a,b). When light of different wavelengths was compared at an irradiance of *ca.* 10 W m^{-2} (*ca.* 3000–3500 lux), blue had the greatest inhibitory effect; white and red light caused a similar but smaller reduction in the rate of cell division. Far-red light on the contrary, stimulated growth.

Fridborg and Eriksson (1975a) found that callus or suspension cultures of *Nicotiana tabacum, Happlopappus gracilis,* haploid *N. sylvestris* and *Allium cepa,* were inhibited to varying degrees by continuous blue to near-U.V. light; but that the growth inhibition could be partially overcome by the cytokinin, 2-iP. For maximum growth, tobacco callus required 10 times more cytokinin in blue light than in white light.

White (26 μmol m^{-2} s^{-1}) and blue (27.5 μmol m^{-2} s^{-1}) light inhibited, but did not prevent, growth and embryogenesis of carrot suspensions. The highest number of embryoids was obtained when the suspensions were kept in the dark (or in red or green light, which produced the same response as dark treatment). Michler and Lineberger (1987) who obtained these results, suggested that red and blue light spectra could be used with advantage to manipulate carrot embryogenesis and embryo growth: as embryos grew, blue light also encouraged the formation of secondary embryos; red light hastened development towards the heart stage; while ABA synthesis at this time was most pronounced under blue light.

Possible causes of light-inhibited growth. The initial cell divisions in explants of artichoke tissue were found by Fraser *et al.* (1967) to be suppressed by light, and Yeoman and Davidson (1971) later showed that:

— cells were sensitised to light by 2,4-D (there was no effect in the absence of auxin);

— the cells have a light sensitive phase; exposure before or after this produced no response.

The conclusion drawn from this work was that light reduced the amount of DNA replication by destroying vitamin B$_{12}$, so inhibiting the activity of a nucleic acid-synthesis precursor. Klein (1964) thought that the action spectrum of light which reduced the growth of *Parthenocissus tricuspicata,* was similar to the absorption spectrum of B_{12} vitamin. This vitamin, which is known to be present in higher plants (Fries, 1962) plays a part in regulatory nucleic acid biosynthesis.

Alternative causes of growth inhibition induced by higher levels of blue or near-U.V. light might be:

- increased production of phenolic compounds which interfere with growth regulator activity (Andersen and Kasperbauer, 1973),

- destruction of cytochrome oxidase which is involved in respiratory processes (El-Mansy and Salisbury, 1971),

- enhanced biosynthesis of gibberellins (Beauchesne et al., 1970). Evidence in favour of this hypothesis was obtained by Fridborg and Eriksson (1975a) who found that the inhibitor of gibberellin synthesis, chlormequat (CCC), stimulated the growth of *Haplopappus gracilis* callus and cell suspensions grown in blue light. Cells and tissues of this plant were also inhibited by the addition to the medium of 0.1 mg/l gibberellic acid. However, in callus cultures of some other plants, gibberellic acid is found to stimulate growth.

- inhibition of natural cytokinin synthesis, or production of abscisic acid which is antagonistic to cytokinin.

Growth inhibition by high incident flux densities of near-U.V. and blue light could also be caused by the accelerated metabolism of the auxin IAA (Fridborg and Eriksson, 1975a) and may occur by the photo-degradation of this natural auxin in the presence of light-sensitised riboflavin (vitamin B_2) (Galston and Hillman, 1961), or some other kind of flavonoid. Flavoprotein inhibitors can prevent callus growth in the light (Seibert et al. 1975). Alternatively light may alter the oxidation of IAA by peroxidase enzymes, by regulating the levels of co-factors and inhibitors of the enzyme (Stickland and Sunderland, 1972b). Reductants such as ascorbic acid and polyphenols, inhibit the oxidation of IAA by riboflavin; possibly it is on account of the natural occurrence of these compounds, that some plant cells are able to grow and divide in the light. In most cultures, cells are stimulated to divide in the light by externally supplied auxins. Marcotrigiano and Stimart (1981) found that in the light, hypocotyls of *Paulownia* required 3 mg/l IAA in the medium to produce shoots at the maximum rate, whereas under continual darkness only 1 mg/l IAA was necessary. Cytokinin (kinetin, 3 mg/l) was required at the same concentration under both regimes. Similar observations on shoot formation from callus were made by Fridborg and Eriksson (*loc. cit.*).

The reaction of plant cells to light *in vitro* depends on their previous history. Light can inhibit callus colony formation from plated suspension cultured cells (Street, 1977c) and protoplasts obtained from cell suspensions invariably grow in the dark, but light is inhibitory (Reinert et al., 1977). However, callus growth from mesophyll protoplasts takes place if they are first incubated in a low illumination (*e.g.* 300 lux) for a short while before being transferred to light of 3000 lux (Enzmann-Becker, 1973).

Blue light inhibition of axillary shoot proliferation. In a series of publications, Letouzé has described how the axillary buds of decapitated willow (*Salix babylonica*) cuttings remain dormant in blue light (*id.*, 1970). The growth inhibition could be overcome by red light (or cytokinin treatment) and the red light promotion was reversed by subsequent exposure to blue light (*id.*, 1974; 1975). In the presence of added growth substances the light-mediated control of bud growth may not be apparent. A negative effect on shoot proliferation of fruit trees has been noted with light of 320–380 nm (Rugini et al., 1987).

Behrouz and Lineberger (1981a,b) have investigated the interaction between white, blue, red or green light (15 μmol m^{-2} s^{-1}) and growth regulators, on the proliferation of shoots in shoot cultures of Juneberry. The regulants incorporated into the medium were 0.1 mg/l NAA + 2.5 mg/l BAP. The greatest number of shoots was produced by using blue or white light together with the auxin and cytokinin.

Somewhat similar results were obtained by Norton et al. (1988a; Norton and Norton, 1988c) in shoot cultures of *Spiraea*. Without the presence of the cytokinin BAP, these produced the same number of axillary shoots in red, blue or white (control) light. However there was significantly more shoot proliferation than in the control in red light when 0.25 mg/l BAP was added to the medium, but less when the rate was increased to 0.5 mg/l. These results support the hypothesis that in many plants, omission of blue light (or irradiance with red — see below) can mimic or replace cytokinin dependency (Fig. 79). A few plants seem to behave differently. In the presence of 5 μM BAP, axillary shoot proliferation of *Vitis* shoot cultures was greater in blue light than in red, especially if the medium contained only 5 μM Mn^{2+}, instead of 100 μM, as in **MS** medium (Chée, 1986).

U.V. light can induce specific enzyme activity. When chlorophyll-free cell cultures of parsley (*Petroselinum hortense*) are irradiated with light of a wavelength below 350 nm (particularly U.V. light, 290 nm), there are changes in the composition of messenger RNA. This leads to the induction of enzymes which are specifically concerned with the formation of some particular fla-

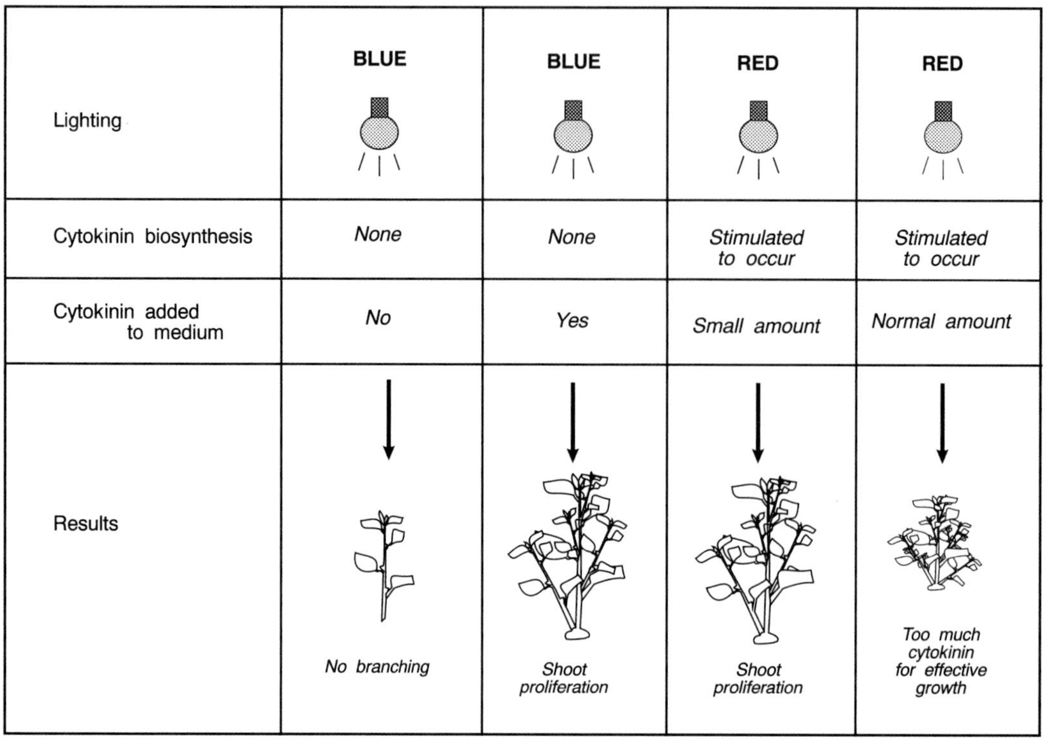

Lighting	BLUE	BLUE	RED	RED
Cytokinin biosynthesis	None	None	Stimulated to occur	Stimulated to occur
Cytokinin added to medium	No	Yes	Small amount	Normal amount
Results	No branching	Shoot proliferation	Shoot proliferation	Too much cytokinin for effective growth

Fig. 79. An hypothesis to explain how the colour of light and cytokinin may interact to modify shoot proliferation.

vonoid glycoside secondary products (Hahlbrock, 1977; Hahlbrock *et al.*, 1980).

The phytochrome system.

Seeds of some varieties of plants which are stimulated to germinate by red light, can alternatively be induced into growth by cytokinin treatment (Miller, 1956); but cytokinins are much more effective at promoting germination if seeds are kept in sufficient light to break their dormancy. Miller (1958) and Khan (1966) showed that with *Xanthium*, kinetin depended on a reversible phytochrome effect to overcome seed dormancy, its stimulatory effect being reversed by far red light. In other words, red light and cytokinin were complementary.

Kadkade and co-workers have reported on phytochrome systems in lettuce and pine. In hypocotyl callus cultures of the former, Kadkade and Seibert (1977) showed two phytochrome-sensitive systems to be in operation. Both callus growth and shoot organogenesis were greatly improved by daily 5 minute exposures to red light, and generally unaffected by similar far-red light treatments. The promotion caused by red light was reversed by afterwards placing the tissues in far-red light.

In most instances where red light specifically influences growth or morphogenesis in tissue cultures, it appears to have either the same effect as, or to reinforce, the addition of cytokinin to the medium. Red light, or polychromatic light containing a high proportion of red wavelengths, usually promotes axillary shoot growth (Fig 79). The response has been shown to be phytochrome dependent, because a short FR treatment at the end of a white light photoperiod can prevent branching (Tucker, 1976). Both red light and cytokinins promote bulblet formation in *Achimenes longifera* (Deutch, 1974).

Duckweed (*Lemna gibba*) cultured on a simple medium will not grow in the dark. The addition of a cytokinin will induce some growth as will periodic exposure to red light. Combining the cytokinin treatment (0.6 mg/l kinetin) with an eight-hourly exposure to 15 minutes of red light, produces the greatest growth response, the effect of which is reversed by far-red irradiation (Cleland, 1976). The promotory effect of red light on the growth of *Crepis capillaris* cells could be completely replaced by the addition of 1 mg/l kinetin to the medium, but kinetin had no effect on green cells cultured under blue light (Hüsemann and Reinert, 1976).

Shoot formation. Cultured root segments of *Convolvulus arvensis* showed enhanced shoot bud development under a light regime which only provided 10 s of red light (655 nm) per day (at an irradiance of approximately 0.6 W m^{-2}). This enhancing effect was reversed by far-red light (Bonnett, 1972). Under the same cultural conditions, the geotropic behaviour of roots of this weed was shown to be affected by the phytochrome system, as well as gravity. The roots grew horizontally in the dark, but showed a far-red reversible normal geotropic response on exposure to red light (Tepfer and Bonnett, 1972).

The involvement of phytochrome in shoot regeneration from callus was demonstrated by Bagga *et al.* (1985). When dark-grown leaf discs of *Brassica oleracea* botrytis, which had begun to form callus, were irradiated with only 5 minutes red light each day, they initiated shoots when transferred to continuous light. Explants for which the red light treatment had been followed by 10 minutes far-red, did not. The cultures were grown throughout on **Gamborg *et al.* (1968) B5** medium with 2 mg/l NAA and 0.5 mg/l BAP.

An interaction between light and benzyladenine (BAP) was demonstrated by Baraldi *et al.* (1988a) for the promotion of shoot formation in *Prunus*. The number of shoots formed under blue, far-red and white light was highly dependent on the rate of photon fluence, but there was no difference in the rate of proliferation in different levels of red light, suggesting that the BAP induction of shoot formation is promoted by a low energy response of phytochrome.

The bulbing of tulip has been found to be enhanced under sources emitting light with a low red to far-red ratio (Alderson and Taeb, 1990).

Root formation. A phytochrome-mediated response was demonstrated in cultured pea roots by Furuya and Torrey (1964): low levels of incident red light would inhibit the initiation of lateral roots in cultured root segments, and the effect could be reversed by far-red wavelengths. In *Helianthus tuberosus* however, red light (optimum at around 660 nm) has been reported to induce adventitious root formation (Letouzé and Beauchesne, 1969). To explain these contrasting results, Thorpe (1980) suggested that the formation of lateral and adventitious roots might be influenced by light in different ways.

Other work has tended to support a phytochrome-regulated stimulation of adventitious root formation. The *ex vitro* rooting of azalea microcuttings was consistently better if shoot cultures had been kept for two weeks in far red light followed by 2 weeks of red illumination, than if the red light treatment preceded the far-red (Read and Economou, 1983). This result was confirmed by Economou (1986), who obtained enhanced rooting of micropropagated *Rhododendron* shoots by giving cultures 15 minutes red light at the end of a 14 h cool-white day. Chée and Pool (1989) obtained improved rooting of *Vitis* cuttings in red light or in fluorescent lighting supplying a relatively high proportion light in the red wavebands. Shoots of *Prunus* 'GF655/2' kept in far red light required auxin for *in vitro* rooting, but others kept in red light did not (Baraldi *et al.*, 1988a).

Respiration. In protoplasts isolated from the leaf intercallary meristems of barley, respiration is partly controlled by phytochrome and a blue light receptor, blue light being able to reverse an inhibitory effect of abscisic acid (Owen *et al.*, 1987).

Green–Yellow light

Light in the yellow-red wavelengths has been found to promote shoot proliferation of fruit tree cultures (Rugini *et al.*, 1987; Loreti *et al.*, 1991). Tran Thanh Van *et al.* (1987) reported that 75% hypocotyl fragments of *Pseudotsuga menziesii* formed adventitious buds when cultured under monochromatic light of 550 nm (green/yellow), whereas only 35% of similar explants produced buds in white light (170 μmol m^{-2} s^{-1}), and light of 550 nm was found to suppress the growth of *Parthenocissus* crown gall callus (Klein, 1964). The combined results suggest that light of these wavelengths actively induces the destruction of auxin.

Photosynthesis

Light induced chlorophyll formation.

The development of chloroplasts. Chlorophyll, the green pigment in plants required for photosynthesis, is formed within the cell in organelles called chloroplasts. A chloroplast is one type of plant plastid, but plastids may become starch-containing (when they are called amyloplasts), or they may contain other coloured pigments (when they are called chromoplasts — found, for instance, in the cells of flowers and the skins of fruits), or oil, or stored protein. Given appropriate stimuli, amyloplasts can be converted to chloroplasts and *vice versa*. An undifferentiated plastid is sometimes called a 'proplastid'. Seedlings germinated in the dark contain plastids in their leaves, called etioplasts. These are already partly differentiated into chloroplasts and although they do not contain chlorophyll, they do possess some other accessory carotenoid pigments, one or more crystalline centres (called 'prolamellar bodies') and some other characteristics of a fully differentiated chloroplast. Buds induced to form from callus in the dark by high cytokinin concentrations, form etiolated shoot systems in which the plastids are similar to etioplasts (Stetler and Laetsch, 1968).

By contrast, in dark-grown cells of suspension or callus cultures, the plastids contain starch, do not have pro-lamellar bodies, and have only a few thylakoids without pigmentation (Bergmann and Berger, 1966; Stetler and Laetsch, 1968). (Thylakoids are series of membrane sacs on which chlorophyll is packaged within a chloroplast). In this respect tissue-cultured cells are akin to the undif-ferentiated cells of a potato tuber, where the plastids are amyloplasts and take several days to begin convertion into chloroplasts after the tubers are exposed to light.

Chlorophyll formation in tissue cultures. When callus or suspension cultures are transferred to light, they may develop chloroplasts and begin photosynthesis, but sel-dom become autotrophic (pages 24 and 204). Greening generally proceeds very slowly compared to the rate in etiolated plant shoots, and cultures may take 8 weeks to reach maximum chlorophyll content. The ability to form chloroplasts seems to depend on the presence of non-di-viding cells within cell aggregates, because when green callus tissue is used to initiate suspension cultures, chlo-roplasts de-differentiate and the level of pigment is re-duced (Yeoman and Street, 1977). Sometimes the forma-tion of green areas on otherwise colourless calluses is a first sign of the commencement of morphogenesis.

The chloroplasts formed in tissue cultured cells tend to be more variable in structure than those in leaf cells. They may not develop at a simultaneous rate and can possess aberrantly-shaped thylakoids (Davey et al., 1971).

In a few plant species (e.g. some conifers), proplastids can become differentiated into chloroplasts in darkened buds (Sundqvist et al., 1980). Most plants though, require some sort of light stimulus to initiate the differentiation of chloroplasts and the formation of chlorophyll. Several pigment systems may be involved. Light may be inter-cepted by:

— the chlorophyll precursor, protochlorophyllide that is present in dark-grown leaves;

— the phytochrome system;

— by the pigment system sensitive to blue and near-U.V. light.

Generally in whole plants, and also in most tissue cultures (Blackwell et al., 1969), chlorophyll synthesis is particu-larly stimulated by red light. Protochlorophyllide has an absorption maximum at 634 nm and is converted by red light (or the red components of white light) to chloro-phyll(ide) (Bjorn, 1976), the absorption maximum of phytochrome P_r being 650–660 nm. In tissue cultures which may lack the biosynthetic precursors of chloro-phyll, the phytochrome system is probably especially

responsible for converting protochlorophyllide into chlo-rophyll (Satter and Galston, 1976) as it is in potato tubers (Morris et al., 1979). However, some plants require light in the near-U.V. to blue, part of the spectrum (i.e. 370–450 nm) for the development of chloroplasts. The induc-tive effect of blue light is then often enhanced by red light treatment before or afterwards (Sundqvist et al., 1980).

Callus and suspension cultured cells of tobacco only develop chlorophyll in blue light (Bergmann and Berger, 1966; Kamiya et al., 1981), which affects the both the nuclear and plastid genomes (Richter and Wessel, 1985). In Chenopodium rubrum, blue light promotes changes in the transcription of genes which regulate the de novo synthesis of plastid and nuclear RNAs (Richter et al., 1990). Chlorophyll retention of tobacco callus also re-quires blue light, for although photosynthesis occurs in green callus kept in red light, the quantity of chlorophyll in the tissues slowly declines (Bergmann and Balz, 1966).

Again emphasizing the similarity between red-light and cytokinin-induced effects, cytokinins added to the me-dium have frequently been noted to promote chlorophyll development in callus or suspension cultures (Bandiera and Morpugo, 1970; Kaul and Sabharwal, 1971; El Hin-nawiy, 1974) or even to be essential for chlorophyll formation in light (Stetler and Laetsch, 1968; Tandeau de Marsac and Peaud-Lenoel, 1972a,b). Formation of pho-tosynthetic enzymes is also promoted by cytokinins, or independently by continuous far-red light (Feierabend, 1969).

Daylength (photoperiod)

Daylength influences plants in two ways:

- By regulating the amount of radiant energy inter-cepted. Growth of photosynthetically-dependent plants is proportional to the length of time that they are exposed to natural sunlight or artificial light;

- Through a controlling mechanism whereby plants are able to recognise changes in the environment. For this purpose plants are able to sense changes in the duration of light provided each day (pho-toperiod).

Genuine photoperiodic effects on plants are energized by light of relatively low irradiance (ca. 0.3 W m^{-2}, Cathey and Campbell, 1980) and are generally associated with the phytochrome system. The P_{fr} form of the phyto-chrome pigment is gradually accumulated during day-light hours and reverts progressively to P_r during dark-ness. Length of day can influence natural growth substance levels within cultured plant tissues: long days have the same kind of effect as exposure to red light; long nights (short days) promote far-red phytochrome responses. Generally it has been found that plants grown on a long photoperiod show a higher endogenous auxin content than those in short days, regardless of the photoperiodic requirement of the plant for flowering (Hillman and Galston, 1961).

Where cultured plant organs or tissues are not autotrophic, and are grown under lighting of relatively low irradiance, the effects of varying daylength on *in vitro* cultures are most likely to be due to photoperiod. However, total intercepted light energy may govern the biosynthesis of key metabolic products in green cultures (*e.g.* in shoot cultures) even though the level of chlorophyll is low and photosynthesis insufficient to sustain normal growth. As the total light energy supplied by photoperiods of different intervals is variable when provided by light of the same flux density, it is not always possible to be sure which of the two mechanisms mentioned above is responsible for many effects described in the literature.

The most well-known effect of photoperiod is the regulation of flowering in many plant species. Short day plants such as chrysanthemum, require to be exposed to short days (*i.e.* 8–10 h of light and 14–16 h of darkness per day) for flowering to be induced, while in long day plants (*e.g.* wheat and barley) flowering is only initiated when they are kept in 14–16 h of light per day. There are many variations on this pattern, including species where flowering takes place independently of day length (*e.g.* tomato).

As with other plant responses that are naturally regulated by light, some of the effects which daylength might have on morphogenesis, may be replaced by additions of synthetic growth regulators to the culture medium. Sometimes however, light of the correct daylength is indispensible: the induction of flower formation in cultured shoot apices or stem explants is the best example, and here, the same photoperiodic treatments as would cause flowering to occur in the intact plant, have generally been found to be essential *in vitro*.

Murashige (1978) pointed out that plants needing specific photoperiods for vegetative growth and development are very likely to manifest this need during *in vitro* culture. However, the photoperiod requisite for flowering may not be the same as that necessary for optimum regeneration of shoots and roots, or for shoot proliferation. For example, although entire plants of *Kalanchoë pinnata* flower under short days, they naturally produce foliar plantlets under long days. Shoot cultures of cucumber (a

short day plant) develop maximum foliation under long days (Rute *et al.*, 1978).

Both the formation and growth of vegetative organs may be influenced by the daylength under which tissue cultures are maintained. Some examples which seem to be related to photoperiod are provided here, and other instances illustrating the effects of light and dark on morphogenesis have been placed in the section on irradiance that follows.

Daylength effects in shoot cultures

Benefit from long days. Haramaki (1971) observed that gloxinia plantlets regenerated from shoot cultures were etiolated and had small leaves when given 8 h illumination of 1075 lux daily. Longer 16 h daylengths gave thicker, stouter and darker leaves, similar to those produced on plants grown under 3200 lux. Shoot cultures of *Pelargonium* have been established and encouraged to form multiple shoots in continuous fluorescent light of 500 lux (Debergh and Maene, 1977) and seedling shoot tips of *Pharbitis nil* (a short day plant) also grew and produced plantlets equally well in long days of 16 or 24 hours (Bapat and Rao, 1977b). In 8 or 12 h photoperiods, shoot and root growth was inhibited. Roots grew well in the dark however, although of course in these conditions the shoots were etiolated. By contrast, apple shoot cultures required 16 h light of 60 μmol m^{-2} s^{-1} fluence for the maximum rate of shoot proliferation. The internode length of 'Delicious', 'Triple Delicious' and 'Vermont Spur Delicious' was less in 24 h than in 16 h days, although that of 'Empire' was greater (Yae *et al.*, 1987).

Short day plants. Shoot cultures of 'Rougen' grapevine had a requirement for short days. They grew, and later shoots formed roots, only in 10 h days, soon becoming necrotic when the daylength was 15, 16 or 24 h (Chée and Pool, 1982a,b). Where, as in *Camellia japonica*, shoot multiplication in shoot cultures is as rapid in a 12 h day as in one of 18 h, propagation under the shorter photoperiod can lead to a saving in lighting costs (Samartin, 1989). However, although *Dianthus caryophyllus* can be propagated in 12 h photoperiods, Stimart (1986) reports that in commercial practice, shoots have been found to flower *in vitro* under these conditions: most shoots are vegetative in a 16 h day.

Interaction with temperature. An interaction between temperature and daylength was observed by Rahman and Blake (1988a) in *Artocarpus heterophyllus* shoot cultures grown under light of 85 μmol m^2 s^{-1}. An optimum number of axillary shoots was produced at 25°C in either a 12 or a 16 h day, but the maximum dry weight of harvested shoots occurred in a 12 h day at a temperature of 30°C. Photosynthesis appeared to contribute to growth, because shoot production was much less in the dark or in an 8 h day.

Adventitious shoot formation

Although shoot morphogenesis is generally stimulated by light, the most favourable daylength can vary from one genus to another. The following examples illustrate the kind of variation which is experienced. In few, if any, of the cited experiments was it discovered whether the observed effects of daylength were due to photoperiod, or the total irradiance received by the cultures.

The formation of adventitious shoots from twin bulb scales of onion was more rapid in long days than in short days (Hussey and Falavigna, 1980), and this seems to be the case in lily too, where continuous light enhances shoot and root formation, and darkness promotes bulb growth (Stimart and Aacher, 1978c). Under a PPF of 160 μmol m^{-2} s^{-1} at 25°C, meristematic explants of *Capsicum annuum* formed adventitious shoots much more rapidly under a daylength of 12 h, than in 16 h days, or in continuous light (Phillips and Hubstenberger, 1985). Similarly, in the experiments of Pillai and Hildebrandt (1969), the callus of *Pelargonium* did not turn green and form adventitious buds in continuous high illumination (21 500 lux from Grolux tubes and incandescent lamps). Shoot regeneration was optimal when these callus cultures were maintained in a photoperiod of 15–16 h. By contrast, shoot regeneration from *Brassica* callus was greater in continuous light than in a daylength of 16 hours (6000 lux, 20°C) (Jain *et al.*, 1988b) and shoots formed directly from leaf segments of *Peperomia scandens* in continuous light of 2700 lux (Kukulczanka *et al.*, 1977).

Heide (1964) found that adventitious shoots were produced more freely from begonia leaf cuttings when the cuttings themselves and/or the mother plants from which they had been taken, were kept in short days. Callus derived from the anther wall of *Hevea* only gave rise to somatic embryos when grown under 8 h days or when transferred from a 16 h to an 8 h photoperiod (Wan Abdul *et al.*, 1981), and although the formation of *Pyrus serotina* callus was not affected by daylength, shoot morphogenesis was promoted by short days or culture in the dark (Hiratsuka and Katagiri, 1988).

Adventitious root formation

The rooting of cuttings taken directly from stock plants is influenced by the length of the days in which the plants have been grown. Effects due to total incident radiation (availability of stored carbohydrates) and daylength (photomophogenesis) can be seen (see page 256 and Chapter 14).

Illuminance and irradiance ('light intensity')

Intensity is a property of a light source and, strictly according to physical definitions, describes its radiant or luminous flux per solid angle (page 213). The word 'intensity' is however colloquially used to describe either luminous or radiant flux density and appears widely in early plant tissue culture literature, especially when the physiological effects of light were thought to be due to the total amount of energy that had been incident on an organ or tissue, rather than to daylength or phytochrome-controlled processes.

'Intensity' influences the total light energy received by plant cultures. The induction of chlorophyll formation in plant organs or callus or cell cultures, is accompanied by increased activity (or *de novo* synthesis) of key enzymes in photosynthesis (Koth, 1974) although, as explained previously, the level of carbon fixation which normally occurs in callus cultures is well below that of leaf mesophyll cells. However, the improved growth of some types of green callus in light can be due to the enhanced availablity of photosynthetically derived carbohydrate (Bergmann and Balz, 1966).

Daylight may provide irradiance of *ca.* 200–700 W m^{-2} (equivalent to an illuminance of *ca.* 50 000–150 000 lux, see Table 16), but plant cultures are typically grown in flux densities which are about 10 times less than daylight and have a different spectral composition. There are several reasons why low irradiance light is used:

— provision of high levels of artificial lighting is expensive and generates unwanted heat;

— cultures in sealed vessels become overheated in high irradiances due to the glasshouse effect (Pierik, 1987);

— the technology of plant tissue culture has evolved using non-autotrophic tissues supplied with a carbohydrate.

Most research workers measure irradiance (or illuminance) immediately above the culture vessel. The light actually incident upon tissues growing inside partially covered glass or plastic-ware will of course be less than this. Examples of the lighting used for several different kinds of tissue cultures are given in tables within Chapter 12.

Callus growth

Callus of many plants can be initiated and maintained in the dark and it has been said that there is no point in culturing tissues in the light if they do not contain chlorophyll. Callus of some plants may not grow at all in the light, or its growth may be severely inhibited (page 222). Callus initiated on explants intended for indirect shoot regeneration is often initiated in the dark at Stage I, and is then moved to the light at Stage II when organogenesis is to be instigated.

However, some callus tissues grow better in the light than in the dark. In geranium an optimum level of incident light for the growth of callus depended on the variety of plant from which stem explants were derived (Hammerschlag, 1978). In two varieties, growth was best when the tissues were illuminated with 1000 or 5000 lux, in another it was most rapid only in 5000 lux. In all three varieties growth was reduced when the callus was kept in 10 000 lux. Inhibition of callus growth by high illuminance could be associated with increased production of growth inhibitors. The production of phenolic compounds is stimulated by light in callus cultures of some species (particularly those lacking chlorophyll), and greater amounts are accumulated as illuminance is increased (Davies, 1972a).

Shoot growth and proliferation

From experiments with shoot tip propagation of several different kinds of plants, Murashige (1974) suggested that an optimum level of illumination for Stages I and II might be 1000 lux (*ca.* 14–15 μmol m^{-2} s^{-1}) from Grolux or white fluorescent tubes; from the literature, it seems that, at these stages, cultures of many herbaceous plants are maintained in photon flux densities of 7–120 μmol m^{-2} s^{-1} (1.5–9.5 W m^{-2}; equivalent to an illuminance of about 0.5–10 klux) (Chapter 12). However, culture initiation under low irradiance may help to prevent blackening in the cultures of sensitive species (Chapter 13); a 16 hour day is most common.

Plants of many genera (*e.g. Aster, Chrysanthemum* and the Caryophyllaceae) require relatively high irradiances for optimum shoot multiplication, and culture in low lighting causes shoots to become succulent and vitreous (hyperhydric), and hence of poor quality. *Hosta* shoot cultures require high light to commence proliferation, but thereafter are able to tolerate light of both high and low irradiance (Stimart, 1986). *Brunnera macrophylla* callus must be kept in complete darkness for adventitious shoot formation (Stimart, 1986). In some plants, shoot proliferation in shoot cultures, or direct shoot formation from explants, is enhanced by using high levels of irradiation

at Stage II. Haramaki (1971) for instance, thought that *Sinningia* shoot cultures were best maintained at 3000–10 000 lux (*ca.* 40–150 μmol m^{-2} s^{-1}); in lower illumination the shoot tips formed callus. Dalton and Dale (1981) found that more tillers were produced from *Lolium multiflorum* in 12 000 lux (*ca.* 35 W m^{-2}) than in 9 600 lux, provided that BAP was present in the medium.

High lighting levels are also required for some woody species. Axillary shoot proliferation in shoot cultures of an *Ulmus* hybrid required an irradiance of *ca.* 9.7 W m^{-2} (45 μmol m^{-2} s^{-1}), but higher (possibly 14, and certainly 36.5 W m^{-2}) were inhibitory to shoot development (Fink *et al.*, 1986). However, in *Castanea* shoot cultures, multiplication was most rapid at 27°C with 33 W m^{-2} irradiance, and the best shoot elongation occurred at 34°C in 22 W m^{-2} (Chauvin and Salesses, 1988). McGranahan *et al.* (1987) reported using 9.7–12.0 W m^{-2} (45–60 μmol m^{-2} s^{-1}) for *Juglans*, while Evers (1984) obtained an optimum rate of growth of *Pseudotsuga menziesii* under 36.4 W m^{-2} or 24.5 W m^{-2}, depending on the time of year at which isolations were made.

Cultures needing low irradiance. There are plants sensitive to high light *in vitro* and these can be multiplied satisfactorily in light of relatively low fluence: *Dicentra spectabilis* is an example. Gloxinia plantlets obtained through shoot culture were progressively larger and their leaf size greater, when illuminated with about 3 200 lux, but in 10 700 lux there was very little growth and leaves were small and discoloured. Callus was present in 320 lux, but absent at the higher flux densities (Haramaki, 1971).

Miller and Murashige (1976) showed that the rate of shoot proliferation of *Cordyline terminalis* was greatest in an illumination of only 300 lux, whereas three other tropical species of foliage ornamentals multiplied most rapidly in 3 000 or 10 000 lux. Cultures of *Phalaenopsis* orchids produced axillary shoots more freely from flower stalk cuttings in 0.25 W m^{-2} than in 2.34 W m^{-2} irradiance (Tanaka *et al.*, 1988c), but the rate of shoot multiplication in *Lythrum virgatum* cultures was no different in 0.3–3.2 W m^{-2} (Heuser, 1983).

Although Einset and Alexander (1985), Hildebrandt and Harney (1983) and Welander (1987) had mainly grown *Syringa* plants at 8–10 W m^{-2}, Pierik *et al.* (1986; 1988c) preferred to utilise 4–5 W m^{-2} for single node cultures of *S. vulgaris*, because stems were more elongated at this irradiance. Shoots grown in 1–3 W m^{-2} had thin stems and very small leaves. In practical micropropagation work, it would be important to ascertain that any increased shoot production at higher lighting levels was cost effective.

Although the multiplication of axillary shoots of *Asparagus* was satisfactory in 1 000 lux, higher illuminance of 3 000–10 000 lux was essential at Stage III to cause shoots to initiate needle-like cladophylls. An illumination of 30 000 lux was excessive (Hasegawa *et al.*, 1973). Zygotic embryos of *Populus deltoides* grown in reduced light produced more vigorous shoots than those grown at higher light intensities (Kouider *et al.*, 1984b).

Storage. Where light is necessary for the storage of cultures, a PPF of 10–15 μmol m^{-2} s^{-1} is usually employed (see Chapter 6).

Morphogenesis

Flower buds. The formation of floral buds (rather than vegetative shoot buds) on cultured explants has usually been found to require the presence of light. In pieces of cold-treated chicory root, the inductive action of light took place during the first few days of culture and presumably during bud initiation. Very thin stem explants of tobacco consisting of just a few cell layers similarly required light to form flower buds, and unless light was supplied during days 7–10 of culture they formed vegetative shoot buds instead (Tran Thanh Van, 1980; Trinh and Tran Thanh Van, 1981). The formation of tobacco flower buds in this system appears to be promoted by long days and high flux densities (Tran Thanh Van, 1977). Red light was also more promotive than far-red light or darkness.

Adventitious shoots. Adventitious shoot formation can take place in the dark, but it is usually greater in the light; for example, more shoots were produced directly from strawberry leaf discs or from a short intervening callus phase, in light of 1000 lux illuminance, than in the dark (Nehra *et al.*, 1988).

Direct shoot formation in endive leaf fragments was reduced by a short period of darkness during culture (Legrand, 1972). Continuous darkness was especially inhibitory if interrupted by 3 days of continuous 600 lux fluorescent light at the beginning or after the first 3 days (Legrand, 1974). A similar situation has been discovered in *Heloniopsis orientalis*, where morphogenesis was inhibited in darkness unless one of several sugars was added to the medium during the first few days of treatment (Kato, 1978a). From these results it seemed that shoot formation *was* dependent on photosynthesis, an hypothesis which appeared to be confirmed when it was found that in the absence of sugar, bud initiation was inhibited in CO_2-free air and by chemical inhibitors of photosynthesis. White, red, blue and far-red light were effective promoters, but not green light (Kato, 1978b).

Shoot regeneration from seedling leaf discs of *Brassica oleracea* did *not* appear to be influenced by photosynthesis, because more shoots were produced at 30 μmol m^{-2} s^{-1} than at 100 or 200 μmol m^{-2} s^{-1}. The reverse was true for root segments (Lazzeri and Dunwell, 1986b).

Adventitious roots. The formation of adventitious roots on cuttings seems to be affected by light energy (see Chapter 14). In many plants, the induction of roots is promoted by darkness or light of low fluence, apparently because natural auxin levels increase in these conditions, whereas they are decreased by light of high fluence. For root formation and root growth though, cuttings or explants require high energy imputs, and supplying mother plants with supplementary illumination (see Chapter 8), culturing cuttings with sucrose, or placing cuttings with root primordia in high light prior to root induction, can all promote root growth.

Root formation from green photosynthetic *Cymbidium* protocorms appeared to depend on how they were illuminated. In the dark, or in light of *ca.* 1250 lux, protocorms gave rise only to shoots, whereas both roots and shoots were formed in *ca.* 2200–2500 lux (Ueda and Torikata, 1972). It was thought that root formation was associated with nitrogen metabolism which was enhanced as illuminance and photosynthesis increased.

Cotyledons of *Cucumis melo* cultured in the light formed either shoots or morphogenic callus, whereas those cultured in the dark, formed either roots or friable non-morphogenic callus (Mackay and Ng, 1988).

Morphogenesis in callus cultures. Light is not always essential for adventitious shoot formation from callus, although sprouting is frequently enhanced under illuminated conditions (*e.g.* in *Anthurium* — Pierik *et al.*, 1974b). A strong correlation between carbohydrate availability and organogenesis in callus cultures has been reported (page 325), and when optimum levels of sugars are provided, light may have only a regulatory effect (*i.e.* it is not required for photosynthesis). Shoot regeneration from *Arabidopsis* callus on an induction medium was enhanced if the tissue had been previously cultured in continuous low illuminance (less than 1000 lux), rather than in darkness, but higher illuminance (more than 4000 lux) greatly reduced the percentage of regenerating calluses (Negrutiu and Jacobs, 1978a). Callus of tobacco grown on Lin and Staba (1961) medium, supplemented with 15% coconut milk and 2 mg/l kinetin, was induced to form somatic embryos by high illuminance (10 000–15 000 lux) (Haccius and Lakshmanan, 1965).

Flux densities for other stages of micropropagation

As with other aspects of the cultural environment, light 'intensity' at each propagation stage may need to be varied for particular plants or for methods of micropropagation other than shoot culture. Unfortunately, the most suitable level can vary even from one cultivar to another. In *Begonia* × *hiemalis* adventitious shoot formation of one variety was improved when cultured in 6000 lux rather than 3000 lux, but two other varieties did not respond in this way (Welander, 1978a).

For the micropropagation of deciduous azaleas, Economou and Read (1986a) found that 30–75 μmol m^{-2} s^{-1} was better than 10 μmol m^{-2} s^{-1}; 10–75 μmol m^{-2} s^{-1} was required during the shoot multiplication stage (although 75 μmol m^{-2} s^{-1} produced shoots of less good quality); the highest percentage of rooted shoots was obtained when Stage III cultures were kept under an irradiance of 10 μmol m^{-2} s^{-1}.

An illuminance of 3 000–10 000 lux (*ca.* 40–150 μmol m^{-2} s^{-1}) was suggested by Murashige (1974) at Stage III to achieve maximum rates of transfer of shoots or plantlets to an exterior environment, and many laboratories find that 40–75 μmol m^{-2} s^{-1} is adequate. In lower flux densities shoots may be etiolated with pale green leaves. Daylengths of 16 h are usually employed.

Sweet gum plants grown under high irradiances (50–315 μmol m^{-2} s^{-1} from metal halide lamps) either *in vivo* or *in vitro*, were found to have larger cells and a more compact mesophyll than those grown in low light. But all *in vitro* plants had smaller, thinner leaves and smaller mesophyll cells than *in vivo* plants, and except at 315 μmol m^{-2} s^{-1}, significantly greater stomatal densities (Lee *et al.*, 1988).

High light levels can be beneficial for special purposes, such as germinating seedlings from which explants are to be excised (Lazzeri and Dunwell, 1986a), or germinating somatic embryos (McGranahan *et al.*, 1987), when irradiances of *ca.* 135–200 μmol m^{-2} s^{-1} may be necessary.

Darkness

Although light is invariably essential for the growth of normal green shoots and plantlets, unorganised cell and tissue cultures can frequently be grown in its absence, and darkness may be beneficial to growth and morphogenesis. Darkness is also used to etiolate shoots. Treating light-grown seedlings to 2–3 days darkness can sometimes help to elongate hypocotyls or epicotyls before explants are excised (Jagannathan and Marcotrigiano, 1986).

Excised green leaves of *Heloniopsis* grown in the light tend to produce a preponderance of shoot initials at the apex (distally). In darkness however, most green and etiolated leaves tended to develop buds at the base (Kato, 1978a). Scale sections of *Lilium longiflorum* regenerated a small number of large bulblets in the dark, each having only a few leaves. Bulblets produced in illuminated cultures were small and bore many leaves, and leaf dry weight was double that of the bulbs (Leshem *et al.*, 1982).

A short period of darkness sometimes promotes shoot morphogenesis. Adventitious buds did not form on swollen needle primordia of *Picea pungens* unless cultures were kept in the dark for 8 days. Subsequent shoot development required 16 h under 1000 lux illumination (Misson *et al.*, 1982).

Establishing cultures

As explained in Chapter 12, keeping cultures in the dark at Stage I can help in establishing explants. This is primarily because visible blackening of the tissues is reduced, although sometimes the formation of less obvious growth inhibitors may also be prevented.

An interaction between the culture medium and light was demonstrated by Stimart and Ascher (1981c). *Paphiopedilum* seed germinated best on **Burgeff (1936) EG-1** medium in the light, but the highest germination scores on **Thomale (1954)GD** medium occurred in the dark. Although dark-grown seedlings were initially etiolated, they quickly regreened in the light and after one month were indistinguishable from plants germinated in the light.

Callus growth

Callus growth does not take place in some plants unless light is excluded from cultures, for example *Hosta* scape explants only produce callus in the dark (Stimart, 1986). *Magnolia* shoot tip callus ceased to grow if moved to even low light and would not resume growth until transferred twice to fresh medium during a 6 week period (Biederman, 1987). In other species, light may be necessary for callus initiation, but once callus has been obtained, it can be subcultured and maintained in the dark. Where light causes shoot formation to occur [e.g in *Anthurium scherzerianum*, Geier (1986)], shoot development may be at the expense of callus growth and so callus induction and multiplication may need to be carried out in the dark.

Morphogenesis

Light is often necessary for the formation of adventitious shoots from callus or explants, but this is not always the case. In *Freesia hybrida*, the requirement for light or dark varied with the plant variety. Callus from young ovaries of some cultivars could produce shoots in the dark, while that from other cultivars required to be incubated in the light (Bach, 1987). Bhatt *et al.* (1979) failed to regenerate shoots from *Solanum khasianum* in the light, but did obtain shoots and roots in the dark.

Sometimes light controls the type of morphogenesis which takes place. Callus from the gametophyte generation of the moss *Physcomitrium coorgense*, only regenerated sporophytes if cultured in the dark, but gave rise to both sporophytes and gametophytes in diffuse daylight (Lal, 1963). Leaf explants of *Solanum melongena* produced callus and roots in the dark, but rooted shoots when cultures were moved to the light (Macchia *et al.*, 1983).

However, in some species caulogenesis or embryogenesis can occur in continuous darkness. For example, fragments of the corms of *Crocus sativus* cultured in darkness on an agar medium, formed miniature corms, which also proliferated (Homès *et al.*, 1987). Sometimes darkness is essential to morphogenesis; for example, scape explants of *Hosta* only form callus and adventitious shoots in the dark (Stimart, 1986). Embryogenic callus was seen on young leaflets of *Euphorbia longan* after 2½ months culture in the dark. Embryos grew to maturity after transfer to another medium in the dark, but required 16 h light per day for germination. There was precocious germination if embryos were exposed to light prematurely (Litz, 1988).

A brief period of darkness. Occasionally morphogenesis can be enhanced if explants are kept in the dark for a certain period. The formation of adventitious buds on young flower buds of *Freesia* was greatly improved if the explants were grown in the dark before being transferred to the light (Pierik and Steegmans, 1975a). Similarly,

keeping segments of apple leaves in the dark for the first three weeks of culture, strongly enhanced the subsequent regeneration of adventitious shoots and embryo-like structures (Welander, 1988). Meyer (1982) and Dai *et al.* (1987) found that more shoots were formed from *Rhododendron* floral explants if they were cultured in the dark for at least two weeks, before being moved to the light.

Maintaining anther cultures of some species in the dark for an initial period can increase the proportion of anthers producing somatic embryos or the frequency with which anther—derived callus is obtained (Sunderland and Roberts, 1977; Sangwan-Norreel, 1977; Nair *et al.*, 1983).

Rooting

Treatment of mother plants or cuttings with a period of darkness, or light of very low fluence, frequently favours the initiation of adventitious roots on cuttings (see page 236. Its use to enhance the induction of adventitious roots on cuttings of micropropagated plants, is descibed in Chapter 14.

Review articles

Light and lighting systems for horticultural crops has been reviewed by Cathey and Campbell (1980). Their paper describes artificial light sources in some detail.

8

Factors affecting Growth and Morphogenesis

II. Tissue Dependent Factors

Growth and morphogenesis in culture are governed by properties of explanted tissues which are additional to the immediate effects of their genetic identity described in the previous chapter (although interactions with genotype certainly occur). For convenience, we have grouped these tissue dependent factors under three headings, *viz*. the influence of:

- the part of the plant's total genetic code that is expressed;

- the manner in which mother plants have been treated;

- the physical and physiological condition of the explants used.

In practice these factors are frequently inter-related. Their effect will often be mediated by the levels of naturally-occurring plant growth substances which explants contain (Chapter 11).

EPIGENETIC EXPRESSION AND CELL DETERMINATION

As explained in Chapter 3, individual plant cells may translate only certain parts of the total genetic information (the genome) they contain. Expression of particular sections of the genotype can result in cell differentiation, the growth of distinct organs and a characteristic pattern of plant development. Such differential expression (or *determination*) may also be required for the maintenance and function of distinct tissues. Some kinds of gene expression are persistent and result in plant cells having an ability to continue over long periods in various patterns

231

of growth, physiological function, and development. Although gene function can be changed by external environmental stimuli, a 'long-term memory' (Swartz, 1991) may persist within cells and be passed on through successive cell generations until a new environmental stimulus is experienced. The results are seen in self-perpetuating changes in form and function, the cause of which is not understood. The most satisfactory explanation is that they are due to epigenetic patterns of gene expression which are stable and heritable during successive mitotic divisions but which are potentially reversible and are not passed on to sexual progeny.

Examples of some of the semi-permanent states which can be induced and maintained in tissue cultures are:—

- phenotypic characteristics of the phase of growth of the tissue from which the explant is obtained;

- the expression of male or femaleness in flowers;

- the commitment of cells to produce organs of one particular type;

- the capacity or *competence* of plant tissues for growth and/or morphogenesis;

- *habituation*, in which cells no longer have a requirement for particular additives such as vitamins or growth regulants (see Chapter 11).

Each of these kinds of partial genomic expression may be induced or modified by tissue culture, particularly by growth regulants added to a tissue culture medium.

The predetermination of cells and tissues can often be changed in culture by cell differentiation and cell division, leading to the direct formation of organogenetic meristems or callus. But if the tissue is not competent to undergo these changes, or the growth regulants in the medium are not suitable, previously predicated developmental pathways may not be interrupted. Some aspects of determination may nevertheless survive in newly-established cultures and can occasionally persist for many callus transfers.

PHASES OF GROWTH

The sequence of stages through which an higher plant has passed in its development from a fertilized egg to an adult organism, is known as its *ontogeny* or ontogenesis.

In the *juvenile phase*, a young seedling plant displays one or more distinctive characteristics of both a morphological and physiological nature, which distinguish it from an adult. The juvenile phenotype gradually disappears during subsequent growth, and under natural conditions it is replaced by the adult (mature) phase in those parts of the plant in which *maturation* has occurred (the developmental switch which enables the tissues to be capable of flowering). In some plants, a 'transitional phase' of development can be distinguished between the juvenile and adult phases during which the potential to flower gradually increases.

The traditional definition of juvenility as "that stage of the life cycle during which flowers cannot be induced to form", causes difficulty. Attainment and maintenance of the ability, or potential, to flower is the only consistent criterion by which to assess the termination of the juvenile period, and it is often difficult to devise methods to promote flowering which will not also advance maturation (Hackett, 1985). In many conifers flowering can be induced on juvenile shoots by gibberellins or auxin/gibberellin mixtures (Pharis *et al.*, 1976, 1980; Pharis and Kuo, 1977; Ross *et al.*, 1981; Pharis and King, 1985), and some plants, probably mutants, seem to be incapable of flowering even though they have apparently reached an adult status.

In considering the relationship between juvenility and plant propagation, it is therefore more helpful to regard juvenility as a syndrome of phenotypic features which are gradually modified as the plant moves to an adult phase, the ability to produce sexual organs, normally being the final transition. This view was adopted by Bonga (1982a), who defined as 'juvenile', those parts or cells of a plant in which there is a distinct preponderance of typical juvenile characteristics over mature ones, and as 'mature' those parts or cells in which most or all of the juvenile characteristics have been replaced.

In general, the duration of the juvenile phase is proportional to the potential ultimate size of the plant, being shortest in annual herbaceous species and progressively longer and more noticeable in perennial and woody plants. In trees it may sometimes persist for many years.

Characteristics of juvenile plants

There are numerous substantive phenotypic attributes associated with juvenility, but they vary considerably between species. Commonly, the leaves on young plants are of a different shape to those on mature parts and may be simple rather than compound (or occasionally the reverse); juvenile leaves may also have a special type of cuticle and be arranged with a distinct phyllotaxis. Compared to their mature counterparts, young plants may have a modified resistance to pests and diseases. Juvenility in woody plants is manifest by prolonged vigorous shoot growth.

The rooting of cuttings. To the plant propagator, the most important attribute of juvenile shoots is their ability to provide cuttings which readily form adventitious roots. Cuttings taken from adult shoots of plants can be rooted, but the frequency of success is low, especially in woody plants. The change from juvenile to adult phase is the most serious constraint to rooting in shrubs and trees (Howard, 1990). Most of the difficulty experienced in rooting mature shoots seems to be caused by their altered physiology, but can also be due to greater contamination with micro-organisms. Cuttings or explants taken from mature shoots are frequently more liable than juvenile material to suffer necrosis, especially when surface sterilised and placed in culture (Hanus and Rohr, 1987). For tissue culture, juvenile explants are usually most readily established in culture and grow and proliferate at a more rapid rate than adult material. This is particularly true in tree species, where micropropagation of adult material is often impossible.

Trees and shrubs

In addition to the characteristics above, in trees and shrubs, juvenile shoots and leaves sometimes have a distinct colour: shoots may have a different kind of bark; display prolonged vigorous growth; and sometimes have characteristic growth habits, and retain their leaves in winter. Stems or leaves may possess spines or thorns, which are not present elsewhere. Plants derived from cuttings taken from juvenile parts of a tree often have more branches and gain height more rapidly than those from mature parts. The degree of physiological maturity (juvenile to adult) in trees is often called their 'maturation state'.

Plagiotropic growth. The leading shoots of woody plants typically grow vertically upwards (*orthotropic* growth), while lateral branches tend to grow at a more horizontal angle (*plagiotropic* growth). In adult angiosperms there will usually be several orthotropic shoots, but most gynosperms usually have only one. In some New Zealand species, plagiotropy can be an adaptation which allows a plant to build up a large root system in exposed locations during the juvenile phase before tall wind-susceptible orthotropic shoots emerge (Beckett, 1979).

Although plagiotropic laterals are formed during the juvenile phase of woody plants (*e.g.* those of angiosperms tend to grow more horizontally than those formed during the adult phase, Fig. 80), in most plants an orthotropic habit of growth re-appears if such shoots are rooted as cuttings. The orthotropic habit of *adult laterals* can however be persistent in some broad-leafed trees and shrubs (*e.g.* in *Eucalyptus cladocalyx* — Maggs and Alexander, 1967; *Coffea* spp. — Sondahl and Sharp, 1979) and particularly in conifers. If shoots from the lateral branches of some coniferous plants are rooted as cuttings, plants are obtained where the leading shoot retains a prostrate or inclined growth habit for one or more years before eventually becoming erect. Sometimes plagiotropism appears to be permanent (*e.g.* in *Araucaria* spp. — Bonga, 1982a; Haines and de Fossard, 1977: and in *Pseudotsuga menziesii* — Ritchie and Long, 1986). In these cases normal plants can only be obtained by rooting cuttings or grafting scions taken from vertical stems (or sometimes from juvenile shoots).

The progression of phasic development

The juvenile or adult phase is expressed by many cells within a plant, but is particularly evident in the apical meristems from which new organs are initiated: the meristems of juvenile shoots are usually smaller than those on their mature counterparts and are composed of cells with small nuclei. Meristems are thus 'determined' to give rise to juvenile or adult organs or tissue in the same way that they can be programmed to give rise to shoots, roots or differentiated cells (Chapter 1). When the determination of a meristem which results in a specific growth characteristic depends on its position on a plant, it can be said to be an example of *topophysis* (see page 264) (Bonga, 1982a).

Both juvenile and adult phases of growth result from persistent and stable kinds of gene expression in the shoot meristems. As cells divide, the expression is transmitted to daughter cells, and continues when shoots are propagated from cuttings, or are grafted. It may then be gradually changed by new environmental conditions, or be retained for several years. The change of an apical meristem from a juvenile condition, to one with the form and function of the adult phase (and *vice versa*), generally takes place progressively (*homoblastic development*). Some features of the plant phenotype may change at a different pace to others. For example, although seedling trees of Douglas fir have not been found to flower until they are 20 years old, 100% of cuttings from a 9-year-old tree could be rooted, but only 5% of those from a tree aged 15 years (Clark, 1982). For some characters, particularly the ability to flower, the switch from one phase to the other is more abrupt and the phenotype characteristic of each phase quite distinct (*heteroblastic development*). In many *Eucalyptus* species leaf shapes are distinct, either juvenile, intermediate, or adult (Durand-Cresswell *et al.*, 1982).

The juvenile form appears in new growth from seedlings and seems to be associated with the proximity of shoot apical meristems to the roots of the plant, and the presence of a normal unrestricted root system. As the physical distance between the shoot tip/s and the roots increases with growth, the juvenile condition of shoot meristem/s disappears. *Nicotiana sylvestris* plants do not flower if, each time the plants begin to run to flower, their shoot tips are removed and re–rooted (Dennin and McDaniel, 1985). One suggestion to explain the early development of adult features in micropropagated conifers is that, compared to seedlings, the plants have poorly developed root systems (Mohammed and Vidaver, 1988).

Parts of a plant close to the ground, may retain juvenile functions throughout the development of the plant (Nozeran, 1978a), but this is not readily seen until new shoots arise. New shoots with some juvenile characteristics therefore often appear from epicormic outgrowths at the base of a mature tree or from the trunk, from so-called spheroblasts (nodular growths), or from lignotubers (in most *Eucalyptus* species) (Fig. 80).

Juvenile shoots of these kinds do not always arise adventitiously, and may sometimes grow from buds formed during the early life of the tree which have remained suppressed and dormant. They can often be induced to form on the lower part of trees by partial girdling, or coppicing. Lignotubers are swellings at the base of the stem which arise on the lower nodes of seedlings. They typically possess many vegetative buds and associated vascular tissue with substantial food reserves. Although the lignotubers are covered by subsequent stem growth, their dormant buds produce juvenile shoots, especially if the upper part of the tree is killed (*e.g.* by fire or frost), or if the tree is cut down or severely pruned (Chattaway, 1976; Gonçalves *et al.*, 1979).

In fruit trees, such as apple, repeated pruning (hedging) or severe annual pruning back to ground level in winter can be successful in inducing the formation of rejuvenated shoots with an improved rooting ability. When non-flowering shoots with juvenile characteristics are formed on mature woody plants, they are termed juvenile reversion shoots.

Although shoots arising from adventitious buds on mature plants usually have a juvenile morphology, they generally give rise to plants that flower in a shorter time than seed-derived plants and so may not be 'completely juvenile' (see below). Adventitious shoots with a juvenile phenotype occur naturally on some trees on mature wood ('water shoots') and as root suckers in many species. The features of juvenility found on adventitious and basal shoots can be short-lived and liable to disappear quickly as the shoots elongate. The roots from which suckers arise seem to retain a juvenile state for a long period.

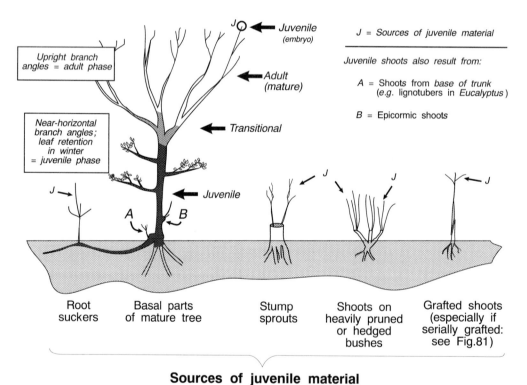

Fig. 80. Some typical juvenility patterns in a deciduous dicotyledenous tree, showing where juvenile shoots may be obtained.

Natural reversion

It has been proposed that flower formation is the stage at which juvenility is normally re-initiated (Meyer, 1984). A reversion to a juvenile state certainly seems to occur within the maternal tissues of the floral organs from which zygotic embryos are derived; it is fully apparent in zygotic embryos, but is not related to sexual fertilisation, because apomictic embryos also give rise to juvenile seedlings [for example, plants derived from the nucellar embryos of *Citrus* are juvenile (Swingle, 1932 *in* Brink, 1962)]. An indication of the juvenile status of inflorescences, flowers and embryos, is that unlike other tissues of the stock plant in close proximity, they have often regained an ability to form adventitious shoots and somatic embryos *in vitro*, and that the plantlets derived from these sources have juvenile characteristics.

Artificial induction of juvenility

Re-rooting and grafting. A partial juvenility or rejuvenation, can sometimes be restored on mature shoots by rooting the apex as a cutting (Lee and Rao, 1986), espe-

cially if the rooting process is repeated several times (Dennin and McDaniel, 1985), *i.e.* a cutting is taken and after a short period of growth on its own roots, the apex is removed and re-rooted. Shoots (and particularly isolated shoot apices) grafted onto juvenile rootstocks can also regain a juvenile status (Debergh and Maene, 1985), but again the process may have to be repeated several times ('cascade grafting') to reinforce juvenile traits (Fig. 81). The rejuvenation of adult shoots by grafting is stimulated by leaves on the juvenile rootstock, but inhibited by leaves on the adult scion (Hackett, 1976). Successful re-juvenation also depends on there being little mature wood on the scion: the greater the quantity the smaller number of successful reversions (Stoutemeyer and Britt, 1961). In practice therefore single or repeated *micro*grafting (Chapter 2) is frequently used for rejuvenation using small shoot tips as scions (Franclet, 1987; Monteuuis *et al*, 1987; Pliego-Alfaro and Murashige, 1987).

Co-culture. Frank and Renner (1956) discovered that the terminal and axillary buds on adult shoots of *Hedera helix* could be induced to revert to the juvenile form, if the shoots were grown in the same containers as juvenile plants. Reversion did not occur unless the adult shoots

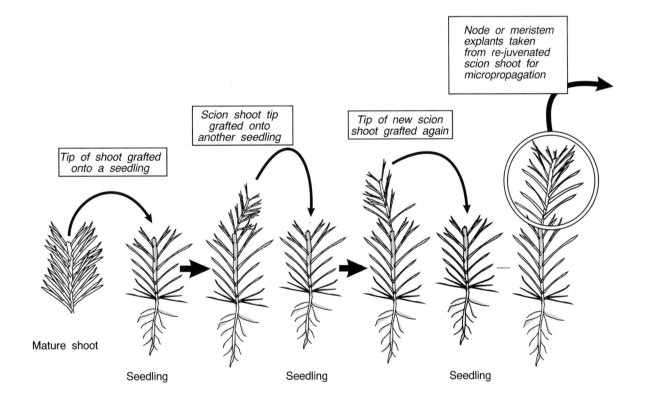

Fig. 81. Cascade grafting to induce rejuvenation .
The drawing shows the use of the technique in a gynosperm. The same method can be used for broad-leafed plants.

produced adventitious roots, suggesting that some substance, produced and excreted by the juvenile plants, had to be taken up by the adult roots.

Unfortunately it is difficult or impossible to induce root formation on adult shoots of many species. Were it not so, co- culture *in vivo* or *in vitro* might provide a means of rejuvenating woody plants. It would nevertheless be interesting to see whether rejuvenation could be induced by adult explants being grown in the same medium as seedling-derived, or rejuvenated cultures.

Etiolation. Darkness or light of low irradiance, which leads to skotomorphogenesis (Chapter 7) and the formation of pale elongated shoots and small unexpanded leaves (*etiolation*) has several applications in micropropagation. Its use to reduce contamination has been mentioned in Chapter 5, and the the application of a brief exposure to darkness to elongate *in vitro* shoots to make them more manageable for rooting, is discussed in Chapter 12.

Etiolation may also improve the facility with which explants from adult material can be cultured *in vitro*. It has, for example, been found to be an effective treatment for preparing mature sweet chestnut shoots for culture. In late May (early summer), newly-grown sweet chestnut shoots 10–15 cm in length were stripped of leaves and (while still on the tree), wrapped in foil for 4 months. When shoot explants were taken from this material, not only was a high proportion established *in vitro* (79% *vs*. 22% in the controls), but there was also a rapid rate of shoot proliferation. From these results, Ballester *et al*. (1989) proposed that etiolation brings about physiological rejuvenation of adult shoots, because it has no beneficial effect on seedling material (Hansen and Lazarte, 1984; Bennett and Davies, 1984b, 1986). It is most effective when applied to the new young shoots which arise from severely pruned plants.

Etiolation has been known for many years to enhance the capacity of shoots to form roots, particularly those of woody species. It can also enhance direct root formation from other explants. For example, Leroux (1968) found that pea seedling internodes rooted more readily when they had been derived from seedlings grown in the dark rather than in 600 lux, and Hansen and Eriksen (1974), and Hansen (1975) obtained similar results, finding that the number of roots formed in the light, decreased as plants were grown in progressively higher irradiances. The greatest number of roots was formed on explants taken from plants grown in 7.4 W m^2 (*ca*. 2700 lux), and smallest on those in 68.1 W m^2 (*ca*. 25 000 lux).

The promotion of rooting would appear to give more weight to the hypothesis that etiolation induces juvenility, because ease of rooting is another characteristic of juve-

nile material. However the rooting of cuttings taken from seedling or herbaceous material is sometimes also improved by dark treatment. *Pelargonium* petioles formed the highest numbers of roots in response to nitrogen and sucrose in an *in vitro* medium, when they were derived from stock plants that had been maintained under an irradiance of 2.5 rather than 11.6 or 23.0 W m^2 (Welander, 1978b).

The stimulus to root formation provided by etiolation can be provoked in a shoot which is to be used as a cutting by:

- dark-treating the whole stock plant before cuttings are excised.

- dark-treating potential cuttings before they are excised;

- dark-treating the potential rooting zone before the cutting is excised from a stock plant;

    There is a minimum length of stem from which light needs to be excluded (Delargy and Wright, 1979).

- dark-treating cuttings after excision;

- dark-treating the rooting zone after the cutting is excised;

One technique used to enhance the rooting of cuttings taken from woody plants, is to keep stock plants in the dark until they produce etiolated shoots 5–10 cm in length. Alternatively, a node immediately behind the apex, which will later serve as the rooting zone, is blanched with black adhesive tape (Bassuk and Maynard, 1987). For the large scale production of cuttings, shoot banding is coupled with hard pruning (page 234). In the traditional 'stool–bed' or 'stool layering' technique, the rooting of cuttings was improved by:

- severe pruning to ground level annually;

- mounding up the soil (keeps light from shoot bases);

- maintaining moisture at the rooting zone.

A more recent adaptation of this method is to cover heavily pruned hedges with dense shading for a few weeks at the start of the growing season. Absolute darkness is not necessary and a low level of lighting (*ca*. 1% PAR) allows the shoots to retain some of their chlorophyll (Howard, 1990). Black polythene enclosures, into which small holes or clear windows have been inserted, are suitable; the elevated temperature within such tents is also beneficial. Cuttings are taken from the etiolated shoots, and dipped in auxin solution before being placed in a suitable rooting substrate.

The use of a dark treatment (etiolation) to promote the rooting of micropropagated plant material is described in Chapter 14.

High temperatures. Above-normal temperatures have been found to promote the growth of juvenile shoots from adult plant material (Fisher, 1954; Hudson and Williams, 1955). Reversal to the juvenile phase was more pronounced in *Hedera canariensis* if grafts of adult scions onto juvenile rootstocks were grown at 27°C, rather than at lower temperatures (Stoutemeyer and Britt, 1961). Providing bottom heat at 15°C above the ambient temperature, induced the formation of juvenile basal shoots in potted plants of *Hamamelis japonica, Magnolia soulangeana* and *M. stellata* (Debergh and Maene, 1985). The shoots were sufficiently re-juvenated to furnish suitable explants for tissue cultures.

Growth regulator treatments. Spraying (Abo El-Nil, 1982) or injecting adult shoots of some plants with cytokinins can induce a reversion to a semi-juvenile state. This treatment may also increase the number of axillary shoots on the plant from which explants can be taken (see later). To obtain shoot material which is sufficiently re-juvenated for tissue culture, spraying with cytokinin is sometimes preceded by one or more of the other treatments mentioned above, such as taking cuttings, hedging, or grafting (Clark, 1982; Pierik, 1990a,b). David *et al.* (1982a) sprayed rooted cuttings of *Pinus pinaster* with 2.2. mg/l BAP every week from March to May; this to stimulated *in vitro* morphogenesis from shoot and leaf explants.

A juvenile phase of growth can sometimes be induced on adult forms of *Hedera helix* plants by spraying them with gibberellic acid. However, treating mother plants with gibberellin can result in poor explant establishment from some species (*e.g.* meristem tips of *Pistacia vera* — Barghchi, 1986a): it may also result in the failure of explants to form roots, or an inhibition of adventitious shoot formation, and so should be used with caution. Spraying woody stock plants with a mixture of a cytokinin and a gibberellin can also be effective in inducing vigorous (juvenile) new growth.

A reversion of adult shoots to the juvenile form occurred most noticeably in raspberry, when plants had well developed basal crown-galls induced by *Agrobacterium tumefasciens* (Hudson and Williams, 1955). Genes located in the t-DNA of the *Agrobacterium* plasmid (Chapter 3) cause tumour formation, partly by inducing transformed cells to synthesize above-normal levels of cytokinins (Akiyoshi *et al.*, 1983, 1984).

The effect of phase of growth on tissue cultures

Direct effect

Establishment. It is possible to initiate cultures of unorganised tissues from meristematic tissues of mature trees: for instance callus from the cambium of 100-tear-old *Castanea sativa* trees (Jacquiot, 1950). Establishing organs such as shoot tips from mature parts of trees is usually difficult. However there are instances of where this has been possible (Table 17).

In many woody plants, it is only juvenile explants which can be established in culture, *e.g. Fagus sylvatica, Quercus robur* (Ahuja, 1986). Shoot tip explants of the apple cultivars 'Redspur' and 'Goldspur', could be established more readily if they were taken from newly grafted shoots, rather than directly from orchard trees (Jones *et al.*, 1985). Nodal segments obtained directly from 10 year- old *Fagraea fragrans* trees did not grow in culture, but the same explants taken from rooted cuttings of a 10 year-old tree were established without difficulty (Lee and Rao, 1986).

Adult explants often produce more phenolic substances (which blacken the medium), than juvenile ones. For example, because *Alnus glutinosa* adult shoot apices gave rise to phenolic substances, they had to be transferred to new medium every two days to prevent blackening, while adult ones did not (Lavarde, 1987). Establishment is improved if the mother plants have been given one of the rejuvenating treatments described above, but even then explants of some species may be difficult to establish in culture. It was necessary to trim the bases of those of *Juglans regia* and transfer them at 2 day intervals during the first 3 months of culture. After this time cultures were more easily managed and only required to be transferred at 7 day intervals (McGranahan *et al.*, 1988a).

Adult shoot tips from a clone of *Castanea sativa* showed symptoms of mineral imbalance when cultured under light of 50 or 80 μmol m^{-2} s^{-1}, but not at 30 μmol m^{-2} s^{-1} (Mullins, 1987).

Growth rate, shoot proliferation, and organogenesis. Besides affecting establishment, the relative maturity of the explant nearly always has major effect on the growth and morphogenesis of plant tissues and organs in culture. Zygotic embryos or pieces taken from germinated seedlings are therefore reliable explants for embryogenesis or morphogenesis.

Table 17. Some example of successful establishment (and sometimes propagation) from vegetative explants of mature trees.

Plant	Age Years	Explant	Result	Reference
Eucalyptus bridgesiana	5	Nodes	Axillary shoots	Durand-Cresswell & Nitsch (1977)
Eucalyptus camaldulensis	Mature tree	Node	Shoot proliferation	Gupta *et al.* (1983)
Eucalyptus citriodora	20	Vegetative buds	Shoot proliferation	Gupta *et al.* (1981)
Eucalyptus spp.	5	Node	Rooted plantlet	Durand- Cresswell & Nitsch (1977)
Eucalyptus grandis	4	Node	Rooted plantlet	Durand- Cresswell & Nitsch (1977)
	5	Crown bud	Rooted plantlet	Durand- Cresswell & Nitsch (1977)
Eucalyptus macarthurii	5	Crown bud	Rooted plantlet	Durand- Cresswell & Nitsch (1977)
Oxydendrum arboreum	24	Tips of forced shoots	Shoot culture	Banko and Stefani (1989)
Tectonia grandis	100	Vegetative buds	Shoot growth: some shoots rooted	Gupta *et al.* (1980)

There are numerous examples in the literature to show that explants derived from the juvenile phase are most tractable in culture. For illustration:

— the rate of survival and the subsequent growth rate of juvenile blueberry explants is much higher than those of adult explants (Smagula and Lyrene, 1984);

— the most rapid initial shoot proliferation of *Prunus avium* shoot cultures was from explants derived from root suckers of a mature tree. In cultures established from 1 year-old and 5 year-old trees, the rate was lower, and explants from mature trees could not be established (Pevalek-Kozlina and Jelaska, 1987);

— only juvenile shoots of *Sequoia sempervirens* produced axillary shoots. Buds from more mature parts of the tree did not proliferate (Ball, 1978).

— in shoot cultures of *Pistacia*, apical dominance was found to be greater even in the shoots grown from apical and axillary buds of 1 year-old seedlings, than in newly germinated seedlings; the difference in the rate of axillary branching disappeared after a few subcultures (Barghchi, 1986b).

Rejuvenation. In the genus *Castanea*, Chevre and Salesses (1987) found that truly juvenile shoot tips from seedlings could be explanted and propagated by shoot culture, but adult material (for example of the hybrid *C. crenata × C. sativa*) required to be rejuvenated first of all in layer beds. *C. sativa* shoot tips isolated from the seedlings obtained by embryo culture, gave shoots which proliferated more rapidly and rooted more easily than those derived from axillary bud explants (Piagnani and Eccher, 1988). Chevre *et al.* (1983) noted a difference in the axillary shoots obtained from juvenile and mature buds of this species. The former elongated in the normal **MS** multiplication medium containing 1 mg/l BAP, while the latter required to be transferred to **MS** with 1 mg/l IAA, 1 mg/l adenine and 0.5% activated charcoal, to stop shoot proliferation and induce shoot elongation.

Only single node cuttings, and not axillary and terminal buds from 2 year-old *Feijoa (Acca) sellowiana* seedlings would produce shoots in culture. The response of single node cuttings declined with age, and only 12% of those from a 3 year-old plant sprouted *in vitro*. However, nodal explants taken from freshly- formed shoots on 3 year-old coppiced trees, all produced shoots but the capacity to do so disappeared once the coppice-shoots were 4 months old. By this time the shoots had lost their juvenile leaf form and were thickened and coated with epicuticular wax (Bhojwani *et al.*, 1987).

Rooting. In conventional propagation, it is found that cuttings from mature parts of a plant are frequently more difficult to root than those taken from juvenile shoots. This is also observed *in vitro*, especially in shoots derived from newly-established node or shoot cultures. Thus de Fossard *et al.* (1977) were able to root the nodes of seedlings of several *Eucalyptus* species, but could not get any roots to form on nodes derived from mature trees. Although Sankara Rao and Venkateswara (1985) could establish shoot cultures from both juvenile and mature nodes of *Eucalyptus grandis*, 60% of the microcuttings from juvenile shoots formed roots, but only 35% rooting occurred on those from the mature source. Similar results were obtained with *Camellia sasanqua* (where 60% of mature shoots and 90% of juvenile shoots rooted within 3 weeks of treatment with IBA). A gradient in rooting potential may even be seen between juvenile material from two different sources. For instance in *Quercus robur*, 83% of the shoots derived from zygotic embryos were successfully rooted compared to 63% of those from stump sprouts), possibly reflecting a difference in the degree of re-juvenation in the two kinds of shoot (Vieitez *et al.*, 1985a).

There are exceptions: shoots produced by shoot culture from juvenile or adult phases of an apple rootstock could both be rooted although their response to phloroglucinol was different (Welander and Huntrieser, 1981).

Callus cultures. Studies on the morphology and behaviour of callus illustrate the cellular basis of the maturation state. Callus cells derived from juvenile and adult phases of the same plant have different characteristics that are maintained consistently *in vitro* over prolonged periods. English ivy (*Hedera helix*) callus, derived from the juvenile stage, has been found to be composed of larger cells, to have faster growth rate, to produce roots more freely (Stoutemeyer and Britt, 1965; Polito and Alliata, 1981; Alliata and Polito, 1982) and to be more prone to develop variant cell lines (Robbins and Hervey, 1970; Banks, 1979b) than callus from the adult form. Callus from juvenile tissue of *Robinia pseudo-acacia* and *Castanea vulgaris* has also been noted to proliferate more rapidly than that obtained from adult zones (Trippi, 1963).

Callus cultures originating from juvenile reversion stems of ivy, regenerated adventitious shoots, whereas those from mature stems gave rise to somatic embryos (Banks, 1979a). Adventitious shoots could be regenerated from callus derived from seedling internodes of *Vitis vinifera* or *Vitis vinifera* × *V. rupestris*, but not from callus of similar adult explants (Rajasekaran and Mullins, 1982).

Rejuvenation induced by *in vitro* culture

A characteristic feature of adult tissues *in vitro*, is that they become more easily managed after a period of time. Most researchers consider that the marked changes wich are observed in the characteristics of the cultured material are due its having become rejuvenated; shoots or plantlets assume one or more of the phenotypic characteristics of plants in the juvenile phase of growth described below, such as a smaller leaf size and an improved capacity for adventitious root formation.

However, workers who consider juvenility to be the total reversal of maturation (*e.g.* Mullins, 1985; Mullins *et al.*, 1986), question whether tissue culture does really produce a juvenile state, because plantlets sometimes flower *in vitro*, and plants derived from tissue cultures usually flower well before those grown from seed. The use of alternative terms such as 're-invigoration' or 'apparent rejuvenation' (Pierik, 1990a,b) is then preferred. However, so many different characteristics of juvenilty are reported in different species of plants which have been micropropagated by shoot culture, others prefer to think that a 'partial rejuvenation' occurs, which is some of the way towards 'complete rejuvenation' (Bonga, 1982a), and that separate features of juvenility are independently controlled.

Plants from adventitious shoots and embryos

Banks (1979a) suggested that all *de novo* meristems (*i.e.* both adventitious shoots and somatic embryos) arising in tissue cultures will be intrinsically juvenile. Plants obtained from somatic embryos initiated in culture are invariably found to be similar to true seedlings and fully juvenile, whether they come from nucellar callus (Spiegel-Roy and Kochba, 1980), or are derived from other adult tissues (Banks, 1979a,b). Banks, however, did add a note of caution in quoting observations of Staritsky, that coffee plants grown from somatic embryos (which were derived from callus of mature plant origin) flowered when 2–3 years old, rather than at 4–5 years as is customary for normal seedlings. Bonga (1982a) has suggested that some adventitious embryos which are stunted or abnormal, may have arisen from tissues where some maturity persisted and rejuvenation was almost, but not entirely, completed.

Shoot cultures

In most plants proliferative shoot cultures are very readily obtained from juvenile explants. However a degree of apparent rejuvenation often takes place after cultures of adult shoots have been maintained for some while *in vitro*. The rate of growth typically improves and is accompanied by an increase in the production of axillary shoots. The production of axillary shoots by cultures of *Coffea arabica* cv. 'Mundo Nova' may serve as an example (Sondahl *et al.*, 1985):

Age of culture	Number of buds produced per node
First 60 days	1.3
Next 60 days	4.5
3rd 60 day period	7.5

As the rate of shoot proliferation increases, separated shoots become easier to root. This apparent re-invigoration is often accompanied by other symptoms of the juvenile phenotype which are also seen in plantlets established *ex vitro*. In temperate hardwood trees, McCown and McCown (1987) have identified three phases in the establishment of shoot cultures. They are particularly obvious in cultures of woody plants where progression through the stage can be equated with a rejuvenation process:

- *an isolation phase*, during which shoots grow rapidly, but when the only axillary shoots produced are those which have grown from buds on the original explant.

- *a stabilization phase*, in which cultures often become quiescent and at best only show unpredictable episodic growth. The duration of this phase is usually short in *Salix* and *Ulmus*, longer in *Acer* and *Fraxinus*, and very long (sometimes many months) in *Fagus* and *Quercus*. *Stabilized cultures* which have passed through this phase have acquired some apparent juvenility.

- *a production phase* (Stage II in conventional terminology — Chapter 2), when shoot proliferation is possible and when shoots can be moved to subsequent stages for rooting and transfer *extra vitrum*.

Although normal cuttings of grapevines perpetuate the adult form, in the cultivar 'Cabernet Sauvignon', Mullins *et al.* (1979) obtained juvenile shoots (that had never been previously recorded) by rooting *in vitro* cuttings from the same very small stem apices on several successive occasions. Moncousin (1982) records similar results with shoot cultures of globe artichoke. As cuttings were successively propagated *in vitro*, the shoots gradually became equivalent to seedlings in that their rooting capacity increased, and plants came to require a cold treatment to flower. This is in agreement with the findings of other authors (see review by Zimmerman, 1972). The phase change from adult to juvenile, induced during shoot cul-

ture of *Episcia*, is disadvantageous because in the juvenile state, plants do not have multicoloured foliage. Although characteristic leaf colour eventually returns, the sale of young plants can be difficult (Bilkey and McCown, 1979).

Symptoms of partial rejuvenation

Leaf form. Lyrene (1980, 1981) found that *Vaccinium* plants obtained by micropropagation of adult explants (using lateral shoot proliferation induced by high cytokinin) assumed juvenile characteristics with small leaves, short internodes and thin stems, like those of seedlings. From the *in vitro* culture of stem nodes, Snir (1981) produced plantlets of raspberry which also had primary leaves like those of seedlings, and similar results were obtained by Whitehead and Giles (1977) with several species of poplar. Nozeran *et al.* (1977) obtained juvenile potato plants from single node cultures, and Denton *et al.* (1977) mention how potato plants grown directly from shoot cultures retained a juvenile leaf form in the field well after it was lost from plants raised normally from tubers. Cultures of this kind are as easy to subculture as juvenile stock (Smagula and Lyrene, 1984).

Plantlets of raspberry, resulting from the *in vitro* culture of stem nodes, had primary leaves like those of seedlings (Snir, 1981): similar results were obtained by Whitehead and Giles (1977) with several species of poplar. Leaves which were transitional from adult to juvenile were produced on nodal explants of *Carica pubescens* × *C. stipulata*. Plantlets which were eventually obtained had juvenile leaves for the first 10 nodes. There was then a gradual transition to an adult leaf shape at about node 15 (Cohen and Cooper, 1982). Shoots regenerated from cotyledon fragments of *Olea europea* gave rise to plantlets with a juvenile phyllotaxis and leaf form (Canãs and Benbadis, 1988).

Shoots produced from shoot culture of vines, using fragmented shoot apices as the explant, closely resembled seedlings in being without tendrils, having spiral phyllotaxy, and the absence of sinuses on the leaves (Skene and Barlass, 1981). Vines without tendrils were also obtained by Favre and Grenan (1979) when they cultured plantlets on a simple macronutrient and micronutrient solution containing sucrose. Tendrils, flowers and sometimes berries were obtained when vitamins were added to the medium.

An increased rate of growth and proliferation. Progressive subcultures often lead to an increased rate of growth of shoots and shoot multiplication. In *Juglans regia*, increased tractabilty of the explants was accompanied by the the production of axillary shoots with small fine-featured leaves, and an increased growth rate

(McGranahan *et al.*, 1988a). This pattern is typical of many shoot cultures. Even cultures initiated from seedling material may become invigorated after several transfers: growth of shoots initiated from *Betula platyphylla* var. *azechuanica* seedlings became more rapid after several monthly subcultures, and shoot multiplication was progressively easier to stimulate (McCown and Amos, 1979).

Micropropagated plants frequently produce many lateral branches during the first few months of growth *extra vitrum*. This is often taken to be a direct result of residual cytokinin within young plants, left over from the *in vitro* treatment used to induce shoot proliferation. It has been associated with the presence of an excessive cytokinin concentration during culture (page 441), or too many subcultures on a cytokinin-containing proliferation medium before plants are rooted (Capellades Queralt *et al.*, 1991). It is possible that, in some species, supernumerary branching in plants resulting from micropropagation, could be a symptom of their rejuvenation.

The rooting of microcuttings. Shoots which have been cultured *in vitro* nearly always root much more freely than cuttings from the mature part of a plant (Lyrene, 1981). Usually the improvement is not immediately apparent, but begins after several passages; then the speed and frequency with which rooting can be induced, characteristically increase during successive subcultures. This has been especially noted in many kinds of woody plants, for example, *Malus × domestica* (Sriskandarajah and Mullins, 1982; Mullins *et al.*, 1986); *Feijoa* (in Bhojwani and Razdan, 1983).

Eucalyptus marginata explants of seedling origin had an high multiplication rate immediately they were introduced to culture, producing up to 10 axillary shoots during the first 4 weeks. Adult explants gave rise to an average of about 3 shoots in the same period and some adult shoots did not start to multiply until they had been cultured for 6–10 months (McComb and Bennett, 1982). Eventually there was an enhanced rate of shoot proliferation, accompanied by an improvement in the readiness of the shoots to form roots. Similar results were obtained with *E. citriodora* by Gupta *et al.* (1981).

Occasionally a very large number of subcultures may be required before any appreciable change in rooting capacity is observed. The number of roots formed per shoot of *Actinidia chinensis* (and the rate of shoot multiplication) was significantly greater after the 28th (shoot tip) subculture than after the third (Standardi, 1982). Similarly, after 30 subcultures the same percentage of rooting was found in the apple rootsock 'A2' derived from juvenile or mature sources, but even after this period there was a difference in the two types of plant material: that from

adult explants required a higher concentration of the auxin IBA for optimum root initiation and was less sensitive than that with a juvenile origin, to supra-optimal IBA doses (Welander and Snygg, 1987). Some other more typical results are given in Chapter 14.

In vitro rejuvenation was necessary before a rapid rate of shoot growth and adventitious root formation was possible in single node cultures of *Syringa vulgaris*. This was attained by frequent subculturing. Some varieties required many subcultures before rejuvenation occurred (Pierik *et al.* 1988c).

Woody plants recently derived from micropropagation may retain the effects of rejuvenation *in vitro* when they are grown and propagated conventionally. An increased rooting potential has been found to last for 1–2 years in *Rhododendron* and at least 10 years in the plum rootstock *Prunus institia cv.* 'Pixy'.

In contrast with usual experience, a *loss* of rooting capacity has been noted in some woody plants which have been subcultured for one or more years. Alderson *et al.* (1988) reported that the rose variety 'Dainty Dinah' became more difficult to root the longer it was cultured, although in the same experiments, the rooting of 'Dicjana' improved; Patena *et al.* (1988) record that shoots from cultures of 'Golden Delicious' apple harvested during the first 1½ years, rooted readily. Those taken from subsequent subcultures showed a gradual decrease in rooting until eventually, they did not root at all.

The 'rejuvenation' effect is often not apparent in herbaceous plants (but see Chapter 12 for exceptions), and Geier (1986) found that shoots from shoot cultures of *Anthurium scherzerianum* formed roots more slowly with each cycle of multiplication. After 3 subcultures, roots only appeared after two transfers on a regulant-free medium. Possibly this was due to an accumulation of cytokinin (used for multiplication) in the tissues?

Susceptibility to pathogens. A change in micropropagated plants of one strawberry cultivar in their resistance to two root rotting fungi, was discovered by Shoemaker and Swartz (1985). Tissue culture propagated plants, and juvenile selfed seedlings, of 'Raritan' were more susceptible than runner plants. The disease reaction shifted towards that of runner plants as time elapsed. Rancillac and Nourisseau (1989) say that micropropagated strawberry plants have a greater resistance to cold than normal runner plants, but that field plantings of the cultivars 'Gorella' and 'Belrubi' originating from beyond 18–30 subcultures, have shown an increased suscepibility to pathogens, and 'Gorella' to early senescence. Fruit quality is always worse on strawberries from beyond the 15th subculture.

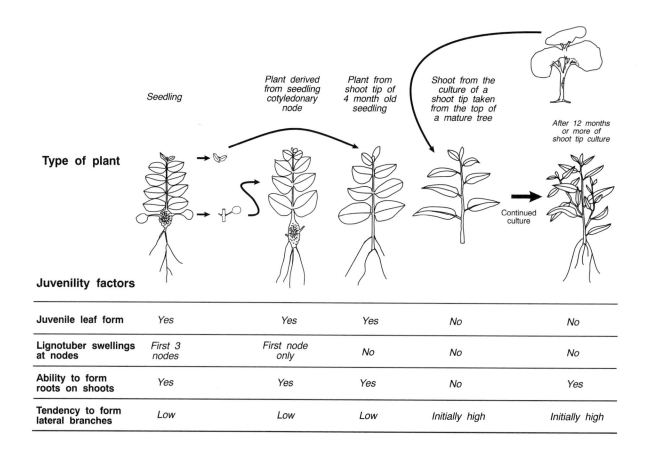

Fig. 82. The independent expression of four characteristics of juvenility in seedlings and micropropagated plants of *Eucalytus marginata*
[after Bennett and McComb (1986). The authors kindly provided the drawing above].

Type of plant	Seedling	Plant derived from seedling cotyledonary node	Plant from shoot tip of 4 month old seedling	Shoot from the culture of a shoot tip taken from the top of a mature tree	After 12 months or more of shoot tip culture
Juvenile leaf form	Yes	Yes	Yes	No	No
Lignotuber swellings at nodes	First 3 nodes	First node only	No	No	No
Ability to form roots on shoots	Yes	Yes	Yes	No	Yes
Tendency to form lateral branches	Low	Low	Low	Initially high	Initially high

Plagiotropism. Most coniferous trees quickly gain the aspect of maturity which conveys a long-term memory of plagiotropism on laterals. Even though many features of juvenility can be re-established in explants by pretreatment of the stock plant material (such as hormone sprays and grafting, and repeated transfers *in vitro*), it is often found that a proportion of young trees originating from shoot multiplication *in vitro* (particularly those of conifers *e.g.* 40% of loblolly pine plants — Leach, 1979;), have a leading shoot with a plagiotropic habit. Although in some species plagiotropism of the leading shoot often disappears after the plant has been 2–3 years in the field (Ritchie and Long, 1986), delay in shoot extension and contorted growth of the main shoot is usually unacceptable for commercial plantings. Plagiotropy imposes a severe restriction on the vegetative multiplication of plants intended for normal planting. It is more likely to result from the micropropagation of adult material. This was the case in *Cunninghamia lanceolata*, where 93% of the plants obtained from shoot cultures initiated from the nodes of a juvenile clone, had orthotropic growth (which

was comparable to that of seedlings), whereas only orthotropic plants were obtained from cultures initiated from the basal side shoots of an adult clone (Engelmann *et al.*, 1987). Because of this problem, explants for conifer micropropagation are frequently taken from plagiotropic branches of mature trees, where this is practicable. However there is a suggestion that orthotropic main shoot growth depends on a young plant having a strong root system. In many woody species, the root system of microcuttings is often of a poorer quality than that of seedlings (McKeand and Allen, 1984). In *Sequioa sempervirens*, plagiotropic growth and poor vigour following micropropagation, are a characteristic of some clones (Boulay, 1987), suggesting that there is a genetic component.

The regulation of maturation

The mature state occurs as cells which were capable of giving rise to organs with juvenile attributes produce others with different capabilities. Although the expression of juvenile or mature traits is an attribute of individual plant cells, it is difficult to distinguish at the molecular level. Some workers have found characteristic potassium to calcium ratios and peroxidase activities in juvenile tissues (reviewed by Boulay, 1987), but as yet there is no simple test which can be applied to a cell to determine its maturity state. It has been proposed that maturation may involve methylation of particular gene sequences (Hood and Libby, 1978) and/or an alteration in the rate of transcription of certain genes (Davies and Hartmann, 1988).

Separate juvenile characteristics

As explained above, some researchers maintain that although plants have been induced to show one or more features of juvenile growth through tissue culture, they cannot be considered to be juvenile or re-juvenated, because some other feature associated with seedling juvenility is missing. However, such results could be explained if the phenotypic characteristics associated with the juvenile phase are capable of independent expression, that is to say, juvenility is not an 'all or nothing' phenomenon.

A good example of the separate expression of juvenile characteristics is provided by the experiment of Bennett and McComb (1986) (Fig. 82). Seedlings of *Eucalyptus marginata* have juvenile leaves which are ovate, sessile and opposite, and produce lignotuberous swellings at nodes 1–3[‡]. Shoots from the cotyledonary node of such seedlings also have juvenile leaves, root easily, and produce a lignotuber: those grown *in vitro* from the shoot tips of 4 month-old seedlings root readily and have juvenile leaves but do not form lignotubers. Shoots initiated from shoot apices of the crown of mature trees have leaves with a mature form and cannot be rooted until they have been cultured for 12 months: shoots then still have a mature leaf shape, are initially more branched than shoots from juvenile explants (Bennett *et al.*, 1986) and may produce flower buds 13 months after transfer from culture.

In vitro flowering

There are many records of flowering having been induced either directly or indirectly *in vitro* from *mature* organs or tissues, such as shoot tips (or other pre-formed meristems); explanted sections of roots, stems, petioles and leaves (Scorza, 1982); or from thin cell layers of epidermal and subepidermal tissues (Tran Thanh Van and Trinh, 1978; Van den Ende *et al.*, 1984a; Altamura *et al.*,

1986; Apelbaum *et al.*, 1988; Bridgen and Veilleux, 1988). These reports fall into two categories:

a) flowers or floral structures produced by parts of a plant committed to flower (the plant having already received an appropriate stimulus). For example,

- explants taken from flowering shoots which show a gradient of flowering potential that decreases the further the explant is from the apex (Tran Thanh Van, 1973a; Croes *et al.*, 1985);

- explants from peduncles, scapes, flower buds, or floral organs (and callus derived from them) which can give rise to flowers or floral structures.

b) flowering induced on adult, but non-committed parts of a plant which are predisposed to flower formation if given an appropriate stimulus. There are many examples of this kind, in which it is often found that:

- flowering occurs much more rapidly than it would *in vivo*,

- flowering is induced in response to photoperiods or vernalisation treatments which are effective in the whole plant,

- induction is influenced by applied growth regulants and the cultural environment,

- explants respond to treatments which are not effective on similar seedling (juvenile) material.

But flowering has also been induced on *juvenile* seedlings or seedling-derived tissues of several plants during culture (Table 18). On the basis of the usual assumption 'that the capacity to flower is the ultimate criterion by which to judge whether or not a plant tissue is mature', one would have to conclude that *in vitro* culture is not only capable of inducing rejuvenation, but also maturation. On the other hand, in seedling material the commitment to flowering appears not to have depended on the prior acquisition of other features of maturity, such as an inability of shoots to form adventitious roots and an adult leaf form. This seems to support the hypothesis that the features of juvenility or maturity are not inseparably associated (*i.e.* a plant is not either completely mature or completely juvenile), but that each feature of juvenility or maturity can be independently influenced by prevailing stimuli. Features of *in vitro* culture which can promote the induction of flowering include:

1. The absence of buds (Pierik, 1967).

2. Size of the explant (Margara *et al.*, 1966).

[‡] These nodes are usually very close together at soil level, so eventually there appears to be one swelling, not three.

Table 18. Examples of *in vitro* flowering on shoots or plants which have been derived from seedlings.

Plant	Explant	Type of culture	Notes	Reference
Bambusa arundinacea *Dendrocalamus brandesii*	Coleoptile sections	Direct, then shoot culture	Shoots flowered after 3 subcultures.	Nadgauda *et al.* (1990)
Dendrocalamus hamiltonii	Epicoltyls, Single nodes	Shoot	Highest proportion of flowering shoots after 8 weeks on 44 μM BAP then to **MS** with no PGRs.	Chambers *et al.* (1991)
Brassica campestris var. *pekinensis*	Seedling shoot tip	Shoot	Some plants flowered in vitro, rest bolted in greenhouse.	Paek *et al.* (1987)
Brassica juncea *B. campestris*	Cotyledon	Callus	Regenerated plants flowered *in vitro*.	Jain *et al.* (1988b)
Carthamus tinctorius	Cotyledon	Direct	Capitula produced on cotyledons. These had florets which later bloomed *in vitro*.	Tejovathi & Anwar (1984)
Cucumis sativus cv. 'Superpickle'	Seedling hypocotyl	Callus	Shoots from somatic embryos and adventitious shoots flowered *in vitro*.	Rajasekaran *et al.* (1983)
Cuminum cyminum	Leaf and hypocotyl	Callus	Plants from adventitious shoots flowered after 3 weeks on a rooting medium	Jha *et al.* (1983)
Glycine max cv. 'Impala'	Seedling	Plant	The proportion of seedlings which flowered depended on a S.D. photoperiod, low salt medium without NH_4NO_3, and the presence of sucrose.	Dickens & Van Staden (1985)
Helianthus annuus	Seedling plumule	Shoot	Flowering depended on sucrose in mod. **White** medium and on there being *no* root system on the plumular shoots.	Hendrickson (1954)
	Shoot tips	Shoot	Precocious flowering *in vitro* or immediately after planting *extra vitrum*	Lupi *et al.* (1987)
Mesembryanthemum floribundum	Root, stem or leaf	Callus	Seedlings arising from somatic embryos flowered when very small	Mehra & Mehra (1972)
Panax ginseng	Root pith	Callus	Embryogenesis. Somatic embryos, the plantlets from which flowered *in vitro*.	Chang & Hsing (1980a)
	Flower buds	Embryogenic callus	Shoots flowered on ½**MS** with 0.5 mg/l GA_3 and 1 mg/l BAP	Shoyama *et al.* (1988)
	Mature zygotic embryos	Direct	Somatic embryos, the plantlets from which flowered *in vitro*.	Lee et al. (1990)

3. The absence of roots (Hendrickson, 1954; Dennin and McDaniel, 1985).

4. In some species, a stimulatory photoperiod applied to the stock plant before explant excision, reinforced by, or substituted with, a similar treatment applied to the culture (Simmonds, 1981; Lawson and Goodwin, 1986).

5. In some species, a cold vernalisation period may be required, but the requirement can often be overcome by cultural treatments.

6. A low concentration of auxin, especially IAA or NAA (Konishi et al., 1982; Scorza, 1982; Handro, 1983).

7. A correct combination of growth regulants; cytokinins are commonly required (Scorza, 1982; Gertsson, 1988b) and a high cytokinin to auxin ratio is frequently necessary (Tanimoto and Harada, 1982b).

8. The presence of sugar (Nitsch and Nitsch, 1965; Tanimoto and Harada, 1981c; 1982c); the correct concentration may be critical (Simmonds, 1981, 1982).

9. The constituents of the culture medium, for example, low levels of nitrogen (Tanimoto and Harada, 1981a; Simmonds, 1982; Dickens and Van Staden, 1985; Wada and Shinozaki, 1985); a low concentration of ammonium ions (Simmonds, 1981; Tannimoto and Harada, 1979, 1981a, 1982c); an increase in the concentration of vitamins (Chaturvedi and Sharma, 1977).

10. The physical condition of the medium (Bouniols and Margara, 1968; Cousson and Tran Thanh Van, 1981).

Flowering of micropropagated plants

Even though micropropagated plantlets may display some characteristics which are clearly juvenile, a mature form re-appears when they are grown-on out of doors and they are soon capable of flowering, indicating that *either* the rejuvenation process which occurs during culture is not as complete as that which is found in seedlings, *or* that flowering has been hastened by the *in vitro* process.

It seems obvious to expect that treatments which can enhance flowering *in vitro* will have a carry-over effect and also tend to promote the early flowering of plants *extra vitrum*, and this does occur. For example some plantlets obtained from shoot culture of Chinese cabbage (normally a biennial plant which has a cold requirement for flower induction), flowered *in vitro* without any cold treatment, and the rest bolted and flowered when planted in the greenhouse (Paek *et al.*, 1987). *Helianthus annuus* is very prone to premature flowering *in vitro*. Lupi *et al.* (1987) found that many shoots derived from shoot cultures, produced flower buds precociously in culture (in which case they could not be rooted), or soon after they had been rooted and transferred to pots. However, if shoots were rooted in the dark, subsequent premature flowering was suppressed.

Premature flowering *extra vitrum* without it having occurred *in vitro*, is also experienced, for example in *Oncidium* orchids (Kerbauy, 1984c); in some plants of *Paulownia tomentosa* obtained from shoots regenerated directly from seedling hypocotyls (Fig. 73) (Jagannathan and Marcotrigiano, 1986). The temperature at which *Senecio × hybridus* was cultured, and the BAP concentration in the medium, influenced subsequent growth, rate of development and number of flowers on micropropagated plants when they were afterwards grown in soil in a growth room (Gertsson, 1988b).

That flowering habits can be altered in the long term by *in vitro* culture has been shown by experience with strawberries. An unusual promotion of flower formation has been found in the cultivar 'Gorella'. Plants derived from advanced shoot subcultures produce an increased number of flowers per inflorescence (Boxus, 1987; Dijkstra, 1987; Rancillac *et al.*, 1987). This is disadvantageous because although more fruits are produced, they are unacceptably small. Kinet and Parmentier (1989) have called the accentuation of flowering in strawberry, *'hyperflowering'*. They found that normal 'Gorella' plants resulted from micropropagation until about the 18th subculture, but that some time after this there was a sudden population shift and the distribution curve of number of flowers per plant moved sharply upwards. All plants from the 29th and the 58th subcultures had extra flowers. Hyperflowering was apparent in both the first and second inflorescences of these plants and also persisted to affect their progeny produced from stolons. Boxus (1989) has suggested that hyperflowering might be caused by growth regulator habituation induced through a protracted contact with high concentrations of growth regulants in the culture medium.

Micropropagated trees and shrubs usually flower well in advance of those established from true seedlings, for example apples after 14 months to 2 years in the orchard (Zimmerman, 1981, 1984a). *Anigozanthus* plants derived from seed usually flower in 9–18 months, whereas those derived from shoot culture can flower in less than 4 months (McComb and Newton, 1981), or even very shortly after deflasking (Laweson and Goodwin, 1986). *Punica granatum* plants flowered only 8 months after field planting, *Eucalyptus* after 2 years instead of the 5–10 years with normal seedlings (Mascarenhas *et al.*, 1982b); and *Juglans regia* flowered after only 10–24 months from being transferred from culture (McGranahan *et al.*, 1988a). Grapevines propagated by shoot culture, flower in the first season after planting outside, whereas seedlings take several seasons to flower (Skene and Barlass, 1981).

Persistence of other juvenile traits

Although plants produced by *in vitro* methods are seldom as juvenile as seedlings, either in the number, or persistence, of the phenotypic characters displayed, the ability to produce roots readily on cuttings has been retained in some micropropagated fruit trees over at least 9 years, even though they have flowered.

Some clones of strawberry plants derived from shoot cultures have been noticed to be more susceptible to fungal pathogens during an initial period of several months (Rancillac *et al.*, 1987), which in some cases is comparable to the increased susceptibility of seedling plants (Shoemaker and Swartz, 1985). It seems therefore that susceptibility of tissue cultured material is associated with its increased juvenilty (Boxus, 1989).

Growth regulators.

There is evidence that the degree of maturation of plant tissues is controlled by plant growth substances or growth regulators. However, the maturity status of meristems is apparently not immediately changed by the availability of such compounds, but only slowly, over a period of time. Above-normal temperatures have been found to promote the reversion of adult shoots to a juvenile form *in vivo* (see above). It is therefore probable that the consistently high temperatures at which plant cultures are usually maintained to ensure the maximum rate of growth and proliferation, will favour reversion to the juvenile condition, and interact with growth regulator effects.

Characteristically, juvenile tissues possess high concentrations of auxin protectors and therefore contain relatively high levels of the natural auxin, IAA (Chapter 11).

Cytokinins.   Cytokinin growth substances which are produced within plant roots seem to be particularly implicated in the induction of the juvenile state. The availability of these compounds decreases as the distance between shoots and root increases, and the degree of maturation of the tissues increases. As explained previously, treating the shoots of stock plants with cytokinins and gibberellins can induce some degree of rejuvenation. As cytokinins are apparently implicated in the re-introduction of a juvenile phenotype *in vivo*, it is tempting to speculate that it is their presence in plant culture media which is mainly responsible for inducing a phase change. However the level of BAP in the culture medium does not affect the tendency of strawberries to produce an abundance of runners after tissue culture propagation (Marcotrigiano *et al.*, 1984) and neither the time of BAP application, nor the amount, affected the change of disease susceptibility noted in one cultivar (Shoemaker and Swartz, (1985) — see above).

Shoot proliferation in shoot cultures of *Actinidia chinensis* increases after several subcultures (Standardi, 1982), but Monette (1986a, 1987) showed that this apparent rejuvenation is due to the length of time that the shoots are in contact with the medium, rather than the number of transfers or divisions they have undergone: material subcultured every 2 weeks and shoots of the same age which had been stored for 52 weeks at 8°C on a medium containing 4 mg/l BAP, produced the same number of shoots.

Gibberellic acid. Shoot 'invigoration' and the rooting potential of the cherry rootstock '46-1 Mazzard', increased during 6 consecutive subcultures when it was in the same culture vessel as the easy–to–root cultivar, 'Colt'. Ranjit and Kester (1988) thought the rejuvenation was brought about by gibberellin released into the medium by 'Colt', because similar results were obtained by adding 0.1–0.25 mg/l (but not 0.5 mg/l or more) gibberellic acid to the medium. Rooting of '46-1 Mazzard' depended on transfer to a medium without gibberellin for root initiation.

Abscisic acid. Swartz (1991) has suggested that growth inhibitors, especially abscisic acid (ABA), may be responsible for maintaining maturity. A diminished synthesis of ABA and availability to meristems during *in vitro* culture could lead to the restoration of partial juvenility. The hormone is synthesized in plastids which are changed in number and function by etiolation and during tissue culture, either by dedifferentiation, or by the low light irradiances in which cultures are usually grown. An

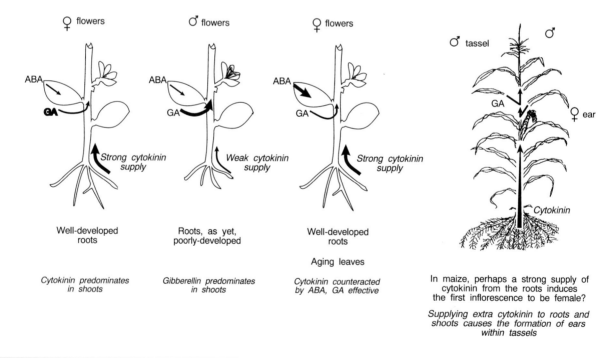

Fig. 83. How the sex of flowers may be regulated by plant growth substances [after Chailakhyan and Khryanin, 1980].

above-average level of ABA can induce flowering *in vitro* (see Chapter 11).

Review articles

A collection of review articles on the effects of juvenility on woody plants was published in *Acta Horticulturae*, volume **56**. Juvenility and rejuvenation has also been reviewed by Bonga (1982a), Greenwood (1987), Hackett (1985), Pierik (1990a,b) and Swartz (1991).

THE SEX OF FLOWERS

Sexual expression is genetically controlled in those species in which male and female organs are borne on different unisexual individuals (*dioecious* plants). In these species, female plants usually have a pair of identical **X** chromosomes, while males have one **X** and one dissimilar **Y** chromosome and are heterogametic. The sex of any particular plant is therefore determined at the time of fertilisation. However, the sexual phenotype of a plant at any one time may not only be influenced by genotype but also by many environmental factors, such as daylength, light 'intensity' and temperature. Genetic and environmental control are probably mediated through the action of natural plant growth substances, because it is found that the development of flowers (Mullins, 1980), and particularly sex expression, can be modified by plant growth regulators applied in culture media, taken up through plant roots, or sprayed or injected into stems.

A *monoecious* plant has both male and female organs, but in different flowers: the male program is often expressed before the female (Durand and Durand, 1984). Growth regulators can also influence the sex of flowers formed on monoecious plants. The application of auxins, ethylene and cytokinins tends to promote femaleness in plants, and gibberellins maleness, but the action of gibberellins can be negated by abscisic acid. In dioecious plants it has been shown that femaleness is promoted by the presence of roots, and maleness by leaves (especially if roots are not present). This led Chailakhyan and Khryanin (1980) to propose the scheme shown in Fig. 83 to explain how the sex of flowers might normally be controlled by the balance of growth regulants. It is not a complete picture: for example, cytokinins induce and promote pistil development in male grapevines (Mullins, 1980), and Wu *et al.* (1990) found a higher level of auxin in the leaves of male *Melandrium album* plants than in female ones.

In some dioecious plants, the differentiation of shoot apices with the capacity to give rise to plants which will bear either male or female flowers, takes place quite early in development. In such cases, culture of isolated embryos on media containing gibberellic acid or a cytokinin, results in nearly all plants becoming respectively either male or female (Chailakhyan and Khryanin (1980).

Abnormalites in flower structure have been reported in plants regenerated from tissue culture, but they are usually interpreted as being due to a changed genotype (somaclonal variation). In the case of oil palms micropropagated by somatic embryogenesis, this seems less certain. Although they have not commenced flowering until four or more years after field planting, many clones established from somatic embryos, which otherwise appear to be phenotypically normal, have been found to contain a proportion of plants with abnormal inflorescences. Both male and female flowers (which are borne in separate inflorescences on the same tree) are apparently more female than normal: in male flowers, stamens develop into fleshy pseudocarpels, while in female flowers there is excessive carpel formation leading to fruit abortion (Corley *et al.*, 1986; Jones, 1988; Dublin *et al.*, 1990). The floral abnormalities seem to be particularly associated with the length of time that tissues were cultured before plant regeneration (Corley *et al.*, 1986) and Dublin *et al.* (1990) have suggested that they may have an epigenetic cause related to a disorder in the availability of endogenous plant growth regulators: possibly this is habituation (see pages 232 and 475).

MORPHOGENIC DETERMINATION

As mentioned in Chapter 1, the cells of plant meristems can become committed or determined to initiate just one specific type of organ. At exactly what stage of development the determination of root, shoot and leaf meristems takes place has been the subject of controversy. There is evidence that commitment need not occur at the same time that the meristem is initiated and that for a period (that may vary according to origin and situation), meristems can exhibit some plasticity in their developmental pattern.

Newly-formed primordia in shoot apices are found to be capable of such flexibility. For example, by culturing isolated leaf primordia, Kuehnert *et al.* (Kuehnert, 1972) found, in a series of studies, that the youngest primordium in a shoot apex of the fern *Osmunda cinnamonea* should be regarded as a completely undetermined outgrowth of the apex with the capability of developing either as a shoot, as a leaf with an axillary bud, or solely as a leaf. Uncommitted primordia in the apex of specialized lateral buds of grapevine can develop as either shoot, tendril, or inflorescence primordia (Mullins, 1980) and in *Impatiens balsamia*, primordia which would normally develop as

Table 19. Examples of floral parts being regenerated from floral explants.

Structures observed	References
Style-like structures on ovule explants of *Nicotiana tabacum*	Haccius et al. (1974) Hicks and McHughen (1974)
	Matsuzaki et al. (1984)
Stigmatoid outgrowths on undifferentiated stamen primordia of *Nicotiana tabacum* and *N. debneyi*	Hicks (1975)
	Hicks and Sand (1977)
Anthers on anther callus of *Cyclamen persicum*	Geier (1978)
Adventitious flower buds on inflorescence pedicels of *Begonia franconis*	Berghoef and Bruinsma (1979c)
Stigma and style-like structures on stigma callus of *Crocus sativus*	Himeno and Sano (1987)
	Koyama *et al.* (1987)
	Namera *et al.* (1987)
	Sano and Himeno (1987)
	Fakhrai and Evans (1990)
Stigmas and stigma-like structures on ovary callus of *Crocus chrysanthus*. *Direct formation of stigma-like stuctures on anthers, petals and ovaries of Crocus sativus*	Fakhrai and Evans (1989, 1990)

petals, can be made to switch to becoming leaves by an inappropriate photoperiod until they are 0.5–1.0 mm in length. Potential leaf primordia of *Impatiens* are not completely determined to this type of development until they are about 750 μm in length (Battey and Lyndon, 1988).

The meristematic centres formed on tissue *in vitro* from which adventitious organs may arise (meristemoids or promeristemoids), behave in a similar fashion to primordia in the shoot apex and are often uncommitted to a definite developmental pathway for a short period after their inception (page 29).

Persistence of a determined state

The cells of established shoot meristems change their pattern of development when they cease being vegetative and instead produce floral structures. Reversion from floral to vegetative status is fairly common and can be induced in the floral buds of some plants by appropriate cultural treatments. The use of this technique as a method of micropropagation of some plants has been mentioned in Chapters 1 and 2. On the other hand, once they are fully differentiated, root apical meristems continue unerringly

in the pattern of their development, and their further culture almost invariably leads to the formation of roots, unless cells of the meristem are disorganised into callus growth. Similarly, "once a leaf has been determined at the shoot apex, its subsequent development is essentially controlled within the leaf itself" (Steeves and Sussex, 1957).

Although the programming of meristems to adopt one particular growth pattern probably results from the semipermanent functioning (or epigenetic expression) of just a certain proportion of the genes in the complete genome, the orderly development of a characteristic plant form depends upon the sequential formation of meristems of different kinds. This suggests that normally some kinds of epigenetic expression need to be operational before others can be instituted; thus perhaps cells need to be committed to shoot (rather than root) development, before leaf meristems can be formed? Against this argument is the fact that leaf-initiating calluses have been occasionally discovered in which rudimentary leaves have been formed directly, apparently without the prior production of a shoot meristem (*e.g.* Steck *et al.* 1971; Venverloo, 1973; Bowes, 1976b; Negrutiu *et al.*, 1979; Maeda *et al.*, 1982b).

Cells which are strongly determined towards a particular kind of development, frequently retain this capacity

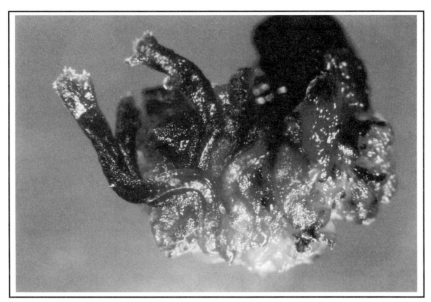

Fig. 84. Stigmas differentiating from ovary-derived callus of *Crocus sativus* (Saffron) [Fakhrai and Evans, 1989)

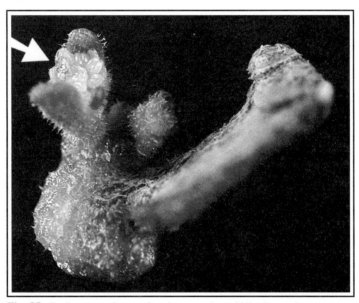

Fig. 85. Rudimentary flowers forming on callus of *Nicotiana tabacum.*

through several cell divisions *in vitro*. It is seen in the capacity of parts of the embryo to regenerate somatic embryos or embryogenic callus (Chapter 2). Callus formed from the tubers of *Corydalis turtachaninovii* seedlings was reported to have a tendency to regenerate tuber-like structures (Anon, 1981c). Those parts of a plant which have become determined to produce floral structures can also retain a similar commitment in explants which are conveyed to culture (Table 19; Figs. 84 and 85).

Flower buds can also be induced to develop *in vitro* directly from superficial cells of thin cell layers excised from floral branches of *Nicotiana tabacum* plants (Tran Thanh Van, 1973a; Van den Ende *et al.*, 1984a). Culturing axillary shoots of *Pseudotsuga menziesii* on a medium which promoted the re-juvenation of vegetative meristems, did not alter the phase-specific development of buds already programmed to become female cones (Gupta and Durzan, 1987a).

The induction of determination

The commitment of cells is usually modified through alterations in the *in vitro* environment, particularly by changing the availability of plant growth regulators. For morphogenesis to be possible, cells must be able to respond to growth regulating chemicals, that is to say they must be *competent* (see Chapter 1). The nature of the internal information factors governing cell competence are largely unknown, but they probably include natural growth substance levels within cells at the time of excision and the capacity of cells to synthesize growth substances or essential metabolites.

Competence

In tissues of some plants, competence can be demonstrated by having two media, one without growth regulants (basal medium, BM) and the other containing growth regulators known to cause shoot formation (shoot inducing medium, SIM). In the experiments of Attfield and Evans (1991b), after a varying period of culture on BM, *Nicotiana tabacum* leaf segments were transferred for induction on SIM for a specified time, and were then cultured (or re-cultured) on BM for 15 d until shoots could be counted. Explants never produced shoots if left on BM, but the longer they were on this medium (**MS** medium), the shorter was the period they required on SIM (**MS** medium plus 5 µM BAP) for shoot induction to occur.

The most rapid way to induce any given degree of shoot formation was to place the explants directly onto SIM, or give them a short 1–2 day exposure to basal medium first of all (Fig. 86). This suggests that 2 days was the minimum time the explants required to gain competence and that growth regulants were not required during this period. Keeping them on basal medium longer than this to begin with, lessened the exposure to BAP which was necessary to induce determination, but increased the total 'medium *plus* growth regulator' induction time for determination.

The induction of morphogenesis thus seems to depend on the combined effect of the medium (competence) and the presence of the correct combination of growth regulators (determination). Competence can be gained on media with or without growth regulators: *e.g.* BM, SIM, a root-

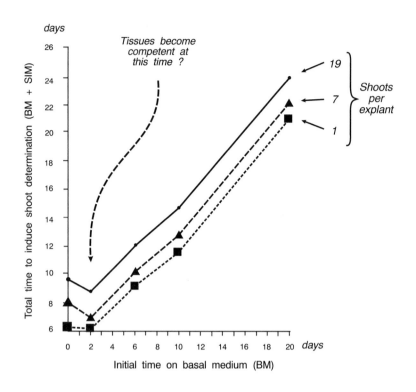

Fig. 86. The development of competence in *Nicotiana tabacum* leaf segments [after Attfield and Evans, 1991b].

The total time to induce shoot formation was shortened by preculture on BM for more than 2 days, suggesting that the tissues became competent during the initial 2-day period.

inducing medium, or a callus-inducing medium (Christianson and Warnick, 1985). It is possible that competence occurs through cells possessing, or coming to possess, a particular level of natural growth regulating substances.

Tissues of different plants vary in their competence. Direct or indirect morphogenesis occurs readily only in some plant species, or may even be restricted to certain varieties within species. Changing the medium, and /or the growth regulators added to it, may induce morphogenesis in recalcitrant tissues, but there are still some kinds of plants in which it has not been satisfactorily achieved.

The part of a plant from which an explant is derived has a major influence on direct organ formation or on the capacity of derived callus tissues to undergo morphogenesis. This suggests possible mechanisms for genetic control, *i.e.* that competence:

1. results from the pleitropic expression of genes which were only functional in certain tissues of the whole plant:

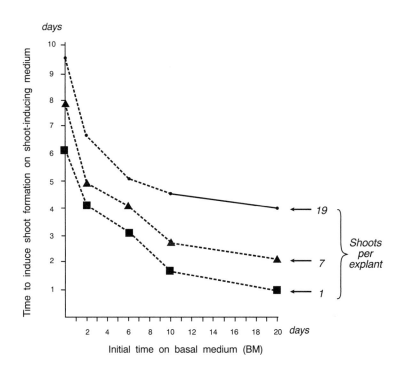

Fig. 87. The effect of the period of exposure of *Nicotiana tabacum* leaf segments to SIM on the number of shoots produced [after Attfield and Evans, 1991b]. The longer the shoot segments were retained on BM, the shorter was the subsequent exposure to SIM necessary to induce any given degree of shoot formation.

ments of *Torenia fournieri* were cultured by Chlyah (1974), the sub- epidermal paren- chyma showed no organogenetic capacity; root initials arose from cells surrounding the vascular bundles. However, if cultured alone in an appropriate medium, the sub- epidermal layers were able to initiate roots, and if they were cultured when only in con- tact with the stem epidermis (the other tis- sues having been removed), they formed shoot primordia.

Determination

Morphological determination is found not to be an 'all or nothing' event: the longer tobacco explants of Attfield and Evans (see above) were kept on SIM (up to 12 days) before transfer to BM, the more shoots they produced. Either more cells became deter- mined as the treatment was continued or determined cells were more able to prolifer- ate (Fig. 87). Shoot formation in *Pinus strobus* cotyledons was also increased the longer they were exposed to BAP (5–50 μM) (up to 21 days), but with these explants a marked reduction in shoot formation oc- curred when they were pre- cultured for even 3 days on a basal medium and after 14 days of pre- culture they had lost their com- petence to produce shoots (Biondi and Thorpe, 1982a; Flinn *et al.*, 1988). In this case the cells of the explant were already competent when transferred to the medium. The commitment of the *Nico- tiana* explants of Attfield and Evans (1991b) to produce roots was also reduced the longer they were cultured on basal medium before being transferred to a root-inducing medium (RIM). A progressively smaller number of roots was initiated, presumably because a smaller number of sites was influenced. Thus although determination took place on RIM after 10 days pre-culture in basal medium, only *ca.* 4 roots were produced per explant, compared with 35–40 roots when the explants were placed into RIM immediately they were excised.

The control of development

The methods whereby epigenetic messages are unfolded are not fully understood. R.Holliday (1989) has sug- gested three possible routes:

- A complex of DNA and bound proteins deter- mines which genes are expressed at any one time. The complexes remain tightly bound during DNA replication.

2. is controlled by specific gene sequences which have a common effect in all tissues, but

a). which happened to be expressed in certain tissues at the time of excision;

b). which were capable of being expressed in certain tissues because of the developmental state of the cells (*i.e* the epigenotype of the tissue).

Several callus strains differing both morphologically and with regard to morphogenetic capacity may sometimes arise from one explanted piece of tissue (Fig. 23, Chapter 2). Street (1979) suggested that this might happen either because cell layers or tissues varied in their morphoge- netic competence as they occurred on the plant, or be- cause competence was induced during callus formation in only certain cells. In these circumstances, callus cul- tures may consist of morphogenetically competent and non-competent cells or zones. Failure to isolate a compe- tent cell line may result in its disappearance by the overgrowth of non-competent tissues.

It has also been shown that adjacent tissue layers can have correlative effects on each other. When intact stem seg-

- Genetic sequences are themselves altered in specific ways to determine a particular developmental outcome. These alterations maintain their fideliity during chromosome replication.

- The expression of genes is regulated according to whether cytosine groups have methyl groups attached to them. Only non-methylated genes are transcribed and translated (page 73).

The last is the most favoured hypothesis. It is proposed that diffusible protein molecules move between cells and engender changes in the methylation patterns of nuclear DNA within a cell when they become bound to receptors on the cell membrane. DNA is restored to a non-methylated state during the process of meiotic cell division.

Growth regulants may bring about the suppression or activation of appropriate parts of the genome by directly altering the rate of transcription of certain genes (Rogler and Dahmus, 1974; Domoney and Timmins, 1980; Davies and Hartmann, 1988), this being induced by the methylation or demethylation of DNA (Swartz, 1991). Presumably, in mutants which have a permanent juvenile phenotype, genes regulating the adult phase are either incapable of being expressed, or those responsible for juvenility cannot be suppressed.

MOTHER PLANT TREATMENT

Plants used as a source of primary explants for tissue cultures are usually termed *mother plants* or *stock plants*. Results obtained *in vitro* can be influenced by the way that mother plants are treated and by the environment in which they have been grown. It is generally recognised that the best explant material is derived from healthy and vigorous plants which have been maintained in active growth without stress. Those growing in the field are subject to high rates of contamination and a variable environment. The reduction in contamination which can occur from using plants reared in a greenhouse or other enclosed environment has been discussed in Chapter 4. For obtaining uniform explant material there are often clear advantages in rearing mother plants in growth rooms under controlled conditions. If this is not possible, then a greenhouse is usually a satisfactory alternative. Herbaceous species are readily treated in this way, but difficulties may be experienced with many woody species. Wherever possible cuttings should be rooted and grown in pots. In some cases heavy contamination of one kind of explant can justify the search for another technique of micropropagation, using another type of explant which is less contaminated, or more easily sterilised (*e.g.* the use of dormant flower buds for the propagation of *Rhododendron* instead of shoot tips — Dai *et al.*, 1987).

As a minimum precaution against the contamination of cultures and the propagation of systemic diseases, mother plants having any history of disease or showing any disease symptoms should be rejected unless there is absolutely no alternative source of material. Where there is a possiblility that plants may harbour hidden pathogens, it may be necessary to utilise the methods of pathogen indexing and elimination, which have been discussed in Chapter 5.

Nutrition

Explants which are most suitable for *in vitro* culture, are generally obtained from stock plants which have received adequate mineral nutrition. Barker *et al.* (1977) could culture adult nodes of *Eucalyptus* most successfully if they were excised from healthy well-watered and well-fertilised trees. Lateral buds of asparagus were readily grown into intact plants when they were derived from strong mother plant shoots (Yang and Clore, 1973, 1974a), and explants of papaya were more responsive to *in vitro* culture if the mother plant had been given fertilizer and water consistently in the field (Litz and Conover, 1977).

For critical work, or to 'fine tune' a particular micropropagation protocol so that the maximum rate of multiplication is achieved, it may be necessary to feed stock plants with a specially adjusted mixture of inorganic salts. The growth of mother plants by hydroponic techniques is then necessary (Garton *et al.*, 1983). Hansen and Eriksen (1974) emphasized that the nutritional status of stock plants may influence the growth and morphogenesis of explants and since then the effect of mineral nutrition has been investigated in a number of species. Read *et al.* (1983) concluded that it had little effect on *in vitro* culture of tomato, but found that a high level of nutrients (probably due to excessive nitrogen) inhibited the direct rooting of cuttings *in vivo*. Later work (Read and Economou, 1987) showed that supplying tomato stock plants with either very low or very high rates of inorganic nitrogen, reduced the number of shoots which could be regenerated from cultured leaf segments. Nitrogen and potassium nutrition were also found to affect the results obtained from tissue culturing several *Salix* clones. The number of plantlets that could be regenerated from explanted tomato tissue was increased if stock plants were pre-treated with NH_4NO_3 or $NaH_2PO_4.H_2O$ for a short period. Prolonged treatment caused impaired *in vitro* shoot regeneration (Reynolds, J.F. *et al.*, 1982).

Disease status

Usually the presence of any kind of plant disease is a reason for rejecting mother plants, because infectious organisms are liable to cause the death of cultures, to have a debilitating and negative effect on them, or to be transmitted to propagated plants (Chapter 5). Greño *et al.* (1988) found that shoot cultures of several *Citrus* species were affected by the presence of the virus and virus-like agents:

> *Citrus* tristeza virus (CTV)
> *Citrus* infectious variegation virus (CIVV)
> Psorosis
> Vein enation
> *Citrus* cachexia viroid (CCaV)
> *Citrus* exocortis viroid complex

In general, infection of the mother plant reduced the number and size of shoots which developed. Similarly, the production of axillary shoots, and the number of plants finally established, tended to be lower in infected cultures than in healthy ones. The actual responses obtained varied both according to the host plant and the pathogen. In some hosts a pathogen might have no effect. As some host-pathogen combinations do not present symptoms on plants in either the greenhouse or the field, but can result in poor *in vitro* growth, Greño *et al.* have suggested that the presence of latent virus infections could be a cause of the difficulties, sometimes experienced, in defining standard micropropagation protocols for perennial plants; and of variation between the plants finally obtained.

Time of sampling

Changes in temperature, daylength, light quality and water stress throughout the year will result in mother plants having altered levels of stored carbohydrates, proteins and growth substances within their tissues. The relative age of tissues and organs changes as a growing season progresses (see below) and the level of contamination found on explants, especially those taken from field-grown plants, will also vary at different seasons (Chapter 3). It is, therefore, to be expected that results from tissue cultures will vary according to the time of year at which explants are excised, or according to the artificial conditions under which mother plants were grown.

A greater amount of callus was produced from unfertilised ovules of glasshouse-grown plants of *Gerbera jamesonii* in experiments started in the autumn, but callus obtained in the spring had a higher morphogenic capacity (Cappadocia *et al.*, 1988). It was possible to obtain callus from shoot apices and sub-apical tissue of *Pinus sylvestris* all through the year, but calli frequently died after 3–5 months in culture. The highest percentages of surviving and growing calli was obtained from explants collected in December to January and April, May and June (Hohtola, 1988). The best callus proliferation from *Pinus strobus* shoot segments, however, occurred in early spring (Kaul, 1985).

Shoot regeneration from greenhouse-grown *Peperomia* leaf segments was greatest when leaves were taken in summer, somewhat less in spring, and poor in winter (Kukulczanka *et al.*, 1977). Shoot cultures of *Spiraea × bumalda* produced the largest number of shoots from explants introduced to culture during May and June. There was another smaller peak in proliferation rate in September, but explants taken in April, late July or October, produced very few shoots (Norton and Norton, 1988d). Bud explants of mature trees of *Larix occidentalis* gathered in June produced multiple axillary buds more rapidly than those taken at other times of the year (in 3–6 weeks compared to 3–4 months at other times) and moreover a higher proportion of the explants responded to *in vitro* culture (Chesick *et al.*, 1990).

Results from *in vitro* culture show that the external environment provided during any one year, affects even closely related species of stock plants in different ways. Moreover, as conditions are not the same from one year to the next, explants taken from field-grown plants of any one genotype, may have to be treated in different ways in each successive year to obtain the same result (Bennici *et al.*, 1988). *Prunus mariana* shoot tips taken from field grown material during 1969 developed into plants most readily if the explants had been taken during active tree growth during June to August. In 1970 the optimum time was advanced by one month (Monsion and Dunez, 1971).

Changes in natural growth substances. Where mother plants are not kept in growth rooms under constant conditions, their tissues are likely to experience seasonally-induced changes in natural growth substance levels, and/or the systems which control them. This can mean that the concentrations of exogenous growth regulators necessary to induce growth or morphogenesis *in vitro* may need to be adjusted periodically.

Most workers have concluded that variations in growth substance levels have been responsible for seasonal effects, and convincing correlations have been made with natural auxin and inhibitor levels within explanted tissues

(Quoirin *et al.* 1975). Shoot formation on *Nicotiana glauca* internode fragments was promoted by the addition of only a cytokinin (2-iP) to the medium, when explants were taken in the spring (a period when endogenous auxin levels were high); both 2-iP and an auxin (IAA) were required to achieve the same results in summer and autumn (Paulet and Ketata, 1969). In tomato, TIBA was found to have different effects on shoot regeneration from stem explants depending on whether explants were taken in December/January or June/July (Cassells, 1979).

The level of irradiance during culture had the greatest effect on the weight of callus produced from *Pelargonium* stem explants when they were excised from plants in winter rather than summer. Hammerschlag (1978) suggested that this might reflect seasonal variations in growth substances such as IAA and ABA.

Sampling during active growth

Generally, cultures are established most readily from explants gathered at the start of, or during, active growth of the mother plant, but the best time of year for sampling may depend on the kind of culture to be grown, on the particular genotype to be used, and on the relative amounts of contamination (Chapter 4) and browning of the explant (Chapter 13) occurring at each season. The best time for sampling is usually when stock plants are producing new vigorous shoots (*i.e.* in temperate regions, in spring in early summer), but many exceptions have been observed.

The proportion of *Prunus* 'Accolade' meristems which gave rise to established shoots with a rosette of leaves, increased in batches excised from field-grown trees as sampling progressed from early December (winter) to May; the time taken in culture for explants to grow into shoots at the rosette stage also declined over the same period (Quoirin *et al.* 1974). Potato buds excised in spring or early summer rooted better than those taken later in the year (Mellor and Stace-Smith, 1969), and a greater proportion of *Castanea sativa* cuttings produced callus *in vitro* if excised and cultured in March (spring) rather than in December (Borrod, 1971). However, in a *Castanea* hybrid, the proportion of December-gathered cuttings forming callus was high, and the poorest rate of culture establishment occurred with explants taken in July.

Exceptions to the general rule. Although the best time for sampling usually coincides with the period when stock plants are in active growth, this is not always the case. Bulblet initiation *in vitro* from bulbs of *Tulipa* 'Hageri' was best in May, when the mother bulbs were growing vigorously, but in 'Apeldoorn' it was best in

August, at harvest time (Nishiuchi, 1979). Similarly sections of the immature floral stems of *Tulipa* 'Merry Widow' bulbs only gave rise to direct adventitious buds when explants were taken from dormant bulbs. Once the bulbs had entered a stage of active growth, the capacity to produce shoots practically disappeared. Callus continued to be formed, but it too was not produced once the floral stem had begun active extension growth (Wright and Alderson, 1980). The formation of adventitious buds from cylinders cut from the base of scale leaves of *Lilium speciosum* was high when explants were taken during spring and autumn, but practically nil in summer and winter (Robb, 1957).

Sexually mature plants of the small ornamental tree *Halesia carolina*, produced the most rapid rate of shoot growth in the greenhouse 4–6 weeks after bud break. Shoot tips excised at this time formed proliferating shoot cultures more slowly than similar explants excised either *before* (0–2 weeks from bud break) or *after* the phase of rapid elongation (8–12 weeks from bud break) (Brand and Lineberger, 1986).

Plants in greenhouses and growth rooms. Some of the effects of the changing environment out of doors which may influence the viability and regenerative capacity of explants, can be eliminated or reduced by growing mother plants in a glasshouse or growth room. *Eucalyptus grandis* nodes rooted most easily when they were taken in April (spring) from plants grown out of doors, but when stock plants were kept in growth rooms, no combination of daylength and temperature could be clearly defined as optimal, and it seemed that the rooting potential of adult plant nodes was best stimulated by a change in the environment of the parent plant (Durand-Cresswell and Nitsch, 1977).

Even in growth rooms, the variability of explants may not be entirely eliminated. The buds on single node explants of *Prosopis juliflora,* taken from the same mother plants grown in a heated glasshouse under supplementary lighting, declined in their capacity to produce shoots with progressive samplings between November (early winter) and March. The cause was unclear. It might have been due to the nutrition or increasing age of the mother plants, or changes in the temperature or total irradiance to which they were exposed (Wainwright and England, 1987).

Persistence of the sampling time effect. Sometimes the effect of the time of year at which explants were taken can persist for some while in cultures. For example, the rooting of shoots obtained from the shoot culture of *Prunus* species and hybrids, was better where the original explants had been collected in mid-June rather than in mid-July (Ranjit *et al.*, 1988a).

Pruning

Cutting back stock plants to induce the growth of juvenile shoots has been descibed earlier in this chapter. When initiating shoot cultures, it can also be advantageous to prune old herbaceous or woody plants to obtain a flush of new shoots bearing young, smaller and less contaminated buds (Read, 1988).

Sampling from dormant material

Although cultures are often best established from plant material that is in active growth, it is sometimes possible to induce growth or morphogenesis upon explants removed from plants in a naturally dormant state. In some cases dormancy is broken by excising a meristem from a dormant bud. Ochatt and Caso (1982) for instance, found it possible to establish shoot cultures of 'Red-leaf' peach from explants excised from dormant winter buds. Lateral buds of apple show varying degrees of dormancy *in vitro* depending on the physiological state of the shoot from which they are taken; they can be capable of growth even when taken from shoots which have formed a resting terminal bud (Powell *et al.* 1980). Lane (1978) suggested growth of lateral buds was possible because bud scales are removed during dissection. These contain growth inhibitors, and naturally restrict the movement of oxygen and other gases to the meristem.

In some species it may be obligatory to utilise dormant material for explants. Shoot initials were formed on needles of *Picea* buds gathered in the Northern hemisphere from September to April, but not from April onwards (Misson *et al.* 1982). Similarly, adventitious bud formation on root cuttings of many plants (especially woody species) only occurs if material is taken from stock plants during a dormant period, usually in winter and early spring (Browse, 1980). On other occasions, actively growing shoots, suitable as meristem or shoot tip explants, have been obtained from dormant buds of woody temperate species, by grafting them onto seedling rootstocks that are grown under controlled conditions.

Chilling. Frequently growth may be induced by chilling small trees, grafted seedlings, or cut shoots, for several weeks before buds are excised; but this treatment is not always entirely effective (Borkowska and Powell, 1979). A proportion of buds may still fail to grow, or shoot elongation may not occur, resulting in the formation of rosetted plants. Powell *et al.* (1980) found that chilling intact shoots of apple before bud excision, could promote greater elongation of bursting buds, but did not necessar-

ily induce a greater number of bud explants to assume active growth.

With *Prunus* 'Accolade', the percentage of buds growing in culture was proportional to the duration of storage at 4°C (Quoirin *et al.* 1975); a short cold treatment (10°C for 12 h) stimulated growth of dormant lateral buds of *Passiflora* (Muralidhar and Mehta, 1982). Immature bulbils of *Laportea* were capable of *in vitro* growth in the light, whereas mature bulbils failed to sprout unless they had been previously chilled, when they would grow in the light or darkness. Mature bulbil dormancy could also be overcome by GA_3 and BAP (Tanno, 1977). Potato tubers which had been stored for under 6 months at 4–6°C were found to provide disc explants which most consistently formed multiple adventitious shoots after transformation with *Agrobacterium* (Sheerman and Bevan, 1988).

Forcing shoots of temperate woody perennials. The technique of forcing buds on severed defoliated shoots, mentioned in Chapter 4 and on page 257, is very useful for obtaining out of season explants from dormant material. Not only are explants relatively contaminant-free, but they may also be more readily established in culture than explants taken during spring and summer, and less prone to produce polyphenol exudates (Chapter 13). Marks *et al.* (1987) found that varieties of plants responded to treatment in different ways, but used the method successfully for *Quercus robur* 'Fastigiata', various *Acer* species and clones, and for clones of *Crataegus*.

Tropical plants. Whereas plants native to temperate climates show just one cycle of growth and dormancy per year, many tropical plants go through several cycles. *Citrus* for instance, normally has 3–4 flushes of shoot growth during the year, and this can affect the behaviour of explanted material. The time taken for buds of *C. sinensis* to sprout in culture was shown by Altman and Goren (1974) to follow a cyclical pattern. Buds which were all initiated on the tree during the spring flush, took 20–25 days to commence growth if excised during April (late spring) or during the following January (winter, when the buds were 10 months old). By contrast, buds commenced growth in 2–4 days if excised and cultured during June–July (when 4 months old) or during the following February–March (11–12 months old). The shortest cultural periods roughly coincided with the natural summer and spring flushes.

Shoot tips of cocoa were found by Orchard *et al.* (1979) only to be capable of continued growth *in vitro* if the buds, from which they were excised, had reached a late stage of bursting, in which bud leaves were fully green. It was thought that at this stage the shoot apex was more readily released from dormancy by growth regulators in the medium (kinetin, or kinetin plus GA_3).

The environment in which mother plants are grown

The environment in which stock plants are grown, including treatments such as fertilizer applications, chemical sprays and watering routines, is very likely to modify the results obtained *in vitro* from explanted tissues or organs: the subject was reviewed by Read and Economou (1987). To standardise the results, it is necessary to grow stock plants under conditions which are as similar as possible from one occasion to another. This will usually mean that the plants have to be kept in growth rooms.

Lighting

The direct effects of light on explanted tissues have been described in the previous chapter. Changes brought about in an intact plant by the wavelength, photon fluence, or daylength of light, are also very likely to affect the growth or morphogenesis of cultured explants.

Flux density. Growth in 22°C and 12 h of high irradiance was found to be the most effective mother plant treatment for obtaining growth and shoot formation of single node explants of *Eucalyptus* (Cresswell and Nitsch, 1975). Stock plants of tomato grown under a reduced light 'intensity' gave the highest yield of tomato protoplasts (Cassells and Barlass, 1978).

Pelargonium petioles formed the highest numbers of roots in response to nitrogen and sucrose in an *in vitro* medium, when they were derived from stock plants that had been maintained under an irradiance of 2.5 rather than 11.6 or 23.0 W m^{-2} (Welander, 1978b). The etiolation of mother plants to enhance subsequent rooting is discussed in Chapter 14.

Wavelength. The branching of intact *Petunia hybrida* plants can be modified through the phytochrome system. Plants grown in 10 h white light, terminated by 30 minutes red light (RP —red light plants), become short and branched, but when the light period is terminated by 30 minutes far-red light (FRP — far red light plants), tall single-stemmed plants are obtained. Leaf discs cut from RP stock plants tend to produce a greater fresh- and dry-weight of callus and a larger number of adventitious shoots than those removed from FRP stocks. The differences in growth and differentiation *in vitro* were probably due to altered natural growth substance levels in the two groups of plants. Extractable free IAA auxin was higher in FRP than in RP (Read *et al.*, 1978a; Suriyajantratong, 1979).

Daylength. The inductive effects of daylength can be carried over from the mother plant into culture, but usually the direct action of daylength on the culture is more important. For example, the flowering of *Glycine max* is induced by short days; nodes cut from aseptic seedlings grown in long days produced shoots which did not flower under long days *in vitro*. Some nodes cut from seedlings kept in short days did produce flowering shoots in short days, but in the reverse situation (seedling in L.D., explant in S.D.), some shoots produced both flowers and fruits. The best flowering and fruiting occurred where both seedlings and explants were maintained in short days, particularly if the seedlings had been grown on **MS** salts (Dickens and Van Staden, 1985).

Hilding and Welander (1976) found that the most effective combination of auxin and cytokinin to induce morphogenesis in petiole explants of *Begonia × hiemalis* varied according to whether stock plants had been grown under long or short days. Leaf petioles of this plant only produced adventitious shoots and roots if they were taken from plants kept in 15–16 h days at 18°–20°C. There was no organogenesis on those taken from plants grown in short days (7–8 h at 15°C) (Welander, 1977). Similar results were obtained by Simmonds and Nelson (1989). By contrast Dunwell and Perry (1973) found that anthers taken from *Nicotiana tabacum* stock plants kept in an 8 h high irradiance photoperiod, produced the greatest numbers of haploid plants from cultured anthers.

In some genera, rooting occurs most readily on shoots harvested from plants kept in long days or, like those of *Acer rubrum*, when the stock plants have been given supplementary illumination (Lane and Still, 1981): cuttings of other genera root most readily when the stock plants from which they were taken have been kept in short days (Nanda *et al.*, 1967). Sometimes the optimum daylength has been found to vary between species within a genus (Hansen, 1987).

Temperature

The temperature at which stock plants have been grown would be expected to influence the results of *in vitro* experiments, but has not been extensively investigated. That it can be important is shown by results of Appelgren and Heide:

> Leaf discs of *Streptocarpus* produced more shoots and roots per disc when mother plants were grown at 12°C rather than 18°C or 24°C (Appelgren and Heide, 1972), and explants from *Begonia × hiemalis* stock plants maintained in growth rooms, formed shoots and roots most freely when the growth room temperature was 15°C rather than 18°C or 21°C (Appelgren, 1976). When greenhouse-grown plants were used as a source, the optimum cultural temperature for morphogenesis varied according to the time of year at which explants were removed. For those taken in October, 18°C was optimal; for those in December, 15°C; and in February, 21°C.

The temperature and length of time at which bulbs have been stored can affect the subsequent production of adventitious bulblets *in vitro*. Scale explants from *Lilium longiflorum* bulbs, produced a smaller number of larger bulblets, if they had been taken from bulbs stored for less than 110 days, than those taken from bulbs stored for a longer period (Stimart and Ascher, 1981b). An effect of storage temperature on subsequent bulblet size has also been demonstrated in *Hyacinthus*. In addition, explants from bulbs kept at 5°C for 35 days, produced a larger number of bulblets than those taken from bulbs stored for a longer period at this temperature (Ko, 1986: reported in Read, 1988).

Growth regulator pre-treatments

Some research workers have applied growth regulators to intact mother plants *before* explants have been taken. As explained above, sprays of gibberellin and/or cytokinin are often effective in introducing some degree of re-juvenation (or re-invigoration) of woody plants, enabling explants to be cultured where previously it was impossible, and frequently inducing axillary bud break and increasing the number of shoots from which explants can be taken.

Instead of treating mother plants with growth regulants, several workers have used such compounds to pretreat explants, or a detached part of a plant from which explants will eventually be excised. The method of germinating seeds on a medium containing a high cytokinin level to obtain multiple shoot formation, has been mentioned in Chapter 2.

Altering the growth of mother plants. Treating mother plants with cytokinins can increase the number of axillary shoots they produce, thus providing more shoots from which explants can be obtained. A mixture of BAP and GA$_3$ in lanolin paste smeared onto buds, or spraying stems 3 times with a solution of 500mg/l BAP plus 100 mg/l GA$_3$, caused dormant axillary buds on the stems of papaya plants to sprout, thereby providing material for cuttings, or as explants for micropropagation (Reuveni and Schlesinger, 1990).

Cordyline terminalis stock plants given foliar sprays of 0.5–1.0 mg/l BAP, could be induced to produce many more axillary shoots if they were sprayed with the cytokinin BAP (dissolved in 1% dimethylsulphoxide) several times, at weekly intervals (Maene and Debergh, 1982). McGranahan *et al.* (1988) applied weekly sprays of 100 mg/l BAP plus 50 mg/l gibberellic acid to *Juglans regia*, and Norton and Norton (1988d) found that the most effective treatments to increase the number of shoots produced by *Spiraea × bumalda* mother plants, was to spray them to run off with 500 mg/l BAP or 1500 mg/l

2-iP (dissolved in DMSO). Injecting the stems of *Hamamelis* and *Magnolia* with a 0.5 mg/l BAP solution, induced the formation of basal buds (Debergh and Maene, 1985) and the production of cuttings from *Gerbera jamesonii* plants was increased by removing all the leaves, washing off the soil from the crowns, and spraying them twice with cytokinin at 1–3 week intervals (Zieslin *et al.*, 1988).

Effects on *in vitro* results. In some cases, treating mother plants, or excised plant material, with cytokinins can also increase the rate of proliferation in shoot cultures originated from excised buds. Read and Yang (1987) report that shoot proliferation from shoot tips of *Philadelphus* and *Dirca* was increased by introducing BAP into the solution into which twigs were placed for forcing in early spring (Chapter 4 and above), and Donkers and Evers (1987) obtained a significant increase in the multiplication rate from certain buds, if flushed shoots of *Platanus × acerifolia* had been sprayed with 45 mg/l BAP in 50% ethanol.

Adventitious shoot formation can laso be influenced by cytokinin pre-treatments. Economou and Read (1980) discovered that if leaves of *Petunia* were dipped into solutions of BAP (*e.g.* 30 s in 400 mg/l), adventitious shoots developed freely when segments of the leaves were later cultured on a cytokinin-free medium. Results were similar to those obtained when a cytokinin was incorporated into the medium. A similar effect can be obtained by treating *Petunia* plants with red light (page 256).

Oka and Ohyama (1981) obtained adventitious bud formation from mulberry leaf explants when seedling mother plants or *in vitro* shoots were pre-treated with BAP. It was subsequently found that if mulberry seedlings were germinated on **MS** medium containing high cytokinin levels (particularly of 2Cl–4PU), shoot formation was strongly stimulated on various seedling explants when they were subsequently cultured (Ohyama and Oka, 1982).

Growth retardants. De Langhe and de Bruijne (1976) found that the shoot forming ability of cultured shoot explants of tomato was stimulated when the parental plants had been previously pre-treated with chlormequat, but that if this compound was added instead to the culture medium, it was ineffective. This observation was confirmed by Read *et al.* (1978a,b). A 400 mg/l foliar spray of chlormequat on tomato stock plants enhanced the number of shoots obtained from leaf explants. It was also observed that shoots excised from *Dahlia* leaves gave rise to increased amounts of callus if the mother plants had been grown in short days or had been sprayed with a 2500 mg/l daminozide solution (Gavinlertvatana *et al.*, 1979).

Frett and Smagula (1981a) and Scorza *et al.* (1982) have reported beneficial effects from pretreating lowbush blueberry and cranberry plants with the herbicide, glyphosate. In the latter case, dipping attached stems into a glyphosate solution for 30 seconds increased the production of axillary and adventitious shoots from excised stem segments.

Treatment with auxins or gibberellic acid. Pre-treating wheat plants with sprays of 2,4-D and several other herbicides during the first week of embryo development caused multiple shoot formation from the embryos at a later stage (Ferguson and McEwan, 1970). This appears to occur through the *in vivo* formation of adventitious embryos (Ferguson *et al.* 1979). Preece (1987) reported that pretreating stock plants with gibberellic acid can inhibit adventitious shoot formation and rooting when explants are subsequently cultured with BAP.

THE EXPLANT

The kind of explant chosen, its size, age, and the manner in which it is cultured, can all affect whether tissue cultures can be successfully initiated, and whether morphogenesis can be induced.

THE AGE OF EXPLANTED TISSUES

The successful culture of plant material *in vitro* is greatly influenced by the age of the tissue or organ which is used as the initial explant. The age of any piece of tissue can be measured in three ways, *i.e.* by:

— **The age of the organ or whole plant from which it is derived.** This is the period of time which has elapsed from the growth of a plant from a bud or embryo, or from the initiation of a particular organ or tissue.

— **Physiological or Ontogenetic age** or phase of growth. In this sense a piece of tissue can be categorised as being 'young' or 'old', according to whether it is derived from a part of a plant in a juvenile or adult phase of growth. The marked effects of 'maturation state' on plant tissue cultures have been discussed in the section on phases of growth at the beginning of this chapter.

— **The degree of differentiation.** In this concept, the youngest parts of a plant are undifferentiated meristematic cells, while differentiated cells of organs, sequentially derived from the meristems, are older. Developmentally, the cells of the apical meristems of most plants have a theoretical capacity to enjoy 'perpetual youth' and to live for ever if the apex of the plant is continually re-rooted *in vivo* or subcultured *in vitro*.

Once a culture has been initiated from explanted material, a fourth age factor becomes operational, namely the:

— **Period of culture**, the time span from when the culture or the passage was first commenced.

Each of these components of tissue age may influence whether an explant from a stock plant or from a previous *in vitro* culture, can be used to initiate a culture, and may modify the direct or indirect morphogenetic potential of the tissue. Ontogenetic age, and the age of the organ, appear to be the most important factors, although in practice it is sometimes impossible to decide which of the first three age factors above is decisive. The shoot apex of a seedling is young in all senses, but although the stem apex from a 50 year-old tree is old in the material sense, it is youthful in that it is undifferentiated.

Ontogenetic age

Explants taken from juvenile plant tissue, particularly that of seedlings, are usually highly responsive. This can be a genuine effect of material age, but usually reflects the juvenile state of seedling tissues. The difficulty which is often experienced in growing and manipulating older tissues can be frustrating, because it is usually desirable to propagate mature plants of proven worth.

Age of the organ or plant

In general, explants taken from newly originated organs are most likely to be capable of growth and organogenesis *in vitro*.

Callus initiation

Growth regulator requirements for callus initiation frequently differ according to the age of the explanted tissue. On a modified **Linsmaier and Skoog (1965)** medium, maximum growth of callus from stem explants taken from 2 week-old *Pelargonium* plants, occurred in the

Table 20. The optimum time for taking explants from *Pyrus serotina* fruits for callus formation and indirect shoot regeneration [from Hiratsuka and Katagiri, 1988].

Explant	Optimum age for sampling (weeks after pollination)	
	For callus formation	For adventitious shoots
Immature seed	7–10	Multiple shoots during 8–10
Endosperm	2–4 only	None
Zygotic embryos	2–3 good 4–7 less good 9–10 good	9–10 (later embryos dormant)

presence of 5 mg/l NAA + 5 mg/l kinetin; but these concentrations inhibited callus formation from similar explants taken from 2 year-old plants. Optimum callus proliferation from the latter occurred with 0.2 mg/l of both regulants (Hammerschlag and Bottino, 1981). The formation of meristemoids, and eventually shoots and roots, occurred only on the young explants cultured on 0.2 mg/l NAA and 0.2 mg/l kinetin.

Indirect morphogenesis

In experiments of Takayama and Misawa (1982b), most segments derived from young leaves of *Begonia* produced buds and roots, whereas those derived from mature leaves usually died. An effect of age was even detected amongst the leaves taken from micropropagated shoots of *Malus × domestica*. With an appropriate combination of growth regulants, adventitious shoots formed on the leaves, but the proportion of explants on which morphogenesis was observed, and the number of new shoots per explant, was greatest in the 3 or 4 leaves nearest the tip of each shoot (Fasolo *et al.*, 1988a). Pierik (1969) and Pierik and Steegmans (1975c) found that the rhizogenic potential of *Rhododendron* stem segments decreased with the age of the shoot from which they were obtained, and in the cultivar which rooted least readily, rooting occurred only on segments of soft young stems.

Young tissues do not invariably provide the most highly morphogenetic explants. Callus formed more readily on various explants from fully-grown plants of *Parthenium hysterophorus* than on young seedlings or cotyledons (Wickham *et al.* 1980). Similarly, callus growth and shoot development was more rapid on *Solanum laciniatum* cut from mature leaves which had just completed

full expansion. By contrast, young unexpanded leaves yielded explants which soon expanded and callused but produced shoots slowly, and really old leaves gave rise to callus and shoots after an even greater time interval. The number of shoots regenerated from the three types of tissue was eventually very similar (Davies and Dale, 1979).

Frequently the pattern of regeneration changes as a tissue ages and then the effect of polarity (see later) on growth and morphogenesis may become more pronounced. Tanimoto and Harada (1980) took leaf discs from the second pair of unfolded leaves of 9, 14, 18 and 24 week-old plants of *Perilla frutescens*. Explants from the younger plants formed most buds from primary callus. No shoot initiation occurred in callus derived from 24 week-old plants. Young leaves of *Heloniopsis* showed none of the polarity in bud formation present in older leaves (Kato, 1974), and in *Chamaenerion angustifolium* and *Armoracia rusticana*, organs developed along the undamaged margins of young root segments without callusing of the cut ends (Emery, 1955; Doré, 1955), but callusing of the cut ends leading to organogenesis can occur in old roots (Emery, 1955; Bowes, 1976b). Young leaves of *Echeveria elegans* tended to produce roots sooner than they produced shoots, while in older leaves the reverse occurred (Raju and Mann, 1970).

For some types of cultures it may be necessary to excise explants at a fairly precise age. For example, to obtain embryo growth and germination from ovaries of *Brassica juncea*, it was necessary to culture 5–7 day-old ovaries. Those which were 4 or 9 days old were unsatisfactory (Mohapatra and Bajaj, 1988). Immature embryos (without testa and endosperm) of *Malus × domestica* which were 0–4 weeks old produced only callus when cultured, those which were 6.5 to *ca.* 14 weeks produced multiple shoots, whereas mature embryos (14 weeks) grew normally with a shoot and a root pole (Kouider *et al.*, 1985). Depending on whether callus or shoot regeneration was required, seed-derived tissues of *Pyrus serotina* were best excised at the times shown in Table 20.

Explants for shoot cultures. In temperate plants where shoots are newly initiated each year from resting buds, shoots can be said to become progressively older as the season advances. Explants for shoot tip or meristem explants are usually best dissected from young shoots (Kaul, 1985, 1986), or from buds just before the spring flush (Kurz, 1986). On the other hand, lateral buds most capable of growth or shoot proliferation may not necessarily be those nearest the apex of a shoot. Single node explants of *Vitis rotundifolia* taken from the basal 10 nodes of non-lignified shoots bearing at least 25 nodes, were better than those from the 10 distal nodes (Sudarsono and Goldy, 1991).

Length of shoots

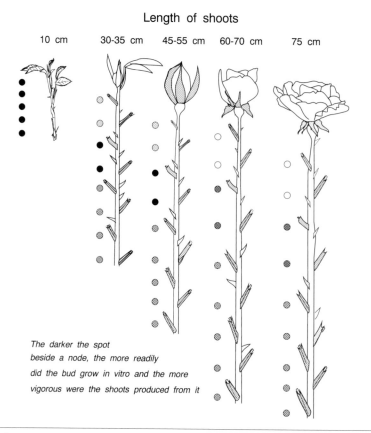

Fig. 88. Selection of single node explants of *Rosa*   [after Mederos and Rodríguez Enríquez, 1988].

Selection of an explant of the optimum 'age' for micropropagation can sometimes be complex. In *Rosa hybrida*, single node explants (1 cm of stem plus a bud) were best taken from the new shoots which grew after bushes were pruned when the shoots were *ca*. 10 cm and had 6 axillary buds. All the lateral buds were then capable of growing *in vitro*. Much less reliable explants were obtained from shoots which had extended until they bore terminal flower buds. Explants which grew well and produced vigorous shoots could then only be obtained from middle order buds, but by the time the shoots were over 60 cm in length, growth of cultured buds was erratic (Fig. 88) (Mederos and Rodríguez Enríquez, 1987). A similar observation was made by Kouadio and Phan (1987) with single node explants from tomato plants at the seventh leaf stage. Buds from nodes 1–3 grew slowly in culture, those from nodes 4 and 5 grew most rapidly, while those from node 6 grew slightly less quickly.

The capacity of meristems in onion flower heads to give rise to shoots, was highest when they were at a primordial stage. Some shoots were produced while pollen meiosis was taking place, but after this the ability of the flower heads to form shoots fell to zero (Dunstan and Short, 1979a).

Degree of differentiation

Explants of young tissues still undergoing cell division generally form callus more readily than those from older parts of a plant, and there is a much greater chance that the callus will be capable of organogenesis. This is particularly the case in the Gramineae, where callus cultures have not been initiated from mature leaves or stems, but only from young leaves or inflorescences, seed embryos or nodes. Callus derived from cotyledons excised from 2–4 week-old seedlings of *Pseudotsuga menziesii* had a greater capacity for caulogenesis than that which originated from older seedlings (Abo El-Nil and Wochok, 1977).

Zygotic embryos as explants.

In a great many species, embryogenic callus can be very reliably obtained from immature zygotic embryos. To improve the yield of embryogenic callus, zygotic embryos of wheat have been classified into the five developmental stages shown in Table 21. The highest yields of callus have been found to be produced using embryos at stages II and III (He *et al.*, 1986). Competence of zygotic embryos of *Picea* for somatic embryogenesis has been shown to be limited to a specific stage of development prior to the accumulation of storage proteins (Roberts *et al.*, 1989b).

In dicotyledons also, embryogenic callus may only be obtained from zygotic embryos once they have reached a critical size. To obtain embryogenic callus from zygotic embryos of *Castanea sativa* in Spain, it was necessary not to excise the embryos from fruits until the end of August. Those explanted before this time only produced a small callus, or no callus at all (Vieitez *et al.*, 1990). Guerra and Handro (1988) postulated that the induction of direct somatic embryogenesis on *Euterpe edulis* zygotic embryos depended on a subtle interaction between the developmental stage of the explants and the auxin 2,4-D in the medium. Mature embryos of *Iris pumila* gave rise to embryogenic callus once they had been germinated *in vitro*, but immature embryos only produced non-embryogenic callus (Radojević *et al.*, 1987b).

Explant age

Plant age and the degree of differentiation of tissues are often inter-related and produce interactive effects *in vitro*. Both the size and degree of development of certain organs, particularly cotyledons, hypocotyls and epicotyls (Fig. 73), depends on plant age. Thus the direct formation of adventitious shoots has been found to occur most readily from *Pinus glauca* cotyledons excised from 7–8 day-old seedlings. Prior to that the rate of shoot formation was slower, and after 8 days, the capacity of the explants to produce shoots declined rapidly (Toivonen and Kartha, 1988). A higher proportion of *Cucumis melo* tissue cultures produced adventitious shoots when they were initiated from small leaves (0.3–0.5 mm) from young (14 day-old) seedlings than from leaves of the same size from older seedlings (21, 28, and 35 days), or from larger leaves (0.6–0.9 mm or 1.0–1.2 mm) from seedlings of any of these ages (Kathal *et al.*, 1988).

Period of culture

The period of time during which callus tissues have been maintained in culture commonly influences their morphogenetic potential. There is often a short period (one or more subcultures) during which morphogenesis increases (*e.g.* Reinert and Backs, 1968; Reinert *et al.* 1971). This is followed by a period of high regenerative ability and then the capacity of the tissues to undergo morphogenesis often declines (see below). Adventitious shoot formation from *Arabidopsis* callus was increased if the normal subculture interval of 4 weeks was increased to 8 weeks

Table 21. Stages in the development of wheat embryos [He *et al.*, 1986].

Stage	Days after anthesis	Length	Appearance of scutellum	Characteristics of embryos
I	<13	0.9	Transparent	—
II	12–13	0.9–1.5	Transparent	Visible
III	15–17	1.5–1.7	Transparent	A sharp ventral scale
IV	16–24	1.3–2.5	Opaque	No visible lateral root primordia
V	22	2.5	Opaque	Obvious lateral root primordia

just before transfer to a regeneration medium (Negrutiu and Jacobs, 1978a).

Loss of regenerative ability

Some callus tissues retain a capacity to regenerate shoots in response to well-known stimuli, over long periods. Stimart *et al.* (1980) for instance, obtained shoot regeneration from *Lilium* callus maintained in culture for 3 years, and Sheridan (1974) found that a regenerative capacity was still present in callus of this species after 8 years of subculturing. Callus of *Dioscorea* (Grewal *et al.* 1977), of *Solanum nigrum* (Mandal and Gadgil, 1979), of *Datura innoxia* (Forche *et al.*, 1981) and of *Lavendula angustifolia* (Webb *et al.*, 1984) maintained a morphogenetic capacity for at least two years; corn and oat calluses have been reported that remained morphogenetically competent for up to 18 months (Rice *et al.* 1979). The shoot-forming capacity of root and embryo callus of rice can be extended over a very long period if the callus is cultured with 2% sucrose plus either 3% mannitol or 3% sorbitol in the medium (Kavi Kishor and Reddy, 1986). However in conventional media, the facility with which morphogenesis may be induced from cultured plant cells very commonly decreases as the tissue is serially subcultured. The reasons for the loss of regenerative ability are still uncertain and may vary in different circumstances. Several theories have been advanced in the past to explain the effect:

- **Genetic variation in the cell population**. One widely-held theory is that cells are preferentially selected during culture for their ability to proliferate most rapidly under the chosen cultural conditions, and that this attribute is incompatible with the ability to undergo morphogenesis. Such a selection pressure will operate whenever there is appropriate genetic variation in the cell population, and can result in the loss of cells retaining the genetic information for totipotency (Sacristan and Melchers, 1969; Smith and Street, 1974; Orton, 1980).

— **The existence of a substance promoting morphogenesis** which is present in freshly isolated explants and which slowly diminishes during growth *in vitro* (Reinert and Backs, 1968). The converse of this hypothesis would be that an inhibitor of morphogenesis accumulates with time.

— **An epigenetic change in the cultured cells**. The genotype of cells is essentially conserved, but mechanisms regulating the genetic information governing morphogenesis become inoperative or lost during subculture. The tissue could be considered to have become dedifferentiated with respect to morphogenesis (Rice *et al.* 1979).

These hypotheses represent two contrasting ideas:

i) that non-competent cells have permanently lost their totipotency,

ii) that morphogenic competence has only been impaired.

In some circumstances both factors could be operative, but in most instances the second alternative now seems more likely, so that loss of regenerative ability is due only to the lack of competence.

Genetic variation as a cause. As explained in Chapter 3, there is considerable evidence to show that the *in vitro* culture of organised cells or tissues can lead to the formation of sufficient genetic variation in the resulting cell population for selection to be possible, leading to the accumulation of incompetent genotypes. Although the natural (or artificially-induced) occurrence of cells having aneuploid chromosome numbers does not necessarily prevent morphogenesis in calluses (Chapter 1), it seems clear that gross variations in the genetic make-up of callus cells will prevent plant regeneration (Rice and Carlson, 1975). In tobacco, Novak and Vyskot (1975) and Nuti Ronchi *et al.* (1981) found that many shoots or plants regenerated with aneuploid chromosome numbers, were weak and died in the course of development. The chromosome complements were presumably too unbalanced to permit survival. Moreover aneuploidy is now known to be only one of the genetic changes that can be induced by callus and cell culture and so other karyotypic alterations may be even more responsible.

The argument that morphogenetic capacity is lost during an active selection for cells capable of high rates of growth, has usually been based on the observation that regenerative capacity of a cell population decreases as karyotypic abnormalities increase. Loss of regenerative ability is not always dependent on the occurrence of karyological diversity in a cell population. For example, one race of *Brachycome* lost its capacity to regenerate embryoids in 2 months, and its ability to produce roots, in 7 months. The cells remained strictly diploid over the whole of this period and beyond (Gould, 1978).

Epigenetic change as a cause. Rather than being due to the disappearance by selection of cells possessing the necesssary genetic information for organogenesis, loss of morphogenetic potential may be caused by a changed pattern of gene expression brought about by the cultural environment, and may be an epigenetic phenomenon (as, some would believe, are habituation and physiological phase).

In experiments of Northcote (1979), bean tissue remained undifferentiated on a 'maintenance' medium containing 2,4-D, and normally differentiated on an 'induction' medium containing NAA (no 2,4-D) and the cytokinin, kinetin. However, after more than four transfers on the maintenance medium, the ability of the tissue to differentiate on the induction medium progressively declined. Cloning experiments showed that selection for the inability to differentiate, was not being practised, and after about 30 transfers on maintenance medium, the ability of the cells to differentiate was often restored quite suddenly over one transfer. Other tests indicated no loss of genetic information from the cell population, which simply did not respond to the normal rates of NAA and kinetin.

The non-regenerative condition of callus could be caused by the direct effects of media components, particularly growth regulators, on genetic expression. One possibility is that genes responsible for morphogenesis become methylated *in vitro* and so incapable of expression. Alternatively failure to regerate organs might be induced by a changed pattern of endogenous growth substance synthesis. It is not clear whether the non-regenerative condition of callus, and the ability to grow autonomously in culture are correlated, or can exist as two separate conditions. Some habituated tissues have been observed to show a reduced, or lost morphogenetic potential (Lutz, 1971).

There have been some reports of the restoration of morphogenesis in 'old' cultures previously considered to be morphogenetically incompetent. A 17-year old cell line of tobacco, which had lost its ability to regenerate plants for 8 years, was re-induced to give rise to shoots (and hence plantlets) by a series of subcultures on a shoot-inducing medium (Rice *et al.*, 1979). At each subculture sectors of the callus which were greener and more compact were selected for transfer. During the third subculture some cultures formed abnormal leaf-like structures and after further rounds of selection, normal shoots were eventually obtained. Traynor and Flashman (1981) obtained shoot formation in tobacco callus lines which had been maintained for 3–17 years on various media by subculture on a medium containing low levels of IAA (*e.g.* 0.05 mg/l) and high (15–25 mg/l) concentrations of 2-iP.

Although media alterations did not restore the morphogenetic capacity of 'old' *Solanum laciniatum* callus, Chandler *et al.* (1982) noticed that whereas large explants from young cultures initiated shoots and small ones did not, the reverse was true of old cultures. Shoot formation was also initiated much more slowly in cultures of old tissue. The authors suggested that these observations were consistent with the gradual accumulation of an inhibitor of morphogenesis in the tissues. In other circumstances it is possible to conjecture on the absence of a promotor being responsible for the failure of morphogenesis. Sometimes shoot regeneration from primary callus only occurs when the original explant is still attached (*e.g.* from *Chrysanthemum* leaves — Khalid *et al.*, 1989).

Altered morphogenic potential. Plant cells may not only show a gradual loss of regenerative capacity the longer they are cultured, but also an *altered* morphogenetic potential. There are many reports in the literature of, for example, altered sensitivity to applied growth substances for shoot bud initiation, or tissues forming only roots where previously both shoot and roots had been differentiated. These events could also be explained in terms of a new epigenetic gene expression and/or an altered pattern of endogenous hormone synthesis, although an explanation based on genuine genetic change is usually preferred (Chapter 3).

THE NATURE OF AN EXPLANT

The manner in which explant derivation can influence growth and morphogenetic potential has been partly covered in the preceding paragraphs where it will be seen that variation in competence or regenerative capacity can be found between explants from different organs and also between tissues within the same organ. The highest rate of micropropagation will often depend not only on the selection of the most suitable explant, but also on the discovery of the correct combination of growth regulators (Chapter 11), and/or the best medium (Mathews, 1987) for that organ or tissue. The results obtained from any one type of explant can vary between even closely related genotypes. In wheat, only embryo axis calli of the cultivar 'Buch Napostá' produced adventitious shoots, but they could be obtained from embryo axis and plumule calli in the hybrid cultivar 'H81199' (Elena and Ginzo, 1988).

For meristem, shoot, or node culture, there is usually only a limited range of explants which can be used. Survival and growth of shoot tips from the apex of growing shoots are generally better than those of lateral buds, although the latter can frequently be employed satisfactorily. In some plants (*e.g. Eucalyptus*), a node bearing a bud is a more reliable initial explant for shoot cultures than a dissected shoot apex.

Explants from hairy organs are usually difficult to decontaminate (Chapter 4). This was the case with hairy softwood explants of *Leucospermum* (Proteacea), which also failed to grow, probably because the prominent indumentum caused explants to be perpetually covered by a layer of liquid (Ben-Jaacov and Jacobs, 1986).

Type and position

Explants for adventitious shoot regeneration

Choice of the correct explant is important when propagation is to be based on direct or indirect shoot initiation. Although in some species, explants from many organs are capable of producing adventitious shoots, it is usually found that those excised from different organs or from different tissues within an organ, vary in morphogenic capacity. Thus in *Brassica carinata*, 86% of cotyledon explants produced shoots, 74% of hypocotyl segments, but only 26% of root segments (Jaiswal *et al.*, 1987).

In such circumstances, it would be necessary, for efficient micropropagation, to select the type which had the highest capacity for regeneration. However, in some plants the availability of competent tissues can be limited, so that there is little choice. One of the best examples is that of direct or indirect embryogenesis, where ovules, nucellus tissue, nucellar embryos, zygotic embryos or parts of young seedlings, or very young leaves, commonly provide the best explants for obtaining somatic embryos or embryogenic callus.

In *Jasminium*, where explants show a remarkable capacity to produce callus *in vitro*, Khoder *et al.* (1979) obtained callus cultures from the shoot apex, petals, anthers, stem internodes, and flower peduncles, but shoot regeneration was only obtained from shoot apex callus. Callus derived from seedlings and inflorescence explants of various *Cymbopogon* species had a higher morphogenic capacity than that arising from seeds, culms, roots or rhizomes (Jagadish Chandra and Sreenath, 1982). Different regenerative capacities are often found in mature leaf tissues. To obtain callus formation and/or organogenesis, it is frequently beneficial to include a portion of midrib or leaf vein in pieces of leaf lamina used as explants (Kato, 1974). In *Armoracia rusticana*, more direct shoot formation took place on leaf segments with part of a lateral vein, than on those which included part of the midrib (Górecka, 1987).

Accessory organs. The presence of a leaf petiole on 1 cm node explants of *Rosa hybrida* inhibited shoot growth *in vitro* (Mederos and Rodríguez Enríquez, 1987) but the greatest potential for direct shoot regeneration from the basal portion of the ray florets of *Chrysanthemum × morifolium* occurred when a pistil was still attached (Khalid *et al.*, 1989). Explants taken from the base of the immature floral stems within tulip bulbs generally produced more adventitious shoots than segments bearing nodes (Taeb and Alderson, 1987). In these experiments an interaction was found between explant position and the time of year at which explants were placed into culture. Explants from the base or the first node of the stem produced less shoots when cut from stored bulbs during November to March, whereas production of shoots from the second node was enhanced during this period.

Topophysis

Strictly positional effects on regeneration (*e.g.* where similar buds from the top and bottom of a plant behave differently *in vitro*), are examples of *topophysis* (an effect of position upon the observed characteristics of a plant). In experiments with trees, positional effects are sometimes further divided into *cyclophysis* (differential effects exhibited by parts of the same age, but different position) and *periphysis* (distinctive characteristics shown by parts of the same age and position which have been subjected to different physical exposure) (Oleson, 1978; Pierik, 1987).

Growth regulator requirements

Explants of different origin react to growth regulators in distinct ways and, as with choice of explant, this is particularly obvious in the formation of adventitious shoots. In some species, one type of explant may respond to a particular growth regulator treatment while another does not; in others the time taken to respond may vary. The proximal halves of the leaf lamina of *Citrus mitis* developed adventitious buds in 3½ weeks when cultured with 2 mg/l BAP, but the distal halves of the same leaves only regenerated shoots after at least 10 weeks in culture (Sim *et al.*, 1989).

The optimum dosage of growth regulators to induce morphogenesis often varies according to the size and type of explant from a single plant. In *Brassica carinata*

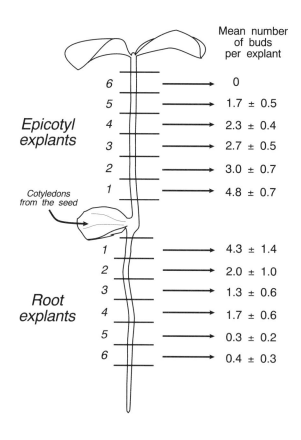

Fig. 89. The number of shoot buds formed on successive explants (1 cm-long) from the epicotyls and roots of *Citrus* seedlings [after Burger and Hackett, 1986].

(Jaiswal *et al.*, 1987), the greatest number of adventitious shoots was obtained by adding to **MS** medium:

> 5.0 µM BAP for cotyledon explants;
>
> 0.5 µM BAP for hypocotyl explants;
>
> 1.0 µM BAP for root sections.

The best medium for regenerating shoots from cotyledon-derived callus of *Lotononis bainesii*, contained 1 mg/l NAA and either 0.1 or 1 mg/l BAP, while for leaf callus it was necessary to use 0.01 mg/l NAA and 0.1 mg/l BAP (Bovo *et al.*, 1986).

In some instances it may even be advantageous to vary the regulatory compounds used for different kinds of explant. Adventitious shoots were obtained in greatest numbers from petiole sections of *Oxalis tuberosa* using 3 mg/l BAP and 3 mg/l NAA, but the best regeneration from internode sections occurred when they were grown on a medium with 3 mg/l zeatin plus 3 mg/l NAA (Khan *et al.*, 1988).

Natural growth factors

It is very probable that variations in the levels of endogenous growth substances are often responsible for the success of tissue cultures. Many of the influences of mother plant and explant origin discussed on previous pages, could be interpreted in this way. The hypothesis seems particular relevant to the varying morphogenic potential of explants of different origins, or those from mother plants in different stages of growth, especially where a morphogenic gradient can be demonstrated.

Seedling cotyledons can be a source of growth factors (Kamisaka and Shibata, 1977) and in many species, explants from the epicotyl or hypocotyl of seedlings have a high morphogenic potential. Is this because these tissues are especially juvenile, or because the cotyledons are a source of a diffusible growth promoting substance? The possibility that the latter might be the true explanation is well demonstrated by the potential of epicotyl or root sections of *Citrus sinensis* 'Valencia' seedlings to produce buds. As is shown in Fig. 89, this decreased the further the explants were from the cotyledon (Burger and Hackett, 1986).

Size

There is frequently an optimum size for explants used to initiate tissue cultures. Very small explants, whether they are shoot (or meristem) tips, fragments of whole plant tissues, or pieces of callus, do not survive well in culture, but large explants may be difficult to decontaminate effectively or less easily manipulated. A good example is provided by the work of Davies and Dale (1979) with leaf discs of *Solanum laciniatum*. Those smaller than 2 mm in diameter showed a high mortality rate, although if they survived they ultimately produced as many shoots as 5 mm discs. Discs 10 mm across showed the same basic type of growth pattern as 5 mm ones, but often developed convolutions and thereby lost some contact with the medium. Shoot tip explants of apple with 4–6 leaves were less liable to hyperhydricity than smaller ones with only two apical leaves (Standardi and Micheli, 1988).

Direct and indirect morphogenesis

Direct and indirect morphogenesis on explants also frequently depends on explant size. In *Brassica oleracea* small discs of vars. *fruticosa* and *acephela* showed the greatest increase in area and fresh weight, but the lowest frequency of root production (Dunwell, 1981b); and 7 mm discs of var. *italica* leaves produced 10 times more shoots per disc than 4 mm ones (Lazzeri and Dunwell, 1986b). Similarly, as stem internode sections of *Bacopa monnieri* were increased in length from 1 to 4 mm, a greater proportion of them formed shoot buds, and the number of shoots per explant increased. The efficiency of shoot production (*i.e.* the number of shoots formed per mm of internode) was however inversely proportional to explant length, except that those smaller than 1 mm failed to show any organ formation (Thakur and Ganapathi, 1978). The same situation was found in *Hyacinthus*, where the number of bulblets per bulb scale explant increased as explant length was enlarged from 1 cm to 3 cm, although the number of bulblets per unit length of explant was thereby decreased (Paek, 1982). Hypocotyl explants of *Albizia richardiana* which were 1 mm in length only produced a large amount of callus, whereas shoot buds were produced on 10 mm sections (Tomar and Gupta, 1988a).

On cultured pieces of *Convolvulus* roots, where new shoots arose from pre-existing meristematic primordia, the number of regenerated shoots and roots per explant increased as length increased, but here the number of roots and shoots produced per unit length of explant was largely independent of explant size, except that very small segments (1.5 mm) were again incapable of organ formation (Bonnett and Torrey, 1965).

Root formation from *Populus* callus was found to depend on the size of the callus pieces subcultured (Winton, 1968b). The greatest number of roots occurred on the largest callus pieces, grown from the biggest explants, of the oldest tissue sources. This suggests that root initiation was influenced by the degree of tissue differentiation. By contrast the frequency of leaf (shoot) formation in *Arabidopsis* callus was highest when small callus pieces (75 mg) were used as inocula on an induction medium. A larger inoculum size (250 mg) favoured continued callus proliferation at the expense of morphogenesis (Negrutiu and Jacobs, 1978a).

Explants for shoot cultures

In *Camellia japonica* shoot culture, both the size of the explants cut from *in vitro* shoots and their age, seemed to influence axillary shoot formation. The highest rate of proliferation occurred where shoot cultures were initiated from nodal segments or from the tips of small axillary shoots. Explants comprising 13–14 mm shoot tips from either the main axis or large axillary shoots gave a low multiplication rate (Vieitez *et al.*, 1989). Two-node segments of *Berberis thunbergii* produced more shoots per bud than single-node explants (Uno and Preece, 1987) and shoot growth from *Pistacia* explants bearing 3 axillary buds was greater than on those with two or one bud (Barghchi, 1986b), but small rhizome segments of *Alstroemeria* hybrids with one bud, gave a higher multiplication rate *in vitro* than larger ones (Pierik *et al.*, 1988b).

METHOD OF CULTURE

Inoculation density

The need for a minimum inoculation density to induce cell or tissue growth *in vitro* has been mentioned in Chapter 1. Besides affecting cell growth, inoculation density is occasionally reported to affect cell differentiation, morphogenesis or shoot proliferation.

Evidence for conditioning factors

After incubating suspension cultures of wild carrot for 10 days, both the number of somatic embryos formed and the growth stage which the embryos had reached, were found to depend on the amount of inoculum used to start the cultures. Increasing dilutions of the inoculum resulted in undifferentiated cell growth. Not only were less embyos formed than would have been predicted from the reduced inoculum size, but those present were progressively smaller in size and less well-developed (Halperin, 1967). Inoculum size was also found (by Verma and Durzan, 1980) to be an important factor in carrot embryogenesis, and Hari (1980) showed that cells do not reach their full embryonic potential at either low or high densities. It was concluded that cells produced an active metabolite (present in conditioned media) essential for complete embryogenesis.

By culturing pieces of embryogenic *Oryza sativa* callus of different weights in a constant volume of medium, or pieces of constant weight in different volumes of medium, Raghava Ram and Nabors (1985) found that the optimum rate of plant regeneration occurred when the ratio of callus to medium was 6.5–7.5 mg ml^{-1}. Plant regeneration was considerably reduced and callus growth increased when larger amounts of callus were used: the tissue often died when smaller pieces of callus were explanted. These results were thought to be caused by the release of a conditioning factor into the medium.

Nutrient supply

The smaller the size of an explant, or the number of explants on a given quantity of medium, the greater should be the availability of nutrients to the cultured tissues; but a high volume of medium per explant may not necessarily result in the best rate of propagation, for the condition is akin to inoculating suspension or callus cultures at low densities, and essential conditioning factors may become limiting. That conditioning factors can be important with whole plant explants is suggested by results of Dunwell (1981a): an interaction between medium composition and explant density was noted with

Brassica oleracea leaf disc explants. When 5 discs were placed on a dish, glutamine increased growth on **MS** medium, whereas when there were 10 discs per dish, it reduced growth.

An explant density effect was reported by Pierik and Steegmans (1972). When 10 seedlings of a *Cattleya* orchid were inoculated into a single flask of liquid medium, they formed protocorms and plantlets, but no protocorms were produced when the inoculum was only 2 plants per flask. Similarly, lateral buds of asparagus on **MS** medium produced more shoots and roots when many were put into the same flask. The effect was thought to be due to a substance diffusing from the explants, because growth could be promoted in the same fashion at lower densities by addition of an auxin and cytokinin (Matsubara, 1973; Matsubara and Clore, 1974).

One result indicating that nutrient supply *can be* important is that of Chun *et al.* (1986). The accumulation of dry weight and the number of axillary shoots per explant in Stage II *Populus* shoot cultures was best when only one shoot was subcultured into each vessel, but the greatest number of shoots *per vessel* (*i.e.* the maximum rate of practical shoot multiplication), occurred when 2 or 3 shoots were explanted into each container. The effect was independent of the size of the container used, and as the amount of medium was constant throughout, Chun *et al.* concluded that competition for nutrients was able to limit growth and shoot proliferation.

In culturing tuber discs of potato to study the formation of tracheids, Phillips and Dodds (1977) found by accident that the number of elements produced was greatly increased when the volume of medium per disc was reduced to below 0.2 ml. Above this figure (*e.g.* 0.5 ml per disc) there was a sharp decrease. The effect seemed not to be due to medium conditioning but might have been related to depletion of some inhibitory factor in the medium.

Effects of polarity

The orientation of explants

Positions on entire or sectioned organs of plants are given relative to the crown (the junction of shoot and root). The morphologically uppermost surface of shoot or leaf explants is said to be *distal*; that of root explants *proximal* to this point. The lower side of leaves is said to be *abaxial* and the upper side *adaxial* (see Fig. 90).

Polarity depends on cells having a capacity for the electrogenic exchange of hydrogen ions (H+) and potassium ions at the plasma membrane (plasmalemma). Auxin promoted H$^+$ efflux in basal cells probably sets up and maintains an electrical potential diference in tissues

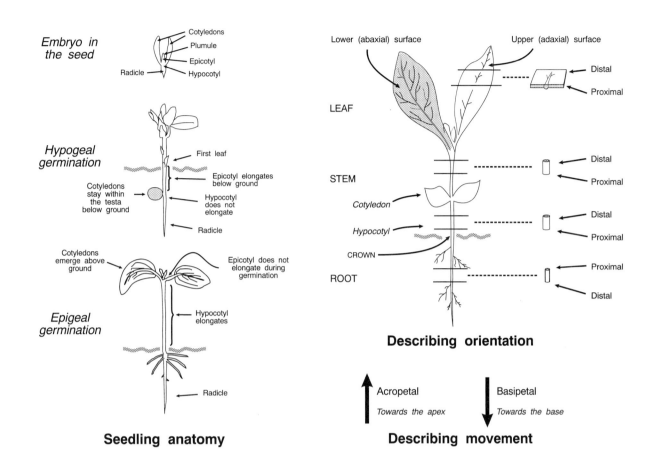

Fig. 90. Explant terminology — seedling explants and explant orientation.

(positive at the apex, negative at the base) which maintains and reinforces auxin transport (Raven, 1979). Excision depolarizes shoot and root tissue, but subsequent washing, ageing or incubation in an aqueous aerated medium restores the cell potential and allows re-polarization to take place, normally within 4–6 h in roots and within 12–16 h in pea epicotyl tissue (Hanson and Trewavas, 1982). Cultured explants usually show a marked polarity in cell proliferation and morphogenesis. This may be related to both the position and/or orientation which the organ or piece of tissue had on the intact plant, and also to its orientation within the culture vessel. Polarity of regeneration varies in different genotypes (even between varieties within a species) and can sometimes be reversed by growth regulator treatments.

Position on the mother plant

Polarity in stem and root sections. Stem and root pieces normally produce shoots from the morphologically up-

permost cut end, and roots from the lower end. Segments of dandelion root, for example, show a very strong polarity (Bowes, 1976a). This is first apparent as a polarity in callus formation. At the distal end of a root segment the phloem proliferates markedly, producing a pronounced callus from which adventitious roots arise. There is much less callus formation at the proximal end of the explant where shoots arise adventitiously from superficial callus-derived meristems. Polarity of regeneration developed slowly in cultured *Epilobium* root segments: buds and roots were formed at first along the whole length of cuttings, but gradually bud initiation came to be localised towards the proximal ends, and root intiation towards the distal ends (Emery, 1955). When the hypocotyls of *Capsicum* seedlings were cut into 6 equal segments, shoots were only produced from apical sections, central sections produced mostly roots, while abundant callus growth occurred on basal segments (Fari and Czako, 1981). Segments of the inflorescence stalk of *Gladiolus* produce callus and roots at the basal end, followed by the formation of buds and cormlets at the distal end (Ziv *et al.* 1970).

Gradients in morphogenesis. It is usually found that when a complete organ is cut into pieces, the various segments differ in their morphogenic capability. There is frequently a gradient in morphogenesis in progressive sections. For example, in *Helianthus annuus*, 5mm sections from the middle of the hypocotyl have been found to be the best explants for obtaining callus capable of regenerating adventitious shoots (Greco *et al.*, 1984). The morphogenic capacity of sections of *Citrus sinensis*, epicotyls and roots has been mentioned previously (page 265 and Fig. 89). The observed gradients were apparent on **Murashige and Tucker (1969)** medium containg 2 mg/l BAP and 0.02 mg/l NAA; less shoots were formed on all sections, and the gradients were not apparent when the concentration of both regulants was 2 mg/l (Burger and Hackett, 1986).

Pedicel sections of the flowers of *Lilium longiflorum* were found by Liu and Burger (1986) to show a gradient in the formation of buds. The section taken from nearest the receptacle (the most distal section) formed the greatest number (nearly 5 times more than the next adjacent section), especially if it was placed upside down on the medium (see below).

Polarity in whole leaves and leaf pieces

Although in some species adventitious buds can be formed over the entire surface of detached leaves, shoots and roots more usually arise at the base of leaves or leaf fragments, *i.e.* at the lower *proximal* end (*i.e.* that nearer the stem — see Fig. 90). This polarity in the capacity of leaf tissues to regenerate adventitious shoots, can be seen in the relative number of shoot buds produced over the surface of an entire leaf, but is more commonly manifested when leaves are cut into sections. The regenerative capacity of leaf fragments cut from detached leaves is then usually greater in those from the proximal end than in those from the distal region. This may occur in some plants because the proximal region of the leaf contains more meristematic cells than distal regions. There was a higher rate of shoot regeneration in sections cut from the proximal half of *Malus* leaves (Welander, 1988) while in *Echeveria elegans* (Crassulaceae), shoots were formed only in the proximal region of entire detached leaves and at the proximal ends of half-leaf segments (Raju and Mann, 1971). In this plant, shoot formation from the base of distal leaf halves was much slower than that from proximal halves. Similarly, the proximal halves of the leaves of *Citrus mitis* seedlings formed direct adventitious shoots after 31/2) weeks of culture on a medium containing 2 mg/l BAP, but shoot regeneration from the distal halves was much slower and only started after 10

weeks of culture: only a few shoots had formed after 12 weeks (Sim *et al.*, 1989).

Callus originating from cotyledon fragments proximal to embryo axes of *Olea europea* was most likely to regenerate shoots (Cãnas and Benbadis, 1988) and morphogenesis occurred on more of the explants (81%) cut from the basal region of Douglas fir cotyledons than on explants taken from the middle (69%) or distal parts (52%) and grown under equivalent conditions (Cheng, 1976a, 1977). However in *Heloniopsis orientalis* (Liliaceae), shoot buds are formed more frequently from the distal parts (see Fig.90) of mature leaves than from proximal segments (Kato, 1974).

A greater number of protocorm-like bodies were produced from explants of proximal leaf tissue in *Phalaenopsis* orchids, than from distal explants (Tanaka *et al.* 1975). Sections cut from the inner part of head lettuce leaves tended to produce callus and only a few shoots, while those from the periphery of leaves all gave rise to shoots (Koevary *et al.* 1978).

Differences between leaf surfaces. Some plants are able to produce callus or to regenerate organs from either leaf surface, but in the Mexican Snowball plant, Raju and Mann (1970) obtained shoots only on the adaxial surface of explants. In *Phalaenopsis* and *Vanda* orchids, protocorms were formed from primordia developed on the adaxial surfaces of either small leaf fragments or whole immature leaves (Tanaka *et al.*, 1975). Contrary to this, regenerative callus only arose from the lower (abaxial) epidermis of *Bryophyllum daigremontianum*, and other leaf tissues never produced buds under the same culture conditions (Bigot, 1976). The abaxial surface of *Ipomoea batatas* leaves formed more embryogenic callus than the adaxial surface (Liu and Cantliffe, 1984). The leaf surface from which adventitious shoots may arise is usually genetically determined. Yanagawa and Sakanishi (1980) showed that regenerative capacity was high on the adaxial surface of bulb scale explants from plants in the Liliaceae, and on the abaxial surface of Amaryllidaceae. Shoot regeneration therefore occurs most frequently on the side of the scale in which the vascular bundles are sited, suggesting that the bundles provide cell division stimuli.

Explants taken from the bulb scales of bulbous plants regenerate adventitious shoots and bulblets more freely if cut from the basal (proximal) part of the bulb scale rather than from the distal region (Hackett, 1969b). Adventitious shoot formation is always much higher if some part of the basal plate of the bulb is included with the scale explant. *Lilium rubellum* can be propagated from bulblets formed directly on leaf segments. Explants derived from the base of the leaf had a higher regenerative capacity than those taken from the leaf apex. In this plant, leaves from the upper part of the stem produced bulblets more readily than those from the base. The capacity of leaves to form bulblets decreased with the approach of flowering and at, or shortly after flowering, it disappeared completely (Niimi and Onozawa, 1979).

Growth regulators and polarity

Natural polarity of regenerative events is normally supposed to be due to the movement of growth substances within plant tissues, particularly the polar (*i.e.* from the shoot apex towards the root tip) transport of IAA auxin (see page 433). Thus IAA movement is naturally basipetal in the stem and acropetal in roots. These patterns may not be apparent in small tissue sections, which would explain why polarity of organogenesis is not usually found in very small explants, but tends to increase as explant size is increased (Thakur and Ganapathi, 1978). The addition of auxin and cytokinin growth regulators to culture media may reinforce the normally observed polarity of explants, induce regeneration from unresponsive parts of organs, or lead to the disappearance or reversal of polar trends.

A reversal of polarity was instanced by Cutter (1962). *Zamioculcas zamiifolia* leaves or leaf pieces produced tuberous swellings from their proximal ends from which roots and one or more shoot buds arose. Regeneration could also be induced from a distal cut surface if it was spot-treated with a concentrated NAA solution (186 mg/l). Loss of polarity following the application of growth regulators has been instanced in cauliflower, rape and *Begonia*. On media without growth regulators, cauliflower petiole explants produced roots and shoots at their proximal pole, but this polarity was cancelled if 1.9 mg/l NAA was added to the medium, when numerous roots were formed all over the explant. Shoots formed all over the explant when 2.3 mg/l BA was administered instead (Margara, 1969b).

Shoot formation occurred at the morphological base of rape flower stalks placed on media containing relatively low concentrations of auxin and cytokinin, but this polarity was not apparent when the concentration of growth regulants was increased (Margara and Leydecker, 1978). Cultured without growth regulators, discs cut from the leaves of *Begonia rex* regenerated a root at the base of the longest vein, but the presence of 5 mg/l kinetin abolished the polarity of organogenesis. Adventitious shoots then arose over the whole area of both sides of the leaf (Schraudolf and Reinert, 1959). Auxin and cytokinin became essential additions to **Linsmaier and Skoog (1965)** medium to produce bulblet, callus and root formation from explants cut from the distal (and normally non-regenerative) part of *Lilium longiflorum* bulb scales (Dinnis

and Ascher, 1976). Legrand (1972) noticed that the polarity of shoot regeneration from *Endiva* leaf fragments was progressively reversed, the longer they were cultured in darkness.

Interactions between growth substances and the normal polarity of explants can be complex. For instance, in the work of Bigot *et al.* (1977), sections taken from tomato hypocotyls tended to have a greater capacity to produce shoots the nearer the root they were taken (*c.f.* page 265). The region of the hypocotyl to show maximum regenerative ability, varied according to the variety of plant and according to the growth regulators in the medium. There was a greater difference in the regenerative ability of distal and proximal ends when 2.1 mg/l IAA and 1.0 mg/l 2-iP were used together, than when 1 mg/l 2-iP was used alone. Zimmerman *et al.* (1988b) found that more hyperhydric plants of *Petunia* were obtained from distal nodal segments of normal plants than from proximal segments.

A morphactin (*n*-butyl-9-hydroxyfluorene-9-carboxylic acid) added to the medium at a concentration of 3.5 μM, caused the roots of *Heloniopsis* plantlets to swell and produce semi-organised buds at their extremities (Kato, 1976). When excised leaves were exposed to the compound, shoot buds were initiated over the entire surface, rather than in a polarised fashion (Kato, 1978a). These results were thought to be consistent with the known ability of morphactins to bring about a redistribution of natural growth substances.

The positioning of explants *in vitro*

Growth or morphogenesis from explants can be influenced by the way that the explant is placed into or upon the medium. The effects noted may sometimes be due entirely to polarity; on other occasions they can be attributable to the effect of positioning on the availability of nutrients and growth regulators to those parts of the explant which are competent.

Embryo explants. The supply of nutritional factors is often of critical importance when excised embryos are cultured. For instance, rye embryos all germinated precociously when placed by Dunwell and Cornish (1980) with their scutellum on the medium, but only 35% did so if the embryonic axis was in contact with it. Embryo explants of *Nuytsia* (a parasitic plant) developed as normal seedlings on a solidified White's medium if placed vertically with the hypocotyl partially embedded, but the cotyledons callused if they touched the agar (Nag and Johri, 1976). Embryos of pine and Douglas fir initiated adventitious buds much more freely and rapidly if cultured in an inverted position, with their cotyledonary ends in the medium, rather than their radical ends (Kadkade and Jopson, 1977). A greater surface of the explant is then in contact with the medium (Aitken-Christie *et al.*, 1985).

Leaf explants. Positioning can be particularly important with leaf explants. Leaf segments of *Gasteria* and *Haworthia* produced more somatic embryos when prone on agar than when placed upright (Beyl and Sharma, 1983). Discs cut from young leaves of the strawberry cultivar 'Redcoat,' produced more adventitious shoots when their *ad*axial surface was kept in contact with the medium than when placed the other way up (Nehra *et al.*., 1988). Similar results were obtained with segments of *Malus × domestica* and *Malus pumila* leaves. Welander (1988) suggested that one explanation, besides polarity for this observation might be that the *ad*axial surface is the most responsive to nutrients being the last tissue of the leaf to cease growing and dividing.

However, the best multiple shoot formation in response to BAP, adventitious root formation in response to the auxins NAA, IAA and IBA, and callus formation in response to 2,4-D and NAA, occurred when the *ab*axial surface of leaf sections of a *Populus* hybrid was in contact with the medium (Park and Son, 1988a). Similarly somatic embryos are formed directly from cells of the *ab*axial epidermis of the cotyledons dissected from immature soybean seeds. Hepher *et al.* (1988) suggested that the embryogenic potential of this tissue was associated with its role as a nutrient transfer tissue.

Bulb scale explants. Bulb scale explants of *Lilium longiflorum* produced far more bulblets per section when the abaxial (convex) surface was touching the medium than when their adaxial surface was in contact (Hackett, 1969b). This result has been confirmed by Lesham *et al.* (1982) who obtained many more and larger bulbs, more roots and less callus, when the abaxial (rather than the adaxial) surface of scale segment was downwards on the medium. In all cases, bulblets developed only on the adaxial side of the scale. A similar result was described by Niederwieser and Vcelar (1990) with leaf sections of *Lachenalia* (Liliaceae) hybrids. Although adventitious buds were produced on the adaxial surface, regardless of the orientation of the explants, the best results occurred when the abaxial surface was in contact with the medium, because if the explants were the other way up, buds grew to form a hard callus-like tissue or were thickened and abnormal.

Stem and root explants. The organogenesis obtained on root or stem sections is also liable to differ according to whether the explants are normally orientated or inverted on the medium. Shoots regenerated from the upper (proximal) surface when dandelion root sections were placed distal side (*i.e.* the side that would normally be

nearest to the root tip) downwards on the medium. Reversed, with the proximal side in contact with the agar, they produced a mound of callus from the upper (distal) surface (Booth and Satchuthananthavale, 1974). Adventitious roots formed from *Acinidia deliciosa* callus formed shoots at their proximal end if they were detached from the callus and inserted vertically with the root tip in the agar medium, but produced shoots along much of their length from the proximal end if placed horizontally (Revilla and Power, 1988).

When the basal ends of white spruce hypocotyl sections were placed in the medium, almost all the explants produced scale-like organs which could be subcultured to give buds and shoots, but only roots were formed on 50% of the sections if they were cultured with their apical ends downwards (Campbell and Durzan, 1978).

Discs cut from the inflorescence stalk of gladiolus developed callus and root primordia from their basal ends when that end was placed on the medium, but if explants were cultured in an inverted position, morphogenesis was more rapid. Roots were again formed at the proximal end (now uppermost), and one or two buds developed at the distal end (in the medium). Subsequent leaf growth turned the explant over. Subcultured correctly orientated on the same medium, explants eventually developed clusters of cormlets and one or two shoots (Ziv *et al.* 1970). It was similarly advantageous to invert scape sections of asparagus (Takatori *et al.* 1968) and *Narcissus* (Seabrook *et al.* 1976) to obtain any morphogenetic response.

It has been suggested that inversion may overcome the polar transport of natural auxin, but this was not the case with tulip. Stalk explants elongated only when they were inverted on a medium containing IAA, and growth was due to basipetal (polar) auxin movement (Gabryszewska and Saniewski, 1983). Pierik and Steegmans (1975e) thought that the strong promotion of rooting from the proximal end of *Rhododendron* stem segments, when they were inverted on a solidified medium, was probably due to a better oxygen supply.

Explant position is not invariably important. Stem sections of olive produced callus and roots from the end immersed in the medium, regardless of whether it was proximal or distal (Scaramuzzzi and de Gaetano, 1974); in *Echeveria elegans*, leaf freagments produced shoots always at the proximal cut end even if they were inverted (Raju and Mann, 1971); and direct shoot regeneration occurred to the same extent on petiole segments of *Saintpaulia*, regardless of their orientation (Harney and Knap, 1979).

Explants for shoot cultures. Placing shoot culture explants on their sides or inverting them in the medium, can sometimes help to remove apical dominance, can promote the synchronous growth of axillary shoots and often induces faster shoot initiation and more shoots than are obtained from a vertical orientation. A horizontal placement has been effective with shoot tips of pear (Lane, 1979b), those of some apple cultivars (Yae *et al.*, 1987; Gološin and Radojević, 1987) and several different woody plants (McClelland and Smith, 1990) (see Chapter 2).

Zimmerman and Fordham (1989) found that 2–3 times more axillary shoots were produced in culture if subcultured apple shoots were placed in the medium upside down. Inversion was particularly effective for cv. 'Delicious' and strains of it ('Triple Red', 'Redchief', 'Starkspur Supreme', and 'Vermont Spur'). Besides increasing the rate of proliferation, inversion also eliminated the tendency of the shoots of these cultivars to senesce after subculturing. Two-node explants of *Berberis thunbergii* produced axillary shoots more rapidly if stood vertically in the agar than if placed horizontally (Uno and Preece, 1987).

COMPETITION BETWEEN MERISTEMS

The first organogenetic meristems formed *in vitro* can inhibit the development of further structures of the same kind (see Chapter 1). New shoot meristems appear equidistantly, on the surface of the explants composed of thin cell layers (Tran Thanh Van *et al.* 1974), suggesting that immediately a meristem is formed, it sends out a message inhibiting the initiation of another meristem in its near vicinity. That the inhibitor could be auxin, is suggested by experiments of Cassells (1979) (see page 434).

The inhibiting effect of meristems on further morphogenesis and on the development of pre-formed organs, increases as meristems enlarge. Removing shootlets as they are formed may therefore facilitate continuous adventitious shoot production from explants or callus tissue, whereas if the tissue is left undisturbed, the total number of shoots may be small. Von Arnold and Eriksson (1978) found that out of 10–30 buds formed on Norway spruce embryo explants, only about 3 would elongate unless those which had reached 3–5 mm high were excised. The large number of shoots formed on *Pinus radiata* cultures wes mutually inhibitory to further growth unless the nodular meristematic tissue from which the shoots had been produced was subdivided and the pieces moved to fresh medium (Aitkin *et al.* 1981).

Competition can also occur between somatic embryos. Although many embryos were formed from scutellar callus of *Pennisetum americanum*, only 2–3 plantlets were produced from each explant if it was transferred to a 2,4-D-free medium in one piece. If the callus was divided into 4–5 pieces, one plant was generally produced from each segment (Vasil and Vasil, 1981a). Gharyal and Maheshwari (1981) showed that direct embryoid formation would persist on *Albizia_lebbek* hypocotyl explants, providing that recognisable embryos were continually removed, as they appeared, and were then cultured separately.

WOUNDING

In the natural environment the wounding of plants by pruning, grazing or mechanical abrasion often stimulates callus formation and/or morphogenesis. All explants transferred to culture are subjected to wounding during their isolation. The smaller the explant, the greater the proportion of wounded surface. In many instances, damage causes the release of inhibitory substances (Chapter 11), but it also induces the natural production of ethylene gas which frequently provides a stimulus to the formation of unorganised tissue or adventitious shoots and roots. The physiological changes in tissues which bring about these responses (the so-called *wound reaction*) are discussed in Chapter 11. The advantage to be gained from wounding can be such that explants are sometimes given additional damage, above that induced by excision (*e.g.* leaves of *Coronaria varia* scratched or peeled before

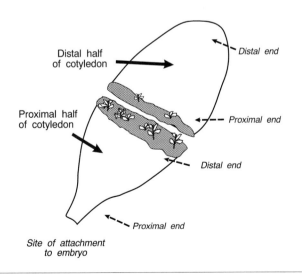

Fig. 91. The polarity of adventitious shoot formation on *Pyrus malus* cotyledon pieces [after Browning et al., 1987].

incubation to induce callus formation — Mariotti and Arcioni, 1983).

Wounding during isolation

Morphogenesis frequently occurs at the cut surface of explants. On cotyledons from *Pyrus malus* seed embryos which were cut into halves, the production of a small amount of callus, followed by multiple adventitious shoots, occurred more frequently from the distal cut surface of proximal sections, than on the proximal end of distal sections (Browning *et al.*, 1987) (Fig. 91). Although the cut edges of *Ipomoea batatas* leaves did not form embryogenic callus, it was formed on the cut edges of stem and leaf explants (Liu and Cantcliffe, 1984). Fragmentation of young expanding leaves of *Malus* into 14 sections improved the capacity of the leaf tissue to form adventitious shoots and embryo-like structures (Welander, 1988).

If cultured intact, all embryo axes of the apple cultivar 'Delicious' and 55% of those of cv. 'Winesap' formed only callus, but if cut into 3 roughly equal sections (root, hypocotyl and plumule), a high proportion of the plumule and hypocotyl pieces of both cultivars formed adventitious shoots. None of the embryo root sections of 'Delicious' formed shoots and only 11% of 'Winesap' ones. Korban and Skirvin (1985) suggested that sectioning had either removed a factor which was inhibiting morphogenesis (possibly one contained in the root zone), or had increased the activity of a promotory substance.

Some explants are insensitive to treatment with growth regulators unless they are damage or sectioned. Axillary buds (areoles) of the cactus *Opuntia polycantha* were insensitive to auxin or cytokinin in the medium unless they were wounded in some way. Then the majority formed adventitious roots in response to 10 mg/l NAA and shoots in response to 10 mg/l BAP (Mauseth and Halperin, 1975). In some species, splitting a shoot tip explant in half along its longitudinal axis can practically double the number of axillary shoots produced (*e.g.* in *Yucca elephantipes*, Bentz *et al.*, 1988).

Additional wounding

Inflicting further wounds to an explant after excision can often increase morphogenesis. For example, cuts across the leaf lamina and main veins of mature phase leaf explants of *Liquidambar styraciflua* var. 'Mariane' significantly increased the number of adventitious shoots produced per explant. The treatment was not effective in the variety 'Variegata' which was naturally highly organogenic (Brand and Lineberger, 1988).

Morphogenesis usually occurs at the site of the wounds. Thus the increased adventitious shoot formation on wounded leaves taken from proliferating shoot cultures of *Vaccinium corymbosum* mainly occurred along points of injury (Callow *et al.*, 1988). Park and Son (1988a) noted that leaves removed from cultured shoots of *Populus nigra* × *P. maximowiczii*, formed adventitious shoots or roots on their outer surfaces, depending on the growth regulators in the medium. However, if the leaves were punctured in several locations (five was optimal) with a pin, morphogenesis occurred at the margins of the perforations. The authors suggested that wounding promoted the transfer of endogenous hormones to the location of the scarring, causing there to be a more suitable level of growth promotors for morphogenesis. This hypothesis seems to agree with results of (Norizaku *et al.*, 1985): although injury did not increase the uptake of BAP into leaf sections of *Torenia fournieri*, transverse cuts across explants cultured in the presence of this regulant, significantly increased the formation of buds within 0.5 cm of the site. Longitudinal (transverse) cuts caused buds to be produced over the entire surface of the explant: without wounding they occurred mainly at its cut ends.

In some *Lachenalia* hybrids, bud formation on the adaxial surface of leaf sections was promoted by two superficial transverse cuts in the centre of either the adaxial or abaxial sides. Buds invariably occurred on the distal side of the cut (Niederwieser and Vcela, 1990).

Root formation

The improved formation of adventitious roots on cuttings which can result from wounding is described in Chapter 14.

9

The Components of Culture Media

Plant tissues and organs are grown *in vitro* on artificial media which supply the nutrients necessary for growth. The success of plant tissue culture as a means of plant propagation is greatly influenced by the nature of the culture medium used. For healthy and vigorous growth, intact plants need to take up from the soil:

- relatively large amounts of some inorganic elements (the so-called *major plant nutrients*) — salts of nitrogen (N), potassium (K), calcium (Ca), phosphorus (P), magnesium (Mg) and sulphur (S); and,

- small quantities of other elements (*minor plant nutrients* or trace elements) — iron (Fe), sodium (Na), chlorine (Cl), manganese (Mn), zinc (Zn), boron (B), copper (Cu), molybdenum (Mo) and (possibly) nickel (Ni).

These are the elements which are *essential*. The requirement for certain others, such as cobalt and aluminium, is uncertain. According to Epstein (1971), an element can be considered to be essential for plant growth if either:

1) a plant grown in a medium adequately purged of that element, fails to grow properly or to complete its life cycle; or,

2) it is a constituent of a molecule that is known to be an essential metabolite.

Plant tissue culture media provide not only these major (*macro-*) and minor (*micro-*) nutrients, but usually a carbohydrate too (sucrose is most common) to replace the carbon which the plant normally fixes from the atmosphere by photosynthesis. To improve growth, many media also include trace amounts of certain organic compounds, notably vitamins, amino acids and plant growth regulators.

In early media 'undefined' components such as fruit juices, yeast extracts and protein hydrolysates, were frequently used in place of defined vitamins or amino acids, or even as further supplements. As it is important that a medium should be the same each time it is prepared, materials which can vary in their composition are best avoided if at all possible, although improved results are sometimes obtained by their addition. Coconut milk, for instance, is still frquently used, and banana homogenate has been a popular addition to media for orchid culture.

Plant tissue culture media are therefore made up from some or all of the following components:

- *macronutrients* (always employed);

- *micronutrients* (nearly always employed, although sometimes just one element, iron, has been used);

- *vitamins* (generally incorporated, although the actual number of compounds added, varies greatly);

- *amino acids* and other nitrogen supplements (usually omitted, but sometimes used with advantage);

- *sugar/s* (nearly always added, but omitted for some specialised purposes);

- *undefined supplements* (which, when used, contribute some of the five components above and also plant growth substances or regulants);

- *buffers* (have seldom been used in the past, but recent work suggests that the addition of organic acids or buffers could be beneficial in some circumstances);

- *a solidifying agent* (used when a semi-solid medium is required. Agar or a gellan gum are the most common choices).

Growth regulating chemicals, particularly auxins and cytokinins, are very important components of culture media, but their selection, and the concentrations adopted, depend on the plant species and the purpose of the culture. Growth regulators are therefore considered in this book in a separate chapter and are not treated here as components which distinguish one medium from another. The discussion and descriptions that follow therefore deal with what are often referred to as 'basal' or 'basic' media.

(Note however that some authors refer to just the inorganic compounds which they have used as their 'basal medium' or 'basal salts').

Extra-cellular enzymes

Cultured plant cells secrete numerous enzymes into culture media which may alter the availability of the nutrients provided, or convert secreted secondary products into nutrients. For example, peroxidase (Moreno *et al.,* 1990), acid phosphatase, amylase, glucanase, IAA oxidase, isopolyphenol oxidases, esterase, and β- glucosidase activity, has been found in the medium in which suspension cultures have been grown (Berger *et al.,* 1988). The presence of extracellular enzymes accounts for at least some of the improved growth which is often possible on conditioned media.

Published media

Many different media have been devised since the early days of plant tissue culture. The individual compositions of some of the most important and useful of these formulations are listed in tables at the end of Chapter 10.[†] The sections which follow discuss the nature, derivation and use of the ingredients within each of the broad classes of medium components.

MACRONUTRIENT SALTS

Plants absorb the nutrients they require from soils, almost entirely as ions. An ion is an atom, or a group of atoms, which has gained either a positive charge (a *cation*) or a negative charge (an *anion*). Macro-nutrients (and most micronutrients) are provided for plant culture media from salts. In weak aqueous solutions, such as plant media, each soluble salt dissociates into two ions, one positively charged, the other negatively charged.

Calcium, magnesium and potassium are absorbed by plant cells (normally those of the root) as the respective cations Ca^{2+}, Mg^{2+} and K^+); nitrogen is mainly absorbed in the form of ammonium (the cation, NH_4^+) or nitrate (the anion, NO_3^-); phosphorus as the phosphate ions $(HPO_4)^{2-}$ and $(H_2PO_4)^-$; and sulphur as the sulphate ion $(SO_4)^{2-}$.

The most important step in deriving a plant tissue culture medium is the selection of macronutrient ions in the correct concentration and balance. The salts normally used to provide the macroelements in tissue culture media also provide ions of the elements sodium (Na) and chlorine (Cl). Because plant cells tolerate high concentrations of Na^+ and Cl^- without injury, these ions are frequently given little importance when contemplating media changes. Salts containing them are considered as convenient sources of N, K, Ca or Mg, because they effectively permit the addition of just one of the major nutrients.

In the whole plant, nutrients are either taken up passively, or through active mechanisms involving the expenditure of energy. Active uptake is generally less dependent on ionic concentration than passive uptake. Both systems are however influenced by the concentration of other elements, pH, temperature, and the biochemical or physiological status of the plant tissues. These factors can in turn be controlled by the solution presented to the roots, or they may dictate the ionic balance of an ideal solution.

†   The names of published media in this, and other chapters, are given in bold type.

For example, Mg^{2+} competes with other cations for uptake. Under conditions of high K^+ or Ca^{2+} concentrations, Mg deficiency can result, and *vice versa*. Active uptake of phosphate falls off if the pH of the solution should become slightly alkaline when the $(H_2PO_4)^-$ ion becomes changed to $(HPO_4)^{2-}$. There is some evidence that ammonium is utilised more readily than nitrate at low temperatures and that uptake may be enhanced by high carbohydrate levels within plant cells. Calcium is not absorbed efficiently and concentrations within plant tissues tend to be proportional to those in the soil. Plants are comparatively insensitive to sulphate ions, but high concentrations of dissolved phosphate can depress growth, probably through competitively reducing the uptake of the minor elements Zn, Fe and Cu. Although the biochemistry and physiology of nutrient uptake in tissue cultures may be similar, it is unlikely to be identical.

When explants are first placed onto a nutrient medium, there is often an initial leakage of ions from damaged cells, especially metallic cations (Na^+, Ca^{2+}, K^+, Mg^{2+}) for the first 1–2 days, so that the concentration in the plant tissues actually decreases (Chaillou and Chaussat, 1986). Cells then commence active absorption and the internal concentration slowly rises. Phosphate and nitrogen (particularly ammonium) are absorbed more rapidly than other ions. Nitrate in a medium very similar to that of **Wood and Braun (1961) B** medium, was reduced by *Catharanthus roseus* suspensions from 24 mM to 5 mM in 15 days, while Na^+, K^+, and SO_4^{2-}, fell to only just over half the original concentrations in the same time (MacCarthy *et al*, 1980). Carnation shoot cultures were found to use 31–75% Mg^{2+}, and 29–41% Ca^{2+} in **MS** medium during a 4 week period (Dencso, 1987).

Some comparative reviews of whole plant mineral nutrition will be found in Mengel and Kirkby (1982), Hewitt and Smith (1975) and Epstein (1971).

FORMS OF NITROGEN

Nitrogen is essential to plant life. Clarkson and Hanson (1980) summarise the role of N in nutrition as "a carbon substitute which, because of its different valency, is capable of introducing an essential distortion into the symetry of carbon chemistry, enabling the formation of compounds with unique structures and properties of coordination, basicity, charge, reactivity, and oxidation-reduction".

Both growth and morphogenesis in tissue cultures is markedly influenced by the availability of nitrogen and the form in which it is presented. The removal of oxygen from a chemical compound and its replacement by hydrogen, is termed *reduction*. Compared to the nitrate ion,

NO_3^- (which is a highly oxidized form of nitrogen), the ammonium ion, NH_4^+, is the most highly 'reduced' form. Plants utilise reduced nitrogen for their metabolism, and within the plant, nitrogen exists almost entirely in the reduced form. As a source of reduced nitrogen, plant cultures are especially able to use primary amines:

$$R– NH_2$$

and amides:

$$R– C\,O– NH– R'$$

(where R and R' are functional groups)

The primary amines which are most commonly employed in culture media are ammonia, NH_3 (which dissolved in water becomes the ion, NH_4^+) and amino acids.

Amides are less commonly added to culture media: those which are able to be used by plants are particularly

$$NH_2 – CO– NH_2 \qquad \text{(urea)},$$

and ureides, which include allantoin and allantoic acid (Kirby, 1982) (Fig. 92). Allantoin or allantoic acid are sometimes more efficient nitrogen sources than urea (Lea *et al*., 1979).

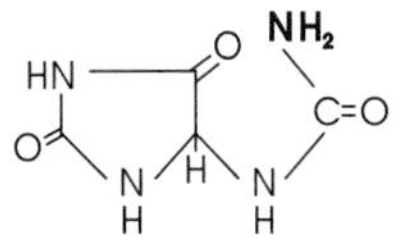

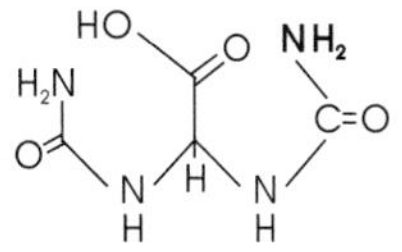

Fig. 92. The structures of allantoin and allantoic acid.

Most media contain more nitrate than ammonium ions (Table 49), but as plant tissue culture media are usually not deliberately buffered, the adopted concentrations of ammonium and nitrate ions have probably been more due to practical pH control, than to the requirement of the plant tissues for one form of nitrogen or another (see section on pH later in this Chapter). Uptake of nitrate only takes place effectively in an acid pH, but is accompanied by extrusion of anions from the plant, leading to the medium gradually becoming less acid. By contrast, uptake of ammonium results in the cells excreting protons (H^+) into the medium, making it more acid (Table 27, page 296). The exchange of ions preserves the charge balance of the tissues and may also assist in the disposal of an excess of protons or hydroxyl (OH^-) ions generated during metabolism (Raven, 1986). Uptake of nitrogen by cell suspension cultures of *Nicotiana tabacum* is an active (energy-dependent) process (Heimer and Filner, 1971) and is dependent on a supply of oxygen (Buwalda and Greenway, 1989).

Plant culture media are usually started at pH 5.4–5.8. When both nitrate and ammonium ions are present, there is then a rapid uptake of ammonium which causes the pH to fall to *ca.* 4.2–4.6. As this happens, further ammonium uptake is inhibited, but uptake of nitrate ion is stimulated, causing the pH to rise. In unbuffered media, efficient nitrogen uptake can therefore depend on the presence of both ions. Unless otherwise stated, comments in this section on the roles of nitrate and ammonium refer to observations on unbuffered media.

There is generally a close correlation in tissue cultures between uptake of nitrogen, cell growth and the conversion of nitrogen to organic materials. A readily available supply of nitrogen seems to be important to maintain cultured cells in an undifferentiated state. The depletion of nitrogen in batch cultures, triggers an increase in the metabolism of some nitrogen-free compounds based on phenylpropanes (such as lignin), which are associated with the differentiation of secondarily-thickened cells (Hahlbrock, 1974). However, the growth in culture of differentiated cotton fibres composed largely of cellulose, is nitrate-dependent; the presence of some reduced nitrogen in the culture medium decreased the proportion of cultured embryos which produced fibres, and particularly in the absence of boron, promoted the cells of the embryos to revert to callus formation (Birnbaum *et al.*, 1974).

Nitrate ions

Nitrate ions are an important source of nitrogen for most plant cultures, and nearly all published media provide the majority of their available nitrogen in this form. However, once within the cell, nitrate has to be reduced to ammonium before being utilised biosynthetically. Why not simply supply nitrogen as NH_4^+ and avoid the use of NO_3^- altogether? The reason lies in the latent toxicity of the ammonium ion in high concentration, and in the need to control the pH of the medium.

Conversion of nitrate to ammonium is brought about firstly by one, or possibly two, nitrate reductase enzymes, which reduce NO_3^- to nitrite (NO_2^-). One nitrate reductase enzyme is thought to be located in the cytoplasm, while the second may be bound to membranes (Nato *et al.*, 1990). The NO_2^- produced by the action of nitrate reductase is reduced to NH_4^+ by a nitrite reductase enzyme located in plastids (Fig. 93). Reduction of nitrate to ammonia requires the cell to expend energy. The ammo-

nium ions produced are incorporated into amino acids and other nitrogen-containing compounds. Nitrate and nitrite reductase enzymes are substrate induced, and their activity is regulated directly by the level of nitrate-nitrite ions within cultured cells (Chroboczek-Kelker and Filner, 1971; Hahlbrock, 1974), but also apparently by the products of the assimilation of reduced nitrogen (see below).

Unlike the ammonium ion, nitrate is not toxic and, in many plants, much is transported to the shoots for assimilation. On the other hand, the nitrite ion can become toxic should it accumulate within plant tissues or in the medium, for example when growth conditions are not favourable to high nitrite reductase activity and when nitrate is the only nitrogen source (Jordan and Fletcher, 1979; Grimes and Hodges, 1990). In *Pinus pinaster*, nitrate reductase is induced by the presence of KNO_3, and plants regenerated *in vitro* exhibit an ability to reduce nitrate similar to that of seedlings (Faye *et al.*, 1986).

For most types of culture, the nitrate ion needs to be presented together with a reduced form of nitrogen (usually the NH_4^+ ion), and tissues will usually fail to grow on a medium with NO_3^- as the only nitrogen source (Hunault, 1985).

Reduced nitrogen

In the natural environment and under most cropping conditions, plant roots usually encounter little reduced nitrogen, because bacteria rapidly oxidize available sources (Hiatt, 1978). An exception is forest soils of mountainous regions of the northern hemisphere, where nitrates are not usually available (Durzan, 1976). If NH_4^+, and other reduced nitrogen compounds *are* available, (and this is particularly the case in the aseptic *in vitro* environment), they can be taken up and effectively utilized by plants. In fact the uptake of reduced nitrogen gives a plant an ergonomic advantage because the conversion of nitrate to ammonium ions (an energy-requiring process) is not necessary. The free ammonium ion can cause toxicity, which, at least in whole plants, can lead to an increase in ethylene evolution (Barker and Corey, 1987; Corey and Barker, 1987). Shoots grown on an unbuffered medium containing a high proportion of ammonium ions may become stunted or hyperhydric. These effects can sometimes be reversed by transfer to a medium containing a high proportion of NO_3^- or to one where NO_3^- is the only N source (Mott *et al.*, 1985). Hyperhydricity is the *in vitro* formation of abnormal organs which are brittle and have a water-soaked appearance (Chapter 13).

Growth of plant cultures may also be impaired in media containing high concentrations of NH_4^+ even when high concentrations of NO_3^- are present. Growth inhibition

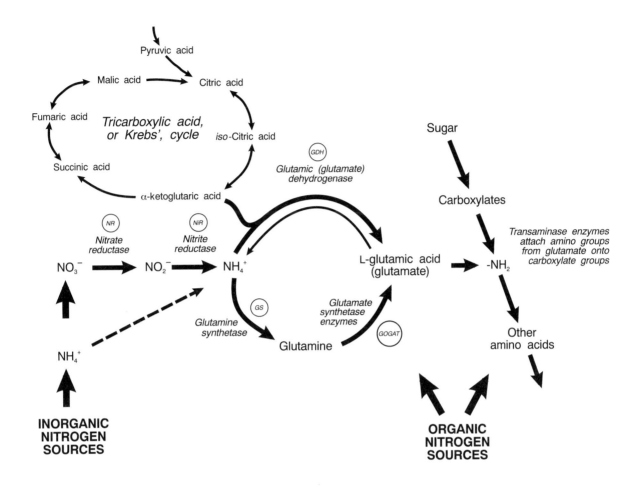

Fig. 93. The metabolism of nitrate and ammonium ions.

may not only be due to depressed pH (Mott *et al.*, 1985), but may reflect a toxicity induced the accumulation of excess ammonium ions. In normal circumstances the toxic effect of ammonium is avoided by conversion of the ion into amino acids. There are two routes by which this takes place (Fig. 93), the most important of which, under normal circumstances, is that by which L-glutamic acid is produced from glutamine through the action of glutamine synthetase (GS) and glutamate synthetase (GOGAT) enzymes. Compounds which block the action of GS can be used as herbicides (De Greef *et al.*, 1989).

The reaction of α-ketoglutaric acid with NH_4^+ is usually less important, but seems to have increased significance when there is an excess of ammonium ions (Furuhashi and Takahashi, 1982). Detoxification and ammonium assimilation may then be limited by the availabilty of

α-ketoglutaric acid, but this may be increased *in vitro* by adding to the medium one or more acids which are Krebs' (tri-carboxylic acid) cycle intermediates (see page 278). Their addition can stimulate growth of some cultures on media containing high levels of NH_4^+ (Gamborg, 1970).

In comparison with media having only nitrate as the nitrogen source, the presence of the ammonium ion in media usually leads to rapid amino acid and protein synthesis, and this takes place at the expense of the synthesis of carbohydrate compounds. This diversion of cellular metabolism can be disadvantageous in some shoot cultures, and can contribute towards the formation of hyperhydric shoots. Hyperhydricity no longer occurs when NH_4^+ is eliminated from the medium or greatly reduced. It is possible that adding an organic acid to the medium might also alleviate the symptoms on some plants.

A supply of reduced nitrogen in addition to nitrate, appears to be beneficial for at least two processes involved with cell division:

— **the formation of a cell wall.** Without a complete cell wall, protoplasts require a factor capable of inducing wall formation. Freshly-isolated protoplasts may contain sufficient of this substance to promote wall formation for just a few divisions. The wall-forming factor is only effective when NH_4^+ is present in the medium (Meyer and Abel, 1975a,b): glutamine does not substitute for NH_4^+:

— **the activity of growth regulators.** (see below)

There are several reports in the literature that, with constant amounts of NO_3^-, ammonium sulphate has not provided such a good source of NH_4^+ as ammonium nitrate or ammonium chloride (De Jong *et al.*, 1974; Steward and Hsu, 1977; Singh, 1978; Kamada and Harada, 1979b). Possibly the reason is that a medium containing ammonium sulphate has a greater tendency to become acid (Harris, 1956), than one containing less sulphate ions. This would result if the presence of sulphate ions accelerated the uptake of NH_4^+, or slowed the uptake of NO_3^- (see the section on pH later in this chapter). Ammonium sulphate has been used as the only source of the ammonium ion in some media used for the culture of legumes, including **Gamborg *et al.* (1968) B5**.

Ammonium as the sole nitrogen source

pH adjustment. If plant tissues are presented with a medium containing only NH_4^+ nitrogen, the pH falls steadily as the ion is taken up (for example a decrease of 0.9 pH units in 15 days in *Asparagus* callus — Hunault, 1985). Growth and morphogenesis is possible in suspension cultures containing only NH_4^+ ions, providing the pH of the medium is frequently adjusted by the addition of a base (Martin *et al.*, 1977), or the medium is buffered (see below). In wild carrot, the induction of embryogenesis required the medium to be adjusted to pH 5.4 at 8 hourly intervals (Dougall and Verma, 1978). Without adjustment, the pH of media containing only NH_4^+ falls rapidly to a point where cells cannot grow (Dougall, 1981).

When buffers are added. Ammonium can also serve as the only nitrogen source when the medium is buffered (see the section on pH, below). Tobacco cells could be grown on a medium containing NH_4^+ nitrogen if the organic acid ion, succinate, was added to the medium. Gamborg and Shyluk (1970) found that cultured cells could be grown without frequent pH adjustment on a medium containing only NH_4^+ nitrogen, when a carbox-

ylic acid was present. The organic acids appeared to minimize the acidification of the medium through NH_4^+ uptake. Similarly *Asparagus* internode callus grew just as well on NH_4^+ as the only nitrogen source as on a medium containing both NH_4^+ and NO_3^-, but only when organic acids (such as citrate, or malate) or MES buffer were added to the medium. When media were buffered with MES, the best callus growth occurred when the pH was 5.5 (Hunault, 1985).

The additional effect of organic acids. Although Krebs' cycle organic acids can act as buffers (above, and page 301), they may also act as substrates for amino acid synthesis from NH_4^+. To be assimilated into amino acids *via* the GDH enzyme, the ammonium ion must react with α-ketoglutaric acid which is produced by the Krebs' cycle (Fig 93). Its availability may govern the rate at which ammonium can be metabolised by this route. The rate of assimilation might be expected to be improved by supplying the plant with α-ketoglutarate directly, or by supplying acids which are intermediates in the Krebs' cycle (citrate, *iso*-citrate, succinate, fumarate or malate), for then the natural production of α-ketoglutarate should increase (Gamborg, 1970).

This hypothesis was confirmed by Behrend and Mateles (1976), who concluded that succinate, or other Krebs' cycle acids, acted mainly as a nutrient, replacing α-ketoglutarate as it was withdrawn from the cycle during NH_4^+ metabolism and amino acid synthesis. Depletion of α-ketoglutarate causes the cycle to cease unless it, or another intermediate, is replaced. The optimum molar ratio of NH_4^+ to succinate, was 1.5 (*e.g.* 10 mM NH_4^+: 15 mM succinate). Chaleff (1983a) thought that the growth of rice callus on **Chaleff (1983a) R3(NH₄)** medium, containing 34 mM of only ammonium nitrogen, **[Chaleff(1983a)R3 NH4 medium]** was enabled by the presence of 20 mM succinate or α-ketoglutarate, partly by the buffering capacity of the acids, and partly by their metabolism within the plant, where they may serve as substrate for amino acid synthesis. Similar conclusions have been reached by other workers (*e.g.* Fukunaga *et al.*, 1978; Dougall and Weyrauch, 1980; Hunault, 1985; Molnar, 1988b), who have found that compounds such as ammonium malate and ammonium citrate are effective nitrogen sources.

Orange juice promotes the growth of *Citrus* callus. Einset (1978) thought that this was not due to the effect of citric acid, but Erner and Reuveni (1981) showed that citric acid, particularly at concentrations above the 5.2 mM found in the juice used by Einset, does indeed promote the growth of *Citrus* callus; it had a more pronounced effect than other Krebs' cycle acids, perhaps due to the distinctive biochemistry of the genus.

Organic acids not only enhance ammonium assimilation when NH_4^+ provides the only source of nitrogen, but may sometimes also do so when nitrate ions are in attendance. The weight of rice anther callus was increased on **Chaleff (1983a) R3** medium, if 20 mM succinate [**Chaleff (1983a) R3 Succ.** medium] or α-ketoglutarate was added (Chaleff (1983a). Similarly the rate of growth of *Brassica nigra* suspensions on **MS** medium, was improved either by adding adding amino acids, or 15 mM succinate. An equivalent improvement (apparently due entirely to buffering) only occurred through adding 300 mM MES buffer (Molnar, 1988b). However, the presence of organic acids may be detrimental to morphogenesis. In Chaleff's experiment, the presence of succinate in **R3** medium markedly decreased the frequency of anther callus formation.

Photosynthesis. Although plants grown on nutrient solutions containing only NH_4^+ nitrogen have been found to possess abnormally high levels of PEP enzyme (Arnozis *et al.*, 1988), the enzyme facilitating CO_2 fixation in photosynthesis, media containing high levels of NH_4^+ tend to inhibit chlorophyll synthesis (Yoshida and Kohno, 1982) and photosynthesis.

Urea

Plants are able to absorb urea, but like the ammonium ion, it is not a substance which is normally available in soils in the natural environment. It is however produced as a by–product of nitrogen metabolism; small quantities are found in many higher plants, which are able to utilise urea as a source of nitrogen, providing it is first converted to ammonium ions by the enzyme urease. At least in legumes, urease requires the microelement nickel for activity (see below). In conifers, the epidermal cells of cotyledons and cotyledons are capable of urease induction and ammonium ion formation (Durzan, 1987).

Urea can be used as the sole nitrogen source for cultures, but growth is less rapid than when ammonium and nitrate ions are supplied (Kirkby *et al.*, 1987); urease enzyme increases after cultures have been maintained for several passages on a urea-based medium (King, 1977; Skokut and Filner, 1980). Although the metabolism of urea, like that of other reduced nitrogen compounds, causes the production of excess hydrogen ions, less are predicted to be secreted into the medium than during the utilisation of NH_4^+ (Raven, 1986), so that urea is less suitable than ammonium to balance the pH of media containing NO_3^-. Nitrate ions are utilized in preference to urea when both nitrogen sources are available (King, 1977). Urea is able to serve as a reduced nitrogen source during embryogenesis (Durzan, 1987), but has been used in relatively few culture media, and of these, none has been widely adopted (George, E.F. *et al.*, 1987).

Media with nitrate <u>and</u> ammonium ions

Most intact plants, tissues and organs take up nitrogen more effectively, and grow more rapidly, on nutrient solutions containing both nitrate and ammonium ions, than they do on solutions containing just one of these sources. Although in most media, reduced nitrogen is present in lower concentration than nitrate, some morphogenic events depend on its presence, and it can be used in plant cultures in a regulatory role. Adventitious organs may also develop abnormally if NH_4^+ is missing (Drew, 1987).

Possible explanations which have been put forward for the regulatory effect of NH_4^+ are:

1. that the reduction and assimilation of NO_3^- is assisted by the presence of of NH_4^+ or the products of its assimilation (Bayley *et al.* 1972a,b; Mohanty and Fletcher, 1978; 1980). When grown on a medium containing a small amount of NH_4^+ nitrogen in addition to nitrate, suspension cultured cells of 'Paul's Scarlet' rose accumulated twice as much protein as when grown on a medium containing only nitrate, even though ammonium finally accounted for only 10% of the total protein nitrogen (Mohanty and Fletcher, 1980).

   Dougall (1977) considered this to be an oversimplified interpretation, moreover nitrate reductase activity is effectively increased by the presence of NO_3^- (Müller and Mendel, 1982) and in some plants, a high concentration of NH_4^+ inhibits nitrate reductase activity (see below).

2. that ammonium ions effectively buffer plant nutrient media in the presence of nitrate and so enhance nitrate uptake (see the section on pH later in this chapter).

Cultures of some plants *are* capable of growing with only NO_3^- nitrogen (*e.g.* cell cultures of *Reseda luteoli*, soybean, wheat, flax and horse radish — Gamborg, 1970; callus of *Medicago sativa* — Walker and Sato, 1981), although yields are generally better when the medium is supplemented with NH_4^+. Craven *et al.* (1972) with carrot, and Mohanty and Fletcher (1978) with *Rosa* 'Paul's Scarlet', found that the presence of NH_4^+ was particularly important during the first few days of a suspension culture. After that cells increase in cell number and dry weight more rapidly on NO_3^- nitrogen alone.

The response of plant cultures to nitrate and ammonium ions depends to a large extent on the enzymes shown in Fig. 93, and the manner in which their activities are increased or inhibited in different tissues by the presence of the ions. These factors vary according to the degree of differentiation of the tissue (Suzuki and Nata, 1982), its physiological age, and its genotype. For example, the high level of NH_4^+ in **MS** medium inhibited the activity of glutamate synthetase enzyme in soybean suspension cultures (Gamborg and Shyluk, 1970), while in *N. tabacum*, a peak of glutamate dehydrogenase (GDH) appeared to exist at 10 mM NH_4^+ (Lazar and Collins, 1981). The activity of GDH and NADH-dependent GOGAT developed rapidly in cultured tobacco cells, while nitrate reductase and ferridoxin-dependent GOGAT activity increased more slowly during growth. By contrast, in sunflower cultures, the specific activity of GDH and ferridoxin-dependent GOGAT only reached a maximum at the end of growth, and the presence of 15 mM NH_4^+ inhibited the activity of nitrate reductase, indicating that the cells were entirely dependent on the reduced nitrogen in the medium (Lenee and Chupeau, 1989).

In consequence of such variation, the relative concentrations of ammonium and nitrate in media may need to be altered for different cultures.

The correct balance of ions

When trying to find media formulations suitable for different plant species and different kinds of cultures, two important factors to be considered are:—

- The total concentration of nitrogen in the medium;

- The ratio of nitrate to ammomium ions.

There is a high proportion of NH_4^+ nitrogen in **MS** medium [ratio of NO_3^- to NH_4^+, 66 : 34 (1.9)] and the quantity of total nitrogen is much higher than that in the majority of other media. For some cultures, the total amount of nitrogen is too high and the balance between the two forms in the medium is not optimal.

It is noticeable that in several media used for legume culture, there is a greater proportion of NO_3^- to NH_4^+ ions than in **MS** medium. Evans *et al.* (1976) found that soybean leaf callus grew more rapidly and formed more adventitious roots when the ammonium nitrate in **MS** medium was replaced with 500 mg/l ammonium sulphate. A reduction in the ammonium level of their medium for the callus culture of red clover, was also found to be necessary by Phillips and Collins (1979a, 1980) to obtain optimum growth rates of suspension cultured cells. A similar adjustment can be beneficial in other genera. Eriksson (1965) was able to enhance the growth rate of cell cultures of *Haplopappus gracilis* when he reduced the ammonium nitrate concentration to 75% of that in **MS** medium, and doubled the potassium dihydrogen phosphate level.

Table 22 lists examples of where changes to the nitrogen content of **MS** medium resulted in improved *in vitro* growth or morphogenesis. It will be seen that the balance between NO_3^- and NH_4^+ in these different experiments has varied widely. This implies that the ratio between the two ions either needs to be specifically adjusted for each plant species, or that the total nitrogen content of the medium is the most important determinant of growth or morphogenesis. Only occasionally is an even higher concentration of nitrate than that in **MS** medium beneficial. Trolinder and Goodin (1988b) found that the best growth of globular somatic embryos of *Gossypium* was on **MS** medium with an extra 1.9 g/l KNO_3.

There are reports that adjustments to the nitrogen content and ratio of NO_3^- to NH_4^+, can be advantageous in media containing low concentrations of salts (Table 23). Biedermann (1987) found that even quite small adjustments could be made advantageously to the NO_3^- content of a low salt medium [that of **Biedermann (1987)**] for the shoot culture of different *Magnolia* species and hybrids, but too great a proportion of NO_3^- was toxic.

The nitrate–ammonium ratio for various purposes

Root growth. Root growth is often depressed by NH_4^+ and promoted by NO_3^-. Media for isolated root culture contain no NH_4^+, or very little. Although roots are able to take up nitrate ions from solutions which become progressively more alkaline as assimilation proceeds, the same may not be true of cells, tissues and organs *in vitro*.

Shoot cultures. Media containing only nitrate nitrogen are used for the shoot culture of some plants, for example strawberry (Boxus, 1974a), which can be cultured with 10.9 mM NO_3^- alone; supplementing the medium with 6 mM NH_4^+ causes phytotoxicity (Damiano, 1980a). However, shoot cultures of strawberry grown without NH_4^+ can become chlorotic: adding a small amount of NH_4NO_3 (or another source of reduced nitrogen) to the medium at the last proliferation stage, or to the rooting medium, may then give more fully developed plants with green leaves (Zimmerman, 1981; Piagnani and Eccher, 1988). On some occasions it is necessary to eliminate or reduce NH_4^+ from the medium for shoot cultures to prevent hyperhydricity (Chapter 13).

Nitrogen supply and morphogenesis

Morphogenesis is influenced by the total amount of nitrogen provided in the medium and, for most purposes, a supply of both reduced nitrogen and nitrate seems to be necessary. The requirement for both forms of nitrogen in a particular plant species can only be determined by a carefully controlled experiment: simply leaving out one component of a normal medium gives an incomplete picture. For example, cotyledons of lettuce failed to initiate buds when NH_4NO_3 was omitted from **Miller (1961a)** salts and instead formed masses of callus (Doerschug and Miller, 1967): was this result due to the elimination of

NH$_4^+$, or to reducing the total nitrogen content of the medium to one third of its original value?

Where the nitrate/ammonium balance was important. The importance of the relative proportions of NO$_3^-$ and NH$_4^+$ has been demonstrated during indirect morphogenesis and the growth of regenerated plants. Grimes and Hodges (1990) found that although the initial cellular events which led to plant regeneration from embryo callus of indica rice, were supported in media in which total nitrogen ranged from 25 to 45 mM and the NO$_3^-$ to NH$_4^+$ ratio varied from 50:50 to 85:15 (Table 23), differ-

entiation and growth were affected by very small alterations to the NO$_3^-$ to NH$_4^+$ ratio. Changing it from 80:20 (**N6**) medium, to 75:20, brought about a 3-fold increase in plant height and root growth, whereas lowering it below 75:25, resulted in short shoots with thick roots. Atypical growth, resulting from an unsuitable balance of nitrate and ammonium, has also been noted in other plants. It gave rise to abnormal leaves in *Adiantum capillus- veneris* (Pais and Casal, 1987); the absence of ammonium in the medium caused newly initiated roots of *Carica papaya* to be abnormally thickened, and to have

Table 22. Examples of adjustments to the nitrogen content of **MS** medium which resulted in improved growth or morphogenesis. In each case, only the NH$_4^+$ and NO$_3^-$ content was changed, the rest of the medium being the same (except K$^+$ and Cl$^-$).

Plant species	Type of culture	Results	NO$_3^-$ mM	NH$_4^+$ mM	Ratio of NO$_3^-$ to NH$_4^+$	Total N mM	Reference
Murashige and Skoog (1962)			**39.40**	**20.61**	**66:34 (1.91)**	**60.01**	
Nicotiana tabacum	Callus	Optimum callus growth	39.4	20.61	66:34 (1.91)	60.01	Murashige and Skoog (1962)
Nicotiana tabacum	Callus	Equal callus growth and shoot formation	40.0	20	67:33 (2.00)	60.0	Behki and Lesley (1980)
			48.0	12.0	80:20 (4.00)	60.0	
			52.0	8.0	87:13 (6.50)	60.0	
	Callus	Callus growth and root formation	24.0	12.0	67:33 (2.00)	36.0	
Dioscorea spp.	Callus	Callus growth and adventitious plantlets	6.25	6.25	50:50 (1.00)	15.0	Asokan *et al.* (1983)
Diospyros kaki	Shoot	Shoot proliferation	19.7	20.61	49:51 (0.96)	40.31	Sugiura *et al.* (1986)
Rubus idaeus	Shoot	Shoot proliferation	19.7	10.30	66:34 (1.91)	30.0	Welander (1987a)
Prunus avium	Shoot	Shoot proliferation	29.09	10.31	74:26 (2.82)	39.40	Righetti *et al.* (1988)
Castanea sativa and *Castanea* hybrids	Shoot	Shoot proliferation	18.00	3.00	86:14 (6.00)	21.0	Piagnani and Eccher (1988)
Peltophorum pterocarpum	Anther	Callus from anthers and shoot regeneration	34.7	9.99	78:22 (3.47)	44.6	Lakshmana Rao and De (1987)
Euphorbia esula	Suspension	Plant regeneration	18.00	8.00	67:33 (2.25)	27mM	Davis *et al.* (1988)
Gossypium hirsutum	Somatic embryo	Growth of globular somatic embryos	58.2	10.30	85:15 (5.65)	68.5	Trolinder and Goodin (1988b)
Haplopappus gracillis	Suspension	Improved growth rate †	33.78	14.99	69:31 (2.25)	8.77	Eriksson (1965)
Oryza sativa	Protoplast	Cell division	18.79	1.01	95:5 (18.53)	19.80	Yamada *et al.* (1986)

†   Medium also contained double the **MS** phosphate level

few lateral branches (Drew, 1987). As mentioned in Chapter 6, shoot cultures may survive low temperature storage more effectively when maintained on a medium containing less NH_4NO_3 than in **MS** medium (Moriguchi and Yamaki, 1989).

By comparing different strengths of **Heller(1953; 1955)** and **MS** media, and varying the NH_4NO_3 and $NaNO_3$ levels in both, David (1972) was led to the conclusion that the principal ingredient in **MS** favouring differentiation in Maritime pine explants is NH_4NO_3. However in embryonic explants of *Pinus strobus*, adventitious shoot

formation was better on **Schenk and Hildebrant (1972)** medium than on **MS** (which induced more callus formation). The difference in the ammonium level of the two media was mainly responsible (Flinn and Webb, 1986).

Morphogenesis influenced by total available nitrogen. Others have found that the *total* nitrogen content of culture media influences morphogenesis more than the relative ammonium concentration. Results of Margara and Leydecker (1978) indicated that adventitious shoot formation from rapeseed callus was optimal in media containing 30–45 mM total nitrogen. The percentage of

Table 23. Examples of beneficial and harmful adjustments to the total nitrogen, and the NO_3^- to NH_4^+ ratio, in low salt media .

Basic medium in which N modified	Plant species or variety	Type of culture and results	NO_3^- mM	NH_4^+ mM	Ratio of NO_3^- to NH_4^+	Total N mM	Reference
Biederman (1987)			**8.62**	**6.25**	**58:42 (1.38)**	**14.87**	
Magnolia stellata		Shoot culture: maximum shoot proliferation	10.99	6.25	64:36 (1.76)	17.24	Biederman (1987)
Magnolia 'Elizabeth'		Shoot culture: maximum shoot proliferation	8.62–10.99	6.25	From 58:42 (1.38) to 64:36 (1.76)	14.87–17.24	
Magnolia 'Yellow Bird', and '#149'		Shoot culture: maximum shoot proliferation	7.43	6.25	54:46 (1.19)	13.68	
Magnolia (all vars.)		Shoot culture: death of the cultures of all varieties	25.04	6.25	80:20 (4.01)	31.29	
Chu *et al.* (1975) N6			**28.00**	**7.00**	**80:20 (4.00)**	**35.00**	
Oryza sativa		Callus induction from immature embryos	28.00	7.00	80:20 (4.00)	35.00	Grimes and Hodges (1990)
		Plant regeneration after callus induction with 2,4-D	12.5–38.25	22.5–3.75	From 50:50 (1.0) to 85:15 (5.66)	25.00–45.00	
		Optimum no. of plants per zygotic embryo	18.75	6.25	75:25 (3.00)	25.00	
		Media giving poor regeneration	100 <17.5	0 >17.5	100:0 (∞) <50:50 (<1.0)	35.00	
		Optimum plantlet growth	26.25	8.75	75:25 (3.00)	35.00	

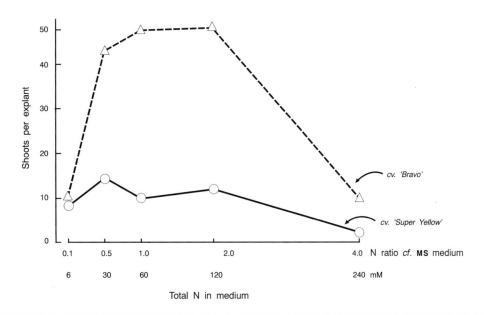

Fig. 94. The number of adventitious shoots formed directly on Chrysanthemum explants with increasing total nitrogen concentration in an otherwise normal **MS** medium. [From data of Roest and Bokelmann, 1975].

explants forming shoots was reduced on media containing smaller or greater amounts (*e.g.* on **MS** medium). Increasing the ratio of NH_4^+ to total N in media, from 0.20 to 0.33 was also detrimental. Similarly, Gertsson (1988c) found that a small number of adventitious shoots was obtained on petiole segments of *Senecio × hybridus* when the total nitrogen in **MS** medium was increased to 75 mM, but that an increased number of shoots was produced when the total nitrogen was reduced to 30 mM (while keeping the same ratio of NO_3^- to NH_4^+). Shoot production was more than doubled if, at the same time as the total N was reduced, the potassium ion concentration was fixed at 15 mM, instead of 20 mM.

The total amount of nitrogen in a medium was shown by Roest and Bokelmann (1975) to affect the number of adventitious shoots formed directly on *Chrysanthemum* pedicels. The combined amount of $KNO_3 + NH_4NO_3$ in **MS** medium (60 mM), was adjusted as is shown in Fig.94, while the ratio of NO_3^- to NH_4^+ (66:34) was unchanged. From 30–120 mM total nitrogen was optimal. However there was clearly a strong effect of genotype, because the cultivar 'Bravo' was much more sensitive to increased nitrogen than 'Super Yellow'.

Nitrogen × sugar interaction. The enhancement of morphogenesis caused by high nitrogen levels may not be apparent unless there is an adequate sucrose concentration in the medium (Margara and Rancillac, 1966; Gamborg *et al*. 1974). In *Dendrobium*, the uptake of NO_3^- is slower than that of NH_4^+. Uptake is dependent on the

nature and concentration of the sugar in the medium, being slower in the presence of fructose than when sucrose or glucose are supplied (Hew *et al*., 1988). The rate of growth of *Rosa* 'Paul's Scarlet' suspensions was influenced by the ratio of NO_3^- to sucrose in the medium. A high ratio favoured the accumulation of reduced nitrogen, but not the most rapid rate of cell growth (Fletcher, 1980).

Embryogenesis and embryo growth. It is accepted that the presence of some reduced nitrogen is necessary for somatic embryogenesis in cell and callus cultures (Halperin and Wetherell, 1965; Reinert *et al.* 1967); but although reduced nitrogen compounds are beneficial to somatic embryo induction, apparently they are not essential until the stage of embryo development (Kamada and Harada, 1979b). A relatively high level of both nitrate and ammonium ions then seems to be required. Some workers have also noted enhanced embryogenesis and/or improved embryo growth when media have been supplemented with amino acids in addition to NO_3^- and NH_4^+ (page 289).

Street (1979) thought that an optimum level of NH_4^+ for embryogenesis was about 10 mM (from NH_4Cl) in the presence of 12–40 mM NO_3 (from KNO_3): that is:

[NO_3^- to NH_4^+ ratio, from 55:45 to 80:20; Total N 22–50 mM]

Walker and Sato (1981) obtained no embryogenesis in alfalfa callus in the absence of either ammonium or nitrate ions. Miller's medium [**Miller (1961a; 1963)**] (12.5 mM NH_4^+) supported a high rate of embryogenesis:

[NO_3^- to NH_4^+ ratio, 68:32; Total N 39.1 mM],

but only a small number of embryos were produced on **Schenk and Hildebrandt (1972)** medium (**SH**):

[NO_3^- to NH_4^+ ratio, 90:10, Total N 27.32 mM],

unless it was supplemented with NH_4^+ from either ammonium carbamate, ammonium chloride or ammonium sulphate. An optimal level of ammonium in **SH** medium was 12.5 mM:

[NO_3^- to NH_4^+ ratio, then 66:34, total N, 37.22],

although embryogenesis was still at a high level with 100 mM ammonium ion:

[NO_3^- to NH_4^+ ratio, then, 20:80; total N, 124.72 mM].

By contrast, *Coffea arabica* leaf callus, which was formed on a medium containing **MS** salts, was induced to become embryogenic by first being cultured on a medium with ½ **MS** salts (and high auxin):

[NO_3^- to NH_4^+ ratio, 66:34; total N, 30.0 mM],

and then moved to another medium containing ½ **MS** salts with an extra 2850 mg/l KNO_3:

[NO_3^- to NH_4^+ ratio, 82:18; total N, 58.2 mM] (and low auxin)
(Sondahl and Sharp, 1977a).

Zygotic embryos. The presence of some reduced nitrogen in the growth medium is also required for the continued growth of zygotic embryos in culture. Nitrate alone is insufficient (Mauney *et al.* 1967; Norstog, 1967, 1973). An optimum concentration of NH_4^+ for the development of barley embryos in culture was 6.4 mM (Umbeck and Norstog, 1979). A similar provision seems to be necessary in most plants for the *in vitro* growth of somatic embryos (Chapters 12 and 14).

Flower bud formation and growth. Nitrate was essential for the formation of adventitious buds on leaf segments of *Begonia franconis*. The greatest proportion of flower buds was obtained with 5 mM NO_3^- and 1.5 mM NH_4^+. Above this level, NH_4^+ promoted vegetative sprouts (Berghoef and Bruinsma, 1979c). The best *in vitro* growth of *Begonia franconis* flower buds detached from young inflorescences, occurred on a medium with 10–15 mM total nitrogen (NO_3^- to NH_4^+ ratio, 50:50 to 67:33) (Berghoef and Bruinsma, 1979a). Detached flower buds of *Cleome iberidella* were found to grow best *in vitro* with 25 mM total nitrogen (NO_3^- to NH_4^+ ratio, 80:20) (De Jong and Bruinsma, 1974; De Jong *et al.* 1974), but the complete omission of NH_4NO_3 from **MS** medium, where the salts had been diluted to ⅕ their original concentration, promoted the development (but not the initiation) of adventitious floral buds of *Torenia fournieri* (Tanimoto and Harada, 1979, 1981a, 1982c).

Effect on the action of growth regulants. The ratio of NO_3^- to NH_4^+ present in the culture medium has been found to affect the activity of plant growth substances and plant growth regulators. The mechanisms by which this occurs are not fully elucidated.

It has been noted, for example, that cells will divide with less added cytokinin when the proportion of reduced nitrogen is reasonably high. To induce tobacco protoplasts to divide, it was necessary to add 0.5–2 mg/l BAP to a medium containing only NO_3^- nitrogen. The presence of glutamine or NH_4^+ in the medium together with NO_3^-, reduced the cytokinin requirement, and division proceeded without *any* added cytokinin when urea, NH_4^+, or glutamine were the sole N-sources of the medium (Meyer and Abel, 1975b). Sargent and King (1974) found that soybean cells were dependent on cytokinin when cultured in a medium containing NO_3^- nitrogen, but independent of cytokinin when NH_4^+ was present as well.

The relative proportion of nitrate and ammonium ions also affects the response of cells to auxin growth regulators in terms of both cell division and morphogenesis. It is possible that this is through the control of intracellular pH (see below). Carrot cultures that produce somatic embryos when transferred from a high- to a low-auxin medium, can also be induced into embryogenesis in a high-auxin medium, if it contains adequate reduced nitrogen. Only root initials are formed in high-auxin media which do not contain reduced nitrogen (Halperin, 1967). The number of plants regenerated from rice callus grown on **Chu** *et al.* **(1975)** medium containing 0.5 mg/l 2,4-D, depended on the ratio of NO_3^- to NH_4^+. It was high in the unaltered medium (ratio 4:1), but considerably less if, with the same total N, the ratio of the two ions was changed to 1:1 (Grimes and Hodges, 1990).

Cells of *Antirrhinum majus* regenerated from isolated protoplasts were stimulated to divide with a reduced quantity of auxin in a medium containing 39.77 mM total nitrogen [NO_3^- to NH_4^+ ratio, 39:77 (2.98)] by adding further ammonium ion to give a total nitrogen content of 54.72 mM [NO_3^- to NH_4^+ ratio, 54:46 (1.19)]. or, alternatively, 400 mg/l of casein hydrolysate (Poirier-Hamon *et al.* 1974).

In experiments of Koetje *et al.* (1989) and Grimes and Hodges (1990) (Table 23), when the NO_3^- to NH_4^+ ratio in **N6** medium was 80:20, there was a strong dose response curve to the auxin 2,4-D with 0.5 mg/l being the best concentration to induce embryogenesis in *Oryza sativa* callus; if the medium was modified, so that the NO_3^- to NH_4^+ ratio was 66:34 or 50:50, 2,4-D was less effective, and there was little difference in the number of plants regenerated between 0.5 and 3 mg/l 2,4-D. The ratio of NO_3^- to NH_4^+ therefore seemed either to to alter the sensitivity of cells to the auxin, or to affect its uptake or rate of metabolism.

Table 24. The effect of total nitrogen, and the NO_3^- to NH_4^+ ratio, on the type of organ produced by alfalfa cells which had been cultured on a root-inducing medium. [Walker and Sato, 1981].

Type of organ produced	NH_4^+ mM	Total N mM	Ratio of NO_3^- to NH_4^+
Roots	<2.5	27.2	From 100:0 to 91:9
Roots *and* somatic embryos	12.5–37.5	37.3–62.3	From 66:34 to 40:60
Somatic embryos	50.0–100	74.7–124.7	From 33:67 to 20:80

Walker and Sato (1981) also found that the proportion of ammonium ion in the medium can influence the way in which growth regulants control morphogenesis. Having been placed for 3 days on a medium which would normally induce root formation [**Schenk and Hildebrandt (1972)** medium containing 5 μM 2,4-D and 50 μM kinetin], suspension cultured cells were subsequently plated on a modification of the same medium (which contains 24.8 mM NO_3^-) without regulants, in which the concentration of NH_4^+ had been adjusted to various levels. Table 24 shows that the morphogenesis experienced, depended on the concentration of ammonia in the regeneration medium. Media containing high levels of ammonium ion would have tended to become acid, especially as the extra ammonium was added as ammonium sulphate (see page 278). Possibly this affected the uptake or action of the regulants?

Amino acids

The need for amino acid additions

Amino acids can be added to plant media to satisfy the requirement of cultures for reduced nitrogen, but as they are expensive to purchase, they will only be used in media for mass propagation where this results in improved results. For most tissue culture purposes, the addition of amino acids may be unnecessary, providing media contain adequate amounts, and correct proportions, of nitrate and ammonium ions. For example, Murashige and Skoog (1962) found that when cultures were grown on media such as **Heller (1953; 1955)**, **Nitsch and Nitsch (1956) N1**, and **Hildebrandt** *et al.* **(1946) Tobacco,** containing sub-optimal amounts of inorganic chemicals, a casein hydrolysate (consisting mainly of a mixture of amino acids, see

later) substantially increased the yield of tobacco callus, whereas it gave only marginal increases in yield when added to their revised **MS** medium. Arginine (0.287 mM) increased the growth of sugar cane callus and suspension cultures grown on **Nickell and Maretzski (1969)** medium (Nickell and Maretzski, 1969) but was without effect on cultures of this plant grown on a medium based on **Scowcroft and Adamson (1976) CS5** macronutrients (Larkin, 1982)

It is noticeable from the literature that organic supplements (particularly amino acids) have been especially beneficial for growth or morphogenesis when cells or tissues were cultured on media such as **White (1943a)**, which do not contain ammonium ions. White (1937b) and Bonner and Addicott (1937), for example, used known amino acids to replace the variable mixture provided by yeast extract. For the culture of *Picea glauca* callus, Reinert and White (1956) supplemented **Risser and White (1964)** medium with 17 supplementary amino acids, and similar, or greater numbers, were used by Torrey and Reinert (1961) and Filner (1965) in **White (1943a)** medium for the culture of carrot, *Convolvulus arvensis*, *Haplopappus gracilis* and tobacco tissues.

Dependence on the nitrate to ammonium ratio. Grimes and Hodges (1990) found that when both NO_3^- and NH_4^+ are present in the medium, the response to organic nitrogen depends on the ratio of these two ions. Twice as many plants were regenerated from embryogenic rice callus when 1g/l CH was added to **Chu** *et al.* **(1975) N6** medium, providing the proportion of NO_3^- to NH_4^+ was also changed to 1 (50:50). There was little response to CH with the same amount of total N in the medium, if the NO_3^-/NH_4^+ ratio was 4 (*i.e.* 80%:20%, as in the original medium), or more.

Amino acids as the sole N source

As most of the inorganic nitrogen supplied in culture media is converted by plant tissues to amino acids, which are then assimilated into proteins, it should be possible to culture plants on media in which amino acids are the only nitrogen source. This has been demonstrated: for example, *Nicotiana tabacum* callus can be cultured on **MS** salts lacking NO_3^- and NH_4^+ (but with an extra 20.6 mM K^+), if 0.1 mM glycine, 1mM arginine, 2 mM aspartic acid and 6 mM glutamine are added (Müller and Grafe, 1978); wild carrot suspensions can be grown on a medium containing glutamine or casein hydrolysate as the sole nitrogen source (Anderson, J.O., 1976). Amino acids provide plant cells with an immediately available source of nitrogen, and uptake can be much more rapid than that of inorganic nitrogen in the same medium (Thom *et al.* 1981). Only the L - form of amino acids is biologically active.

Amino acids can also provide reduced nitrogen in culture media in place of NH_4^+ and as a supplement to NO_3^-. However they are usually employed as minor additions to media containing both NH_4^+ and NO_3^-. Uptake of amino acids into cultured tissues causes a decrease in the pH of the medium, similar to that which occurs when NH_4^+ ions are absorbed.

Sugar-based amines such as glucosamine and galactosamine can also serve as a source of reduced nitrogen in morphogenesis (Margara, 1969a; Margara and Leydecker, 1978).

Biologically-active amino acids

Amino acids are classified according to their stereoisomers and according to the relative positions of the amino group and the acidic radical. Only the L- isomers of the α- amino acids are important for plant tissue culture media. They have the general structure:

$$NH_2$$
$$|$$
$$R - CH - COOH$$

β-Amino acids , which have the general structure:

$$NH_2$$
$$|$$
$$R - CH\ CH_2 - COOH$$

(where R = functional groups)

are present in plants but tend to result from secondary metabolism.

Unfortunately the particular amino acid, or mixture of amino acids, which promotes growth or morphogenesis in one species, may not do so in another. For instance, L-α-alanine, glutamine, asparagine, aspartic acid, glutamic acid, arginine and proline could serve as a source of reduced nitrogen in a medium containing 20 mM NO_3^-, and were effective in promoting embryogenesis in *Daucus carota* callus and suspensions, but lysine, valine, histidine, leucine and methionine were ineffective (Kamada and Harada, 1982).

Competitive inhibition. Some amino acids are growth inhibitory at fairly low concentrations and this is particularly observed when mixtures of two or more amino acids are added to media. Inhibition is thought to be due to the competitive interaction of one compound with another. In oat embryo cultures, phenylalanine and L-tyrosine antagonise each other, as do L-leucine and DL-valine, DL-isoleucine and DL-valine, and L- arginine and L-lysine (Harris, 1956).

Lysine and threonine often exert a co-operative inhibition when present together, but do not inhibit growth when added to a medium singly (Cattoir-Reynaerts *et al.* 1981).

Glycine. Glycine is an ingredient of many media. It has usually been added in small amounts, and has been included by some workers amongst the vitamin ingredients. Despite frequent use, it is difficult to find hard evidence that glycine is really essential for so many tissue cultures, but possibly it helps to protect cell membranes from osmotic and temperature stress (Orczyk and Malepszy, 1985).

White (1939b) showed that isolated tomato roots grew better when his medium was supplemented with glycine rather than yeast extract and that glycine could replace the mixture of nine amino acids that had been used earlier. It was employed as an organic component by Skoog (1944) and continued to be used in his laboratory until the experiments of Murashige and Skoog (1962). They adopted the kinds and amounts of organic growth factors specified by White (1943a) and so retained 2 mg/l glycine in their medium without further testing.

Linsmaier and Skoog (1965), furthering the study of medium components to organic ingredients, omitted glycine from **MS** medium and discovered that low concentrations of it had no visible effect on the growth of tobacco callus, while at 20 mg/l it depressed growth. No doubt the success of **MS** medium has caused the 2 mg/l glycine of Skoog (1944) to be copied in many subsequent experiments. Many workers overlook the later Linsmaier and Skoog paper.

Casein and other protein hydrolysates. Proteins which have been hydrolysed by acid, or enzymes, and so broken down into smaller molecules, are less costly than identified amino acids. The degree of degradation varies: some protein hydrolysates consist of mixtures of amino acids together with other nitrogenous compounds such as peptide fragments, vitamins, and elements which might (if they can form inorganic ions, or are associated with organic compounds which can be taken up by plant tissues) be able to serve as macro- or micro-elements. Peptones are prepared from one or several proteins in a similar fashion but generally consist of low molecular weight proteins. Although protein hydrolysates are a convenient source of substances which may promote plant growth, they are by nature relatively undefined supplements. The proportion of individual amino acids in different hydrolysates depends on the nature of the source protein and the method by which the product has been prepared (Table 25).

The hydrolysate most commonly used in culture media is that of the milk protein, casein, although lactalbumin hydrolysate has been employed (La Motte and Lersten, 1971). Peptones and tryptone have been used less frequently, although there are reports of their having been added to media with advantage (*e.g.* Muralidhar and

Table 25. Some analyses of the amino acids in casein hydrolysates and in yeast extract (mg per gram).

| Amino acid | Casein hydrolysate | | | Yeast extract |
	Acid hyrolysis D	Pancreatic enzyme hydrolysis D	N-Z-Amine =	 I
Alanine			16.4	
Arginine	14	26		7.8
Aspartic acid	37	51		51
Cystine	3	3.0		
Glutamic acid	142	170	152.9	65
Glycine	10	18		24
Histidine	7	24		9.4
Isolecine	27	50		29
Leucine	35	71		36
Lysine	37	53	51.4	40
Methionine	17	24		7.9
Phenylalanine	7	38	28.9	22
Proline	40	115	55.4	
Threonine	25	35		34
Trytophan		9		8.8
Tyrosine	31	23	20.8	6.0
Valine	41	56		34

D = As given by Bridson (1978)

= = Given in the 1991 Sigma Chemical Company catalogue.

I = Given by Sandstedt and Skoog (1960) (ex the Sigma Chemical Company) and identically in Bridson (1978).

Mehta, 1982; Pierik *et al.*, 1988a). Casein hydrolysates can be a source of calcium, phosphate, several microelements, vitamins and, most importantly, a mixture of up to 18 amino acids. Several casein hydrolysates (CH) are available commercially but their value for plant tissue culture can vary considerably. Acid hydrolysis can denature some amino acids and so products prepared by enzymatic hydolysis are to be preferred. The best can be excellent sources of reduced nitrogen, as they can contain a relatively large amount of glutamine.

Casein hydrolysate produces an improvement in the growth of *Cardamine pratensis* and *Silene alba* suspensions, only if the medium is deficient in phosphorus. Glutamine has the same effect; it is the most common amino acid in CH, and its synthesis requires ATP. For these reasons, Bister-Miel *et al.* (1985) concluded that CH overcomes the shortage of glutamine when there is insufficient phosphorus for adequate biosynthesis.

However several investigators have concluded that casein hydrolysate itself, is more effective for plant culture than the addition of the major amino acids which it provides. This has led to speculation that CH might contain some unknown growth-promoting factor (Inoue and Maeda, 1982). In prepared mixtures of amino acids resembling those in CH, competitive inhibition between some of the constituents is often observed. For instance, the induction of embryogenesis in carrot cell suspensions on a medium containing glutamine as the only nitrogen source, was partly inhibited by the further addition of L-amino acids similar in composition to those in CH. This suppression was mainly caused by the L-tyrosine in the mixture (Anderson, J.O., 1976).

There may be a limit to the amount of CH which can be safely added to a medium. Anstis and Northcote (1973) reported that the brand of CH known as 'N-Z-amine'™, can produce toxic substances if concentrated solutions are heated, or if solutions are frozen and thawed several times. Possibly these are reasons why mixtures of amino acids occasionally provide more valuable supplements than CH. *Nicotiana tabacum* callus grew better on a nitrogen-free **MS** medium when a mixture of the amino acids L-glutamine (6 mM), L–aspartic acid (2 mM), L-arginine (1 mM) and glycine (0.1 mM) was added, rather than 2 g/l casein hydrolysate (which would have provided about 2 mM glutamine, 0.6 mM aspartic acid, 0.2 mM arginine and 0.3 mM glycine) (Müller and Grafe, 1978).

Beneficial effects of amino acid additions

Improved growth. The growth rate of cell suspensions is frequently increased by the addition of casein hydrolysate or one or more amino acids (particularly glutamine) to media containing both nitrate and ammonium ions. Some workers have included a mixture of several amino acids in their medium without commenting on how they improved growth. In other cases the benefit resulting from a specific compound has been clearly shown. The lag phase of growth in suspensions of *Pseudotsuga menziesii* cultured on **Cheng (1977; 1978a)** medium was eliminated by the addition of 50 mM glutamine, and the final dry weight of cells was 4 times that produced on the unammended medium (Kirby, 1982). Similarly the rate of growth of *Actinidia chinensis* suspensions was improved by the addition of 5mM glutamine (Suezawa *et al.*, 1988) and those of *Prunus amygdalus* cv. 'Ferragnes' could not be maintained unless 0.2% casamino acids was added to the medium (Rugini and Verma, 1982). Molnar (1988b) found that the growth of *Brassica nigra* cell suspensions was improved by adding 1–4 g/l CH or a mixture of 4 mM alanine, 4 mM glutamine and 1 mM glutamic acid. In this case the medium contained **MS** salts (but less iron) and **B5** vitamins.

Amino acid supplements have also been used to boost the rate of growth of callus cultures. For instance, Short and Torrey (1972b) added 5 amino acids and urea to a medium containing **MS** salts for the culture of pea root callus, and Sandstedt and Skoog (1960) found that aspartic and glutamic acids promoted the growth of tobacco callus as much as a mixture of several amino acids (such as found in yeast extract). Glutamic acid seemed to be primarily responsible for the growth promotion of sweet clover callus caused by casein hydrolysate on a medium containing 26.6 mM NO_3^-, 12.5 mM NH_4^+ and 2.0 mM PO_4^{3-} (Taira *et al*. 1977).

Amino acids are often added to media for protoplast culture. It was essential to add 2 mM glutamine and 2 mM asparagine to a medium containing **MS** salts, to obtain cell division, colony growth and plantlet differentiation from *Trigonella* protoplasts (Shekhawat and Galston, 1983b).

Shoot cultures. Many shoot cultures are grown on MS medium containing glycine, although in most cases the amino acid is probably not an essential ingredient. Usually it is unnecessary to add amino acids to media supporting shoot cultures, but methionine may represent a special case. Druart (1988) found that adding 50–100 mg/l L-methionine to the medium seemed to stimulate cytokinin activity and caused cultures of *Prunus glandulosa* var. *sinensis* to have high propagation rates through several subcultures. This promotive effect of L-methionine was thought to be due to it acting as a precursor of ethylene (see page 455). Glutamine inhibited the growth of apical domes excised from *Coleus blumei* shoots (Smith, 1981a) and 50–100 mg/l glutamic acid inhibited shoot growth, the formation of axillary buds and shoot proliferation in cultures of woody plants (Druart, *loc. cit.*).

L-Citrulline is an important intermediate in nitrogen metabolism in the genus *Alnus*. The addition of 1.66 mM (4.99 mM NH_2) to **WPM** medium improved the growth of *A. cordata* and *A. subcordata* shoot cultures (Cremiere *et al.*, 1987).

Contaminants grow more rapidly on media containing amino acids. Casein hydrolysate is therefore sometimes added to the media for Stage I shoot cultures so that infected explants can be rejected quickly (Schulze, 1988). The health of shoots grown from seedling shoot tips of *Feijoa (Acca) sellowiana* was improved when 500 mg/l CH was added to **Boxus (1974a)** medium (which does not contain ammonium ions).

Organogenesis. The provision of amino acids can enhance morphogenesis, either when they provide the only source of reduced nitrogen, or when they are used as a supplement to a medium containing both NO_3^- and NH_4^+. In a medium containing 25 mM nitrate, but no NH_4^+, direct adventitious shoot formation on cauliflower peduncle explants was induced by the addition of a mixture of the amino acids asparagine, proline, tyrosine and phenylalanine, each at a concentration of only 0.1 mM. (Margara, 1969b). A high rate of adventitious shoot regeneration and embryogenesis, from *Beta vulgaris* petioles or petiole callus, was achieved on a medium comprised of several amino acids and a complex vitamin mixture with **MS** salts (Freytag *et al.*, 1988). The addition of CH to **MS** medium was found to be essential for shoot formation from callus (Chand and Roy, 1981).

Adding only 1–10 mg/l of either L-leucine or L-isoleucine to **Gamborg *et al.* (1968) B5** medium, decreased callus growth of *Brassica oleracea* var capitata, but increased adventitious shoot formation. Basu *et al.* (1989) thought that this might be due to these amino acids being negative effectors of threonine deaminase (TD) enzyme, the activity of which was diminished in their presence. Threonine, methionine and pyruvic acid which increased callus growth in this species, enhanced TD activity.

There are several examples of the amino acid L-asparagine being able to stimulate morphogenesis. This may be because it too can be a precursor of ethylene (Durzan, 1982a) (see page 455), the biosynthesis of which may be increased by greater substrate availability. Kamada and Harada (1977) found that the addition of 5 mM L- asparagine stimulated both callus and bud formation in stem segments of *Torenia fournieri*, while alanine (and, to a lesser extent, glutamic acid) increased flower bud formation from *Torenia* internode segments when both an auxin and a cytokinin were present. An increase in the number of adventitious buds formed on the cotyledons and hypocotyl of *Chamaecyparis obtusa* seedlings occurred when 1.37 mM glutamine and 1.51 mM asparagine were added together to **Campbell and Durzan (1975)** medium, but not when they were supplied on their own (Ishii 1986). L-asparagine was also added to **MS** medium by Green and Phillips (1975), to obtain plant regeneration from tissue cultures of maize; adding it to **Finer and Nagasawa (1988) 10A4ON** medium caused there to be more embryogenic clumps in *Glycine max* suspension cultures (Finer and Nagasawa, 1988).

Amino acid additions do not invariably enhance morphogenesis. Supplementing **Linsmaier and Skoog (1965)** medium with 0.5–5 mM glutamine, caused callus of *Zamia latifolia* to show greatly decreased organogenesis (Webb and Rivera, 1981) and ammending **Linsmaier and Skoog (1965)** medium with 100 mg/l CH, prevented adventitious shoot formation from stem internode callus of apple and cherry rootstocks (James *et al.*, 1984).

Table 26. Some examples of the promotion of embryogenesis by amino acids in media containing NO_3^- and NH_4^+.

Plant species	Type of culture	Basal medium used	Amino acid supplements	Reference
Aesculus hippocastrum	Zygotic embryo callus	**MS**	CH (250 mg/l) plus proline (250 mg/l)	Radojevic (1988)
Dactylis glomerata	Suspension-derived callus	**Schenk and Hildebrandt (1972)**	CH (1.5 g/l)	Gray *et al.* (1984)
Daucus carota	Hypocotyl callus	**Gamborg et al. (1968) B5**	Proline (100mM) plus serine (100mM)	Nuti Ronchi *et al.* (1984)
Dioscorea rotundata	Callus ex zygotic embryos	**MS**	CH (1 g/l)	Osifo (1988)
Glycine max	Suspension	**Kartha et al. (1974a)**	L-Aspagine (5mM)	Finer and Nagasawa (1988)
Gossypium klotzschianum	Suspension	**Gamborg et al. (1968) B5**	Glutamine (10 mM)	Price and Smith (1979a,b).
Larix decidua	Gametophyte callus	**Litvay et al. (1981) LM**	Glutamine (500 mg/l) plus CH (1 g/l)	Nagmani and Bonga (1985)
Nigella sativa		**MS**	CH (100–500 mg/l)	Bannerjee and Gupta (1976)
Trigonella foenum-graecum	Leaf callus	**MS**	CH (50 mg/l) (500 mg/l inhibitory)	Gupta *et al.* (1987)
Triticum aestivum	Anther	**Chu and Hill (1988) MN6**	Serine, proline, arinine, aspartic acid, and alanine (each at 40 mg/l) plus glutamine (400 mg/l)	Chu and Hill (1988)
Vitis vinifera	Anther	½ **MS**	CH (250 mg/l)	Mauro *et al.* (1986)
Zea mays	Zygotic embryo callus	**Chu et al. (1975) N6**	Proline (20–25 mM)	Kamo *et al.* (1985) Armstrong and Green (1985)

Embryogenesis. The presence the ammonium ion is usually sufficient for the induction of embryogenesis in callus or suspension cultures containing NO_3^-, but on media where NH_4^+ is lacking [*e.g.* **White (1954)**], casein hydrolysate, or an amino acid such as alanine, or glutamine, is often promotory (Ranga Swamy, 1958; Ammirato and Steward, 1971; Street, 1979). For embryogenesis in carrot cultures, Wetherell and Dougall (1976) have shown that in a medium containing potassium nitrate, reduced nitrogen in the form of ammonium chloride matched the effectiveness of an equivalent concentration of nitrogen from casein hydrolysate. Casein hydrolysate could be replaced by glutamine, glutamic acid, urea or alanine. Suspensions of wild carrot cells grew and produced somatic embryos on a medium containing either glutamine or CH as the sole nitrogen source (Anderson, J.O., 1976).

There have also been many reports of embryogenesis being promoted by the addition of casein hydrolysate, or one or more specific amino acids, when both NO_3^- and NH_4^+ were available in the medium. Some examples are given in Table 26. In many cases, embryogenic callus and/or embryo formation did not occur without the presence of the amino acid source, suggesting that without amino acid, the medium was deficient in NH_4^+ or total nitrogen. Armstrong and Green (1985) found that the frequency of friable callus and somatic embryo formation from immature embryos of *Zea mays* increased almost linearly with the addition of up to 25 mM proline to **Chu et al. (1975) N6** medium [total N, 34.99 mM; NO_3/NH_4 ratio, 3.99], but there was no benefit from adding proline to **MS** medium [total N, 60.01 mM; NO_3/NH_4 ratio, 1.91] (containing 150 mg/l asparagine hydrate).

The growth of somatic embryos can also be affected by the availability of reduced nitrogen. That of *Coronilla varia* embryos was poor on **Gamborg *et al.* (1968) B5** medium (Total N 26.74 mM; NH$_4^+$ 2.02 mM), unless 10 mM asparagine or 20 mM NH$_4$Cl was added to the medium, or unless the embryos were moved to **Saunders and Bingham (1972) BOi2Y** medium, which has 37.81 mM total inorganic N, 12.49 mM NH$_4^+$ and 2000 mg/l casein hydrolysate (approx. 9.9 mM NH$_4^+$ equivalence) (Moyer and Gustine, 1984). However, the germination of *Triticum aestivum* somatic embryos was completely prevented by adding 800 mg/l CH to **MS** medium (Ozias Akins and Vasil, 1982; Carman *et al.*, 1988a).

Culture of immature cotyledons. Young storage cotyledons isolated from immature zygotic embryos accumulate protein efficiently when cultured with amino acids in a medium without nitrate and ammonium ions. A medium such as that of **Millerd *et al.* (1975)**, or of **Thompson *et al.* (1977)** is normally used, but where the effect of different amino acids on protein assimilation is being studied, the amino acid content of the medium is varied. Glutamine is often found to be the most efficient nitrogen source for this purpose (Thompson *et al.*, 1977; Haga and Sodek, 1987), but protein increase from culture with asparagine and glutamate (glutamic acid) is usually also significant (Lea *et al.*, 1979).

Causes of the stimulatory effect of amino acids

We may conclude therefore, that many cultural purposes, amino acids are not essential media components; but their addition as identified pure compounds, or more cheaply through casein hydrolysates, can be an easy way of ensuring against medium deficiency, or of providing a source of nitrogen that is immediately available to cultured cells or tissues. An observation by Murashige and Skoog (1962) that the presence of casein hydrolysate allowed vigorous organ development over a broader range of IAA and kinetin levels, may be of significance.

In gram moles per litre, amino acids can be a much more efficient source of reduced nitrogen than ammonium compounds. For instance, the mixture of amino acids provided by 400 mg/l of casein hydrolysate (containing at most as much reduced nitrogen as 3.3 mM NH$_4^+$) was as effective as 14.95 mM NH$_4$Cl in stimulating the division of protoplast-derived cells of *Antirrhinum* (Poirier-Hamon *et al.* 1974).

Why should this be, and why can additions of amino acids (sometimes in comparatively small amounts) stimulate growth or morphogenesis when added to media which already contain large amounts of NH$_4^+$? Some hypotheses which have been advanced are:

- **Conservation of ATP — alleviating phosphate deficiency.** Durzan (1982) points out that when plant tissues take up the ammonium ion, they consume adenosine tri-phosphate (ATP) in converting it to amino acids. If suitable amino acids are available from the medium, some of ATP may be conserved. Bister-Miel *et al.* (1985) noted that CH promoted growth in cultures where phosphate became growth-limiting. They suggested that amino acids compensated for phosphate deficiency. With the plant well supplied with amino acids, some of the phosphate which is normally used for ATP production can be diverted to other uses. Several authors have pointed out that CH itself is also a source of phosphate. For example, Bridson (1978) and some chemical catalogues, show that some casein hydrolysates normally contain about 1.3 g P$_2$O$_5$ per 100g. The addition of 2 g/l of CH will therefore increase the phosphate content of **MS** medium by 11% and that of **White (1954)** medium by 44% (assuming complete phosphate availability).

- **A capacity to act as chelating agents.** Some amino acids can act as chelating agents (see page 309)

- **Enhanced nitrogen assimilation.** Glutamine and glutamic acid are directly involved in the assimilation of NH$_4^+$ (Fig. 76). A direct supply of these amino acids should therefore enhance the utilization of both nitrate and ammonium nitrogen and its conversion into amino acids.

- **A replacement for toxic ammonium ions.** Certain plant tissues are particularly sensitive to NH$_4^+$. Ochatt and Caso (1986) and Ochatt and Power (1988a, b) found that protoplasts of *Pyrus* spp. would not tolerate the ion, and that to obtain sustained cell division it was necessary to eliminate it from **MS** medium, and use 50 mg/l casein hydrolysate as a source of reduced nitrogen. CH can however be extremely toxic to freshly isolated protoplasts of some species and varieties of plants (Ranch and Widholm, 1980; Russell and McCown, 1988a). Conifer tissues too are unable to cope with high concentrations of NH$_4^+$, but cultures can be supplied with equivalent levels of reduced nitrogen in the form of amino acids without the occurrence of toxicity (Durzan, 1982). In soybean suspension cultures, the high level of ammonium in **MS** medium has been shown to inhibit isocitrate dehydrogenase (a Krebs' cycle enzyme) and glutamine synthetase, which contribute towards the the conversion of NH_4^+ to glutamine (Gamborg and Shyluk, 1970).

- **Adjustment of intracellular pH.** As intracellular pH is important for the activation of sea urchin eggs, and amino acids can promote embryogenesis, Nuti Ronchi *et al.* (1984) speculated that the uptake and assimilation of amino acids might help to regulate cellular pH in plants.

As mentioned in Chapter 1, there is commonly a minimum inoculation density below which growth cannot be initiated *in vitro*. This minimum varies according to both the source of the cells and the nature of the medium. It can usually be lowered by employing a 'conditioned' medium (*i.e.* a fresh medium into which the products of another medium in which cells are actively growing, have been added). Alternatively, initial growth at low densities can be supported by the close presence of other actively growing plant cells ('nurse cultures'). Compounds responsible for this effect must be freely diffusible from living cells and could include growth substances, reducing sugars, vitamins and amino acids. Addition of such supplements has been found to overcome the inhibited growth of some cells at low densities (Kao and Michayluk, 1975).

PHOSPHATE

Phosphorus is a vital element in plant biochemistry. It occurs in compounds which are involved in energy transfer, protein and nucleic acid synthesis and contributes to the structure of nucleic acids. Phosphorus is absorbed into plants in the form of phosphate ions by an active process, which requires the expenditure of respiratory energy. It is used in plants as the fully oxidized orthophosphate (PO_4^{3-}) form. When phosphate is depleted from **MS** medium, there is an increase in free amino acids in *Catharanthus roseus* cells, because protein synthesis has ceased and degradation of proteins is occurring (Ukaji and Ashihara, 1987).

In modern culture media the element is provided as soluble sodium or potassium mono- and di-hydrogen phosphates. The di- and mono-valent phosphate anions respectively provided by these chemicals are interconvertible in solution depending on pH.

Monovalent $H_2PO_4^-$ predominates at pH values below 7, characteristic of most tissue culture media, and it is this ion which is most readily absorbed into plants (Devlin, 1975). Conversion of $H_2PO_4^-$ into divalent HPO_4^{2-} begins to occur as solutions become more alkaline. The divalent ion is said to be only sparingly available to plants but Hagen and Hopkins (1955) and Jacobsen *et al.* (1958)

thought that its absorbtion could be significant, because even though the ion is normally at a relatively low concentration in nutrient solutions, its affinity with the site of absorption is greater than that of the mono-valent form. Trivalent PO_4^{3-}, which appears in alkaline solutions, is not generally absorbed by plants; however phosphate may be made available to plants from this source through the action of phosphatase enzymes (see below).

Because both salts of both $H_2PO_4^-$ and HPO_4^{2-} have been added to culture media, it is not possible to calculate a common ionic equivalence for phosphate in a macronutrient composition, except by expressing it as PO_4^{3-}: the equivalence of phosphate as the trivalent ion in Table 48 at the end of Chapter 10, therefore *does not* indicate that PO_4^{3-} was the form of phosphate available to the plant. In nearly all cases the predominant available ion will have been $H_2PO_4^-$: its molarity and equivalence can be calculated by dividing the value given for PO_4^{3-} by 3.

In some early tissue culture media, all (*e.g.* Bouharmont, 1961), or part (*e.g.* Vacin and Went, 1949), of the phosphorus was supplied as sparingly-soluble phosphates. A slow rate of phosphorus availability seems to be possible from such compounds. The optimum rate of uptake of phosphate (HPO_4^{2-}) into cultured *Petunia* cells occurred at pH 4 (Chin and Miller, 1982) but Zink and Veliky (1979) did not observe any decline in the absorption of phosphate by *Ipomoea* suspension cultures at pH 6.5, when HPO_4^{2-} and $H_2PO_4^-$ were present in approximately equal concentrations. Plant tissue cultures secrete phosphatase enzymes into the medium (Ciarrocchi *et al.*, 1981) which could release phosphate ions from some organic phosphates.

High concentrations of dissolved phosphate can depress growth, possibly because calcium and some microelements are precipitated from solution and/or their uptake reduced. Although the concentration of phosphate introduced into plant culture media, has been as high has 19.8 mM, the average level is 1.7 mM and most media contain about 1.3 mM. However there are reports that such typical levels may be too low for some purposes.

Uptake

The rate of uptake of phosphate ions depends on genotype, but is usually fairly constant and proportional to the growth rate of the culture. Phosphate (starting concentration 2.64 mM) and sucrose were the only nutrients completely depleted in *Catharanthus roseus* batch suspension cultures, and the period of growth could be prolonged by increasing the levels of both (MacCarthy *et al.*, 1980). **MS** medium contains only 1.25 mM phosphate which may be insufficient for suspension cultures of some plants. The phosphate in **MS** medium was insufficient for *Cardamine pratensis* suspension cultures, all having been absorbed in 5 days: it was however adequate for *Silene alba* suspensions (Bister-Miel *et al.*, 1985).

The phosphate in **MS** medium is also inadequate for static cultures of some plants, or where a large amount of tissue or organs are supported on a small amount of medium (for example where many separate shoots are explanted together in a static shoot culture). The concentration of the ion is then likely to be reduced almost to zero over several weeks (Barroso *et al.*, 1985; Singha *et al.*, 1987b; Lumsden *et al.*, 1990). Although growth can continue for a short while after the medium is depleted of phosphate, for some purposes it has been found to be beneficial to increase the phosphate concentration to 1.86 mM (Jones and Murashige, 1974), 2.48 mM (Murashige *et al.*, 1972b; Murashige, 1974; Jakobek *et al.*, 1986), 3.1 mM (Miller and Murashige, 1976) or 3.71 mM (Thorpe and Murashige, 1968a, 1970), for example, to induce adventitious shoot formation from callus, or to increase the rate of shoot multiplication in shoot cultures.

When phosphate levels are increased to obtain a more rapid rate of growth of a culture, it can be advisable to investigate the simultaneous enhancement of the level of *myo*-inositol in the medium (see page 315).

POTASSIUM

Potassium is the major cation (+ve ion) within plants which counterbalances the negative charge of inorganic and organic anions. Potassium ions are transported quickly across cell membranes and two of their major roles are regulating the pH and osmotic environment within cells. Potassium, calcium, sodium and chloride ions conserve their electrical charges within the plant, unlike the cation NH_4^+ and the anions NO_3^-, SO_4^{2-}, and $H_2PO_4^-$, which are rapidly incorporated into organic molecules. In intact plants, potassium ions are thought to cycle. They move, associated with cations (particularly NO_3^-), upwards from the roots in the xylem. As nitrate is reduced to ammonia and assimilated, carboxylic acid ions (RCO_3^-, malate) are produced. These become associated with the released K^+ ions and are transported in the phloem to the roots, where they are decarboxylated, releasing K^+ for further anion transport (Ben-Zioni *et al.*, 1971). Carboxylate transported to the roots gives rise to OH^- ion which is excreted into the medium to counterbalance NO_3^- uptake (Touraine *et al.*, 1988). Potassium ions will clearly have a similar role in cultured tissues, but obvious transport mechanisms will usually be absent.

Many proteins show a high specificity for potassium which, acting as a cofactor, alters their configuration so that they become active enzymes. Potassium ions also neutralise organic anions produced in the cytoplasm, and so stabilise the pH and osmotic potential of the cell. In whole plants, deficiency of potassium results in loss of cell turgor, flaccid tissues and an increased susceptibility to drought, salinity, frost damage and fungal attack. A high potassium to calcium ratio is said to be characteristic of the juvenile stage in woody plants (Boulay, 1987). Potassium deficiency in plant culture media is said to lead to hyperhydricity (Pasqualetto *et al.*, 1988b), and a decrease in the rate of absorbtion of phosphate (Chin and Miller, 1982). However quite wide variations in the potassium content of **MS** medium had little effect on the growth or proliferation of cultured peach shoots (Loreti *et al.*, 1988).

Lavee and Hoffman (1971) reported that the optimum rate of callus growth of two apple clones was achieved in a medium containing 3.5 mM K^+: when the concentration was much higher than this, or when it was less than 1.4 mM, the callus grew less vigorously. However, the growth rate of wild carrot suspensions was said by Brown *et al.* (1976) to be at, or near, the maximum when K^+ concentration was 1 mM: for embryogenesis 10–50 mM K^+ was required. Uptake of potassium into plants is reduced in the absence of calcium (Devlin, 1975).

Within a large sample of different macronutrient compositions, it is found that authors have tended to relate the concentration of potassium to the level of nitrate. This is correlated with a coefficient of 0.78, $P<0.001$ (George *et al*, 1988). The average concentration of potassium in these media was 13.6 mM and the most common value (median), 10.5 mM. **Murashige and Skoog (1962)** medium contains 20.04 mM K^+.

SODIUM

Sodium ions (Na^+) are taken up into plants, but in most cases they are not required for growth and development and many plants actively secrete them from their roots to maintain a low internal concentration. The element can function as an osmotic stabilizer in halophytic plants; these have become adapted so that, in saline soils with low water potential, they can accumulate abnormally high concentrations of Na^+ ion in vacuoles, and thereby maintain sufficient turgor for growth.

The element does appear to have a beneficial nutritional effect on some plants. Small amounts of sodium chloride (*e.g.* 230 mg/l) can stimulate the growth of plants in the families Chenopodiaceae and Compositae even when there is no limitation on the availability of K^+ (Brownell, 1979). In other plants such as wheat, oats, cotton and cauliflower (Sharma and Singh, 1990), sodium can partially replace potassium, but is not essential.

Sodium only appears to be *essential* to those salt-tolerant plants which have a C_4 (crassulacean acid) metabolism.

Examples are *Bryophyllum tubiflorum* (Crassulaceae) and *Mesembryanthemum crystallimum* (Aizoaceae). In these plants the element is necessary for CO_2 fixation in photosynthesis.

Most macronutrient formulations do not contain any sodium at all, and the average concentration in 615 different preparations was 1.9 mM (George *et al.*, 1988). Even if the element is not deliberately added as a macronutrient, small amounts are incorporated in most media from the salts added to provide micronutrients. Plant macronutrient preparations containing high concentrations of both sodium and chloride ions are not well formulated.

MAGNESIUM

Magnesium is an essential component of the chlorophyll molecule and is also required non-specifically for the activity of many enzymes, especially those involved in the transfer of phosphate. The magnesium ion is mobile and diffuses freely within plants and thus, like potassium, serves as a cation balancing and neutralising anions and organic acids. Macklon and Sim (1976) estimated there to be 2.1 mM Mg^{2+} in the cytoplasm of *Allium cepa* roots while McClendon (1976) put the general cytoplasmic requirement of plants as high as 16 mM. Plant culture media invariably contain relatively low concentrations of magnesium (average 6.8 mM, median 5.3 mM). Very often $MgSO_4$ is used as the unique source of both magnesium and sulphate ions.

Walker and Sato (1981) found there to be a large reduction in the number of somatic embryos formed from *Medicago sativa* callus when Mg^{2+} was omitted from the medium.

SULPHUR

The sulphur utilised by plants is mainly absorbed as SO_4^{2-}, which is the usual source of the element in plant culture media. Uptake is coupled to nitrogen assimilation (Reuveny *et al.*, 1980), and is said to be independent of pH. It results in the excretion of OH^- ions by the plant, making the medium more alkaline. However, according to Mengel and Kirkby (1982), plants are relatively insensitive to high sulphate levels and only when the concentration is in the region of 50 mM, is growth adversely affected. Although sulphur is mainly absorbed by plants in the oxidized form, that which is incorporated into chemical compounds is mainly as reduced –SH, –S– or –S–S– groups. Sulphur is used by plants in lipid synthesis and in regulating the structure of proteins through the formation of S—S bridges. The sulphur-containing amino acids cysteine, cystine and methionine become incorporated into proteins. The element also acts as a ligand joining ions of iron, zinc and copper to metalloproteins and enzymes. The reactive sites of some enzymes are —SH groups. Sulphur is therefore an essential element and deficiency results in a lack of protein synthesis. Sulphur-deficient plants are rigid, brittle and thin-stemmed.

Growth and protein synthesis in tobacco cell suspensions were reduced on a medium containing only 0.6 mM SO_4^{2-} instead of 1.73 mM (Klapheck *et al.*, 1982) and when the supply of S in the medium was used up, large amounts of soluble nitrogen accumulated in the cells. Most media contain from 2–5 meq/l SO_4^{2-}.

CALCIUM

As a major cation, calcium helps to balance anions within the plant, but unlike potassium and magnesium, it is not readily mobile. Because of its capacity to link biological molecules together, the element is involved in the structure and physiological properties of cell membranes and the middle lamella of cell walls. The enzyme β- (1→3)-glucan synthase depends on calcium ions, and cellulose synthesis by cultured cells does not occur unless there are at least micro-molar quantities of Ca^{2+} in the medium. Many other plant enzymes are also calcium-dependent and calcium is a cofactor in the enzymes responsible for the hydrolysis of ATP.

Although calcium can be present in millimolar concentrations within the plant as a whole, calcium ions are pumped out of the cytoplasm of cells to maintain the concentration at around only 0.1 μM. This active removal of Ca^{2+} from the protoplasm is necessary to prevents the precipitation of phosphate (and the consequent disruption of phosphate-dependent metabolism) and interference with the function of Mg^{2+}. The review by Hepler and Wayne (1985) shows how the uniquely low intra-cellular concentration of Ca^{2+} allows plants to use calcium as a chemical 'second messenger'; regulatory mechanisms are initiated when Ca^{2+} binds with the protein calmodulin, which is thus enabled to modify enzyme activities. A temporary increase in Ca^{2+} concentration to 1 or 10 μM does not significantly alter the ionic environment within the cell, but is yet sufficient to trigger fundamental cell processes such as polarized growth (for example that of embryos — Shelton *et al.*, 1981), response to gravity and plant growth substances, cytoplasmic streaming, and mitosis (Ferguson and Drøbak, 1988; Poovaiah, 1988). Physiological and developmental processes which are initiated through the action of phytochrome are also dependent on the presence of Ca^{2+}.

Large quantities of calcium can be deposited outside the protoplast, in cell vacuoles and in cell walls. Calcification strengthens plant cell walls and is thought to increase the resistance of a plant to infection. By forming insoluble salts with organic acids, calcium immobilises some potentially damaging by-products. The element gives protection against the effects of heavy metals and conveys some resistance to excessively saline conditions and low pH.

The Ca^{2+} ion is involved in *in vitro* morphogenesis and is required for many of the responses induced by plant growth substances, particularly auxins and cytokinins. In the moss *Funaria*, cytokinin causes an increase in membrane-associated Ca^{2+} specifically in those areas which are undergoing differentiation to become a bud (Saunders and Hepler, 1981). Protocorm formation from callus of *Dendrobium fibriatum* was poor on **Mitra *et al*. (1976) A** medium when calcium was omitted (Mitra *et al*., 1976) and in *Torenia* stem segments, adventitious bud formation induced by cytokinin seems to be mediated, at least in part, by an increase in the level of Ca^{2+} within cells (Tanimoto and Harada, 1986).

Calcium deficiency

Shoot tip necrosis. Calcium deficiency in plants results in poor root growth and in the blackening and curling of the margins of apical leaves, often followed by a cessation of growth and death of the shoot tip. The latter symptoms are similar to aluminium toxicity (Wyn Jones and Hunt, 1967). Tip necrosis has been especially observed in shoot cultures, sometimes associated with hyperhydricity. It often occurs after several subcultures have been accomplished (*e.g.* in *Cercis canadensis* — Yusnita *et al.*, 1990). After death of the tip, shoots often produce lateral branches, and in extreme cases the tips of these will also die and branch again. The cause of tip necrosis has not always been determined [*e.g.* in *Pistacia* shoot cultures (Barghchi, 1986b), where shoots showing symptoms may die after planting out (Martinelli, 1988)]. The occurrence of necrosis was reduced in *Pistacia* (Barghchi *loc. cit.*) and *Prunus tenella* (Alderson *et al.*, 1987) by more frequent subculturing, but this is a costly and time-consuming practice.

Tip necrosis was found in *Psidium guajava* shoot cultures after prolonged subculturing, if shoots were allowed to grow longer than 3 cm, and was common in rapidly growing cultures (Amin and Jaiswal, 1988); it occurred on *Sequoiadendron giganteum* shoots only when they were grown on relatively dilute media (Monteuuis *et al*, 1987). Necrosis of *Rosa hybrida* 'White Dream', was

cured by adding 0.1 mg/l GA_3 to the medium (Valle and Boxus, 1987a).

Analysis of necrotic apices has shown them to be deficient in calcium (Debergh, 1988), and a shortage of this element has been associated with tip necrosis in *Amelanchier*, *Betula*, *Populus*, *Sequoia*, *Ulmus* and other woody plants, although the extent of damage is variable even between genotypes within a species (Sha *et al.*, 1985). As calcium is not remobilised within plant tissues, actively growing shoots need a constant fresh supply of ions in the transpiration stream. An inadequate supply of calcium can result from limited uptake of the ion, and inadequate transport, the latter being caused by the absence of transpiration due to the high humidity in the culture vessel. A remedy can sometimes be obtained by reducing the culture temperature so that the rate of shoot growth matches calcium supply, using vessels which promote better gas exchange (thereby increasing the transpiration and xylem transport), or by increasing the concentration of calcium in the medium (McCown and Sellmar, 1987). The last two remedies can have drawbacks: the medium will dry out if there is too free gas exchange; adding extra calcium ions to the medium is not always effective (*e.g.* in cultures of *Castanea sativa* — Mullins, 1987); and can introduce undesirable anions. Chloride toxity can result if too much calcium chloride is added to the medium (see below). To solve this difficulty, McCown *et al.* (Zeldin and McCown, 1986; Russell and McCown, 1988) added 6 mM calcium gluconate to **Lloyd and McCown (1981) WPM** medium to correct Ca^{2+} deficiency, without altering the concentrations of the customary anions. There is a limit to the concentration of calcium which can be employed in tissue culture media because several of its compounds have limited solubility.

Tip necrosis sometimes also occurs during the weaning of cuttings or plantlets in mist (see Chapter 14).

CHLORIDE

The chloride ion (Cl^-) has been found to be essential for plant growth (Broyer *et al.*, 1954; Johnson *et al.*, 1957; Ozanne *et al.*, 1957; Ozanne, 1958), but seems to be involved in few biological reactions and only very small quantities are really necessary. Rains (1976) listed chlorine as a micronutrient. The chloride ion is freely transported and many plants can tolerate the presence of high concentrations without showing toxicity. The chief role of chloride seems to be in the maintenance of turgor and in balancing rapid changes in the level of free cations such as K^+, Mg^{2+} and Na^+. Plants deprived of Cl^- are liable to wilting (Johnson *et al.*, 1957).

In isolated chloroplasts, chloride (together with Mn^{2+}) ions are required for oxygen evolution in photosystem II of photosynthesis (Bové *et al.*, 1963; Mengel and Kirkby, 1982; Shkolnik, 1984), although there has been some doubt whether this requirement exists *in vivo* (Terry, 1977). Chloride ions are best taken into plants at slightly acid pH (Jacobson *et al.*, 1971).

The most common concentration in culture media is 3 mM, the average 6 mM. **MS** medium contains 6 mM Cl^-; **Quoirin and Lepoivre (1977)** medium, 0.123 μM. Some species are sensitive to chloride ions. McCown and Sellmer (1987) reported that too high a concentration, seemed to cause woody species to have yellow leaves and weak stems: sometimes tissues collapsed and died. An excess of Cl^- has been thought to be one cause of the induction of hyperhydricity, and omission of the ion does seem to prevent the development of these symptoms in *Prunus* (Chapter 13). Pevalek-Kozlina and Jelaska (1987) deliberately omitted chloride ions from **WPM** medium for the shoot culture of *Prunus avium* and obtained infrequent hyperhydricity in only one genotype. The presence of 7 mM Cl^- can be toxic to pine suspension cultures (Teasdale, 1987).

As chlorine has only a relatively small nutritional significance, steps are sometimes taken to reduce the concentration of chloride ion in culture media, but in order to adjust the concentration of other ions, it is then often necessary to make a marked increase in SO_4^{2-}. For example, using ammonium sulphate instead of ammonium chloride to supply NH_4^+ in **Eeuwens (1976) Y3** medium, would increase the sulphate level from 2 to 12 meq/l (from 1 to 6 mM).

EFFECT OF pH ON CULTURES

pH CONTROL WITHIN THE PLANT

The relative acidity or alkalinity of a solution is assessed by its pH. This is a measure of the hydrogen ion activity (concentration) in solution. The greater the activity of H^+ ions, the more acid the solution. As pH is defined as the negative logarithm of hydrogen ion activity, acid solutions have low pH values (0–7) and alkaline solutions, high values (7–14). Solutions of pH 4 are therefore more acid than those of pH 5; solutions of pH 9 are more alkaline than those of pH 8. Pure water, without any dissolved gases such as CO_2, has a neutral pH of 7.

The pH of a culture medium must be such that it will not disrupt the function of plant cell membranes or the buffered pH of the cytoplasm. But within these physiologically acceptable limits it also:

— governs whether salts will remain in a soluble form;

— influences the uptake of medium ingredients and plant growth regulator additives, and

— affects the gelling efficiency of agar.

This means that the effective range of pH for media is restricted. As will be explained, medium pH is altered during culture, but an initial pH can often be selected to ensure the availability of nutrients and the most rapid rate of culture growth. In culture media, detrimental effects of an adverse pH are generally related to ion availability and nutrient uptake rather than cell damage.

The pH of the cytoplasm of plant cells is tightly regulated. It was believed to be in the range of 6.5–8.0 (Smith and Raven, 1979) but more recent measurements place it in the range 6.7–7.7 (Felle, 1988; Kurkdjian and Guern, 1989; Hüsemann *et al.*, 1990). Intracellular vacuoles are thought to be used in the maintenance of cytoplasmic pH. Their pH is usully somewhat lower than that of the cytoplasm (*i.e. ca.* 4.0–6.0). Plant cells typically generate an excess of acidic compounds during metabolism which have to be neutralised (Felle, 1988). One of the most important ways by which this is accomplished is for H^+ (protons), or K^+ (cations) to be pumped out of the cell, in exchange for anions (*e.g.* OH^-), thereby decreasing the extracellar pH.

Plant cells also compensate for an excess of H^+ by the degradation of organic acids. Synthesis of organic acids, such as malate, from neutral precursors is used to increase H^+ concentration when the cytoplasmic pH rises, for instance if plants are grown in alkaline soils (Raven and Smith, 1976; Findenegg *et al.*, 1986). In intact plants, there is usually a downwards gradient from the low pH external to the cell, to higher pH levels in more mature parts, and this enables the upwards transport of non-electrolytic compounds such as sugars and amino acids (Böttger, 1986).

Altering the pH of the external solution surrounding roots or cells can alter the pH of the cell (Smith and Raven, 1979). Because of necessary controls, the pH of the cytoplasm may be only slightly altered, that of vacuoles may show a more marked change. Changing the pH of the medium in which photo-autotrophic *Chenopodium rubrum* suspensions were cultured from 4.5 to 6.3, caused the pH of the cytoplasm to rise from 7.4 to 7.6 and that of the cell vacuoles to increase from 5.3 to 6.6. The increase in cytoplasmic pH caused there to be a marked diversion of carbon metabolism, away from sugar and starch, into the production of lipids, amino acids and proteins (Hüsemann *et al.*, 1990). Changing the pH of the medium can thus have a regulatory role on plant cultures which is similar to that of plant growth regulating chemicals, one of the actions of which is to modify intracellular pH and the quantity of free calcium ions. Auxins can modify cytoplasmic pH by triggering the release of H^+ from cells. In plant tissue culture these ions can acidify the medium (Kurkdjian *et al.*, 1982). Proton release is thought to be the first step in acid-triggered and turgor-triggered growth (Schubert and Matzke, 1985).

THE pH OF MEDIA

The uptake of ions and molecules

The uptake of negatively charged ions (*anions*) is favoured at acid pH, while that of *cations* (positively charged) is best when the pH is increased. As mentioned on page 275, the relative uptake of nutrient cations and anions will alter the pH of the medium. The release of hydroxyl ions from the plant in exchange for nitrate ions results in media becoming more alkaline; when ammonium ions are taken up in exchange for protons, media become more acid (Table 27).

Nitrate and ammonium ions

The uptake of ammonium and nitrate ions is markedly affected by pH. Excised plant roots can be grown with NH_4^+ as the sole source of nitrogen providing the pH is maintained within the range 6.8 to 7.2 and iron is available in a chelated form. At pH levels below 6.4 the roots grow slowly on ammonium alone and have an abnormal appearance (Sheat *et al.* 1959). This accords with experiments on intact plants where ammonium as the only source of nitrogen is found to be poorly taken up at low pH. It was most effectively utilised in *Asparagus* in a medium buffered at pH 5.5. At low pH (*ca.* 4 or less) the ability of the roots of most plants to take up ions of any kind may be impaired, there may be a loss of soluble cell constituents and growth of both the main axis and that of laterals is depressed (Asher, 1978).

Nitrate on the other hand, is not readily absorbed by plant cells at neutral pH or above (Martin and Rose, 1976). Growth of tumour callus of *Rumex acetosa* on a nitrate-containing medium was greater at pH 3.5 than pH 5.0 (Nickell and Burkholder, 1950), while Chevre *et al* (1983) reported that axillary bud multiplication in shoot cultures of *Castanea* was most satisfactory when the pH of **MS** was reduced to 4 and the Ca^{2+} and Mg^{2+} concentrations were doubled.

pH stabilization. One of the chief advantages of having both NO_3^- and NH_4^+ ions in the medium is that uptake of one provides a better pH environment for the uptake of the other. The pH of the medium is thereby stabilized. Uptake of nitrate ions by plant cells leads to a drift towards an alkaline pH, while NH_4^+ uptake results in a more rapid shift towards acidity (Street, 1969; Behrend and Mateles, 1975; Hyndman *et al.* 1982b). For each equivalent of ammonium incorporated into organic matter, about 0.8–1 H^+ (proton) equivalents are released into the external medium; for each equivalent of nitrate assimilated, 1–1.2 proton equivalents are removed from the medium (Fuggi *et al.*, 1981). Raven (1986) calculated that there should be no change of pH resulting from NO_3^- or NH_4^+ uptake, when the ratio of the two is 2 to 1.

The pH shifts caused by uptake of nitrate and ammonium during culture (see above) can lead to a situation of nitrogen deficiency if either is used as the sole nitrogen source without the addition of a buffer (see later) (Hyndman *et al.* 1982b). The uptake of NH_4^+, when this is the only source of nitrogen is only efficient when a buffer or an organic acid is also present in the medium. In media containing both NO_3^- and NH_4^+ with an initial pH of 5–6,

Table 27. The uptake of ions and its consequence in plant culture media.

Uptake	Anion	Cation
	e.g. NH_4^+	e.g. NO_3^-
Rate	Best in alkaline or weakly acid solutions	Best in relatively acid solutions
Consequence	Protons (H^+) extruded by plant	Hydroxyl (OH^-) ions extruded by plant
	Medium becomes more ACID	Medium becomes more ALKALINE

preferential uptake of NH_4^+ causes the pH to drop during the early growth of the culture. This results in increased NO_3^- utilisation (Martin and Rose, 1976) and a gradual pH rise. The final pH of the medium depends on the relative proportions of NO_3^- and NH_4^+ which are provided (Gamborg *et al.* 1968). After 7 days of root culture, **White (1943a)** medium (containing only nitrate), adjusted to pH 4.8–4.9, had a pH of 5.8–6.0 (Street *et al.* 1951, 1952), but Sheat *et al.* (1959) could stabilize the medium at pH 5.8 by having one fiftieth of the total amount of nitrogen as ammonium ion, the rest as nitrate. Changes in the pH of a medium do however vary from one kind of plant to another.

Media differing in total nitrogen levels (but all having the same ratio of nitrate to ammonium as **MS** medium), had a final pH of *ca.* 4.5 after being used for Stage III root initiation on rose shoots, whereas those containing ammonium alone had a final pH of *ca.* 4.1 (Hyndman *et al.* 1982b). A similar observation with **MS** medium itself was made by Delfel and Smith (1980). No matter what the starting value in the range 4.5–8.0, the final pH after culture of *Cephalotaxus* callus was always 4.2. The medium of **De Jong *et al.* (1974)** always had a pH of 4.8–5.0 after *Begonia* buds had been cultured, whatever the starting pH in the range 4.0–6.5. This is not to say that the initial pH was unimportant, because there was an optimum for growth and development (see later) (Berghoef and Bruinsma, 1979c).

Other ions

The availability and uptake of other inorganic ions and organic molecules is also affected by pH. As explained above, the uptake of phosphate is most efficient from acid solutions. *Petunia* cells took up phosphate most rapidly at pH 4 and its uptake declined as the pH was raised (Chin and Miller, 1982). Vacin and Went (1949) noted the formation of iron phosphate complexes in their medium by pH changes. Insoluble iron phosphates can also be formed in **MS** medium at pH 6.2 or above unless the proportion of EDTA to iron is increased (Dalton *et al.* 1983).

The uptake of Cl^- ions into barley roots is favoured by low pH, but Jacobson *et al.* (1971) noticed that it was only notably less at high pH in solutions strongly stirred by high aeration. They therefore suggested that H^+ ions secreted from plant roots as a result of the uptake of anions, can maintain a zone of reduced pH in the Nernst layer (Chapter 7). In plant tissue culture, uptake of ions and molecules may therefore more liable to be affected by adverse pH in agitated liquid media, than in media solidified by agar.

Organic compounds

Lysine uptake into tobacco cells was found by Harrington and Henke (1981) to be stimulated by low pH. The net uptake into cells of plant growth regulators which are weak lipophilic acids (such as IAA, NAA, 2,4-D and abscisic acid) will be greater, the more acid the medium and the greater the difference between its pH and that of the cell cytoplasm (Rubery, 1980). Shvetsov and Gamburg (1981) did in fact find that the rate of 2,4-D uptake into cultured corn cells increased as the pH of the medium fell from 5.5 to 4. But as previously mentioned, auxins can themselves modify intra- and extra-cellular pH. Adding 2,4-D to a medium increased the uptake of nicotine into culture of *Acer pseudoplatanus* cells (Kurkdjian *et al.* 1982).

Choosing the pH of culture media

Starting pH

Many plant cells and tissues *in vitro*, will tolerate pH in the range of about 4.0–7.2; those inoculated into media adjusted to pH 2.5–3.0 or 8.0 will probably die (Butenko *et al.*, 1984). Best results are usually obtained in slightly acid conditions. In a random sample of papers on micropropagation, the average initial pH adopted for several different media was found to be 5.6 (mode 5.7) but that adjustments to as low as 3.5 and as high as 7.1 had been made.

The pH for most plant cultures is thus lower than that which is optimum for hydroponic cultures, where intact plants with their roots in aerated solution usually grow most rapidly when the pH of the solution is in the range 6.0–7.3 (De Capite, 1948; Sholto Douglas, 1976; Cooper, 1979).

Suspension cultured cells of *Ipomoea*, grew satisfactorily in **Rose and Martin (1975) P2** medium adjusted initially to pH 5.6 or pH 6.3, but the yield of dry cells was less at two extremes (pH 4.8 and pH 7.1). Martin and Rose (1976) supposed that a low yield of cells from a culture started at pH 7.1 was due to the inability of the culture to utilise NO_3^-, but the cause of a reduction in growth at pH 4.8 was less obvious. It might have resulted from the plant having to expend energy to maintain an appropriate physiological pH internally.

Kartha (1981a) found that pH 5.6–5.8 supported the growth of most meristem tips in culture and that cassava meristems did not grow for a prolonged period on a medium adjusted to pH 4.8. The optimum pH (before autoclaving) for the growth of carnation shoot tips on **Linsmaier and Skoog (1965)** medium, was 5.5–6.5. When the medium was supplemented with 4 mg/l adenine sulphate and 2 g/l casein hydrolysate, the optimum pH was 5, and on media adjusted to 6.0 and 6.5, there was significantly less growth (Davis *et al.* 1977). Shoot proliferation in *Camellia sasanqua* shoot cultures was best when the pH of a medium with ½**MS** salts was adjusted to 5–5.5. Only in these flasks was the capacity of juvenile explants to produce more shoots than adult ones really pronounced (Torres and Carlisi, 1986).

Norstog and Smith (1963) suggested that the pH of the medium used for the culture of isolated zygotic embryos, should not be greater than 5.2.

pH adjustment

Because there is then no need to take special aseptic precautions, and it is impractical to adjust pH once medium has been dispensed into small lots, the pH of a medium is usually adjusted with acid or alkali *before* autoclaving. According to Krieg and Gerhardt (1981), agar is partially hydrolysed if autoclaved at pH 6 or less and will not solidify so effectively when cooled. They recommend that agar media for bacteriological purposes should be sterilised at a pH greater than 6 and, if necessary, should be adjusted to acid conditions with sterile acid *after* autoclaving, when they have cooled to 45–50°C. The degree of hydrolysis in plant culture media autoclaved at pH 5.6–5.7, is presumably small.

The effect of autoclaving. Autoclaving changes the pH of media. In media without sugars, the change is usually small unless the phosphate concentration is low, when more significant fluctuations occur. Media autoclaved with sucrose generally have a slightly lower pH than those autoclaved without it, but if maltose, glucose, or fructose have been added instead of sucrose, the post-autoclave pH is significantly reduced (Owen *et al.*, 1991).

The pH of liquid media containing **MS** salts (e.g. **Linsmaier and Skoog (1965)** or **Skirvin and Chu (1979a)** media) containing 3–3.4% sucrose, has been found to fall during autoclaving from an adjusted level of 5.7, to pH 5.17 (Singha, 1982c) to pH 5.5 (Owen *et al.*, 1991), or pH 4.6 (Skirvin *et al.*, 1986). The drop in pH may vary according to the pH to which the medium was initially adjusted. In the experiments of (Skirvin *et al.*, *loc. cit.*), the pH of a medium adjusted to 5.0, fell to 4.2; one adjusted to 6.4, fell to 5.1; that set at pH 8.5, fell to 8.1.

Most agars cause the pH of media to increase immediately they are dissolved. Knudson (1946) noticed that the pH of his medium shifted from 4.6–4.7 to 5.4–5.5 once agar had been added and dissolved; and Singha (1982c) discovered that the unadjusted pH of **MS** medium rose from pH 4 to pH 5.2, depending on the amount of agar added. However if a medium containing agar is adjusted to pH 5.7, and then autoclaved, the medium becomes

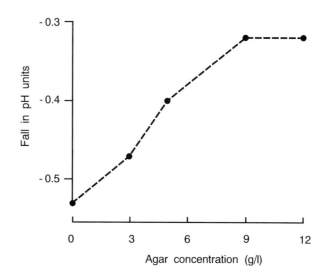

Fig. 95. The decline in the pH of **Linsmaier and Skoog (1965)** medium after autoclaving in the presence of various amounts of 'Phytagar' [from Singha, 1982c]. The medium was adjusted to pH 5.7 before autoclaving.

more *acid* than if agar had not been added, the fall in pH being generally in proportion to the amount of agar present (Fig. 95).

The effect of storage. The pH of autoclaved plant media tends to fall if they are stored. Vacin and Went (1949) noted that autoclaving just accelerated a drop in the pH of **Knudson (1946) C** medium, as solutions left to stand showed similar changes. Sterilisation by filtration (see below) was not a satisfactory alternative, as it too effected pH changes. The compounds particularly responsible were thought to be unchelated ferrous sulphate (when the pH had initially been set between 3 to 6), and calcium nitrate (when the original pH was 6 to 9). Complex iron phosphates, unavailable to plants, were produced from the ferrous sulphate, but if iron was added as ferric citrate or ferric tartrate (chelates), no significant pH changes resulted from autoclaving, and plants showed no iron-deficiency symptoms.

Skirvin *et al.* (1986) found that both with and without agar, autoclaved **MS** medium tended to become more acid after 6 weeks storage, for example:

| | **MS** medium | |
Time	Liquid	With 0.6% Difco Bacto agar
Starting pH	5.7	5.7
After autoclaving	4.6	4.6
6 weeks later	4.1	4.4

To minimise a change in the pH of stored media, it is suggested that they are kept in the dark: Owen *et al.*, 1991) reported that and the pH of **MS** containing 0.1M sucrose or 0.8% Phytagar, remained relatively stable after autoclaving if kept in the dark at 4°C, but fell by up to 0.8 units if stored in the light at 25°C.

Hydrolysis. Some organic components of culture media are liable to be hydrolysed by autoclaving in acid media. The degree of hydrolysis of different brands of agar may be one factor influencing the incidence of hyperhydricity in plant cultures (see Chapter 13). Agar media may not solidify satisfactorily when the initial pH has been adjusted to 4–4.5. The reduction in pH which occurs in most media *during* autoclaving may also cause unsatisfactory gelling of agar which has been added in low concentrations. Part of the sucrose added to plant culture media adjusted to pH 5.5 is also hydrolysed during autoclaving: the proportion degraded increases if the pH of the medium is much less than this. Hydrolysis of sucrose is, however, not necessarily detrimental (page 324).

Activated charcoal. The presence of activated charcoal can alter the pH of a medium (see page 471).

Initiating cultures at low pH

Plants of the family Ericaceae which only grow well on acid soils (*e.g.* rhododendrons and blueberries), have been said to grow best on media such as **Anderson (1975), Anderson (1978a; 1980a)** and **Lloyd and McCown (1981) WPM**, when the pH is first set to *ca.* 4.5 (Anderson, 1975; Skirvin, 1981), but for highly calcifuge species such as *Magnolia × soulangiana*, a starting pH of 3.5 can result in the highest rate of shoot proliferation in shoot cultures (Howard and Marks, 1987). Chevre *et al.* (1983) state that chestnut shoot cultures grew and proliferated best at pH 4 provided **MS** medium was modified by doubling the usual levels of calcium and magnesium.

De Jong *et al.* (1974), using a specially developed medium, found that a low pH value favoured the growth of floral organs. A similar result was seen by Berghoef and Bruinsma (1979c) with *Begonia* buds. Growth was greatest when the pH of the medium was initially adjusted to acid, 4.5–5.0 being optimal. At pH 4.0 the buds became glassy.

Before the discovery of effective chelating agents for plant cultures, root cultures were grown on media with a low pH. Tomato roots were, for instance, unable to grow on media similar to those of **White (1943a)**, when the pH rose to 5.2 (Street *et al.* 1951). Boll and Street (1951) were able to show that the depression of growth at high pH was due to the loss of Fe from the medium and that it could be overcome by adding a chelated form of iron (see page 308). Using FeEDTA, Torrey (1956) discovered that

isolated pea roots [grown on a medium containing **Bonner and Devirian (1939) A** macronutrients, which do not contain NH_4^+], grew optimally at pH 6.0–6.4 but were clearly inhibited at pH 7.0 or greater; and Street (1969) reported that growth of tomato roots could be obtained between pH 4.0 and pH 7.2, if EDTA was present in the medium. Because agar does not gel properly when the initial pH of the medium is adjusted to 4, it is necessary to use liquid media for low pH cultures; or employ another gelling agent, or a mechanical support.

Some other cultures may also be beneficially started at low pH, which may indicate that the tissues have an initial requirement for NO_3^-. Embryogenesis of *Pelargonium* was induced more effectively if **MS**, or other media, were adjusted to pH 4.5–5.0 before autoclaving (rather than pH 5.5 and above) (Marsolais *et al.*, 1991).

pH changes during culture

Due to the differential uptake of anions and cations into plant tissues, the pH of culture media does not usually stay constant, but changes as ions and compounds are absorbed by the plant.

It is usual for media containing nitrate and ammonium ions to decline slowly in pH during a passage, after being adjusted initially to pH 5.4–5.7, Sometimes after a preliminary decrease, the pH may begin to rise and return to a value close to, or even well above that at which the culture was initiated. The pH of **White (1954)** medium, which contains only NO_3^- nitrogen, drifted from an initial 5.0 to 5.5 towards neutrality as callus was cultured on it (Klein and Manos, 1960).

With some cultures, the initial pH of the medium may have little effect. Cell suspension cultures of *Dioscorea deltoides* in the medium of **Kaul and Staba (1968)** [containing **MS** salts], adjusted to a pH either 3.5, 4.3, 5.8 or 6.3, all had a pH of 4.6–4.7 within 10 h of inoculation. There was a further fall to pH 4.0–4.2 in the next 2–3 days, but during the following 15–17 days the pH was 4.7–5.0, finally rising to pH 6.0–6.3 on about day 19 (Butenko *et al.*, 1984). Similarly, Skirvin *et al.* (1986) found that **MS** medium adjusted to pH 3.33, 5.11, 6.63, or 7.98 before autoclaving, and then used for the culture of *Cucumis melo* callus, had a pH after 48 h in the range 4.6–5.0. Visseur (1987) also reported that although the pH of his medium (similar macronutrients to **MS** but more Ca^{2+} and PO_4^{3-}) decreased if it was solidified with agar, but on a 2-phase medium, the final pH was 6.9 ± 0.4 irrespective of whether it was initially 4.8, 5.5 or 6.2.

Despite the above remarks, it should be noted that the nature of the pH drift which occurs in any one medium, differs widely, according to the species of plant grown upon it. The pH of the medium supporting shoot cultures of *Disanthus cercidifolius* changed from 5.5 to 6.5 over a 6 week period, necessitating frequent subculturing to prevent the onset of senescence, whereas in the medium in which shoots of the calcifuge *Lapageria rosea* were grown, the pH, initially set to 3.5–5.0, only changed to 3.8–4.1 (Howard and Marks, 1987). Note also that the reversion of media to a homeostatic pH, may be due to the presence of both NO_3^- and NH_4^+ ions (Dougall, 1980). Adjustment of media containing only one of these nitrogen sources to a range of pH levels, would be expected to result in a more variable set of final values.

As the pH of media deviate from the original titration level, simple unmonitored cultures may not provide the most favourable pH for different phases of growth and differentiation. In *Rosa* 'Paul's Scarlet' suspensions, the optimum pH for the cell division phase was 5.2–5.4: pH 5.5–6.0 was best for the cell expansion phase (Nesius and Fletcher, 1973). The maximum growth rate of *Daucus carota* habituated callus on **White (1954)** medium with iron as Fe–EDTA, occurred at pH 6.0 (Klein and Manos, 1960).

It has been suggested that acidification of media is partly due to the accumulation of carbon dioxide in tightly closed culture flasks (Leva *et al.*, 1984), but the decrease in pH associated with incubating anther cultures with 5% CO_2 was found by Johansson and Eriksson (1984) to be only *ca.* 0.1 units. Removal of CO_2 from an aerated cell suspension culture of *Poinsettia* resulted in an increase of about 0.2 pH-units (Preil, 1991).

Auxin action. Auxin plant growth regulators promote cell growth by inducing the efflux of H^+ ions through the cell wall (Chapter 11). Hydrogen ion efflux from the cell is accompanied by potassium ion influx. When cultures are incubated in a medium containing an auxin, the medium will therefore become more acid while the pH of the cell sap will rise. The extent of these changes was

found by Kurkdjian *et al.* (1982) to be proportional to auxin (2,4-D) concentration.

Differentiation and Morphogenesis

Differentiation and morphogenesis are frequently found to be pH-dependent. The growth of callus and the formation of adventitious organs from thin cell layers excised from superficial tissues of the inflorescence rachis of *Nicotiana*, depended on the initial pH of **Linsmaier and Skoog (1965)** medium containing 0.5 μM IBA and 3 μM kinetin (Table 28) (Mutaftschiev *et al.*, 1987). The types of callus produced from the plumules of *Hevea* seedlings differed according to the pH of the medium devised by Chua (1966). Soft and spongy callus formed at acid (5.4) or alkaline (8.0) pH. A compact callus was obtained between pH 6.2 and 6.8.

Adventitious root formation

There are several reports in the literature which show that the pH of the medium can influence root formation of some plants *in vitro*. A slightly acid pH seems to be preferred by most species. Zatkyo and Molnar (1986), who showed a close correlation between the acidity of the medium (pH 7.0 to 3.0) and the rooting of *Vitis*, *Ribes nigrum* and *Aronia melancarpa* shoots, suggested that this was because acidity is necessary for auxin action.

Sharma *et al.* (1981a) found it advantageous to reduce the pH of the medium to 4.5 to induce rooting of *Bougainvillea* shoots and a reduction of the pH of **MS** medium to 4.0 (accompanied by incubation in the dark) was required for reliable root formation of two *Santalum* species (Barlass *et al.*, 1980) and *Correa decumbens* and *Prostanthera striatifolia* (Williams *et al.*, 1984; 1985). Other Australian woody species rooted satisfactorily at pH 5.5 and pH 4 was inhibitory (Williams *et al.*, *loc. cit.*). Shoots from

---

Table 28. The influence of the initial pH of **Linsmaier and Skoog (1965)** medium on morphogenesis in thin cell layers of *Nicotiana* [data of Mutaftschiev *et al.*, 1987].

Initial pH of the medium	Mean no. organs per explant	Mean percentage of explants forming:			
		Callus	Roots	Vegetative buds	Flowers
3.8	4 ±2	60 ±10	40 ±10	0	0
5.0	2 ±1	90 ±10	10 ±10	0	0
6.1	20 ±10	0	0	100	0
6.8	6 ±2	0	0	20 ±10	80 ±10

carnation meristem tips rooted more readily at pH 5.5 than pH 6.0 (Stone, 1963), and rooting of excised potato buds was best at pH 5.7, root formation being inhibited at pH 4.8 and at pH 6.2 or above (Mellor and Stace-Smith, 1969). Direct root formation on *Nautilocalyx* leaf segments was retarded if a modified **MS** medium containing IAA was adjusted initially to an acid pH (3.5 or 4.0) or a neutral pH (6.5). Good and rapid root formation occurred when the medium was adjusted to between pH 5.0 to 6.3 (Venverloo, 1976).

Direct formation of roots from *Lilium auratum* bulb scales occurred when **MS** medium was adjusted within the range 4–7 but was optimal at pH 6. The pH range for adventitious bulblet formation in this plant was from 4 to 8, but most bulblets were produced when the initial pH was between 5 and 7 (Takayama and Misawa, 1979).

Substrates which are to acid or too alkaline can adversely affect rooting *extra vitrum* (Chapter 14).

Embryogenesis

Smith and Krikorian (1989) discovered that pre-globular stage pro-embryos (PGSP) of carrot could be made to proliferate from tissues capable of direct embryo formation, with no auxin, on a medium containing 1–5 mM NH_4^+ (and no nitrate). Somatic embryos were formed when this tissue was moved to **MS** medium. The pH of the 'ammonium-nitrogen' medium fell from 5.5 to 4.0 in each subculture period, and it was later found (Smith and Krikorian, 1990a,b) that culture on a medium of low pH was essential for the maintenance of PGSP cultures. Sustained culture at a pH equal or greater than 5.7, with no auxin, allowed somatic embryo development.

A similar observation to that of Smith and Krikorian had been made by (Stuart *et al.*, 1987). Although the pH of a suspension culture of alfalfa 'Regen-S' cells in a modified **Schenk and Hildebrandt (1972)** medium with 15 mM NH_4^+ was adjusted to 5.8, it quickly fell back to pH 4.4–5.0 in a few hours. The pH then gradually increased as somatic embryos were produced, until at day 14 it was 5.0. In certain suspension cultures, the pH was titrated daily to 5.5, but on each occasion soon returned to nearly the same pH as that in flasks which were untouched. Even so, the pH-adjusted suspensions produced more embryos than the controls.

The ammonium ion has been found to be essential for embryogenesis (page 283). Is one of its functions to reduce the pH of the medium through rapid uptake and metabolism, thereby facilitating the uptake of nitrate, upon which embryogenesis is really dependent?

Control of pH

Buffering

Vacin and Went (1949) investigated the effect on pH of each compound in their medium. The chemicals which seemed to be most instrumental in changing pH were $FeSO_4.7H_2O$ and $Ca(NO_3)_2.4H_2O$. Replacing the former with ferric tartrate at a weight which maintained the original molar concentration of iron, and substituting $Ca_3(PO_4)_2$ and KNO_3, for $Ca(NO_3)_2.4H_2O$, they found that the solution was more effectively buffered. While amino acids also showed promise as buffering agents, KH_2PO_4 was ineffective unless it was at high concentration. In some early experiments attempts were made to stabilise pH by incorporating a mixture of KH_2PO_4 and K_2HPO_4 into a medium (see Kordan, 1959, for example), but Street and Henshaw (1966) found that significant buffering was only achieved by soluble phosphates at levels inhibitory to plant growth. For this reason Sheat *et al.* (1959) proposed the buffering of plant root culture media with sparingly-soluble calcium phosphates, but unfortunately if these compounds are autoclaved with other medium constituents, they absorb micronutrients which then become unavailable.

A buffer is a compound which can poise the pH level at a selected level: effective buffers should maintain the pH with little change as culture proceeds. Plant tissue culture media are normally poorly buffered. However, pH is stabilised to a certain extent when tissues are cultured in media containing both nitrate and ammonium ions. Agar and Gelrite gelling agents may have a slight buffering capacity (Scherer, 1988).

Organic acids. Many organic acids can act as buffers in plant culture media. By stabilizing pH at *ca.* pH 5.5, they can facilitate the uptake of NH_4^+ when this is the only source of nitrogen, and by their own metabolism, assist the conversion of NH_4^+ into amino acids (page 278). There can be improvement to growth from adding organic acids to media containing both NH_4^+ and NO_3^-, but this is not always the case.

Norstog and Smith (1963) noted that 0.75 mM malic acid was an effective buffer and appeared to enhance the effect of the glutamine and alanine which they added to their medium. Vyskot and Bezdek (1984) found that the buffering capacity of **MS** medium was increased by adding either 1.25 mM sodium citrate or 1.97 mM citric acid plus 6.07 mM dibasic sodium phosphate. Citric acid and some other organic acids have been noted to enhance the growth of *Citrus* callus when added to the medium (presumably that of **Murashige and Tucker, 1969**) (Erner and Reuveni, 1981). For the propagation of various cacti from axillary buds, Vyskot and Jara (1984) added sodium citrate to **MS** medium to increase its buffering capacity.

Recognised biological buffers. Unlike organic acids, conventional buffers are not metabolised by the plant, but can poise pH levels very effectively. Compounds which have been used in plant culture media for critical purposes such as protoplast isolation and culture, and culture of cells at very low inoculation densities, include:

Tris	Tris(hydroxymethyl)aminomethane;
Tricine	N-tris(hydroxymethyl)methylglycine;
MES	2-(N-morpholino)ethanesulphonic acid;
HEPES	4-(2-hydroxyethyl)-1-piperazine(2-ethanesulphonic acid); and
CAPS	3-cyclohexylamino-1-propanesulphonic acid.

Such compounds may have biological effects which are unrelated to their buffering capacity. Depending on the plant species, they have been known to kill protoplasts or greatly increase the rate of cell division and/or plant regeneration (Conrad *et al.*, 1981).

MES is one of the few highly effective and commercially available buffers with significant buffering capacity in the pH range 5–6 to which plant culture media are usually adjusted and has only a low capacity to complex with micronutrients. It is not toxic to most plants, although there are some which are sensitive.

During the culture of thin cell layers of *Nicotiana*, Tiburcio *et al.* (1989) found that the pH of **LS** medium could be kept close to 5.8 for 28 days by adding 50 mM MES, whereas without the buffer pH gradually decreased to 5.25. Regulating pH with MES alters the type of morphogenesis which occurr in this (and other) tissues (page 300).

Parfitt *et al.* (1988) found 10 mM MES to be an effective buffer in four different media used for tobacco, carrot and tomato callus cultures, and peach and carnation shoot cultures, although stabilizing pH did *not* result in superior growth. The tobacco, peach and carnation cultures were damaged by 50 mM MES: Tris was toxic at all concentrations tested, although Klein and Manos (1960) had found that the addition of only 0.5 mM Tris effectively increased the fresh weight of callus which could be grown on **White (1954)** medium when iron was chelated with EDTA.

MES has also been used successfully to buffer many cultures initiated from single protoplasts (Müller *et al.*, 1983) and its inclusion in the culture medium can be essential for the survival of individual cells and their division to form callus colonies (e.g those of *Datura innoxia* — Koop *et al.*, 1983). MES was found to be somewhat toxic to single protoplasts of *Brassica napus*, but 'Polybuffer 74'™ (PB-74, a mixture of polyaminosulphonates), allowed excellent microcolony growth in the pH range 5.5–7.0 (Spangenberg *et al.*, 1986). Used at $\frac{1}{100}$ of the commercially available solution, it has a buffering capacity of a 1.3 mM buffer at its pK value (Koop *et al.*, 1983).

Banana homogenate is widely used in orchid micropropagation media. Ernst (1974) noted that it appeared to buffer the medium in which slipper orchid seedlings were being grown.

MICRONUTRIENTS

Plant requirements for microelements have only been elucidated over the past 40–50 years. Before the end of the last century, it had been realised that too little iron caused chlorophyll deficiency in plants, but the importance of other elements took many years to prove conclusively. Mazé, for example, used hydroponic techniques during the years 1914–1919 to show that zinc, manganese and boron improved the growth of maize plants. Sommer and Lipman (1926) also showed the essentiality of boron, and Sommer (1931) of copper, but uncertainty over which elements were really indispensible to growth still existed in 1933 when Hoagland and Snyder proposed two supplementary nutrient solutions for water culture which in total contained 26 elements. It took several further years to prove that molybdenum (Arnon and Stout, 1939) and cobalt in very small amounts, were most important for healthy plant growth. Early plant tissue culture work was to both profit from, and contribute to the findings of previous hydroponic studies. Our understanding has been enhanced by investigations into the biochemical role of minor elements.

Early use for plant tissue cultures

At the time of the early plant tissue culture experiments, uncertainty still existed over the nature of the essential microelements. Many tissues were undoubtedly grown successfully because they were cultured on media prepared from impure chemicals (see below) or solidified with agar, which acted as a micronutrient source (see page 338).

In the first instance, the advantage of adding various micronutrients to culture media, was mainly evaluated by their capability of individual elements to improve the growth of undifferentiated callus or isolated root cultures. Knudson (1922) incorporated Fe and Mn in his very successful media for the non-symbiotic germination of orchid seeds, and, following a recommendation by Berthelot (1934), Gautheret (1939) and Nobécourt (1937) included (in addition to iron) copper, cobalt, nickel, titanium and beryllium to their tissue culture media. By 1946, Hildebrandt et al. had studied the optimum requirements of B, Mn, Zn, Fe (and I) for the culture of tobacco and sunflower tumour callus. Surprisingly, with the exception of Mn, they arrived at significantly different concentrations of these elements for the two species (Table 13). Burkholder and Nickell (1949) added Mo for the first time. The advantage of adding five micronutrients to tissue culture media was perhaps first well demonstrated by Heller in 1953. When he examined the effect of mineral deficiencies in carrot callus previously grown on **Gautheret (1942)** medium, he found that death of the culture occurred in 3 to 5 passages in the absence of either Fe, B, Mn, Zn or Cu, but in one to two passages, when either N, K, Ca, Mg, S or P were missing. This demonstrates that although a ready supply of macro-elements is indispensible, explanted tissues can retain sufficient microelements for at least limited growth over several cell generations.

Zinc was found to be necessary for the normal development of tomato root systems (Eltinge and Reed, 1940), and without Cu, roots ceased to grow (Glasstone, 1947). Hannay and Street (1954) showed that Mo and Mn were also essential for root growth.

Micronutrients through trace impurities

Micronutrients tend to be added to modern media by the addition of fairly standard chemicals (Table 50). Street (1977b) rightly emphasised that even analytical grade chemicals contain traces of impurities that will provide a hidden supply of micronutrients to a medium. An illustration of this, comes from the work of Dalton et al. (1983) who found traces of silicon (Si) in a precipitate from **MS** medium which had been made up with analytical grade laboratory chemicals. Gelling agents contain inorganic elements but whether cultures can utilize them is unclear. Scherer et al. (1988) calculated that 0.2% Gelrite could theoretically contribute 190 mg/l of microelements (especially Na, Al, Sr, Ti, Cu and V) and 0.8% agar 320 mg/l (particularly SO_4^{2-} and Si).

Amounts of contaminating substances in chemicals would have been greater in times past, so that an early medium such as **Knudson (1922; 1943) B**, prepared today with highly purified chemicals, will not have quite the same composition as when it was first used by Knudson in 1922; the addition of some micronutrients might improve the results obtained from a present-day formulation of such early media.

Optimum micro-element concentrations

Most modern culture media use the microelements of **Gamborg et al. (1968) B5** medium, or the more concentrated mixtures in **MS** or **Bourgin and Nitsch (1967) H** media. Several research workers have continued to use **Heller (1953)** micro-nutrient formulation, even though higher levels are now normally recommended. Quoirin and Lepoivre (1977) showed clearly that in conjunction with **MS** or their **Quoirin and Lepoivre (1977) B** macro-elements, the concentration of Mn in Heller's salts should be increased by 100 fold to obtain the most effective growth of *Prunus* meristems.

Cell growth and morphogenesis of some species may even be promoted by increasing the level of micronutrients above that recommended by Murashige and Skoog (1962). The induction and maintenance of callus and growth of cell suspensions of juvenile and mature organs of both Douglas fir and loblolly pine, was said to be improved on **Litvay et al. (1981) LM** medium in which Mg, B, Zn, Mo, Co and I were at 5 times the concentration of **MS** micro-elements, and Mn and Cu at 1.25 and 20 times respectively (Litvay et al. 1981; Verma et al. 1982). Other authors to have employed high micronutrient levels are Barwale et al. (1986) who found that the induction of adventitious shoots from callus of 54 genotypes of *Glycine max* was assisted by adding four times the normal concentration of minor salts to **MS** medium.

A further example where more concentrated micro-elements seemed to promote morphogenesis is provided by the work of Wang, Z. et al. (1980, 1981). Embryogenesis could be induced most effectively in callus derived from *Hevea brasiliensis* anthers, by doubling the concentration of microelements in **MS** medium, while at the same time reducing the level of macronutrients to 60–80% of the original.

Despite these reports, few research workers seem to have accepted the need for such high micronutrient levels. To diminish the occurrence of hyperhydricity in shoot culture of carnation, Dencso (1987) reduced the level of micronutrients (except iron, which was as recommended by Dalton et al., 1983) to $\frac{1}{10}$ those in **MS** medium, but this mixture was inadequate for *Gerbera* shoot cultures and the rate of propagation was less than that with the normal **MS** formulation.

The need for macronutrient concentrations to be optimised as the first step in media development seems to be emphasised by results of Eeuwens (1976). In an experiment with factorial combinations of the macro- and micro-nutrient components of four media, his **Eeuwens (1976) Y3** micronutrients gave a considerable improvement in the growth of coconut callus, compared with other micro-element mixtures, when they were used with **Y3** and **MS** macronutrients, but not when used with those of **White (1942)** or **Heller (1953; 1955)**.

Cellular differentiation and morphogenesis

Welander (1977) obtained evidence which suggested that plant cells are more demanding for minor elements when undergoing morphogenesis. Petiole explants of *Begonia* × *hiemalis* produced callus on media without micronutrients, but would only produce adventitious shoot buds directly when micronutrients were added to the macronutrient formulation. The presence of iron is particularly important for adventitious shoot and root formation (Legrand, 1975).

That mineral nutrition can influence cellular differentiation in combination with growth hormones, was shown by Beasley *et al.* (1974). Cotton ovules cultured on a basic medium containing 5.0 μM IAA and 0.5 μM GA₃, required 2 μM calcium (normally present in the medium) for the ovules to develop fibres. Magnesium and boron were essential for fibre elongation.

THE BIOCHEMICAL ROLE OF MICRONUTRIENTS

The essential micronutrient metals Fe, Mn, Zn, B, Cu, Co and Mo are components of plant cell proteins of metabolic and physiological importance. At least five of these elements are, for instance, necessary for chlorophyll synthesis and chloroplast function (Sundqvist *et al.*, 1980). Micronutrients have roles in the functioning of the genetic apparatus and several are involved with the activity of growth substances.

Manganese

Manganese (Mn) is one of the most important microelements and has been included in the majority of plant tissue culture media. It is generally added in similar concentrations to those of iron and boron, *i.e.* between 25–150 μM. Manganese has similar chemical properties

to Mg^{2+} and is apparently able to replace magnesium in some enzyme systems (Hewitt, 1948). However there is normally 50- to 100-fold more Mg^{2+} than Mn^{2+} within plant tissues, and so it is unlikely that there is a frequent substitution between the uses of the two elements.

The most probable role for the element is in definition of the structure of metalloproteins involved in respiration and photosynthesis (Clarkson and Hanson, 1980). It is known to be required for the activity of several enzymes, which include decarboxylases, dehydrogenases, kinases and oxidases and super-oxide dismutase enzymes. Manganese is necessary for the maintenance of chloroplast ultra-structure. The evolution of oxygen during photosystem II of the photosynthetic process, is dependent on an Mn–containing enzyme and is proportional to Mn content (Mengel and Kirkby, 1982; Shkolnik, 1984).

In tissue cultures, omission of Mn ions from **Doerschug and Miller (1967)** medium reduced the number of buds initiated on lettuce cotyledons. A high level of manganese could compensate for the lack of molybdenum in the growth of excised tomato roots (and *vice versa*) (Hannay and Street, 1954). Natural auxin levels are thought to be reduced in the presence of Mn^{2+} because the activity of IAA-oxidase is increased. This is possibly due to Mn^{2+} or Mn-containing enzymes inactivating oxidase inhibitors, or because manganous ions are one of the cofactors for IAA oxidases in plant cells (Galston and Hillman, 1961). Manganese complexed with EDTA increased the oxidation of naturally-occurring IAA, but not the synthetic auxins NAA or 2,4-D (MacLachlan and Waygood, 1956). However, Chée (1986) has suggested that, at least in blue light, Mn^{2+} tends to cause the maintenance or *increase* in IAA levels within tissues by inactivating a co-factor of IAA oxidase. When the Mn^{2+} level in **MS** medium was reduced from 100 μM to 5 μM, the production in blue light, of axillary shoots by *Vitis* shoot cultures was increased.

Zinc

Zinc deficient plants suffer from reduced enzyme activities and a consequent diminution in protein, nucleic acid and chlorphyll synthesis. Molybdenum- and zinc-deficient plants have a decreased chlorophyll content and poorly developed chloroplasts. Plants deprived of zinc often have short internodes and small leaves.

Zinc is a component of stable metallo-enzymes with many diverse functions, making it difficult to predict the unifying chemical property of the element which is responsible for its essentiality (Clarkson and Hanson, 1980). In bacteria, Zn is present in RNA and DNA polymerase enzymes, deficiency resulting in a sharp decrease in RNA levels. DNA polymerase is concerned with the repair of incorrectly formed pieces of DNA in DNA replication, and RNA polymerase locates the point on the DNA genome at which initiation of RNA synthesis is to take place. Divalent Mg^{2+}, Mn^{2+} or Co^{2+} are also required for activation of these enzymes (Eichhorn, 1980).

When Eriksson (1965) added 15 mg/l $Na_2ZnEDTA$ to *Haplopappus gracilis* cell cultures, he obtained a 15% increase in cell dry weight which was thought to be due to the presence of zinc rather than the chelating agent.

There is a close relationship between the zinc nutrition of plants and their auxin content (Skoog, 1940). It has been suggested that zinc is a component of an enzyme concerned with the synthesis of the IAA precursor, tryptophan (Tsui, 1948). The importance of Zn for tryptophan synthesis is especially noticeable in crown gall callus which normally produces sufficient endogenous auxin to maintain growth on a medium without synthetic auxins, but which becomes auxin-deficient and ceases to grow in the absence of Zn (Klein *et al.* 1962).

The concentration of Zn^{2+} added to cultured media has varied widely, and has ranged from 0.1–70 μM, which seems to indicate that an excess of Zn^{2+} ions is not especially toxic. Generally the level used is 2–30 times that of copper.

Boron

The role of boron in plant biochemistry and physiology is still largely unknown. A review has been provided by Lewis (1980). The element is required for the metabolism of phenolic acids, and for lignin biosynthesis: it is probably a component, or co–factor of the enzyme which converts *p*-coumaric acid to caffeate and 5-hydroxyferulate. Boron is necessary for the maintenance of meristematic activity, most likely because it is involved in the synthesis of N-bases (uracil in particular); these are required for RNA synthesis (Mengel and Kirkby, 1982). It is also thought to be involved in the maintenance of membrane structure and function, possibly by stabilizing natural metal chelates which are important in wall and membrane structure and function (Pollard *et al.*, 1977; Clarkson and Hanson, 1980).

Boron is concerned with the regulating the activities of phenolase enzymes; these bring about the biosynthesis of the phenylpropane compounds, which are polymerized to form lignin. Lignin biosynthesis does not take place in the absence of boron. Boron also mediates the action of phytochrome and the response of plants to gravity (Tanada, 1978).

Use in culture media

In the soil, boron occurs in the form of boric acid and it is this compound which is generally employed as the source of the element in tissue cultures. Uptake of boric acid occurs most readily at acid pH, possibly in the undissociated form (Oertli and Grgurevic, 1974) or as $H_2BO_3^-$ (Devlin, 1975). A wide range of boron concentrations has been used in media, the most usual concentrations being between from 50 and 100 μM: **MS** medium contains 100 μM. Bowen (1979) found boron to be toxic to sugarcane suspensions above 2 mg/l (185 μM), but there are a few reports of higher concentrations being employed (Table 29). High concentrations of boron may have a regulatory function; for example, 1.6–6.5 mM have been used in simple media to stimulate pollen germination (Brewbaker and Kwack, 1963; Taylor, 1972).

Boric acid reacts with some organic compounds having two adjacent *cis*–hydroxyl groups (Greenwood, 1973). This includes *o*–diphenols, hexahydric alcohols such as mannitol and sorbitol (commonly used in plant tissue culture as osmotic agents), and several other sugars, but excludes sucrose which forms only a weak association. Once the element is complexed it appears to be unavailable to plants. This led Lewis (1980) to suggest that because boric acid was required for lignin biosynthesis, vascular plants were led, during evolution, to use sucrose exclusively for the transport of carbohydrate reserves.

Although the addition of sugar alcohols and alternative sugars to sucrose can be beneficial during plant tissue culture (see later in this chapter), it is clearly necessary to return to a sucrose-based medium for long-term culture, or boron deficiency may result.

Deficiency symptoms

Boron is thought to promote the destruction of natural auxin and increase its translocation. Endogenous IAA levels increase in the absence of boron and translocation is reduced, the compound probably being retained at the site of synthesis (Goldbach and Amberger, 1986). Plants suffering from boron deficiency have restricted root systems (Odhnoff, 1957; Whittington, 1959) and a reduced capacity to absorb $H_2PO_4^-$ and some other ions. High levels of auxins can have the same effect on growth and ion uptake (Pollard *et al.*, 1977). Neales (1959, 1964) showed that isolated roots stopped growing unless a minimum concentration of boron was present (although the necessity for the element was not so apparent when cultures were grown in borosilicate glass vessels). Inhibition of root elongation in the absence of boron has been shown to be due to the cessation of mitosis and the inhibition of DNA synthesis (Moore and Hirsch, 1981).

Table 29. Examples of cultures grown with unusually high concentrations of boron.

Plant	Concentration of boron µM	Type of culture	Reference
Antirrhinum majus	323	Embryos from protoplast colonies	Poirier-Hamon *et al.* (1974)
Brassica napus *Capsella bursa-pastoris*	200	Embryo	Monnier (1976)
Citrus medica	646	Anther callus	Drira and Benbadis (1975)
Hevea brasiliensis	320	Anther: plant regeneration	Chen, Z.(1984)
Hordeum crosses	242	Embryo rescue	Jensen (1974
Larix decidua	250	Direct morphogenesis	Bonga (1984)
	250	Callus & embryogenesis	Nagmani & Bonga (1985)
Lycopersicon esculentum	242	Isolated root	Street & McGregor (1952)
Nicotiana tabacum	323	Protoplast culture	Ohyama & Nitsch (1972)
Petunia hybrida	566	Callus and root formation	Sangwan and Norreel (1975)
Prunus amygdalus	200	Shoot	Hisajima (1982a)

Boron deficiency also results in depressed cytokinin synthesis. Cell division is inhibited in the absence of boron, apparently because there is a decrease in nuclear RNA synthesis (Ali and Jarvis, 1988). However, deficiency often leads to increased cambial growth in intact dicotyledonous plants.

Cotton ovules which otherwise develop fibres when cultured, commence extensive callus formation when placed on a medium deficient in boron. On the other hand, the growth rate of callus cultures of *Helianthus annuus* and *Daucus carota* (Krosing, 1978), and cell cultures of sugar cane (Bowen, 1979), was much reduced when boron was not present in the growth medium.

Adventitious root formation

Boron is thought to promote the destruction of auxin. Although auxin is required for the formation of adventitious root initials, boron is necessary in light grown-plants for the growth of these primordia (Middleton *et al.*, 1978); possibly boron enhances the destruction of auxin in these circumstances, which in high concentrations is inhibitory to root growth (Jarvis, 1986)? An interaction between boron and auxins in the rooting of cuttings has been noticed in several species (Hemberg, 1951; Weiser, 1959; Weiser and Blaney, 1960; Bowen *et al.* 1975) and a supply of exogenous borate has been shown to be essential (Ali and Jarvis, 1988). However, excessive boron concentrations lead to a reduction in the number of roots formed (Jarvis, 1986).

Copper and molybdenum

Copper is an essential micronutrient, even though plants normally contain only a few parts per million of the element. Two kinds of copper ions exist; they are the monovalent cuprous [Cu(I)] ion, and the divalent cupric [Cu(II)] ion: the former is easily oxidized to the latter; the latter is easily reduced. The element becomes attached to enzymes, many of which bind to, and react with oxygen. They include the cytochrome oxidase enzyme system, responsible for oxidative respiration, and superoxide dismutase (an enzyme which contains both copper and zinc atoms). Detrimental superoxide radicals, which are formed from molecular oxygen during electron transfer reactions, are reacted by superoxide dismutase with water (page 199). Copper atoms occur in plastocyanin, a pigment participating in electron transfer.

Several copper-dependent enzymes are involved in the oxidation and hydroxylation of phenolic compounds, such as ABA and dopamine (Lerch, 1981). The hydroxylation of monophenols by copper-containing enzymes leads to the construction of important polymeric constituents of plants, such as lignin. These same enzymes can lead to the blackening of freshly isolated explants (Chapter 13). Copper is a constituent of ascorbic acid oxidase and the characteristic growth regulatory effects of ethylene are thought to depend on its metabolism by an enzyme which contains copper atoms.

High concentrations of copper can be toxic. Most culture media include *ca.* 0.1–1.0 µM Cu^{2+}. Ions are usually added through copper sulphate, although occasionally cupric chloride or cupric nitrate have been employed. In hydroponic culture of *Trifolium pratense*, uptake of copper into the plant depended on the amount of nitrate in solution. Uptake was considerably reduced when NO_3^- was depleted (Jarvis, 1984).

Plants utilise hexavalent molybdenum and absorb the element as the molybdate ion (MoO_4^{2-}). This is normally added to culture media as sodium molybdate at concentrations up to 1 µM. Considerably higher levels have occasionally been introduced [*e.g.* in the media of **Abou-Mandour (1977b)** and **Asahira and Kano (1977)**] apparently without adverse effect, although Teasdale (1987) found pine suspension cultures were injured by 50 µM. Molybdenum is a component of several plant enzymes, two being nitrate reductase and nitrogenase, in which it is a cofactor together with iron: it is thesefore essential for nitrogen utilisation. Tissues and organs presented with NO_3^- in a molybdenum-deficient medium can shown symptoms of nitrate toxicity because the ion is not reduced to ammonia.

Cobalt

Cobalt was found to have been included in approximately half of a large sample of published plant culture media (George, E.F. *et al.*, 1987). The concentration most commonly added to a medium is *ca.* 0.1 µM, although ten times this amount has sometimes been used. Cobalt is the metal component of Vitamin B_{12} which is concerned with nucleic acid synthesis (Fries, 1962), but evidence that the element has any marked stimulatory effect on growth or morphogenesis in plant tissue cultures is hard to find.

Murashige and Skoog (1962) included Co in their medium because it had been shown to be required by lower plants (Holm-Hansen *et al.*, 1954) and that it might have a role in regulating morphogenesis in higher plants (Miller, 1954; Salisbury, 1959). However no stimulatory effect on the growth of tobacco callus was observed by adding cobalt chloride to the medium at several concentrations from 0.1 µM and above, and at 80.0 and 160 µM the compound was toxic. Similarly Schenk and Hildebrandt (1972) obtained no clear evidence for a Co requirement in tests on a wide variety of plants, but retained the element in their medium because they occasionally observed an apparent stimulation to the callus growth of some monocotyledons. *Pinus* suspension cultures do not require cobalt (Teasdale, 1987).

Advantage from adding cobalt to plant culture media might be derived from the fact that the element can have a protective action against metal chelate toxicity and it is able to inhibit oxidative reactions catalysed by ions of copper and iron (Albert, 1958). The Co^{2+} ion can inhibit ethylene synthesis (see Chapter 11).

Aluminium and nickel

Several workers, following Heller (1953), have included aluminium and nickel in their micronutrient formulations (Chapter 10). The general benefit of adding these metals does not seem to have been adequately demonstrated.

In most plants Ni^{2+} is not absolutely required for normal growth and development (Mishra and Kar, 1975). However, the ion is a component of urease enzymes (Dixon *et al.*, 1975; Polacco, 1977a) which convert urea to ammonia and has been shown to be an essential micronutrient for some legumes. In tissue cultures the presence of 0.1 µM Ni^{2+} strongly stimulates the growth of soybean cells in a medium containing only urea as a nitrogen source. Slow growth occurs on urea without the deliberate addition of nickel, possibly supported by trace amounts of the element remaining in the cells (Polacco, 1977b). Cells and tissues are not normally grown with urea as a nitrogen source, and as urease is the only enzyme which has been shown to have a nickel component, it could be argued that nickel is not essential. However, without it soybean plants grown hydroponically, accumulate toxic concentrations of urea (2.5%) in necrotic lesions on their leaf tips, whether supplied with inorganic nitrogen, or with nitrogen compounds obtained from bacterial symbiotic nitrogen fixation. These symptoms can be alleviated in plants growing in hydroponic culture by adding 1 µg/l Ni to the nutrient solution. Absence of nickel in a hydroponic solution also results in reduced early growth and delayed nodulation (Eskew *et al.*, 1983).

Despite these findings nickel has not been added deliberately to tissue culture media for soybean or other legumes. Possibly urea toxicity has been avoided because, in tissue cultures, urea diffuses into the medium (Teasdale, 1987). Quoirin and Lepoivre (1977) showed that at the concentrations recommended by Heller, Al^{3+} and Ni^{2+} were without effect on the growth of *Prunus* meristems and were inhibitory at higher levels. If it is thought that Ni should be added to a culture medium, 0.1 µM is probably sufficient.

Aluminium has been said to be necessary for the growth of some ferns (Taubock, 1942), but is not generally added to tissue culture media for fern propagation.

Iodine

Iodine is not recognised as an essential element for the nutrition of higher plants (Rains, 1976), although it may be necessary for the growth of some algae, and small amounts do accumulate in higher plants (*ca*.12 and 3 mol/kg dry weight in terrrestrial and aquatic plants respectively — Raven, 1986). However, the iodide ion has been added to many tissue culture media (*e.g.* to 65% of the micronutrient formulations in Chapter 10).

The practice of including iodide in plant culture media began with the report by White (1938b) that it improved the growth of tomato roots cultured *in vitro*. Hannay (1956) obtained similar results and found that root growth declined in the absence of iodine which could be supplied not only from potassium iodide, but also from iodoacetate or methylene iodide, compounds which would only provide iodide ions very slowly in solution by hydrolysis. Street (1966) thought that these results indicated that iodine could be an essential nutrient element, but an alternative hypothesis is that any beneficial effect may result from the ability of iodide ions to act as a reducing agent (George *et al.*, 1988). Oxidants convert iodide ions to free iodine. Eeuwens (1976) introduced potassium iodide into his **Y3** medium at 0.05 mM (ten times the level used by Murashige and Skoog), as it prevented the browning of coconut palm tissue cultures. The presence of 0.06 M potassium iodide slightly improved the survival and growth of cultured *Prunus* meristems (Quoirin and Lepoivre, 1977b).

Although Gautheret (1942) and White (1943a) had recommended the addition of iodine to media for callus culture, Hildebrandt *et al.* (1946) obtained no statistically significant benefit from adding potassium iodide to tumour callus cultures of tobacco and sunflower. However, as the average weight of tobacco callus was 11% less without it, the compound was included (at different levels) in both of the media they devised. Once again iodine also had no appreciable effect on tobacco callus yield in the experiments of Murashige and Skoog (1962), but was nevertheless included in their final medium. Other workers have omitted iodine from **MS** medium (*e.g.* Roest and Bokelmann, 1975; Périnet *et al.*, 1988; Gamborg, 1991) or from new media formulations without any apparent ill effects. However, Teasdale *et al.* (1986); Teasdale, (1987) reported a definite requirement of *Pinus taeda* suspensions for 25 μM KI when they were grown on **Litvay *et al.* (1981) LM** medium.

There seems, at least in some plants, to be an interaction between iodine and light. Eriksson (1965) left KI out of his modification of **MS** medium, finding that it was toxic to *Haplopappus gracilis* cells cultured in darkness: shoot production in *Vitis* shoot cultures kept in blue light was reduced when iodine was present in the medium (Chée, 1986), but the growth of roots on rooted shoots was increased. Chée thought that these results supported the hypothesis that iodine enhanced the destruction and/or the lateral transport of IAA auxin. This seems to be

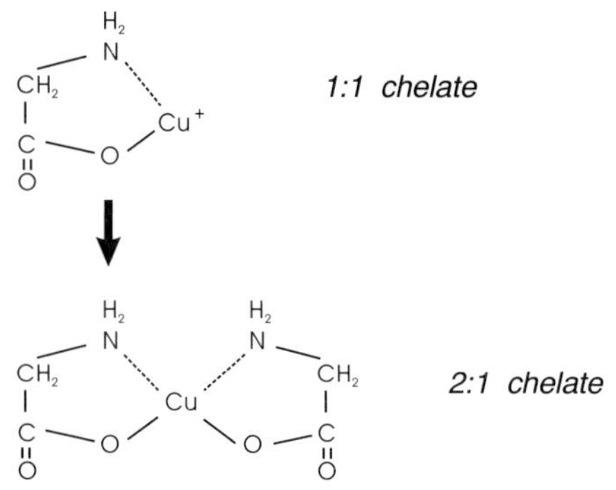

Fig. 96. Copper chelated with the amino acid, glycine.

inconsistent with the suggestion that I^- acts mainly as a reducing agent.

Silicon

The silicate ion is not normally added to tissue culture media, although it is likely to be present in low concentrations. Deliberate addition to the medium might, however, improve the growth of some plants. Adatia and Besford (1986) found that cucumber plants depleted silicate from a hydroponic solution and in consequence their leaves were more rigid, had a higher fresh weight per unit area and a higher chlorophyll content than the controls. The resistance of the plants to powdery mildew was also much increased.

CHELATING AGENTS

Some organic compounds are capable of forming complexes with metal cations, in which the metal is held with fairly tight chemical bonds. The complexes formed may be linear or ring-shaped, in which case the complex is called a *chelate* (from the Greek word meaning a crab's claw). Metals can be bound (or sequestered) by a chelating agent and held in solution under conditions where free ions would react with anions to form insoluble compounds, and some complexes can be more chemically reactive than the metals themselves. For example, Cu^{2+} complexed with amino acids is *more* active biologically than the free ion (Cruickshank *et al.*, 1987). Chelating agents vary in their sequestering capacity (or *avidity*) according to chemical structure and their degree of ionisation, which changes with the pH of the solution. Copper is chelated by amino acids at relatively high pH, but in conditions of greater acidity, it is more liable to be complexed with organic acid ligands (White *et al.*, 1981). The higher the stability of a complex, the higher the avidity of the complexing agent. One, and in many cases, two or three molecules of a complexing agent may associate with one metal ion, depending on its valency.

Despite tight bonding, there is always an equilibrium between different chelate complexes and between ions in solution. Complexing agents also associate with some metal ions more readily than with others. In general Fe^{3+} (for agents able to complex with trivalent ions) complexes have a higher stability than those of Cu^{2+}, then (in descending order), Ni^{2+}, Al^{3+} (where possible), Zn^{2+}, Co^{2+}, Fe^{2+}, Mn^{2+} and Ca^{2+} (Albert, 1958; Reilley and Schmid, 1958). For a chelated metal ion to be utilised by a plant there must be some mechanism whereby the complex can be broken. This could occur if it is absorbed directly and the ion displaced by another more avid binding agent, or if the complex is biochemically denatured. Metals in very stable complexes can be unavailable to plants; copper in EDTA chelates may be an example (Coombes et al., 1977). High concentrations of avid chelating agents are phytotoxic, probably because they competitively withdraw essential elements from enzymes.

Naturally-occurring compounds act as chelating agents. Within the plant very many constituents such as proteins, peptides, porphyrins, carboxylic acids and amino acids have this property (Albert, 1958; Martin, 1979): some of those with high avidity are metal-containing enzymes. Amino acids are able to complex with divalent metals (Fig. 96). Grasses are thought to secrete a chelating agent from their roots to assist the uptake of iron (Römheld and Marschner, 1986).

There are also synthetic chelating agents with high avidities (stability constants) for divalent and trivalent ions. Some are listed in Table 30, and the structure of those most commonly used in plant culture media is illustrated in Fig. 97. The application of synthetic chelating agents and chelated micronutrients to the roots of some plants growing in alkaline soils can improve growth by supplying essential metals such as iron and zinc which are otherwise unavailable. The addition of such compounds to tissue culture media can help to make macro- and micronutrients more accessible to plant cells.

Table 30. Some common chelating agents: abbreviations and chemical names.

EDTA	Ethylenediaminetetraacetic acid
EGTA	Ethleneglycol-bis(2-aminoethylether)tetraacetic acid
EDDHA	Ethylenediamine-di(o-hydroxyphenyl)acetic acid
DTPA	Diethylenetriaminepentaacetic acid
DHPTA	1,3-diamino-2-hydroxypropane-tetraacetic acid

Iron and iron chelates

A key property of iron is its capacity to be oxidized easily from the ferrous [Fe(II)] to the ferric [Fe(III)] state, and for ferric compounds to be readily reduced back to the ferrous form. In plants, iron is primarily used in the chloroplasts, mitochondria and peroxisomes of plants for effecting oxidation/reduction (redox) reactions. The element is required for the formation of amino laevulinic acid and protoporphyrinogen (which are respectively early and late precursors of chlorophyll) and deficiency leads to marked leaf chlorosis. Iron is also a component of ferredoxin proteins which function as electron carriers in photosynthesis.

Iron is therefore an essential micronutrient for plant tissue culture media and can be taken up into plants as either ferrous (Fe^{2+}) or ferric (Fe^{3+}) ions. In early experiments, ferrous sulphate or ferric citrate or tartrate were used in media as a source of the element. Citric and and tartaric acids can act as chelating agents for some divalent metals (Bobtelsky and Jordan, 1945), but are not very efficient at keeping iron in solution (Fig. 97). If Fe^{2+} and Fe^{3+} ions escape from the chelating agent, they are liable to be precipitated as iron phosphate. The iron may then not be available to plant cells, unless the pH of the medium falls sufficiently to bring free ions back into solution. The problem of precipitation is more severe in aerated media and where the pH of the medium drifts towards alkalinity. Under these conditions Fe^{2+} (ferrous) ions are oxidized to Fe^{3+} (ferric) ions and unchelated ferric ions may then also be converted to insoluble $Fe(OH)_3$. For plant hydroponic culture, the advantages of adding iron to nutrient solutions in the form of a chelate with EDTA was first recognised in the 1950's (Jacobson, 1951; Weinstein et al. 1951). Street et al. (1952) soon found that iron in this form was less toxic and could be utilised by in vitro cultures of isolated tomato roots over a wider pH range than ferric citrate. Klein and Manos (1960) showed that callus cultures of several species grew more rapidly on **White (1954)** medium if Fe^{3+} ions from $Fe_2(SO_4)_3$ were chelated with EDTA, rather than added to the medium from the pure compound, and Doerschug and Miller (1967), that 0.036 mM Fe from NaFeEDTA was as effective as 0.067 mM Fe as ferric citrate, in promoting shoot bud initiation on lettuce cotyledons. Iron presented as ferric sulphate (0.025 mM Fe) was much less effective than either chelated form.

Skoog and co-workers began to use EDTA in media for tobacco callus cultures in 1956 and discussed their findings in the same paper that describes **MS** medium (Murashige and Skoog, 1962). The addition of an iron (Fe)–EDTA chelate once again greatly improved the availability of the element. Following this publication,

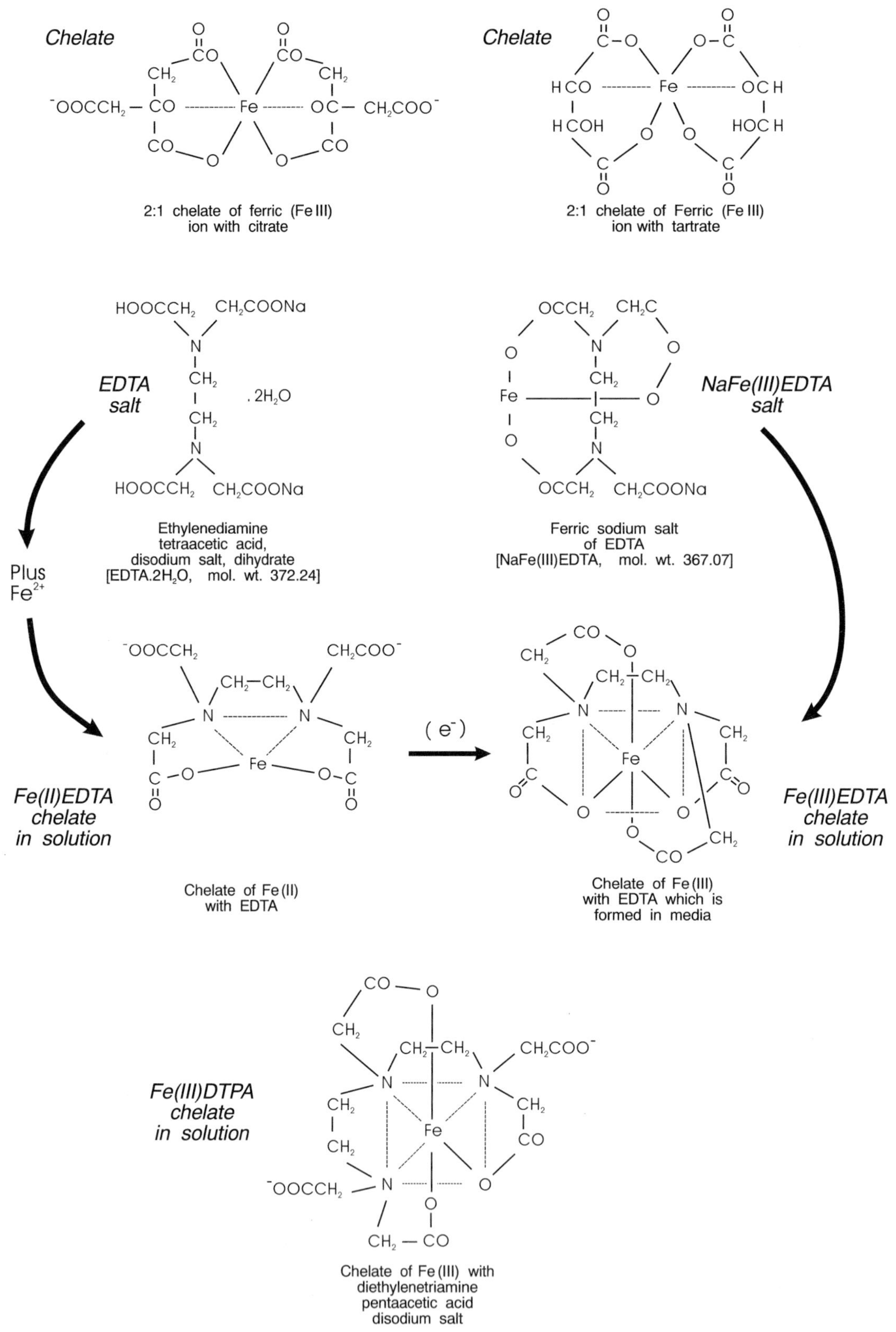

Fig. 97. Chemical structures of some chelating agents and iron chelates.

(Fe)–EDTA complexes were rapidly recognised to give generally improved growth of all types of plant cultures (Nitsch, 1969). EDTA has now become almost a standard medium component and is generally preferred to other alternative chelating agents (Table 30).

Preparation and use

(Fe)-EDTA chelates for tissue cultures are prepared in either of two ways.

- A ferric or ferrous salt is dissolved in water with EDTA and the solution is heated;

- A ready-prepared salt of iron salt of EDTA is dissolved and heated.

Heating can take place during the preparation of chelate stock solutions, or during the autoclaving of a medium (actual methods of preparation are described in Chapter 10).

The form of iron complexed is invariably Fe(III). If iron has been provided from ferrous salts, it is oxidised during heating in aerated solutions. The rate of oxidation of the ferrous ion is enhanced in some complexes and retarded in others (Albert, 1958). That of Fe^{2+}-EDTA is extremely rapid (Kolthoff and Auerbach (1952). Only a small proportion of Fe^{2+} is likely to remain: its chelate with EDTA is much less stable than the Fe(III) complex. Iron is however thought to be absorbed into plants in the ferrous form. Uptake of iron from EDTA probably occurs when molecules of Fe(III)–chelate bind to the outer plasma membrane (the plasmalemma) of the cytoplasm, where Fe(III) is reduced to Fe(II) and freed from the chelate (Römheld and Marschner, 1983).

In most recent plant tissue culture work, EDTA has been added to media at an equimolar concentration with iron, where it will theoretically form a chelate with all the iron in solution. However, it has been found in practice that the Fe(III)-EDTA chelate, although stable at pH 2–3, is liable to lose some of its bound iron in culture media at higher pH levels; the displaced iron may form insoluble ferric hydroxides and iron phosphate (Dalton *et al.*, 1983). If this occurs, free EDTA will tend to form chelates with other metal ions in solution. Some micronutrients complexed with EDTA may then not be available to the plant tissues. Re-complexing may also happen if the EDTA to Fe ratio is increased by decreasing the amount of iron added to the medium (as has been proposed to solve the precipitation problem, see page 347). It is not possible to add very much more than 0.1 mM EDTA to culture media because the chelating agent can become toxic to some plants (see below).

Hill-Cottingham and Lloyd-Jones (1961) showed that tomato plants absorbed iron from FeEDTA more rapidly than they absorbed EDTA itself, but concluded that both Fe and Fe- chelate were probably taken up. They postulated that EDTA liberated by the absorption of Fe, would chelate other metals in the nutrient solution in the order shown on page 309. Teasdale(1987) calculated that in many media, nearly all the copper and zinc, and some manganese ions might be secondarily chelated, but it is unclear whether micronutrients in this form are freely available to plant tissues. One presumes they are, for deficiency symptoms are not reported from *in vitro* cultures.

Ambiguous descriptions.

In many early papers on plant tissue culture, the authors of scientific papers have failed to describe which form of EDTA was used in experiments, or have ascribed weights to EDTA which should refer to its hydrated sodium salts. Singh and Krikorian (1980) drew attention to this lack of precision. They assumed that in papers where Na_2EDTA is described as a medium constituent, it indicates the use of the anhydrous salt (which would give 11 mol/l excess of EDTA to iron, with unknown consequences). However, the disodium salt of EDTA is generally made as the dihydrate (*Beilstein's Handbuch der Organischen Chemie*) and this is the form which will almost invariably have been used, Na_2EDTA merely being a shorthand way of indicating the hydrated salt without being intended as a precise chemical formula.

Further confusion has arisen through workers using ready-prepared iron-EDTA salts in media without specifying the weight or molar concentration of actual Fe used. Mono- , di- , tri- , and tetra-sodium salts of EDTA are possible, each with different (and sometimes alternative) hydrates (see Chapter 10), so that when a research report states only that a certain weight of 'FeEDTA' was used, it is impossible to calculate the concentration of iron that was employed with any certainty. Molar concentrations of iron in micronutrient formulations are therefore not always given in the table of micronutrient compositions in Chapter 10.

The compound 'monosodium ferric EDTA' with the formula NaFeEDTA (no water of hydration) exists, and is nowadays commonly selected as a source of chelated iron. However in some papers 'NaEDTA' has been used as an abbreviation for some other form of iron-EDTA salt. For example the paper of Eeuwens (1976) describing **Y3** medium, says that to incorporate 0.05 mM iron, 32.5 mg/l 'sodium ferric EDTA' was used. The weight required using a compound with the strict molecular formula NaFeEDTA would be 18.35 mg/l. Hackett (1970) employed 'Na₄FeEDTA'. Gamborg and Shyluk (1981) and Gamborg (1982a) said that to prepare **B5** or **MS** medium with 0.1 mM Fe, 43 mg/l of 'ferric EDTA' or 'Fe–versenate' (EDTA) should be weighed. The compound recommended in these papers was probably the Na₂FeEDTA.2H₂O chelate (theoretical mol. Wt. 428.2) as was the 'FeEDTA' (13% iron) employed by Davis *et al.* (1977).

Alternatives to EDTA

A few other chelating agents have been used in culture media in place of EDTA. The **B5** medium of Gamborg *et al.* (1968) was originally formulated with 28 mg/l of the iron chelate 'Sequestrene 330 Fe'. According to Heberle-Bors (1980), 'Sequestrene 330 Fe' is FeDTPA (Table 7), containing 10% iron (Anon, 1978b). This means that the concentration of Fe in **B5** medium was originally 0.05 mM. Gamborg and Shyluk (1981) have proposed more recently that the level of Fe should be increased to 0.1 mM. **B5** medium is now often used with 0.1 mM FeEDTA, but some researchers still prefer FeDTPA, for example (Garton and Moses, 1986) used it in place of FeEDTA in **Lloyd and McCown (1981) WPM** medium for shoot culture of several woody plants.

Growth regulatory effects of chelating agents.

Although most iron, complexed to chelating agents such as EDTA, EDDHA and DTPA (Table 30) is absorbed as uncomplexed ions by plant roots, there is evidence that the chelating agents themselves can be taken up into plant tissues (Weinstein *et al.* 1951; Tiffin *et al.* 1960; Tiffin and Brown, 1961). Chelating compounds such as EDTA, in low concentrations, exert growth effects on plants which are similar to those produced by auxins. The effects include elongation of oat coleoptiles (Heath and Clark, 1956a.b), and etiolated lupin hypocotyls (Weinstein *et al.* 1956), the promotion of leaf epinasty (Weinstein *et al.* 1956) and the inhibition of root growth (Burstrom, 1961, 1963). Hypotheses put forward to explain these observations have included:

- that chelating agents act as auxin synergists by sequestering Ca from the cell wall (Thimann and Takahashi, 1958);

- that the biological properties of the natural auxin IAA may be related to an ability to chelate ions; other chelating agents therefore mimic its action (Heath and Clark, 1960).

Burstrom (1960) noted that EDTA inhibited root growth in darkness (not in light) but that the growth inhibition could be overcome by addition of Fe³⁺ or several other metal ions (Burstrom, 1961). He recognised that reversal

of EDTA action by a metal does not mean that the metal is physiologically active but that it might only release another cation which had previously been made unavailable to the tissue by chelation.

Effects in tissue cultures.

Growth and morphogenesis in tissue cultures has been noted on several occasions to be influenced by chelating agents other than EDTA. It has not always been clear whether the observed effects were caused by the chelation of metal ions, or by the chelating agent *per se*.

The growth rate of potato shoot tips was increased by 0.01–0.3 mg/l 8-hydroxyquinoline (8-HQ) when cultured on a medium which also contained EDTA (Goodwin, 1966), and more callus cultures of a haploid tobacco variety formed shoots in the absence of growth regulators when DHPTA was added to **Kasperbauer and Reinert (1967)** medium which normally contains 22.4 mg/l EDTA. The DHPTA appears to have been used in addition to the EDTA, not as a replacement, and was not effective on callus of a diploid tobacco (Kochhar *et al.* (1970). In the same experimental system, Fe-DHPTA and Fe-EDDHA were more effective in promoting shoot formation from the haploid-derived tissue than Fe with CDTA, citric acid or tartaric acid (Kochhar *et al.*, 1971).

The inclusion of EDTA into a liquid nutrient medium caused the small aquatic plant *Lemna perpusilla* to flower only in short day conditions whereas normally the plants were day-neutral (Hillman, 1959, 1961). In the related species *Wolffia microscopica*, plants did not flower unless EDTA was present in the medium, and then did so in response to short days (Maheshwari and Chauhan, 1963). When, however, Maheshwari and Seth (1966) substituted Fe-EDDHA for EDTA and ferric citrate, they found that plants not only flowered more freely under short days, but also did so under long days. The physiological effect of EDTA and EDDHA as chelating agents was thus clearly different. This was again shown by Chopra and Rashid (1969b) who found that the moss *Anoectangium thomsonii* did not form buds as other mosses do, when grown on a simple medium containing ferric citrate or Fe-EDTA, but did so when 5–20 mg/l Fe-EDDHA was added to the medium instead. An optimum concentration was between 5 and 8 mg/l. Rashid also discovered that haploid embryoids developed more freely from *in vitro* cultures of *Atropa belladonna* pollen microspores when Fe-EDDHA was incorporated into the medium, rather than Fe-EDTA (Rashid and Street, 1973). Heberle-Bors (1980) did not obtain the same result, and found that FeEDTA was superior to FeEDDHA for the production of pollen plants from anthers of this species and of two

Nicotianas. In tobacco, the production of haploid plants was greatest with FeEDTA, next best with FeDTPA, FeEGTA, FeEDDHA, and poorest with Fe citrate. Each complex was tested at or about the same iron concentration. Heberle-Bors also showed that chelating agents are differentially absorbed by activated charcoal.

Toxicity caused by chelating agents

Although low concentrations of EDTA markedly stimulate the growth of whole plants in hydroponic cultures by making iron more readily available, the compound begins to be toxic at higher levels. By comparisons with observations on animal tissues, Weinstein *et al.* (1951) suggested that toxicity arose through competition between EDTA and enzymes (and other physiologically-active complexes) in the plant, for metals essential to their activity. This will occur if the avidity of the chelating agent is greater than the metal binding capacity of proteins on the surface of cells (Albert, 1958).

Toxicity can also occur in *in vitro* cultures. Legrand (1975) found that an optimum rate of adventitious shoot initiation occurred in endive leaf segments when only 7.5 mg/l EDTA (one fifth the concentration used in **MS** medium) was employed. In these circumstances, higher levels of EDTA were clearly inhibitory and more than 55 mg/l prevented shoot formation. Dalton *et al.* (1983) found that 0.3 mM EDTA (compared to the 0.1 mM in **MS** medium) reduced the growth rate of *Ocimum* cell suspensions.

Cultured flower buds of *Begonia franconis* died within a few days if cultured with a high level of FeEDTA (1–1.5 mM, *i.e.* 10–15 times the normal level) together with 0.4–1.6 mM $H_2PO_4^-$. Berghoef and Bruinsma (1979a) thought that Fe^{3+} released from the FeEDTA complex, had precipitated the phosphate. Necrosis was avoided by increasing $H_2PO_4^-$ concentration to 6.4 mM.

Tissues may be damaged by culture in media containing synthetic chelating agents where the pH approaches neutrality, because at these pH levels, EDTA and EGTA have been shown to remove calcium ions from the membranes of mitochondria and this inhibits NAD(P)H oxidation and respiration (Moller and Palmer, 1981). Chelating agents have been found to inhibit the action of the growth substance ethylene (see Chapter 11) and are thought to do so by sequestering Cu ions within plant tissues, thereby interfering with the synthesis or action of a Cu-containing enzyme responsible for ethylene metabolism. EDTA can also inhibit the activity of plant polyphenol oxidase enzymes *in vitro* (Weinstein *et al.* 1951) and D.L. Smith (1968) thought that this might occur because EDTA made Cu ions less available for enzyme incorporation, when he found the chelating agent was able to prevent the blackening of freshly-isolated *Carex flacca* shoot tips (see Chapter 13). Several oxidative reactions are also biochemically catalysed by ions such as Cu^{2+}, Co^{2+} and Zn^{2+}, and where this is the case (*e.g.* the oxidation of glutathione — Martin, 1979; chatecol amine oxidation - Gergely and Kiss, 1979), chelating agents such as EDTA and CDTA are inhibitory.

MICRO-ORGANIC SUPPLEMENTS

Growth and morphogenesis of plant tissue cultures can be improved by small amounts of some organic nutrients. These are mainly vitamins (including some substances that are not strictly animal vitamins), amino acids and certain undefined supplements.

VITAMINS

Vitamins are compounds required by animals in very small amounts as necessary ancillary food factors. Absence from the diet leads to abnormal growth and development and an unhealthy condition. Many of the same substances are also needed by plant cells as essential intermediates or metabolic catalysts, but intact plants, unlike animals, are able to produce their own requirements. Cultured plant cells and tissues can however be-

come deficient in some factors; growth and survival is then improved by their addition to the culture medium.

In early work, the requirements of tissue cultures for trace amounts of certain organic substances were satisfied by 'undefined' supplements such as fruit juices, coconut milk, yeast or malt extracts and hydrolysed casein. These supplements can contribute vitamins, amino acids and growth regulants to a culture medium. The use of undefined supplements has declined as the need for specific organic compounds has been defined, and these have become listed in catalogues as pure chemicals.

The development of vitamin mixtures

The vitamins most frequently used in plant tissue culture media are thiamine (Vit. B_1), nicotinic acid (niacin) and pyridoxine (Vit. B_6) and, apart from these three compounds, and *myo*–inositol, there is little common agreement about which other vitamins are really essential.

The advantage of adding thiamine was discovered almost simultaneously by Bonner (1937, 1938a), Robbins and Bartley (1937) and White (1937a). Nicotinic acid and pyridoxine appear, in addition to thiamine, in media published by Bonner (1940a), Gautheret (1942) and White (1943b); this was following the findings of Bonner and Devirian (1939) that nicotinic acid improved the growth of isolated roots of tomato, pea and radish; and the papers of Robbins and Schmidt (1939a,b) which indicated that pyridoxine was also required for tomato root culture. These four vitamins; *myo*–inositol, thiamine, nicotinic acid, and pyridoxine, are ingredients of **Murashige and Skoog (1962)** medium and have been used in varying proportions for the culture of tissues of many plant species (Chapter 10). However unless there has been research on the requirements of a particular plant tissue or organ, it is not possible to conclude that all the vitamins which have been in a particular experiment were essential.

The requirements of cells for added vitamins, vary according to the nature of the plant and the type of culture. Welander (1977) found that **Nitsch and Nitsch (1965)** vitamins were not necessary, or were even inhibitory, to direct shoot formation on petiole explants of *Begonia* × *hiemalis*. Roest and Bokelmann (1975) on the other hand, obtained increased shoot formation on *Chrysanthemum* pedicels when **MS** vitamins were present. Callus of *Pinus strobus* grew best when the level of inositol in **MS** medium was reduced to 50 mg/l whereas that of *P. echinata* proliferated most rapidly when no inositol was present (Kaul and Kochbar, 1985).

Research workers often tend to adopt a 'belt and braces' attitude to minor media components, and add unusual supplements just to ensure that there is no missing factor which will limit the success of their experiment. Sometimes complex mixtures of as many as nine or ten vitamins have been employed.

Experimentation often shows that some vitamins can be omitted from recommended media. Although four vitamins were used in **MS** medium, later work at Professor Skoog's laboratory showed that the optimum rate of growth of tobacco callus tissue on **MS** salts required the addition of only *myo*-inositol and thiamine. The level of thiamine was increased four-fold over that used by Murashige and Skoog, but nicotinic acid, pyridoxine and glycine (amino acid) were unnecessary (Linsmaier and Skoog, 1965). A similar simplification of the **MS** vitamins was made by Earle and Torrey (1965b) for the culture of *Convolvulus* callus.

Soczek and Hempel (1988) found that in the medium of **Murashige et al. (1974)** devised for the shoot culture of *Gerbera jamesonii*, thiamine, pyridoxine, and inositol could be omitted without any reduction in the rate of shoot multiplication of their local cultivars. Ishihara and Katano (1982) found that *Malus* shoot cultures could be grown on **MS** salts alone, and that inositol and thiamine were largely unnecessary.

Specific compounds

myo-Inositol

Myo-inositol (also sometimes described as *meso*-inositol or *i*-inositol), is the only one of the nine theoretical stereoisomers of inositol which has significant biological importance. Medically it has been classed as a member of the Vitamin B complex and is required for the growth of yeast and many mammalian cells in tissue culture. Rats and mice require it for hair growth and can develop dermatitis when it is not in the diet. In the media tables in Chapter 10, *myo*-inositol has been classed as a plant 'vitamin', but note that some authors think that it should be regarded as a supplementary carbohydrate.

Historical use in tissue cultures. *myo*-Inositol was first shown by Jacquiot (1951) to favour bud formation by elm cambial tissue when supplied at 20–1000 mg/l. Necrosis was retarded, though the proliferation of the callus was not promoted. *myo*-Inositol at 100 mg/l was also used by Morel and Wetmore (1951a) in combination with six other vitamins for the culture of callus from the monocotyledon *Amorphophallus rivieri* (Araceae). Bud initials appeared on some cultures and both roots and buds on others, according to the concentration of auxin employed. The vitamin was adopted by both Wood and Braun (1961) and Murashige and Skoog (1962) in combination with thiamine, nicotinic acid and pyridoxine in their preferred media for the culture of *Catharanthus roseus* and *Nicotiana tabacum* respectively. Many other workers have since included it in culture media with favourable results on the rate of callus growth or the induction of morphogenesis. Letham (1966) found that *myo*-inositol interacted with cytokinin to promote cell division in carrot phloem explants.

Occurrence and biochemistry. Part of the growth promoting property of coconut milk is due to its *myo*-inositol content (Pollard *et al.* 1961). Coconut milk also contains *scyllo*-inositol (Table 31). This can also promote growth, but to a smaller extent than the *myo*-isomer (Pollard *et al.*, 1961). Inositol is a constituent of yeast extract (Steiner *et al.*, 1969; Steiner and Lester, 1972) and small quantities may also be contained in commercial agar (Wolter and Skoog, 1966).

myo–Inositol is a natural constituent of plants and the much is often incorporated into phosphatidyl-inositol, which may be an important factor in the functioning of membranes (Jung et al., 1972; Harran and Dickinson, 1978). The phosphatidylinositol cycle controls various cellular responses in animal cells and yeasts, but evidence of it playing a similar role in plants is only just being accumulated. Enzymes which are thought to be involved in the cycle have been observed to have activities in plants, and lithium chloride (which inhibits *myo*-inositol–1–phosphatase and decreases the cycle) inhibits callus formation in *Brassica oleracea* (Bagga *et al.*, 1987), and callus growth in *Amaranthus paniculatus* (Das *et al.*, 1987). In both plants the inhibition is reversed by *myo*-inositol.

As the *myo*-inositol molecule has six hydroxyl units, it can react with up to six acid molecules forming various esters. It appears that inositol phosphates act as second messengers to the primary action of auxin in plants: phytic acid (inositol hexa-phosphate) is one of these. Added to culture media it can promote tissue growth, if it can serve as a source of inositol (Watanabe *et al.*, 1971). In some species, auxin can be stored and transported as IAA-*myo*-inositol ester (Chapter 11). *o*-Methyl-inositol is present in quite large quantities in legumes; inositol methyl ethers are known to occur in plants of several other families, although their function is unknown (Phillips and Smith, 1974).

The stimulatory effect of *myo*-inositol in plant cultures probably arises partly from the participation of the compound in biosynthetic pathways leading to the formation of the pectin and hemicelluloses needed in cell walls (Loewus *et al.*, 1962; Loewus, 1974; Loewus and Loewus, 1980; Harran and Dickinson, 1978; Verma and Dougall, 1979; Loewus and Loewus, 1980) and may have a role in the uptake and utilization of ions (Wood and Braun, 1961).

In the experiments of Staudt (1984) mentioned below, when the PO_4^{3-} content of the medium was increased to 4.41 mM, the rate of callus growth of cv. 'Aris' was progressively enhanced as the *myo*-inositol in the medium was put up to 4000 mg/l. This result seems to stress the importance of inositol-containing phospholipids for growth.

Activity in tissue cultures. Cultured plant tissues vary in their capacity for *myo*-inositol biosynthesis. Intact shoots are usually able to produce their own requirements, but although many unorganised tissues are able to grow slowly without the vitamin being added to the medium (Murashige, 1974), the addition of a small quantity is frequently found to stimulate cell division. The compound has been discovered to be essential to some plants. In the opinion of Kaul and Sabharwal (1975), this includes all monocotyledons, the media for which, if they do not contain inositol, need to be complemented with coconut milk, or yeast extract.

Fraxinus pennsylvanica callus had an absolute requirement for 10 mg/l *myo*-inositol to achieve maximum growth; higher levels, up to 250 mg/l had no further effect on fresh or dry weight yields (Wolter and Skoog, 1966). The formation of shoot buds on callus of *Haworthia* spp. was shown to be dependent on the availability of *myo*-inositol (Kaul and Sabharwal, 1972, 1975). In a revised **Linsmaier and Skoog (1965)** medium [**Staudt (1984)** containing 1.84 mM PO_4^{3-}], callus tissue of *Vitis vinifera* cv. 'Müller-Thurgan' did not require *myo*-inositol for growth, but that of *Vitis vinifera* × *V. riparia* cv. 'Aris' *was* dependent on it and the rate of growth increased as the level of *myo*-inositol was increased up to 250 mg/l (Staudt, 1984).

Gupta *et al.* (1988) found that it was essential to add 5 g/l *myo*-inositol to **Gupta and Durzan (1985) DCR-1** medium to induce embryogenesis (embryonal suspensor masses) from female gametophyte tissue of *Pseudotsuga menziesii* and *Pinus taeda*. The concentration necessary seems insufficient to have acted as an osmotic stimulus (see page 335). *myo*- Inositol reduced the rate of proliferation in shoot cultures of *Euphorbia fulgens* (Zhang *et al.*, 1986).

Thiamine

Thiamine (Vit. B_1, aneurin), in the form of thiamine pyrophosphate, is an essential co-factor in carbohydrate metabolism and is directly involved in the biosynthesis of some amino acids. It has been added to plant culture media more frequently than any other vitamin. Tissues of most plants seem to require it for growth, the need becoming more apparent with consecutive passages, but some cultured cells are self sufficient. The maize suspension cultures of Polikarpochkina *et al.* (1979) showed much less growth in passage 2, and died in the third passage when thiamine was omitted from the medium.

MS medium contains 0.3 µM thiamine: That this may not be sufficient to obtain optimum results from some cultures is illustrated by the results of Barwale *et al.* (1986): increasing the concentration of thiamine HCl in **MS** medium to 5 µM, increased the frequency with which zygotic embryos of *Glycine max* formed somatic embryos from 33% to 58%. Adding 30 µM nicotinic acid (normally 4 µM) inproved the occurrence of embryogenesis even further to 76%.

There can be an interaction between thiamine and cytokinin growth regulators. Digby and Skoog (1966) discovered that normal callus cultures of tobacco produced an adequate level of thiamine to support growth providing a relatively high level of kinetin (*ca.* 1 mg/l) was added to the medium, but the tissue failed to grow when moved to a medium with less added kinetin unless thiamine was provided.

Sometimes a change from a thiamine-requiring to a thiamine-sufficient state occurs during culture (see HABITU-ATION — Chapter 11). In rice callus, thiamine influenced morphogenesis in a way that depended on which state the cells were in. Presence of the vitamin in a pre-culture (Stage I) medium caused thiamine-sufficient callus to form root primordia on an induction (Stage II) medium, but suppressed the stimulating effect of kinetin on Stage II shoot formation in thiamine-requiring callus. It was essential to omit thiamine from the Stage I medium to induce thiamine-sufficient callus to produce shoots at Stage II (Inoue and Maeda, 1982).

Other vitamins

Pantothenic acid. Pantothenic acid plays an important role in the growth of certain tissues. It favoured callus production by hawthorn stem fragments (Morel, 1946) and stimulated tissue proliferation in willow and black henbane (Telle and Gautheret, 1947; Gautheret, 1948). However, pantothenic acid showed no effects with carrot, vine and Virginia creeper tissues which synthesise it in significant amounts (*ca.* 1 μg/ml).

Vitamin C. The effect of vitamin C (L-ascorbic acid) as a component of culture media has been discussed on page 200. The compound is also used during explant isolation and to prevent blackening (see Chapter 13).

Vitamin D. Some vitamins in the D group, notably vitamin D_2 and D_3 can have a growth regulatory effect on plant tissue cultures. Their effect is discussed in Chapter 11.

Vitamin E. The anti-oxidant activity of vitamin E (α-tocopherol), is discussed on page 201.

Other vitamins. Evidence has been obtained that folic acid slows tissue proliferation in the dark, while enhancing it in the light. This is probably because it is hydrolysed in the light to *p*-aminobenzoic acid (PAB). In the presence of auxin, PAB has been shown to have a weak growth-stimulatory effect on cultured plant tissues (de Capite, 1952a,b).

Riboflavin which is a component of some vitamin mixtures, has been found to inhibit callus formation. It may also improve the growth and quality of shoots (Drew and Smith, 1986). Suppression of callus growth can mean that the vitamin may either inhibit or stimulate root formation on cuttings (Chapter 14). Glycine is occasionally de-scribed as a vitamin in plant tissue cultures: its use has been described in the section on amino acids.

Adenine. Adenine (or adenine sulphate) has been widely used in tissue culture media, but because it mainly gives rise to effects which are similar to those produced by cytokinins, it is considered in the chapter on plant growth regulators.

Stability

Some vitamins are heat-labile; see the section on medium preparation in Chapter 10.

UNDEFINED SUPPLEMENTS

Many undefined supplements were employed in early tissue culture media. Their use has slowly declined as the balance between inorganic salts has been improved and as the effect of amino acids and growth substances has become better understood. Nevertheless several supplements of uncertain and variable composition are still in common use.

The first successful cultures of plant tissue involved the use of yeast extract (Robbins, 1922b; White, 1934a). Other undefined additions made to plant tissue culture media have been:

— meat, malt and yeast extracts and fibrin digest;

— juices, pulps and extracts from various fruits (Steward and Shantz, 1959; Ranga Swamy, 1963; Guha and Maheshwari, 1964, 1967), including those from bananas and tomatoes (La Rue, 1949);

— the fluids which nourish immature zygotic embryos;

— extracts of seedlings (Saalbach and Koblitz, 1978) or plant leaves (Borkird and Sink, 1983);

— the extract of boiled potatoes and corn steep liquor (Fox and Miller, 1959);

— plant sap or the extract of roots or rhizomes. Plant roots are thought to be the main site of cytokinin synthesis in plants (Chapter 11).

— protein (usually casein) hydrolysates (containing a mixture of all the amino acids present in the original protein). Casein hydrolysates are sometimes termed casamino acids: they are discussed on page 286).

Many of these ammendments can be a source of amino acids, peptides, vitamins and plant growth substances.

Those which have been most widely used are described below.

Yeast extract

Yeast extract (YE) is used less as an ingredient of plant media nowadays than in former times, when it was added as a source of amino acids and vitamins, especially inositol and thiamine (Vitamin B₁) (Bonner and Addicott, 1937; Robbins and Bartley, 1937). In a medium consisting only of macro- and micro- nutrients, the provision of yeast extract was often found to be essential for tissue growth (White, 1934a; Robbins and Bartley, 1937). The vitamin content of yeast extract distinguishes it from casein hydrolysate (CH), so that in such media CH, or amino acids alone, could not be substituted for YE (Straus and La Rue, 1954; Nickell and Maretzki, 1969). It was soon found that amino acids such as glycine, lysine and arginine, and vitamins such as thiamin and nicotinic acid, could serve as replacements for YE, for example in the growth of tomato roots (Skinner and Street, 1954), or sugar cane cell suspensions (Nickell and Maretzki, 1969).

The percentage of amino acids in a typical yeast extract is high (*e.g.* 7% amino nitrogen — Nickell and Maretzki, 1969; Bridson, 1978; Thom *et al.*, 1981), but there is less glutamic acid than in casein, or other protein hydrolysates (Table 26, page 286). Malt extract contains little nitrogen (*ca.* 0.5% in total).

Yeast extract is typically added to media in concentrations of 0.1—1 g/l: occasionally 5, 10 and even 20 g/l (Morel and Muller, 1964) have been included. It normally only enhances growth in media containing relatively low concentrations of nitrogen, or where vitamins are lacking. Addition of 125–5000 mg/l YE to **MS** medium completely inhibited the growth of green callus of 5 different plants whereas small quantities added to **Vasil and Hildebrandt (1966) THS** medium (which contained 0.6 times the quantity of NO_3^- and NH_4^+ ions, and unlike **MS**, did not contain nicotinic acid or pyridoxine), gave more vigorous growth of carrot, endive and lettuce callus, than occurred on **MS**. There was still no growth of parsley and tomato callus on THS medium: these tissues only grew well on unmodified **MS** (Vasil and Hildebrandt, 1966c).

Stage I media are sometimes fortified with yeast extract to reveal the presence of micro-organisms which may have escaped decontamination procedures (Chapter 5): it is then omitted at later stages of culture.

Yeast extract has been shown to have some unusual properties which may relate to its amino acid content. It elicits phytoalexin accumulation in several plant species, and in *Glycyrrhiza echinata* suspensions it stimulated chalcone synthase activity, leading to the formation of

narengin (Ayabe *et al.*, 1988). On **Monnier (1976, 1978)** medium, 1 g/l yeast extract was found to inhibit the growth of immature zygotic embryos of *Linum*, an effect which, when 0.05 mg/l BAP and 400 mg/l glutamine was added, induced the direct formation of adventitious embryos (Pretova and Williams, 1986).

> Yeast extract is now purchased directly from chemical suppliers. In the 1930s and 1940s it was prepared in the laboratory. Brink *et al.* (1944) macerated yeast in water, which was then boiled for 30 minutes and, after cooling, the starchy material was removed by centrifugation. However, Robbins and Bartley (1937) found that the active components of yeast could be extracted with 80% ethanol.

Potato extract

Workers in China found that there was a sharp increase in the number of pollen plants produced from wheat anthers when they were cultured on an agar solidified medium containing only an extract of boiled potatoes, 0.1 mM FeEDTA, 9% sucrose and growth regulators. Potato extract alone, or potato extract combined with components of conventional culture media (Chuang *et al.,* 1978; 1981), has since been found to provide a useful medium for the anther culture of wheat and some other cereal plants. Sopory *et al.* (1978) obtained the initiation of embryogenesis from potato anthers, on potato extract alone, and Lichter (1981) found it beneficial to add 2.5 g/l Difco potato extract to a medium for *Brassica napus* anther culture, but it was omitted by Chuong and Beversdorf (1985) when they repeated this work. We are not aware of potato extract being added to media for micropropagation, apart from occasional reports of its use for orchid propagation. Sagawa and Kunisaki (1982) supplemented 1 litre of **Vacin and Went (1949)** medium with the extract from 100g potatoes boiled for 5 minutes, and Harvais (1982) added 5% of an extract from 200g potatoes boiled in 1 litre water, to his orchid medium.

> Potato extract is prepared as follows:
>
> To prepare a medium containing 20% potato extract, 200g of fresh potato tubers are cleaned with water, and any sprouts which may be present are removed. The tubers are cut into small pieces and then boiled in 400–600 ml of distilled water for 25–30 minutes. The liquid in which the potatoes were boiled plus the potato macerate, is filtered through 2 layers of cheese cloth. Chuang *et al.* (1978; 1981) also extracted the remaining potato pieces once more with water and combined the two liquors. The liquid extract is mixed immediately with other medium components. Potatoes that have not been long in storage give the best results (Anon, 1976; Nitzsche and Wenzel, 1977; Chuang *et al.*, 1978; 1981).

Banana homogenate

Homogenised banana fruit is sometimes added to media for the culture of orchids and is often reported to promote growth. The reason for its stimulatory effect has not been explained. One suggestion mentioned above (page 302), is that it might help to stabilise the pH of the medium. Pierik *et al.* (1988a) found that it was slightly inhibitory to the germination of *Paphiopedilum ciliolare* seedlings, but promoted the growth of seedlings once germination had taken place.

Fluids which nourish immature embryos

The liquid which is present in the embryo sac of immature fruits of *Aesculus* (*e.g. A. woerlitzensis*) (Shantz and Steward, 1956, 1964; Steward and Shantz, 1956, 1959; Steward and Rao, 1970) and *Juglans regia* (Steward and Caplin, 1952) has been found to have a strong growth-promoting effect on some plant tissues cultured on simple media, although growth inhibition has occasionally been reported (Fonnesbech, 1972b). Fluid from the immature female gametophyte of *Ginkgo biloba* (Steward and Caplin, 1952) and extracts from the female gametophyte of *Pseudotsuga menziesii* (Mapes and Zaerr, 1981) and immature *Zea mays* grains (less than two weeks after pollination) can have a similar effect . The most readily obtained fluid with this kind of activity is coconut milk.

Coconut milk

When added to a medium containing auxin, the liquid endosperm of *Cocos nucifera* fruits can induce plant cells to divide and grow rapidly. The fluid is most commonly referred to as coconut milk although Tulecke *et al.* (1961) maintained that the correct English term is 'coconut water', because the term coconut milk also describes the white liquid obtained by grating the solid white coconut endosperm (the 'meat') in water, and this is *not* generally used in tissue culture media.

Coconut milk was first used in tissue cultures by Van Overbeek *et al.* (1941, 1942) who found that its addition to a culture medium was necessary for the development of very young embryos of *Datura stramonium*. Gautheret (1942) found that coconut milk could be used to initiate and maintain growth in tissue cultures of several plants, and Caplin and Steward (1948) showed that callus derived from phloem tissue explants of *Daucus carota* roots grew much more rapidly when 15% coconut milk was added to a medium containing IAA. Unlike other undefined supplements to culture media (such as yeast extract, malt extract and casein hydrolysate), coconut milk has

proved harder to replace by fully defined media. The liquid has been found to be beneficial for inducing growth of both callus and suspension cultures and for the induction of morphogenesis. Although commercial plant tissue culture laboratories (particularly those in temperate countries) would endeavour not to use this ingredient on account of its cost, it is still frequently employed for special purposes in research.

It is possible to get callus growth on coconut milk alone (Steward *et al.*, 1952), but normally it is added to a recognised medium. Effective stimulation only occurs when relatively large quantities are added to a medium; the incorporation of 10–15 percent by volume, is quite usual. For instance, Burnet and Ibrahim (1973) found that 20% coconut milk (*i.e.* one-fifth of the final volume of the medium) was required for the initiation and continued growth of callus tissue of various *Citrus* species in **MS** medium; Rangan (1974) has obtained improved growth of *Panicum miliaceum* in **MS** medium using 2,4-D in the presence of 15% coconut milk. By contrast, Vasil and co-workers (*e.g.* Vasil and Vasil, 1981a,b) needed to add only 5% coconut milk to **MS** medium to obtain somatic embryogenesis from cereal callus and suspension cultures.

Many workers try to avoid having to use coconut milk in their protocols. It is an undefined supplement whose composition can vary considerably (Swedlund and Locy, 1988). However, adding coconut milk to media often provides a simple way to obtain satisfactory growth or morphogenesis without the need to work out a suitably defined formulation. Suggestions that coconut milk is essential for a particular purpose, need to be treated with some caution. For instance, in the culture of embryogenic callus from root and petiole explants of *Daucus carota*, coconut milk can be replaced satisfactorily either by adenine or kinetin, showing that it did not contribute any unique substances required for embryogenesis (Halperin and Wetherell, 1964).

Preparation. Ready prepared coconut milk can be purchased from some chemical suppliers, but the liquid from fresh nuts (obtained from the greengrocer), is usually perfectly adequate. One nut will usually yield at least 100 ml. The milk is most simply drained from dehusked coconuts by drilling holes through two of the micropyles. Only normal uncontaminated milk should be used and so nuts should be extracted one by one, and the liquid endosperm from each examined to ascertain that it is unfermented before addition to a bulk supply. Milk from green but mature coconuts may contain slightly different quantities of substances to that in the nuts purchased in the local market (Table 31) and has been said to be a more effective stimulant in plant media than that from ripe fruits, but Morel and Wetmore (1951a) found to the

Table 31. Substances identified as components of coconut milk from mature green fruits and market-purchased fruits .

SUBSTANCE	QUANTITY/REFERENCE		SUBSTANCE	QUANTITY/REFERENCE	
	Mature green fruits	Mature fresh fruits		Mature green fruits	Mature fresh fruits
Amino acids (mg/l)			**Sugars** (g/l)		
Alanine	127.3 (14)	312 (13), 177.1 (14)	Sucrose	9.2 (14)	8.9 (14)
Arginine	25.6 (14)	133 (13), 16.8 (14)	Glucose	7.3 (14)	2.5 (14)
Aspartic acid	35.9 (14)	65 (13), 5.4(14)	Fructose	5.3 (14)	2.5 (14)
Asparagine	10.1 (14)	*ca*.60 (13), 10.1 (14)	**Sugar alcohols** (g/l)		
γ-Aminobutyric acid	34.6 (14)	820 (13), 168.8 (14)	Mannitol		(1)
Glutamic acid	70.8 (14)	240 (13), 78.7 (14)	Sorbitol		15.0 (12), (17)
Glutamine	45.4 (14)	*ca.* 60 (13),13.4 (14)	*myo*-Inositol		0.1 (12), (17)
Glycine	9.7 (14)	13.9 (14)	*scyllo*-Inositol		0.5 (12), (17)
Histidine	6.3 (14)	Trace (13, 14)	**Vitamins** (mg/l)		
Homoserine	— (14)	5.2 (14)	Nicotinic acid		0.64 (4)
Hydroxyproline		Trace (13, 14)	Pantothenic acid		0.52 (4)
Lysine	21.4	65.8 (14)	Biotin, Riboflavin		0.02 (4)
Methionine	16.9 (14)	8 (13), Trace (14)	Riboflavin		0.01 (4)
Phenylalanine	— (14)	12 (13), 10.2 (14)	Folic acid		0.003 (4)
Proline	31.9	97 (13), 21.6 (14)	Thiamine, pyridoxine		Trace (4)
Serine	45.3 (14)				
Typtophan		39 (13)	**Growth substances** (mg/l)		
Threonine	16.2 (2)	44 (13) 26.3 (14)	Auxin		0.07 (7), (28)
Tyrosine	6.4 (14)	16 (13) 3.1 (14)	Gibberellin		Yes (10, 28)
Valine	20.6 (14)	27 (13) 15.1 (14)	1,3-Diphenylurea		5.8 (8), (6,17)
Other nitrogenous compounds			Zeatin		(22, 26)
Ammonium		(19)	Zeatin glucoside		(26)
Ethanolamine		(19)	Zeatin riboside		(20), (24) (25)
Dihydroxyphenylalanine		(19)	6-Oxypurine growth promoter		(27)
Inorganic elements (mg/100g dry wt.)			Unknown cytokinin/s		6, (18) (22)
Potassium		312.0 (3)	**Other** (mg/l)		
Sodium		105 (3)	RNA-polymerase		(23)
Phosphorus		37.0 (3)	RNA-phosphorus,	20.0 (14)	35.4 (14)
Magnesium		30.0 (3)	DNA-phosphorus	0.1 (14)	3.5 (14)
			Uracil, Adenine	21	
Organic acids (Meq/ml)			Leucoanthocyanins		(11) (15, 17)
Malic acid	34.3 (14)	12.0 (14)	Phyllococosine		(16)
Shikimic, Quinic and 2 unknowns	0.6 (14)	0.41 (2)	Acid phosphatase		(5, 9)
			Diastase		(2)
Pyrrolidone carboxylic acid	0.4 (14)	0.2 (14)	Dehydrogenase		(5)
Citric acid	0.4 (14)	0.3 (14)	Peroxidase		(5)
Succinic acid	— (14)	0.3 (14)	Catalase		(5)

References

(1) Dunstan (1906),   (2) DeKruijff (1906),   (3) McCance and Widdowson (1940),   (4) Vandenbelt (1945),   (5) Sadasivan (1951),   (6) Shantz and Steward (1952),   (7) Paris and Duhamet (1953),   (8) Shantz and Steward (1955),   (9) Wilson and Cutter (1955),   (10) Radley and Dear (1958),   (11) Steward and Shantz (1959),   (12) Pollard *et al.* (1961),   (13) Figures of Steward *et al.* (1961), given by Raghavan (1977b),   (14) Tulecke *et al.* (1961),   (15) Steward and Mohan Ram (1961),   (16) Kuraishi and Okumura (1961),   (17) Steward (1963),   (18) Zwar *et al.* (1963),   (19) Steward *et al.* (1964),   (20)Letham (1968),   (21) Steward *et al.* (1969),   (22) Zwar and Bruce (1970),   (23)Mondal et al. (1972),   (24) Letham (1974),   (25) Van Staden and Drewes (1975),   (26) Van Staden (1976),   (27) Letham (1982),   (28) Dix and Van Staden (1982).

contrary. Tulecke *et al.* (1961) discovered that the milk from highly immature coconuts contained smaller quantities of the substances normally present in mature nuts.

Coconut milk is usually strained through cloth and deproteinized by being heated to 80—100°C for about 10 minutes while being stirred. It is then allowed to settle and the supernatant is separated from the co–agulated proteins by filtration through paper. The liquid is stored frozen at -20°C. Borkird and Sink (1983) did not boil the milk from fresh ripe coconuts, but having filtered it through several layers of cheesecloth, adjusted the pH to 10 with 2 N NaOH and then kept it overnight at 4°C. The following day the pH was re-adjusted to 7.0 with 5 N HCl, and the preparation was refiltered before being stored frozen at –20°C.

Some workers autoclave media containing coconut milk; others filter- sterilise coconut milk and add it to a medium after autoclaving has been carried out. Morel and Wetmore (*loc. cit.*) used filter sterilisation, but found that the milk lost its potency if stood sterile (but presumably unfrozen) for 3 months. Street (1977b) advocated autoclaving coconut milk after it had been boiled and filtered; it was then stored at –20°C until required.

Active ingredients. The remarkable growth stimulating property of coconut milk has led to attempts to isolate and identify the active principles. This has proved to be difficult because the fractions into which coconut milk has been separated, each possess only a small proportion of the total activity and the different components appear to act synergistically. Substances so far identified include amino acids, organic acids, nucleic acids, purines, sugars, sugar alcohols, vitamins, growth substances and minerals (Table 31). The variable nature of the product is illustrated in the table by the analytical results obtained by different authors.

Auxin activity. The liquid has been found to have some auxin activity which is increased by autoclaving, probably because the growth substance exists in a bound form and is released by hydrolysis. But although coconut milk can stimulate the growth of some *in vitro* cultures in the absence of exogenous auxin, it normally contains little of this kind of growth regulator, and an additional exogenous supply is generally required. In modern media, where organic compounds are often added in defined amounts, the main benefit from using coconut milk is almost certainly due to its providing highly active natural cytokinin growth substances.

Cytokinin activity. Coconut milk was shown to have cytokinin activity by Kuraishi and Okumura (1961), and recognised natural cytokinin substances have since been isolated (Letham, 1968; 9-β-D-ribo-furanosyl zeatin:

Zwar and Bruce, 1970; zeatin and several unidentified ones: Shantz and Steward, 1955; N, N′-diphenyl urea), but the levels of these compounds in various samples of coconut milk have not been published. An unusual cytokinin-like growth promoter, 2(3-methylbut-2-enylamino)-purin-6-one, was isolated by Letham (1982).

Because coconut milk contains natural cytokinins, adding it to media often has the same effect as adding a recognised cytokinin. This means that a beneficial effect on growth or morphogenesis is often dependent on the presence of an auxin. Steward and Caplin (1951) showed that there was a synergistic action between 2,4-D and coconut milk in stimulating the growth of potato tuber tissue. Lin and Staba (1961) similarly found that coconut milk gave significantly improved callus growth on seedling explants of peppermint and spearmint initiated by 2,4-D, but only slightly improved the growth initiated by the auxin 2-BTOA (2-benzothiazoleoxyacetic acid). The occurrence of gibberellin-like substances in coconut milk has also been reported (Radley and Dear, 1958).

Suboptimum stimulation and inhibition. In cases where optimal concentrations of growth adjuvants have been determined, it has been found that the level of the same or analogous substances in coconut milk may be suboptimal. La Motte (1960) noted that 150 mg/l of tyrosine most effectively induced morphogenesis in tobacco callus cultures, but coconut milk added at 15% would provide only 0.96 mg/l of this substance (Tulecke *et al.* 1961). Fresh and autoclaved coconut milk from mature nuts has proved inhibitory to growth or morphogenesis (Noh *et al.*, 1988) in some instances. It is not known which ingredients cause the inhibition but the growth of cultured embryos seems particularly liable to be prevented, suggesting that the compound responsible might be a natural dormancy-inducing factor such as abscisic acid. Van Overbeek *et al.* (1942, 1944) found that a factor was present in coconut milk which was essential for the growth of *Datura stramonium* embryos, but that heating the milk or allowing it to stand could lead to a release of toxic substances. These could be removed by shaking with alcohols or ether, or lead acetate precipitation. Duhamet and Mentzer (1955) isolated nine fractions of coconut milk by chromatography, and found one of these to be inhibitory to cultured crown gall tissues of black salsify when more than 10–20% coconut milk was incorporated into the medium. Norstog (1965b) showed that autoclaved coconut milk could inhibit the growth of barley embryos but that filter-sterilised milk was stimulatory. Autoclaved or filter-sterilized coconut milk inhibited the growth of wheat embryo-shoot apices (Smith, 1967).

ORGANIC ACIDS

Organic acids can have three roles in plant culture media:

- they may act as chelating agents, improving the availability of some micronutrients,
- they can buffer the medium against pH change,
- they may act as nutrients.

A beneficial effect is largely restricted to the acids of the Krebs' cycle (see page 278). Dougall *et al.* (1979) found that 20 mM succinate, malate or fumarate supported maximum growth of wild carrot cells when the medium was initially adjusted to pH4.5. Although 1 mM glutarate, adipate, pimelate, suberate, azelate or phthalate controlled the ph of the medium, little or no cell growth took place.

Use as buffers

The addition of organic acids to plant media is not a recent development. Various authors have found that some organic acids and their sodium or potassium salts, stabilise the pH of hydroponic solutions (Trelease and Trelease, 1933) or *in vitro* media (Van Overbeek *et al.*, 1941, 1942; Arnow *et al.*, 1953), although it must be admitted that they are not as effective as synthetic biological buffers in this respect (page 301). Norstog and Smith (1963) discovered that 100 mg/l malic acid acted as an effective buffering agent in their medium for barley embryo culture and also appeared to enhance growth in the presence of glutamine and alanine. Malic acid, now at 1000 mg/l was retained in the improved **Norstog (1973) Barley II** medium. In the experiments of Schenk and Hildebrandt (1972), low levels of citrate and succinate ions did not impede callus growth of a wide variety of plants, and appeared to be stimulatory in some species. The acids were also effective buffers between pH 5 and pH 6, but autoclaving a medium containing sodium citrate or citric acid caused a substantial pH increase.

Complexing with metals

Divalent organic acids such as citric, maleic, malic and malonic (depending on species) are found in the xylem sap of plants, where together with amino acids, they can complex with metal ions and assist their transport (White *et al.*, 1981). These acids can also be secreted from cultured cells and tissues into the growth medium, and will contribute to the conditioning effect. Ojima and Ohira (1980) found that malic and citric acids, which were released into the medium by rice cells during the latter half of a passage, were able to make unchelated ferric iron available, so correcting an iron deficiency.

Nutritional role

As explained on page 278, adding Krebs' cycle organic acids to the medium can enhance the metabolism of NH_4^+. Gamborg and Shyluk (1970) found that some organic acids could promote ammonium utilisation, and the incorporatiion of small quantities of sodium pyruvate, citric, malic and fumaric acids into the medium, was one factor which enabled Kao and Michayluk (1975) to culture *Vicia hajastana* cells at low density. Their mixture of organic acid ions has been copied into many other media designed for protoplast culture. Cultures may not tolerate the addition of a large quantity of a free acid, which will acidify the medium. For example *Triticale* anther callus grew well on **Chu *et al.* (1975)** N6 medium, supplemented with 35 mg/l of a mixture of sodium pyruvate, malic acid, fumaric acid, citric acid, but not when 100 mg/l was added (Chien and Kao, 1983). When organic anions are added to the medium from the sodium or potassium salts of an acid, there are metallic cations to counterbalance the organic anions, and it seems to be possible to add larger quantities without toxicity. 5 mM (1240 mg/l $.3H_2O$) potassium succinate enhanced the growth of cultured peach embryos (Ramming, 1990), and adding 15 mM (4052 mg/l $.4H_2O$) sodium succinate to **MS** medium (while also increasing the sucrose content from 3% to 6%), increased the cell volume and dry weight of *Brassica nigra* suspensions by 2.7 times (Molnar, 1988b).

Some plants seem to derive nutitional benefit from the presence of one particular organic acid. Murashige and Tucker (1969) showed that orange juice, added to a medium containing **MS** salts, promoted the growth of *Citrus* albedo callus. Malic and other Krebs' cycle acids, also have a similar effect; of these, citric acid produces the most pronounced growth stimulation. A concentration of up to 10.4 mM can be effective (Goldschmidt, 1976; Einset, 1978; Erner and Reuveni, 1981). Succulent plants, in particular those in the family Crassulaceae, such as *Bryophyllum* and *Kalanchoe*, fix relatively large amounts of carbon dioxide during darkness, converting it into organiic acids, of which malic acid is particularly important. The organic acids are metabolised during daylight hours. In such plants, malic acid might be expected to prove especially efficient in enhancing growth if added to a culture medium. Lassocinski (1985) has shown this to be the case in chlorophyll-deficient cacti of three genera. The addition of L-malic acid to the medium of **Savage *et al.* (1979)**, markedly improved the rate of survival and vigour of small cacti or areoles.

SUGARS — NUTRITIONAL AND REGULATORY EFFECTS

SUGARS AS ENERGY SOURCES

Carbohydrate autotrophy

Only a limited number of plant cell lines have been isolated which are *autotrophic* when cultured *in vitro*. Autotrophic cells are capable of fully supplying their own carbohydrate needs by carbon dioxide assimilation during photosynthesis (Bergmann, 1967; Tandeau de Marsac and Peaud–Lenoel, 1972a,b; Chandler *et al.* 1972; Anon, 1980a; Larosa *et al.* 1981). Many autotrophic cultures have only been capable of relatively slow growth (*e.g.* Fukami and Hildebrandt, 1967), especially in the ambient atmosphere where the concentration of carbon dioxide is low (see page 204).

Normally for the culture of either cells, tissues or organs, it is necessary to incorporate a carbon source into the medium. Sucrose is almost universally used for micropropagation purposes as it is so generally utilisable by tissue cultures. Refined white domestic sugar is sufficiently pure for most practical purposes. The presence of sucrose in tissue culture media specifically inhibits chlorophyll formation and photosynthesis (see later), making autotrophic growth less feasible.

Alternatives to sucrose

Other sugars

The selection of sucrose as the most suitable energy source for cultures follows many comparisons between possible alternatives. Some of the first work of this kind on the carbohydrate nutrition of plant tissue was done by Gautheret (1945) using normal carrot tissue. Sucrose was found to be the best source of carbon followed by glucose, maltose and raffinose; fructose was less effective and mannose and lactose were the least suitable. The findings of this and other work is summarized in Table 32. Sucrose has almost invariably been found to be the best carbohydrate; glucose is generally found to support growth equally well, and in a few plants it may result in better *in vitro* growth than sucrose, or promote organogenesis where sucrose will not; but being more expensive than sucrose, glucose will only be preferred for micropropagation where it produces clearly advantageous results.

Multiplication of *Alnus crispa*, *A. cordata* and *A. rubra* shoot cultures was best on glucose, while that of *A. glutinosa* was best on sucrose (Tremblay and Lalonde, 1984; Tremblay *et al.*, 1984; Barghchi, 1988). Direct shoot formation from *Capsicum annuum* leaf discs in a 16 h day required the presence of glucose (Phillips and Hubstenberger, 1985). Glucose is required for the culture of isolated roots of wheat (Furguson, 1967) and some other monocotyledons (Bhojwani and Razdan, 1983).

Some other monosaccarides such as arabinose and xylose; disaccharides such as cellobiose, maltose and trehalose; and some polysaccharides; all of which are capable of being broken down to glucose and fructose (Table 32), can also sometimes be used as partial replacements for sucrose (Straus and LaRue, 1954; Sievert and Hildebrandt, 1965; Yatazawa *et al.* 1967; Smith and Stone, 1973; Minocha and Halperin, 1974; Zaghmout and Torres, 1985). In *Phaseolus* callus, Jeffs and Northcote (1967) found that sucrose could be replaced by maltose and trehalose (all three sugars have an alpha-glucosyl radical at the non-reducing end) but not by glucose or fructose alone or in combination, or by several other different sugars. Galactose has been said to be toxic to most plant tissues; it inhibits the growth of orchids and other plants in concentrations as low as 0.01% (0.9 mM) (Ernst *et al.*, 1971; Arditti and Ernst, 1984). Although it may not be able to contribute to the carbon nutrition of cultured tissues, galactose has been found to reduce or overcome hyperhydricity in shoot cultures (Druart, 1988) (Chapter 13). Fructose has also been reported to be effective in preventing hyperhydricity (Rugini *et al.*, 1987).

There are some situations where fructose supports growth just as well as sucrose or glucose (Steffen *et al.*, 1988), and occasionally it gives better results. Some orchid species have been reported to grow better on fructose than glucose (Ernst, 1967; Ernst *et al.*, 1971; Arditti, 1979). Fructose was the best sugar for the production of adventitious shoots from *Glycine max* cotyledonary nodes, especially if the concentration of nutrient salts supplied was inadequate (Wright *et al.*, 1986). Shoot and leaf growth and axillary shoot formation in *Castanea* shoot cultures, was stimulated when sucrose was replaced by 30 g/l fructose. The growth of basal callus was reduced and it was possible to propagate from mature explants of *C. crenata*, although this was not possible on the same medium supplemented with sucrose (Chauvin and Salesses, 1988). However, fructose was reported to be toxic to carrot tissue if, as the sole source of carbon, it was autoclaved with **White (1943a)A** medium. When filter sterilized, fructose supported the growth of callus cultures which had a final weight 70% of those grown on sucrose (Pollard *et al.*, 1961).

Sucrose in culture media is usually hydrolysed totally, or partially, into the component monosaccharides glucose

Table 32. The main sugars which can be utiliized by plants. The value of a sugar for carbon nutrition is indicated by the size of the type.

SUGAR	Reducing Capacity	Products of hydrolytic/enzymatic breakdown
Monosaccharides		
Hexoses		
Glucose	Reducing sugar	None
Fructose	Reducing sugar	None
Galactose	Reducing sugar	None
Mannose	Reducing sugar	None
Pentoses		
Arabinose	Slow reduction	None
Ribose	Slow reduction	None
Xylose	Slow reduction	None
Disaccharides		
Sucrose	Non-reducing	Glucose, fructose
Maltose	Reducing sugar	Glucose
Cellobiose	Reducing sugar	Glucose
Trehalose	Non-reducing	Glucose
Lactose	Reducing sugar	Glucose, galactose
Trisaccharides		
Raffinose	Non-reducing	Glucose, galactose, fructose

and fructose (see below), and so it is logical to compare the efficacy of combinations of these two sugars with that of sucrose. Kromer and Kukulczanka (1985) found that meristem tips of *Canna indica* survived better on a mixture of 25 g/l glucose plus 5 g/l fructose, than on 30 g/l sucrose. Germination of *Paphiopedilum* orchid seeds was best on a medium containing 5g/l fructose plus 5 g/l glucose; a mixture of 7.5 g/l of each sugar was optimal for further growth of the seedlings (Pierik *et al.*, 1988a).

The general superiority of sucrose over glucose for the culture of organised plant tissues such as isolated roots, may be on account of the more effective translocation of sucrose to apical meristems (Butcher and Street, 1964).

Plant species vary in their ability to utilise unusual sugars. For instance, although Gautheret (1945) could grow carrot callus on maltose, Mathes *et al.* (1973) obtained only minimal growth of *Acer* tissue on media supplemented with this sugar. Similarly, growth of soybean tissue on maltose is normally very slow, but variant strains of cells have been selected which can utilise it (Limberg *et al.*

1979), perhaps because the new genotypes possessed an improved capacity for its active transport.

The disaccharide, lactose, has been detected in only a few plants. When added to tissue culture media it has been found to induce the activity of β-galactosidase enzyme which can be secreted into the medium. The hydrolysis of lactose to galactose and glucose then permits the growth of *Nemesia strumosa* and *Petunia hybrida* callus, and cucumber suspensions (Hess *et al.*, 1979; Callebaut and Motte, 1988). Rodríguez and Lorenzo Martin (1987) found that adding 30 g/l lactose to **MS** medium instead of sucrose, increased the number of shoots produced by a *Musa accuminata* shoot culture, but no new shoots were produced on subsequent subculture, although they were when sucrose was present.

Corn syrups. Kinnersley and Henderson (1988) have shown that certain corn syrups can be used as carbon sources in plant culture media and that they may induce morphogenesis which is not provoked by supplementing with sucrose. Embryogenesis was induced in a 10-year old non-embryogenic cell line of *Daucus carota* and plantlets were obtained from *Nicotiana tabacum* anthers by using syrups. Those used contained a mixture of glucose, maltose, maltotriose and higher polysaccharides. Their stimulatory effect was reproduced by mixtures of maltose and glucose. Somatic embryos were produced in greater numbers from *Petunia* anthers when they were cultured with maltose, rather than sucrose or glucose (Raquin, 1983) and this sugar has also been found to be highly effective in promoting embryogenesis in alfalfa cultures (Strickland *et al.*, 1987). Transfer from a medium containing sucrose or glucose to one supplemented with maltose has been used by Stuart *et al.* (1986) and Redenbaugh *et al.* (1987b) to enhance the conversion of embryos of alfalfa (see Chapter 14).

Sugar alcohols. Sugar alcohols are not usually metabolised by plant tissues and generally cannot be used as carbon sources. For this reason mannitol and sorbitol are frequently employed as osmotica to modify the water potential of a culture medium. In these circumstances, sufficient sucrose must also be present to supply the energy requirement of the tissue. Adding either mannitol or sorbitol to the medium may make boron unavailable (page 305).

Mannitol may occasionally be metabolised (*e.g.* by *Fraxinus* tissues — Wolter and Skoog, 1966), but sorbitol is more liable to be broken down; it has been found to support the growth of apple callus (Chong and Taper, 1972, 1974a,b), and that of other rosaceous plants (Coffin *et al.* 1976), occasionally giving rise to more vigorous growth than can be obtained on sucrose. The ability of Rosaceae to use sorbitol as a carbon source is reported to be variety dependent: Albrecht (1986) found that shoot cultures of one crabapple variety required sorbitol for growth, and would not grow on sucrose; another benefitted from being grown on a mixture of sorbitol and sucrose, and the growth of a third suffered if any sucrose was replaced by sorbitol. The apple rootstock 'Ottawa 3' produced abnormal shoots on sorbitol (Chong and Pua, 1985).

The cyclic hexahydric alcohol *myo*-inositol, does not seem to provide a source of energy (Meryl Smith and Stone, 1973) and its beneficial effect on the growth of cultured tissues when used as a supplementary nutrient must depend on its participation in biosynthetic pathways (see under VITAMINS).

Starch. Cultured cells of a few plants are able to utilise starch in the growth medium and appear to do so by release of extracellular amylases (Nickell and Burkholder, 1950). Growth rates of these cultures are increased by the addition of gibberellic acid, probably because it increases the synthesis or secretion of amylase enzymes (Maretzki *et al.*, 1971, 1974).

Hydrolysis of sucrose

The remainder of this section on sugars, is devoted to the apparent effects of sucrose concentration on cell differentiation and morphogenesis. Reports on the subject should be tempered with the knowledge that some or all of the sucrose in the medium is liable to be broken down into its constituent hexose sugars, and that such *inversion* will also occur within plant tissues, where reducing sugar levels of at least 0.5 per cent are likely to occur (Helgeson *et al.*, 1972).

Autoclaving. A partial hydrolysis of sucrose takes place during the autoclaving of media (Ball, 1953; Wolter and Skoog, 1966), the extent being greater when the compound is dissolved together with other medium constituents than when it is autoclaved in pure aqueous solution (Ferguson *et al.*, 1958). In a fungal medium, not dissimilar to a plant culture medium, Bretzloff (1954) found that sucrose inversion during autoclaving (15 min at 15 lbs/in^2) was dependent on pH in the following way:

pH 3.0	100 %
pH 3.4	75 %
pH 3.8	40 %
pH 4.2	25 %
pH 4.7	12.5%
pH 5.0	10 %
pH 6.0	0 %

These results suggest that the proportion of sucrose hydrolysed by autoclaving media at conventional pH levels (5.5–5.8) should be negligible. Most evidence suggests

that this is not the case, and that 10–15% sucrose can be converted into glucose and fructose. Cultures of some plants grow better in media containing autoclaved (rather than filter-sterilised) sucrose (Ball, 1953; Guha and Johri, 1966; Johri and Guha, 1963; Verma and Van Huystee, 1971; White, 1932), suggesting that the cells benefit from the availability of glucose and/or fructose. However, Nitsch and Nitsch (1956) noted that glucose only supported the growth of *Helianthus* callus if it had been autoclaved, and Romberger and Tabor (1971) that the growth of *Picea* shoot apices was less when the medium contained sucrose autoclaved separately in water (or sucose autoclaved with only the organic constituents of the medium), than when all the constituents had been autoclaved together. They suggested that a stimulatory substance might be released when sugars are autoclaved with agar.

In other species there has been no difference between the growth of cultures supplied with autoclaved or filter sterilised sucrose (Mathes *et al.*, 1973), or growth has been less on a medium containing autoclaved, instead of filter sterilised, sucrose (Stehsel and Caplin, 1969).

Enzymatic breakdown. Sucrose in the medium is also inverted into monosaccharides during the *in vitro* culture of plant material. This occurs by the action of invertase located in the plant cell walls (Burstrom, 1957; Yoshida *et al.*, 1973), or by the release of extracellular enzyme (King and Street, 1977). In most cultures, inversion of sucrose into glucose and fructose, takes place in the medium; but because the secretion of invertase enzymes varies, the degree to which it occurs differs from one kind of plant to another. After 28 days on a medium containing either 3 or 4% sucrose, single explants of *Hemerocallis* and *Delphinium* had used 20–30% of the sugar. Of that which remained in the medium which had supported *Hemerocallis*, about 45% was sucrose, while only 5% was sucrose in the media in which *Delphinium* had been grown. In both cases the rest of the sucrose had been inverted (Lumsden *et al.*, 1990).

The sucrose-inverting capacity of tomato root cultures was greatest in media of pH 3.6–4.7. Activity sharply declined in less acid media (Weston and Street, 1968). Helgeson *et al.* (1972) found that ommission of IAA auxin from the medium in which tobacco callus was cultured, caused there to be a marked rise in reducing sugar due to the progressive hydrolysis of sucrose, both in the medium and in the tissue. A temporary increase in reducing sugars also occurred at the end of lag phase when newly transferred callus pieces started to grow rapidly.

In cultures of some species, uptake of sugar may depend on the prior extracellular hydrolysis of sugar. This is the

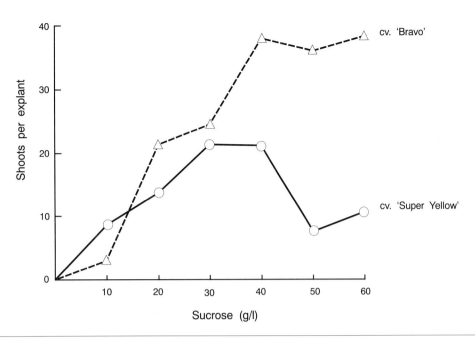

Fig. 98. The effect of sucrose concentration on direct adventitious shoot formation from flower pedicels of two chrysanthemum cultivars [from data of Roest and Bokelmann, 1975].

case in sugar cane (Komor *et al.*, 1981); and possibly also in *Dendrobium* orchids (Hew *et al.*, 1988) and carrot (Kanabus *et al.*, 1986). Nearly all the sucrose in suspension cultures of sugar cane and sugar beet was hydrolysed in 3 days (Thom *et al.*, 1981; Zamski and Wyse, 1985) and *Daucus carota* suspensions have been reported to hydrolyse all of the sucrose in the medium into the constituent hexoses, within 3 days (Kanabus *et al.*, 1986) or within 24 h (Dijkema *et al.*, 1990).

The growth of shoots from non-dormant buds of mulberry is not promoted by sucrose, only by maltose, glucose or fructose. Even though mulberry tissue hydrolysed sucrose into component monosaccharides, shoots did not develop. In the presence of 3% fructose, sucrose was actually inhibitory to shoot development at concentrations as low as 0.2% (Oka and Ohyama, 1982).

Uptake

The uptake of sugar molecules into plant tissues appears to be partly through passive permeation and partly through active transport. The extent of the two mechanisms may vary. Active uptake is associated with the withdrawal of protons (H^+) from the medium. Charge compensation is effected by the excretion of a cation (H^+ or K^+) (Komor *et al.*, 1977; 1981). Glucose was taken up preferentially by carrot suspensions during the first 7 days of a 14 day passage; fructose uptake followed during days 7–9 (Dijkema *et al.*, 1990). At concentrations below 200

mM, glucose was taken up more rapidly into strawberry fruit discs and protoplasts than either sucrose or fructose (Scott and Breen, 1988).

Effective concentrations

In most of the comparisons between the nutritional capabilities of sugars discussed above, the criterion of excellence has been the most rapid growth of unorganised callus or suspension-cultured cells. For this purpose 2–4% sucrose w/v is usually optimal. Similar concentrations are also used in media employed for micropropagation, but laboratories probably pay insufficient attention to the effects of sucrose on morphogenesis (see below) and plantlet development. Sucrose levels in culture media which result in good callus growth, may not be optimal for morphogenesis, and either lower or higher levels may be more effective.

The optimum concentration of sucrose to induce morphogenesis or growth differs between different genotypes, sometimes even between those which are closely related. For instance, Damiano *et al.* (1987) found that the concentration of sucrose necessary to produce the best rate of shoot proliferation in *Eucalyptus gunnii* shoot cultures varied between clones. The influence of sucrose concentration on direct shoot formation from *Chrysanthemum* explants varied with plant cultivar (Fig. 98).

Experiments of Molnar (1988b) have shown that the optimum level of sucrose may depend upon the other ammendments added to a culture medium. The most rapid growth of *Brassica nigra* suspensions on one containing **MS** salts (but less iron, and **B5** vitamins), occurred when 2% sucrose was added. However, when it was supplemented with 1–4 g/l casein hydrolysate, or a mixture of 3 defined amino acids, growth was increased on up to 6% sucrose. A similar result was obtained if, instead of the amino acids, 15 mM sodium succinate was added. There was an extended growth period and the harvested dry weight of the culture was 2.8 times that on the original medium with 2% sucrose.

The respiration rate of cultured plant tissues rises as the concentration of added sucrose or glucose is increased. In wheat callus it was found to reach a maximum when 90 g/l (0.263 M) was added to the medium, even though 20 g/l produced the highest rate of growth and number of adventitious shoots (Galiba and Erdei, 1986). The uptake of inorganic ions can be dependent on sugar concentration and the benefit of adding increased quantities of nutrients to a medium may not be apparent unless the amount of sugar is increased at the same time (Gamborg *et al.*, 1974).

Cell differentiation

Formation of vascular elements. Although sugars are clearly involved in the differentiation of xylem and phloem elements in cultured cells, it is still uncertain whether they have a regulatory role apart from providing a carbon energy source necessary for active cell metabolism. Sucrose is generally required to be present in addition to IAA before tracheid elements are differentiated in tissue cultures. The number of both sieve and xylem elements formed (and possibly the proportion of each kind—Wetmore and Rier, 1963; Rier and Beslow, 1967), depends on sucrose concentration (Aloni, 1980). In *Helianthus tuberosus* tuber slices, although sucrose, glucose and trehalose were best for supporting cell division and tracheid formation, maltose was only a moderately effective carbon source (Minocha and Halperin, 1974). Shininger (1979) has concluded that only carbohydrates which enable significant cell division are capable of promoting tracheary element formation. The occurrence of lignin in cultured cells is not invariably associated with thickened cell walls. Sycamore suspension cultures produced large amounts of lignin when grown on a medium with abnormally high sucrose (more than 6%) and 2,4-D levels. It was deposited within the cells and released into the medium (Carceller *et al.* 1971).

Chlorophyll formation. Levels of sucrose normally used to support the growth of tissue cultures are often inhibitory to chlorophyll synthesis (Rier and Chen, 1964; Edelman and Hanson, 1972), but the degree of inhibition does vary according to the species of plant from which

the tissue was derived. In experiments of Hildebrandt *et al.* (1963) and Fukami and Hildebrandt (1967), for example, carrot and rose callus had a high chlorophyll content on **Hildebrandt *et al.* (1946) Tobacco** medium with 2–8% sucrose; but tissue of endive, lettuce and spinach only produced large amounts of the pigment on a medium with no added sucrose (although a small amount of sugar was probably supplied by 15–16% coconut milk).

Cymbidium protocorms contain high chlorophyll levels only if they are cultured on media containing 0.2–0.5% sucrose. Their degree of greening declines rapidly when they are grown on sucrose concentrations higher than this (Vanséveren-Van Espen, 1973). Likewise, orchid protocorm-like bodies will not become green, and cannot develop into plantlets if sucrose is present in the medium beyond the stage of their differentiation from the explants (see Chapter 17). Where added sucrose does reduce chlorophyll formation, it is thought that the synthesis of 5-aminolaevulinic acid (ALA — a precursor of the porphyrin molecules of which chlorophyll is composed) is reduced due to an inhibition of the activity of the enzyme ALA synthase (Pamplin and Chapman, 1975). Sugars apart from sucrose are not inhibitory (Edelman and Hanson, 1972; El Hinnawiy, 1974). It has been said that cells grown on sucrose for prolonged periods may permanently lose the ability to synthesise chlorophyll (Van Huystee, 1977). Plastids become converted to amyloplasts packed with starch, and this may change the expression of plastid DNA (Gunning and Steer, 1975), or result in a reduction of plastid RNA (Rosner *et al.* 1977).

A small amount of photosynthesis may be carried out by cultured shoots providing they are not maintained on media containing a high concentration of sucrose. Photosynthesis increased in *Rosa* shoot cultures when they were grown initially on 20 or 40 g/l sucrose which was decreased to 10 g/l in successive subcultures (Langford and Wainwright, 1987). An increase in photosynthesis occurs when sucrose is omitted from the medium in which rooted plantlets are growing (Short *et al.*, 1987), but these treatments are not successful in ensuring a greater survival of plantlets when they are transferred *extra vitrum* (Chapter 14).

STARCH ACCUMULATION AND MORPHOGENESIS

Starch deposition preceeding morphogenesis. Cells of callus and suspension cultures commonly accumulate starch in their plastids and it is particularly prevalent in cells at the stationary phase. Starch in cells of rice suspensions had different chemical properties to that in the endosperm of seeds (Landry and Smyth, 1988).

In searching for features which might be related to later morphogenetic events in *Nicotiana* callus, Murashige and co-workers (Murashige and Nakano, 1968; Thorpe and Murashige, 1968a,b) noticed that starch accumulated preferentially in cells sited where shoot primordia ultimately formed. The starch is produced from sucrose supplied in the culture medium (Thorpe *et al.*, 1986). As a result of this work, it was suggested that starch accumulation might be a prerequisite of morphogenesis. In tobacco, starch presumably acts as a direct cellular reserve of the energy required for morphogenesis, because it disappears rapidly as meristemoids and shoot primordia are formed (Thorpe and Meier, 1974; 1975). Morphogenesis is an energy-demanding process, and callus maintained on a shoot-inducing medium does have a greater respiration rate than similar tissue kept on a non-inductive medium (Thorpe and Murashige, 1970; Thorpe and Meier, 1972). Organ-forming callus of tobacco has been found to accumulate starch prior to shoot or root formation whereas callus not capable of morphogenesis did not do so (Kavi Kishor and Mehta, 1982).

Morphogenesis without starch deposition. Cells of other plants which become committed to initiate organs do not necessarily accumulate starch as a preliminary to morphogenesis and it seems likely that the occurrence of this phenomenon is species-related. The deposition of starch was observed as an early manifestation of organogenesis in *Pinus coulteri* embryos (Patel and Berlyn, 1983), but not in those of *Picea abies* (Von Arnold, 1987). Although zygotic embryos of the latter species immediately began to accumulate starch (particularly in the chloroplasts of cell in the cortex), when they were placed on a medium containing sucrose, it was never observed in meristematic cells from which adventitious buds developed (Von Arnold, 1987).

Meristematic centres in bulb scales of *Nerine bowdenii* can be detected as groups of cells from which starch is *absent* (Grootaarts *et al.*, 1981). Starch was not accumulated in caulogenic callus of *Rosa persica* × *R. xanthina* initiated from recently- initiated shoot cultures, but cells did accumulate starch when the shoot forming capacity of the callus was lost after more than three passages (Lloyd *et al.*, 1988). Callus derived from barley embryos, was noted to accumulate starch very rapidly and this was accompanied by a reduction in osmotic pressure within the cells (Granatek and Cockerline, 1978). Gibberellic acid, which in this plant could be used to induce shoot formation, brought about an increase in cell osmolarity.

There are some further examples where a diminution of the amount of stored carbohydrate in cultured tissues has restored or improved their organogenetic capacity. A salt-tolerant line of alfalfa cells which showed no ability for shoot regeneration after three and a half years in culture on 3% sucrose, was induced to form shoots and plantlets by being cultured for one passage of 24 days on 1% sucrose, before being returned to a medium containing 3% sucrose and a high 2,4-D level (Rains *et al.* 1980, and personal communication). Cells which in 3% sucrose were full of starch, became starch-depleted during culture on a lower sucrose level. The number of somatic embryos formed by embryogenic 'Shamouti' orange callus, was increased when sucrose was omitted from the medium for one passage, before being returned to **Murashige and Tucker (1969)** medium, with 5–6% sucrose (Kochba and Button, 1974).

Unusual sugars

In some plants, unusual sugars are able to regulate morphogenesis and differentiation. Galactose stimulates embryogenesis in *Citrus* cultures (Kochba *et al.*, 1978b) and can enhance the maturation of alfalfa embryos (Chapter 14). Callus of *Cucumis sativus* grew most rapidly on raffinose, and was capable of forming roots when grown on this sugar; somatic embryos were only differentiated when the callus was cultured on sucrose (88–175 mM), but if a small amount of stachyose (0.3 mM) was added 88 mM sucrose, the callus produced adventitious shoots instead (Kim and Janick, 1989b). Stachyose is the major translocated carbohydrate in cucurbits.

OSMOTIC EFFECT OF MEDIA INGREDIENTS

Besides having a purely nutritive effect, solutions of inorganic salts and sugars, which compose tissue culture media, influence plant cell growth through their osmotic properties. A discussion is most conveniently accommodated at this point, as many of the papers published on the subject stress the osmotic effects of added sugars.

Osmotic and water potentials

Water movement into and out of a plant cell is governed by the relative concentrations of dissolved substances in the external and internal solutions, and by the pressure exerted by its restraining cell wall. The manner of defining the respective forces has changed in recent years, and as both old and new terminology are found in the tissue culture literature, the following brief description may assist the reader. More detailed explanations can be found in many text books on plant physiology.

In the older concept, cells were considered to take up water by suction (*i.e.* by exerting a negative pressure) induced by the osmotically active concentration of dissolved substances within the cell. The suction force or *suction pressure* (SP) was defined as that resulting from the *osmotic pressure of the cell sap* (OP_{cs}) minus the *osmotic pressure of the external solution* (OP_{ext}), and the pressure exerted on, and stretching the cell wall, *turgor pressure* (TP) — so called because it is at a maximum when the cells are turgid. This may be represented by the equations:

$$SP = (OP_{cs} - OP_{ext}) - TP$$

or $$SP = OP_{cs} - (OP_{ext} + TP).$$

These definitions devised by botanists, are not satisfactory thermodynamically because water should be considered to move down an energy gradient, losing energy as it does so. The term *water potential* (Ψ - Greek capital letter *psi*) is now used, and solutions of compounds in water are said to exert an *osmotic potential*. As the potential of pure water is defined as being zero, and dissolved substances cause it to be reduced, solutions have osmotic potentials, ψ_s (or ψ_π — Greek small letter *psi*) which are negative in value. Water is said to move from a region of high potential (having a less negative value) to one that is lower (having a more negative value). Both osmotic pressure and osmotic potential are used as terms in tissue culture literature and are equivalent except that they are opposite in sign (*i.e.* an OP of + 6 bar equals a ψ_s of - 6 bar). Thermodynamically, the cell's turgor pressure is defined as a positive *pressure potential* (ψ_p). The water potential of a cell (Ψ_{cell}) is then equal to the sum of its osmotic and pressure potentials plus the force holding water in microcapillaries or bound to the cell wall matrix (ψ_m) :

$$\Psi_{cell} = \psi_s + \psi_p + \psi_m$$

Modern statements of the older suction pressure concept are therefore that the difference in water potential (Δ_ψ) (*i.e.* the direction of water movement) between a cell and solution outside is given by:

$$\Delta_\psi = (\psi_{s\ inside\ cell} - \psi_{s\ outside\ cell}) - \psi_p$$

or $$\Delta_\psi = \Psi_{cell} - \psi_{\pi_{outside}}$$

and when $$\Delta_\psi = 0 \quad \text{(at equilibrium)}$$

$$\psi_{\pi\ outside} = \Psi_{cell}$$

The force of water movement between two cells, 'A' and 'B', of different water potential, is given by:

$$\Delta_\psi = \Psi_{cell_A} - \Psi_{cell\ B}$$

the direction of movement being towards the more negative water potential.

The osmotic potential (pressure) of solutions is determined by their molar concentration and by temperature. The water potential of a plant tissue culture medium (Ψ_{tcm}) is equivalent to the osmotic potential of the dissolved compounds (ψ_s). There is no pressure potential but, if they are added, substances such as agar, Gelrite, or polythylene glycol contribute a matric potential (ψ_m):

$$\Psi_{tcm} = \psi_s + \psi_m$$

Osmotic pressure and water potential are measured in standard pressure units thus:

$$1 \text{ bar} = 0.987 \text{ atm}$$
$$= 10^6 \text{ dynes cm}^{-2}$$
$$= 10^5 \text{ Pa} \quad (0.1 \text{ MPa} = 1 \text{ bar}).$$

Whereas molarity is defined as number of gram moles of a substance in one litre of a solution (*i.e.* one litre of solution requires less than one litre of solvent) (see page 352), molality is the number of gram moles of solute per kilogram of solvent, and thus, unlike osmotic potential (osmolarity, measured in pressure units) *is independent of temperature*. It is therefore more convenient to give measurements of osmotic pressure in *osmolality* units. The *osmole* (Os) is defined as:

The unit of the osmolality of a solution exerting an osmotic pressure equal to that of an ideal non-dissociating substance which has a concentration of one mole of solute per kilogram of solvent.

The osmolality of a very dilute solution of a substance which does not dissociate into ions, will be the same as its molality (*i.e.* g moles per kilogram of solvent). The osmolality of a weak solution of a salt, or salts, which has completely dissociated into ions, will equal that of the total molality of the ions.

The osmotic potential of dilute solutions approximates to Van't Hoff's equation:

$$\psi = - c\,R\,T$$

where c = concentration of solutes in molesperlitre
R = the gas constant, and

T = temperature °K.

From the above equation, at 0°C one litre of a solution containing 1 mole of an undissociated compound, or 1 mole of ions, could be expected to have an osmolality of 1 Os/kg, and an osmotic (water) potential of:

$$\Psi = -1 \times 0.082054 \times 273.16$$
$$\quad\quad \text{mole} \quad\quad \text{atm. per mole per °C} \quad\quad \text{°K}$$

$$= -22.414 \text{ atm}$$

Thus, although in practice the Van't Hoff equation must be corrected by the osmotic coefficient, ϕ :

$$\psi = - \varphi\,c\,R\,T \quad\quad \text{(Lang, 1967)},$$

it is possible to give approximate figures for converting osmolality into osmotic potential pressure units. These are shown in Table 33. This table can also be used to estimate the osmotic potential of non-dissociating molecules such as sugars or mannitol. Thus at 25°C, 30 g/l sucrose (molecular wt. 342.3) should exert an osmotic potential of:

$$-2.4789 \times \frac{30}{342.3} = -0.217 \text{ MPa}$$

The observed potential is –0.223 MPa (Table 34).

A definition. The osmotic properties of solutions can be difficult to describe without confusion. In this book, the addition of solutes to a solvent (which makes the osmotic or water potential more negative, but makes the osmolality of the solution increase to a larger positive value), has been said to REDUCE, or make smaller, the osmotic potential of solutions. MS medium containing 3% sucrose (osmolality, *ca*. 186 mOsm/kg; ψ_s = *ca*. –461 kPa at 25°C) is thus described as having a lower water potential than the medium of **White (1954)** supplemented with 2% sucrose (osmolality, *ca*. 78 mOsm/kg; ψ_s = *ca*. –193 kPa at 25°C).

The osmotic potential of media

The contribution of nutrient salts.

Inorganic salts dissociate into ions when they are dissolved in water, so that the water potential of their solutions does not depend on the molality (or molarity) of undissociated compounds, but on the molality (or molarity) of their ions. Thus a solution of KCl with a molality of 0.1, will have a theoretical osmolalty of 0.2, because in solution it dissociates into 0.1 mole K^+ and 0.1 mole

Cl^-. Osmolality of a solution of mixed salts is dependent on the total molality of ions in solution.

Dissociation may not be complete, especially when several different compounds are dissolved together as in plant culture media, which is a further reason why calculated predictions of water potential may be imprecise. In practice, osmotic potentials should be determined by actual measurement with an osmometer. Clearly though, osmotic potential of a culture medium is related to the concentration of solutes, particularly that of the macronutrients and sugar.

Of the inorganic salts in nutrient media, the macronutrients contribute most to the final osmotic (water) potential because of their greater concentration. The osmolality of these relatively dilute solutions is very similar to the total osmolarity *of the constituent ions* at 0°C, and can therefore be estimated from the total molarity of the macronutrient ions, which is given in the last column of Table 49. Thus based on its macronutrient composition, a liquid **Murashige and Skoog (1962)** medium (without sugar) with a total macronutrient ion concentration of 95.75 mM, will have an osmolality of *ca*. 0.0958 osmoles (Osm) per kilogram of water solvent (95.8 mOsm/kg), at 25°C, an osmotic potential of *ca*. –0.237 MPa (237 kPa). Estimates of osmolality derived in this way agree closely to actual measurements of osmolality or osmolarity for named media given in the papers of Yoshida *et al.* (1973), Kavi Kishor and Reddy (1986) and Lazzeri *et al.* (1988).

The total osmotic potential of solutes.

The approximate total osmotic potential of a medium due to dissolved substances (Ψ_s), can be estimated from:

$$\Psi_s \approx \psi_{s \text{ macronutrients}} + \psi_{s \text{ sugars}}$$

Table 33. Factors by which osmolality (Os/kg) should be multiplied to estimate an equivalent osmotic potential in pressure units.

For conversion to	Multiply Os/kg by the factor shown for an appropriate temperature ‡				
	0°C	**15°C**	**20°C**	**25°C**	30°C
Atm	-22.414	-23.645	-24.055	-24.465	-24.875
bar	-22.711	-23.958	-24.374	-24.789	-25.205
dyne/cm^2	-22.711×10^6	-23.958×10^6	-24.374×10^6	-24.789×10^6	-25.205×10^6
MPa	-2.2711	-2.3958	-2.4374	-2.4789	-2.5205
kPa	-2271.1	-2395.8	-2437.4	-2478.9	-2520.5

‡ Divide pressure units by the figures shown to find approximate osmolality

(e.g. 223 kPa $= \frac{223}{1000} \times \frac{1}{2.4789} = 0.089$ Os/kg or 89 mOs/kg).

When 3% w/v sucrose is added to **Murashige and Skoog (1962)** medium, the osmolality of a filter sterilised preparation rises from 0.096 to 0.186 Osm/kg and at 25°C, the osmotic potential of the medium decreases from –0.237 to –0.460 MPa. Sugars are thus responsible for much of the osmotic potential of normal plant culture media. Even without any inversion to monosaccharides, the addition of 3% w/v sucrose is responsible for over four fifths of the total osmotic potential of **White (1954)** medium, 60% of that of **Schenk and Hildebrandt (1972)**, and for just under one half that of **MS**.

The water potential of media solidified with gels is more negative than that of a liquid medium, due to their matric potential, but this component is probably relatively small (Amador and Stewart, 1987). In the following sections, the matric potential of semi- solid media containing *ca.* 6 g/l agar has been assumed to be – 0.01 MPa at 25°C, but as adding extra agar to media helps to prevent hyperhydricity (Chapter 13), it is possible that this is an underestimate.

The contribution of sugars

The osmolality and osmotic potential of sucrose solutions can be read from Table 34. Those of mannitol and sorbitol solutions *of equivalent molarities* will be approximately comparable. At concentrations up to 3% w/v, the osmolality of sucrose is close to molarity. It will be seen that

Table 34. The osmolality and osmotic potential of sucrose solutions of different concentrations.

Sucrose Concentration		Osmolality	Osmotic potential at 25°C
(% w/v)	mM	Os/kg	MPa
0.5	14.61	0.015	- 0.037
1.0	29.21	0.030	- 0.074
1.5	43.82	0.045	- 0.112
2.0	58.43	0.060	- 0.149
2.5	73.04	0.075	- 0.186
3.0	87.64	0.090	- 0.223
4.0	116.86	0.121	- 0.300
6.0	175.28	0.186	- 0.461
8.0	233.71	0.253	- 0.627
10.0	292.14	0.324	- 0.803
12.0	350.57	0.396	- 0.982

the osmotic potential (in MPa) of sucrose solutions at 25°C can be roughly estimated by multiplying the % weight/volume concentration by –0.075: that of the monosaccharides fructose, glucose, mannitol and sorbitol (which have a molecular weight approximately 0.52 times that of sucrose), by multiplying by –0.14.

If any of the sucrose in a medium becomes hydrolysed into monosaccharides, the osmotic potential of the combined sugar components (sucrose + glucose + fructose), ($\psi_{s\ sugars}$), will be lower (more negative) than would be estimated from Table 34. The effect can be seen in Table 35. From this data it seems that 40–50% of the sucrose added to **MS** medium by Lazzeri *et al.* (1988) was broken down into monosaccharides during autoclaving. Hydrolysis of sucrose by plant-derived invertase enzymes will also have a similar effect on osmotic potential. In some suspension cultures, all sucrose remaining in the medium is inverted within 24 h.

A fully inverted sucrose solution would have almost double the negative potential of the original solution, but as the appearance of glucose and fructose by enzymatic hydrolysis usually occurs concurrently with the uptake of sugars by the tissues, it will tend to have a stabilizing effect on osmotic potential during the passage of a culture. Reported measurements of the osmolality of **MS** medium containing 3% sucrose, after autoclaving, are:

Gelling agent	mOs/kg	Reference
0.65% Phytagar	230	Lazzeri *et al.* (1988)
0.6–0.925% agar	240 ±20	Scherer *et al.* (1988)
0.2–0.4% Gelrite	230 ±50	Scherer *et al.* (1988)

Decreasing osmotic potential with other osmotica.

By adding soluble substances in place of some of the sugar in a medium, it can be shown that sugars not only act as a carbohydrate source, but also as osmoregulants. Osmotica employed for the deliberate modification of osmotic potential, should be largely lacking other biological effects. Those most frequently selected are the sugar alcohols mannitol and sorbitol, which are usually not metabolised by plants (although instances are reported — Thompson and Thorpe, 1981). Sodium sulphate and sodium choride have also been used in some experiments.

Protoplast isolation and culture. The osmotic potential of a plant cell is counterbalanced by the pressure potential exerted by the cell wall. To safely remove the cell wall during protoplast isolation (see Chapter 1) without damaging the plasma membrane, it has been found necessary to plasmolyse cells before wall-degrading enzymes are used. This is done by placing the cells in a solution of lower water potential than that of the cell.

Glucose, sucrose and especially mannitol and sorbitol, are usually added to protoplast isolation media for this purpose, either singly or in combination, at a total concentration of 0.35–0.7 M. These addenda are then retained in the subsequent protoplast culture medium, their concentration being progressively reduced as cell colonies start to grow. Tobacco cell suspensions take up only a very small amount of mannitol from solution (Thompson and Thorpe, 1981) and its effect as an osmotic agent appears to be exerted outside the cell (Thorpe, 1982). When protoplasts were isolated from *Pseudotsuga* and *Pinus* suspensions, which required a high concentration of inositol to induce embryogenesis (see page 315), it was found to be essential to add 60 g/l (0.33 M) *myo*-inositol (plus 30 g/l sucrose, 20 g/l glucose and 10 g/l sorbitol) to the isolation and culture media (Gupta *et al.*, 1988). Mannitol and further amounts of sorbitol could not serve as substitutes.

Osmotic effects on growth and morphogenesis

Solutions of different concentrations partly exert their effect on growth and morphogenesis by their nutritional value, and partly through their varying osmotic potential. Lapeña *et al.* (1988) estimated that three quarters of the sucrose necessary to promote the optimum rate of direct adventitious shoot formation from *Digitalis obscura* hypocotyls, was required to supply energy, while the surplus regulated morphogenesis osmotically.

How osmotic potential influences cellular processes is still far from clear. Cells maintained in an environment with low (highly negative) osmotic potential, lose water and in consequence the water potential of the cell decreases. This brings about changes in metabolism and cells accumulate high levels of proline. The activity of the main respiratory pathway of cells (the cytochrome pathway) is reduced in conditions of osmotic stress, in favour of an alternative oxidase system (de Klerk-Kiebert and Van der Plas, 1985).

Equilibrium between the water potential of the medium and that of *Echinopsis* callus, only occurred when the callus was dead. Normally the water potential of the medium was greater so that water flowed into the callus (Kirkham and Holder, 1981). Clearly this situation could not occur in media which were too concentrated, and Cleland (1977) proposed that a critical water potential needs to be established within a cell before cell expansion and cell division, can occur. The osmotic concentration of culture media could therefore be expected to influence the rate of cell division or the success of morphogenesis of the cells or tissues they support. Both the inorganic and organic components will be contributory. The cells of many plants which are natives of sea- shores or deserts (*e.g.* many cacti) characteristically have a low water potential (Ψ_{cell}) and in consequence may need to be cultured in media of relatively low (highly negative) osmotic potentials (Lassocinski, 1985). Sucrose concentrations of 4.5–6% have sometimes been found to be beneficial for such plants (Sachar and Iyer, 1959; Johnson and Emino, 1979; Mauseth, 1979; Lassocinski, 1985).

Above normal sucrose concentrations can often be beneficial in media for anther culture (e.g 13% sucrose in **Gamborg *et al.* (1968) B5** medium — Chuong and Beversdorf, 1985), and for the culture of immature embryos (*e.g.* 10% sucose in **MS** medium — Stafford and Davies, 1979; 12.5% in **Phillips and Collins (1979a) L2.** medium — Phillips *et al.*, 1982).

Table 35. The predicted osmolality of MS medium, and the osmolality actually observed after autoclaving [from data given by Lazzeri *et al.*, 1988].

Components of medium	Predicted osmolality (no sucrose hydrolysis)				Observed total osmolality
	Salts	Agar	Sucrose	Total	
	mOsm/Kg	mOsm/Kg	mOsm/kg	mOsm/Kg	mOsm/kg
MS medium + agar	96	4	–	100	–
MS + agar + 0.5% sucrose	96	4	15	115	115
MS + agar + 1.0% sucrose	96	4	30	130	140
MS + agar + 2.0% sucrose	96	4	60	160	184
MS + agar + 4.0% sucrose	96	4	121	221	276

Balance between ψ_s of medium and sugar. If the osmotic potential of the medium does indeed influence the growth of tissue cultures, one might expect the sucrose concentration which is optimal for growth, to vary from one medium to another, more sucrose being required in dilute media than in more concentrated ones. Evans *et al.* (1976) found this was so with cultures of soybean tissue. Maximum rates of callus growth were obtained in media containing either:

(i) 50–75% of **MS** basal salts + 3–4% sucrose, or,

(ii) 75–100% of **MS** basal salts + 2% sucrose.

Similarly Yoshida *et al.* (1973) obtained equally good growth rates of *Nicotiana glutinosa* callus with nutrient media in which

(i) the salts exerted –0.274 MPa and sucrose –0.223 MPa, or

(ii) the salts exerted –0.365 MPa and sucrose –0.091 MPa.

It was essential to add 60 g/l sucrose ($\psi_{s\ sucrose}$ = –0.461 MPa at 25°C) to the 'MEDIUM' salts of **de Fossard et al. (1974)** ($\psi_{s\ medium}$ = –0.135 MPa) to obtain germination and seedling growth from immature zygotic embryos of tomato. However, if the 'HIGH' salts ($\psi_{s\ medium}$ = –0.260 MPa) were used, 60 g/l sucrose gave only slightly better growth than 2.1 g/l ($\psi_{s\ sucrose}$ = –0.156 MPa) (Neal and Topoleski, 1983).

Callus and cell growth

A detailed examination of osmotic effects of culture media on callus cultures was conducted by Kimball *et al.* (1975). Various organic substances were added to a modified **Miller (1961a)** medium (which included 2% sucrose), to decrease the osmotic potential (ψ_s) from –0.290 MPa. Surprisingly, the greatest callus growth was said to occurr at –1.290 to –1.490 MPa (unusually low potentials which normally inhibit growth — see later) in the presence of mannitol or sorbitol, and between –1.090 to –1.290 MPa when extra sucrose or glucose were added. On the standard medium, many cells of the callus were irregularly shaped; as the osmotic potential of the solution was decreased there were fewer irregularities and at about ψ_s –1.090 MPa all the cells were spherical. The percentage dry matter of cultures also increased as ψ_s was decreased.

Doley and Leyton (1970) found that increasing the water (osmotic) potential of half **White (1963)** medium by –0.100 or –0.200 MPa through adding more sucrose (and/or polyethylene glycol), caused the rate of callus growth from the cut ends of *Fraxinus* stem sections to be lower than on a standard medium. At the reduced water

potential, callus had suberised surfaces and grew through the activity of a vascular cambium. It also contained more lignified xylem and sclereids. At each potential there was an optimal IAA concentration for xylem differentiation.

Senescence and the inhibition of cell division. When the concentration of sucrose in a high salt medium such as **MS** is increased above 4–5 per cent, there begins to be a progressive inhibition of cell growth in many types of culture. This appears to be an osmotic effect because addition of other osmotically-active substances (such as mannitol and polyethyleneglycol) to the medium causes a similar response (Maretzki *et al.* 1972). Usually, high concentrations of sucrose are not toxic, at least not in the short term, and cell growth resumes when tissues or organs are transferred to media containing normal levels of sugar. Increase of ψ_s is one method of extending the shelf life of cultures (Chapter 6). Pech and Romani (1979) found that the addition of 0.4 M mannitol to **MS** medium (modified organics), was able to prevent the rapid cell lysis and death which occurred when 2,4-D was withdrawn from pear suspension cultures.

Tissue water content. The water content of cultured tissues decreases as the level of sucrose in the medium is increased. Isolated embryos of barley were grown by Dunwell (1981b) on **MS** medium in sucrose concentrations up to 12 per cent. Dry weight increased as the sucrose concentration was raised to 6 or 9 per cent and shoot length of some varieties was also greater than on 3 per cent sucrose. Water content of the developing plantlets was inversely proportional to the sucrose level.

The dry weight of *Lilium auratum* bulbs and roots on **MS** medium increased as the sucrose concentration was augmented to 90 g/l but decreased dramatically with 150 g/l because growth was inhibited. The fresh weight/dry weight ratio of both kinds of tissue once again declined progressively as sucrose was added to the medium (0–150 g/l). In a medium containing 30 mg/l sucrose, the number and fresh weight of bulblets increased as **MS** salt strength was raised from one eighth to two times its normal concentration. An interaction between salt and sucrose concentrations was demonstrated in that optimum dry weight of bulbs could be obtained in either single strength **MS** + 120 g/l sucrose (osmolality, without sucrose inversion = *ca.* 492 mOs/kg; ψ_s = *ca.* – 1.22 MPa), or double strength **MS** + 60 g/l sucrose (osmolality, without sucrose inversion = *ca.* 378 mOs/kg; ψ_s = *ca.* – 0.94 MPa) (Takayama and Misawa, 1979).

Morphogenesis

The osmotic effect of sucrose in culture solutions was well demonstrated by a series of experiments on tobacco callus by Thorpe *et al.* (1978) and Brown *et al.* (1979):

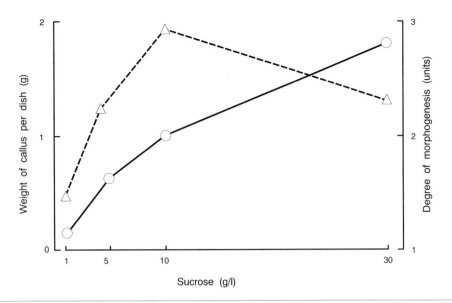

Fig. 99. The effect of sucrose concentration on the growth and morphogenesis of tobacco callus.
[Drawn from data for four lines of tobacco callus in Barg and Umiel, 1977].

Callus growth = solid line

Morphogenesis (line of dashes): Scale was   1 = No differentiation.

2 = Dark green callus with meristemoids.

3 = Leafy shoots.

rates of callus growth and shoot regeneration which were optimal on culture media containing 3 per cent sucrose, could be maintained when the sugar was replaced partially by osmotically equivalent levels of mannitol. The optimal ψ_s (medium plus sucrose) here was between -0.4 and -0.6 MPa, and increasing sucrose levels above 3 per cent brought a progressive decrease in shoot regeneration. Similar results were obtained by Barg and Umiel (1977a), but when they kept the osmotic potential of the culture solution roughly constant by additions of mannitol, the sucrose concentrations optimal for tobacco callus growth or morphogenesis were not the same (Fig. 99).

Brown and Thorpe (1980a) subsequently found that callus of *Nicotiana* capable of forming shoots, had a water potential (Ψ) of -0.8 MPa, while non-shoot-forming callus had a Ψ of -0.4 MPa. The two relationships were:

Shoot forming callus

$$\Psi_{cell} = \psi_s + \psi_p + \psi_m$$

$$-0.8 = -1. + 0.4 + 0 \text{ MPa}$$

Non-shoot-forming callus

$$\Psi_{cell} = \psi_s + \psi_p + \psi_m$$

$$-0.4 = -0. + 0.3 + 0 \text{ MPa}$$

†   The actual units in the paper are misprinted.

Correct water potential. An optimum rate of growth and adventitious shoot formation of wheat callus occurred on **MS** medium containing 2% sucrose. Only a small number of shoots were produced on the medium supplemented with 1% sucrose, but if mannitol was added so that the total Ψ_s was the same as when 2% sucrose was present, the formation of adventitious shoots was stimulated (Galiba and Erdei, 1986). Very similar results were obtained by Lapeña *et al.* (1988). A small number of shoot buds were produced from *Digitalis obscura* hypocotyls on **MS** medium containing 1% sucrose: more than twice as many if the medium contained 2% sucrose (total Ψ_s given as -0.336 MPa[†]), or 1% sucrose plus mannitol to again give a total ψ_s. equal to -0.336 MPa.

Water potential can modify commitment. Morphogenesis can also be regulated by altering the water potential of media. Shepard and Totten (1977) found that very small (*ca.* 1–2 mm) calluses formed from potato mesophyll protoplasts were unable to survive in 1 or 2% sucrose, and the base of larger (5–10 mm) ones turned brown, while the upper portions turned green but formed roots and no shoots. The calli became fully green only on 0.2–0.5% sucrose. At these levels shoots were formed in the presence of 0.2–0.3 M mannitol. When the level of mannitol was reduced to 0.05 M, the proportion of calli differentiating shoots fell from 61% to 2%. The possibility of an osmotic affect was suggested because equimolar concentrations of *myo*-inositol were just as effective in promoting shoot regeneration.

Another way to modify morphogenesis is to increase the ionic concentration of the medium. Pith phloem callus of tobacco proliferates on **Zapata *et al.* (1983) MY1** medium supplemented with 10^{-5} M IAA and 2.5×10^{-6} M kinetin, but forms shoots on **Murashige *et al.* (1972b)** medium containing 10^{-5} M and 10^{-5} M kinetin. These two media contain very similar macronutrients (total ionic concentrations, respectively 96 and 101 mM), yet adding 0.5–1.0% sodium sulphate (additional osmolality 89–130 mOsm/kg) *decreased* the shoot formation of callus grown on the shoot-forming medium, but increased it on the medium which previously only supported callus proliferation (Pua *et al.*, 1985a). Callus cultured in the presence of sodium sulphate retained its shoot-producing capacity over a long period, although the effect was not permanent (Pua *et al.*, 1985b; Chandler *et al.*, 1987). In these experiments shoot formation was also enhanced by sodium chloride and mannitol.

Increasing the level of sucrose from 1, to 3 per cent in **MS** medium containing 0.3 mg/l IAA, induced tobacco callus to form shoots, while further increasing it to 6 per cent resulted in root differentiation (Rawal and Mehta, 1982; Mehta, 1982). The formation of adventitious shoots from *Nicotiana tabacum* pith callus is inhibited on a medium with **MS** salts if 10–15% sucrose is added. Preferential zones of cell division and meristemoids produced in 3% sucrose then become disorganised into parenchymatous tissue (Hammersley-Straw and Thorpe, 1988).

It should be noted that auxin which has a very important influence on the growth and morphogenesis of cultured plant cells, causes their osmotic potential to be altered (Van Overbeek, 1942; Hackett, 1952; Ketellapper, 1953). When tobacco callus is grown on a medium which promotes shoot regeneration, the cells have a greater osmotic pressure (or more negative water potential) than callus grown on a non-inductive medium (Brown and Thorpe, 1980a; Brown, 1982).

Apogamous buds on ferns. Whittier and Steeves (1960) found a very clear effect of glucose concentration on the formation of apogamous buds on prothalli of the fern *Pteridium*. (Apogamous buds give rise to the leafy and spore-producing generation of the plant which has the haploid genetic constitution of the prothallus). Bud formation was greatest between 2–3% glucose (optimum 2.5%). Results which confirm this observation were obtained by Menon and Lal (1972) in the moss *Physcomitrium pyriforme*. Here apogamous sporophytes

were formed most freely in low sucrose concentrations (0.5–2%) and low light conditions (50–100 lux), and were not produced at all when prothalli were cultured in 6% sucrose or high light (5000–6000 lux). Whittier and Steeves (*loc. cit.*) noted that they could not obtain the same rate of apogamous bud production by using 0.25% glucose plus mannitol or polyethyleneglycol; on the other hand, adding these osmotica to 2.5% glucose (so that the osmotic potential of the solution was equivalent to 8% sucrose) did reduce bud formation. It therefore appeared that the stimulatory effect of glucose on morphogenesis was mainly due to its action as a respiratory substrate, but that inhibition might be caused by an excessively depressed osmotic potential.

Differentiation of floral buds. Pieces of cold-stored chicory root were found by Margara and Rancillac (1966) to require more sucrose (up to 68 g/l; 199 mM) to form floral shoots than to produce vegetative shoots (as little as 17 g/l; 50 mM). Tran Thanh Van and co-workers (Tran Thanh Van and Trinh, 1978) have similarly shown that the specific formation of vegetative buds, flower buds, callus or roots by thin cell layers excised from tobacco stems, could be controlled by selecting appropriate concentrations of sugars and of auxin and cytokinin growth regulators.

Root formation and root growth

Media of small osmotic potential are usually employed for the induction and growth of roots on micropropagated shoots. High salt levels are frequently inhibitory to root initiation. When high salt levels have used for Stage II of shoot cultures, it is common to select a low salts medium (*e.g.* ¼ or ½ **MS**), when detached shoots are required to be rooted at Stage III. By testing four concentrations of **MS** salts (quarter, half, three quarters and full strength) against four levels of sucrose (1, 2, 3 and 4%), Harris and Stevenson (1979) found that correct salt concentration (¼ or ½ **MS**) was more important than sucrose concentration for root induction on grapevine cuttings *in vitro*. As mentioned earlier in this Chapter, the benefit of low salt levels for root initiation may be due more to the need for a low nitrogen level, than for an increased osmotic potential. Dunstan (1982) showed that microcuttings of several tree-fruit rootstocks rooted best on ⅓–½ **MS** salts, but that in media of these concentrations, the amount of added sugar was not critical, although it was essential for there to be some present. For the best rooting of *Castanea*, it was important to place shoots in ½ **Lloyd and McCown (1981) WPM** medium containing 4% sucrose (Serres, 1988).

There are reports that an excessive sugar concentration can inhibit root formation. Green cotyledons of *Sinapis alba* and *Raphanus sativus* were found by Lovell *et al.*

(1972) to form roots in 2% sucrose in the dark, but not in light of 5500 lux luminous intensity. In the light, rooting did occur if the explants were kept in water, or (to a lesser extent) if they were treated with DCMU (a chemical inhibitor of photosynthesis) before culture in 2% sucrose. The authors of this paper suggested that sugars were produced within the plant tissues during photosynthesis which, added to the sucrose absorbed from the medium, provided too great a total sugar concentration for rooting. Rahman and Blake (1988b) reached the same conclusion in experiments on *Artocarpus heterophyllus*. When shoots of this plant were kept on a rooting medium in the dark, the number and weight of roots formed on shoots, increased with the inclusion of up to 80 g/l sucrose. The optimum sucrose concentration was 40 g/l if the shoots were grown in the light.

Root formation on avocado cuttings in 0.3 × **MS** salts [plus **Linsmaier and Skoog (1965)** vitamins] was satisfactory with 1.5, 3 or 6% sucrose, and only reduced when 9% sucrose was added (Pliego- Alfaro, 1988).

Although 4% (and occasionally 8%) sucrose has been used in media for isolated root culture, 2% has been used in the great majority of cases (Butcher and Street, 1964). In an investigation into the effects of sucrose concentration on the growth of tomato roots, Street and McGregor (1952) found that although sucrose concentrations of between 1.5 and 2.5% caused the same rate of increase of root fresh weight, 1.5% sucrose was optimal. It produced the best rate of growth of the main root axis, and the greatest number and total length of lateral roots.

Embryogenesis

The osmotic potential of a medium can influence whether somatic embryogenesis can occur and, at least in some plants, regulate the proper development of embryos. As will be shown below, a low osmotic potential is often favourable, but this is not always the case. For instance immature cotyledons of *Glycine max* produced somatic embryos on **Phillips and Collins (1979) L2** medium containing less than 2% sucrose, but not if the concentration of sugar was increased above this level (Lippmann and Lippmann, 1984).

Embryo formation. Placing tissues in solutions with high osmotic potential will cause cells to become plasmolysed, leading to the breaking of cytoplasmic interconnections between adjacent cells (*plasmodesmata*). Wetherell (1984) has suggested that when cells and cell groups of higher plants are isolated by this process, they become enabled to develop independently, and express their totipotency. He points out that the isolation of cells of lower plants induces regeneration, and plasmolysis has long been known to initiate regeneration in multicellulr

algae, the leaves of mosses, fern prothallia and the gemmae of liverworts (Narayanaswami and LaRue, 1955; Miller, 1968). Carrot cell cultures pre-plasmolysed for 45 min in 0.5–1.0 M sucrose or 1.0 M sorbitol gave rise to many more somatic embryos when incubated in **Wetherell (1969)** medium with 0.5 mg/l 2,4-D than if they had not been pre-treated in this way. Moreover embryo formation was more closely synchronized.

Callus derived from hypocotyls of *Albizia richardiana*, produced the greatest numbers of adventitious shoots on **B5** medium containing 4% sucrose, but somatic embryos grew most readily when 2% sucrose was added. At least 1% sucrose was necessary for any kind of morphogenesis to take place (Tomar and Gupta, 1988a). A similar result was obtained by Culafić *et al.* (1987b) with callus from axillary buds of *Rumex acetosella*: adventitious shoots were produced on a medium containing **MS** salts and 2% sucrose (Ψ_s = *ca.* –0.39 MPa at 25°C), but embryogenesis occurred when the sucrose concentration was increased to 6% ($\psi_{s\ sucrose}$ = –0.46 MPa, Ψ_s = *ca.* –0.70 MPa at 25°C) or if the medium was supplemented with 2% sucrose plus 21.3 g/l mannitol or sorbitol (which together have the same osmolality as 6% sucrose).

A low (highly negative) osmotic potential helps to induce somatic embryogenesis in some other plants. Adding 10–30 g/l sorbitol to **Kumar** *et al.* **(1988)** L- 6 medium (total macronutient ions 64.26 mM; 20 g/l sucrose), caused there to be a high level of embryogenesis in *Vigna aconitifolia* suspensions and the capacity for embryogenesis to be retained in long-term cultures. The formation of somatic embryos in ovary callus of *Fuchsia hybrida* was accelerated by adding 5% sucrose to **B5** medium (Dabin and Beguin, 1987), and the induction of embryogenic callus of *Euphorbia longan* required the culture of young leaflets on **B5** medium with 6% sucrose (Litz, 1988). There are exceptions. The proportion of *Ipomoea batatas* somatic embryos forming shoots was greatest when a medium containing **MS** inorganics contained 1.6%, rather than 3% sucrose (Chée *et al.*, 1990).

Embryo growth. Protocorm proliferation of orchids is most rapid when tissue is cultured in high concentrations of sucrose, but for plantlet growth, the level of sucrose must be reduced (Homes and Vanseveran-Van Espen, 1973). The induction of embryogenic callus from immature seed embryos of *Zea mays* was best on **MS** medium with 12% sucrose (Lu *et al.*, 1982), and Ho and Vasil (1983) used 6–10% sucrose in **MS** medium to promote the formation of pro-embryoids from young leaves of *Saccharum officinarum*. However, in the experiments of Ahloowalia and Maretski (1983), somatic embryo formation from callus of this plant was best on **MS** medium with 3% sucrose, but growth of the embryos into complete

Table 36. The relative humidities within culture vessels which would be expected to result from the use of plant culture media of various osmolalities or water potentials.

Relative humidity in vessel %	Osmolality mOs/kg	Water potential (kPa) at temperature :			
		15°C	20°C	25°C	30°C
98	1121.4	−2686.6	−2733.2	−2779.8	−2826.4
99	557.9	−1336.5	−1359.7	−1382.9	−1406.1
99.5	278.2	−666.6	−678.1	−689.7	−701.3
99.75	138.9	−332.8	−338.7	−344.4	−350.2

plantlets required that the embryos should be cultured first on **MS** medium with 6% sucrose and then on ½ **MS** with 3% sucrose.

When cultured on **Sears and Deckard (1982)** medium, embryogenesis in callus initiated from immature embryos of 'Chinese Spring' and some other varieties of wheat was incomplete, because shoot apices germinated and grew before embryos had properly formed. More typical somatic embryos could be obtained by adding 40 mM sodium or potassium chloride to the medium. The salts had to be removed to allow plantlets to develop normally (Galiba and Yamada, 1988). Transferring somatic embryos to a medium of lower (more negative) water potential is often necessary to ensure their further growth and/or germination (Chapter 14).

Culture of isolated embryos. High sucrose levels are often required in media for the culture of zygotic embryos if they are isolated when immature. The use of 50–120 g/l sucrose in media is then reported, the higher concentrations usually being added to very weak salt mixtures. Embryos which are more fully developed when excised, grow satisfactorily in a medium with 10–30 g/l sugar.

Anther culture. The use of high concentrations of sucrose is commonly reported in papers on anther culture where the addition of 5–20% sucrose to the culture medium is found to assist the development of somatic embryos from pollen microspores. This appears to be due to an osmotic regulation of morphogenesis (Sunderland and Dunwell, 1977), for once embryoid development has commenced, such high levels of sucrose are no longer required, or may be inhibitory. The temporary presence of high sucrose concentrations is said to prevent the proliferation of callus from diploid cells of the anther that

would otherwise swamp the growth of the pollen-derived embryoids.

The concentration of macronutrient ions generally used in anther culture media is not especially low. In a sample of reports it was found to be 68.7 mM (George E.F. *et al.*, 1987), and so the total Ψ_s (salts plus sucrose) of many anther culture media is in the range −0.55 to −1.15 MPa.

Relative humidity

The vapour pressure of water is reduced by dissolving substances in it. This means that the relative humidity of the air within culture vessels is dependent on the water potential of the medium according to the equation:

$$\Psi = \frac{1000\, R\, T}{W_a}\, \ln_e \left(\frac{p}{p_0}\right) \cdot \left(p - c\frac{dp}{dc}\right)$$

(after Glasstone, 1947)

where: Ψ, R and T are as in the Van't Hoff equation, W_a is the molecular weight of water, c is the concentration of the solution in moles per litre, and p_0 and p are respectively the vapour pressures of water and the solution.

If the change in vapour pressure dependent on the density of the solution, $p - c\frac{dp}{dc}$, is treated as unity (legitimate perhaps for very dilute solutions, or when the equation is expressed in molality, rather than molarity), it is possible to estimate relative humidity ($100\frac{p}{p_0}$) above tissue culture media of known water potentials, from:

$$\Psi = \frac{1000\, R\, T}{18.016}\, \ln_e \left(\frac{p}{p_0}\right), \qquad \text{(Lang, 1967)}$$

The relative humidity above most plant tissue cultures is thus calculated to be in the range 99.25–99.75% (Table 36), the osmolality of some typical media being:

Medium	Osmolality[‡] mOs/kg
White (1963), liquid, 2% sucrose	106
MS, agar, 3% sucrose	230
MS, agar, 6% sucrose	359
MS, agar, 12% sucrose (unusual)	659

[‡] 50% hydrolysis of sucrose into monosaccharides assumed to have taken place during autoclaving.

SUPPORT SYSTEMS

Although plant cultures can be grown in liquid media, for many purposes there are advantages in supporting explants, or cultures, above the surface of the medium. Agar solidified media were first used for this purpose by analogy with the techniques developed in bacteriology.

Mechanical supports

White (1953) tried growing carrot tissue in a liquid medium contained in tubes that were lined with perforated cellophane (the tissue being placed between the glass and cellophane). It was hoped that flat sheets of tissue would result, but callus grew spherically as usual. Growth was more rapid in liquid medium without cellophane, and tissue weight was finally greatest on an agar–supplemented medium. Previously Heller and Gautheret (1949a) had tried supporting cultures on glass-cloth having an oil or plastic binder, but decided that there was too great a risk of the binders or the glass adding undefined supplements to the medium (crushed boro-sillicate glass is a source of boron). Eventually they found (Heller and Gautheret, 1949b) that tissues could be satisfactorily cultured on pieces of ashless filter paper moistened by being in contact with (but not submerged in) liquid medium. Very small explants such as meristem tips which may be lost if placed in a rotated or agitated liquid medium, can be successfully cultured if placed in the centre of an M- or ∩-shaped strip of filter paper (sometimes called 'Heller' supports). When the folded paper is placed in a tube of liquid medium, the side arms act as a wick (Goodwin, 1966). This method of support ensures

excellent tissue aeration but the extra time required for preparation and insertion has meant that paper wicks are only used for special purposes such as the initial cultural stages of single small explants which are otherwise difficult to establish. Whether explants grow best on agar or on filter paper supports, varies from one species of plant to another. Davis *et al.* (1977) found that carnation shoot tips grew less well on filter paper bridges than on 0.6% agar, but axillary bud explants of a protea (*Leucospermum*) would not survive on agar and had to be kept on bridges for 3–4 months. After this they could be moved to an agar medium: prolonged culture on bridges resulted in hyperhydricity (Kunisaki, 1990).

To support seedling–derived shoots of *Pinus caribaea* above a liquid medium, Skidmore *et al.* (1988) drilled holes in a polystyrene Petri dish which was inverted in a larger container (Fig. 100). A somewhat similar method of support has sometimes been used for large scale multiplication (Chapter 16), and in experimental micropropagation systems, where explants have not been placed in liquid or solid media, but continuously irrigated with nutrient mists (Fox, 1980).

Porous materials. As would be expected, tissues or organs can be grown on inert and porous materials other than paper, if they have been wetted with a liquid medium. Aeration of the tissues and of roots which might grow into the porous substrate is usually better than it would be in agar or static liquid. Shoots of many plants grow and root satisfactorily on rockwool moistened with a liquid medium. For example, Tanaka *et al.* (1991) grew several different kinds of plants on rockwool 'Multiblocks' (Grodania A.S., Denmark) within the porous plastic bags described on page 115.

Cheng and her co-workers have used 100% polyester fleece to support cultures of Douglas fir that were irrigated with liquid media in Petri dishes. In the first instance plantlets were regenerated from cotyledon explants placed on 3 mm-thick fabric (Cheng and Voqui, 1977; Cheng, 1978a). When a protoplast suspension was dispersed over fabric of 0.5 mm thickness, numerous colonies were produced in 12 days, whereas in the absence of the support, cell colonies failed to proliferate beyond the 20 cell stage. A major advantage in using this type of fabric support is that media can be changed simply and quickly without disturbing the tissues. The system has been used for protoplast culture of other plants (*e.g.* Russell and McCown, 1986a).

Cultures can be grown on foam supports, providing the material selected has no toxic components. For instance,

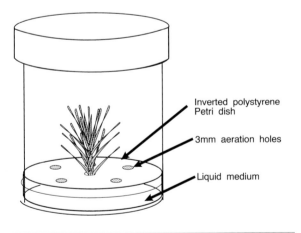

Fig. 100. The method of supporting *Pinus* shoots used by Skidmore *et al.* (1988).

Inverted polystyrene Petri dish

3mm aeration holes

Liquid medium

the successful culture of *Picea, Citrus* and *Nicotiana* on polyurethane foam has been reported from Gutman and Shiryaeva (1980) and Scherer (1988). Conner and Meredith (1984) found that cells grew more rapidly than on agar, if they were plated onto filter papers which were then placed on top of polyurethane foam pads saturated with medium. A buoyant polypropylene membrane floated on top of a liquid medium has been used by Chin *et al.* (1988) to culture *Asparagus* cells and protoplasts. The membrane (Celgard 3500, Questar Corp., Charlotte, N.C.) has a pore size of 0.04 μm and is autoclavable. Shoot culture of some plants *e.g.* certain insectivorous plants (Woodward *et al.*, 1991) is highly successful when they are supported on rockwool soaked with a liquid medium.

Rooting. The use of mechanical supporting materials during Stage III, when shoots are being rooted before transfer to the external environment, is discussed in Chapter 14.

GELLING AGENTS

Plant organs and tissues are most suitably retained above the surface of a culture medium by increasing its viscosity with some kind of gelling agent. Ideally, the material chosen should be capable of being sterilised by autoclaving, in which case the thickened medium should be liquid when hot, but viscous when cool. Several suitable products are now available for gelling plant media but the results obtained on each may differ considerably. The selection of the most suitable material in terms of both the rate and cost of propagation has become another task in building up a suitable protocol for the tissue culture propagation of any particular plant.

Agar

Agar has traditionally been used as the preferred gelling agent for tissue cultures, and is very widely employed for the preparation of semi-solid culture media. For this purpose it has the same advantages that have made it so widely used for the culture of bacteria, namely:-

- with water it forms gels that melt at *ca.* 100°C and solidify at *ca.* 45°C. This means that the gels are stable at all feasible incubation temperatures;

- gels are not digested by plant enzymes;

- agar does not strongly react with media constituents.

Agar is thought to be composed of a complex mixture of related polysaccharides built up from the sugar, galactose. These range from an uncharged neutral polymer fraction, called *agarose* with the capacity to form strong gels, to highly charged anionic polysaccharides sometimes called *agaropectins* which give agar its viscosity. Agar is a natural product extracted from species of red algae (especially *Gelidium amansii* and algae in the phylum Rhodophyta) which are collected from the sea in several different countries. It varies in nature according to country of origin, the year of collection and the way in which it has been extracted and processed. The proportion of agarose to total polysaccharides can vary from 50 to 90% (Adrian and Assoumani, 1983). This means that there may be big differences in the properties of the products offered by laboratory suppliers. Depending on the nature of the particular agar selected, concentrations between 0.5 and 1% w/v usually produce semi-solid gels.

Firmness of the gel produced by a given concentration varies according to brand (Debergh, 1982), and according to the pH during autoclaving; agar is partly hydrolysed if it is autoclaved in an acid medium (page 290). Some agars may not be suitable for use at low concentrations (Bridson, 1978). An inhibition of gelling may take place in the presence of 0.8 to 1.0 per cent charcoal (Horner *et al.* 1977).

Differences between brands of agar

Purity. Various brands and grades of agar are available commercially which differ in the amounts of impurities they contain and their gelling capabilities. Both of these characteristics can alter the chemical and physical properties of a medium. The gelling capacity of Difco brands of agar increased with increasing purity *i.e.* 'Noble' > 'Purified' > 'Bacto' (Debergh, 1983). As the degree of firmness produced by any given concentration of agar varies greatly between different brands, the kind used experimentally should always be described (Debergh, 1982). It is usually unnecessary to use highly purified agar for commercial micropropagation work, which is fortuitous since the high cost would be disadvantageous. Boxus (1978) reported the successful use of a relatively cheap agar for industrial micropropagation.

White (1953) suggested that some agars may have a nutritional role since tissues might be able to utilise the carbohydrates, traces of amino acids and vitamins therein (Day, 1942); for this reason he recommended that agar should not be used in critical experiments on tissue metabolism. Agar contains small amounts of macro- and micro-elements; particularly calcium, sodium, potassium, and phosphate, all of which may supplement the ingredients of the actual culture medium (Debergh, 1982, 1983; Scherer *et al.*, 1988). As the agaropectin polysaccharide has sulphate ester groups on some of the sugar units, agar always contains a large amount of sulphur which is reactive (*e.g.* with blood serum).

Some impurities can be removed from cheaper agar brands by prior soaking and/or washing in distilled water at room temperature over a 24 hour period. If then rinsed in ethanol, spread thinly on trays, and placed in a ventilated oven at 60°C for 24 hours, all of the water is excluded. A blender or similar apparatus may be necessary to finally convert the agar back into a powdered form (Lane, 1982). This treatment will not remove insoluble or tightly bound impurities, but may remove some component/s which help to prevent hyperhydricity. Nairn (1988) found that 0.8% Difco 'Bacto' agar did not cause *Pinus radiata* shoots to become hyperhydric, but symptoms were marked if cultures were plated on a medium containing this agar which had been washed in distilled water. Agars contain phenolic substances (Scherer *et al.*, 1988) and less pure grades may contain long chain fatty acids, inhibitory to the growth of some bacteria, which can be removed by exposure to activated charcoal (see page 470).

Fortunately the effects of inorganic impurities in agar do not seem to be appreciable. Nutrient levels in shoot tip explants of crabapple and pear after 8 weeks of culture on **Singha *et al.* (1985)** medium, were dependent on both the concentration and brand of agar employed, but variations in shoot proliferation and growth were not explained by the macro- or micro-elements in either the agar brands or the explants. However, Debergh (1983) discoverd that there was a significant amount of soluble copper in Difco 'Bacto' agar, which may accelerate the blackening of tissues (see page Chapter 13).

Romberger and Tabor (1971) showed vigour and dry weight increase of cultured Norway spruce shoot apices to be best on purified Difco agar, and least good on Difco highly pure 'Noble' agar. The widely used Difco 'Bacto' agar produced intermediate results. By contrast the best initial growth of carnation shoot tips occurred on 0.6% Difco 'Noble' agar and on the same concentration of Difco 'Bacto' agar, explants had only half the fresh weight (Davis *et al.* 1977). Banks-Izen and Polito (1980) noted that callus growth was slower on 'Bacto' agar than on Gibco 'Phytagar'.

Shoot proliferation in shoot cultures of *Malus baccata* × *M. pumila* was slightly faster on T.C. agar (KC Biological Inc.) than on 'Bacto' agar, but culture on 'Bacto' agar gave the fastest rate of increase of *Pyrus communis* 'Seckel' (Singha, 1984). A ten-fold difference in the regeneration rate of sugar cane was observed by Anders *et al.* (1988) on media gelled with the best and least effective of 7 brands of agar.

Agar concentration. To ensure adequate contact between tissue and medium, a lower concentration of agar is used for plant cultures than in most media prepared for the culture of bacteria. Plant media are not firmly gelled, but only rendered semi-solid. Depending on brand, concentrations of between 0.7–1.0% agar are used in many academic experiments, but as agar can be the most expensive component of plant media, most commercial laboratories use only the minimum possible concentration. Providing the gel is sufficiently firm to prevent the tissues sinking, a semi-fluid medium can often be beneficial to growth due to better diffusion of media ingredients. A weak gel is also readily removed from plantlets that are to be transferred to soil at Stage III. The lowest concentration of agar which can be used will depend on the purity and brand which has been chosen and the pH of the medium, and is about 0.4–0.5% (Von Arnold and Eriksson, 1979a).

Inadequate concentrations of agar either do not support explants or may lead to the induction of hyperhydricity. In cultures of susceptible plants, hyperhydricity decreases as the agar concentration is raised, but in cultures of growing shoots there is invariably an accompanying reduction in the rate of growth and/or proliferation. An intermediate concentration of agar can often be selected, at which there is a reasonable rate of shoot multiplication and at which there is only a small amount of hyperhydricity. For carnation shoot cultures, Hakkaart and Versluijs (1983) used 8–10 g/l agar: when the medium contained 6 g/l most shoots were glassy; at 12 g/l plant growth was severely reduced.

When 4 g/l of several alternative Dicfo agar were added to **Davis *et al.* (1977)** MS-3 medium adjusted to pH 5.5, 'Noble' agar solidified, but 'Purified' and 'Bacto' agars only gelled partially. There was a high rate of fresh and dry weight increase of shoot tips on such partially gelled media, but it was mainly due to abnormal hyperhydric leaves which were in contact with the medium or had fallen over and sunk below the surface. The growth rate of cultures declined as the concentration of agar was increased: the best results were obtained on 0.6% 'Noble' agar.

Shoot cultures of *Cynara scolymus* grown on **Debergh *et al.*, 1981** medium became hyperhydric on 0.6% Difco 'Bacto' agar, but glassiness decreased as the agar concentration was increased. There were no symptoms in cultures on 1.1% agar, but the rate of shoot proliferation was then considerably decreased (Debergh *et al.*, 1981).

Singha (1982a,c) found that **Linsmaier and Skoog (1965)** medium with 0.3% Phytagar did not gel satisfactorily, probably because of the acidification of the medium during autoclaving, but nevertheless the loose gel was capable of supporting the explant. The highest fresh weights and dry weight of 'Almey' crabapple and 'Seckel' pear were obtained on this medium but shoots were succulent and fragile. Shoot proliferation of the crabapple was best on 0.3% Phytagar, but only single shoots of pear were produced on filter paper bridges or on 0.3% agar, and shoot proliferation of this plant required an agar concentration of above 0.6%.

According to Loreti and Pasqualetto (1986), hyperhydricity can sometimes be overcome by substituting one brand of agar for another. Rugini and Verma (1983) used an agar (0.7 g/l) and pectin (0.5 g/l) mixture to prevent hyperhydricity (see Chapter 13) in almond shoot cultures. A mixture of pectin and agar can be a less expensive substitute for agar. A semi-solid medium consisting of 2 g/l agar plus 8–10 g/l pectin, was employed for shoot culture of strawberry and some other plants (Zimmerman, 1979).

Physical effects of agar gels

Agar has adsorptive properties which have not been fully evaluated and White (1953) thought that it might remove harmful metabolic products. The growth of callus or plant organs on solidified media is generally less rapid than in liquid culture. Furthermore, dry weight increase on a solid medium tends to be inversely related to the concentration of the agar incorporated. Growth on hard gels is therefore inhibited (see above), but morphogenesis may be improved when explants or callus cultures are maintained on agar-supplemented media. There are several physical effects which might explain these observations.

Reduced diffusion. Romberger and Tabor (1971) calculated that only the diffusion of large molecules was likely to be restricted through an agar gel, and it was thought that this would not lead to the accumulation of toxic metabolites in the cultured tissues. They suggested a more likely cause of reduced growth rates might be the immobilisation of the enzyme invertase released from culture tissues.

Invertase immobilisation would result in a reduced availability of glucose and fructose in the tissues. However, there is good reason to believe that the absorption of inorganic ions will also be restricted. The uptake of nitrate ions into shoots and plantlets cultured on agar, is apparently less than when they are grown on a liquid medium (Faye et al., 1986).

The availability of medium ingredients to tissues cultured on agar, compared to those in shaken liquid culture, will be reduced by the medium having a decreased water potential, and an increased viscosity (which will limit diffusion); and by the fact that less than half of the explant, or callus surface, is in contact with the medium.

The decrease in water potential which results from the matric potential of agar, will limit ion uptake which is closely associated with the rate of water influx into tissues. Tissue surfaces within agar will receive only a limited supply of oxygen (Chapter 7). Microelements and phosphate may be absorbed into the agar matrix and so become less available to cultures (Debergh, 1983).

Tissue water content and nutrient uptake. An agar-solidified medium will have a lower (more negative) water potential than its liquid equivalent (Debergh et al. 1981) and this may be partly responsible for the morphogenetic responses which sometimes occur preferentially on agar. The proline content of explants rises as agar concentration is increased, indicating that they are under greater water stress. Chicory root explants produced flower buds when continuously illuminated on a medium supplemented with 45 g/l sucrose and 12 g/l agar. But when they were supported on filter paper soaked in the same medium without agar, they produced only vegetative buds. The formation of flower buds was correlated with the water content of tissue, which was lower on agar than on filter paper (Bouniols and Margara, 1968).

Medium hardness increases linearly with agar concentration, and the contact between explant and medium decreases, causing the uptake into the explant of growth regulators, mineral ions and organic susbstances, to be reduced (Debergh, 1982). Ma and Shii (1974) reported that shoots were formed from meristematic centres on banana callus providing the medium contained 0.5% agar or less, but not when the agar concentration was 1%. Callus derived from potato tubers grew most rapidly on 1% agar and less well on either higher or lower concentrations. On media containing 0.6 or 0.8% agar, the callus was white and wet, while on higher levels it was hard, drier and of a red-brown colour (Anstis and Northcote, 1973).

Skirvin (1981) points out that the rate of water evaporation from media increases as agar levels are reduced, and that some precautions may be necessary to preserve a semi-solid condition.

Agarose

Agarose is the high gel strength moiety of agar. It consists of β-D (1→3)galactopyranose and 3,6-anhydro α-L (1→4)galactopyranose linked into polymer chains of 20–160 monosaccharide units. Agaropectin with its sulphate side groups is largely removed (Shillito et al., 1983). There are several different commercial products available which have been extracted from agar and treated to remove most of the residual sulphate side groupings. Because preparation involves additional processes, agarose is much more expensive than agar, and its use is only warranted for valuable cultures. In research, it has been employed particularly in protoplast (Lorz *et al.*, 1983; Shillito *et al.*, 1983) and anther culture (Chaleff and Stolarz, 1981). Brands may differ widely in their suitability for these applications. A concentration of *ca.* 0.4% of the most suitable kinds is usually adequate. Agarose derivatives are available which melt and gel at temperatures below 30°C, making them especially suitable for testing media ingredients which are heat-labile, or for the preparation of 'beads' (see later). Low melting-point agarose is prepared by introducing hydroxyethyl groups into the agarose molecules (Shillito *et al.*, 1983).

In shoot cultures, adding agarose to the medium may induce hyperhydricity. In *Picea abies* and *Pinus radiata*, low concentrations of agarose produced glassy shoots even though they made the medium firmer than an equivalent concentration of agar (Von Arnold and Eriksson, 1984; Nairn, 1988). Hyperhydricity is absent on media with high levels of agarose (*e.g.* 1.5–2%) but, as happens with extra agar, shoot growth is then suppressed.

Gelrite

One alternative gelling agent which is is being used to an increasing extent, is Gelrite™ (Kelco Division of Merck and Co.). Gelrite is a gellan gum – a hetero-polysaccharide produced by the bacterium *Pseudomonas elodea* which is comprised of linked K-glucuronate, rhamnose and cellobiose molecules (Kang *et al*, 1982). The commercial product contains significant quantities of potassium, sodium, calcium and magnesium (Pasqualetto *et al.*, 1988b; Scherer *et al.*, 1988), but is said to be free of the organic impurities found in agar. Heating in the presence of cations such as K^+, Ca^{2+}, Mg^{2+} at a concentration of 0.1% or less, causes the polysaccharide to form gels. It is unclear whether these cations afterwards remain fully available to plant cultures. Some researchers (*e.g.* Gawel *et al.*, 1986; 1990; Trolinder and Goodin, 1987; Umbeck *et al.*, 1987) add an extra 750 mg/l $MgCl_2$ to a medium containing **MS** salts to aid the gelling of 1.6 g/l Gelrite. In most other reports on the use of Gelrite, cations in the medium have apparently been sufficient to produce a gel.

The commercial deacetylated and purified polysaccharide forms firm non-elastic gels which have a strength equivalent to that of agar at approximately ½–¼ the concentration. Gelling is very rapid, the setting point being determined by the concentration of the polysaccharide and that of the cation, and varies between 35–50°C (Kang *et al.*, 1982). Water in a Gelrite gel seems to be only lightly bound, so that diffusion of water soluble substances is more rapid than through agar (Scherer, 1988).

Gelrite is an attractive alternative to agar for plant tissue culture because its cost per litre of medium is less, and it produces a clear gel which assists the proper observation of cultures and their possible contamination. It has proved to be a suitable gelling agent for tissue cultures of many herbaceous plants and there are reports of its successful use for callus culture, the direct and indirect formation of adventitious organs and somatic embryos, shoot culture of herbaceous and semi-woody species and the rooting of plantlets. In most cases the results have been as good as those obtainable on agar solidified media: in many instances superior results have been obtained.

Anders *et al.* (1988) described considerable improvements in the number of plants regenerated (presumably *via* indirect embryogenesis) from several sugar cane varieties cultured on Gelrite, rather than the most productive brand of agar and Koetje *et al.* (1989) found that embryogenesis of rice resulted in many more plants if callus was cultured on **Chu *et al.* (1975) N6** medium solidified with Gelrite rather than Bacto-agar, on which the growth of calli was severely reduced.

The same problem may arise using low concentrations of Gelrite as occurs with low levels of agar: shoots and particularly those in shoot cultures of some woody species, are liable to become hyperhydric. The incidence of glassy shoots may then be reduced by increasing the concentration of gelling agent, but as shown by the results

Table 37. The effect of concentration of Gelrite on the proportion of hyperhydric plants in three genera of the Rosaceae [data of Turner and Singha, 1990].

Gelrite concentration % w/v	Species	Hyperhydric plants %
0.1	*Geum quellyon*	100
	Malus (crabapple)	100
	Pyrus communis	100
0.2	*Geum quellyon*	80
	Malus (crabapple)	80
	Pyrus communis	100
0.4	*Geum quellyon*	20–40
	Malus (crabapple)	20–40
	Pyrus communis	100

of Turner and Singha (1990) (Table 37), there can be sharp differences in the response of different species. In these experiments, the highest rate of shoot proliferation of *Geum* occurred in 0.2% Gelrite (greater than on 0.6% Phytagar™), and that of *Malus* on 0.4% Gelrite.

Agar plus Gelrite

Pasqualetto *et al.* (1986) discovered that shoot cultures of *Malus domestica* 'Gala' were always hyperhydric on media solidified with Gelrite, but that the syndrome could be avoided, without a marked decrease in shoot proliferation, by adding 1–1.5 g/l Gelrite *and* 2–3 g/l Sigma agar to the medium. This technique was also used successfully for shoot cultures of *Pinus radiata* by Nairn (1988). Vitrescence occurred after 4 transfers on a medium gelled with 2 g/l Gelrite. A satisfactory alternative gel for routine use was the mixture of 1.94 g/l Gelrite *plus* 0.24 g/l Difco 'Bacto' agar. Any hyperhydric shoots that occurred were placed on a medium with 1.8 g/l Gelrite *plus* 0.8 g/l agar, which corrected the phenomenon, providing only a low concentration of BAP was present.

Alternative gelling agents

Starch

Sorvari (1986a,c) found that the frequency of plantlet formation from barley anther cultures was much greater if the anthers were plated on a medium solidified with 5% corn starch, or barley starch, than with agar. Corn starch only formed a weak gel and so it was necessary to place a polyester net on its surface to prevent the explants sinking. On medium containing barley starch, adventitious shoots were formed from potato discs in 3 weeks, instead of the 5–14 weeks which it took on an agar-solidified medium (Sorvari, 1986b).

That starches can be used instead of agar has been confirmed by Henderson and Kinnersley (1988). The growth of wild carrot and embryogenic carrot callus cultures was found to be slightly better on media gelled with corn starch than with agar. A food grade starch, such as that available in supermarkets, could be used (Corn Products Code 3005), but it was easier to dispense a modified starch with a reduced molecular weight (Code 5061) derived from the above by acid hydrolysis. Henderson and Kinersley found that they had to use more than 7% starch in the medium to obtain a stable gel capable of supporting tissues. In their growth tests 12% starch was used, which could be a disadvantage, considering that gels of comparable strength were produced by using 0.9% Difco 'Bacto' agar.

κ-Carrageenan

The experimental use of this gelling agent in plant tissue cultures is decribed by Ichi *et al.* (1986). Like Gelrite, κ-carrageenan requires the presence of cations for gelation. When incorporated into **Linsmaier and Skoog (1965)** medium at 0.6% w/v, the gel strength was slightly less than that of 0.2% Gelrite or 0.8% of an extra pure agar. Tissues seemed to grow on the gel slightly better than they did on the agar solidified medium.

Gelatin

Gelatin at a concentration of *ca.* 10% has been tried for solidifying plant tissue culture media, but is currently little used as it melts at *ca.* 30–35°C and forms a good substrate for the growth of bacteria.

Alginans

Alginic acid is a linear heteropolymer extracted from various species of brown algae. It is a co-polymer of 1,4-β-D-mannuronic acid and 1,4-α-L-guluronic acid residues (Larkin *et al.*, 1988): the sodium salt is generally employed for tissue cultures.

Adaoha Mbanaso and Roscoe (1982) advocated the use of alginate for gelling media intended for protoplast culture. Particular advantages were were said to be that:

- solutions are gelled by adding Ca ions. This enabled protoplasts to be suspended in the medium. Plant cells mixed with cooling agar gels are usually damaged (*e.g.* Button and Botha, 1975);

- gels can be liquified (so releasing protoplasts or cell colonies for transfer) by adding sodium citrate;

- gels are stable at normal culture temperatures.

Disadvantages are that:-

- solutions cannot be autoclaved without unacceptable alginate breakdown (sterilisation was carried out at 90°C for 20 mins);

- alginate reacts with divalent metal cations so there is a possibility of it causing nutrient deprivation.

Miscellaneous gels

Adaoha Mbanaso and Roscoe (1982) mentioned that they had successfully grown plant tissue cultures on media solidified with methocel (methylcellulose, a compound that is used to increase the viscosity of animal media) but that solutions were difficult to handle. Dispersions of microcrystalline cellulose were however successfully used by George *et al.* (1983) to support shoots of several *Brassica* species on **Linsmaier and Skoog (1965)** medium.

Native cellulose (degree of polymerization >500) was acid hydrolysed, which led to the removal of amorphous fractions and chain degradation so that a cellulose powder (CGA) containing predominantly the crystalline fractions of the initial sample could be recovered. For tissue culture media 10–12% CGA was required to produce a gel of sufficient viscosity after autoclaving. Plants supported on a medium solidified with CGA were generally of a better quality than those grown on agar, and rooted more freely.

Bead culture and immobilised cells

Bead culture

Several authors have captured cells or protoplasts in 'beads' of agar, agarose (Shillito *et al.*, 1983) or alginate (Draget *et al.*, 1988). Spherical agar beads are formed if molten agar is dropped into corn oil. One way of producing agarose beads containing protoplasts is to mix a culture medium with warm agarose and then add a protoplast suspension. The medium is poured into a Petri dish, and when solidified, cut into pieces which are incubated in static or agitated liquid medium. Bead culture allows protoplasts to be plated densely but yet exposed to a large pool of medium which can help to dilute inhibitors and toxic substances. As the protoplasts grow, cell colonies can be picked from the beads and transferred, or they can be left so that cells grow out into the medium to form a suspension (Horn H.E. *et al.*, 1988). Larkin *et al.* (1988) describe culturing protoplasts in beads of 1.5% alginate. Growth was enabled at low plating densities by adding nurse beads containing the same kind of protoplasts at high density. The nurse beads were marked with activated charcoal.

Immobilized cells

Much research is devoted to the extraction of plant secondary products from cultured cells, but yields are generally lower than may be obtained from whole plants. Amounts of secondary metabolites are usually greater in differentiated and/or slow-growing cells than in those which are growing quickly in an undifferentiated form. By immobilizing cells in a suitable gel, their rate of growth can be slowed and the production of secondary products enhanced. Several methods of immobilization have been employed. One involves incorporating suspension culture cells into molten agar and then dipping nylon pan scrubbers into the mixture. These 'baskets' of embedded cells are then placed into glass columns. Similar 'baskets' of immobilized cells can be produced by dipping pieces of a porous inert carrier (*e.g.* pieces of plastic foam) into an inoculated medium containing sodium alginate. The alginate is then solidified by placing the alginate-soaked carrier into a calcium chloride solution (Lindsey and Yeoman, 1983).

10

The Derivation, Preparation, and Use of Plant Culture Media

THE DEVELOPMENT OF PLANT CULTURE MEDIA

The definition of a medium

In this text, a medium is defined as a formulation of inorganic salts and organic compounds (apart from major carbohydrate sources and plant growth regulators), used for the nutrition of plant cultures.

As explained on page 349, plant culture media are given the name of their authors and the year in which the description first appeared; suffixed by letters or numbers which the authors by which the authors may have originally described their composition, or by ones which may be necessary to distinguish between several un-named compositions, mentioned in a single paper, article, or book.

In some publications, a 'medium' has been regarded as a complete mixture of nutrients *and* growth regulators, but this approach makes it very difficult to name distinct recipes and construct comparative tables: even a well known medium such as **Murashige and Skoog (1962)** would have to be classified into numerous subsidiary versions each time a sucrose level had been changed, glucose used instead of sucrose, or one growth regulator

substituted for another. The media listed later in this chapter therefore exclude plant growth regulators and common sugars such as sucrose and glucose, used conventionally as the main energy source.

EARLY NUTRIENT SALT SOLUTIONS

The gradual appreciation of the requirements of plants for inorganic ions, led to the formulation of nutrient solutions which could be used to maintain complete plants in hydroponic (water) culture, or to serve as liquid feeds for soil-grown plants; the consequences of this work eventually led to the development of the fertilizer industry.

Solutions developed for the hydroponic culture of intact plants were often used as the nutrient salts of early plant tissue culture media. The macronutrients of two such solutions, those of **Knop (1865)** and **Pfeffer (1900)**, were originally defined by the ratio between the weights of salts used. In Knop's solution the ratio of calcium nitrate, to potassium nitrate, to potassium dihydrogen phosphate, to magnesium sulphate, was 4:1:1:1. Pfeffer's solution additionally had potassium chloride, making the overall weight ratio 8:2:2:2:1. When the solutions came to be used in tissue culture media it became necessary to define the actual weights of compounds that were required. This has led to some variation in their stated composition. For example, Knop's solution has been taken as having either 1000 mg/l 6.09 mM calcium nitrate (*e.g.* Kotte, 1922; Lang, 1921; Bell and Coombe, 1965), 800 mg/l 4.87 mM (*e.g.* Miller, 1931; Sanders and Ziebur, 1958; Hewitt, 1963), 4.23 mM (Gautheret, 1933, 1959; Nobécourt, 1937). Pfeffer (1900) gave two ways of making up 'good nutrient solutions', one had 571 mg/l calcium nitrate, the other 1333 mg/l. However, Heller (1953) accredits Pfeffer's solution with 800 mg/l, and Robbins (1922a) describes a modified Pfeffer's solution containing 333 mg/l calcium nitrate. The situation has been further complicated by the fact that in many of the early papers it was not stated whether anhydrous or hydrated salts were used. Some subsequent authors have made one assumption, some the opposite: result confusion!

In Tables 47 and 48 we have listed the most commonly accepted versions of these two solutions and have therefore adjusted any reference to them accordingly. A later nutrient solution which has found employment in tissue culture, largely in the rooting of shoots, is frequently referred to as 'Hoagland's solution'. A composition was outlined by Hoagland (1920) but clearly stated by Hoagland and Snyder (1933) and Hoagland and Arnon (1938).

A requirement for iron was recognised by Knop and Pfeffer, but by the time Hoagland's solution was devised, the importance of other minor elements was appreciated, although which ones were of real significance had still to be decided.

EARLY MEDIA FOR *IN VITRO* CULTURE

Early plant tissue culture media were developed by research workers studying unrelated problems and only since the late 1950's onwards, has the complexity of *in vitro* nutrition been considered in a more unified fashion. Media developed separately before then for culturing isolated roots, seed embryos or callus, were all characterised by having a low overall concentration of inorganic ions, especially those of potassium and nitrate, and by providing nitrogen solely in the form of nitrate. Media developed for the germination of orchid seeds were similar except that they did contain ammonium ions (Knudson, 1922, 1943; Vacin and Went, 1949).

A significant amount of plant tissue culture work in the period 1930–1940 was concerned with the culture and nutrition of excised roots. The relatively dilute media devised for this purpose, now have another application in the induction and growth of roots on excised shoots that have been propagated by tissue culture. The root culture media of White have frequently been used for this purpose (*i.e.* **White, 1943a; 1954; 1963**) (*e.g.* with *Gypsophila paniculata*, Kusey *et al.* 1980; *Tectona grandis*, Gupta *et al.* 1980).

Early media for callus cultures

Callus cultures were at first initiated on dilute media which were the same as, or very similar to, those that had been employed for root culture. Nobécourt (1937) for example, used a slightly modified half-diluted **Knop (1865)** solution to establish carrot callus cultures. In the first major experimental study of nutritional requirements of plant callus cultures, Hildebrandt *et al.* (1946) developed improved media for the culture of tumour tissues of tobacco and sunflower from **White (1943a)** medium, using a triangulation method. The macro-elements required by sunflower tissue were found to be higher than those needed by tobacco, and the chosen levels of PO_4^{3-}, Ca^{2+}, Mg^{2+} and SO_4^{2-} were as high as in many media developed more recently for the culture of normal tissues. Concentrations of NO_3^- and K^+, although higher than those used by White (*loc. cit.*), were still much lower than are now customary.

Mineral nutrition was also investigated by Burkholder and Nickell (1949), using callus derived from sorrel tumour tissue. They found a need for a large increase in the PO_4^{3-} concentration to 23.98 meq/l, a level that has not since been found necessary in any work on normal tissues. Heller (1953) developed a solution of macronutrients which gave significantly better callus growth than could be obtained by using the media of **Gautheret (1939)** or **White (1943a)**. The new medium contained higher levels of K^+ and NO_3^-, but a lower level of Ca^{2+}. Heller noted that vigorous colonies of carrot callus tissue required more K^+ than slowly growing ones, while the situation was reversed for Ca^{2+}.

Major formulation advances

The most significant improvements that have been made in the composition of macronutrient solutions for general purpose tissue culture media, have involved the introduction of nitrogen in the form of the ammonium ion (NH_4^+) together with the use of higher concentrations of nitrate (NO_3^-) and potassium (K^+). These changes have permitted better callus growth; and have enabled direct and indirect shoot formation, embryogenesis; and axillary shoot proliferation in a very wide range of tissue cultures.

The introduction of ammonium ions

Intact plants can be grown in nutrient solutions containing only nitrate nitrogen. Solutions of this nature proved to be suitable for the aseptic culture of isolated plant roots so that early workers on plant tissue culture all assumed that ammonium ions were unnecessary. Early media, such as those of **Bonner (1940a,b), Gautheret (1942), White (1943a), Hildebrandt** *et al.* **(1946)** and **Miller and Skoog (1953)**, relied solely on nitrate nitrogen. Nevertheless, as long ago as 1922, Knudson discovered that orchid seeds could be germinated *in vitro* on a medium containing ammonium ions, and using **Knudson C (1922; 1943)** medium (which contained 7.6 mM NH_4^+ in addition to 8.5 mM NO_3^-), Morel (1960) obtained his pioneering result in the micropropagation field with the *in vitro* formation of protocorms and protocorm proliferation from orchid shoot tips. The importance of ammonium ions for the growth of orchid seedlings has been emphasised by later investigators (Uesato, 1973; Ichihashi and Yamashita, 1977; Ichihashi, 1979). It is unlikely that Morel would have demonstrated a method for orchid micropropagation had he not used a medium containing NH_4^+, because this ion has since been shown to be essential for adventitious protocorm development (De Bruijne and Debergh, 1974).

Nitsch and Nitsch (1956) were perhaps the first to use significantly higher levels of NO_3^- and potassium (K^+), in their studies on tissue culture of the Jerusalem artichoke, but they concluded that NH_4^+ was undesirable, because as little as 0.1 mM of ammonium chloride caused there to be less growth. This was attributed to the "well-known inhibitory effect of the ammonium ions", although the subsequent successful development of media containing NH_4^+ to as high a level as 20 mM, makes this observation surprising.

At about the same time, work began on the optimisation of culture media in Professor Skoog's laboratory. Here, the presence of the ammonium ion *was* found to improve the growth of tobacco callus; in a progressive series of media, improved results were obtained by gradually increasing the concentration of both NO_3^- and NH_4^+ (Miller *et al.* 1956; Miller, 1961a; Murashige and Skoog, 1962). Wood and Braun (1961), investigating the growth of both normal and crown-gall tumour cells of *Vinca rosea* (*Catharanthus roseus*), obtained independent evidence for the benefit of adding ammonium to a modified White's medium. The resulting concentrations of NO_3^-, NH_4^+, K^+ and $H_2PO_4^-$ were very close to those selected for **Miller (1961a)** medium.

As explained in Chapter 9, modern research has tended to emphasise that for many cultural purposes, it is important to optimise the ratio of nitrate to ammonium ions.

MEDIA WHICH ARE WIDELY USED

Murashige and Skoog (1962) medium

Work on improved media formulations in Professor Skoog's laboratory culminated in 1962 in Murashige and Skoog's publication on the inorganic salts required for the optimum growth of tissue cultures of tobacco. Their revised medium (abbreviated to **MS** medium in this book), contained 40 mM N as NO_3^- and 20 mM as NH_4^+. This was a five fold increase in the total nitrogen used in one of the laboratory's earlier media (**Miller** *et al.* **1956**), 15 times that in **Hildebrandt** *et al.* **(1946) Tobacco** medium, and 19 times that in **White (1943a)**. The improved growth of cells and tissues on **MS** medium is undoubtedly largely due to this increase in ammonium and nitrate concentration. For instance, callus growth from *Ginkgo biloba* embryos was similar to that on **MS** medium on White (1963) medium providing 1650 mg/l NH_4NO_3 was added (Webb *et al.*, 1986).

For **MS** medium, potassium was also increased approximately 11-fold to 20 mM, and phosphorus 13-fold over the 1956 levels to 1.25 mM. The concentration of other macronutrients was also raised, but by smaller factors. The revised medium gave a 167% increase in callus dry weight over that given by the **Hildebrandt** *et al.* **(1946) Tobacco** medium. Although Murashige and Skoog's macroelements were developed for the culture of tobacco callus, their recipe has proved to be eminently satisfactory for the tissue culture of numerous plant species for micropropagation purposes, and undoubtedly it has been used more than any other for plant tissue culture work. In addition, many other media are based on the **MS** macronutrients (see Table 47). Inevitably components of the medium have also been modified in different ways.

The change most frequently made to **MS** macronutrients, has been to alter the quantities of KNO_3 and NH_4NO_3, while leaving the rest of the salts at the original level. These adjustments have altered both the total nitrogen content of a medium and the ratio of NO_3^- to NH_4^+, factors which, as explained in Chapter 9, can be of importance for obtaining optimum growth and morphogenesis in particular species. There may also be a benefit from adding an organic acid to the medium (see pages 278 and 301); for example, Molnar (1988b) obtained greatly improved growth of *Brassica nigra* suspensions on a medium containing **MS** salts, by adding 15 mM sodium succinate. One method of preventing the browning of explants is to soak them in a mixture of citric acid and ascorbic acid. Several researchers have also put these compounds into Stage I culture media for the same purpose, and entries in Tables 47 and 55, showing addition of citric acid to **MS** and other media, represent this usage. For the reasons given in Chapter 9, it would be expected that the citric acid would also promote growth.

The only criticism of **MS** medium has been that the phosphate level is too low for the sustained growth of many cultures. As mentioned in Chapter 9, the medium has been modified on several occasions to contain higher levels of this ion. A precipitate may form in **MS** medium which is unlikely to be noticed in small volumes, or if agar has been added. Analysis has showed that the precipitate consists mainly of phosphate and iron, with smaller amounts of Ca, K, N, Zn and Mn and traces of C, Mg, H, Si, Mo, S, Cu and Co. The composition of the medium thus changes, and after 7 days, up to 50% of Fe and 13% of PO_4^{3-} can be precipitated from solution. Elements precipitated from a medium should be unavailable, but although Dalton *et al.* (1983) found that the chlorophyll content of *Ocimum basilicum* cells was significantly higher in **MS** medium supplied with the Fe^{2+} and EDTA in the ration 0.033 mM to 0.1 mM, their dry weight and packed cell volume was the same as in the normal medium. There are two 'tidied' versions of **MS** medium in which weights of salts have been adjusted to provide non- fractional mole (and therefore ion equivalent) values. They are those of de Fossard (1976) (called **Murashige and Skoog (1962) a:deF** medium, and **Margara (1978) N60** medium; both are given in the tables at the end of this chapter.

Gamborg *et al.* (1968) B5 medium

The **B5** medium developed by Gamborg *et al.* (1968) for the culture of soybean cell suspensions has also been employed in many different investigations subsequently. It differed from Gamborg and Eveleigh's (1968) **PRL-4** formulation, principally in that it contained much higher levels of NO_3^- and K^+. **B5** is similar to **PRL-4** in containing only a low concentration of NH_4^+, because the growth of soybean cells was found to be depressed when the concentration exceeded 2 mM NH_4^+. Variations in the concentration of Ca^{2+} and Mg^{2+} (in the ranges 1–4 mM and 0.5–3 mM respectively) gave no difference in the dry weight yield of cells and 1 mM of each was chosen. A level of 1 mM for phosphorus appeared to be optimal. Several modified versions of **B5** have been proposed (see Media for Monocotyledons, page 348).

De Greef and Jacobs (1979) used a new macronutrient solution for the *in vitro* culture of sugar beet from which they obtained a cell line with high regenerative capacity. The derivation of the medium is not discussed, but their

Table 38. How the callus of 37 different plant species grew on **SH** medium.

Growth rate index	Species response	
	Number of species	% species responding
5 (high)	12	32
4	7	19
3	11	19
2	5	14
1 (low)	2	5

formulation appears to be a modification of the Gamborg and Eveleigh **PRL-4** recipe in which the concentrations of the NO_3^- and K^+ ions have been increased. Another medium derived from **B5** is that of **Savage *et al.* (1979)**. (Note that in recent publications Gamborg has advocated an iron level for **B5** above that originally used — see the section on chelating agents in Chapter 9).

Schenk and Hildebrandt (1972) medium

The medium of **Schenk and Hildebrandt (1972), (SH)**, is similarly well-known. It was introduced for the induction and culture of callus of both monocotyledons and dicotyledons. From a different starting point, Schenk and Hildebrandt reached final ionic concentrations which are very similar to those of **Gamborg *et al.* (1968)**, though with slightly higher levels of Ca^{2+}, Mg^{2+} and $H_2PO_4^-$. Any further increase in the concentration of these ions caused precipitates and decreased growth. Schenk and Hildebrandt examined the growth of callus tissues from some 37 plant species on their medium, and published growth rate indices ranging in scale from 5 (excellent growth) down to 1 (poor growth). Results in the most favourable environment are shown in Table 38.

Schenk and Hildebrandt tested their medium against several others and reported that it supported better callus growth in all but two cases. However the growth regulators added to each medium were not identical and so the results presented are not strictly comparable. For instance, the growth indices given in their paper for **MS** medium are those obtained in conjuction with 5 mg/l kinetin and 0.1 mg/l NAA, while **SH** medium was supplemented with 2 mg/l PCPA, 0.5 mg/l 2,4-D and 0.1 mg/l kinetin. Nevertheless **SH** medium does clearly provide a satisfactory *in vitro* substrate, and has been fairly widely used in tissue culture work, particularly for legumes.

Anderson (1978a; 1980a) medium

Anderson formulated a medium for shoot culture of *Rhododendron* in which the concentration of nitrate, ammonium ,and potassium ions, was one quarter that in **MS** medium, but where the level of PO_4^{3-} and iron was doubled. The medium is unusual in that, for a post-Murashige and Skoog formulation, its total ionic concentration is low. This is consistent with other media devised for woody species. Others have confirmed that not only rhododendrons, but other Ericaceae, can be propagated satisfactorily on the medium.

Lloyd and McCown (1980) WPM medium

'Woody Plant Medium' was developed for the shoot culture of trees and shrubs such as *Betula, Kalmia, Rosa and Rhododendron* (Lloyd and McCown, 1980, 1981; McCown and Lloyd, 1981). It has the same NO_3^- and NH_4^+ concentrations as Anderson's medium (above), more potassium, and a high level of sulphate ions; but the **MS** level of phosphate, and less Cl^-. **WPM** is widely used for the propagation of ornamental shrubs and trees in commercial laboratories.

Some woody plants are particularly susceptible to chloride ions. Pevalek-Kozlina and Jelaska (1987) therefore utilised a version of WPM medium without Cl^- and found that *Prunus avium* shoot cultures could be propagated on it with much less likelihood of hyperhydricity than on WPM. Composition of the revised **WPM** medium is not given in this paper, but a macronutrient salt mixture to meet the specification has been calculated for Table 48.

MEDIA FOR PARTICULAR SPECIES

Much of the development of macronutrient solutions since 1962 has been concerned with trying to optimise the levels of the various salts for the tissue culture and propagation of particular species. This work has naturally been concentrated on classes of crops in which culture and morphogenesis has not so far been very successful. Media formulations have therefore appeared especially for monocotyledons (*e.g.* cereals and coconut), legumes and for woody plants (see section on species-related concentration adjustment, following).

Media originally devised for monocotyledons

Satisfactory growth and morphogenesis in callus and suspension cultures of several cereals has been achieved using **MS** medium, showing special media do not necessarily have to be devised for plant regeneration and micropropagation in cereals and grasses (see Chapter 17).

Inevitably though, there have been many attempts to find improved mixtures for some genera.

An attempt to improve the growth of callus from tissues of mature coconut palms, and subsequent morphogenesis, led Eeuwens (1976) to a new macronutrient formulation which had half the NO_3^- and NH_4^+ concentrations of **MS** medium, but twice the level of K^+. To do this, it was necessary to add the potassium as KCl, greatly increasing the concentration of Cl^-. It was assumed that this could be disregarded. **Eeuwens (1976) Y3** medium is considered further in the section on micronutrients.

In working on the nutrition of suspension cultures of rice cells, Ohira *et al.* (1973) found that it was beneficial to increase the concentrations of NO_3^- and NH_4^+ in **Gamborg *et al.* (1968) B5** medium. Potassium levels above 20 mM caused little change in yield, but the concentration of the ion was increased to 40 mM to provide the necessary NO_3^- level. Phosphorus at levels below 1 mM was inadequate, so the level was increased to 2 mM. Both Ca^{2+} and Mg^{2+} were adequate at 1mM, higher concentrations causing reduced cell growth.

A similar but less extreme modification of the **B5** medium was proposed by Dunstan and Short (1977a) for the improved growth of onion tissue cultures. They once again used higher levels of NO_3^-, NH_4^+ and $H_2PO_4^-$.

Media for legume culture

Suspension cultures were used in much of the early work on media for legumes (Hildebrandt *et al.*, 1963; Dougall, 1964; Mehta, 1966). **B5** medium was developed from observations on the growth of soybean cell suspensions and uses $(NH_4)_2SO_4$ as the reduced nitrogen source. Evans *et al.* (1976) also found that soybean callus grew better when the molar concentration of NH_4^+ in **MS** medium was reduced to about one third. This was accomplished by replacing the NH_4NO_3 with 3.8 mM $(NH_4)_2SO_4$. Although the regeneration of plants from legume callus cultures is difficult, Scowcroft and Adamson (1976) were able to achieve it in *Stylosanthes hamata*, using a modified **Schenk and Hildebrandt (1972)** medium. The ionic concentrations of macronutrients were finally very close to those of **MS**, but the new medium had more phosphate.

Phillips and Collins (1979a) investigated the nutritional requirements for plant regeneration from red clover callus cultures. Little callus initiation and proliferation was obtained with **MS**, **SH**, or **B5** media. After an extensive study, they developed **Phillips and Collins (1979a) L2** medium, which has a composition intermediate between the media of **MS** and **SH** for NO_3^-, NH_4^+ and K^+; but which contained higher levels of Ca^{2+}, Mg^{2+} and SO_4^{2-} than either of these media. Once again, the adopted phosphate level (3 mM) was higher than in most other tissue culture media, which perhaps indicates a requirement of some legumes. Phillips and Collins (1980) developed a slightly different medium (**SL2**) for red clover suspension cultures, obtaining better results when the concentrations of Ca^{2+}, Mg^{2+}, Cl^- and NH_4^+ were lower than those in **L2** medium.

A comparison of the above media and others which have been used for legumes [*e.g.* those of **Hahlbrock *et al.* (1974)**; **Reynolds *et al.* (1982a)**; **Maheswaran and Williams (1984) EC6**; and **Finer and Nagasawa(1988) 10A40N**], shows that compared to **MS** medium, all have a lower total nitrogen content, a smaller proportion of ammonium to total nitrogen, and more sulphate ions.

Simple media

Although plant tissue culture media can be complex, it is interesting to note that shoot cultures of some plants can be grown on home-made preparations, using materials which would be available to amateur horticulturalists or schools. Brand and Bridgen (1986) found that cultures of African violet (*Saintpaulia*), *Tradescantia* and Boston fern (*Nephrolepis exaltata* 'Bostoniensis') could be grown on a medium made up from:

Table sugar	1/8 cup (23g)
Soluble fertilizer	1 cup of dilution[†] (240 ml)
Tap water[‡]	1 cup (240 ml)
Inositol tablet	1/2 tablet (125 mg)
Agar flakes	2 tablespoons
Optional ingredients	
Vitamin tablet[¶]	1/4 tablet
Coconut milk	4 tablespoons
Lime tablet	1/2–1 tablet[§]

† A proprietary soluble fertilizer which contains micronutrients should be chosen. The authors used 'Rapid-Gro fertilizer'; the solution was prepared from 1/4 teaspoon per U.S. gallon.

‡ If water is very alkaline it may be necessary to use distilled water.

¶ It is important that the vitamin mixture includes thiamine. The authors used 'One-a-day' dietary vitamin tablets, which also contain iron.

§ Used where the pH of tap water is low.

No doubt other readily propagated plants could be cultured on similar media, authough sucess would be limited if auxin and cytokinin could not be obtained.

Kozai and co-workers (Kozai *et al.*, 1987b; Kozai and Iwanani, 1987; Kozai and Sekimoto, 1988; Kozai, 1989) have found that simple media containing only macronutrients and micronutrients, such as those used for hydroponic culture, are adequate for cultures maintained in light of very high flux density with CO_2 enrichment (see page 205).

THE COMPOSITION OF CULTURE MEDIA

Describing media

Media are usually described by listing the weights or molar quantities of the chemicals from which they were prepared. [An explanation of some of the terms used in describing the components of plant culture media, including an illustration of the calculation of molarity and equivalence, has been included in pages 352 and 353]. A complete list of the ingredients is not necessary when the mixture used has been the same as, or very close to that described in a previous scientific paper. It has therefore been agreed by convention to give media the name of their authors. Subsidiary letters or numbers are sometimes to the name; this may be the original code name given to the medium by the author/s, or have been added to distinguish between several different media which the inventors may have been using in comparative experiments. In nearly all cases plant culture media have been described in a published document, and so the name of a medium is the same as the bibliographic reference to the publication. The paper in which each medium listed in this book is first described can therefore be accessed by looking up the inventor/s and the date of the medium, in the bibliography.

The number of compounds which has been used in plant culture media is large, and so to draw up tables which permit a comparison between components, it is necessary to assign chemicals to convenient groupings. The six components which have been used in the tables at the end of this Chapter are:

1.	Macronutrients	Table 48
2.	Micronutrients	Table 50
3.	Vitamins	Table 52
4.	Amino acids	Table 53
5.	Unusual sugars and long-chain alcohols	Table 54
6.	Organic acids and buffers	Table 55

The chemicals necessary to prepare a medium are conveniently listed under each of these headings.

The composition of different media can be explained by setting out a full list of the ingredients required for each, but many media utilise common groups of components. Individual listing then becomes cumbersome when more than a few media are to be compared, and also makes the similarities between media less obvious. For the first edition of *Plant Propagation by Tissue Culture* (George and Sherington, 1984), Dr. G. S. Davy conceived the idea of extending the medium naming principle to the separate components of a medium. The medium of **Sangwan and Harada (1975)** can therefore be said to be composed of:

- the macronutrients of **Murashige and Skoog (1962)** medium,
- the micronutrients of **Cresswell and Nitsch (1975)** medium, and
- the vitamins of **Nitsch and Nitsch (1965) K and S** media.

In its entirety, **Sangwan and Harada (1975)** medium was different to other media published prior to 1975, even though each of the three major components (macronutrients, micronutrients and vitamins) had been described previously by other persons. Many other media are original because a unique mixture of chemicals has been used to *prepare* one or more of the components.

Using Dr. Davy's approach, it is necessary to have a master table, the **DERIVATION** table (Table 47), which shows from which components each medium is comprised, but subsequent tables of the weights and molar concentrations of separate ingredients, can be of considerably reduced length. In our 1984 listing, media were regarded as being distinct if they were composed of a unique combination of macronutrients, micronutrients, vitamins, and amino acids; the increasing complexity of media, particularly those used for protoplast culture, has necessitated the inclusion of organic acids and/or buffers, and unusual sugars as two further groups of media components.

Published media

A very wide range of media has been described for plant culture. Unfortunately most descriptions of alternative preparations are not accompanied by evidence that the new medium was necessarily better than another for that type of culture. Thus although one knows that a mixture can be associated with certain results, it is impossible in many cases to say whether a different medium would not have produced the same, or a better result.

The composition of a range of published plant culture media is given in the tables at the end of this chapter. Media described at the beginning of this chapter are included because they are either unmodified, or, with some adaptation they produce good results with cultures of many different species. For much more comprehensive tables, from which the composition of very many media can be related to plant species and type of culture, the reader is referred to the books by George E.F. *et al.* (1987; 1988).

The number of media used by a micropropagation laboratory will depend on the types of cultures being grown and on the range of plant species which are to be multiplied.

A comprehensive list of media is useful for:

- selecting the most appropriate medium for a particular species or type of culture. Some of the uses to which the media listed in Table 47 have been put, are given in Table 46, and media which have been employed in the propagation of particular species are mentioned in other chapters.

- quickly discovering the composition of media referred to in research papers;

- appreciating the range of compositions which have been used in plant tissue culture work in the past, and devising improvements;

- comparing the concentration and balance of nutrients used for types of culture or plant species.

- providing a list of the 'correct' versions of media.

Amongst the media listed in Table 47, approximately 100 unique formulations have been devised for each of the macronutrients, micronutrient and vitamin components, but changes leading to a unique recipe have sometimes been trivial and one is led to doubt their value. In many recent papers, authors have employed **MS** macro- and micro- nutrients, but have used minor modifications of the vitamin component. We have not been able to include all such variations.

Mistaken attribution

In this, and previous publications we have tried to identify media and their major components by the names of the authors by whom they were first described and the year in which the publication was made. The derivation of a medium is ascribed to the earliest publication known to us to contain an adequate description. There may therefore be mistakes in the attribution of some media or media components, for the list of plant tissue culture publications available to us has been far from complete. In addition, when an original group of components has been listed by different authors in the same year, there is often no way of telling who was the originator, or whether both parties devised the composition independently. We apologise to those authors of a medium who find their invention ascribed to someone else. Errors of these and other kinds will be corrected if you contact the publishers, whose address is given at the front of this book. Reprints of the original publication would be appreciated.

Some papers are referenced frequently in the plant tissue culture literature as the 'source' of a particular medium, even though the actual medium referred to was devised by other author/s at an earlier date. Examples of such discrepancies are identified in the medium 'derivation table' (Table 47).

Ambiguous descriptions

In the early literature, it was customary to describe the salts used in media by name, or by the molecular formula of anhydrous salts. This has led to confusion as to whether hydrated or anhydrous salts were originally intended: in consequence there are frequently several versions of early media which may differ considerably. For example, a specified weight of $MgSO_4$ would give a solution in which the molarity of Mg^{2+} and SO_4^{2+} was about twice that in a solution prepared from the same weight of $MgSO_4.7H_2O$. In most recent publications (*i.e.* after *ca.* 1940) hydrates have been specified where they are the most readily available and stable form of a compound.

When collecting comparative information on early media, it is only by careful research that one can determine whether anhydrous or hydrated chemicals were originally employed. Often commonly-available hydrates were employed, an anhydrous formula being written only as a convenient shorthand. Unfortunately many subsequent researchers have consulted only one paper in a series, and then described their own interpretation of it as the substantive original. Subsequent copying has then caused the circulation of several versions of some media. Many versions of White's medium have been circulated. White (1934a) presents no problems because quantities are recorded in moles, but in White (1939b) the salts are listed by chemical name. However, the weights given correspond to anhydrous salts in the molar concentrations given by White (1934a). By giving both weights and molar concentrations, White (1943a) again made it clear that he was referring to anhydrous salts. A discussion on the authentic version of White's medium has been provided by Singh and Krikorian (1981).

In other cases where formulae indicate the use of anhydrous salts, one is left in doubt as to what the author actually used. A particular case is the composition of Knudson's solution B. Knudson's papers in 1922 and 1925 show the calcium nitrate and ferric phosphate to be anhydrous, while in a later paper (1943), Knudson used the same weights, but for hydrated salts. We have assumed in this instance that the salts originally used were the hydrates. The true nature of Blaydes' medium also causes problems.

Erroneous descriptions

As plant culture media have many separate components, it is easy for mistakes to be made in reproducing named media, both in original experimentation and in subsequent published desriptions. It would clearly be advantageous to have a single document which could be relied upon to give the 'true' version. One of the objectives of George *et al.*, in publishing the 1987 book of media, was to try to provide an authorive list, whose correctness would be accepted or challenged, so that an authoritative list would always be available. The publishers have been notified of only a very few errors; whether this means that the listings are gaining acceptance, or are largely ignored, is difficult to ascertain. The book is seldom referred to in the bibliographies accompanying experimental work, but this is probably because authors prefer to refer to original source documents when desciding their media.

A further reason for using an authoritative listing of media is that *it is often not possible to deduce the authoritative version of a medium by consulting a single paper*. This is especially true of early media, where ingredients may be described by name or chemical formulae in such a way that the actual nature of the components is unclear. It is only by looking at a series of papers by the same, and other authors, that the true nature of a medium may become apparent. Even modern papers may contain misprints or mistakes: two examples are the original paper describing **Nitsch and Nitsch (1969)** and the 1972b paper of Gresshoff and Doy describing their 1972 **DBM 1 and DBM 2** media; errors in both of which were subsequently corrected.

Sometimes a medium given in a paper has been formerly published by someone else; for example, the true version of the medium given by Nitsch and Nitsch (1969), is not an original, but was first published by Bourgin and Nitsch in 1967.

Molar and ionic compositions

In addition to the tables giving the weight of ingredients from which media may be prepared, Tables 49, 51, 52, and 53, also indicate the molarity of nutrients.

The ions in macronutrient solutions

Table 49 shows the equivalence of the ions which appear in solution when specified macronutrient mixtures of salts are dissolved. Equivalence permits a convenient comparison between the ions in different media and has

CHEMICAL DEFINITIONS — MOLECULAR WEIGHTS AND MOLARITY

Compounds and salts

A compound is a unique substance composed of atoms of two or more elements. A salt is a compound which in solution yields ions other than hydrogen (H^+) or hydroxyl (OH^-).

Ions

An ion is an atom or group of atoms which carries a positive or negative electric charge.

> The atomic weights of elements encountered in compounds used for plant tissue culture media, are given in Tables 40 and 41.

Formula weight

The formula weight (or molecular weight) of a chemical compound is the sum of the atomic weights of the elements of which it is composed.

The chemical formula for potassium nitrate is KNO_3. It is composed of one atom of potassium, one atom of nitrogen and 3 atoms of oxygen. The formula weight is calculated as follows:

Chemical symbol	Atomic weight	Number of atoms	Weight
K	39.102	1	39.102
N	14.0067	1	14.0067
O	15.9994	3	47.9982
Formula weight			101.11

Gram molecular weight

The formula weight (molecular weight) of a compound expressed in grams is its **gram molecular weight**. This is also known as a **gram mole** or **mole** (abbreviated to **mol**). One mole of KNO_3 thus has a mass of 101.1 g.

Molarity

A molar solution is prepared by dissolving one mole of a substance (the *solute*) in sufficient solvent (water in the case of culture media) to make one litre of solution. **Molarity** is thus the number of moles of compound dissolved in one litre of solution. The quantity of solvent therefore varies with the mass of solute dissolved. Molarity is still commonly (and conveniently) expressed by the suffix M, although the accepted SI unit is mol l^{-1} (or kmol m^{-3}).

Quantity	Alternative methods of description		
	M	*SI*	*SI*
A solution of 101.1 g KNO_3 in 1 litre of water contains	1 M	1 mol l^{-1}	1 kmol m^{-3}
A solution containing $1/1\,000$ mole per litre contains	1 mM	1 mmol l^{-1}	1 mol m^{-3}
A solution containing $1/1\,000\,000$ mole per litre contains	1 μM	1 μmol l^{-1}	1 mmol m^{-3}
A 1 mM (10^{-3}M) solution of KNO_3 therefore contains	0.1011 g/l	0.1011 g l^{-1}	101.1 g m^{-3}
	101.1 mg/l	101.1 mg l^{-1}	101.1 g m^{-3}
A 1 μM (10^{-6}M) solution of KNO_3 therefore contains	0.1011 mg/l	0.1011 mg l^{-1} l^{-1}	101.1 mg m^{-3}
	101.1 μg/l	101.1 μg l^{-1}	101.1 mg m^{-3}

Molality

A molal solution (1 mol kg^{-1}) is prepared by dissolving one mole of substance in one kilogram of solvent. Molality is temperature independent and so is more convenient than molarity for thermodynamic calculations.

CHEMICAL DEFINITIONS — CALCULATING MOLARITY AND EQUIVALENCE

Ions

An ion is an atom or a group of atoms which is positively or negatively charged. Positive ions are formed when neutral atoms or molecules lose one or more electrons; negative ions are produced when one or more electrons are gained. Negatively charged ions are called *anions*; positively charged ones, *cations*.

Association between cations and anions leads to the formation of *acids*, *alkalis* and *salts*. When a compound of this kind is dissolved in water, the attraction between the ions is nullified and the compound *dissociates* into ions. The number of electrical charges carried by an ion denotes its *valency*. A cation with a valency of one (e.g. Na^+) will associate with an anion of single valence (e.g. Cl^-): Ca^{2+} forms a salt with two Cl^- ions.

Why use molarity units?

A mole of whatever compound contains the same number (Avagadro's number, 6.023×10^{23}) of molecules. The relative biological activities of compounds can therefore be compared readily when the effective quantities have been expressed in moles. Reactions between chemicals take place in molar proportions. If the compound is a salt, then the molarity of its constituent ions can also be found by multiplying their number by the molarity of the molecule. Thus 20 µM $CuSO_4$ contains 20 µM Cu^{2+}, and 20 µM SO_4^{2-}; 10 mM $(NH_4)_2SO_4$ yields 20 mM NH_4^+, and 10 mM SO_4^{2-}.

> If 3 mg/l 2,4-D induces callus formation to the same extent as 2.5 mg/l IAA, which is the most effective auxin? The formula weight of 2,4-D is 221.04, that of IAA, 175.19.
>
> $$\text{Molarity of 2,4-D} = \frac{3 \text{ mg. } l^{-1}}{221.04} = 13.6 \text{ µM,}$$
>
> $$\text{that of IAA} = \frac{2.5 \text{ mg. } l^{-1}}{175.19} = 14.2 \text{ µM .}$$
>
> **Answer:** 2,4-D, because a smaller number of molecules is involved.

The same number of Cu^{2+} ions will be placed in solution from 20 µM $CuSO_4$ and 20 µM $CuSO_4.5H_2O$; the statement that "20 µM $CuSO_4$ was used" is therefore unambiguous. However, to write that "3.19 mg/l $CuSO_4$ was added to the medium" leaves the reader wondering "Was 20 µM $CuSO_4$, or 12.8 µM $CuSO_4.5H_2O$, really used?" The *disadvantage* of presenting molar values is that the reader has to recalculate how much compound to use to repeat your work. Describing amounts in both mole and mass (weight) values is therefore helpful.

Equivalence

The *equivalent* has been abandoned as an SI term, but is still useful for considering the concentration of ions in solution. This is because ions combine to form compounds in quantities proportional to their *equivalent weights* (i.e. the formula weight divided by the valency of the ion). Thus although 20 milli-moles per litre ($\equiv$ 20 mM) $(NH_4)_2SO_4$ contributes 20 mM SO_4^{2-} and 40 mM NH_4^+ to a solution, it provides 40 milli-equivalents (meq) SO_4^{2-} and 40 meq NH_4^+. Notice that whereas molarities of cations and anions are not necessarily equal, the sum of the cation equivalents always equals the sum of anion equivalents. This remains the case when, as in a culture medium, several different salts have been dissolved together.

$$\text{Equivalent weight} = \frac{\text{Actual wt. of compound}}{\text{formula weight} / \text{valency}}$$

$$= \frac{\text{Actual wt. of compound}}{\text{formula weight}} \times \text{valency}$$

$$= \text{mole} \times \text{valency}$$

$$\text{Equivalent wt. per litre} = \text{mole per litre} \times \text{valency}$$

$$= \text{molarity} \times \text{valency}$$

Calculating molarity

A solution of 2.643 g/l $(NH_4)_2SO_4$ has a molarity of: $\dfrac{2.643 \text{ g/l}}{132.15} = 20 \text{ mmol } l^{-1}$ (mM)

	molarity of salt	*no. ions*	*molarity of ion*
The molarity of NH_4^+ =	20 mmol l^{-1}	× 2 =	40 mmol l^{-1}
The molarity of SO_4^{2-} =	20 mmol l^{-1}	× 1 =	20 mmol l^{-1}

> Multiply the molarity of an ion by its valency to get equivalence.

Calculating equivalence

	molarity of salt	*no. ions*	*valency*	*equivalence*
The equivalence of NH_4^+ =	20 mmol l^{-1}	× 2	× 1 =	40 meq

> Divide the equivalence of an ion by its valency to get molarity.

the advantage that the sum of the equivalence of cations in solution equals that of the anions. Where there are multiple ions in solution, this provides a useful check that calculations have been correctly carried out. Molarities of ions can be readily obtained from equivalents, as explained on page 345 and in the heading to Table 49.

Macronutrient compositions, in particular, should be listed according to the molar concentration, or equivalence, of the ions they contain, and not according to the weights of the particular compounds used by the inventors. This is because it is usually possible to prepare the same mixture of ions from more than one mixture of inorganic salts (see below). A macronutrient composition should therefore be defined as *a mixture of major nutrient ions of specified concentrations*. Describing macronutrients only by weights of salts, does not allow a true comparison between different mixtures. It is only by listing media according to the molar concentration or equivalence of ions, that three aspects of composition become apparent:

- the actual ions provided;

- the balance between the major ions;

- the total ionic concentration of the medium.

The macronutrient mixtures devised by different authors differ both in the relative proportion of essential ions and in their total concentration. When a large sample of published macronutrient preparations is compared, it is found that several, apparently unique, formulations contain very similar proportions of some major ions, and differ mainly in total concentration. Chloride or ammonium ions have been ommitted from several media, and on rare occasions even those of nitrate, phosphate or magnesium have been left out, either ill-advisedly or for special purposes. Sodium is often only included unintentionally through the selection of sodium salts to provide other ions. A low concentration of sodium, chloride and sulphate ions is usually provided from the salts added to the medium to provide micronutrients.

Calculating equivalence. At the concentrations used for plant nutrition, salts used can be assumed to dissociate completely into ions. Assuming that the pH of the solution is unchanged, the total equivalence of positively charged ions (cations) in solution should equal that of those which are negatively charged (anions). The equivalence of each ion can be found relatively quickly using a calculator, as shown on page 345.

For example, if a solution contains 400 mg/ $MgSO_4.7H_2O$ and 1651.9 mg/l $(NH_4)_2.SO_4$, the milliequivalence of sulphate (SO_4^{2-}) ions will be:

$$\left(\frac{400.0}{246.50} \times 1 \times 2\right) + \left(\frac{1651.9}{132.15} \times 1 \times 2\right) = 28.24 \text{ meq/l}$$

that of ammonium (NH_4^+) ions:

$$\left(\frac{1651.9}{132.15} \times 2 \times 1\right) = 25.00 \text{ meq/l}$$

and that of Mg^{2+} ions:

$$\left(\frac{400.0}{246.50} \times 1 \times 2\right) = 3.24 \text{ meq/l}$$

The total equivalence of the cations in solution (25.0 + 3.24 meq/l) is thus equal to the equivalence of the anion (28.24 meq/l).

Although phosphate is mainly taken up into plants as the $H_2PO_4^-$ ion; mono- , di- and even tri-basic phosphates have been added to culture media. As has been explained in Chapter 9, the calculation of cation and anion equivalents which are equal, is simplified if the phosphate anion is taken to have a valence of 3, being partly balanced by hypothetical hydrogen cations. Note therefore that although a concentration of H^+ ions is given in Table 49, this does *not* correlate with the pH of the medium and in reality the ions will be associated with $(H_2PO_4)^-$ or $(HPO_4)^{2-}$.

If the compositions of several macronutrient compositions are to be compared, a program which can be run on a microcomputer is of great assistance. A textual version of one written in BASIC, which lists the molarity of ions and elements in alternative media formulations, was published by Ó Ríordáin and Grant (1984): another BASIC program ('ION–1') for the calculation of the ionic equivalence of macronutrient solutions is given in George *et al.* (1988).

A disadvantage of defining media by the equivalence of ions, is that having made a choice of preferred concentrations on paper, it is not easy to calculate the weights of salts which should then be used to prepare the composition. Another computer program in BASIC ('ION–2') which will do this, will also be found in George *et al.* (1988). †ION–2 can also be used to work out alternative mixtures of salts for making up any particular macronutrient formulation.

We have said that a given mixture of macronutrient ions can frequently be prepared just as well from weights and combinations of salts, other than those originally described. This is not generally realised, but as Table 39 above illustrates, **Murashige and Skoog (1962)** macronu-

---

†   Updated versions of **ION-1** and **ION-2** are obtainable on disc for a small fee from the publishers of this book.

Table 39. Two alternative recipes for **MS** macronutrients.

Salts	Original MS ingredients mg/l	Alternative MS ingredients mg/l
KNO₃	1900.0	1295.0
NH₄NO₃	1650.0	1650.0
Ca(NO₃)₂.4H₂O	—	706.1
CaCl₂.2H₂O	440.0	—
MgSO₄.7H₂O	370.0	—
MgCl₂.6H₂O	—	305.0
KH₂PO₄	170.0	170.0
KCl	—	222.3
K₂SO₄	—	261.4

Constituents of both formulations

Ions	Equivalence meq/l	Molar concentration mM
NO_3^-	39.4	39.4
PO_4^{3-}	3.75	1.25
SO_4^{2-}	3.0	1.5
Cl^-	5.99	5.99
K^+	20.04	20.04
Ca^{2+}	5.99	2.99
Na^+	0	0
Mg^{2+}	3.00	1.5
NH_4^+	20.61	20.61
$[H^+]$	2.50	—
Sum of I^+ or I^-	52.14	—

trients can be made up using $Ca(NO_3)_2.4H_2O$, $MgCl_2.6H_2O$, KCl and K_2SO_4 in place of $CaCl_2.2H_2O$ and $MgSO_4.7_2O$. The alternative mixture of salts is less elegant than the original, but provides the same nutrient ions. A similar substitution of one salt for another can be used in the preparation of other media, and is a method whereby the cost of preparing any particular mixture of macronutrient ions can be minimised. Calculations such as these are greatly facilitated by the **ION-2** computer program.

Surprisingly, few published comparisons have been made between the macronutrients in plant media on the basis of their ionic composition. Those which we have discovered being papers of Yoshida *et al.* (1973), Ichihashi *et al.* (Ichihashi and Yamashita, 1977; Ichihashi, 1978,

1979) and Margara (1978) and the book by de Fossard (1976). Margara in fact devised a set of eight media in which the composition of total nitrogen, and then K^+, Ca^{2+} and NH_4^+ ions were varied. Although the point is rather poorly illustrated in his paper, Margara claimed that cultures of different crop species could usually be initiated, and morphogenesis induced more effectively, by selecting the most appropriate of his media, than by utilizing other well-publicised ones. Some of Margara's media are mentioned in his earlier papers but we have used the 1978 reference in the media tables at the end of this chapter, as it contains the most complete list.

Culture-related concentrations.

The total concentration of ions in a macronutrient mixture can be just as important as their relative proportions. The uptake of mineral salts into cultured plant material varies according to the surface to volume ratio of the explant, and whether it is grown on a solid or liquid medium. Large organs (*e.g.* proliferating shoot cultures), or large callus pieces, with a small ratio of surface area to volume, on a semi-solid medium, would be expected to take up nutrients more rapidly from a relatively concentrated medium than from a dilute one. Cultures which require concentrated or relatively dilute media are in fact commonly found. Roots, with cells specially adapted for nutrient uptake, take up salts more efficiently than other organs, or unorganised tissues, and grow well in a medium of low total salt concentration. Dilute media are also found to be most suitable for root initiation on isolated shoots and for germinating seeds *in vitro*. It can therefore be important to suit the medium, and in particular the concentrations of macronutrients, as much to the type of culture as to the species of plant being grown. As is shown below, morphogenesis can also be promoted by adjustment of ions in the medium.

The concentration of dissolved substances, especially macronutrients and sucrose, also determines the osmotic potential of a solution, a factor known to influence growth and morphogenesis (Chapter 9). Selection of an appropriate concentration of sugar can be especially important.

Species-related concentrations

Adjustment to the ionic concentration will also become necessary when one or more ions are inhibitory to a species, or to a group of plants. Woody plant tissues, for instance, have frequently been found to grow best *in vitro* in media containing reduced concentrations of one (Durzan *et al.* 1973; Anderson, 1975) or more (Washer *et al.*, 1977; de Fossard, 1977; McCown and Lloyd, 1981) ions. Alternatively, some workers have simply employed a reduced concentration of **MS** macroelements for woody

Table 40. Atomic and formular weights of inorganic elements, ions and compounds used in plant culture media.
Compounds marked 'Preferred in tables' , have been used in the media tables of this book.

Compound	Formula weight	Comment	Compound	Formula weight	Comment
Al, Al^{3+}	26.98	Element; ion: atomic weight	Mg, Mg^{2+}	24.31	Element; ion: atomic weight
$AlCl_3$	133.34	Preferred in tables	$MgCl_2.6H_2O$	203.33	
$Al_2(SO_4)_3$	342.14		$Mg(NO_3)_2.6H_2O$	256.43	
$Al_2(SO_4)_3.18H_2O$	666.45		$MgSO_4$	120.39	
B	10.81	Element: atomic weight	$MgSO_4.7H_2O$	246.50	Preferred in tables
Ca,,Ca^{2+}	40.08	Element; ion: atomic weight	Mn, Mn^{2+}	54.94	Element; ion: atomic weight
$CaCl_2$	110.99	Deliquescent	$MnCl_2$	125.84	
$CaCl_2.2H_2O$	147.03	Preferred in tables	$MnCl_2.H_2O$	143.84	
$CaCl_2.6H_2O$	219.09	Alternative hydrate	$MnCl_2.4H_2O$	197.91	
$Ca(NO_3)_2$	164.10		$MnSO_4.H_2O$	169.01	
$Ca(NO_3)_2.4H_2O$	236.15	Preferred in tables	$MnSO_4.4H_2O$	223.06	Preferred in tables
$CaSO_4$	136.15		Mo	95.94	Element: atomic weight
$CaSO_4.2H_2O$	172.18	Slightly soluble. Preferred where specified	MoO_3	143.94	
$CaH_4(PO_4)_2.H_2O$	252.09	Preferred in tables	MoO_4^{2-}	159.93	Ion
$CaH_4(PO_4)_2.2H_2O$	270.11	Alternative hydrate sometimes specified	N	14.01	Element: atomic weight
Co, Co^{2+}	58.93	Element; ion: atomic weight	NO_3^-	62.00	Ion
$CoCl_2$	129.85	Anhydrous form available in catalogues	Na, Na^+	22.99	Element; ion
$CoCl_2.2H_2O$	165.89		NaCl	58.44	
$CoCl_2.6H_2O$	237.95	Preferred in tables	$Na_2EDTA.2H_2O$	372.24	Preferred in tables
$Co(NO_3)_2.6H_2O$	291.05		$Na_3EDTA.2H_2O$	394.22	
$CoSO_4$	155.01		$Na_4EDTA.4H_2O$	452.24	
$CoSO_4.6H_2O$	263.10		$Na_4EDTA.2H_2O$	416.22	
$CoSO_4.7H_2O$	281.10		NaFeEDTA	367.05	
Cu, Cu^{2+}	63.54	Element; ion: atomic weight	$NaFeEDTA.H_2O$	385.07	Martindale Pharmacopoeia
$CuCl_2$	134.45		$NaFeEDTA.2H_2O$	403.07	
$CuCl_2.2H_2O$	170.49	Preferred in tables	$Na_2FeEDTA.2H_2O$	426.06	
$Cu(NO_3)_2.3H_2O$	241.60		$NaFeEDDHA.H_2O$	469.19	
$CuSO_4$	159.61		$Na_4FeDTPA$	570.13	
$CuSO_4.H_2O$	177.62		NaH_2PO_4	119.99	
$CuSO_4.5H_2O$	249.69	Preferred in tables	$NaH_2PO_4.H_2O$	138.01	Preferred in tables
EDTA	292.25	Preferred in tables. See also under Na_nEDTA	$NaH_2PO_4.2H_2O$	156.01	Commonly listed in catalogues
Fe, Fe^{2+}, Fe^{3+}	55.85	Element; ions: atomic weight	$Na_2HPO_4.2H_2O$	178.01	Preferred in tables
Ferric citrate	—	A combination of Fe and citric acid of indefinite composition (Merck Index)	$Na_2HPO_4.7H_2O$	268.09	
$FeC_6H_5O_7.H_2O$	262.97	Fluka chemical catalogue, 1986	$Na_2HPO_4.12H_2O$	358.22	
$FeC_6H_5O_7.3H_2O$	299.00	Formula for ferric citrate given by some sources	$Na_2Mo O_4$	205.94	
$FeC_6H_5O_7.5H_2O$	335.03	Formula for ferric citrate which we have used in tables. Given in several current chemical catalogues	$Na_2MoO_4.2H_2O$	241.98	Preferred in tables
$FeC_6H_5O_7.nH_2O$	—	Ferric citrate according to some authors	$NaNO_3$	85.01	
$FeCl_3$	162.21		Na_2SO_4	142.06	
$FeCl_3.6H_2O$	270.32	Preferred in tables	$Na_2SO_4.10H_2O$	322.22	
$Fe_3[C_3H_5(OH)_2PO_4]_2$	677.75	Ferric glycerophosphate	$Na_2ZnEDTA$	399.57	Used by Eriksson (1965)
$FePO_4.2H_2O$	186.86		NH_4^+	18.04	Ion
$FePO_4.4H_2O$	222.89		NH_4Cl	53.50	
$FeSO_4.7H_2O$	278.03		$NH_4H_2PO_4$	115.04	
$Fe_2(SO_4)_3$	399.90		$(NH_4)_2HPO_4$	132.07	
$Fe_2(C_4H_4O_6).H_2O$	591.60	Ferric tartrate. Preferred in tables	$(NH_4)_2MoO_4$	196.03	
$Fe_2(C_4H_4O_6).2H_2O$	573.93	Ferric tartrate	$(NH_4)_6Mo_7O_{24}.4H_2O$	1235.95	
H_3BO_3	61.84	See MoO_3 also	NH_4NO_3	80.05	
H_2MoO_4	161.97		$(NH_4)_2SO_4$	132.15	
$H_2MoO_4.H_2O$	179.98	Preferred in tables	Ni	58.71	Element: atomic weight
I, I^-	126.90	Element; ion: atomic weight	$NiCl_2.6H_2O$	237.70	Preferred in tables
K, K^+	39.10	Element; ion: atomic weight	$NiSO_4.6H_2O$	262.85	
KCl	74.55		Zn	65.37	Element: atomic weight
KH_2PO_4	136.09		$Zn(NO_3)_2.6H_2O$	297.49	
K_2HPO_4	174.18		$ZnSO_4$	161.44	
KI	166.02		$ZnSO_4.H_2O$	179.45	
KNO_3	101.10		$ZnSO_4.6H_2O$	269.54	
K_2SO_4	174.26		$ZnSO_4.7H_2O$	287.56	Preferred in tables

Table 41. Formula weights of organic compounds used in plant culture media. [For plant growth regulators, see Chapter 11].
Compounds marked 'Preferred in tables' , have been used in the media tables of this book.

Compound	Formula weight	Comment	Compound	Formula weight	Comment
Adenine	135.13	Vit. B$_4$	D-Mannitol	182.17	
Adenine.3H$_2$O	189.13		Mannose	180.16	
Adenine sulphate	368.34	(anhydrous)	2-Mercaptoethanol	78.13	Anitoxidant
Adenine sulphate.2H$_2$O	404.37		MES	195.24	Buffer
Adenosine	267.25		Methionine	149.21	
L-Alanine	89.09		myo-Inositol	180.16	
p-Amino benzoic acid	137.13		Nicotinamide	122.12	
dibasic-Ammonium citrate	226.19		Nicotinic acid	123.11	Vit. B$_3$, Niacin
dibasic-Ammonium citrate	243.22	Preferred in tables	Nitrilotriacetic acid	191.14	
Ammonium hydrogen malate	151.12	Preferred in tables	Ornithine	132.16	
dibasic-Ammonium succinate	152.15		Pantothenic acid	219.24	
Arabinose	150.13		PB 74	—	Buffer.
L-Arginine	174.21		Phenylalanine	165.19	
L-Ascorbic acid	176.12		Potassium acetate	98.14	Anhydrous
L-Ascorbic acid. 3H$_2$O	230.17		di-Potassium succinate.3H$_2$O	248.31	
Aspartic acid	133.10		tri-Potassium citrate.H$_2$O	324.40	
L-Asparagine	132.12		Proline	115.13	
Biotin	244.32	Vit.H	Pyridoxal	167.17	
Calcium acetate.xH$_2$O	158.17	(anhydrous compound)	Pyridoxal. HCl	203.63	
Calcium pantothenate	476.53		Pyridoxin(e)	169.18	Adermin(e), Vit. B$_6$
Cellobiose	342.30		Pyridoxine. HCl	205.64	Vit. B$_6$
Choline	121.18		Raffinose	594.52	
Choline chloride	139.63		Rhamnose	182.17	
trans-Cinnamic acid	148.15		Riboflavin	376.36	
Citric acid	192.12		Ribose	150.13	
Cyanocobalamine	1357.64	Vit. B$_{12}$	Serine	105.09	
Cysteine	121.15		Sodium acetate	82.04	Anydrous. Preferred in tables
Cysteine. HCl	157.61		Sodium acetate.3H$_2$O	136.08	
Cystine	240.29		mono-Sodium citrate	214.11	
Cystine. HCl	275.75		tri-Sodium citrate.2H$_2$O	294.12	Preferred in tables
Cytidilic acid	323.20		tri-Sodium citrate.5H$_2$O	348.17	
1,4-Dithiothreitol	154.24	Antioxidant	mono-Sodium glutamate.H$_2$O	187.13	
Folic acid	441.41	Vit. B$_c$	Sodium pyruvate	110.04	
Fructose	180.16		di-Sodium succinate	162.05	Anhydrous
Fumaric acid	116.07		di-Sodium succinate.6H$_2$O	270.14	Preferred in tables
Galactosamine	179.17		Sorbitol	182.17	
Galactose	180.16		Sorbitol.½H$_2$O	191.18	
Glucosamine	179.17		Spermidine	145.25	
Glucose	180.16		Spermine	202.35	
L-Glutamic acid	147.13		Succinic acid	118.09	
L-Glutamic acid.HCl	183.59		Sucrose	342.30	
Glutamic acid.H$_2$O	165.15		Thiamine. HCl	337.27	Vit. B$_1$, Aneurin
L-Glutamine	146.15		Threonine	119.12	
Glutathione	307.33		α-Tocopherol	430.70	Vit. E (see below)
Glycine	75.07		Trehalose	342.30	
Guanylic acid	367.21		TRIS	121.14	Buffer
HEPES	283.31	buffer	Tryptophane	204.22	
Histidine	155.16		Urea	60.06	
Histidine.2HCl	228.09		Valine	117.15	
Hydroxyroline	131.13		Vitamin A	286.44	Retinol
Isoleucine	131.17		Vitamin B$_{12}$	1357.64	Cyanocobalamine
Lactose	360.31		Vitamin E	430.70	α-Tocopherol
Leucine	131.17		Vitamin E acetate	472.74	
Lysine	146.19		Xylitol	152.15	
Malic acid	134.0		Xylose	150.13	
Maltose	360.31				

plants, instead of specially devised media (Anderson, 1980a; Cheng, 1977; Ma and Wang, 1977).

Shoot cultures of some Bromeliads showed increased survival in Stage I and an improved rate of multiplication in Stage II when **MS** salts were used at a quarter or half strength (Mekers, 1977). However more callus was produced from immature zygotic embryos of wheat on full strength **MS** medium (or 2 × **MS**) than on ½**MS**, and no callus at all formed on 4 × **MS** (He *et al.*, 1988). Bulb scale explants of *Iris hollandica* produced less adventitious bulblets if cultured on a medium with more than ½**MS** salts (Van der Linde *et al.*, 1988). Single node cultures of *Syringa vulgaris* elongated and multiplied most rapidly when grown on a medium with **MS** salts or 1.25 × **MS** salts, but leaf curling and leaf shrinkage occurred at these salt concentrations and was only eliminated when the medium included 1.5 × **MS** salts (Pierik *et al.*, 1988c).

USE OF THE MEDIA TABLES

To determine the composition of any particular medium:

1. **Turn to Table 47.** All the media in this table are unique in their total composition but any given medium may be composed of the macronutrient, micronutrient, vitamin or amino acid constituents of previous workers. Where this is the case, it is indicated by insertion of the appropriate reference into the derivation of the formula used. Where our first record of the use of a macronutrient, micronutrient, vitamin, or amino acid mixture is the same as that which describes the comp,ete medium, the word *Unique* is printed. A completely orignal medium will have *Unique* in all columns.

   Coconut milk and adenine seem to act mainly as growth regulators and so have not been recognised here as distinctive media components. The inclusion of one of these substances in the original description of a medium is however indicated in the second column of the Table 47. The addition of a buffer; an unusual sugar, or a sugar alcohol; or an organic acid; to the medium by the original author/s, is indicated in the last two columns. The quantities of these substances which were included will be found listed in Tables 54 and 55.

   The composition of any particular medium can be found by noting its components in this table, and then turning to the appropriate following tables to discover from which chemicals it can be prepared.

2. **Derive macronutrient salt compositions from Table 48.** Consult the footnotes at the end of the table where instructed to do so. The symbol 'h' adjoining

a figure shows that the author/s originally used an anhydrous compound (or a different hydrate), but that we have entered the weights of the formula given in the column heading, to produce the same molar concentration. Weights are in mg/l.

3. **Derive micronutrient salt compositions from Table 50.** Compositions are given in µg/l unless otherwise stated. The sybol 'h' preceding a weight indicates that the author originally used another hydrate; weights have been adjusted accordingly. The letter 'D' in the column headed *Fe chelates*, indicates that Fe-DTPA (Sequestrene 330) was orinally used: for most practical purposes an equivalent molar concentration of FeEDTA can be substituted.

   Once again it is important to consult notes on a composition where indicated, because other ingredients may be mentioned which it was not possible to tabulate.

4. **Derive vitamin additions from Table 52.** The presence of a footnote is again indicated in the extreme right hand column. Compositions are in µg/l unless otherwise stated.

5. **Derive amino acid supplements from Table 53.** Footnotes are again provided. Compositions are here given in mg/l unless indicated otherwise.

6. **Derive unusual sugars or sugar alcohols from Table 54.**

7. **Derive organic acid supplements or buffers from Table 55.**

Molarities. The macro- and micro-nutrient compositions of media can be compared most effectively by consulting Tables 49 and 51, which respectively, give the milli-equivalence and molarity of macronutrient and micronutrient ions. In addition to the milliequivalent concentrations of the nutrient ions, Table 49 also shows;

- the proportions of nitrogen, potassium and phosphate in each medium;

- the total nitrogen content;

- the relative levels of reduced and unreduced nitrogen;

- the proportion of nitrate to ammonium ions;

- the total molarity of the ions in the composition.

These parameters can help to explain why certain media are especially suited to particular species. They also show much more clearly than the weight tables, the similarities and differences between formulations.

The molarity of vitamin and amino acid compositions is shown in brackets beneath the weight of ingredients in Tables 52 and 53.

CHOICE OF AN APPROPRIATE MEDIUM

Relying on previous experience

Media need to be selected which are appropriate to the species of plant *and* the kind of culture, or the cultural stage being undertaken. When approaching a new situation, it is sensible, in the first instance, to use the media and methods which have been found to be successful by others. If no records can be found for a given cultivar, those appropriate for other cultivars or species within the genus will probably be successful. If no details of work on a genus can be found, a medium used for a plant in the same family could be chosen. Changes can then be made to the original medium to try to improve growth, morphogenesis, or the rate of multiplication.

We have tried to indicate throughout this book, which media have been used successfully for different purposes, and Table 46 gives uses for each of the media listed in subsequent media tables. The book by George E.F. *et al.*(1987) shows the plants and types of culture for which some 2000 media have been employed, and other details can be obtained from reviews on the culture of particular species. To obtain precise details of the methods used by previous workers, it will be necessary to refer to original publications. There is however no one single medium which *must* be used for a given type of culture, and satisfactory growth can often be obtained on media of varied composition. The most suitable formulation will often vary, even between varieties of the same species, so unless a particular cultivar is to be propagated repeatedly in large numbers, there is little point in trying to fully optimise a medium.

To obtain the most effective results from growth regulator treatments, it is usually important to see that the nutritional components of the medium are at the most favourable levels.

Without previous knowledge

Selection of macronutrients

How should one proceed if faced with the problem of finding a suitable medium for a particular kind of culture, without knowledge gained from previous investigations? One approach which limits the amount of experimentation, is to compare, in the first instance, several well-known macronutient formulations. The macronutients of **MS** medium (perhaps at both half and full strength), could be compared with those of one or two other media. For this stage of testing, it would be advisable to use identical micronutrient and vitamin mixtures with each different set of macronutrients; sucrose concentration should also be held constant at 2 or 3%. In whichever medium gave the best results, the next step might be to vary the NO_3^- : NH_4^+ ratio by altering the concentrations of these ions.

Macronutrient and sucrose concentrations. It may be just as important to select the correct total concentration of macronutrients as to choose a particular ratio of ions provided by a named medium. It will be clear from the earlier part of this chapter that sucrose will be found to be a suitable sugar for most cultural purposes, but that selection of the correct concentration of sucrose and mineral salts could be important for obtaining an optimum rate of micropropagation. For example, using **Murashige** *et al.* **(1974)** macro- and micro-elements (supplemented with 100 mg/l *myo*- inositol, 0.4 mg/l thiamine HCl, 3–4 mg/l BAP and 30 g/l sucrose), Harris and Stevenson (1979) obtained twice as many shoots from grapevine shoot cultures on three quarters strength salts, as on full or half-strength. This difference disappeared though when 80 mg/l adenine sulphate was added, implying that medium concentration was only important when cytokinin levels were not quite optimal.

Alternative stratagies

There are clearly many other stratagems by which the many variables described in Chapters 9 and 11 can be optimised; nearly all require cultures to be set up in a large number of different treatments. Albrecht (1986) suggested that 3–5 levels of each of the major inorganic ions (including chelated iron) should be tried. A series of media in which there was represented 3 levels of each of NO_3^-, SO_4^{2-}, PO_4^{3-}, Ca^{2+}, NH_4^+ and NaFeEDTA would require 18 treatments, each requiring to be replicated several times.

De Fossard *et al.* (1974a) have been most notable in recommending an initial 'Broad Spectrum' experiment when a new tissue culture is to be undertaken. Their approach to devising the most suitable combination of ingredients, was to break down a medium into two component parts, namely:

— minerals (macronutrients plus micronutrients), and

— organic constituents (a complete range of vitamins, two amino acids, and sucrose).

Table 42. The comparative costs of **MS** medium prepared from separate chemicals or from purchased ready-prepared packs. The packaged medium did not contain sucrose, agar or growth regulators. The cost of these has been added.

Ingredients	Wt. per 1000 L	Price £ Stirling 1991	Cost per 1000 L £ Stirling 1991	Price £ Stirling 1991	Cost per 1000 L £ Stirling 1991
	g	Prepared from 99.5% pure chemicals		Prepared from 99% pure chemicals	
KNO_3	1 900	35.20/kg	66.88	28.70/5 kg	11.29
NH_4NO_3	1 650	34.20/kg	56.43	32.40/5 kg	10.69
$CaCl_2.2H_2O$	440	93.50/ 5 kg	8.22		
$MgSO_4.7H_2O$	370	35.20/kg (anh)	5.87		
KH_2PO_4	170	46.30/kg	7.87	9.00/kg	1.53
$MnSO_4.4H_2O$	23			7.50/250 g (.H_2O)	0.42
$ZnSO_4.7H_2O$	8.6	8.10/100 g	0.70		
H_3BO_3	6.2	4.50/ 250g	0.11		
KI	8.3	16.50/100 g	1.36		
$CuSO_4.5H_2O$	0.025			4.50/100 g	0.00
$Na_2MoO_4.2H_2O$	0.25			11.00/100 g	0.03
$CoCl_2.6H_2O$	0.025			7.20/25 g	0.01
NaFeEDTA	36.71			12.00/250 g	1.76
myo-Inositol	10.00	8.30/25 g	3.32	10.00/100 g	1.00
Thiamine-HCl	0.1			7.70/25 g	0.03
Nicotinic acid	0.50			3.20/25 g	0.06
Pyridoxine HCl	0.1			11.50/25 g	0.05
Glycine	2			5.40/100 g	0.11
Sucrose (30 g/l)	30 000			0.66/kg	19.80
Agar (6 g/l)	6 000			672.80/25 kg	161.47
Growth regulators					
e.g. NAA (1 mg/l)	1.0			5.90/25 g	0.24
BAP (2 mg/l)	2.0	24.40/5 g	9.76	18.10/5 g	7.24

Medium prepared from separate chemicals	*Investment cost for chemicals*	*Cost of medium*	*Investment cost for chemicals*	*Cost of medium*
Totals	1074.70	344.50	1024.50	231.99
Cost per litre		0.34		0.23

Packaged ready-prepared medium		*Investment cost*	*Cost per litre*
Cost when ordering 1000 × 1 litre packs		1081.27	1.08
Cost when ordering 100 × 10 litre packs		742.27	0.74

Each of these two entire component parts was tested at 3 levels with auxin and cytokinin growth regulators as two further factors (also at three levels), in an experiment with $3 \times 3 \times 3 \times 3$ (*i.e.* 81) treatments. Each treatment was replicated four times. The actual 'high', 'medium', and 'low' level ingredients used in the paper are shown in the media tables at the end of this chapter. Using tobacco callus as a demonstration material, de Fossard *et al.* were able to show that its morphology (*i.e.* normal, compact, sloppy), the rate at which it gained weight, and its mor-phogenic capacity, depended on all four component factors.

By whatever method is employed. the selection of the most suitable medium for a culture can require a considerable amount of experimentation. Closely related genotypes can have different nutritional requirements, and so if a medium is required for use with several related plants, it is advisable to test a preliminary mixture on several of them, before trying to optimise results.

THE PREPARATION OF TISSUE CULTURE MEDIA

Pre-mixed media

Murashige and Skoog (1962) medium, and many other of the more common plant tissue culture media, can be obtained as pre-mixed powders, from specialist chemical suppliers in packages sufficient to prepare various quantities of medium (*e.g.* 1, 5, 10 or 50 litres). It is possible to purchase the complete medium, or in some cases the medium containing the sucrose, agar and growth regulators recommended by the original authors. Components of some media [*i.e.* the nutrient salts (macronutrients + micronutrients), or the vitamins] are also sold separately. There is obviously no opportunity to modify a medium to suit a particular plant genotype when a complete mixture of nutrients, sugars and regulants is purchased. Most companies selling prepared media will also package any other unlisted medium which a customer may wish to use, providing there is a guarantee that the product will be ordered regularly in large quantities.

Packaged preparations avoid the need to store stock solutions, and are particularly valuable when only small quantities of medium are required at any one time. For large scale use, it is cheaper, but less convenient, to formulate the necessary mixtures from basic ingredients. Individual formulation becomes essential when experiments are to be conducted on the effects of changed medium components.

A comparison of the cost of **MS** medium prepared from separate ingredients and from purchased pre-mixes (without sugar, agar or growth regulants) is shown in Table 42. Pre-mixes are 2–4 times more expensive in materials cost, but save the labour costs of weighing chemicals, and preparing and storing stock solutions; their use should also make errors, which commonly occur in media preparation, much less frequent.

Before employing a pre-mixed medium, do ensure that the supplier has correctly interpreted the formulation which you wish to employ! This does not mean that the medium must have been prepared from exactly the same salts as were used in the original description, because a given mixture of ions can be prepared from different compounds (page 354); but the final formulation must have the same composition of essential nutrients, without superfluous ions or organics! Owen and Miller (1992) discovered that one chemical supplier wrongly listed several well-known media in their catalogue; **B5** medium was given as containing 4 times the correct amount of calcium.

A method of preparing a medium from a pre-packaged powder is shown in Fig. 101.

MAKING UP MEDIA

Materials to use

Clean glassware should be used for all media preparation; vessels which are to receive autoclaved medium should obviously have been previously sterilised. Containers become covered with microbe–laden dust in storage, so that once they have been cleaned, they should be placed into bags, or their mouths should be stoppered. It is good practice never to store glassware for long periods.

Water supplies. Tap water contains dissolved salts and other impurities which vary in quantity from one location to another. Laboratory purification of water is usually carried out by distillation, ion exchange, or reverse osmosis; generally two of these processes are combined. Many tissue culture laboratories use water purified by ion exchange followed by distillation; others use double distillation; some which are small avoid in-house purification and purchase distilled water from outside suppliers.

In hard water districts, the prior use of an ion exchange column prevents stills suffering from excessive scaling.

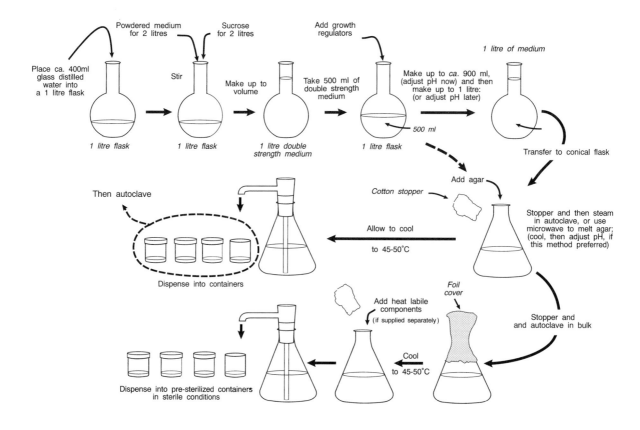

Fig. 101. Suggested steps in preparing a medium from a ready-packaged mixture. [See also Fig. 107.]

Ion exchange columns remove dissolved ions but are liable to release organic compounds from their resins into the water. By contrast, distillation effectively removes large organic molecules, but some ions may be transferred into the distillate, together with volatiles which have low boiling points, such as ammonia and chlorine. Some of these volatiles will evaporate during distillation providing that the cooling water in the condenser is not too cold. However, when a still is first started, such volatiles will distil over before the water in the still reaches boiling point, and they may accumulate preferentially in the initial distillate. Water collected during the first 10-15 minutes of operating a still should therefore be discarded. Inhibitory substances are liable to accumulate in the boiler and they, or their breakdown products, may eventually be transferred to the distilled water reservoir. The boiler of the still should therefore be cleaned on a regular basis after each few hours of operation.

Double distilled water (with the last step from glass) is often said to be essential for preparing media intended for research into plant tissue culture, but for media used in routine micropropagation, water which has been passed through an ion exchange column and then distilled once from a glass still, is usually acceptable. Purified water must be kept in clean vessels which will not introduce contaminating chemicals; prolonged storage is inadvisable.

Chemicals. The chemicals used for preparing media should be of analytical grade, but sucrose purchased as refined grocery sugar is of sufficient purity.

Although chemicals are cheaper when ordered in quantity, it is a mistake to obtain a large amount of any one compound in a single bottle. Chemicals can deteriorate in store; hygroscopic materials become damp and all chemicals are liable to become cross contaminated when jars have been opened and used many times.

Preparation from basic ingredients

Media are normally prepared by dissolving the appropriate chemicals in water; adjusting the pH of the solution;

adding agar or another gelling agent, if necessary; dispensing into culture vessels; and sterilising by autoclaving.

Sometimes it is necessary, or preferred, to autoclave the medium in bulk, before it is dispensed. Agar is degraded and sucrose hydrolysed by being autoclaved in an acid medium (Chapter 9). If the final preparation is required to be acid (*e.g.* pH 4–5), the medium should be autoclaved and its pH adjusted with sterile acid *after* autoclaving, while it is still warm and before it is dispensed (within a laminar flow hood) into sterile vessels. Bulk autoclaving is also necessary when heat labile substances are to be added: they are introduced into the cooled medium, having first been sterilised by ultrafiltration (see below). This treatment is especially suitable for vitamins and growth regulators.

When macronutrients are prepared from individual chemicals, Gamborg (1982a, 1991) suggested that inorganic salts should be dissolved one by one, starting with the nitrate and ammonium sources, to avoid the chance of precipitation.

Stock solutions of ingredients can be prepared to simplify repeated operations. Methods recommended for preparing and using them can vary considerably from one laboratory to another. Three contrasting methods for preparing **MS** medium are given in Figs. 102, 103, and 104.

The preparation of **MS** and other media from stock solutions is also described by Vasil and Hildebrandt (1966c), Veliky and Martin, 1970, Kasperbauer and Collins (1972), Burk *et al.* (1979), Kartha (1984) and Gamborg (1991).

Stock solutions

Macronutrients. When only a small amount of medium is required, or when a medium is only needed infrequently, it is probably best to weigh out and freshly dissolve the macronutrients for each preparation. This approach is indicated in the second and third methods of preparing **MS** medium (Figs. 103 and 104). Otherwise stock solutions are an obvious advantage and are usually prepared at 10–20 times the concentration of the final medium. A separate stock solution of calcium salts, calcium nitrate or calcium chloride (as recommended by Gamborg and Shyluk, 1981; and Gamborg, 1982a) may help to avoid precipitation problems. Precipitation usually occurs if phosphate and calcium sources are mixed at a pH above 6.

Thompson (1977) recommended separate stock solutions (of × 10 concentration) of each of the five major salts in his orchid seed germination medium, and Vasil and Hildebrandt (1966a,c), Mellor and Stace-Smith (1977) and Helgeson (1979) (Fig. 102) used a similar approach

to the formulation of **MS** medium. On the other hand Gamborg (1991) advocated the preparation of a 10 × stock solution containing all the **MS** macronutrients.

Stock solutions of macro-elements can be stored satisfactorily for 1–2 weeks in a dark cool place, but because they may become contaminated with bacteria and algae, they are best kept for longer periods in a refrigerator at *ca.* 2°C, or if possible, frozen and stored in a deep freeze cabinet (page 368). Street (1977b) suggests that stock solutions should first be cleared of solid particles by being passed through a sintered glass filter.

Micronutrients (except iron). All authors agree that micronutrients are most conveniently stored as stock solutions. Usually the stocks are made at 10 or 100 times the final strength of the medium, although some dilute micronutrient formulations [*e.g.* those of **Berthelot (1934)** and **Heller (1953; 1955)**] have been kept as 1000-fold concentrations. It is usually suggested that solutions should be stored in a refrigerator or even in a freezer, but this precaution may be unnecessary. Vasil and Hildebrandt (1966c) ensured that refrigerator-stored stock solutions were never used after 4–6 weeks from preparation, but Mellor and Stace-Smith (1977) found that refrigerated stock solutions could be stored for up to one year without appreciable deterioration. Gamborg and Shyluk (1981) and Gamborg (1982a) recommend that potassium iodide (100-fold concentration) is made up and kept separately in an amber (or black-painted) glass bottle in the refrigerator.

A combination of macro- and micronutrients. Hartmann and Kester (1983) suggested that media are prepared from seven stock solutions (each × 100):

1. Contains nitrates [*i.e.* KNO_3, NH_4NO_3, $Ca(NO_3)_2$];

2. contains sulphates, both macronutrients and micronutrients;

3. contains chlorides and potassium iodide;

4. contains phosphates, H_3BO_3 and $Na_2MoO_4.2H_2O$;

5. a stock solution containing $FeSO_4.7H_2O$ and $Na_2EDTA.2H_2O$;

6. a stock solution of the vitamins which are used, excluding *myo*-inositol;

7. *myo*-inositol.

This approach is similar to that adopted by Helgeson (1979) (see Fig. 102).

Iron. The simplest method of adding iron to tissue culture media is to weigh out a ready-prepared sodium or potassium salt of ferric EDTA, sold in crystalline form (see below). Solutions of Fe-EDTA chelate can however be readily prepared in the laboratory by mixing ferrous sulphate or ferrous chloride with an aqueous solution of

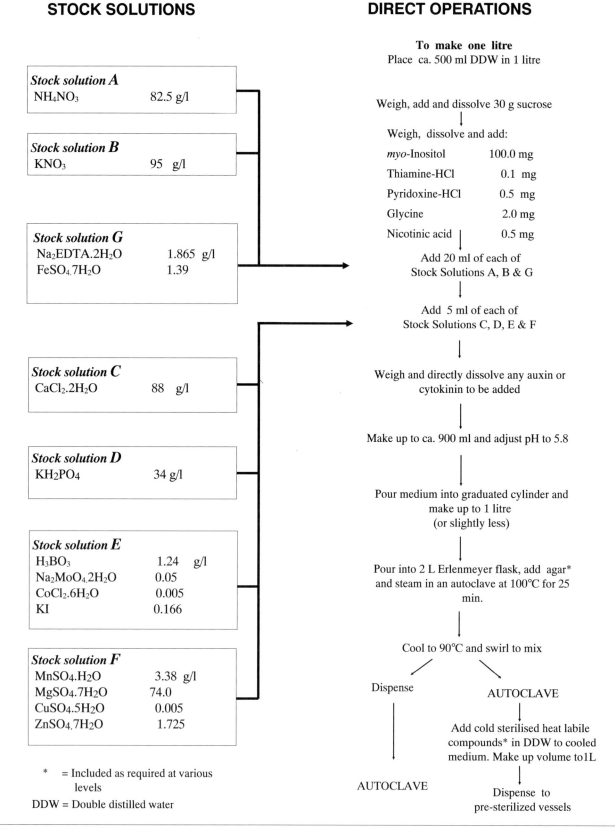

Fig. 102. Alternative methods of preparing MS medium: 1. — According to Helgeson (1979).

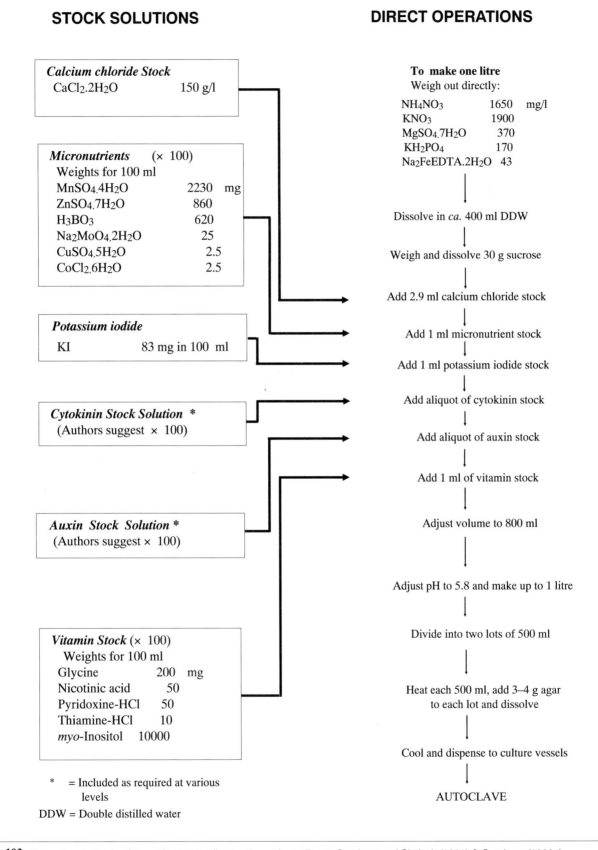

STOCK SOLUTIONS

Calcium chloride Stock
$CaCl_2.2H_2O$ 150 g/l

Micronutrients   (× 100)
Weights for 100 ml
$MnSO_4.4H_2O$ 2230   mg
$ZnSO_4.7H_2O$ 860
H_3BO_3 620
$Na_2MoO_4.2H_2O$ 25
$CuSO_4.5H_2O$ 2.5
$CoCl_2.6H_2O$ 2.5

Potassium iodide
KI   83 mg in 100 ml

Cytokinin Stock Solution *
(Authors suggest × 100)

Auxin Stock Solution *
(Authors suggest × 100)

Vitamin Stock (× 100)
Weights for 100 ml
Glycine   200   mg
Nicotinic acid   50
Pyridoxine-HCl   50
Thiamine-HCl   10
myo-Inositol   10000

*   = Included as required at various
      levels
DDW = Double distilled water

DIRECT OPERATIONS

To make one litre
Weigh out directly:

NH_4NO_3 1650   mg/l
KNO_3 1900
$MgSO_4.7H_2O$ 370
KH_2PO_4 170
$Na_2FeEDTA.2H_2O$ 43

Dissolve in *ca.* 400 ml DDW

Weigh and dissolve 30 g sucrose

Add 2.9 ml calcium chloride stock

Add 1 ml micronutrient stock

Add 1 ml potassium iodide stock

Add aliquot of cytokinin stock

Add aliquot of auxin stock

Add 1 ml of vitamin stock

Adjust volume to 800 ml

Adjust pH to 5.8 and make up to 1 litre

Divide into two lots of 500 ml

Heat each 500 ml, add 3–4 g agar
to each lot and dissolve

Cool and dispense to culture vessels

AUTOCLAVE

Fig. 103. Alternative methods of preparing **MS** medium: 2. — According to Gamborg and Shyluck (1981) & Gamborg (1982a).
Gamborg (1991) advocated preparing a stock solution of the combined MS macronutrients (see text).

STOCK SOLUTIONS

DIRECT OPERATIONS

To make one litre
Weigh out directly:

NH_4NO_3	1650	mg/l
KNO_3	1900	
$MgSO_4.7H_2O$	370	
KH_2PO_4	170	
$CaCl_2.2H_2O$	440	

To make one litre, dissolve the
quantities above in *ca.* 400 m l DDW

Add 10 ml microelement stock solution

↓

Add 5 ml of iron stock solution

↓

Weigh and dissolve 100 mg *myo*-inositol

↓

Add aliquot of cytokinin stock

↓

Weigh out auxin*, dissolve and
add to medium directly

↓

Make up to 800 ml with DDW

↓

Adjust pH to 5.7–5.8

↓

Make up to 1 litre with DDW

↓

Store in refrigerator if necessary

↓

Divide into 2 lots of 100 ml and place
each in 250 ml flask

↓

Add 3 g sucrose and 0.8 g agar* to each 100 ml flask

↓

AUTOCLAVE

↓

Cool to 50°C and add 1 ml filter-sterilised
vitamins to each 100 ml flask

Dispense to pre-sterilized vessels

Micronutrients (× 100)
Weights for 100 ml

$MnSO_4.4H_2O$	2230	mg
$ZnSO_4.7H_2O$	860	
H_3BO_3	620	
KI	83	
$Na_2MoO_4.2H_2O$	25	
$CuSO_4.5H_2O$	2.5	
$CoCl_2.6H_2O$	2.5	

Iron-EDTA (× 100)

Weights for 100 ml stock solution

$FeSO_4.7H_2O$	557	mg
$Na_2EDTA.2H_2O$	745	

Cytokinin Stock Solution *
(Authors suggest × 100)

Vitamin Stock (× 100)
Weights for 100 ml

Glycine	200	mg
Nicotinic acid	50	
Pyridoxine-HCl	50	
Thiamine-HCl	10	

---

* = Included as required at various
levels
DDW = Double distilled water

Fig. 104. Alternative methods of preparing **MS** medium: 3. — According to Dodds and Roberts (1982).

Na$_2$EDTA.2H$_2$O, or with a solution of the compound in potassium, sodium or ammonium hydroxide.

To make up one litre of a 20 mM stock solution, (× 200, according to the original **MS** levels):

> Dissolve 7.44g Na$_2$EDTA.2H$_2$O in *ca.* 900 ml double distilled water. A clear solution should result in 20 minutes at room temperature (25°C). This solution should be heated almost to boiling point before slowly adding 5.56g FeSO$_4$.7H$_2$O (or an equimolar quantity of another ferrous salt) while stirring; a clear yellow solution is obtained of which the pH is *ca.* 2.8. Heating and stirring result in a more stable Fe-EDTA complex (Vasil and Hildebrandt, 1966c) and heat is probably *essential* to enable the the chelation reaction to go to completion. If the mixture is not heated sufficiently, the stock solution has a final pH of *ca.* 1.2 and EDTA free acid is left in solution or precipitated (Dalton *et al.*, 1983). Allow to cool, make up to 1 litre and store *without* adjusting the pH. The stock solution can be kept at room temperature (although some recommend that it be placed in a refrigerator at *ca.* 4°C), but as it is photosensitive, it should be kept in a container which will exclude light, such as red or dark glass. Add 5 ml of the stock solution during the preparation of 1 litre of medium which requires 0.1 mM chelated iron.

The chelate formed upon adding ferrous sulphate or ferrous chloride to an EDTA solution is likely to be one embracing the ferric ion rather than the ferrous. The ferrous ion is rapidly oxidised to Fe(III) in solution and bonding by EDTA makes the ferric chelate much more stable than the ferrous complex (Fig. 97, Chapter 9). Steiner and Van Winden (1970) recommended that the ferrous salts used in the preparation of an Fe(III)-EDTA chelate, should be first dissolved in dilute sulphuric or hydrochloric acid to prevent the formation of ferrous hydroxide; and that once EDTA and a ferrous salt have been mixed, the Fe(II)-EDTA chelate, should be aerated to convert the ferrous iron into a stable dark yellow-brown coloured ferric form. However, such aeration is probably unnecessary and the observed colour change may represent the formation of ferric-hydroxy complexes (Dalton *et al.*, 1983). Because the acidity of the solution will help to avoid displacement of iron from an Fe(III)EDTA chelate, it is unwise to adjust the pH of the stock solution to 5.5 as is sometimes recommended (*e.g.* in Bhojwani and Razdan, 1983).

Equimolar concentrations of Fe and EDTA are used in the majority of plant tissue culture media and if a chelate stock solution is properly prepared from 20 mM ferrous sulphate and 20 mM Na$_2$EDTA by heating (page 366), almost all the ferric ion should be chelated (Dalton *et al.*, 1983). Precipitates in media probably only occur when free iron reaches a concentration where ferric phosphate solubility is exceeded (page 309). This situation may occur as iron is displaced from the chelate in prepared media kept at conventional pH levels for several days. However, Vyskot and Bezdek (1984) found that up to 10% of the iron in their **MS** preparation was not chelated when the molar ratio of Fe(II) to Na$_2$EDTA was 1:1, as is customary. In these conditions iron phosphate precipitates appeared after the medium had been autoclaved; but if the Fe (II): Na$_2$EDTA molar ratio was 1:2, only 1% of the iron in the solution was not chelated, and the heat-sterilized medium remained clear.

These findings are very similar to those of Dalton *et al.* (1983), who recommended that:

- **MS** medium should be made up and stored at pH 3.2 or below, and only readjusted to the required pH (*e.g.* 5.7) immediately before use, and

- the concentration of iron be reduced to one third that in standard **MS** medium, while the EDTA level is kept the same.

Very few workers seem to have accepted the advice Dalton *et al.* and Vyskot and Bezdek, and, as far as we are aware, no major benefit has been demonstrated by culturing plants in media from which precipitates have been eliminated. Adding an excess of EDTA could even be disadvantageous if other micronutrients become chelated with free EDTA, for they may then not be available to cultured tissues (page 309). If a precipitate-free medium *is* required, iron should be added to the medium from a stock solution (× 200) of Fe (0.05 mM) plus EDTA (0.1 mM). This may be prepared as follows:

> Dissolve 7.44g Na$_2$EDTA.2H$_2$O by the procedure described previously, but then add only 2.28 g FeSO$_4$.7H$_2$O (instead of 5.56g). Heat, stir, and cool; make up to 1 litre and once again store in the dark and/or in a darkened bottle.

NaFeEDTA. An anhydrous sodium ferric salt of EDTA (NaFeEDTA) is available from chemical suppliers. When this compound is used as a source of iron, and directly dissolved into a medium shortly before autoclaving, an Fe(III)-EDTA chelate will be formed in high proportion as the medium is heated during autoclaving (see Fig. 97), so than an Fe(III)-EDTA stock solution is unnecessary. If NaFeEDTA *is* used to prepare an iron chelate stock solution, it is advisable that the NaFeEDTA powder should be dissolved in hot water. To make up 1 litre of a 20 mM stock solution:

> Weigh out 7.34 g NaFeEDTA and dissolve in *ca.* 900 ml of near-boiling glass distilled water. Allow to cool, check that the solution is acid, and if necessary adjust to pH 3, make up to 1 litre and store in the dark. Add 5 ml per litre of medium to obtain 0.1 mM Fe.

Vitamins and amino-acids. Vitamins are prepared as 100-fold or 1000-fold concentrates and the solutions stored in the freezer at –20°C. Simple amino acids (*e.g.* glycine) can be added to the vitamin solution if necessary. Most researchers would agree that solutions of organic media constituents should be freshly prepared on each occasion if a freezer is not available, but refrigerated storage has been reported to be adequate (Vasil and Hildebrandt, 1966a,c; Mellor and Stace-Smith, 1977).

Once in solution, vitamins commonly added to plant culture media are more stable in a slightly acid solution than in one above pH 7 (Bridson, 1978). Some organic constituents are heat labile and should be filter sterilised (see below).

Growth regulators. Cytokinins are stable in solution but can be difficult to dissolve. They are usually brought into solution in a few drops of 0.1–1 N HCl, with slight heating. A stock solution (× 100 or × 1000) can be prepared and stored in a refrigerator. Schmitz and Skoog (1970) found that cytokinins could be dissolved in a small volume of dimethylsulfoxide (DMSO) without injury to cultures. Anderson (1975) dissolved both auxins and cytokinins in a small volume of DMSO before adding them to media for *Rhododendron* propagation. An advantage of using this solvent is that it acts as a sterilant, so growth regulators dissolved in it can be added by micro-syringe after the medium has been autoclaved. DMSO has been found to have growth-promoting properties in protoplast cultures (Hahne and Hoffman, 1984; Menczel and Wolfe, 1984; Gupta and Durzan, 1986) but has been found to induce genetic change (Chapter 6) and to damage cell membranes (Parr *et al.*, 1984). It should therefore be used with caution.

Gamborg (1982a) says that 2,4-D and NAA are satisfactory as stock solutions, but Helgeson (1979) and Dodds and Roberts (1982), prefer IAA to be weighed out afresh for each medium preparation, as it is rather unstable when stored. IAA can be dissolved in small amounts of absolute ethanol with gentle warming. Veliky and Martin (1970) prepared stock solutions of growth regulators in 95% ethanol when these compounds were to be added to cell suspensions. However, some workers have recommended that chemicals should not pre-dissolved in ethanol, as this solvent may inhibit tissue cultures (Bonga, 1982d). An alternative is to dissolve auxins (including 2,4-D and NAA) in 1–2 ml of 0.1 N NaOH. Once cytokinins have been dissolved in acid and auxins in alkali, the pH of stock solutions should be brought back to 5.5–5.8 before making up to volume, and before refrigerated storage.

The preparation of coconut milk for addition to media has been described on page 320.

Storage

Ideally, complete autoclaved media, containing regulants, should be stored for as short a time as possible. It is therefore preferable to store stock solutions of media components, or complete mixtures of ingredients, *before* they have been autoclaved and before growth regulators have been added. Solutions should be kept in stoppered

Table 43. The time required to sterilise various volumes of medium by autoclaving at 121°C [Given by Burger (1988)].

Volume of medium per vessel ml	Pre-heating time to reach 121°C min	Total sterilisation time min
20–25	9	24
50	11	26
100	13.5	28.5
250	16.5	31.5
500	20	35
1000	25	40
2000	33	48
3000	40	55
4000	48	63

vessels to prevent evaporation. Autoclaved media can be stored for short periods, but should be kept in presterilised containers in the dark at a cool temperature (*e.g.* at 5°C). Some organic components of media, such as the growth regulators IBA and IAA (especially), are degraded in solution, particularly in the light (Nissen and Sutter, 1988, 1990).

Deep-freeze storage

Prepared stock solutions and complete liquid media can be conveniently stored in a frozen state. It is inconvenient to have to thaw the whole of a frozen stock solution each time a fresh supply of medium is to be prepared. Having prepared a stock solution of vitamins (and/or macro- or micro- nutrients), it is therefore advisable, before freezing, to divide it into small measured volumes that will each be sufficient for a later bulk preparation of medium. These can be frozen and stored in small borosilicate glass or plastic bottles or specially designed plastic bags. To prepare one litre of medium, one 100ml bag of each of the 10× stock solutions of macronutrients, micronutrients, and organics would then be thawed and the solutions mixed. Certain basal media (without growth regulators) can be stored entire in a frozen condition (Kartha, 1984): after thawing, 100 ml of concentrate is then ready to be made up to 1 litre of finished medium. Frozen solutions should not be re-frozen after being thawed, for there is then a risk of precipitates being formed.

According to Gamborg *et al.* (1976) and Gamborg and Shyluk (1981), it is possible to freeze a 10-times concentrated **B5** or **MS** medium complete with macro- and micro-elements, FeEDTA, vitamins and sucrose. They suggest storing 100 ml or 400 ml aliquots in plastic bags in a deep-freeze until required. To prepare one litre of final medium, 100 ml of the concentrate would be thawed, growth regulators added, the pH adjusted and the volume made up with glass distilled water.

Some think that long-term storage of solutions containing organic compounds is inadvisable. Ascorbic acid and glutamine, for example, are known to break down in solution, even at low temperatures (Bonga, 1982d).

Adjusting pH

pH is most commonly adjusted using NaOH (sometimes KOH) or HCl, after all the components of the medium have been mixed just prior to autoclaving. Electrical meters are generally used for this purpose, but some workers have added a colour-changing indicator to their medium to monitor pH during culture growth. Chlorophenol red (1–5 mg/l, Reinert and White, 1956, Risser and White, 1964; Henson, 1979; Binns and Meins, 1980), and bromocresol purple have been employed. Some indicators may be toxic. BDH 4460 inhibited growth of petunia protoplast cultures (Roscoe and Bell, 1981).

Media are usually adjusted to pH 5.5—5.7 (Chapter 9). Murashige and Skoog (1962) found that a pH of 5.7–5.8 was suitable for maintaining all the salts of **MS** medium in the soluble form, even with relatively high phosphate levels (but low enough to permit rapid growth).

Selection of a relatively high pH before autoclaving is usually thought to be necessary with agar media to ensure gelation (page 298). When **MS** medium is used in a liquid form, it may be advantageous to adjust it to pH 5. There is then a reduced tendency for ions to react to form insoluble salts which are precipitated (Miller and Murashige, 1976). Gamborg *et al.* (1968) showed that soybean cell suspensions grew best in liquid **B5** medium adjusted at the outset to pH 4.5–5.5. There was a substantial reduction in cell dry weight from selecting a pH above 5.5. Contamination problems may be less in suspension cultures grown at low pH (Veliky and Martin, 1970).

Although medium pH is nearly always adjusted before autoclaving, heat sterilisation usually results in an increase in acidity (page 298). Mann *et al.*, (1982) found that prior adjustment of a modified **MS** medium to pH 5.7, resulted in a pH of about 5.0 after autoclaving. To achieve a pre-cultural pH of 5.7–5.9, it was necessary to titrate the medium initially to pH 7. This method should reduce the hydrolyis of agar (page 298), but there is an increased risk of a calcium phosphate precipitate being formed by autoclaving media at pH 7 or 8 (Vacin and Went (1949).

Adjustment after sterilisation

The most accurate method of ensuring that the medium has a desired pH, is to make pH adjustments *after* autoclaving. This is obviously not practical where medium is dispensed into small vessels before autoclaving, but can be carried out when a bulk supply is heat sterilised. It is then advisable to bring the pH to 6 before autoclaving, and to readjust it to the desired pH again afterwards.

A method of adjustment after sterilisation described by Sheat *et al.* (1959) involved separation of a small sample of the medium. The test sample and the bulk stock were then autoclaved, and the test portion afterwards titrated with sterile 0.1N NaOH (or HCl) to the selected pH. The necessary volume of the sterile acid or alkali was then calculated, and added aseptically in order to adjust the bulk of the medium to the same pH.

STERILISATION OF MEDIA

Autoclaving

Autoclaves should be fed with demineralised water to prevent scaling. Prepared medium is either sterilised in small bulk lots, or else dispensed into culture vessels which are then autoclaved. Tissue culture media are usually autoclaved at 121°C and 1.05 kg/cm^2 (103.4 KPa, or 15lb/in^2). Efficient sterilisation depends on the air having been removed from the autoclave chamber. To become sterile, a solution then requires to reach 121°C and be kept at this temperature for 15 minutes. The time taken for a sample of medium to reach the effective temperature of 121°C within an autoclave, increases according to the volume of the liquid in a container; actual times may also vary according to the nature of the autoclave. The time necessary for pre-heating within the autoclave is reduced if liquids have been heated prior to

Table 44. Some acids which may result from autoclaving sugars in plant culture media.

Sugar	Acids resulting from oxidation
Sucrose	None directly (but some is hydrolysed during autoclaving to glucose and fructose, see below)
Glucose	Gluconic acid, glycuronic acid
Fructose	Glycollic acid, erythronic acid
Galactose	Galactonic acid, galacturonic acid

Table 45. Heat labile compounds often used in plant culture media .
Sugars are also heat labile (see text).

Compound	Heat degradation	Reference
(±)-ABA	Some	Sigma catalogue
Adenine sulphate		Liau & Boll (1970)
L-Ascorbic acid		Sigma catalogue
L-asparagine		Liau & Boll (1970)
Ca-pantothenate	High	Dodds & Roberts (1982); Sigma catalogue
trans-Cinnamic acid		Sigma catalogue
Cystine		Butenko (1964)
Benzyladenine riboside		Sigma catalogue
Choline chloride		Liau & Boll (1970)
Folic acid		Liau & Boll (1970)
Fructose	Inhibitory substances	Stehsel & Caplin(1969)
Gibberellic acid	Slight	Butenko (1964); Watson & Halperin (1981)
L-Glutamine	High	Liau & Boll (1970); Thompson *et al.*(1977)
IAA	40% loss in 20 min autocl.	Nissen & Sutter (1988); Sigma catalogue
IAA-L-alanine	Slight	Pence &Caruso (1984); Sigma catalogue
IAA-L-aspartic acid	Marked	Pence &Caruso (1984); Sigma catalogue
IAA-glycine	Slight	Pence & Caruso (1984); Sigma catalogue
IAA-L-phenylalanine	Slight	Pence &Caruso (1984); Sigma catalogue
IBA	20% loss in 20 min autocl.	Nissen & Sutter (1988); Sigma catalogue
Kinetin	Some	Sigma catalogue
Malt extract	Inhibitory substances	Solomon(1950)
Nicotinamide		Liau & Boll (1970)
Nicotinic acid		Liau & Boll (1970)
N,N'-diphenylurea	Activity lost by autocl.	Schmitz and Skoog (1970)
Pantothenic acid		*See* Ca-pantothenate
PBA	Some	Sigma catalogue
Phloridzin		Krikorian *et al.* (1982b)
Pyridoxine	Slight	Singh & Krikorian (1981)
Riboflavin		Liau & Boll (1970); Sigma catalogue
2-iP	Some	Sigma catalogue
2-iP riboside		Sigma catalogue
Thiamine (.HCl) (Vit. B$_1$)	High above pH 5.5	Linsmaier and Skoog (1965); Liau & Boll (1970)
L-Tryptophan		(Butenko1964), Sigma catalogue
Urea		Liau & Boll (1970); Peters & Mayne(1974)
Zeatin	Some	Sigma catalogue

being placed therein. This is a sensible stratagem when a bulk supply of a medium is to be sterilised. Volatile substances may contaminate media and glassware if vessels are wrapped in paper during autoclaving (White, 1963). Ethylene can be produced if rubber stoppers or tubing are autoclaved; dissolved in media this can be inhibitory to cultures (Beyer, 1975).

Autoclave preheating times (and hence the total sterilisation times) found by Burger (1988) for sterilising various volumes of liquid, are shown in Table 43. Measurements made by other workers have suggested that somewhat shorter times are necessary. For example, Veliky and Martin (1970), who measured temperatures within their autoclave, found it necessary to use only 30 min at 121°C for 8 litres of medium. The sterilisation of small volumes of media for 15–20 min is commonly reported in the literature, and sterilisation times of 10 min have not been uncommon. There is clearly a risk of contamination if too short a period is used.

Burger (*loc. cit.*) discovered that the time taken to reach 121°C was considerably increased if flasks containing large volumes of liquid were enclosed within heat-resistant bags. If large volumes of media *are* autoclaved for the extended times suggested in Table 43, there is a risk of violent boiling as the autoclaved is cooled. Such problems can be avoided by preparing media in a steriliser sold especially for the purpose, which contains a stainless steel pressure vessel (Bonga, 1982d).

Certain chemicals used in plant culture media are degraded by heating in solution (see below); the degree of spoilage increases with temperature and length of exposure to heat. It is therefore always preferable to autoclave small quantities of media; large volumes should be divided into several smaller lots. *Overheating* media (*i.e.* autoclaving at above 121°C) will also cause excessive breakdown of some components. Tests conducted by Veliky and Martin (1970) showed that growth of cultured cells and tissues was considerably reduced in overheated media. Overheating is especially likely to occur when large volumes of media are autoclaved, and so, when media are required to be autoclaved in bulk (*e.g.* when pre–sterilised culture vessels are to be used), heat labile compounds should be filter–sterilised and added to the medium after autoclaving (Fig. 101). Autoclaved media should be cooled quickly; those containing agar should be dispensed into sterile culture vessels, under aseptic conditions, once they have cooled to 40–50°C, and are still liquid. Autoclaved media should be stored in cool conditions in the dark until required; from 4 to 10°C is variously recommended.

Heat labile compounds

Some organic compounds are partially degraded, or completely broken down, by being autoclaved together with other media constituents. Certain amino acids, vitamins and growth regulators are at risk, together with urea (which is sometimes used as a major source of nitrogen) (Table 45). For most purposes, compounds which are only partly degraded by heat can be co-autoclaved with other constituents of a medium; the risk of degradation is increased if the period of autoclaving is greater than 15–20 minutes. Compounds which are highly susceptible to heat damage should be filter sterilised (see below).

Thiamine is heat labile and is said to break down into its thiazole and pyrimidine moieties. However, Bonner (1938a) and Langridge and Brock (1961) found that isolated pea and tomato roots were able to grow when these two substances were provided separately, suggesting that plants can use them as intermediates for the re-synthesis of thiamine. If this is the case, autoclaving thiamine may not necessarily be detrimental (Singh and Krikorian, 1981). Marques (1986) found that autoclaved thiamine increased the growth of *Coffea* callus, while the filter sterilized vitamin did not.

Autoclaving sugars. Sucrose, and some other di- and trisaccharides, can be hydrolysed during autoclaving, especially at acid pH (Chapter 9). Sucrose is partly hydrolysed into fructose and glucose, but for most purposes this is no disadvantage. Autoclaving sugars also leads to some caramelisation, and to the production of sugar acids from monosaccharides (Table 44). All three processes (hydrolysis, carelmisation, and the formation of acids) proceed at a faster rate when sugars are autoclaved together with the rest of the medium, rather than in aqueous solutions (Ferguson *et al.*, 1958); they can be minimised by autoclaving the sugar, and other components of a medium, as two separate solutions which are mixed aseptically afterwards (Street, 1977b). Dalton (1980) autoclaved the fructose sugar source of his medium, separately at pH 4.

Autoclaving does not normally lead to the accumulation of significant amounts of harmful constituents, unless the period of heating is prolonged; however, the products of caramelisation, and sugar acids (if they occur in high concentration) are likely to inhibit the growth of plant tissues. Inhibitory substances can also be produced when sugars react with other constituents of the medium during autoclaving. Fructose is partially degraded to toxic furfurals. As some fructose is liable to be produced from sucrose during autoclaving (page 324), small amounts of furfural may appear in media autoclaved with sucrose. Stehsel and Caplin (1969) found that autoclaved fructose was especially inhibitory to carrot callus cultures. The degree of inhibition increased when this sugar was autoclaved together with other constituents of the medium. 5–Hydroymethyl–furfural has been thought to result from autoclaving sucrose in a slightly acid medium (Weatherhead *et al.*, 1979).

Autoclaving glucose together with phosphate and amino acids, can produce substances inhibitory to bacterial growth; and glucose can be partially broken down or converted to other sugars by autoclaving with phosphate ions. These reactions occur less frequently in the slightly acid solutions generally used for plant tissue culture work, than at alkaline pH. Nevertheless, Negrutiu and Jacobs (1978a) found that leaf (shoot) formation from

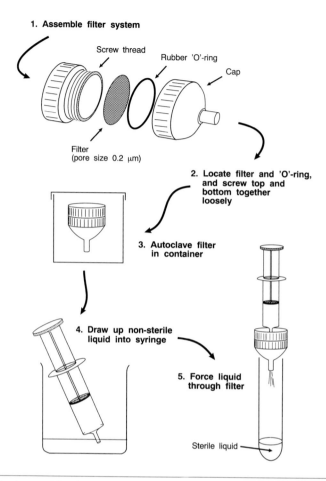

1. Assemble filter system

Screw thread

Rubber 'O'-ring

Cap

Filter
(pore size 0.2 μm)

2. Locate filter and 'O'-ring, and screw top and bottom together loosely

3. Autoclave filter in container

4. Draw up non-sterile liquid into syringe

5. Force liquid through filter

Sterile liquid

Fig. 105. Method of sterilising small volumes of liquid.

Arabidopsis callus was greater when glucose (the sugar used) was filter sterilised rather than autoclaved. An autoclaved mixture of glucose and sucrose was inhibitory to tracheary element differentiation in *Helianthus tuberosus*, whereas the filter sterilised mixture was not (Watson and Halperin, 1981).

Some of the different results obtained from autoclaved or filter-sterilised media, may be related to changes in pH. For example, Rashid and Reinert (1983) obtained a greater frequency of embryo formation from *Nicotiana* pollen cultures when a filter sterilized medium was adjusted to pH 6.8 rather than 5.8: the best results on autoclaved medium occurred when the pH was adjusted to the latter figure. Gametophytes of *Pteridium aquilinum* produced only half the number of apogamous sporophytes on a filter–sterilised medium containing ferric citrate and glucose, than they did on the same medium sterilised by autoclaving. When an FeEDTA chelate was used as the iron source, a filter sterilised medium gave the best result (Whittier, 1964a). A similar result had previously led Ferguson *et al.* (1958) to suggest that sugars

might form a chelate when autoclaved with Fe(III), helping to keep iron in solution.

Growth regulators. Several growth regulators are liable to be denatured by autoclaving. The extent of the degradation of most common auxins and cytokinins is slight and can probably be ignored in routine micropropagation. Although some degradation of the auxins IAA and IBA has been detected in autoclaved media (Table 45), it is possible to compensate for a loss of activity.

The commonly-used cytokinins and auxins are thought to be heat stable, but Negrutiu and Jacobs (1978a) and Jordan *et al.* (1982) reported an advantage from filter-sterilising IAA and kinetin. Harvais (1982) found that cytokinins and auxins were more active in promoting germination and seedling growth of a *Cypripedium* orchid if they were sterilised by membrane filtration instead of autoclaving. A reaction was suspected between the regulants and other medium components during autoclaving. The cytokinin N, N'-diphenylurea, loses activity on autoclaving but not when added to the medium in a

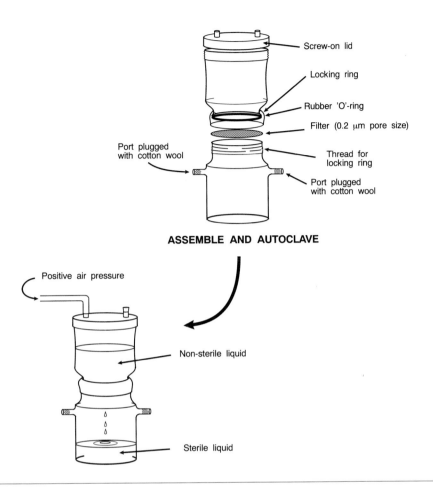

Fig. 106. Apparatus for filter-sterilising large volumes of media components.

small volume of dimethylsulphoxide (Schmitz and Skoog, 1970).

It is generally agreed that gibberellic acid should definitely not be autoclaved as it is hydrolysed by heating in solution, and can be rendered inactive. Nevertheless some workers (*e.g.* Kochba *et al.* 1974; Watson and Halperin, 1981; Kartha, 1984) have reported no significant loss of activity.

Ultrafiltration

Media ingredients that are heat labile are best sterilised by ultrafiltration rather than being autoclaved with other constituents of the medium. However, the process is slower and more costly than autoclaving, and so is only suitable for particular ingredients of a medium or specialised experiments. Solutions to be sterilised are passed though a filter with a pore size not greater than 0.22 µm diameter, into a sterile container. Disposable filter mem-

branes are made for various pieces of apparatus, so that both small and large volumes of liquid can be treated.

Small volumes of growth regulator solutions and vitamin concentrates can be passed through a miniature ultrafiltration unit attached to a syringe, and so dropped aseptically into the autoclaved medium which has been allowed to cool to *ca* 45°C. Large volumes of solution (*e.g.* necessary if the sugar is to be filter-sterilised) require to be passed through a large diameter filter of the same pore size (under pressure or vacuum) into previously autoclaved glassware. Apparatus can be purchased to provide high positive pressure from bottled air or gas cylinders to speed the filter sterilisation of large quantities (*e.g.* 10 litres) of medium.

Some typical ultrafiltration apparatus is illustrated in Figs. 105 and 106. Normally the filter membrane is autoclaved together with the funnel, and with the vacuum flask if large quantities of liquid are to be sterilised. The filter and associated apparatus can also be cold sterilised in isopropanol (Bonga, 1982d). A detergent is often in-

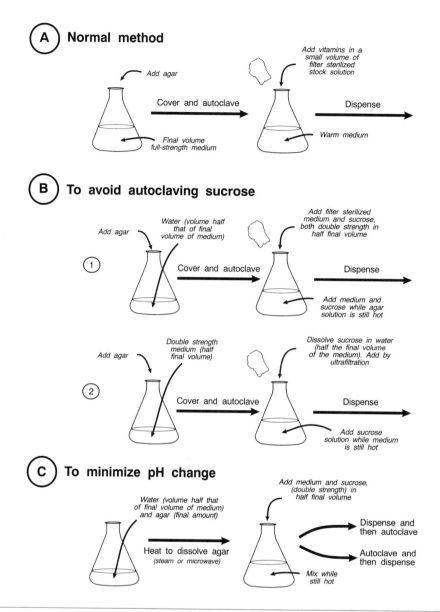

Fig. 107. Alternative methods of adding agar during the preparation of media [see text].

corporated into membrane filters to speed the filtration process. If it is required to eliminate detergent from media for sensitive tests, a membrane can be washed in water before use; the subsequent rate of filtration will be reduced.

Street (1977b) recommended that when very dilute solutions of growth regulators are filter sterilised, the first portion of the filtrate should be rejected, as the solution may initially be reduced in concentration by absorption. Some ultrafiltration screens contain detergents that are harmful to plant tissue cultures.

Other methods of sterilisation

Ferguson *et al.* (1958) found that small amounts of compounds could be effectively sterilised by being treated dry in a sterile container with Analar® ethyl ether. The ether was evaporated below 30°C and the compound then dissolved in sterile distilled water. Chemicals can also be sterilised by being dissolved in DMSO (page 367). Heating for 2–3 minutes in a microwave oven was said to sterilise **MS** medium and **Boxus (1974a)** strawberry medium (Wood and Lundergan, 1981). Media heated for less than two minutes became contaminated. Strawberry shoot tips grew equally well on microwaved and conventionally autoclaved media. Microwave heating can be used to sterilise soil-based potting media. Fungal and bacterial populations are reduced or eliminated by heating in a domestic microwave oven (2450 MHz), although good results require quite a long period of treatment (*e.g.* 24 min at 50% power) (Moore *et al.* 1983).

Addition of agar

If pre-sterilised containers are to be used, the medium is autoclaved in bulk, allowed to cool to 45–50°C and dispensed into the vessels in a laminar flow cabinet or other sterile area. The more common method is to use non-sterile vessels: agar is introduced into the medium which is heated until the agar is dissolved; it is then dispensed into culture vessels which are then covered and autoclaved (Figs. 101 and 107).

Agar is frequently added to a medium after it has been made up to volume:

— agar is put into the medium after its pH has been adjusted and it has been made up to final volume. The medium is transferred to a flask of double the solution volume for this purpose; the solution is then steamed in an autoclave for about 1 minute, or heated in a microwave oven, until the agar has dissolved.

— agar is placed into the medium and dissolved by heating, as above. The pH is adjusted *after* the agar is dissolved; this is thought to be the best method (Owen *et al.*, 1991).

The addition of agar causes the pH of a medium to change; usually media containing agar have a lower pH after autoclaving than comparable liquid media (Chapter 9 and Fig. 95). To avoid an appreciable change following

autoclaving, Murashige and Skoog (1962) recommended that after agar is added, the medium should be preheated for a few minutes in the autoclave before pH adjustment, as suggested above. A slightly different method was suggested by Sarma *et al.* (1990). Noting that when agar was dissolved directly during the autoclaving process (method *A* in Fig 109), the pH of **MS, Gamborg *et al.* (1968) B5** and **Chu *et al.* (1975) N6** media fell sharply after autoclaving, it was discovered that the pH fall could be minimized by:

> Dissolving the agar in water which was heated and stirred until the agar was dissolved. The volume of water used was half that of the final medium. The hot agar solution was added to a similar volume of double strength medium and the whole autoclaved either before, or after, being dispensed to culture vessels (method *C* in Fig. 109). In using this technique, care should be taken not to add the gelling agent to an actively-boiling liquid, as it is then liable to froth up and boil over.

A different approach must be used if it decided not to autoclave sucrose (to prevent hyrolytic breakdown). Agar is then added to either half the final volume of water (method *B1*, Fig. 107) or to half the final volume of medium (method *B2*, Fig. 107); sucrose dissolved in either medium or water is added to the hot agar solution by ultrafiltration.

REVIEWS

More detailed information on procedures to be followed during media preparation will be found in articles by:

Gamborg *et al.* (1976); Street (1977b); Biondi and Thorpe (1981); Gamborg and Shyluk (1981); Bonga (1982d); Gamborg (1982a; 1991); and in the book by Dodds and Roberts (1982).

Table 46. Uses for the plant culture media described in Tables 47 to 55.

Medium	Original and/or subsequent use
Abo El-Nil & Hildebrandt(1976)	Callus culture of *Pelargonium*
Abo El-Nil & Zettler(1976) AZ	Shoot culture of *Colocasia* (Araceae). Callus culture of *Allium*.
Abou-Mandour(1977a)	Used by the author to initiate and culture callus of many species.
Anderson(1975)	Devised for shoot culture of *Rhododendron*; an early version of the 1978;1980 medium.
Anderson(1978;1980)	Shoot culture of *Rhododendron* and otherEricaceae (also *Rubus, Corylus*).
Anderson(1984) R	*Rhododendron* rooting medium.
Asahira & Kano(1977)	Callus culture of *Fragaria*.
Asokan et al.(1984b) 1.	Shoot culture of *Xanthosoma*.
Asokan et al.(1984b) 2.	Rooting of *Xanthosoma* shoots.
Asokan et al.(1984c)	Callus and shoot culture of *Amorphophallus*.
Atanassov & Brown(1984) B5h	Callus culture of *Medicago* spp.
Ault & Blackmon(1985)	Callus and shoot tip culture of Cactaceae.
Bajaj & Pierik(1974)	Callus and suspension cultures of wide range of species. No morphogenesis.
Barnes(1979)	Shoot culture of *Citrullus* (Cucurbitaceae).
Ben-Jaacov & Dax(1981)	Shoot culture, shoot growth and rooting of many species.
Beretta & Eccher(1987)	Shoot culture of *Camellia* hybrid.
Berthelot(1934) Dilution	An early micronutrient mixture.
Blaydes(1966) Version 1.	Same medium as **Miller 1961a; 1963.**
Blaydes(1966) Version 2.	Callus, suspension culture and adventitious shoots in Leguminosae.
Bonner & Devirian(1939) A	Isolated root culture and seed germination, several spp.
Bonner & Devirian(1939) B	Isolated root culture.
Bonner & Devirian(1939) C	Isolated root culture, tomato.
Bonner(1940a) A	Isolated root culture of *Pisum*.
Bonner(1940b) A	Isolated root culture.
Bonner(1940b) B	Isolated root culture.
Bonner(1940b) C	Isolated root culture.
Bourgin & Nitsch(1967) H	Widely used as anther culture medium for dicots. Also suitable for direct adventitious shoot formation, callus growth and, sometimes, indirect embryogenesis.
Bourgin & Nitsch(1967) Simple	Anther culture of dicots.
Boxus(1974a)	Shoot culture of strawberry.
Brown & Lawrence(1968)	Callus growth of *Pinus* spp.
Campbell & Durzan(1975)	Direct shoot formation and shoot culture in Pinaceae.
Canas & Benbadis(1988) OM	Basal medium for *Olea europaea* culture.
Canas & Benbadis(1988) OMc	Callus growth and morphogenesis from *Olea europaea* cotyledon fragments.
Canas & Benbadis(1988) OMe	Root elongation of *Olea europaea*.
Canas & Benbadis(1988) OMr	Rooting of *Olea europaea* shoots.
Chaleff(1983a) R3	Anther culture medium for *Oryza sativa*.
Chaleff(1983a) R3 Succ.	Improved growth of rice anther callus (cf. R3 medium).
Chaleff(1983a) R3 (NH4) MES	Medium with only NH4 nitrogen which supports callus growth.
Chaleff(1983a) R3 (NH4) Succ.	Medium with only NH4 nitrogen which supports callus growth.

Medium	Original and/or subsequent use
Cheng(1977;1978)	Direct adventitious shoots, shoot growth and rooting in Pinaceae.
Chu & Hill(1988) MN6	Anther culture of *Triticum aestivum*.
Chu et al.(1975) N6	Embryogenesis in monocots. from anthers or embryos.
Chu(1978;1981)	Anther culture of monocots.
Cresswell & Nitsch(1975)	Shoot growth and rooting of *Eucalyptus*.
Curir et al.(1988) Exp.	Shoot culture of *Ruscus racemosus*.
Dabin & Bouharmont(1983) A	Shoot tip culture of *Rhododendron simsii*.
Dabin & Bouharmont(1983) B	Shoot tip culture of *Rhododendron simsii* (2 cvs.).
Davis et al.(1977) MS-3.	Shoot culture of *Dianthus caryophyllus*.
De Fossard et al.(1974a) LOW	
De Fossard et al.(1974a) MEDIUM	Media for original broad spectrum experiment.
De Fossard et al.(1974a) HIGH	
De Greef & Jacobs(1979) PGoB	Shoot and callus cultures of *Beta vulgaris*: indirect adventitious shoots.
Debergh & Maene(1977)	Callus, adventitious shoots, rooting in *Pelargonium*.
Debergh et al.(1981)	Shoot culture of *Cynara scolymus*.
Doerschug & Miller(1967)	Direct adventitious shoots in *Lactuca sativa*.
Dudits et al.(1975) T	Callus growth and shoot regeneration in *Triticum*.
Dunstan & Short(1977a) BDS	Callus, embryogenesis, direct shoots, shoot culture in the Alliaceae.
Eccher et al.(1986)	Shoot culture of *Vaccinium corymbosum*.
Economou & Read(1984)	Shoot culture of Ericaceae & Rubiaceae.
Eeuwens & Blake(1977)	Tissue cultures of Palmae.
Eeuwens(1976) Y3	Tissue cultures of Palmae.
Elliott(1970) L-S	Callus and adventitious shoots, shoot growth; several species.
Eriksson(1965) 1.	Callus and suspension cultures, indirect embryogenesis.
Eriksson(1965) 2.	A supplemented version of Medium 1. Low density inocula, callus from suspensions.
Evaldsson & Welander(1985)	Shoot culture of *Cordyline terminalis*.
Evans et al.(1976) HRM	Shown to be better than **MS** for callus growth and adv. root formation in *Glycine max*
Finer & Nagasawa(1988) 10A40N	Embryogenesis in suspension cultures of *Glycine max*.
Franco & Swartz(1985) CBM	Basal medium for *Cupressus lusitanica*. Adventitious shoots, shoot growth.
Franco & Swartz(1985) GDM	Shoot elongation of *Pinus oocarpa*.
Gamborg(1966) PRL-4-C	Callus and suspension cultures of several spp.
Gamborg et al.(1968) B5	Used for callus and suspension cultures and occasionally anther culture in plants of many families. Only rarely is embryogenesis or caulogenesis reported on this medium. Especially suited to plants of the Leguminosae.
Garve et al.(1980)	Callus, suspensions, adventitious shoots and embryogenesis in *Datura & Digitalis*.
Gautheret(1942)	An early callus culture medium.
Green(1982)	Callus and adventitious shoots in the Gramineae.
Gresshoff & Doy(1972a,b) DBM 1.	Anther culture medium for *Arabidopsis & Lycopersicon*.
Gresshoff & Doy(1972a,b) DBM 2.	Medium used for rooting shoots.
Gresshoff & Doy(1972b) DBM 3.	Used for callus subculture in *Lycopersicon*.
Gupta & Durzan(1985)	Shoot culture of Pinaceae.
Gupta et al.(1980) Wh.	Rooting medium used for several broad-leafed tree spp.

Table 46 (Continued). Uses for plant culture media.

Medium	Original and/or subsequent use
Gupta et al.(1981)	Shoot culture and shoot growth of broad-leafed trees, esp. *Eucalyptus*.
Hahlbrock et al.(1974)	Callus and suspension cultures, direct shoots and roots: Leguminosae.
Halperin & Minocha(1973)	Suspension cultures of several species.
Halperin & Wetherell(1965) A	Callus growth in *Daucus carota*.
Halperin & Wetherell(1965) B	Embryogenesis in *Daucus carota*.
Hasegawa(1979)	Shoot culture (esp. in Rosaceae); embryogenic callus and plant regen. in Gramineae.
Heinz & Mee(1969)	A variant of **MS** medium, widely used for the same purposes.
Heller(1953;1955)	Embryo culture of several spp. Direct adventitious shoots, roots and protocorms (in Orchidaceae), but little callus growth.
Hildebrandt et al.(1946) Tobacco	Callus formation and suspension cultures, several spp.
Hildebrandt(1962) C	Callus initiation, maintenance; suspension cultures; several spp.
Horgan & Aitken(1981) 1.	Organised callus, direct adventitious buds and shoot growth in *Pinus*.
Horgan & Aitken(1981) 2.	A rooting medium for *Pinus* shoots.
Hussey(1978a)	Medium with ½**MS** salts. Shoot culture of *Allium*. Rooting.
Jelaska(1987)	Direct adventitious shoots from cotyledons of *Calocedrus*.
Jona & Gribaudo(1987) A	Direct adventitious shoots from *Ficus lyrata* leaves.
Jona & Gribaudo(1987) B	Rooting of *Ficus lyrata* shoots.
Jona & Vigliocco(1985) A	Shoot tip culture of *Prunus persica*.
Jona & Vigliocco(1985) B	Shoot culture and shoot elongation of *Prunus persica*.
Jones & Murashige(1974) A	Shoot culture of ornamental plants.
Jones & Murashige(1974) B	Shoot culture of ornamental plants.
Jones et al.(1977)	Shoot culture of *Malus* and *Prunus*.
Kao & Michayluk(1975) 8.	Protoplast culture of several species
Kao & Michayluk(1975) 8p.	Protoplast culture and initiating suspension cultures with low density inocula.
Kao(1977) Cell	Used in protoplast culture to gradually dilute the two media above. Callus colony growth.
Kartha et al.(1974a)	**MS** salts with **Gamborg (1966) PRL-4-C** vitamins. Widely used as an alternaive to **MS** for shoot and meristem culture
Kasperbauer & Reinert(1967)	Anther culture, callus and indirect shoots/roots in several spp.
Kaul & Staba(1968)	Callus and suspension culture of many spp., sometimes with morphogenesis. Shoot tip culture e.g. *Chrysanthemum, Dioscorea*.
Knop(1865)	Early hydroponic culture solution.
Knudson(1922;1943) B	Early orchid culture medium.
Knudson(1946) C	Orchid culture. Protocorm formation.
Kumar et al.(1988) L-6	Regeneration of somatic embryos of *Vigna aconitifolia*.
Kunisaki(1975)	Shoot culture of *Anthurium* and *Cordyline*.
Kunisaki(1990) 1.	Shoot culture of *Leucospermum* (Proteaceae).
Kunisaki(1990) 2.	Rooting of *Leucospermum* shoots.
Kyte & Briggs(1979) I	Shoot culture of *Rhododendron*.

Medium	Original and/or subsequent use
Kyte & Briggs(1979) R	Rooting medium for *Rhododendron*.
Lin & Staba(1961)	Callus and suspension cultures. Direct and indirect morphogenesis.
Lindemann et al.(1970) 1.	Callus formation in *Cattleya*.
Lindemann et al.(1970) 2.	Protocorm regeneration and proliferation in *Cattleya*
Linsmaier & Skoog(1965)	Simplified version of **MS** medium. Widely used for the same purposes.
Linsmaier-Bednar & Skoog(1967)	**LS** medium without thiamine. Adequate for callus and indirect shoot and root formation in some spp.
Litvay et al.(1981) LM	Suspension culture medium for conifers.
Lloyd & McCown(1981) WPM	Shoot tip culture of woody plants. Widely used.
Maheswaran & Williams(1984) EC6	Used by the authors to induce indict embryogenesis in legumes.
Margara(1977;1978) N15Ca	
Margara(1977;1978) N15K	
Margara(1977;1978) N30Ca	A set of experimental media providing a broad range of macronutrient ions. The set of media was designed to facilitate the selection of an appropriate mixture for any species.
Margara(1977;1978) N30K	
Margara(1977;1978) N30NH4	
Margara(1977;1978) N5Ca	
Margara(1977;1978) N5K	
Miller & Murashige(1976) I.	Shoot culture of ornamentals, e.g. *Cordyline*.
Miller & Murashige(1976) II.	This is **LS** medium with twice the level of PO_4^{3-}. Found to give better shoot proliferation and growth than **MS** or **LS** in shoot cultures of some spp. Has also been used for direct & indirect shoot initiation and embryogenesis.
Miller & Murashige(1976) III.	**LS** medium with 2.5 × the amount of PO_4^{3-}. Indirect embryogenesis in Palmae. Shoot culture of *Nephrolepsis* fern.
Miller & Murashige(1976) IV.	**LS** medium with 3 times the amount of PO_4^{3-}. Shoot culture of *Syngonium*.
Miller & Skoog(1953)	Callus growth and ind. shoot formation in some spp.
Miller et al.(1956)	Callus and ind. morphogenesis in some spp.
Miller(1961a;1963)	Callus growth of several spp. and sometimes shoot and root initiation.
Miller(1968)	Callus growth of several spp. and sometimes shoot and root initiation.
Millerd et al.(1975) 1. and 2.	Media for the growth of isolated cotyledons.
Mitra et al.(1976) A	Callus and protocorm formation in *Dendrobium*.
Mullin et al.(1974) A	Meristem culture of *Fragaria*.
Mullin et al.(1974) B	Shoot growth and multiplication *Fragaria, Castanea*. Adventitious shoots.
Murashige & Skoog(1962)	The most widely used of all plant media. Shoot and single node culture, callus and suspension cultures, direct & indirect shoot formation and embryogenesis. Occasionally used for embryo culture. Usually employed at ½ strength for rooting microcuttings .
Murashige & Skoog(1962) Supplemented	Used for the same purposes as **MS** medium, but the CH supplement seems to make the medium specially suitable for inducing caulogenesis and embryogenesis.
Murashige & Tucker(1969)	All kinds of tissue culture of *Citrus*. Direct & ind. morphogenesis; protoplast culture.
Murashige et al.(1972b)	Single node and shoot culture.
Murashige et al.(1974)	Shoot culture of *Gerbera*.
Nagata & Takebe(1970)	Protoplast culture of *Nicotiana*.
Nagata & Takebe(1971)	Protoplast culture and cell colony growth, many spp.
Nickell & Maretzki(1969) 1.	Callus & suspension cultures of *Saccharum*.

Table 46 (Continued). Uses for plant culture media.

Nitsch & Nitsch(1956) N1.	Callus growth, several spp.
Medium	**Original and/or subsequent use**
Nitsch & Nitsch(1965) K	Callus and direct adventitious shoots and roots, *Plumbago*.
Nitsch & Nitsch(1965) S	Callus. Direct and indirect caulogenesis, embryogenesis, several spp.
Nitsch & Nitsch(1969)	Anther culture of several dicot. plants, esp. Solanaceae.
Nitsch(1951) 1.	Mainly used for ovule/ovary/fruit culture, occasionally for anther culture.
Nitsch(1968) S	Direct and indirect adventitious shoots in several spp., occasionally anther culture.
Norstog(1973) Barley II.	Embryo culture of barley, wheat, *Lilium*. Also suitable for orchid seed germination.
Pevalek-Kozlina & Jelaska(1987) WPM (no Cl⁻)	Shoot culture of chloride-sensitive woody plants.
Pfeffer(1900) A and B	Early callus culture media. Have also been tried for orchid seed germination.
Phillips & Collins(1979a) L2.	Callus, suspensions and indirect embryogenesis *Glycine* and *Trifolium*.
Phillips & Collins(1979a) R	Rooting shoots of *Trifolium* spp.
Phillips & Collins(1980) SL2.	Callus and indirect embryogenesis, *Glycine* and *Trifolium*.
Pierik et al.(1974)	Callus
Quoirin & Lepoivre(1977) A	Shoot tip establishment, *Prunus*.
Quoirin & Lepoivre(1977) B	Shoot culture propagation, *Prunus*.
Ramming et al.(1990)	Culture of immature *Vitis vinifera* embryos.
Ramming(1990)	Culture of immature peach embryos.
Ranga Swamy(1961) I	Embryo and organ culture. Callus. Direct and indirect morphogenesis and embryogenesis (many spp.).
Ratnamba & Chopra(1974)	Direct morphogenesis or callus & indirect morphogenesis
Reynolds et al.(1980)	Direct and indirect caulogenesis & embryogenesis, several spp.
Reynolds et al.(1982)	Direct and indirect embryogenesis im *Glycine max*.
Risser & White(1964)	Callus and growth of *Picea glauca*.
Roca et al.(1978)	Shoot and single node culture of *Solanum*, also ind. shoot formation.
Rodriguez & Lorenzo Martin(1987) MH	Shoot culture of *Musa acuminata*.
Rodriguez(1982b) K(h)	At ½ strength, used for shoot cultures of *Corylus* and rooting of other woody plants.
Roh & Wocial(1989)	Direct adventitious shoots of × *Achimenantha* (Gesneriaceae).
Rose & Martin(1975) P2.	Suspension cultures of *Ipomoea*.
Sangwan & Harada(1975)	Callus and indirect shoot formation,, *Antirrhinum*.
Schenk & Hildebrandt(1972)	Callus and susp. cultures of many spp. Indirect morphogenesis and embryogenesis.
Scowcroft & Adamson(1976) CS5	Callus and susp. culture of *Stylosanthes* (Leguminosae). Indirect shoot formation.
Singha et al.(1985)	Shoot culture of crabapple and pear.
Skirvin & Chu(1978a,b)	Shoot culture of *Prunus* and *Rubus*.
Skoog(1944)	Direct shoot formation, *Kalanchoe*.
Snir & Erez(1980) R	Rooting microcuttings of *Malus* and *Prunus*.

Sommer et al.(1975) 1.	Direct shoot formation, *Eucalyptus* and Pinaceae.
Sommer et al.(1975) 2.	Shoot culture of *Betula*.
Medium	**Original and/or subsequent use**
Sommer et al.(1975) 3.	Rooting medium.
Standardi & Catalano(1985) 1.	Stage I medium for *Actinidia* shoot cultures.
Standardi & Catalano(1985) 2.	Stage II medium for *Actinidia* shoot cultures.
Standardi & Catalano(1985) 3.	Stage III rooting medium for *Actinidia*.
Stapfer & Heuser(1985)	Shoot culture of several spp.; (a modified **WPM** medium).
Staudt(1984) M2.	Callus growth of *Vitis vinifera*.
Staudt(1984) M2-2.	Callus growth of *myo*-inositol- dependent *V. vinifera*.
Strullu et al.(1986)	Shoot growth of *Castanea sativa*.
Syono & Furuya(1972)	**MS** medium without glycine. Often used instead of **MS**: similar uses.
Thomale(1954) GD	Protocorm proliferation and growth in orchids.
Thompson et al.(1977)	A medium for the growth of isolated cotyledons.
Thorpe & Meier(1973) Sf	Callus and ind. shoot formation, *Nicotiana*.
Thorpe & Murashige(1968;1970) Sf	SAME AS **Miller & Murashige(1976) IV**, but has 100 mg/l tyrosine. Used for direct (and indirect) shoot formation in several spp., esp. *Nicotiana*.
Tran Thanh Van(1973)	Shoot culture of several spp.
Tukey(1933) I	Embryo culture of several spp.
Tukey(1933) II	Embryo culture of *Prunus*.
Uchimiya & Murashige(1974) C	Callus and suspension cultures of many spp. Only rarely indirect morphogenesis.
Vacin & Went(1949)	Widely used for orchid culture, protocorm proliferation.
Vasil & Hildebrandt(1966c) C	Callus growth, several species.
Veliky & Martin(1970) 67-V	Callus and suspension cultures, several spp. Indirect organogenesis in *Phaseolus*.
Von Arnold & Eriksson(1977) LP	Direct shoot formation in *Picea*.
Von Arnold & Eriksson(1979) LPm	Direct shoot formation in *Picea*.
Von Arnold & Eriksson(1981) LPm	Shoot growth in *Salix*, callus and indirect embryogenesis in *Picea*.
Wetherell(1969)	Suspension cultures of *Daucus carota*.
White(1942)	White's media were originally used for isolated root culture and callus culture; now also used for rooting the microcuttings of some species.
White(1943a) A	
White(1954)	
White(1963)	
Wood & Braun(1961) A	Legume callus and cell colony growth.
Wood & Braun(1961) B	Callus and suspension culture of some spp.
Yang & Chang(1979)	Shoot culture of *Pyrus* and *Trifolium*. Direct organogenesis in other spp.
Yasuda et al.(1985)	Embryogenic callus of *Coffea arabica*.
Zapata et al.(1983) MY1.	Callus and indirect adventitious shoots, *Oryza*.
Zimmerman & Broome(1980) Z-2.	Shoot tip culture of *Rhododendron* & *Vaccinium*.
Zimmerman & Broome(1980) Z-3.	Shoot culture of *Vaccinium*.
Zimmerman(1984a) WPMm.	Shoot culture of *Malus*.
Ziv et al.(1970)	Originally used for adventitious shoots and corms in *Gladiolus*. Callus and adventitious shoots in other plants.

Table 47. Media Derivations.

Medium	Additions	Macronutrients	Micronutrients	Vitamins	Amino acids/Amides	Sug./Alc.	Org. Acids	Notes
Abo El-Nil & Hildebrandt(1976)		Murashige & Skoog(1962)	Unique	Murashige & Skoog(1962)	Skoog(1944)	—	—	
Abo El-Nil & Zettler(1976) AZ		Unique	Unique	Schenk & Hildebrandt(1972)	Skoog(1944)	—	—	
Abou-Mandour(1977b)		Lin & Staba(1961)	Unique	Nitsch & Nitsch(1965) K & S	Murashige & Skoog(1962) Supplemented	—	—	
Al-Talib & Torrey(1959)		Unique	Unique	Bonner & Devirian(1939) C	Unique	—	—	
Anderson(1975)	AdSh	Unique	Murashige & Skoog(1962)	Linsmaier & Skoog(1965)	None	—	—	
Anderson(1978a;1980a)	AdSh	Unique	Unique	Linsmaier & Skoog(1965)	None	—	—	See notes
Anderson(1984a,b) R		0.25 × Anderson(1978;1980)	0.25 × Anderson(1978;1980)	Linsmaier & Skoog(1965)	None	—	—	
Asahira & Kano(1977)		Murashige & Skoog(1962)	Unique	Unique	Skoog(1944)	—	—	
Asokan et al.(1984b) 1.	AdS	Miller & Murashige(1976) III	Murashige & Skoog(1962)	Gamborg(1966) Modified White	Skoog(1944)	—	—	
Asokan et al.(1984b) 2.		Murashige & Skoog(1962)	Murashige & Skoog(1962)	Unique	Skoog(1944)	—	—	
Asokan et al.(1984c)		Unique	Murashige & Skoog(1962)	None	None	—	—	
Atanassov & Brown(1984) B5h	Ad	Unique	Gamborg et al.(1968) B5	Gamborg(1966) PRL-4-C	Unique	—	—	See notes
Ault & Blackmon(1985)		Unique	Murashige & Skoog(1962)	Venverloo(1973)	None	—	—	
Bajaj & Pierik(1974)		Murashige & Skoog(1962)	Murashige & Skoog(1962)	Murashige & Skoog(1962)	Kavathekar & Ganapathy(1973)	—	—	
Barnes(1979)		Unique	Murashige & Skoog(1962)	Linsmaier-Bednar & Skoog(1967)	None	—	—	
Ben-Jaacov & Dax(1981)		0.5 × Murashige &Skoog(1962)	0.5 × Murashige & Skoog(1962)	Murashige & Skoog(1962)	Skoog(1944)	—	—	
Beretta & Eccher(1987)	20 mg/l Ad	Unique	Unique	Morel & Wetmore(1951b)	None	—	—	See notes
Berthelot(1934) Dilution		—	Unique	—	—	—	—	See notes
Blaydes(1966) Version 1.		SAME AS Miller (1961a;1963)						See notes
Blaydes(1966) Version 2.		Unique	Unique	Bonner & Devirian(1939) C	Skoog(1944)	—	—	See notes
Bonner & Devirian(1939) A		Unique	Bonner & Bonner(1938)	Unique	None	—	—	
Bonner & Devirian(1939) B		As Medium A above	Bonner & Bonner(1938)	Unique	None	—	—	
Bonner & Devirian(1939) C		As Medium A above	Bonner & Bonner(1938)	Unique	None	—	—	
Bonner(1940a) A		Unique	Unique	Bonner & Devirian(1939) A	None	—	—	
Bonner(1940b) A		Bonner(1940a) A	Bonner & Bonner(1938)	Bonner & Devirian(1939) A	None	—	—	
Bonner(1940b) B		Bonner(1940a) A	Bonner & Bonner(1938)	Bonner & Devirian(1939) C	None	—	—	
Bonner(1940b) C		Bonner(1940a) A	Bonner & Bonner(1938)	Unique	None	—	—	
Bourgin & Nitsch(1967) H		Lin & Staba(1961)	Unique	Nitsch & Nitsch(1965) K & S	Skoog(1944)	—	—	

Medium	Additions	Macronutrients	Micronutrients	Vitamins	Amino acids/Amides	Sug./Alc.	Org. Acids	Notes
Bourgin & Nitsch(1967) Simple		Murashige & Skoog(1962)	Bourgin & Nitsch(1967) H	None	None	—	—	
Boxus(1974a)		Knop(1865)	Murashige & Skoog(1962)	Murashige & Skoog(1962)	Skoog(1944)	—	—	
Brown & Lawrence(1968)		Murashige & Skoog(1962)	Murashige & Skoog(1962)	Wood & Brown(1961) A	Unique	—	—	
Campbell & Durzan(1975)		Unique	Murashige & Skoog(1962)	Linsmaier & Skoog(1965)	None	—	—	
Canas & Benbadis(1988) OM		Unique	Unique	Nitsch & Nitsch(1965) K & S	Unique	—	—	
Canas & Benbadis(1988) OMc		Sarwar(1984)	Canas & Benbadis(1988) OM	Nitsch & Nitsch(1965) K & S	Murashige & Skoog(1962) Supplemented	—	—	
Canas & Benbadis(1988) OMe		0.25 × Canas & Benbadis(1988) OM	0.25 × Canas & Benbadis(1988) OM	Unique	Unique	—	—	
Canas & Benbadis(1988) OMr		0.5 × Canas & Benbadis(1988) OM	0.5 × Canas & Benbadis(1988) OM	None	None	—	—	
Chaleff(1983a) R3		Unique	Murashige & Skoog(1962)	Linsmaier & Skoog(1965)	None	—	—	
Chaleff(1983a) R3 Succ.		Chaleff(1983) R3,but see notes	Murashige & Skoog(1962)	Linsmaier & Skoog(1965)	None	—	Y	See notes
Chaleff(1983a) R3 (NH4) MES		Chaleff(1983) R3 (NH4)	Murashige & Skoog(1962)	Linsmaier & Skoog(1965)	None	—	Y	
Chaleff(1983a) R3 (NH4) Succ.		As R3 (NH4) above, but see notes	Murashige & Skoog(1962)	Linsmaier & Skoog(1965)	None	—	Y	See notes
Cheng(1977;1978a)		0.5 × Murashige & Skoog(1962)	Unique	Unique	None	—	—	
Chu & Hill(1988) MN6		Chu et al.(1975) N6	Unique	Skoog(1944)	Skoog(1944)	—	—	
Chu et al.(1975) N6		Unique	Unique	Unique	Skoog(1944)	—	—	
Chu(1978;1981)		Chu et al.(1975) N6	Chu et al.(1975) N6	Unique	Skoog(1944)	—	—	See notes
Cresswell & Nitsch(1975)		0.5 × Knop(1865)	Unique	Nitsch & Nitsch(1965) K & S	Skoog(1944)	—	—	
Curir et al.(1988) Exp.		Unique	Murashige & Skoog(1962)	Unique	Unique	—	—	
Dabin & Bouharmont(1983) A		Unique	Murashige & Skoog(1962)	Murashige & Skoog(1962)	Skoog(1944)	—	—	
Dabin & Bouharmont(1983) B		Unique	Murashige & Skoog(1962)	Murashige & Skoog(1962)	Skoog(1944)	—	—	
Davis et al.(1977) MS-3.		Murashige & Skoog(1962)	Murashige & Skoog(1962)	Unique	Skoog(1944)	—	—	
De Fossard et al.(1974a) LOW		Unique	Unique	Unique	Unique	—	—	See notes
De Fossard et al.(1974a) MEDIUM		Unique	Unique	Unique	Unique	—	—	See notes
De Fossard et al.(1974a) HIGH		Unique	Unique	Unique	Unique	—	—	See notes
De Greef & Jacobs(1979) PGoB		Unique	Unique	Gamborg(1966) PRL-4-C	None	—	—	
Debergh & Maene(1977)		Murashige & Skoog(1962)	Nitsch & Nitsch(1965) K & S	Unique	Matsubara & Nakahira(1966)	—	—	
Debergh et al.(1981)		Murashige & Skoog(1962)	Bourgin & Nitsch(1967) H	Linsmaier & Skoog(1965)	None	—	—	
Doerschug & Miller(1967)		Miller(1961a;1963)	Unique	Unique	None	—	—	
Dudits et al.(1975) T		Unique	Unique	Unique	Unique	—	—	
Dunstan & Short(1977a) BDS		Unique	Gamborg et al(1968) B5	Gamborg(1966) PRL-4-C	None	—	—	
Eccher et al.(1986)	80 mg/l AdS	Unique	Unique	Unique	Skoog(1944)	—	—	
Economou & Read(1984)		Unique	Unique	Linsmaier & Skoog(1965)	None	—	—	
Eeuwens & Blake(1977)		Eeuwens(1976) Y3	Eeuwens(1976) Y3	Venverloo(1973)	Unique	—	—	

MEDIA DERIVATIONS

Medium	CM								Notes
Eeuwens(1976) Y3		Unique	Unique	Unique	None	—	—	—	
Elliott(1970) L-S		Murashige & Skoog(1962)	Elliott(1969) M-S	Unique	None	—	—	—	
Eriksson(1965) 1.		Unique	Unique	Unique	Skoog(1944)	—	—	—	
Eriksson(1965) 2.		As Medium 1. above	As Medium 1. above	Unique	Skoog(1944)	—	—	—	See notes
Evaldsson & Welander(1985)		Quoirin & Lepoivre(1977) B	Murashige & Skoog(1962)	Murashige & Skoog(1962)	Skoog(1944)	—	—	—	
Evans et al.(1976) HRM		Unique	Murashige & Skoog(1962)	Unique	None	—	—	—	
Finer & Nagasawa(1988) 10A40N		Unique	Murashige & Skoog(1962)	Gamborg(1966) PRL-4-C	Unique	—	—	—	
Franco & Swartz(1985) CBM		Lin & Staba(1961)	Unique	Nitsch & Nitsch(1965) K & S	None	—	—	—	
Franco & Swartz(1985) GDM		Gamborg(1966) PRL-4-C	Gresshoff & Doy(1972a,b) DBM-1	Sommer et al.(1975)	None	—	—	—	
Gamborg(1966) PRL-4-C		Unique	Unique	Unique	Unique	—	—	—	
Gamborg & Eveleigh(1968) PRL-4		SAME AS Gamborg(1966) PRL-4-C							See notes
Gamborg et al.(1968) B5		Unique	Unique	Gamborg(1966) PRL-4-C	None	—	—	—	See notes
Garve et al.(1980)		Murashige & Skoog(1962)	Button & Botha(1975)	Unique	Koblitz & Hagen(1962)	—	—	—	
Gautheret(1942)		0.5 × Knop(1865)	Bertholot(1934) Dilution	Bonner & Devirian(1939) C	White(1939b)	—	—	—	
Green(1982)		Murashige & Skoog(1962)	Murashige & Skoog(1962)	White(1939b)	Unique	—	—	—	See notes
Gresshoff & Doy(1972a,b) DBM 1.		Gamborg(1966) PRL-4-C	Unique	Gamborg(1966) PRL-4-C	Unique	—	—	—	See notes
Gresshoff & Doy(1972a,b) DBM 2.		Blaydes(1966) Version 3.	Unique	Gamborg(1966) PRL-4-C	As DBM 1. Medium above	—	—	—	See notes
Gresshoff & Doy(1972b) DBM 3.		Gamborg(1966) PRL-4-C	Gresshoff & Doy(1972a,b) DBM 1.	Unique	None	—	—	—	
Gupta & Durzan(1985)		Unique	Unique	Chu et al.(1975) N6	Skoog(1944)	—	—	—	
Gupta et al.(1980) Wh.		White(1954;1963)	Unique	Bonner & Devirian(1939) C	White(1939b)	—	—	—	
Gupta et al.(1981)		Murashige & Skoog(1962)	Murashige & Skoog(1962)	Unique	Skoog(1944)	—	—	—	
Hahlbrock et al.(1974)		Gamborg et al.(1968) B5	Unique	Gamborg(1966) PRL-4-C	None	—	—	—	
Halperin & Minocha(1973)		Unique	Unique	Unique	None	—	—	—	
Halperin & Wetherell(1965) A		Unique	Lin & Staba(1961)	Halperin(1964)	None	—	—	—	
Halperin & Wetherell(1965) B		Unique	Lin & Staba(1961)	Halperin(1964)	None	—	—	—	
Hasegawa(1979)		Murashige & Skoog(1962)	Murashige & Skoog(1962)	Gamborg(1966) Modified White	Skoog(1944)	—	—	—	
Heinz & Mee(1969)	CM	Murashige & Skoog(1962)	Murashige & Skoog(1962)	Unique	None	—	—	—	
Heller(1953;1955)		Unique	Unique	None	None	—	—	—	
Hildebrandt et al.(1946) Tobacco		Unique	Hildebrandt et al.(1946) Tobacco	Bonner & Devirian(1939) B	White(1939b)	—	—	—	
Hildebrandt(1962) C and D	CM	Hildebrandt et al.(1946) Tobacco	Hildebrandt et al.(1946) Tobacco	Unique	White(1939b)	—	—	—	See notes
Hoagland & Snyder(1933)		Unique	Unique	None	None	—	—	—	
Horgan & Aitken(1981) 1.		Schenk & Hildebrandt(1972)	Unique	Schenk & Hildebrandt(1972)	None	—	—	—	
Horgan & Aitken(1981) 2.		Gamborg(1966) PRL-4-C	As Medium 1. above	Sommer et al.(1975) 1.	None	—	—	—	
Hussey(1978a)		0.5 × Murashige & Skoog(1962)	0.5 × Murashige & Skoog(1962)	Ziv et al.(1970)	None	—	—	—	See notes
Jelaska(1987)		Lloyd & McCown(1981) WPM	Lloyd & McCown(1981) WPM	Gamborg(1966) Modified White	Skoog(1944)	—	—	—	
Jona & Gribaudo(1987) A		Lin & Staba(1961)	Bourgin & Nitsch(1976) H	Unique	Unique	—	—	—	

Medium	Additions	Macronutrients	Micronutrients	Vitamins	Amino acids/Amides	Sug./Alc.	Org. Acids	Notes
Jona & Gribaudo(1987) B		Unique	Poirier-Hamon et al.(1974) Stem	Jona & Gribaudo(1987) A	Jona & Gribaudo(1987) A	—	—	
Jona & Vigliocco(1985) A		Murashige & Skoog(1962)	Unique	Unique	Skoog(1944)	—	—	
Jona & Vigliocco(1985) B		Unique	Unique	Unique	None	—	—	
Jones & Murashige(1974) A	AdSh	Murashige & Skoog(1962)	Murashige & Skoog(1962)	Reinert & Mohr(1967) 1.	Skoog(1944)	—	Y	
Jones & Murashige(1974) B	AdSh	Unique	Murashige & Skoog(1962)	Linsmaier & Skoog(1965)	None	—	—	
Jones et al.(1977)		Murashige & Skoog(1962)	Jones(1967)	Linsmaier & Skoog(1965)	None	—	—	
Kao & Michayluk(1975) 8.	CM	Unique	Gamborg(1966) PRL-4-C	Unique	Kao et al.(1974) 2. & 3.	Y	Y	See notes
Kao & Michayluk(1975) 8p.	CM	As Medium 8. above	Gamborg(1966) PRL-4-C	As Medium 8. above	Kao et al.(1974) 2. & 3.	Y	Y	See notes
Kao(1977) Cell	CM	Kao & Michayluk(1975) 8.	Gamborg et al.(1968) B5	Unique	Kao et al.(1974) 2. & 3.	Y	Y	See notes
Kartha et al.(1974a)		Murashige & Skoog(1962)	Murashige & Skoog(1962)	Gamborg(1966) PRL-4-C	None	—	—	
Kasperbauer & Reinert(1967)		Murashige & Skoog(1962)	Unique	Murashige & Skoog(1962)	Skoog(1944)	—	—	
Kaul & Staba(1968)		Murashige & Skoog(1962)	Murashige & Skoog(1962)	Unique	None	—	—	
Knop(1865)		Unique	See notes	None	None	—	—	See notes
Knudson(1922;1943) B		Unique	Unique	None	None	—	—	See notes
Knudson(1946) C		Knudson(1922;1943) B	Unique	None	None	—	—	
Kumar et al.(1988) L-6		Unique	Murashige & Skoog(1962)	Gamborg(1966) PRL-4-C	Kapoor(1959)	Y	—	See notes
Kunisaki(1975)		Murashige & Skoog(1962)	Murashige & Skoog(1962)	Unique	None	—	—	
Kunisaki(1990) 1.		Unique	Murashige & Skoog(1962)	Kunisaki(1975)	None	—	—	
Kunisaki(1990) 2.		Unique	Murashige & Skoog(1962)	None	None	—	—	
Kyte & Briggs(1979) I	AdS	Anderson(1978;1980)	Unique	Linsmaier & Skoog(1965)	None	—	—	
Kyte & Briggs(1979) R		0.33 × Anderson(1978;1980)	Unique	Unique	None	—	—	
Lin & Staba(1961)		Unique	Unique	Unique	None	—	—	See notes
Lindemann et al.(1970) 1.		Unique	Unique	None	None	—	—	
Lindemann et al.(1970) 2.		As Medium 1. above	As Medium 1. above	Unique	Unique	—	—	
Linsmaier & Skoog(1965)		Murashige & Skoog(1962)	Murashige & Skoog(1962)	Unique	None	—	—	See notes
Linsmaier & Skoog(1965) Supplemented	AdS	Murashige & Skoog(1962)	Murashige & Skoog(1962)	Linsmaier & Skoog(1965) & see notes	See notes	—	—	See notes
Linsmaier-Bednar & Skoog(1967)		Murashige & Skoog(1962)	Murashige & Skoog(1962)	Unique	None	—	—	
Litvay et al.(1981) LM		Unique	Unique	Wood & Braun(1961) A	None	—	—	
Lloyd & McCown(1981) WPM		Unique	Unique	Mullin et al.(1974) B	Skoog(1944)	—	—	See notes
Maheswaran & Williams(1984) EC6		0.5 × Eriksson(1965) 1.	Blake(1966)	None & see notes	Smith(1944)	—	—	See notes
Margara(1977b;1978) N5K		Unique	Unique	None specified	None	—	—	See notes
Margara(1977b;1978) N15Ca		Unique	As for Medium N5K above	None specified	None	—	—	See notes

MEDIA DERIVATIONS

Margara(1977b;1978) N15K		Unique	As for Medium N5K above	None specified	None	–	–	See notes
Margara(1977b;1978) N30Ca		Unique	As for Medium N5K above	None specified	None	–	–	See notes
Margara(1977b;1978) N30K		Unique	As for Medium N5K above	None specified	None	–	–	See notes
Margara(1977b;1978) N30NH4		Unique	As for Medium N5K above	None specified	None	–	–	See notes
Margara(1977b;1978) N45K		Unique	As for Medium N5K above	None specified	None	–	–	See notes
Margara(1977b;1978) N5Ca		Unique	As for Medium N5K above	None specified	None	–	–	See notes
Margara(1978) N60			As for medium N5K above	None specified		–	–	See notes
Miller & Murashige(1976) I.	AdS	Jones & Murashige(1974) B	Murashige & Skoog(1962)	Linsmaier & Skoog(1965)	None	–	–	
Miller & Murashige(1976) II.	AdS	Murashige et al.(1972b)	Murashige & Skoog(1962)	Linsmaier & Skoog(1965)	None	–	–	
Miller & Murashige(1976) III.		Unique	Murashige & Skoog(1962)	Linsmaier & Skoog(1965)	None	–	–	See notes
Miller & Murashige(1976) IV.		Thorpe & Murashige(1968;1970) Sf	Murashige & Skoog(1962)	Linsmaier & Skoog(1965)	None	–	–	
Miller & Skoog(1953)		Unique	White(1938b)	Skoog & Tsui(1948)	Skoog(1944)	–	–	
Miller et al.(1956)		Unique	Unique	Bonner & Devirian(1939) C	Skoog(1944)	–	–	See notes
Miller(1961a;1963)		Unique	Fox & Miller(1959)	Bonner & Devirian(1939) C	Skoog(1944)	–	–	See notes
Miller(1968)		Miller(1961a;1963)	Miller(1965;1967)	Unique	None	–	–	
Millerd et al.(1975) 1.		Unique	Murashige & Skoog(1962)	Linsmaier & Skoog(1965)	Unique	–	–	
Millerd et al.(1975) 2.		Unique	Murashige & Skoog(1962)	Linsmaier & Skoog(1965)	As Medium 1. above	–	–	
Mitra et al.(1976) A		Unique	Unique	Unique	None	–	–	
Molnar(1988b)		Murashige & Skoog(1962)	Unique	Gamborg(1966) PRL-4-C	None	–	Y	See notes
Mullin et al.(1974) A		Knop(1865)	Unique	White(1937c)	None	–	–	
Mullin et al.(1974) B		Knop(1865)	As medium A above	Unique	Skoog(1944)	–	–	
Murashige & Skoog(1962)		Unique	Unique	Unique	Skoog(1944)	–	–	See notes
Murashige & Skoog(1962) Supplemented		Murashige & Skoog(1962)	Murashige & Skoog(1962)	Murashige & Skoog(1962)	Unique	–	–	See notes
Murashige & Skoog(1962) a:deF		Unique	Unique	Unique	Unique	–	–	See notes
Murashige & Tucker(1969)		Murashige & Skoog(1962)	Murashige & Skoog(1962)	Murashige & Skoog(1962)	Skoog(1944)	–	–	See notes
Murashige et al.(1972b)	AdS	Unique	Murashige & Skoog(1962)	Murashige & Skoog(1962) & see notes	Rangan et al.(1968)	–	–	See notes
Murashige et al.(1974)	AdS	Jones & Murashige(1974) B	Murashige & Skoog(1962)	Unique	Thorpe & Murashige(1968;1970) Sf	–	–	See notes
Nagata & Takebe(1970)		Unique	Takebe et al.(1968)	Heinz & Mee(1969)	Skoog(1944)	Y	–	
Nagata & Takebe(1971)		Unique	Murashige & Skoog(1962)	Heinz & Mee(1969)	None	Y	–	
Nickell & Maretzki(1969) 1.		Unique	Unique	Unique & see notes	Unique	–	–	See notes
Nickell & Maretzki(1969) 2.		As Medium 1 above	As Medium 1 above	As Medium 1 above	Unique	–	–	
Nitsch & Nitsch(1956) N1.		Unique	None	None	None	Y	–	
Nitsch & Nitsch(1965) K		0.5 × Knop(1865)	Unique	Unique	Unique	–	–	
Nitsch & Nitsch(1965) S		Murashige & Skoog(1962)	As Medium K above	As Medium K above	As Medium K above	–	–	
Nitsch & Nitsch(1969) H		SAME AS Bourgin & Nitsch(1967) H						See notes
Nitsch(1951) 1.		0.5 × Knop(1865)	Unique	None	None	–	–	

Medium	Additions	Macronutrients	Micronutrients	Vitamins	Amino acids/Amides	Sug./Alc.	Org. Acids	Notes
Nitsch(1968) S		Murashige & Skoog(1962)	Bourgin & Nitsch(1967) H	Nitsch & Nitsch(1965) K & S	Skoog(1944)	—	—	
Norstog(1973) Barley II.		Unique	Graebe & Novelli(1966)	Unique	Unique	—	Y	See notes
Pevalek-Kozlina & Jelaska(1987) WPM (no CT)		Unique	Lloyd & McCown(1981) WPM	Mullin et al.(1974) B	Skoog(1944)	—	—	See notes
Pfeffer(1900) A		Unique	Unique	None	None	—	—	See notes
Pfeffer(1900) B		Unique	As Medium A above	None	None	—	—	See notes
Phillips & Collins(1979a) L2.		Unique	Unique	Unique	None	—	—	
Phillips & Collins(1979a) R		0.5 × Phillips & Collins(1979a) L2.	0.5 × Phillips & Collins(1979a) L2.	Phillips & Collins(1979a) L2.	None	—	—	
Phillips & Collins(1980) SL2.		Unique	Unique	Unique	None	—	—	
Pierik et al.(1974b)		0.5 × Murashige & Skoog(1962)	Murashige & Skoog(1962)	Murashige & Skoog(1962)	Skoog(1944)	—	—	
Quoirin & Lepoivre(1977) A		Murashige & Skoog(1962)	Unique	Jacquiot [Gautheret(1959)]	None	—	—	
Quoirin & Lepoivre(1977) B		Unique	As Medium A above	Jacquiot [Gautheret(1959)]	None	—	—	See notes
Ramming et al.(1990)		Unique	Graebe & Novelli(1966)	Norstog(1973) Barley II	Unique	—	—	
Ramming(1990)		Murashige & Skoog(1962)	Murashige & Skoog(1962)	Murashige & Skoog(1962)	Unique	—	Y	
Ranga Swamy(1961) I		Unique	Unique	Unique	Sachar & Kapoor(1959) NbV	—	—	See notes
Ratnamba & Chopra(1974)		Murashige & Skoog(1962)	Murashige & Skoog(1962)	Nitsch & Nitsch(1965) K & S	Murashige & Skoog(1962) Supplemented	—	—	
Reynolds et al.(1980)	Ad	Unique	Unique	Sangwan & Gorenflot(1975)	Skoog(1944)	—	—	See notes
Reynolds et al.(1982a)	Ad	Gamborg et al.(1968) B5	Gamborg et al.(1968) B5	Gamborg(1966) PRL-4-C	Unique	—	—	
Risser & White(1964)		Unique	Unique	Unique	Unique	—	—	
Roca et al.(1978)		Murashige & Skoog(1962)	Murashige & Skoog(1962)	Unique	Skoog(1944)	—	—	
Rodriguez & Lorenzo Martin(1987) MH		Unique	Murashige & Skoog(1962)	Murashige & Skoog(1962)	Skoog(1944)	—	—	
Rodriguez(1982b) K(h)		Murashige & Skoog(1962)	Murashige & Skoog(1962)	Unique	None	—	—	
Roh & Wocial(1989)		Unique	Cheng(1975) Basal	Heinz & Mee(1969)	None	—	—	
Rose & Martin(1975) P2.		Unique	Murashige & Skoog(1962)	Veliky & Martin(1970) 67-V	None	—	—	
Sangwan & Harada(1975)		Murashige & Skoog(1962)	Veliky & Martin(1970) 67-V	Nitsch & Nitsch(1965) K & S	None	—	—	
Schenk & Hildebrandt(1972)		Unique	Cresswell & Nitsch(1975)	Unique	None	—	—	
Scowcroft & Adamson(1976) CS5		Unique	Schenk & Hildebrandt(1972)	Schenk & Hildebrandt(1972)	None	—	—	
Sears & Deckard(1982)		SAME AS Green(1982)						
Singha et al.(1985)		Murashige & Skoog(1962)	Murashige & Skoog(1962)	Passey & Jones(1983)	None	—	—	
Skirvin & Chu(1978a,b)		Murashige & Skoog(1962)	Murashige & Skoog(1962)	Unique	None	—	—	See notes
Skoog(1944)		Unique	White(1938b)	Bonner & Devirian(1939) B	Unique	—	—	
Snir & Erez(1980) R		0.5 × Murashige & Skoog(1962)	0.5 × Murashige & Skoog(1962)	Unique	None	—	—	
Sommer et al.(1975) 1.		Gamborg(1966) PRL-4-C	Gresshoff & Doy(1972a,b) DBM 1.	Unique	None	—	—	

MEDIA DERIVATIONS

Medium									
Sommer et al.(1975) 2.			Gresshoff & Doy(1972a,b) DBM 1.	As medium 1. above	None	—	—	—	
Sommer et al.(1975) 3.			Unique	As medium 1. above	None	—	—	—	
Standardi & Catalano(1985) 1.		Zimmerman(1984a) Lep	Bourgin & Nitsch(1967) H	Unique	Skoog(1944)	—	—	—	
Standardi & Catalano(1985) 2.		Zimmerman(1984a) Lep	Unique	Elliott(1970) L-S	None	—	—	—	
Standardi & Catalano(1985) 3.		0.5 × Zimmerman(1984) Lep	Unique	Elliott(1970) L-S	None	—	—	—	
Stapfer & Heuser(1985)		Lloyd & McCown(1981) WPM	Lloyd & McCown(1981) WPM	Murashige & Skoog(1962)	None	—	—	—	
Staudt(1984) M2.		Unique	Unique	Unique	None	—	—	—	
Staudt(1984) M2-2.		Unique	Staudt(1984) M2.	Unique	None	—	—	—	
Strullu et al.(1986)		Unique	Unique	Morel & Wetmore(1951b)	None	—	—	—	
Syono & Furuya(1972)		Murashige & Skoog(1962)	Murashige & Skoog(1962)	Murashige & Skoog(1962)	None	—	—	—	See notes
Thomale(1954) GD		Unique	Burgeff(1936) Eg1.	None	None	Y	—	—	See notes
Thompson et al.(1977)		Unique	Unique	Unique	Unique	—	—	—	See notes
Thorpe & Meier(1973) Sf	90 mg/l AdS	Unique	Murashige & Skoog(1962)	Linsmaier & Skoog(1965)	Unique	—	—	—	
Thorpe & Murashige(1968;1970) Sf	AdS	Unique	Unique	Linsmaier & Skoog(1965)	Unique	—	—	—	
Tran Thanh Van(1973a)		Murashige & Skoog(1962)	Murashige & Skoog(1962)	Earle & Torrey(1965b) Callus	None	—	—	—	
Tukey(1933) I		Unique	Unique	None	None	—	—	—	
Tukey(1933) II		Unique	Unique	None	Unique	—	—	—	
Uchimiya & Murashige(1974) C		Murashige & Skoog(1962)	Murashige & Skoog(1962)	Murashige & Tucker(1969)	Unique	—	—	—	
Vacin & Went(1949)		Unique	Unique	None	None	—	—	—	
Vasil & Hildebrandt(1966c) C	CM	Hildebrandt et al.(1946) Tobacco	As Medium T above	Hildebrandt(1962) C	White(1939b)	—	—	—	
Veliky & Martin(1970) 67-V		Unique	Unique	Unique	Gamborg(1966) PRL-4-C	Y	—	—	
Von Arnold & Eriksson(1977) LP		Unique	Unique	Unique	Unique	Y	—	—	
Von Arnold & Eriksson(1979a) LPm		Von Arnold & Eriksson(1977) LP	Von Arnold & Eriksson(1977) LP	Von Arnold & Eriksson(1977) LP	Von Arnold & Eriksson(1977) LP	Y	—	—	
Von Arnold & Eriksson(1981) LPm		Unique	Unique	Unique	Von Arnold & Eriksson(1977) LP	—	—	—	
Wetherell(1969)		Unique	Unique	Unique	None	—	—	—	
White(1942)		Unique	Unique	Not specified	Not specified	—	—	—	See notes
White(1943a) A		White(1942)	White(1942)	Bonner & Devirian(1939) C	White(1939b)	—	—	—	See notes
White(1954)		Unique	Unique	Bonner & Devirian(1939) C	White(1939b)	—	—	—	See notes
White(1963)		Unique	Unique	Bonner & Devirian(1939) C	White(1939b)	—	—	—	See notes
Wood & Braun(1961) A		White(1954)	White(1942)	Unique	Unique	—	—	—	
Wood & Braun(1961) B		Unique	Unique	As Medium A above	White(1939b)	—	—	—	
Yang & Chang(1979)		Murashige & Skoog(1962)	Murashige & Skoog(1962)	Wood & Braun(1961) A	None	—	—	—	
Yasuda et al.(1985)		Unique	Unique	Gamborg(1966) PRL-4-C	None	—	—	—	
Zapata et al.(1983) MY1.		Murashige & Skoog(1962)	Murashige & Skoog(1962)	Murashige & Skoog(1962) & see notes	Unique	—	—	—	See notes
Zimmerman & Broome(1980) Z-2.	80 mg/l AdSh	Unique	Button & Botha(1975)	Linsmaier & Skoog(1965)	None	—	—	—	See notes
Zimmerman & Broome(1980) Z-3.	AdSh	0.5 × Zimmerman & Broome(1980) Z-2.	Unique	Linsmaier & Skoog(1965)	None	—	—	—	
Zimmerman(1984a) WPMm		Unique	Unique	Mullin et al.(1974) B	Skoog(1944)	—	—	—	See notes
Ziv et al.(1970)	AdS	Unique	Murashige & Skoog(1962)	Unique	Skoog(1944)	—	—	—	

Supplementary Notes

Anderson (1978;1980). This medium was first described in 1978, but only in a scientific abstract; the 1980 reference is the first published paper in which it seems to be listed. The medium is also described in full in Anderson(1984) where it is said to be used in commercial laboratories for the propagation of *Kalmia, Arcostaphylos, Vaccinium, Rubus,* and *Corylus* as well as *Rhododendron.* It is commonly known as Anderson's Rhododendron medium. Anderson's rooting medium is of the same composition, but adenine sulphate dihydrate is omitted and 600 mg/l activated charcoal included.

Atanassov & Brown (1984) B5h. Said to be a modification of **Gamborg *et al.* (1968) B5 medium.**

Beretta & Eccher (1987). Said to be a modified version of **Crézé & Beauchesne(1980)** medium.

Berthelot (1934) Dilution. See the notes to the micronutrient table.

Blaydes (1966) Versions 1 and 2. In Blaydes' paper, the weights of salts are given against anhydrous formulae. This has led to several interpretations. We prefer to think that the medium was the same as that of **Miller(1961a;1963)**. Version 2 is an alternative, where the weights of Blaydes are taken to refer to hydrated salts (Saunders & Bingham, 1972, 1975).

Chaleff (1983a) R3 Succ. and R3 (NH₄) Succ. 20 mM succinic acid was added to the medium and the pH adjusted to 6 before autoclaving, with KOH.

Chu (1978; 1981). This medium was published in the proceedings of a meeting held in Peking in 1978. The medium was copied from an English language version of the proceedings published in 1981, but because many authors give the medium a 1978 suffix, both years have been quoted here to avoid confusion.

De Fossard et al. (1974a). In their Broad Spectrum tissue culture experiment, de Fossard *et al.* divided media components into four groups: (1) Macro- & micronutrients (combined); (2) auxins; (3) cytokinins; (4) sucrose and amino acids. The order in which the four groups are referred to is always the same. Each group of constituents could be used independently at one of four levels, viz. zero (not present) (Z); low (L); medium (M) or high (H), to give various combinations of media ingredients. The best combination for any one *in vitro* system was determined by experiment.

In the case of auxins, the HIGH concentration first consisted of 1 mg/l IAA + 2 mg/l IBA + 1 mg/l NAA + 2 mg/l NOA + 2.2 mg/l 2,4-D + 1.9 mg/l CPA. The MEDIUM

concentration of auxins was one tenth of the HIGH concentration and the LOW concentration was one tenth of the MEDIUM. The HIGH concentration of cytokinins consisted of 2.15 mg/l Kin + 2.25 mg/l BAP. The MEDIUM and LOW concentrations of cytokinins were respectively one tenth and one hundredth of the HIGH concentration, as for the auxins.

Eriksson (1965) 2. This version of the medium was only used by Eriksson with small inocula.

Gamborg & Eveleigh (1968) PRL-4. This medium is identical to that of Gamborg(1966) PRL-4-C, except that 28 mg/l Sequestrene 330 Fe (0.05 mM Fe chelated with DTPA) was used instead of 0.05 mM FeEDTA.

Gamborg et al. (1968) B5. This medium originally contained 0.05 mM in the form of Sequestrene 330 Fe. Another commonly used version is the adjustment described by Gamborg(1982) in which 0.1 mM Fe is used supplied by FeEDTA.

Green(1982). A medium of C.E. Green given in Sears & Deckard(1982).

Gresshoff & Doy (1972a,b) DBM 1. & DBM 2. Gresshoff & Doy(1973) make it clear that there was a typographical error in their 1972b paper. It wrongly indicated that the vitamins used were one tenth the concentration given in Gresshoff & Doy(1972a & 1974) DBM 1 & 2 media. The concentrations given in the Vitamin table here are authentic. Sommer *et al.* (1975) employed the one tenth dilution in their version of DBM 1 & 2. McCown & Amos(1979) also added the one tenth vitamin supplement to Gresshoff & Doy salts.

Hoagland & Snyder (1933). This was originally published as a solution for hydroponic plant culture. The macronutrients are often called Hoagland's solution. Note that there is an alternative, incorrect version of Hoagland's solution given by Heller(1953). The micronutrients which were originally recommended to accompany the major salts of Hoagland & Snyder for hydroponic culture, are called A-Z Supplements.

Hussey (1978a). Iron was added as 25 mg/l "ferrous ethylene diamine sulphate". We were not sure what molar concentration of Fe this represented but have supposed it to have been 0.05 mM [i.e. half that in Murashige & Skoog(1962)].

Knop (1865). Variously described by different authorities to contain a trace of FeCl₃, FePO₄ or FeSO₄. Hewitt(1966), quoting Knop(1861), says that Knop used from a trace up to 0.1 g/l FePO₄. The version which we have listed simply as **Knop (1865)** is the one commonly used in plant tissue culture work, especially by

MEDIA DERIVATIONS

European workers. There are several other versions of Knop's solution which differ from each other and from the version listed here.

Knudson (1922;1943) B. The version published in 1922 was revised by Knudson in 1925 and 1943. We give the medium as given in Knudson(1943) which corrects an apparent error and makes it clear which chemical hydrates were used. See the notes to the Macronutrients table.

Kumar et al. (1988) L-6. MS micronutrients were probably used, however the paper says that 22 mg/l $MnSO_4.H_2O$ and 27.85 NaFeEDTA were employed. A transcription error is assumed.

Lin & Staba(1961). The salts were an unpublished formula of Murashige.

Linsmaier & Skoog (1965). The authors termed this medium RM-1964 [cf. Murashige & Skoog(1962)], but we have not met this terminology in the literature.

Linsmaier & Skoog (1965) Supplemented. Some optional constituents were listed for this medium as follows:

p-Aminobenzoic acid	0.1 mg/l
Tyrosine	100.0 mg/l
Amino acid mixture (Lamotte, 1961)	
Casein hydrolysate (Edamine)	1000–3000 mg/l
Braun's supplement:	
Cytidylic acid	200 mg/l
Guanylic acid	200 mg/l
L-Asparagine	500 mg/l
L-Glutamine	500 mg/l
Tobacco leaf extract	
(Murashige & Skoog, 1962).	

Adenine sulphate 40 mg/l and gibberellic acid 1 mg/l were also listed but are considered by the present author to be growth regulating substances and not media components.

Lloyd & McCown (1981) WPM. WPM stands for "Woody Plant Medium". This medium is often referred to as **Lloyd & McCown(1980)** medium because the medium was first given in the 1980 proceedings of the International Plant Propagator's Society; but this was not published until 1981, and the publication date should have precedence.

Maheswaran & Williams (1984) EC6. Extra vitamins would have been provided by the yeast extract added to the medium.

Margara (1977;1978). As with (1969a,b) C medium, no vitamins were specified for use with these media. The macronutrients of N 60 are a 'tidied' version of those of **MS** medium.

Miller & Murashige (1976) III. This formulation is marketed commercially as **Murashige's Fern Multiplication** medium.

Miller et al. (1956). Weights given in the paper were for anhydrous compounds (Miller(1961a; 1963; 1965).

Miller (1961a;1963). This medium has been interpreted in various ways. We believe our version to be correct (see above). An alternative versions of Miller's medium is listed under **Blaydes(1966)**. In describing the components, Miller(1961a) has 500 mg/l $Ca(NO_3)_2.4H_2O$ as the only hydrated salt. In the 1963 paper, 347 mg/l anhydrous $Ca(NO_3)_2$ is given and all other salts have anhydrous formulae. In 1965, 1967 and 1968 papers, Miller gives hydrated formulae with adjusted weights.

Molnar (1988). This medium is almost the same as that of **Kartha et al. (1974a)**. It differs in having slightly more iron.

Murashige & Skoog (1962). The authors termed this medium RM-1962. It is sometimes referred to as **RM** medium, or more commonly, as **MS** medium. We have used the abbreviation **MS** throughout this book.

Murashige & Skoog (1962) Supplemented. The medium is identical to Murashige & Skoog(1962) except that 1000 mg/l CH is added. Casein hydrolysate (Murashige & Skoog used Edamin) was given as an ooptional addition. Tobacco leaf extract was also found to stimulate the growth of tobacco callus, but was finally not recommended as an additive, being an undefined ingredient. Tobacco leaf extract was however given as an optional extra by Linsmaier & Skoog(1965) [see above].
The leaf extract was prepared as follows:

465 kg of tobacco leaves were frozen and, in this state, were ground in a meat grinder and thawed. The juice was then expressed, heated to 100°C, chilled to 5–10°C, centrifuged and then concentrated under reduced pressure. The resulting 216 litres of liquid contained 12.6 kg solids. Growth stimulation was obtained by adding 3.75 g solids (i.e. 5.96 ml of juice) to each litre of MS medium.

Murashige & Skoog (1962) a:deF. This is a 'tidied' version of **MS** medium given by de Fossard (1976) (see the text of Chapter 10). Another 'tidied' version of **MS** macronutrients are those of **Margara (1977b)** N60.

Murashige & Tucker (1969). As given by Skirvin(1981). Adding orange juice (100 ml/l) improved callus growth of *Citrus*. Orange juice may be counted as a source of citric acid and vitamins.

Murashige et al. (1972b). Extra vitamins would have been provided by the malt extract added to the medium.

Murashige et al. (1974). Adenine sulphate was omitted if the medium was used prior to transplanting.

Nickell & Maretzki (1969) 1. Vitamins would also have been provided by the yeast extract added to this medium.

Nitsch & Nitsch (1969). This paper contains a misprint: $FeSO_4.7H_2O$ (but not NaEDTA) was listed as being included at one tenth of the proper concentration. Nitsch(1969) points out the error and says that the intended iron level was (27.85 mg/l) $FeSO_4.7H_2O$. We have however listed the medium in the Micronutrient Table with the lower iron level because some workers have used it in this form [e.g. Chopra & Ratnamba(1975)]. With the higher iron level the medium is the same as that of Bourgin & Nitsch(1967) H.

Norstog (1973) Barley II. Norstog said he used 25 µg/l Na_2MoO_4. We have taken this to be 25 µg of the $2H_2O$ salt. Norstog had used hydrated sodium molybdate formerly. Moreover the medium is usually given as containing this weight of $Na_2MoO_4.2H_2O$, e.g. by Yeung et al. (1981) and Bhojwani & Razdan (1983).

Pevalek-Kozlina & Jelaska (1987). They used a version of WPM without chloride ions. No recipe is given and so an estimated version of the macronutrients is given in Table 48.

Pfeffer (1900) A. In the translation of Pfeffer's book by Ewart(1900), it says that "good nutrient solutions are obtained from calcium nitrate (4 g), potassium nitrate (1 g), magnesium sulphate (1 g), potassium dihydrogen phosphate (1 g) and potassium chloride (0.5 g) when the salts are dissolved in either 7 litres or 3 litres of water". The Pfeffer solution which we have termed medium A in the table, is achieved by dissolving the salts in 5 litres (i.e. an average of 7 litres and 3 litres). This version has been commonly adopted as Pfeffer's solution [e.g. by Knudson(1922;1925); Miller(1931)]. See the supplementary notes to the Micronutrient table regarding the addition of ferric chloride. Heller gives a slightly different version of Pfeffer's solution (see the Macronutrients table notes).

Pfeffer (1900) B. An alternative solution for plant culture given in the 1900 translation of Pfeffer's book. See the supplementary notes to the Micronutrient table regarding the addition of ferric chloride.

Quoirin & Lepoivre (1977) B. We think that the medium is identical to that published by Quoirin et al. (1977). This medium is sometimes called Quoirin's medium, and sometimes attributed to Lepoivre.

Ranga Swamy (1961) 1. Medium 1. is the medium which many Indian researchers have termed 'Modified White's' [see also the notes on White's medium later in this section]. In 1958 Ranga Swamy used a medium very similar to this 1961 version and described the micronutrients as those of Nitsch(1951) plus 0.025 mg/l $CoCl_2$. Nitsch(1951) used 0.025 mg/l $Na_2MoO_4.2H_2O$, but in Ranga Swamy(1961), 0.025 mg/l Na_2MoO_4 (no hydrate) is said to have been used, even though hydrated salts were listed for other micronutrients. Anhydrous sodium molybdate is available and so we must suppose that Ranga Swamy did use the salt in this form. Accordingly, we have entered 29.375 µg/l against it in the Micronutrients table. There is also an anhydrous version of $CoCl_2$ available and we have assumed that Ranga Swamy would have used it [as did Wetmore(1954) — see Wetmore & Rier(1963)], because in contemporary papers by Indian authors, $CoCl_2$ is always referred to as the anhydrate. Note however that Skirvin(1981) lists Ranga Swamy(1961) 1. medium with 25 ug/l of the hydrated Na_2MoO_4 and $CoCl_2$ salts.

Reynolds et al. (1980). In this report the medium was said to contain 38 mg/l Fe citrate. The authors have informed me that this is a misprint: in this and in all subsequent papers 28 mg/l was used. Note that Fe citrate was used in addition to the FeEDTA already in the formulation.

Skirvin & Chu (1978a,b). The composition of this medium is confirmed by Skirvin(1981). No glycine was originally described, but 2 mg/l [i.e. Skoog(1944)] is listed in Skirvin(1981).

Thomale (1954) GD. According to Withner(1959) and Thompson(1977) who assumed that 110 mg/l $Mg(NO_3)_2$ was used by Thomale as the hydrated $(6H_2O)$ salt.

Thompson et al. (1977). A medium designed for the growth of isolated cotyledons.

Thorpe & Meier (1973) Sf. Medium includes 90 mg/l adenine sulphate.

White (1942 to 1963). White developed several media for plant tissue culture. Those published between 1942 and 1963 are often all described as WHITE'S MEDIUM. All the formulations are essentially the same and the various versions and alternatives are given here only for completeness. We recommend that White(1954) [as we have listed it] is used as a standard version of White's medium. This is the same as the standardized version recommended by Singh & Krikorian(1981).

Unfortunately there has been much confusion and lack of clarity in the literature over the precise composition of White's medium. There have been several causes, but in particular:

(1). White listed his medium slightly differently in his successive publications. Authors have frequently stated that they have used White's medium or a "modified White's

MEDIA DERIVATIONS

"medium" without indicating which published version they have employed. Additionally, some modifications, in particular that of Ranga Swamy(1961) 1, have been called "White's medium" by later workers.

(2). The weights of compounds used for White's medium have often been given against the formulae for anhydrous salts. White himself sometimes did this and it is only by studying all his publications that one realises when hydrated salts were intended. Many readers have read a single publication and have assumed that the quoted weights for anhydrous compounds were those for commonly available hydrated salts. These mistakes have been carried over into several textbooks of plant tissue culture, so making them more widespread.

A full review of the many errors in quoting White's medium was provided by Singh & Krikorian(1981). Further comments will be found in the notes to the Macronutrients and Micronutrients tables. Note that the medium of **Ranga Swamy(1961) 1** is so different to White's medium that we have given it a separate entry.

On p. 105 of his 1943 book and on p. 59 of his 1963 one, White seems to indicate that his 1943a A medium was previously used in work published in 1934, 1938 and 1939. We believe this not to be the case: in these papers his 1934 medium is quoted.

White (1963). On page 59 of White's 1963 book, there is a table entitled "Salt Solutions in Common Use for Plant Cell Cultures". One of the media listed is said to be that of "White (1934, 1943a, 1943b)": it is the same as the medium which we have called **White (1943a)** A, except that 0.001 $CuSO_4.5H_2O$ and 0.0001 mg/; MoO_3 are included; a footnote explains that these were added by Boll and Street (1951).

Some people have taken this medium (including the Cu and Mo) to be White's 1963 medium (Owen and Miller, 1992); Singh and Krikorian (1981) in their review of White's media, concluded that the 1943 and the 1963 media were the same, *i.e.* they thought that the medium listed on page 59 (the 1943 medium, ignoring Cu and Mo) was still in use by White in 1963. We think that both these interpretations are mistaken, because on the following page of the book is set out how to prepare **White (1943a)** medium 'modified in current practice'. This is the medium listed in the tables here as **White (1963)**, except that, like other media, it has been listed as a molar solution: White's instructions said that the chemical ingredients should be dissolved in a given volume of water, rather than dissolved and then made up to that volume (giving a molal, rather than a molar solution). We recommend that **White (1963)** should normally be ignored, and that **White (1954)** should be treated as White's medium (see above).

Zapata et al. (1983) MY1. Extra vitamins were provided by the yeast extract added to this medium (see amino acids).

Zimmerman & Broome (1980) Z-2. The medium was employed for culture initiation and shoot multiplication. Also included in the medium are 80 mg/l AdSh, 15 mg/l 2iP, 4 mg/l IAA, 3% sucrose and 0.55% agar.

Zimmerman (1984a) WPMm. A modification of Lloyd & McCown(1981) WPM.

Table 48. Macronutrient compositions. All concentrations are given in mg/l.

Macronutrient author/s	KNO3	NaNO3	NH4NO3	Ca(NO3)2.4H2O	CaCl2.2H2O	MgSO4.7H2O	MgCl2.6H2O	KCl	KH2PO4	K2HPO4	NH4H2PO4	NaH2PO4.H2O	Na2HPO4.2H2O	Na2SO4	K2SO4	(NH4)2SO4	NH4Cl	Notes
Abo El-Nil & Zettler(1976) AZ	2525				220	370					345							
Al-Talib & Torrey(1959)				236		37	71	149	86		57							
Anderson(1975)	950		2000		440	370			170			170						
Anderson(1978a; 1980a)	480		400		440	370						380						
Asokan et al.(1984 c)	950		200		220	185			85							134		
Atanassov & Brown(1984) B5h	3000				h 1020	500						150						
Ault & Blackmon(1985)	1900		1650		440	370			170			150						
Barnes(1979)	1900		1650		440	370			170			100						
Beretta & Eccher(1987)	1200		1000		75	75			270									
Blaydes(1966) Version 2.	1000		1000	347		35		65	300									
Bonner & Devirian(1939) A	85			242		42		61	20									
Bonner(1940 a,b) A	81			236		36		65	20									
Campbell & Durzan(1975)	340		800	980		370		65	170									
Canas & Bendadis(1988) OM	1100		412	600	440	1500		500	340									
Chaleff(1983a) R3(NH4)					440	370			170								1813	
Chu et al.(1975) N6	2830				166	185			400							463		
Curir et al.(1988) Exp.	1200		300	800		300		40	250			120						
Dabin & Bouharmont(1983) A	252.8		165		44	123.3			244.9									
Dabin & Bouharmont(1983) B	250			590.4		250			250									
De Fossard et al.(1974 a) LOW			400.3		147	123.3		141.6	13.6					5.7				
De Fossard et al.(1974 a) MEDIUM	1011		800.5		294.1	369.8						138		63.9				
De Fossard et al.(1974 a) HIGH	2022		1601		441.1	730.5						276		92.3				
De Greef & Jacobs(1979) PGoB	2000				300	500.0		600	250							400		
Dudits et al.(1975) T	1000		1000	260		360		65				165						
Dunstan & Short(1977 a) BDS	2530		320		150	247					230	152				134		
Eccher et al.(1986)	305		480	470		370			205			180						See notes
Economou & Read(1984)	202		400		440	370			408							132		
Eeuwens(1976) Y3	2020				294	247		1492					312				535	

MACRONUTRIENT COMPOSITIONS

Concs. as mg/l

Reference	1	2	3	4	5	6	7	8	9	10	11	12	13
Eriksson(1965) 1.	1900		1200		440	370	340	340					
Evans et al.(1976) HRM	1900				440	370	170	170			500		
Finer & Nagasawa(1988) 10A40N	3033		800.5		440	370	170	170				134	
Gamborg et al.(1968) B5	2500				150	250			150				
Gamborg(1966) PRL-4-C	1000				150	250	300		90	h 37.6		200	
Halperin & Minocha(1973)	4044				h 220	185	68	68					267.5
Halperin & Wetherell(1965) A	6066				h 220	185	68	68					
Heller(1953; 1955)		600			75	250	750		125				
Hildebrandt et al.(1946) Tobacco	80			400		180	65		33	800			
Hoagland & Snyder(1933)	505.5			1180.8		493.0		136.1					See notes
Jona & Gribaudo(1987) B				654.9		123.3	67.1	136.1					
Jona and Vigliocco(1985) B	1820		400	1181		370		348					
Jones & Murashige(1974) B	1900		1650		440	370		170	85				
Kao & Michayluk(1975) 8.	1900		600		600	300	300	170	85				
Knop(1865)	250			1000		250		250			500		See notes
Knudson(1922; 1943) B			1000	1000		250		250					See notes
Kumar et al.(1988) L-6	1000		1000	500	330	179	150	170					
Kunisaki(1990) 1.	475		825		880	740		170					
Kunisaki(1990) 2.	356		619		128	555	113	128					
Lin & Staba(1961)	950		720		h 219.9	185		68					
Lindemann et al.(1970) 1.				h 720	22	h 246	1050	135			1000		See notes
Litvay et al.(1981) LM	1900		1650			1850		340					
Lloyd & McCown(1981) WPM			400	556	96	370		170					See notes
Margara(1977b; 1978) N15 Ca	101		240	944		246	149	136					
Margara(1977b; 1978) N15 K	606		240	354		246	149	136					
Margara(1977b; 1978) N30 Ca	808		480	1180		246	74.5	136					
Margara(1977b; 1978) N30 K	1313		480	590		246	74.5	136					
Margara(1977b; 1978) N30 NH4	606		800	472		246	372.5	136					
Margara(1977b; 1978) N45 K	1818	85	720	944		246	372.5	136					See notes
Margara(1977b; 1978) N5 Ca			80	354	h 292	246	149	136					See notes
Margara(1977b; 1978) N5 K	75.8		80	265.5		246	372.5	136					
Margara(1977b) N60	2022		1601		441.1	369.8		170.1					
Miller & Murashige(1976) III.	1900		1650		440	370		170	255				
Miller & Skoog(1953)	80		400	h 143.9		h 71.7	65	37.5					
Miller et al.(1956)	80		400	h 143.9		h 71.7	65	12					See notes
Miller(1961a; 1963)	1000		1000	500		h 71.7	65	300					See notes
Millerd et al.(1975) 1.					h 582.9	370	400	300					See notes
Millerd et al.(1975) 2.					h 582.9	370	400	1050					See notes

Macronutrient author/s	KNO3	NaNO3	NH4NO3	Ca(NO3)2.4H2O	CaCl2.2H2O	MgSO4.7H2O	MgCl2.6H2O	KCl	KH2PO4	K2HPO4	NH4H2PO4	NaH2PO4.H2O	Na2HPO4.2H2O	Na2SO4	K2SO4	(NH4)2SO4	NH4Cl	Notes
Mitra et al.(1976) A	180			200		250						150				100		
Murashige & Skoog(1962)	1900		1650		440	370			170									
Murashige & Skoog(1962) a:deF	2022		1601		441.1	369.8			204.1									
Murashige et al.(1972 b)	1900		1650		440	370			170			170						
Nagata & Takebe(1970)	101.1				1470.2	246.5			27.2									
Nagata & Takebe(1971)	950		825		220	1233			680									
Nickell & Maretzki(1969) 1.	80			200		175.5		65				16.5		200				
Nitsch & Nitsch(1956) N1.	2000				33	250		1500				250						
Norstog(1973) Barley II					740	740		750	910									See notes
Pevalek-Kozlina & Jelaska(1987) WPM (no Cl⁻)			297.3	709.7		369.8					144.1				110.5			See notes
Pfeffer(1900) A	200			800		200		100	200									See notes
Pfeffer(1900) B	285.7			1142.9		585.7			285.7									See notes
Phillips & Collins(1979 a) L2.	2100		1000		600	435			325			85						
Phillips & Collins(1979 a) SL2.	2100		600		550	400			325			85						
Quoirin & Lepoivre(1977) B	1800		400	200		3600			2700									
Ramming et al.(1990)	160			887.8	h 199	737.1		65				19		200				See notes
Ranga Swamy(1961) 1	80			260	220	360		65	68			h 189.8		200				
Reynolds et al.(1980)	950		720		220	185			68			250						
Risser & White(1964)	80			300		740		65				165		200				
Rodriguez & Lorenzo Martin(1987) MH	3000		800		440	370			170		450							See notes
Rose & Martin(1975) P2.	2200	450		h 144		250			68									
Sarwar(1984)	950		720		166	185					300							
Schenk & Hildebrandt(1972)	2500				200	400					300							
Scowcroft & Adamson(1976) CS5	2505		1240		200	400					460							
Skoog(1944)	80			h 144		h 71.7		65	12.5									
Staudt(1984) M2.	1900		800		450	400			250									See notes
Staudt(1984) M2-2.	1900		800		450	400			350									See notes
Strullu et al.(1986)	375		240	h 354		246		37.5	136							132.5		See notes
Thomale(1954) GD	400		370						300					852.4		60		
Thompson et al.(1977)					440	370		745.5	170									
Thorpe & Meier(1973) Sf	1900		1650		440	370			170			50						
Thorpe & Murashige(1968b; 1970) Sf	1900		1650		440	370			170			340						
Tukey(1933) I	136.4					h 349.0		681.8										See notes
Tukey(1933) II						h 383.9		750										See notes

MACRONUTRIENT COMPOSITIONS

Concs. as mg/l

Reference											See notes
Vacin & Went(1949)	525			250	200	250	250		150	500	See notes
Veliky & Martin(1970) 67-V	800		200	250		340			20	100	
Von Arnold & Eriksson(1977) LP	1900	1200	1760	370	370	340					
Von Arnold & Eriksson(1981) LPm	1900	1200	180	370	370	340					
Wetherell(1969)	4000		h 220	185		68				540	
White(1942)	80		h 287.8	h 737.1	65		16.5	200			See notes
White(1954)	80		287.8	737.1	65		19	200			See notes
White(1963)	80		300	750	65		19	200			See notes
Wood & Braun(1961) B	80	1800	300	720	910		316.5	200		790	
Yasuda et al.(1985)	475		412.5	92.5	110	85					
Zimmerman & Broome(1980) Z-2.	202		160	370		408				198	
Zimmerman(1984 a) Lep.	1800		400	370		272					
Ziv et al.(1970)	1900		1650	370	440		300.7				

Supplementary Notes

Eccher et al.(1986). Specifies 205 mg/l $KH_2PO_4.H_2O$. The use of such a hydrate seems very unlikely. Therefore 205 mg/l KH_2PO_4 (anhydrous) has been entered.

Gamborg et al. (1968) B5. Weights given against molar values were rounded off. Thus as **B5** medium was derived by modification of an original medium which contained 30 mM (given as 3000 mg/l) KNO_3 and 2 mM (given as 500 mg/l) $MgSO_4.7H_2O$, to contain 25 mM KNO_3 and 1 mM $MgSO_4.7H_2O$, the weights used of these two compounds must have been 2500 and 250 mg/l respectively. This interpretation agrees with listings of the medium in later Gamborg papers [e.g. Gamborg (1970)].

Hoagland & Snyder(1933). This is often referred to as 'Hoagland's solution'.

Knop(1865). There is more than one version of Knop's solution (see Derivation Table notes). The one listed here is that which is commonly accepted as Knop's solution in the plant tissue culture literature. It is given in Strasburger's *Textbook of Botany* (Lang, 1921; Harder et al., 1965) *where a trace of ferrous chloride or ferrous sulphate is also prescribed.*

Knudson(1922;1943) B. Also contained 50 mg/l $FePO_4.4H_2O$ and 1000 mg/l $Ca(NO_3)_2.4H_2O$. In 1922 the medium was given as also containing 50 mg/l $Fe_2(PO_4)_3$, and the weight for calcium nitrate was against an anhydrous formula.

Knudson(1925) ammended this to 50 mg/l $FePO_4$ [i.e. instead of $Fe_2(PO_4)_3$] with a 1000 mg/l $Ca(NO_3)_2$. In 1943 Soln. B was said to contain 1000 mg/l $Ca(NO_3)_2.4H_2O$ and 50 mg/l $FePO_4.4H_2O$ and so it is clear that hydrated compounds were always employed.

Lindemann et al.(1970) 1. The authors give 120 mg/l $MgSO_4$ and 500 mg/l $Ca(NO_3)_2$. Equivalent weights of hydrated salts have been entered in the table.

Lloyd & McCown(1981) WPM. Also contained 990 mg/l K_2SO_4.

Margara(1977;1978) N45K. 1 mM $NaNO_3$ inserted to agree with author's table of meq/l.

Margara(1977;1978) N5 Ca. NH_4NO_3 weight ammended to agree with author's table of meq/l.

Miller et al.(1956). Weights of salts given against anhydrous formulae. Other Miller papers lead us to think that these are genuinely anhydrous weights (see Medium derivation table).

Miller(1961a;1963). Compounds mentioned in the paper as being anhydrous are genuinely so (see Medium Derivation table notes).

Millerd et al.(1975) 1 & 2. Also contained 300 mg/l K_2SO_4.

Pevalek-Kozlina & Jelaska(1987) WPM. Used WPM medium without chloride ions. A formulation devised by us which fits this bill and gives the same concentration of major ions as WPM, but more SO_4^{2-} (to compensate for the absence of Cl^-) is given in the table. **Pfeffer(1900) A.** See the notes to the Derivation table. Heller(1953) erroneously gives 250 mg/l KCl instead of the 100 mg/l suggested by Pfeffer.

Pfeffer(1900) B. A little KCl was added in some cases.

Ranga Swamy(1961) 1. The macroelements were originally described as containing 165 mg/l NaH_2PO_4. We believe that this salt commonly exists as the monohydrate; the weight has therefore not been modified.

Sarwar(1984). The macronutrients are an erroneous version of Lin & Staba(1961). They were copied from Long & Kohlenbach(1975), who used the same medium as Kohlenbach & Schmidt(1975). The latter medium uses Lin & Staba(1961) macronutrients.

Staudt(1984) M2. & M2-2. Weights were given against anhydrous formulae, but as rounded figures were used throughout the medium, we have assumed that the weights refer to conventional hydrates and no compensation has been made.

Thomale(1954) GD. Also 110 mg/l $Mg(NO_3)_2.6H_2O$. Withner(1959) and Thompson(1977) assumed that 110 mg/l $Mg(NO_3)$ was used by Thomale as the hydrated (.$6H_2O$) salt. Arditti & Ernst(1977) assumed that weight given for $Mg(NO_3)$ was for an anhydrous compound — see Medium Derivation table notes.

Tukey(1933) I. Following Van Oberbeek et al.(1941) we prefer the assumption that 2 g KNO_3 were added to the original salt mixture for preparing medium I. All the salts were ground together and 1.5 g were dissolved in 1 litre of water. We think that Skirvin(1981) was mistaken when he allowed a total of 2 g/l KNO_3 in the final salt solution. His interpretation gives weights for the other salts of 170.45 mg/l $CaSO_4$, 170.45 mg/l $Ca_3(PO_4)_2$ and 170.45 mg/l $Fe_3(PO_4)_2$. In calculating molar concentrations, we have assumed that $CaSO_4.2H_2O$ and $Fe_3(PO_4)_2.8H_2O$ were used. Neither Tukey nor Van Overbeek et al. indicated whether they employed anhydrous $MgSO_4$ or $MgSO_4.7H_2O$. As an anhydrous form of the chemical is available commercially, we have presumed that it was used originally. Skirvin(1981) took the view that $MgSO_4.7H_2O$ was utilised.

Tukey(1933) II. Also contained 187.5 mg/l $CaSO_4$, 187.5 $Ca_3(PO_4)_2$, 187.5 mg/l $Fe_3(PO_4)_2$. In calculating the molar concentrations, we have assumed that $Ca(SO_4).2H_2O$ and $Fe_3(PO_4)_2.8H_2O$ were used.

Vacin & Went(1949). The medium also contained 200 mg/l $Ca_3(PO_4)_2$.

White(1942). In 1942 White published a review paper in which he showed that the macronutrients in use in his laboratory had been increased in concentration compared to what he had used formerly. No hydrates were given against the salts specified in the 1942 paper, but the same medium is given again on page 103 of White's 1943 book (White,1943a) and here molar concentrations are given against the weights. These make it quite clear that 16.5 mg/l (0.12 mM) $NaH_2PO_4.H_2O$ was used. The same weights of salts are given for White(1943) on page 59 of the (1963) dition of White's second book, *The Cultivation of Animal & Plant Cells*. Thus even though 16.5 mg/l is specified against anhydrous NaH_2PO_4 in 1942, we think it reasonable to assume that both the 1942 and 1943a media are the same. Owen et al. (1992) state that 19 mg/l $NaH_2PO_4.H_2O$ was used: this is incorrect.

White(1954). The macroelement weights of 'White's solution' were wrongly given in the 1954 edition of White's book *The Cultivation of Animal & Plant Cells*, KNO_3 was omitted and the wrong weight of KCl was given. However, 16.5 mg/l NaH_2PO_4 was specified and the reader cautioned to "be sure to make the proper corrections in weights if hydrates of any salts are used". White seemed to have forgotten that he specified 16.5 mg/l $NaH_2PO_4.H_2O$ in 1943.

White(1963). See the notes at the end of the Derivation Table.

Table 49. Ionic composition of macronutrients.

Ionic concentrations are given in meq/l. The total concentration of cations (ΣI^+) equals that of the anions (ΣI^-): *i.e* $\Sigma I = \Sigma I^+ + \Sigma I^-$;
Ratios indicate the relative proportions of NH_4^+ to total N, the proportion of NO_3^- to NH_4^+, and of total N, phosphate and potassium to ΣI^-;
The last column is the total mM ionic concentration (most likely to be proportional to osmotic potential);
To obtain mM concentrations, divide the meq/l figure by the valence of the ion (*i.e.* 3. meq/ NO_3^- ≡ 3.3 mM: 2.5 meq/ Ca^{2+} ≡ 1.25 mM).

Macronutrient author/s	NO_3^- (meq/l)	PO_4^{3-} (meq/l)	SO_4^{2-} (meq/l)	Cl^- (meq/l)	K^+ (meq/l)	Ca^{2+} (meq/l)	Na^+ (meq/l)	Mg^{2+} (meq/l)	NH_4^+ (meq/l)	H^+ (meq/l)	Total N (meq/l)	NH_4^+/N ratio	NO_3^-/NH_4^+ ratio	ΣI^+ (meq/l)	N/ΣI ratio	PO_4^{3-}/ΣI ratio	K^+/ΣI ratio	Total ionic concentration (mM)
Abo El-Nil & Zettler(1976) AZ	24.97	8.99	3	2.99	24.97	2.99		3	2.99	5.99	27.96	0.1	8.35	39.94	0.34	0.1125	0.312	69.4
Al-Talib & Torrey(1959)	1.99	3.38	0.3	2.69	2.63	1.99		0.99	0.49	2.25	2.48	0.19	4.06	8.35	0.14	0.2022	0.157	12.81
Anderson(1975)	34.38	7.44	3	5.98	10.64	5.98	1.23	3	24.98	4.96	59.36	0.42	1.37	50.79	0.58	0.0732	0.104	90.64
Anderson(1978a; 1980a)	9.74	8.26	3	5.98	4.74	5.98	2.75	3	4.99	5.5	14.73	0.33	1.95	26.96	0.27	0.1531	0.087	42.44
Asokan et al.(1984 c)	11.89	1.87	1.5	2.99	10.02	2.99		1.5	2.49	1.24	14.38	0.17	4.77	18.24	0.39	0.0512	0.274	32.24
Atanassov & Brown(1984) B5h	29.67	3.26	6.08	13.87	29.67	13.87	1.08	4.05	2.02	2.17	31.69	0.06	14.68	52.86	0.29	0.0308	0.28	91.56
Ault & Blackmon(1985)	39.4	7	3	5.98	20.04	5.98	1.08	3	20.61	4.67	60.01	0.34	1.91	55.38	0.54	0.0631	0.18	100.1
Barnes(1979)	39.4	5.92	3	5.98	20.04	5.98	0.72	3	20.61	3.94	60.01	0.34	1.91	54.29	0.55	0.0545	0.184	98.65
Beretta & Eccher(1987)	24.36	5.95	0.6	1.02	13.85	1.02		0.6	12.49	3.96	36.85	0.33	1.95	31.92	0.57	0.0931	0.216	58.77
Blaydes(1966) Version 2.	25.32	6.61	0.28	0.87	12.96	2.93		0.28	12.49	4.4	37.81	0.33	2.02	33.06	0.57	0.0999	0.195	59.98
Bonner & Devirian(1939) A	2.89	0.44	0.34	0.81	1.8	2.04		0.34		0.29	2.89	0		4.47	0.32	0.0491	0.201	7.29
Bonner(1940 a,b) A	2.79	0.44	0.29	0.87	1.82	1.99		0.29		0.29	2.79	0		4.39	0.31	0.0501	0.207	7.2
Campbell & Durzan(1975)	21.65	3.74	3	0.87	5.48	8.29		3	9.99	2.49	31.64	0.31	2.16	29.25	0.54	0.0639	0.093	48.87
Canas & Bendadis(1988) OM	21.1	7.49	12.17	12.69	20.08	11.06		12.17	5.14	4.99	26.24	0.19	4.1	53.44	0.24	0.07	0.187	84.19
Chaleff(1983a) R3	30	3.74	3	5.98	26.24	5.98		3	5	2.49	35	0.14	6	42.71	0.4	0.0437	0.307	76.94
Chaleff(1983a) R3 (NH4)		3.74	3	39.87	1.24	5.98		3	33.88	2.49	33.88	1	0	46.59	0.36	0.0401	0.013	84.71
Chu et al.(1975) N6	27.99	8.81	8.5	2.25	30.93	2.25	0.86	1.5	7	5.87	34.99	0.2	3.99	47.55	0.36	0.0926	0.325	83.1
Curir et al.(1988) Exp.	22.39	8.11	2.43	0.53	14.24	6.77		2.43	3.74	5.41	26.13	0.14	5.98	33.45	0.39	0.1212	0.212	55.68
Dabin & Bouharmont(1983) A	4.56	5.39	1	0.59	4.3	0.59		1	2.06	3.59	6.62	0.31	2.21	11.54	0.28	0.2335	0.186	18.19
Dabin & Bouharmont(1983) B	7.47	5.51	2.02		4.3	5		2.02		3.67	7.47	0		14.99	0.24	0.1837	0.143	21.79
De Fossard et al.(1974 a) LOW	5	0.29	1.08	3.89	1.99	1.99	0.08	1	5	0.19	10	0.5	1	10.25	0.48	0.0141	0.097	18.28
De Fossard et al.(1974 a) MEDIUM	20	2.99	3.9	4	10	4	1.89	3	10	1.99	30	0.33	2	30.88	0.48	0.0484	0.161	54.32
De Fossard et al.(1974 a) HIGH	40	5.99	7.22	6	20	6	3.29	5.92	20	3.99	60	0.33	2	59.2	0.5	0.0505	0.168	104.84

Macronutrient author/s	NO3⁻ (meq/l)	PO4³⁻ (meq/l)	SO4²⁻ (meq/l)	Cl⁻ (meq/l)	K⁺ (meq/l)	Ca²⁺ (meq/l)	Na⁺ (meq/l)	Mg²⁺ (meq/l)	NH4⁺ (meq/l)	H⁺ (meq/l)	Total N (meq/l)	NH4⁺/N ratio	NO3⁻/NH4⁺ ratio	ΣI⁺ (meq/l)	N/ΣI ratio	PO4³⁻/ΣI ratio	K⁺/ΣI ratio	Total ionic concentration (mM)
De Greef & Jacobs(1979) PGoB	19.78	5.51	10.11	12.12	29.66	4.08		4.05	6.05	3.67	25.83	0.23	3.26	47.51	0.27	0.0579	0.312	82.23
Dudits et al.(1975) T	24.58	3.58	2.92	0.87	10.76	2.2	1.19	2.92	12.49	2.39	37.07	0.33	1.96	31.95	0.58	0.056	0.168	57.49
Dunstan & Short(1977 a) BDS	29.02	9.3	4.03	2.04	25.02	2.04	1.1	2	8.02	6.2	37.04	0.21	3.61	44.38	0.41	0.1047	0.281	78.53
Eccher et al.(1986)	12.99	8.43	3		4.52	3.98	1.3	3	5.99	5.62	18.98	0.31	2.16	24.41	0.38	0.1726	0.092	38.22
Economou & Read(1984)	6.99	8.99	4.99	5.98	4.99	5.98		3	6.99	5.99	13.98	0.5	1	26.95	0.25	0.1667	0.092	40.92
Eeuwens(1976) Y3	19.98	5.25	2	34.01	39.99	3.99	3.5	2	10	1.75	29.98	0.33	1.99	61.23	0.24	0.0428	0.326	114.97
Eriksson(1965) 1.	33.78	7.49	3	5.98	21.29	5.98		3	14.99	4.99	48.77	0.3	2.25	50.25	0.48	0.0745	0.211	89.51
Evans et al.(1976) HRM	18.79	3.74	10.56	5.98	20.04	5.98		3	7.56	2.49	26.35	0.28	2.49	39.07	0.33	0.047	0.25	65.87
Finer & Nagasawa(1988) 10A40N	40	3.74	3	5.98	31.24	5.98	1.08	3	10	2.49	50	0.2	4	52.71	0.47	0.0354	0.296	96.94
Gamborg et al.(1968) B5	24.72	3.26	4.05	2.04	24.72	2.04		2.02	2.02	2.17	26.74	0.07	12.23	34.05	0.39	0.0478	0.362	61.89
Gamborg(1966) PRL-4-C	9.89	2.59	5.05	6.06	13.91	2.04	1.07	2.02	3.02	1.51	12.91	0.23	3.27	23.57	0.27	0.0549	0.294	40.87
Halperin & Minocha(1973)	40	1.49	1.5	7.99	40.49	2.99		1.5	5	0.99	45	0.11	8	50.97	0.44	0.0146	0.397	97.96
Halperin & Wetherell(1965) A	60	1.49	1.5	2.99	60.49	2.99		1.5		0.99	60	0		65.97	0.45	0.0112	0.458	127.96
Heller(1953; 1955)	7.05	2.71	2.02	11.08	10.06	1.02	7.96	2.02		1.81	7.05	0		22.87	0.15	0.0592	0.219	41.39
Hildebrandt et al.(1946) Tobacco	4.17	0.71	12.72	0.87	1.66	3.38	11.5	1.46		0.47	4.17	0		18.47	0.11	0.0192	0.044	27.68
Hoagland & Snyder(1933)	15	3	4		6	10		4		2	15	0		22	0.34	0.068	0.13	33
Jona & Gribaudo(1987) B	5.54	3	1	0.9	1.9	5.54		1		2	5.54	0		10.44	0.26	0.1436	0.09	15.11
Jona and Vigliocco(1985) B	33	7.67	3		20.55	10		3	4.99	5.11	37.99	0.13	6.61	43.65	0.43	0.0878	0.235	74.2
Jones & Murashige(1974) B	39.4	5.59	3	5.98	20.04	5.98	0.61	3	20.61	3.73	60.01	0.34	1.91	53.97	0.55	0.0517	0.185	98.22
Kao & Michayluk(1975) 8.	26.28	3.74	2.43	12.18	24.06	8.16		2.43	7.49	2.49	33.77	0.22	3.5	44.63	0.37	0.0419	0.269	80.25
Knop(1865)	10.94	5.51	2.02		4.3	8.46		2.02		3.67	10.94	0		18.45	0.29	0.1492	0.116	26.99
Knudson(1922; 1943) B	8.46	5.51	9.59		1.83	8.46		2.02	7.56	3.67	16.02	0.47	1.11	23.54	0.34	0.1169	0.038	33.39
Kumar et al.(1988) L-6.	26.61	3.74	1.45	4.48	11.14	8.72		1.45	12.49	2.49	39.1	0.31	2.13	36.29	0.53	0.0515	0.153	64.26
Kunisaki(1990) 1.	15	3.74	6	13.98	7.95	11.97		6	10.3	2.49	25.3	0.4	1.45	38.71	0.32	0.0483	0.102	62.95
Kunisaki(1990) 2.	11.25	2.82	4.5	3.25	5.97	1.74		4.5	7.73	1.88	18.98	0.4	1.45	21.82	0.43	0.0646	0.136	36.39
Lin & Staba(1961)	18.39	1.49	1.5	2.99	9.89	2.99		1.5	8.99	0.99	27.38	0.32	2.04	24.36	0.56	0.0305	0.202	44.74
Lindemann et al.(1970) 1.	6.09	2.97	17.13	14.08	15.07	6.09		1.99	15.13	1.98	21.22	0.71	0.4	40.26	0.26	0.0368	0.187	65.94
Litvay et al.(1981) LM	49.4	7.49	15.01	0.29	21.29	0.29		15.01	20.61	4.99	60.01	0.34	1.91	62.19	0.48	0.0602	0.171	104.23
Lloyd & McCown(1981) WPM	9.7	3.74	3	1.3	1.24	6.01		3	4.99	2.49	14.69	0.33	1.94	17.73	0.41	0.1054	0.034	26.97
Margara(1977b; 1978) N15 Ca	11.99	2.99	1.99	1.99	3.99	7.99		1.99	2.99	1.99	14.98	0.19	4.01	18.95	0.39	0.0788	0.105	29.93
Margara(1977b; 1978) N15 K	11.99	2.99	1.99	1.99	8.99	2.99		1.99	2.99	1.99	14.98	0.19	4.01	18.95	0.39	0.0788	0.237	32.43
Margara(1977b; 1978) N30 Ca	23.98	2.99	1.99	0.99	9.99	9.99		1.99	5.99	1.99	29.97	0.19	4	29.95	0.5	0.0499	0.166	50.92
Margara(1977b; 1978) N30 K	23.98	2.99	1.99	0.99	14.98	4.99		1.99	5.99	1.99	29.97	0.19	4	29.94	0.5	0.0499	0.25	53.41

IONIC COMPOSITION OF MACRONUTRIENTS

Concs. of ions in meq/l

Macronutrient author/s	NO_3^- (meq/l)	PO_4^{3-} (meq/l)	SO_4^{2-} (meq/l)	Cl^- (meq/l)	K^+ (meq/l)	Ca^{2+} (meq/l)	Na^+ (meq/l)	Mg^{2+} (meq/l)	NH_4^+ (meq/l)	H^+ (meq/l)	Total N (meq/l)	NH_4^+/N ratio	NO_3^-/NH_4^+ ratio	ΣI^+ (meq/l)	N/ΣI ratio	PO_4^{3-}/ΣI ratio	K^+/ΣI ratio	Total ionic concentration (mM)
Margara(1977b; 1978) N30 NH4	19.98	2.99	1.99	4.99	11.99	3.99		1.99	9.99	1.99	29.97	0.33	2	29.95	0.5	0.0499	0.2	53.92
Margara(1977b; 1978) N45 K	35.97	2.99	1.99	4.99	23.97	7.99	0.99	1.99	8.99	1.99	44.96	0.19	4	45.92	0.48	0.0325	0.26	83.88
Margara(1977b; 1978) N5 Ca	3.99	2.99	1.99	5.97	2.99	6.96		1.99	0.99	1.99	4.98	0.19	4.03	14.92	0.16	0.1001	0.1	22.39
Margara(1977b; 1978) N5 K	3.99	2.99	1.99	4.99	6.74	2.24		1.99	0.99	1.99	4.98	0.19	4.03	13.95	0.17	0.1071	0.241	22.8
Margara(1977b; 1978) N60	40	3.75	3	6	21.5	6		3	20	2.5	60	0.33	2	52.75	0.57	0.0355	0.201	97.0
Miller & Murashige(1976) III.	39.4	9.29	3	5.98	20.04	5.98	1.84	3	20.61	6.19	60.01	0.34	1.91	57.66	0.52	0.0805	0.173	103.14
Miller & Skoog(1953)	2	0.82	0.58	0.87	1.93	1.21		0.58	4.99	0.55	2	0		4.27	0.23	0.096	0.225	6.8
Miller et al.(1956)	7	0.26	0.58	0.87	1.75	1.21		0.58	12.49	0.17	11.99	0.41	1.4	8.7	0.68	0.0149	0.1	16.05
Miller(1961a; 1963)	26.61	6.61	0.58	0.87	12.96	4.23		0.58		4.4	39.1	0.31	2.13	34.66	0.56	0.0953	0.186	62.22
Millerd et al.(1975) 1.		6.61	3	13.29	7.56	7.92		3		4.4				22.88	0	0.1443	0.165	34.41
Millerd et al.(1975) 2.		23.14	3	13.29	13.08	7.92	1.08	3		15.43				39.43	0	0.2934	0.165	56.47
Mitra et al.(1976) A	3.47	3.26	3.54		1.78	1.69		2.02	1.51	2.17	4.98	0.3	2.29	10.25	0.24	0.1588	0.086	14.72
Murashige & Skoog(1962)	39.4	3.74	3	5.98	20.04	5.98		3	20.61	2.49	60.01	0.34	1.91	52.12	0.57	0.0358	0.192	95.75
Murashige & Skoog(1962) a:deF	40	4.5	3	6	21.5	6		3	20	3	60	0.33	2.0	53.5	0.56	0.0421	0.2	98.00
Murashige et al.(1972 b)	39.4	7.44	3	5.98	20.04	5.98	1.23	3	20.61	4.96	60.01	0.34	1.91	55.82	0.53	0.0666	0.179	100.69
Nagata & Takebe(1970)	1	0.59	2	19.99	1.19	19.99		2		0.39	1	0		23.57	0.02	0.0125	0.025	34.76
Nagata & Takebe(1971)	19.7	14.99	10	2.99	14.39	2.99		10	10.3	9.99	30	0.34	1.91	47.67	0.31	0.1572	0.15	73.86
Nickell & Maretzki(1969) 1.	2.48	0.35	4.23	0.87	1.66	1.69	2.93	1.42		0.23	2.48	0		7.93	0.15	0.022	0.104	11.95
Nitsc & Nitsch(1956) N1.	19.78	5.43	2.02	20.56	39.9	0.44	1.81	2.02		3.62	19.78	0		47.79	0.2	0.0568	0.417	89.72
Norstog(1973) Barley II		20.06	6	20.12	16.74	10.06		6		13.37				46.17	0	0.2172	0.181	67.94
Pevalek-Kozlina & Jelaska(1987) WPM (no Cl⁻)	9.72	3.75	4.26		1.26	6.01		3	4.96	2.5	14.68	0.33	1.95	17.73	0.41	0.1057	0.035	26.32
Pfeffer(1900) A	8.75	4.4	1.62	1.34	4.78	6.77		1.62		2.93	8.75	0		16.1	0.27	0.1366	0.148	24.27
Pfeffer(1900) B	12.5	6.29	4.75		4.92	9.67		4.75		4.19	12.5	0		23.53	0.26	0.1336	0.104	33.29
Phillips & Collins(1979 a) L2.	33.26	9.01	3.52	8.16	23.15	8.16	0.61	3.52	12.49	6	45.75	0.27	2.66	53.93	0.42	0.0835	0.214	94.27
Phillips & Collins(1979 a) SL2.	28.26	9.01	3.24	7.48	23.15	7.48	0.61	3.24	7.49	6	35.75	0.2	3.77	47.97	0.37	0.0938	0.241	82.97
Quoirin & Lepoivre(1977) B	24.49	59.51	29.2		37.64	1.69		29.2	4.99	39.67	29.48	0.16	4.9	113.19	0.13	0.2628	0.166	156.67
Ramming et al.(1990)	9.1	0.41	8.79	0.87	2.45	7.51	2.95	5.98		0.27	9.1	0		19.16	0.23	0.0106	0.063	26.91
Ranga Swamy(1961) 1	2.99	4.12	5.73	0.87	1.66	2.2	4.19	2.92		2.75	2.99	0		13.72	0.1	0.1502	0.06	19.25
Reynolds et al.(1980)	18.39	6.93	1.5	2.99	9.89	2.99	1.81	1.5	8.99	4.62	27.38	0.32	2.04	29.8	0.45	0.1162	0.165	51.99
Risser & White(1964)	3.33	3.58	8.81	0.87	1.66	2.54	4.01	6		2.39	3.33	0		16.6	0.1	0.1078	0.05	22.12
Rodriguez & Lorenzo Martin(1987) MH	39.66	3.74	3	5.98	30.92	5.98		3	9.99	2.49	49.65	0.2	3.96	52.38	0.47	0.0357	0.295	96.27

Macronutrient author/s	NO3⁻ (meq/l)	PO4³⁻ (meq/l)	SO4²⁻ (meq/l)	Cl⁻ (meq/l)	K⁺ (meq/l)	Ca²⁺ (meq/l)	Na⁺ (meq/l)	Mg²⁺ (meq/l)	NH4⁺ (meq/l)	H⁺ (meq/l)	Total N (meq/l)	NH4⁺/N ratio	NO3⁻/NH4⁺ ratio	ΣI⁺ (meq/l)	N/ΣI ratio	PO4³⁻/ΣI ratio	K⁺/ΣI ratio	Total ionic concentration (mM)
Sarwar(1984)	18.39	1.49	1.5	2.25	9.89	2.25		1.5	8.99	0.99	27.38	0.32	2.04	23.62	0.57	0.0315	0.209	43.63
Schenk & Hildebrandt(1972)	24.72	7.82	3.24	2.72	24.72	2.72		3.24	2.6	5.21	27.32	0.09	9.5	38.49	0.35	0.1015	0.321	67.17
Scowcroft & Adamson(1976) CS5	40.26	11.99	3.24	2.72	24.77	2.72		3.24	19.48	7.99	59.74	0.32	2.06	58.2	0.51	0.1029	0.212	103.81
Skoog(1944)	2.01	0.27	0.58	0.87	1.75	1.21		0.58		0.18	2.01	0		3.72	0.26	0.0362	0.234	6.08
Staudt(1984) M2.	28.78	5.51	3.24	6.12	20.63	6.12		3.24	9.99	3.67	38.77	0.25	2.88	43.65	0.44	0.0631	0.236	77.32
Staudt(1984) M2-2.	28.78	7.71	3.24	6.12	21.36	6.12		3.24	9.99	5.14	38.77	0.25	2.88	45.85	0.42	0.084	0.232	80.26
Strullu et al.(1986)	9.7	2.99	4	0.5	5.21	2.99		1.99	5	1.99	14.7	0.34	1.94	17.18	0.42	0.0869	0.151	27.88
Thomale(1954) GD	8.57	6.61	0.9		6.16		12		5.53	4.4	14.1	0.39	1.54	16.09	0.43	0.2054	0.191	27.31
Thompson et al.(1977)		3.74	15	15.98	11.24	5.98		3		2.49				34.71	0	0.0538	0.161	54.94
Thorpe & Meier(1973) Sf	39.4	4.83	3	5.98	20.04	5.98	0.36	3	20.61	3.22	60.01	0.34	1.91	53.21	0.56	0.0453	0.188	97.21
Thorpe & Murashige(1968b; 1970) Sf	39.4	11.13	3	5.98	20.04	5.98	2.46	3	20.61	7.42	60.01	0.34	1.91	59.51	0.5	0.0935	0.168	105.61
Tukey(1933) I	1.34		2.83	9.14	10.49			2.83			1.34	0		13.32	0.05	0	0.393	23.8
Tukey(1933) II			3.11	10.06	10.06			3.11				0		13.17	0	0	0.381	23.23
Vacin & Went(1949)	5.19	5.51	9.59		7.02	5.98		2.02	7.56	3.67	12.75	0.59	0.68	20.27	0.31	0.1358	0.173	31.08
Veliky & Martin(1970) 67-V	7.91	3.59	3.54	5.4	10.59	2.72	1.31	2.02	1.51	2.28	9.42	0.16	5.23	20.43	0.23	0.0878	0.259	34.33
Von Arnold & Eriksson(1977) LP	33.78	7.49	3	23.94	21.29	23.94		3	14.99	4.99	48.77	0.3	2.25	68.21	0.35	0.0549	0.156	116.45
Von Arnold & Eriksson(1981) LPm	33.78	7.49	3	2.44	21.29	2.44		3	14.99	4.99	48.77	0.3	2.25	46.71	0.52	0.0801	0.227	84.2
Wetherell(1969)	39.56	1.49	1.5	13.08	40.06	2.99	2.93	1.5	10.09	0.99	49.65	0.2	3.92	55.63	0.44	0.0133	0.36	107.27
White(1942)	3.22	0.35	8.79	0.87	1.66	2.43	2.93	5.98		0.23	3.22	0		13.23	0.12	0.0132	0.062	17.62
White(1954)	3.22	0.41	8.79	0.87	1.66	2.43	2.95	5.98		0.27	3.22	0		13.29	0.12	0.0154	0.062	17.7
White(1963)	3.33	0.41	8.9	0.87	1.66	2.54	2.95	6.08		0.27	3.33	0		13.5	0.12	0.0151	0.061	17.97
Wood & Braun(1961) B	24.5	6.87	20.61	12.2	12.99	2.54	26.28	5.84	11.95	4.58	36.45	0.32	2.05	64.18	0.28	0.0535	0.101	109.28
Yasuda et al.(1985)	9.85	1.87	0.75	1.49	5.32	1.49		0.75	5.15	1.24	15	0.34	1.91	13.95	0.53	0.067	0.19	25.16
Zimmerman & Broome(1980) Z-2.	9.99	8.99	5.99		4.99	5.99		3	4.99	5.99	14.98	0.33	2	24.96	0.3	0.18	0.099	36.44
Zimmerman(1984 a) WPMm.	9.59	3.59	14.36	1.79	12.55	6.39		3	4.99	2.39	14.58	0.34	1.92	29.32	0.24	0.061	0.21	44.38
Ziv et al.(1970)	39.4	6.53	3	5.98	18.79	5.98	2.17	3	20.61	4.35	60.01	0.34	1.91	54.9	0.54	0.0594	0.171	99.46

Table 50. Micronutrient compositions. All concentrations are given in mg/l.

Micronutrient author/s	MnSO4.4H2O	MnCl2.2H2O	ZnSO4.7H2O	H3BO3	KI	CuSO4.5H2O	Na2MoO4.2H2O	H2MoO4.H2O	CoCl2.6H2O	AlCl3	NiCl2.6H2O	Ferric citrate	Ferric tartrate	FeSO4.7H2O	Fe2(SO4)3	FeCl3.6H2O	Na2EDTA.2H2O	NaFeEDTA	Fe chelates	EDTA	Notes
Abo El-Nil & Hildebrandt(1976)	22300		8600	6200	830	25	50		25				40000								
Abo El-Nil & Zettler(1976) AZ	11200		4300	6200	830	25	250		25					27900			37300				
Abou-Mandour(1977 b)	25000		10000	10000		25	25000											24000			
Al-Talib & Torrey(1959)	h 5940		1500	1500	75	200										1500					
Anderson(1978 a;1980a)	h 22300		8600	6200	300	25	250		25					55700			74500				
Asahira & Kano(1977)	h 46190		10000	10000	1000	35	25000		35					27800			37300				
Beretta & Eccher(1987)	13400		6300	3700	490	15	150		15					60000			73200				
Berthelot(1934) Dilution	1000		50	25	250	25	25		25		25				25000						See notes
Blake(1966)	2230		860	620	83	2.5	25		2.5					27800			37300				See notes
Blaydes(1966) Version 2.	h 5807		1500	1600	800													32000			
Bonner & Bonner(1938)													1500								
Bonner(1940 a) A												1500									
Bourgin & Nitsch(1967) H	25000		10000	10000		25	250							27850			37250				
Burgeff(1936) Eg 1.														20000							
Button & Botha(1975)	22300		8600	6200	830	25	250		25					55700			74500				See notes
Canas & Benbadis(1988) OM	22300		14300	12400	830	250	250		25					27800			37500				
Cheng(1975) Basal	22300		10510	6200	830	25	250		25					30000			36000				See notes
Cheng(1977 ;1978)	11150		5250	3100	400	13	150		13					6000			7200				
Chu & Hill(1988) MN6	10000		10000	10000	800	25	25		25										D 40000		
Chu et al.(1975) N6	4400		1500	1600	800									27850			37250				
De Fossard et al.(1974 a) LOW	2231		287.560	618.400	83	2.497	2.420		23.795					2780			3722				
De Fossard et al.(1974 a) MEDIUM	11153		5751	3092	415	24.969	24.2		119					13902			18613				
De Fossard et al.(1974 a) HIGH	22306		11502	9275	830	374.500	242		238					27803			37225				
Doerschug & Miller(1967)	h 6470		2700	1600	750													13000			
Dudits et al.(1975) T	h 6600		3000	3000	250	25	250		25					27800						See notes	

Micronutrient author/s	$MnSO_4.4H_2O$	$MnCl_2.2H_2O$	$ZnSO_4.7H_2O$	H_3BO_3	KI	$CuSO_4.5H_2O$	$Na_2MoO_4.2H_2O$	$H_2MoO_4.H_2O$	$CoCl_2.6H_2O$	$AlCl_3$	$NiCl_2.6H_2O$	Ferric citrate	Ferric tartrate	$FeSO_4.7H_2O$	$Fe_2(SO_4)_3$	$FeCl_3.6H_2O$	$Na_2EDTA.2H_2O$	NaFeEDTA	Fe chelates	EDTA	Notes
Eccher et al.(1986)	h 17685		6300	3700	500	15	150							60000			73200				
Economou & Read(1984)	h 22300		8600	6200		25	250		25										D 56000		
Eeuwens(1976) Y3	11200		7200	3100	8300	250	240		240		24			13900			37300	20000			See notes
Elliott(1969) M-S	22300		8600	6200	830	25			25												See notes
Eriksson(1965) 1.	2230		2700	630	800	2.500	25		2.500					27850			37250	32000			
Fox & Miller(1959)	6500			1600	800																See note
Franco & Swartz(1985) CBM	9239		4500	2400	375	10								27800			37300				See notes
Gamborg et al.(1968) B5	h 13200		2000	3000	750	25	250		25										D 28000		
Gamborg(1966) PRL-4-C	h 13200		3000	3000	750	250	250		250					13900			18600				See notes
Graebe & Novellli(1966)	h 3959		500	500		25	25		25			10000									
Gresshoff & Doy(1972 a,b) DBM 1.	h 13200		3000	3000	750	250	250		250					27850			37250				See notes
Gresshoff & Doy(1972 a,b) DBM 2.	h 13200		3000	3000	800	250	250		250					27850			37250				See notes
Gupta & Durzan(1985) DCR	h 29432		8600	6200	830	250	250		25		h 46			37300			37300				See notes
Hahlbrock et al.(1974)	h 13190		2000	3000	750	25	250		25					13900			18630				
Halperin & Minocha(1973)	h 9240		4050	2400	375	10								13900		1000	18600				See notes
Heller(1953 ;1955)	100		1000	1000	10	30				30	30		40000								
Hildebrandt et al.(1946) Tobacco	4500		6000	375	3000			h 30	s 46	s 44	s 50		5000								
Hoagland & Snyder(1933) A-Z Suppl.		389	56	611	28	56	200		200												See notes
Horgan & Aitken(1981) 1.	20000		1000	5000	1000	200	200							1500			2000				See notes
Jona & Vigliocco(1985) A	25139		8627	61840	830	25	242		24									36707			
Jona & Vigliocco(1985) B	1115		8627	12368	83	25	242		24									36707			
Jones(1967)	22300		8600	6200	830	25	250		25									20000			
Kasperbauer & Reinert(1967)	22300		8600	6200	830	25	250		25						10670					22400	
Knop(1865) a:H																					See notes
Knudson(1922 ;1943) B																					See notes
Knudson(1946) C	7500													25000							
Kyte & Briggs(1979) I	h 22305		8600	6200	830	30	250		30					55700			74500				

MICRONUTRIENT COMPOSITIONS

All concs. are given in mg/l

Reference															Notes
Kyte & Briggs(1979) R	h 7435	2867	2067		10	83	10	10			18567	24833			See notes
Lin & Staba(1961)	h 9240	4050	2400	375										39750	See notes
Lindemann et al.(1970) 1.	h 101	h 1006	1014	99	h 29.7		31	h 31.2	5400						
Litvay et al.(1981) LM	h 27720	43000	31000	4150	500	1250	130				27800	37300			See notes
Lloyd & McCown(1981) WPM	h 29430	8600	6200		250	250					27800	37300			See notes
Margara(1977 b;1978) N5K	h 157	500	500	10	100	h 59					35000	30000			
Miller et al.(1956)	6500	2700	1600	800									25000		See notes
Miller(1965; 1967)	14000	3800	1600	800	s362								13200		See notes
Mitra et al.(1976) A	400	50	600	30	50	50					16700	22300			See notes
Molnar(1988b)	22300	8600	6200	830	25	250	s 40.878	25						D 40000	
Mullin et al.(1974) A & B	h 800	50	25	250	25	25	25			2500	13300	15700			See notes
Murashige & Skoog(1962)	22300	8600	6200	830	25	250	25				27850	37250			
Murashige & Skoog(1962) a:deF	22306	8627	6184	830.1	23.79	241.9	23.79				27803	37225			
Nickell & Maretzki(1969) 1.	h 5939	1500	1500	750							h 4090				
Nitsch & Nitsch(1965) K & S	25000	10000	10000		25	250	25				27850	37250			
Nitsch & Nitsch(1969) H	25000	10000	10000		25	250	25				2785	3725			
Nitsch(1951) 1.	3000	500	500		25	25			10000						
Pfeffer(1900) A										8000					See notes
Phillips & Collins(1979 a) L2	h 19800	5000	5000	1000	100	400	100				25000	33600			
Phillips & Collins(1980) SL2	h 17820	4500	4500	900	90	360	90				25000	33600			
Poirier-Hamon et al.(1974) NH4	50000	20000	20000			500					13900	18600			
Poirier-Hamon et al.(1974) Stem	25000	10000	10000		25	250					13900	18600			
Quoirin & Lepoivre(1977) A	10000	1000	1000	10	30						27800	37300			
Ranga Swamy(1961) I	3000	500	500		25	h 29.375	h 45.812		10000						See notes
Reynolds et al.(1980)	25000	10000	10000		25	250			28000		27850	37250			See notes
Risser & White(1964)	h 6600	2500	1500	750									2500		See notes
Schenk & Hildebrandt(1972)	h 13200	1000	5000	1000	200	100	100				15000	20000			
Sommer et al.(1975) 3.	h 6600	2500	1500	750	10	h 1.25					27800	37300			See notes
Standardi & Catalano(1985) 2.	1320	8600	6200	80	25	250	25				27.85	37.25			
Standardi & Catalano(1985) 3.	33	8600	6200	80	25	250	25				27850	37250			
Staudt(1984) M2.	20000	5000	15000	1000	25	250	25				27803	38507			See notes
Strullu et al.(1986)	22300	5700	12400	150	250	250	138	250			27800	37200			See notes

Micronutrient author/s	MnSO$_4$.4H$_2$O	MnCl$_2$.2H$_2$O	ZnSO$_4$.7H$_2$O	H$_3$BO$_3$	KI	CuSO$_4$.5H$_2$O	Na$_2$MoO$_4$.2H$_2$O	H$_2$MoO$_4$.H$_2$O	CoCl$_2$.6H$_2$O	AlCl$_3$	NiCl$_2$.6H$_2$O	Ferric citrate	Ferric tartrate	FeSO$_4$.7H$_2$O	Fe$_2$(SO$_4$)$_3$	FeCl$_3$.6H$_2$O	Na$_2$EDTA.2H$_2$O	NaFeEDTA	Fe chelates	EDTA	Notes
Takebe et al.(1968)					166.02	h 2.497															
Thompson et al.(1977)	22300		8600	6200	830	25	250		25										D 57013		See notes
Tukey(1933) I																					See notes
Tukey(1933) II																					See notes
Vacin & Went(1949)	7500												28000								
Veliky & Martin(1970) 67-V	h 5279		1500	5000	50	250	250		250					13900			18600				
Von Arnold & Eriksson(1977) LP	2230			630	750	2.50	25		2.500					13900			18700				See notes
Von Arnold & Eriksson(1981) LPm	2200			630	750	2.50	25		2.50					14000			19000				

Supplementary Notes

Berthelot(1934) Dilution. Our entry is the modification of Berthelot's micronutrient solution made by Gautheret(1942). Gautheret explains that he omitted calcium from Berthelot's original composition because it was a constituent of the macroelements he had used. He also added iodine following White, because it favoured cell proliferation. In his 1942 paper, Gautheret gives the composition of a stock solution 2000 times the strength quoted here and used 10 drops per litre of medium. White(1943) assumed that 20 drops of an aqueous solution were equivalent to 1 ml. The dilution quoted in the Table is therefore equivalent to 0.5 ml (10 drops) per litre. This is confusing because in another section of his book, Gautheret stated that 1 ml of micronutrients was added per litre of medium. However, the dilution which we have given is confirmed by Gautheret(1959) where he also makes it clear that the weights originally given applied to hydrated salts.

The Dilution of Berthelot's micronutrients given by Gautheret(1942) also contained 169 µg/l Ti$_2$(SO$_4$)$_3$, and 50 µg/l BeSO$_4$.4H$_2$O. Gautheret also included 1 ml/l of concentrated H$_2$SO$_4$ (32N) per litre of × 2000 stock solution, explaining that it helped to prevent the formation of precipitates. There is a discrepancy between Gautheret(1942) and Gautheret(1955;1959) over the weight of titanium used. Gautheret(1955;1959) gives 4.2 x 10^{-8} g/cc Ti. This would mean that 0.169 mg/l Ti$_2$(SO$_4$)$_3$ would have to be used in the Dilution (not 100 µg/l as given by Gautheret(1942) — possibly he used a different Ti compound).

Titanium and berylium are now seldom considered to be elements essential for plant growth. White(1963) omitted them from his listing of Gautheret's version of the Berthelot micronutrients. Note that the preferred Dilution of these micronutrients is not correctly given in White(1963).

Blake(1966). Also contained 300 µg/l 8-hydroxyquinoline which can act as a chelating agent.

Button & Botha(1975). These micronutrients (Murashige & Skoog but with twice the Fe level) are almost the same as those of Kyte & Briggs(1979) 1 and Lyrene(1980).

Cheng(1975) Basal. No source of boron is mentioned in the paper. Boric acid is used in other Cheng media and so we have assumed that the omission was a typographical error.

Dudits et al.(1975) T. The original paper gives 25 µg/l anhydrous copper sulphate.

Elliott(1969) M-S. Also included 180 µg/l (NH$_4$)$_6$Mo$_7$O$_{24}$.4H$_2$O.

Eriksson(1965) 1. Also contained 15 mg/l ZnNa$_2$EDTA. No water of crystallisation is given in the paper but probably 4H$_2$O.

Franco & Swartz(1985) CBM. The medium also contained 0.093 mg/l (NH$_4$)$_6$Mo$_7$O$_{24}$.4H$_2$O.

MICRONUTRIENT COMPOSITIONS

All concs. are given in mg/l

Gamborg et al.(1968) B5. The original paper gives anhydrous copper sulphate but 25 ug/l $CuSO_4.5H_2O$ is given for the medium in Gamborg et al.(1976), and again in Gamborg(1982). Originally 28 mg/l (0.05 mM) Sequestrene 330 Fe (FeDTPA) was used. Other versions of B5 micronutrients use FeEDTA, often at 0.1 mM.

Gamborg(1966) PRL-4-C. Again anhydrous copper sulphate was specified. See note to Gamborg et al.(1968) B5.

Gresshoff & Doy(1972a,b) DBM 1 and 2. In both papers, and in Gresshoff & Doy(1973), the authors say that their micronutrients were based on Gamborg & Eveleigh(1968). This logically gives the weights of salts shown in the table here. But note that in their 1974 paper, Gresshoff & Doy suggest that one tenth Gamborg & Eveleigh(1968) [a medium which is in fact Gamborg(1966) PRL-4-C] micronutrients were used in DBM media. We think that this was a misprint. KI was originally incorporated into the authors' stock solution of macronutrients.

Hahlbrock et al.(1974). These micronutrients are effectively those of Gamborg et al.(1968) B5, but 0.05 mM FeEDTA has been used instead of Sequestrene 330 Fe.

Halperin & Minocha(1973). Also contained 92.5 µg/l $(NH_4)_6Mo_7O_{24}.4H_2O$.

Horgan & Aitken(1981) 1. This medium was said to be as Schenk & Hildebrandt(1972), except for the micronutrients specified here. Iron was not mentioned, and so we have presumed that this was as Schenk & Hildebrandt(1972).

Knop(1865) a:H. Iron supplied as $FePO_4$. See Macroelement table.

Knudson(1922;1943) B. Medium contained 50 mg/l $FePO_4.4H_2O$ as described in the Macronutrients table.

Lin & Staba(1961). Iron as Perma Green Iron 135.

Lloyd & McCown(1981) WPM. The paper gives 22300 µg/l $MnSO_4.H_2O$, but at later dates [e.g. Smith & McCown(1983)] WPM medium is said to include 22300 µg/l $MnSO_4.4H_2O$.

Miller et al.(1956). Anhydrous weights given are assumed to be genuine [see Macronutrient table notes].

Miller(1965;1967). Also contained 100 µg/l $(NH_4)_6Mo_7O_{24}.4H_2O$ and 350 µg/l $Cu(NO_3)_2.3H_2O$. The latter has been represented in the table by an equivalent weight of copper sulphate. We assume that the omission of KI from the 1965 medium was an oversight.

Mitra et al.(1976) A. 50 µg/l $Co(NO_3)_2.6H_2O$ was originally used. An equivalent weight of cobalt chloride has been entered in the table.

Mullin et al.(1974) A & B. The micronutrient solution also contained 1 ml/l H_2SO_4 (32N).

Nitsch & Nitsch(1969). See the notes to the Derivation table.

Pfeffer(1900) A. Pfeffer's solution is often described as containing "a small amount" or "a few drops" of ferric chloride solution. Knudson(1925) standardised this as 8 mg/l $FeCl_3.6H_2O$ [not given as a hydrate in the 1925 paper, but can be assumed to be so from Knudson(1943)], and we suggest that this is taken as a standardised amount for both of the Pfeffer's solutions.

Ranga Swamy(1961) I. See the Medium Derivation Table notes.

Reynolds et al.(1980). This report describes the use of 38000 µg/l Fe citrate. We believe this to be a misprint because in subsequent papers SEM-1 medium contains 28000 µg/l Fe citrate.

Sommer et al.(1975) 3. The medium originally contained 1 µg/l MoO_3. An equivalent weight of molybdic acid has been entered in the table.

Staudt(1984) M2. See Macronutrient table notes. We have entered weights given against anhydrous formulae for conventionally hydrated salts.

Strullu et al.(1986). Also contained 0.375 ug/l $(NH_4)_6Mo_7O_{24}.4H_2O$. The Mo molarity given in Table 51 takes account of this.

Thompson et al.(1977).

Tukey(1933) I. This medium also contained Fe from 170.45 mg/l $Fe(PO_4)_2.8H_2O$ as described in the Macroelements table.

Tukey(1933) II. 187.5 mg/l $Fe_3(PO_4)_2$ was included in the medium, as described in the Macronutrients table.

Von Arnold & Eriksson(1977) LP. The micronutrients also included 10 ug/l ZnEDTA.

Wetherell(1969). Mo as Lin & Staba(1961).

White(1963). White here includes $CuSO_4$ and MoO_3 for the first time.

Yasuda et al.(1985). $MnSO_4.7H_2O$ has been taken to be a misprint for $MnSO_4.4H_2O$.

Table 51. Molar concentrations of micronutrients. Concentrations are given in mM.

Micronutrient author/s	Mn	Zn	B	I	Cu	Mo	Co	Al	Ni	Fe	Total molarity	Notes
Abo El-Nil & Hildebrandt(1976)	99.9731	29.9068	100.25873	4.99939	0.10012	0.20662	0.10506			69.69491	305.24473	
Abo El-Nil & Zettler(1976) AZ	50.2107	14.9534	100.25873	4.99939	0.10012	1.03314	0.10506			100.34888	272.00942	
Abou-Mandour(1977b)	112.07746	34.77535	161.70763		0.10012	103.31432				65.38262	477.3575	
Al-Talib & Torrey(1959)	26.6296	5.2163	24.25614	0.45175	0.80099					5.54897	62.90375	
Anderson(1978a;1980a)	99.9731	29.9068	100.25873	1.80701	0.10012	1.03314	0.10506			200.33809	433.52205	
Asahira & Kano(1977)	207.07432	34.77535	161.70763	6.02337	0.14017	103.31432	0.14708			99.9892	613.17144	
Beretta & Eccher(1987)	60.07352	21.90847	59.83182	2.95145	0.06007	0.61988	0.06303			215.80404	361.31228	
Berthelot(1934) Dilution	4.48309	0.17387	0.40426	1.50584	0.10012		0.10506		0.10517	62.51562	69.39303	
Blake(1966)	9.99731	2.99068	10.02587	0.49993	0.01001	0.10331	0.0105			99.9892	123.62681	
Blaydes(1966) Version 2.	26.03335	5.2163	25.87322	4.81869						87.17683	149.11839	
Bonner & Bonner(1938)										2.61355	2.61355	
Bonner(1940a) A										4.47721	4.47721	
Bourgin & Nitsch(1967) H	112.07746	34.77535	161.70763		0.10012	1.03314				100.16904	409.86274	
Burgeff(1936) Eg 1.										71.93468	71.93468	
Button & Botha(1975)	99.9731	29.9068	100.25873	4.99939	0.10012	1.03314	0.10506			200.33809	436.71443	
Canas & Benbadis(1988) OM	99.9731	49.72875	200.51746	4.99939	1.00124	1.03314	0.10506			99.9892	457.34734	
Cheng(1975) Basal	99.9731	36.54889	100.25873	4.99939	0.10012	1.03314	0.10506			107.90202	350.92045	
Cheng(1977;1978)	49.98655	18.25705	50.12936	2.40934	0.05206	0.61988	0.05463			21.5804	143.08927	
Chu & Hill(1988) MN6	44.83098	34.77535	161.70763	4.81869	0.10012	0.10331	0.10506			71.6243	318.06544	
Chu et al.(1975) N6	19.72563	5.2163	25.87322	4.81869						100.16904	155.80288	
De Fossard et al.(1974a) LOW	10.00179	1	10	0.49993	0.01	0.01	0.1			9.99892	31.62064	
De Fossard et al.(1974a) MEDIUM	50	19.9993	50	2.49969	0.1	0.1	0.5001			50.00179	173.20088	
De Fossard et al.(1974a) HIGH	100	39.9986	149.98382	4.99939	1.49985	1.00008	1.00021			100	398.48195	
Dudits et al.(1975) T	29.58845	10.4326	48.51228		0.10012	1.03314	0.10506			99.9892	189.76085	
Eccher et al.(1986)	79.2836	21.90847	59.83182	3.01168	0.06007	0.61988				215.80404	380.51956	
Economou & Read(1984)	99.9731	29.9068	100.25873		0.10012	1.03314	0.10506			98.22321	329.60016	
Eeuwens(1976) Y3	50.2107	25.03825	50.12936	49.99397	1.00124	0.99181	1.00861		0.10096	49.9946	228.4695	
Elliott(1969) M-S	99.9731	29.9068	100.25873	4.99939	0.10012	1.01946	0.10506			54.48552	290.84818	
Eriksson(1965) 1.	9.99731	37.54035	10.18758		0.01001	0.10331	0.0105			100.16904	158.0181	
Fox & Miller(1959) 29.14014	9.38934	25.87322	4.81869						87.17683	156.39822		
Franco & Swartz(1985) CBM	41.41934	15.6489	38.80983	2.25876	0.04004	0.52672				99.9892	198.69279	See notes
Gamborg et al.(1968) B5	59.1769	6.95507	48.51228	4.51752	0.10012	1.03314	0.10506			49.11121	169.5113	
Gamborg(1966) PRL-4-C	59.1769	10.4326	48.51228	4.51752	1.00124	1.03314	1.05064			49.9946	175.71892	
Graebe & Novelli(1966)	17.74858	1.73876	8.08538		0.10012	0.10331	0.10506			29.84807	57.72928	

MOLAR CONCENTRATIONS OF MICRONUTRIENTS

Concs. are given as µM

Micronutrient author/s	Mn	Zn	B	I	Cu	Mo	Co	Al	Ni	Fe	Total molarity	Notes
Gresshoff & Doy(1972 a,b) DBM 1.	59.1769	10.4326	48.51228	4.51752	1.00124	1.03314	1.05064			100.16904	225.89336	
Gresshoff & Doy(1972 a,b) DBM 2.	59.1769	10.4326	48.51228	4.81869	1.00124	1.03314	1.05064			100.16904	226.19453	
Gupta & Durzan(1985) DCR	131.94656	29.9068	100.25873	4.99939	1.00124	1.03314	0.10506		0.19352	134.15818	403.60262	See notes
Hahlbrock et al.(1974)	59.13207	6.95507	48.51228	4.51752	0.10012	1.03314	0.10506			49.9946	170.34986	
Halperin & Minocha(1973)	41.42383	14.08401	38.80983	2.25876	0.04004	0.52389				49.9946	147.13496	
Heller(1953;1955)	0.4483	3.47753	16.17076	0.06023	0.12014			0.22498	0.1262	3.69931	24.32745	
Hildebrandt et al.(1946) Tobacco	20.17394	20.86521	6.06403	18.07011						69.69491	134.8682	
Hoagland & Snyder(1933) A-Z Supplements	1.96553	0.19474	9.88033	0.16865	0.22427	0.16668	0.19331	0.32998	0.21034	8.71186	22.04569	
Horgan & Aitken(1981) 1.	89.66197	3.47753	80.85381	6.02337	0.80099	0.82651	0.84051			5.3951	187.87979	
Jona & Vigliocco(1985) A	112.70061	30.00069	1000	4.99939	0.10012	1.00008	0.10086			100	1248.90175	
Jona & Vigliocco(1985) B	4.99865	30.00069	200	0.49993	0.10012	1.00008	0.10086			100	336.70033	
Jones(1967)	29.9068	100.25873	4.99939	0.10012	1.03314	0.10506			54.48552	290.86186		
Kasperbauer & Reinert(1967)	99.9731	29.9068	100.25873	4.99939	0.10012	1.03314	0.10506			26.68167	263.05801	See notes
Knop(1865) a:H												See notes
Knudson(1922;1943) B												See notes
Knudson(1946) C	33.62324									89.91835	123.54159	
Kyte & Briggs(1979) I	99.95551	29.9068	100.25873	4.99939	0.12014	1.03314	0.12607			200.33809	436.77787	
Kyte & Briggs(1979) R	33.33183	9.97009	33.42496		0.04004	0.343	0.04202			66.78056	143.9325	
Lin & Staba(1961)	41.42383	14.08401	38.80983	2.25876	0.04004	0.52389	0.10086			100.00000	197.14036	See notes
Lindemann et al.(1970) 1.	0.45279	3.4984	16.39715	0.59631	0.11894	0.56637		0.23248	0.13125	16.11795	37.54527	
Litvay et al.(1981) LM	124.27149	149.53401	501.29366	24.99698	2.00248	5.16571	0.54633			99.9892	907.79986	
Lloyd & McCown(1981) WPM	131.93759	29.9068	100.25873		1.00124	1.03314				99.9892	364.1267	
Margara(1977b;1978) N5K	0.79328	1.73876	8.08538	0.06023	0.40049	0.24382	0.10506			125.88569	137.20765	
Miller et al.(1956)	29.14014	9.38934	25.87322	4.81869						68.1069	137.32829	
Miller(1965;1967)	62.76338	13.21463	16.39715	0.59631	1.44979	0.56637				35.96044	144.64652	
Mitra et al.(1976) A	2.02112	0.17387	9.70245	0.1807	0.20024	0.20662	0.17179			60.06546	72.72225	
Molnar(1988b)	99.9731	29.9068	100.25873	4.99939	0.10012	1.03314	0.10506			71.6243	308.00064	
Mullin et al.(1974) A & B	3.58647	0.17387	0.40426	1.50584	0.10012		0.10506		0.10517	54.08812	60.06891	
Murashige & Skoog(1962)	99.9731	29.9068	100.25873	4.99939	0.10012	1.03314	0.10506			100.16904	336.54538	
Murashige & Skoog(1962) a:deF	100	30.0	100	5	0.1	1	0.1			100	336.20	
Nitsch & Nitsch(1965) K & S	112.07746	34.77535	161.70763		0.10012	1.03314	0.10506			100.16904	409.9678	
Nitsch & Nitsch(1969) H	112.07746	34.77535	161.70763		0.10012	1.03314				10.0169	319.7106	See notes
Nitsch(1951) 1.	13.44929	1.73876	8.08538		0.10012	0.10331				29.84807	53.32493	

Amino acid & amide author/s	Glycine	Alanine	Arginine	Asparagine	Aspartic acid	Cysteine	Glutamine	Glutamic acid	Leucine	Methionine	Phenylalanine	Proline	Serine	Tyrosine	Protein hydrolysates	Yeast/Malt Extract	Notes
Thorpe & Murashige(1968b; 1970) Sf														100.0 (551.91)			
Tukey(1933) II				2000.0 (15137.8)													
Von Arnold & Eriksson(1977) LP	2.0 (26.64)	0.05 (0.56)	0.01 (0.06)			0.02 (0.165)	0.4 (2.736)		0.01 (0.08)		0.01 (0.06)			0.01 (0.06)			See notes
White(1939b)	3.0 (39.96)																
Wood & Braun(1961) A	3.0 (39.96)		"	200.0 (1513.78)			200.0 (1368.46)										See notes
Zapata et al.(1983) MY1.	2.0 (26.64)															10000	

Supplementary Notes

All amino acids mentioned have the L-configuration unless otherwise stated.

Atanassov & Brown(1984) B5h. Also contained 10 mg/l glutathione.

Gresshoff & Doy(1972a,b) DBM 1. Gresshoff & Doy(1973) state that there was a typographical error in their 1972b paper. It wrongly indicated that glycine was used at one tenth the concentration given in Gresshoff & Doy(1972a) for these media. The 4 mg/l glycine given in the table is the correct weight for DBM 1. Note that Gresshoff & Doy(1974) omitted glycine.

Koblitz & Hagen(1962). The medium also contained 26 mg/l g-aminobutyric acid; 0.05 mg/l histidine; 1.2 mg/l hydroxyproline; 2 mg/l lysine; 4.1 mg/l threonine; 2.3 mg/l valine.

Lindemann et al.(1970) 2. Also added 181.6 mg/l guanylic acid and 161.6 mg/l cytidylic acid.

Millerd et al.(1975) 1. Also contained 27.2 mg/l histidine; 46 mg/l isoleucine; 56 mg/l lysine; 33.2 mg/l threonine; and 4.6 mg/l valine.

Murashige & Skoog(1962) Supplemented. The casein hydrolysate originally used was Edamin (a pancreatic digest of casein).

Nickell & Maretzki(1969) 2. Also contained 10 mg/l histidine; 30 mg/l isoleucine; 35 mg/l threonine.

Von Arnold & Eriksson(1977) LP. Amino acids are given in the paper in micrograms per litre. In Von Arnold & Eriksson(1979) it says that the concentration should be in mg/l. We have printed the corrected weights.

Wood & Braun(1961) A. Also contained 100 mg/l cytidylic acid and 100 mg/l guanylic acid.

Table 54. Unusual sugars and long-chain alcohols.

Author/s	UNUSUAL SUGARS								LONG-CHAIN ALCOHOLS			Notes
	Glucose	Fructose	Ribose	Xylose	Mannose	Rhamnose	Cellobiose	Arabinose	Sorbitol	Mannitol	Total Molarity	
	mg/l	mg/l	mg/l	mg/l	mg/l	mg/l	mg/l	mg/l	mg/l (mM)	mg/l (mM)	mM	
Kao & Michayluk(1975) 8	68400	250	250	250	250	250	250		250 (1.37)	250 (1.37)	390.6155	
Kao & Michayluk(1975) 8p	68400	250	250	250	250	250	250		250 (1.37)	250 (1.37)	390.6155	
Kao(1977) Cell	10000	125	125	125	125	125	125		125 (0.69)	125 (0.69)	60.9827	
Kumar et al(1988) L-6									10000 (54.89)		54.8938	
Nagata & Takebe(1970)										127520 (700.0)	700.0055	
Nagata & Takebe(1971)										127520 (700.0)	700.005	
Nitsch & Nitsch (1956) N1.	18000										99.9112	See notes
Thomale(1954) GD	10000	10000									111.0124	
Von Arnold & Eriksson(1977) LP	180			150				150	45500 (249.77)		252.7640	
Von Arnold & Eriksson(1979a) LPm	180			150				150			2.9973	See notes
Von Arnold & Eriksson(1981) LPm	180			150				150			2.9973	See notes

Supplementary notes

Nitsch & Nitsch(1956) N1. The glucose listed was added to the medium in addition to sucrose (0.1 M).

Von Arnold & Eriksson(1979) LPm. When first used by the authors, the medium also included 30 g/l sucrose, in addition to the sugars listed here.

Von Arnold & Eriksson(1981) LPm. When first used by the authors, the medium also included 30 g/l sucrose, in addition to the sugars listed here.

Table 55. Organic acids and buffers.

Organic acid author/s	Weights of additions in mg/l, and their molarities (mM)							Equivalence of cations			Notes
	Citric acid	Fumaric acid	Malic acid	Na pyruvate	Na succinate	K succinate	MES buffer	K+ meq/l	Na+ meq/l	NH4+ meq/l	
Chaleff(1983a) R3 Succ.						4966.2 (20.0)		40.0			See notes
Chaleff(1983a) R3 (NH4) MES							9762 (50.0)				
Chaleff(1983a) R3 (NH+) Succ.						2483.1 (20.0)		20.0			See notes
Jones & Murashige(1974) A	150 (0.78)							2.34*			
Kao & Michayluk(1975) 8 & 8p	40 (0.21)	40 (0.34)	40 (0.30)	20 (0.18)					0.18	1.91*	See notes
Kao(1977) Cell	10 (0.05)	10 (0.09)	10 (0.07)	5 (0.05)					0.05	0.48*	
Molnar(1988b)					4052.1 (15.0)				30.0		
Norstog(1973) Barley II			1000 (7.46)							14.9*	See notes
Ramming (1990)						1240 (4.99)		9.99			

Supplementary notes

Chaleff(1983a) R3 media. The media were adjusted to pH 4 with KOH.
Kao & Michayluk(1975) 8 and 8p. The authors adjusted the media to pH 5.5 with NH4OH.

Norstog(1973) Barley II. Norstog dissolved malic acid in 50 ml water, which was then adjusted to pH 5 with NH4OH before addition.

11

Plant Growth Regulators

GROWTH SUBSTANCES AND GROWTH REGULATORS

Some chemicals occurring naturally within plant tissues (*i.e.* endogenously), have a regulatory, rather than a nutritional role in growth and development. These compounds, which are generally active at very low concentrations, are known as *plant growth substances* (or *plant hormones*). Synthetic chemicals with similar physiological activities to plant growth substances, or compounds having an ability to modify plant growth by some other means, are usually termed *plant growth regulators*. Some of the natural growth substances are prepared synthetically or through fermentation processes and can be purchased from chemical suppliers. When these chemicals have been added to plant tissue culture media, they are termed plant growth regulators in this book, to indicate the fact that they have been applied from outside the tissues (*i.e.* exogenously). There are several recognised classes of plant growth substance:

- auxins,

- cytokinins,

- gibberellins,

- ethylene,

- abscisic acid.

Auxins and cytokinins are by far the most important for regulating growth and morphogenesis in plant tissue and organ cultures; in these classes, synthetic regulators have been discovered with a biological activity which equals or exceeds that of the equivalent growth substances.

No chemical alternatives to the natural gibberellins or abscisic acid are available, but some natural gibberellins are extracted from cultured fungi and are available for use as exogenous regulants. However, several classes of chemicals, which are highly effective in blocking the synthesis of gibberellins within the plant, are very effective growth regulators. They are usually termed:

- anti-gibberellins (or growth retardants).

The gases acetylene and propylene mimic the activity of ethylene, but considerably higher molar concentrations are required to produce the same biological activity. Exogenous ethylene can be used as a growth regulant, but being a gas, it is difficult to administer and to control the available convcentration, except in tightly sealed vessels. However, some chemicals have been invented which are capable of releasing ethylene; effective compounds are taken up into plants as intact molecules, but then break down to release ethylene within the tissues of a plant. One of these ethylene-releasing chemicals is used as a growth regulator for tissue cultures.

Biological effects of growth regulators

The effects of growth regulators are generally not absolute and specific. The responses of cells, tissues and organs *in vitro* can vary according to cultural conditions, the type of explant and the plant genotype. Frequently a combination of two or more compounds of separate kinds is required, either applied simultaneously or sequentially, and there is generally a lag period before the effect of treatment becomes apparent.

Growth and morphogenesis *in vitro* are regulated by the interaction and balance between the growth regulators supplied in the medium, and the growth substances pro-duced endogenously. Besides exerting a direct effect on cellular mechanisms, many synthetic regulants may in fact modify the level of endogenous growth substances, sometimes in a fashion which is heritable over many cell generations. Factors influencing growth and morphogenesis described in Chapter 8, will also frequently exert their influence through changes in internal hormone levels.

The effect produced *in vitro* by a growth regulator is also dependent on the medium on which an organ or tissue is being cultured. By adding 0.5 mg/l 2,4-D to **MS** medium containing 250 μM L-tryptophan, it was possible to obtain approximately 2 plants from each embryo-derived callus of *Oryza sativa*: on **Chu et al. (1975) N6** medium, the same concentration of auxin enabled 9 plantlets to be regenerated (Koetje *et al.* 1989).

AUXINS

Auxins are very widely used in micropropagation work and are incorporated into nutrient media to promote the growth of callus, cell suspensions or organs, and to regulate morphogenesis, especially in conjunction with cytokinins (see later). The choice of compounds and the concentration required will depend on:

- the kind of growth or development required,

- the natural levels of auxin within the explant when it is excised,

- the capacity of the cultured tissues to synthesise auxin naturally, and

- the interaction, if any, between applied synthetic auxins and the natural endogenous substance/s.

NATURALLY OCCURRING AUXINS

Compounds are called auxins if they are capable of controlling various distinctive processes such as cell growth and cell elongation. Auxins are capable of initiating cell division and are involved in the origination of meristems giving rise to either unorganised tissue, or defined organs. In organised tissue, auxins are responsible for the maintenance of apical dominance (but see page 466).

The most commonly detected natural auxin is IAA (3-indolyl-acetic acid) (5).

Precursors of IAA

IAA is formed from the amino acid L-tryptophan (1) and endogenous levels of the auxin increase rapidly in tissues incubated on a medium containing this amino acid (Black *et al.*, 1986). Conversion to IAA normally proceeds *via* indole-3-pyruvic acid (2) or tryptamine (3) (Percival and Purves (1974), but may also occur *via* tryptophol (4) (Rayle and Purvis, 1967; Percival *et al.*, 1973) (Fig. 108). Tryptophol was more effective than IAA for inducing embryogenic callus on *Cucurbita pepo* hypocotyl explants. A higher proportion of genotypes responded to the tryptophol than to IAA, and embryogenesis occurred more rapidly; Jelaska *et al.* (1985) supposed that this was because it was steadily converted to IAA, and was not subject to rapid metabolism, or binding.

As would also be expected, L-tryptophan can also act as an auxin replacement in some plants; in these case it may stimulate growth or induce morphogenesis (*e.g.* callus growth of *Nicotiana glauca* × *N. langsdorfii* hybrids — Cheng, 1972; the formation of embryogenic callus in some rice cultivars — Siriwardana and Nabors, 1983).

Natural levels of IAA

Levels of naturally-occurring auxin in explanted tissues are found to depend on the mother plant from which the explants were derived. The age of the mother plant, the conditions under which it has been growing and the season of the year at which explants are taken, can all be influential (Cassells, 1979).

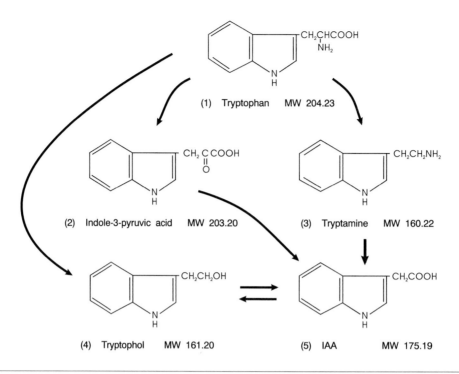

Fig. 108. Routes to the biosynthesis of IAA.

The presence of an associated organised meristem can cause callus to grow more vigorously than otherwise, or to be capable of organogenesis (Fakhrai *et al.*, 1989). This suggests that meristematic cells are particularly active sites for the biosynthesis and/or the release of natural growth factors favouring cell growth (Clare and Collin, 1974).

Sometimes tissues, organs or strains of cells arise in culture which are able to grow without the addition of any auxin to the medium. They are said to be auxin autonomous or *auxin habituated* (see page 473).

MODE OF ACTION OF AUXINS

Growth promotion

Auxins are thought to promote the growth of plant tissues in two ways:

1. by inducing the secretion of hydrogen ions into and through the cell wall. Binding of auxin leads to lipid breakdown and acidification of the wall, increasing its extensibility. Potassium ions are taken into the cell to counteract the electrogenic export of H^+ ions (protons) and this has the effect of decreasing the water potential of the cell so that water enters, and the cell

expands (Rayle and Cleland, 1977; Cleland and Lomax, 1977; Marre, 1977, 1979; Böttger, 1986). This explanation is now commonly accepted to explain the rapid growth–stimulating effect of auxin.

2. by an effect on RNA metabolism (and hence protein synthesis), possibly by inducing the transcription of specific messenger RNA (mRNA) molecules (Trewavas, 1968; Key, 1969; Bevan and Northcote, 1981a,b). The mRNAs are thought to encode proteins which are required for sustained growth. In tobacco cultures, auxins appear to stimulate the synthesis of a β-1,3- glucanase enzyme, which hydrolyses β-1,3- glucan polysaccharides in the cell wall (Felix and Meins, 1985) thereby loosening the wall, and possibly also producing biologically active oligosaccharides (see below — Tran Thanh Van and Mutaftschiev, 1990).

The export of protons from cells, causes there to be an accelerated acidification of the external medium when explants are treated with an auxin (Schubert and Matzke, 1985). Ion exchange may occur because auxin indirectly stimulates the ATP-ase enzyme located in cell membranes which is responsible for the transport of H^+ and OH^- into and out of cells; or because the growth substance increases the permeability of the cell membrane to protons and other ions (Rossignol *et al.*, 1990).

Morphogenesis

Applied auxins seem to be capable of erasing the genetically programmed physiology of whole plant tissues, which had previously determined their differentiated state. Cells which respond to auxin revert to a dedifferentiated state and begin to divide. How auxin brings about this reprogramming is not fully understood, Lo Schiavo *et al.* (1989) found that auxins cause DNA to become more methylated than usual and suggested that this might be necessary for the re-programming of differentiated cells. Tissue-specific programmes specifically associated with differentiation would become eradicated by hypermethylation, with perhaps a small fraction of the cells reaching an ultimate state of dedifferentiation in which they become capable of morphogenesis, or embryogenesis (Terzi and Lo Schiavo, 1990).

AUXIN GROWTH REGULATORS

Commonly-used compounds

Synthetically-prepared IAA is used as an auxin in plant tissue culture media, but it tends to be denatured in culture media (page 423) and rapidly metabolised within plant tissues (see later). However, these attributes can be useful, because in some plants, callus induced by IAA (together with cytokinins) frequently gives rise to shoots or embryos as its effective concentration becomes diminished. IAA has also been used with other regulants to induce direct morphogenesis (including the rooting of microcuttings), and for meristem and shoot cultures (*e.g.* of *Bougainvillea*, Chaturvedi *et al.*, 1978; Sharma A. K. *et al.*, 1981; *Citrullus*, Barnes, 1979; and *Sinningia*, Haramaki, 1971; Grunewaldt, 1977). However, for many purposes, it is necessary or desirable to use one of the many chemical analogues of IAA, which, because they have similar biological properties, are also called auxins. The synthetic auxins most commonly used in tissue cultures are:

2,4-D	**(6)**	2,4-dichlorophenoxyacetic acid
IBA	**(7)**	3-indolebutyric acid, or
		4-(indol-3-yl)butyric acid, or
		1*H*-indole-3-butanoic acid
NAA	**(8)**	1-naphthalene acetic acid, or
(α-NAA)		1-naphthylacetic acid

Together with cytokinins, 2,4-D is used primarily for callus induction and suspension cultures, being replaced

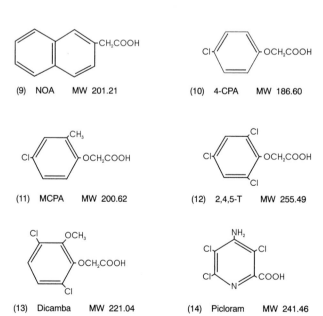

(6) 2,4-D   MW 221.04

(7) IBA   MW 203.24

(8) NAA   MW 186.21

by NAA and IBA when morphogenesis is required. NAA and IBA are favoured auxins for shoot culture.

Other less commonly employed auxins include:

NOA	**(9)**	2-naphthyloxyacetic acid
4-CPA	**(10)**	4-chlorophenoxyacetic acid, or
PCPA		*p*-chlorophenoxyacetic acid
MCPA	**(11)**	2-methyl-4-chlorphenoxyacetic acid
2,4,5-T	**(12)**	2,4,5-trichlorophenoxyacetic acid
dicamba	**(13)**	3,6-dichloroanisic acid (and its dimethylamine salt, Banvel D)
picloram	**(14)**	4-amino-3,5,6-trichloropicolinic acid

(9) NOA   MW 201.21

(10) 4-CPA   MW 186.60

(11) MCPA   MW 200.62

(12) 2,4,5-T   MW 255.49

(13) Dicamba   MW 221.04

(14) Picloram   MW 241.46

2,4,5-T is used only rarely in tissue cultures, and then almost exclusively for the induction of callus and indirect embryogenesis in monocotyledons such as *Avena, Oryza,* and *Panicum.* Heyser *et al.* (1983) found that in *Triticum aestivum,* some varieties produced embryogenic callus with 2,4-D, while others responded only to 2,4,5-T.

Dicamba is often effective in inducing the formation of embryogenic callus in monocotyledons, for example *Dactylis glomerata* (40 µM) (Gray and Conger, 1985); *Musa* (90..5 µM) (Jarret *et al.*, 1985b,c); and rice (4.5–18.1 µM) (Zimny and Lorz, 1986). The use of 9.05µM dicamba permitted the formation of wheat scutellar callus, which produced more somatic embryos in conjunction with 2.6–4.7 µM kinetin, than that induced by the optimum rate of 2,4-D (3.62 µM) (Carman *et al.*, 1988b). This is probably because dicamba is metabolised quickly in wheat (Chang and Vanden Born, 1971), possibly more quickly than 2,4-D.

Picloram is sometimes used to induce and/or maintain callus or suspension cultures of broad-leafed plants; or to induce the formation of embryogenic callus, where it may be more effective than 2,4-D (Beyl *et al.*, 1981; Beyl and Sharma., 1983). The rate required (*e.g.* 0.06–4.0 µM) is generally less than that necessary for other auxins. Mok and Mok (1977) found that the growth rate and yield of callus from different species and varieties of *Phaseolus,* were greater in the presence of picloram than with 2,4-D. Picloram was active at lower concentrations and over a wider range of genotypes. In only a very few instances has this auxin been used for meristem or single node culture and then at very low rates (*e.g.* 0.012–0.4 µM) in combination with a cytokinin.

At high concentrations most synthetic auxins are phytotoxic to field-grown broad-leafed plants: 2,4-D; 2,4,5-T; MCPA; dicamba and picloram have been used commercially as selective herbicides. There are many other chemicals with auxin-like activity besides the ones we have listed, which have seldom been used in plant tissue cultures. An unusual auxin 2-chloro-3(2,3-dichloro-phenyl) propionitrile (CDPPN) **(15)**, which is related to orthonil (PRB-8) **(16)**, was found by Nemeth (1981) to produce up to 90% more shoots in apple shoot cultures than the same concentration of IBA (5 µM).

(15) CDPPN   MW 234.51   (16) Orthonil   MW 214.10

Stability in culture media

IAA and IBA are heat labile and decomposed during autoclaving (see Chapter 10), but IAA is not stable in culture media even if filter sterilised. In the dark there can be more than a ten-fold decrease in concentration over a four week period without the presence of inocula (Campbell and Sutter, 1986; Nissen and Sutter, 1988). The rate of decrease of IAA is even more rapid in the light and is accelerated by the presence of **MS** salts (Dunlap *et al.*, 1986). In liquid **MS** medium incubated at 25°C in a normal 16 h photoperiod, 10 µM (1.75 mg/l) IAA, was reduced to less than the limit of detection (0.05 mg/l) in 14 days (Nissen and Sutter, 1988). IBA is more stable in solution than IAA: 75% remained after 30 days in the dark, 40 % after 30 days in the light. Other auxins such as NAA and 2,4-D are not denatured in media (Dunlap *et al.*, *loc cit.*), but once absorbed within plant tissues, the rate of decay of all auxins may be equally rapid, for they are then not only exposed to physical factors, but may also be subjected to enzymatic degradation.

Physiological activity

Auxins differ in their physiological activity and the extent to which they move within tissues, are bound within cells, or metabolised. In media for micropropagation work, effective concentrations of each growth regulator will vary, and will need to be adjusted according to the genotype of the plant to be cultured, the type of tissue or organ, the nature of the micropropagation method, and the stage of the culture. Although artificial auxins have been available for many years, it is still unclear to what extent their physiological activity is due to their direct mimicry of the action of natural IAA, or to an indirect action in modifying its effective level within tissues.

Mixtures of auxins. Some investigators have employed mixtures of many different auxins (*e.g.* Blackmon *et al.*, 1981b), but as the effect of individual compounds can vary in different genotypes, most researchers prefer to use only one, or at most two compounds. However, a mixture of more than one auxin can be particularly effective for root induction (Chapter 14) and a mixture of a synthetic auxin and IAA has been found by many workers to be more effective than the synthetic compound on its own. A mixture of 2,4-D (or 2,4,5-T) and either IAA or L-tryptophan was found to promote embryogenic callus formation in wheat, pearl millet and some varieties of rice (Nabors *et al.*, 1983). This observation was confirmed by Carman *et al.* (1988b), who found that adding 0.2 mM L-tryptophan to 3.62 µM 2,4-D, consistently enhanced the formation of somatic embryos from scutellum callus of wheat genotypes. There was a decrease in embryo formation when tryptophan was combined with dicamba.

Effects in tissue cultures

Combinations of growth regulators used in the various kinds of cultures that are employed for micropropagation are given in Chapter 12. The following is a summary of the main effects of auxins *in vitro*.

Induction of callus growth

An auxin is generally required to be incorporated into the nutrient medium for the induction of callus from explants. Irvine *et al.* (1983) reported having tested 79 potential regulants for the ability to initiate callus from immature sugar cane leaf tissue. Of the effective compounds, 96% had structures known to be associated with auxin activity.

The auxin most frequently employed to initiate callus cultures is 2,4-D; but as cultures maintained on 2,4-D may be liable to become genetically variable, some investigators prefer to use NAA or IAA, or to transfer callus to a medium containing one of these alternative compounds once it has been initiated by 2,4-D. For callus induction from broad-leafed plants, 2,4-D is generally used at levels between 4.5–13.6 μM (1.0–3.0 mg/l).

Note that to induce callus growth from explants of dicotyledonous plants, a cytokinin is almost always added to the medium in addition to an auxin. The presence of a cytokinin may not be necessary to obtain callus from explants of monocotyledons (Chapter 12), and in these plants a somewhat higher auxin concentration, for example 2,4-D in the range 9.0–45.2 μM (2.0–10.0 mg/l), is usually used. The combined use of auxin and cytokinin in tissue cultures is considered separately in a later section.

Auxins promote cell dispersion in suspension cultures while cytokinins tend to cause cell aggregation. The relatively high levels of auxin added to liquid media for this purpose will prevent morphogenesis, but might induce an embryogenesis if the cells are still competent.

Chlorophyll formation

Whereas cytokinins tend to promote the formation of chlorophyll in callus and suspension cultures, auxins can be inhibitory. Some reduction of chlorophyll formation in the presence of 2,4-D was noted in callus cultures of pea, tomato and potato, by Hildebrandt *et al.* (1963) but *Oxalis dispar* callus was found to turn green only when the auxin content in the medium was reduced to one tenth of that normally used to promote callus growth (*i.e.* 2,4-D reduced from 1 to 0.1 mg/l, or NAA from 10 to 1 mg/l). Compared to callus subcultured to media entirely free of auxin, even a reduced auxin level delayed the appearance of chlorophyll and shortened the period over which it accumulated (Sunderland and Wells, 1968). Similar observations have been made by other workers. Increasing

the concentration of IAA led to a progressive reduction in chloroplast development within chicory callus (Wozny *et al.*, 1973), but in other tests IAA or NAA have been reckoned to be less inhibitory to chlorophyll formation than 2,4-D (Davey *et al.*, 1971).

Morphogenesis

Root and shoot formation. The induction of caulogenesis or rhizogenesis in callus cultures usually requires an adjustment of the levels of auxins and cytokinins that are necessary for callus initiation and growth. An appropriate balance between the two types of regulant is necessary (see later). A high cytokinin to auxin ratio is generally required: it is also necessary for the direct induction of shoots on explants. By contrast, rhizogenesis usually follows treatment with auxin alone, or with mixtures containing more auxin than cytokinin; exogenous cytokinins are commonly inhibitory. Auxin-induced root formation is thought to require, or induce, the promotion of polyamine synthesis (Friedman *et al.*, 1985).

The use of auxins to induce the rooting of separate shoots produced during *in vitro* culture is discussed in Chapter 14.

Embryogenesis

The process of somatic embryogenesis is often initiated in media containing high levels of auxins (especially 2,4-D), but embryos do not develop further until the auxin concentration is reduced (Chapter 12). Sharp *et al.* (1980) proposed that auxin induces an embryogenic determination in a proportion of the cells in callus or suspension cultures but at the same time causes these induced cells to cease division. Division of the 'pro-embryogenic cells' is only resumed, it was suggested, in lower auxin concentrations. There are, however, many recorded exceptions to this general observation, where somatic embryos have appeared in cultures grown on media devoid of auxins. It is possible that in these instances, embryogenesis has been induced by endogenous auxin, the concentration of which has been reduced by metabolism or binding (see below) to permit embryo formation.

The discovery that embryo formation in carrot can be regulated by pH (see page 301), makes it probable that at least some of the regulatory effects of auxins on the formation and maintenance of embryogenic cultures can be ascribed to their capacity to reduce intracellular pH. Embryo formation coincides with the withdrawal of auxin and a rise in cellular pH. However, somatic embryogenesis in carrot has also been found to be induced by an excess of hypochlorite ions (Kiyosue *et al.*, 1989b), subjecting tissues to high osmotic potential (0.7 mM sucrose or 0.6 M mannitol — Kamada *et al.*, 1988; or 0.3

M NaCl — Kiyosue *et al.*, 1989), and by exposure to heavy metal ions, especially by 0.5–1.0 mM Cd^{2+}, Ni^{2+} and Co^{2+} (*i.e.* 0.25–0.5 mM $CdCl_2$, $NiCl_2$ and $CoCl_2$) (Kiyosue *et al.*, 1990). Thus it cannot be assumed that pH is the only controlling factor: a common physiological mechanism by which such different stimuli can induce embryogenesis has yet to be demonstrated.

In the induction of somatic embryogenesis from immature cotyledons of *Glycine max*, Lazzeri *et al.* (1988) discovered a highly significant interaction between the concentration of auxin and sucrose in the medium. The number of embryos obtained was reduced if there was a high concentration of either auxin or sucrose, combined with a low concentration of the other; there was a high frequency of somatic embryo formation with 1–2% sucrose and 6.25–25 mg/l NAA, or 4% sucrose and 50 mg/l NAA. Ranch *et al.* (1986) previously used 5 mg/l 2,4-D with 6% sucrose to obtain maximum embryogenesis in this plant, while Lippmann and Lippmann (1984) found 1 mg/l 2,4-D and 1% sucrose to be satisfactory. Perhaps either directly or indirectly, sugar provides sites through which effective auxin concentrations can be reduced through conjugation?

Organ cultures

An auxin is almost invariably required to promote the initial growth of meristem and shoot tip explants. A low concentration of auxin is often used in conjunction with high levels of cytokinin at Stage II when shoot multiplication is required, although in some cases cytokinin alone is sufficient (see tables in Chapter 12). It is important to choose an auxin at a concentration which will promote growth without inducing callus formation.

AUXIN UPTAKE

IAA, and other synthetic auxins such as NAA and 2,4-D, are rapidly taken up into cultured tissues from media with a pH less than 5–6. The compounds are subsequently absorbed into cells as whole molecules, but dissociation then causes them to be retained within the cell, because the plasmalemma is impermeable to auxin anions (Norris and Bukovak, 1972; Raven, 1979; Edwards and Goldsmith, 1980; Minocha and Nissen, 1985b; Minocha, 1987). The rate of uptake of NAA into tobacco pedicel explants was proportional to the concentration in the medium (Croes and Barendse, 1986).

REGULATION OF AUXIN ACTIVITY

The differentiation, division and morphogenic potential of plant cells can depend not only on the auxins added to the growth medium, but also on the IAA within the cultured tissues, and the interaction between the two. Factors affecting the natural levels of IAA and the activity of this compound, can therefore be important in controlling growth and morphogenesis in plant tissue cultures used for micropropagation.

Auxin action is dependent on the free-availability of boron. In boron-deficient plants, both the translocation of IAA (Goldbach and Amberger, 1986) (see Chapter 9), and nuclear RNA synthesis in response to auxin treatment (Ali and Jarvis, 1988), have been found to be inhibited. This results in a lack of response to auxin in the absence of boron, for example the promotion of rooting by IBA.

Regulation of the level of the auxin IAA could be achieved naturally within plant cells by variation in the rate of its biosynthesis or metabolism, or in the extent of its deactivation. IAA is deactivated by being oxidized and broken down into other compounds, or by being bound to (or conjugated with), other molecules.

IAA is heat-labile, but even if it is filter sterilised before addition to the medium, it is not generally a very effective exogenous regulant for promoting growth or morphogenesis, probably because much is rapidly metabolised. After 8 h growth of carrot suspension cultures with labelled IAA, only 10% of the radioactivity in the cells was free IAA, 45% was IAA–aspartate, and the rest breakdown products of IAA (Shea *et al.*, 1988).

Auxin binding

Both IAA and synthetic auxin regulators react with compounds within the plant. Attachment to small molecules is usually termed *conjugation*, while complexing with proteins, which is required for some kinds of auxin action, is termed *binding*. Conjugation makes auxins temporarily or permanently unavailable. Nakamura *et al.* (1985) concluded that auxin may also be immobilised by compartmentalisation, because plant cells resistant to 2,4-D were also found to be resistant to IAA, NAA and picloram, and neither the rate of uptake of the compounds, nor their rate of metabolism seemed to be responsible.

Binding sites

Auxin receptors. For the regulation of at least some processes involving cell growth and cell division, it is thought that auxins need to become bound to one or more proteins, which because they are involved in the physiologial action of auxin, can be termed *receptors*. One receptor may be situated on cellular membranes (Maan *et al.*, 1985a,b); another within the cell, capable of cycling between cytoplasm and nucleus (Elliott *et al*, 1986; Herber *et al.*, 1988; Brummel and Hall, 1987).

IAA conjugates

As well as becoming bound to molecules involved in auxin action, a proportion of the IAA produced within most plants reacts with other compounds to produce esters, amides or glycosides. This appears to be a mechanism for storing IAA in cells, stabilising the level of free auxin in the plant, and metabolising excess. Auxin in conjugated molecules is protected from oxidative breakdown and may be released again through the action of enzymes as required:

$$IAA + alcohol \rightleftarrows IAA\ ester$$

$$IAA + amino\ acid \rightleftarrows IAA\ amide$$

The proportion of conjugated IAA can differ significantly even between closely related genotypes (Alvarez *et al.*, 1989) and the nature of the complexes formed varies in different plant genera (Bandurski, 1980). Indolacetylaspartic acid, and conjugates with sugars (glycosides), such as glucobrassicin (found in Cruciferae), are commonly found.

The occurrence and activity of auxin esters has been investigated less well than that of the amino acid amide conjugates, but they are known to occur in plants (Cohen and Bandurski, 1982): for example, conjugates of IAA and *myo*-inositol have been reported (Bandurski, 1984; Hall and Bandurski, 1986; Komoszynski and Bandurski, 1986). IAA-inositol and IAA-inositol-galactoside are stored in maize kernels (Bandurski, 1980; Hall and Bandurski, 1986; Komoszynski and Bandurski, 1986) and can be hydrolyzed *in situ* to yield free IAA, or transported to the root and shoot (Nowacki and Bandurski, 1980). Rates of conjugation may be affected by other regulants. Lau and Yang (1973) found that kinetin decreased the rate at which exogenous IAA was conjugated with aspartic acid.

In some cultures, IAA-amino acid conjugates can be of value as growth regulants. Hangarter *et al.* (1980) found that out of several IAA-amino acid conjugates tested, IAA-L-alanine (indole-acetyl-L-alanine) **(17)** and IAA-glycine (indole-acetyl-glycine) **(18)** were better auxin sources for inducing callus growth from tomato hypocotyl segments than other commercially-available auxins. Some other IAA conjugates supported shoot development, instead of the root regeneration induced by free IAA. Hangarter *et al.* suggested that the activity of conjugates might be due to their slow and steady release

of IAA through hydrolysis, but this might not be the complete explanation (Caruso, 1987).

There have been several reports of the successful use of IAA-amino acid conjugates since the publication of Hangarter *et al.* For example, Griesbach (1983) reported that IAA-L-alanine and (particularly) IAA-glycine, were more effective than NAA for the propagation of *Phalaenopsis* orchids; IAA-alanine and IAA-glycine were more effective than IAA in promoting callus formation from tomato leaf discs (Pence and Caruso, 1984); and shoot formation from *Fragaria* callus occurred when 2,4-D was replaced with IAA-β-alanine (Jones *et al.*, 1988). However the effectiveness of conjugates in general, and that of individual compounds, is very genotype-dependent. In carrot suspensions, none of 11 conjugates tested were as effective as IAA, probably because the activity of hydrolytic enzymes was high in these cells (Shea *et al.*, 1988).

Tryptophol [a probable natural precursor of IAA (see above) and also a breakdown product of IAA] can form conjugates with sugars. The glucoside, found in many species (Magnus *et al.*, 1973), can be naturally hydrolysed to release tryptophol (Magnus, 1979). Tryptophol glucoside, and especially, tryptophol arabinoside, are capable of inducing the formation of embryogenic callus in *Cucurbita* (Jelaska *et al.*, 1985).

Conjugates of synthetic auxins

Synthetic auxins may also form conjugated molecules, although possibly not until after some degree of metabolism has taken place. Suspension cultures of wheat metabolise 2,4-D rapidly. Chlorine substitutions on the benzene ring of 2,4-D are replaced by hydroxyl groups; the altered compound is then conjugated with sugars (producing a compounds lacking auxin activity) (Bristol *et al.*, 1977), or with amino acids (producing compounds in

(17) IAA-acetylalanine MW 246.27

(18) IAA-acetylglycine MW 232.24

which auxin activity can be retained). Preliminary metabolism of NAA in tobacco probably involves conjugation with aspartic acid (Croes and Barendse, 1986).

Elimination of auxin by conjugation

In most plant tissues, auxin which is not bound in cultured tissues is probably rapidly diluted when an exogenous supply is withdrawn. Only a 2,4-D–resistant tobacco variant was able to hold auxins within its cells: cells of the wild-type lost significant amounts by washing (Nakamura *et al.*, 1985). However, auxin which is bound or conjugated can be released in physiologically important quantities during a long period. The presence of conjugated auxin may therefore be disadvantageous when a decreased concentration is necessary to induce morphogenesis. The extent and nature of the subsequent release can vary according to plant genotype and according to the auxin used.

Genotypic effects. Montague *et al.* (1981a,b) found that whereas soybean cells conjugated a large amount of 2,4-D with amino acids (forming, for example, 2,4-D–glutamic and 2,4-D–aspartic acids), carrot cells contained mainly free 2,4-D. After prolonged exposure to the auxin, carrot cells released much more of it to an auxin-free medium than did those of soybean. As only the carrot cells become embryogenic on an auxin-free medium, the retention of 2,4-D in soybean cells could be responsible for their inability to undergo morphogenesis.

Two lines of birdsfoot trefoil were found to differ in their tolerance to 2,4-D. The morphogenic behaviour of the more tolerant line was consistent with the hypothesis that it was capable of absorbing 2,4-D more strongly than the other, and that absorbed 2,4-D was slowly released or unloaded when the auxin was withdrawn from the medium. Swanson and Tomes (1980) who obtained this result, pointed out that inactivation of 2,4-D by esterification with sugars has been reported in a number of species.

Chemical structure. The rate at which an effective concentration within cells will be depleted, once an exogenous supply is withdrawn, will vary from one auxinic compound to another. Mehra and Cheema (1980b) could induce callus from *Populus ciliata* stems on **MS** medium containing either 0.09 mg/l NAA + 1.1 mg/l BAP (cytokinin), or 0.2 mg/l IBA + 2.25 mg/l BAP. The presence of BAP in both media was conducive to shoot formation, and if the callus was transferred to **MS** plus only 2.3 mg/l BAP, there was enhanced differentiation. However, at least two subcultures on an auxin-free medium were necessary to eliminate the residual effect of NAA, whereas enhanced shoot regeneration occurred immediately on cultures induced to grow on IBA.

Factors influencing binding

Membrane-located binding sites for NAA in batch cultured tobacco cells increased exponentially with time but did not correspond with the number of cells present. There was no increase in binding during the stationary phase (Vreugdenhil *et al.*, 1981). When any of several cytokinins were added to cultured soybean cells in conjunction with 2,4-D, they inhibited the conjugation of the auxin with amino acids (see above). Upon subsequent transfer to a regulator-free medium, cytokinin-treated cells released more of their 2,4-D than the controls (Montague *et al.*, 1981b).

Auxin metabolism

Increased endogenous concentrations of IAA have been correlated with an elevated rate of synthesis of the IAA precursor tryptophan (Sung, 1979). However, IAA, and to a lesser extent other synthetic auxins such as IBA and IPA (indole-propionic acid) (Wagenknecht and Burris, 1950; Kenton, 1955) are oxidised to inactive compounds by the peroxidase enzymes found in plants. Modification of the rate of oxidation or conjugation seem to be the most important way by which internal IAA levels are naturally regulated.

The activity of enzymes responsible for IAA oxidation probably varies quite widely even within the tissues of different plant varieties. These enzymes exist within cultured cells in multiple forms termed iso-enzymes, the pattern of which can be changed by many factors, including the amount of plant growth regulators added to the medium (Lee, 1971a,b,c). Normal sugar beet callus has been found to have a higher peroxidase activity and to release peroxidases into the medium more freely than auxin–habituated callus (Kevers *et al.*, 1981a, 1982).

Shoot formation in tobacco (Thorpe *et al.*, 1978; Rawal and Mehta, 1982) and sugar beet (Kevers *et al.*, 1981b) has been correlated with an increase in peroxidase activity. In apple shoots, Druart *et al.* (1982) discovered an above-average peroxidase activity during root induction, but a low activity during actual root initiation. Tyrosine and other hydroxylated aromatic compounds have been thought to increase the activity of IAA oxidase enzymes in tissue cultures (Lee, 1962 *in* Thorpe and Murashige, 1970).

Regulation by ethylene

The internal concentration of ethylene within plant tissues appears to regulate auxin biosynthesis (Valdovinos *et al.*, 1967; Krul and Colclasure, 1977). Treatments which alter internal ethylene levels in *Citrus* callus have effects on embryo formation. These include: inhibition in tightly sealed vessels (in which the ethylene level was elevated) (Spiegel-Roy and Kochba, 1980); stimulation by low (0.01–1.0 mg/l) concentrations of ethephon (an ethylene-releasing chemical), Kochba *et al.*, 1978a; inhibition by higher levels (Tisserat and Murashige, 1977a); and stimulation by galactose (Kochba *et al.*, 1978b). Galactose may inhibit auxin biosynthesis (Anker, 1974) by increasing internal ethylene levels (Colclasure and Yopp, 1976).

Inhibitors of IAA-oxidase

The rate at which IAA is oxidised also seems to be regulated by enzyme inhibitors. Relatively large amounts of natural inhibitor/s of IAA oxidase have been said to be present in meristematic and juvenile tissues, but not in normal mature differentiated cells until they are wounded (Stonier and Yoneda, 1967; Stonier, 1969). The normal process of auxin (IAA) inactivation has also been reported to be inhibited in the callus produced following crown-gall infection (the callus is capable of autonomous growth in culture) (Lipetz and Galston, 1959; Platt, 1954; Stonier, 1969; Bouillenne and Gaspar, 1970), and in auxin-habituated callus (Weis, 1967). Growing tobacco cells on media which favour the induction of auxin habituation (see Syono and Furuya, 1974), causes there to be an increase in an inhibitor of auxin destruction (Syono, 1979).

Various reducing agents are effective inhibitors of IAA oxidation (Betz, 1963), so that auxin protector/s may function by keeping the cell at a low redox potential (see Chapter 7 and below). The naturally-occurring reducing agent NADH is able to totally inhibit IAA oxidation, until it is itself oxidized (Stonier *et al.*, 1970). A reduced state is thought to be necessary for cell division and differentiation.

The growth regulatory effects of phenols

Compounds which carry one or more hydroxyl groups on an aromatic ring are termed phenolic compounds. Many mono- , di- and tri-hydroxyphenols and their more complex derivatives found naturally in plant cells are strong reducing agents and can serve as substrates for oxidative enzymes. This has led to two hypotheses as to their growth regulatory activity.

- that when added exogenously, hydroxyphenols act as alternative substrates for oxidative enzymes, and, as discussed above, may spare auxin from oxidative breakdown (Stonier, 1971; Stonier *et al.*, 1970; James and Thurbon, 1981b);

There are many papers on the growth regulating properties of phenolic compounds in tissue cultures. Effects noted from adding phenols to culture media are mainly an enhancement of callus growth, more effective adventitious shoot formation, the improved rooting of shoots, and a greater rate of shoot proliferation in certain shoot cultures. Most plant responses have involved a synergism with auxins, particularly added IAA, so that a mode of action that is dependent on the regulation of internal IAA levels has seemed probable. But some workers (*e.g.* Basu *et al.*, 1969; Hammerschlag, 1982b) have queried whether the stimulatory effect of phenols in promoting rooting is not due to some other function than that of preventing IAA destruction.

Lee (1980) found that, in maize, some phenolic compounds can alter the relative proportions of free and bound IAA. Lee and Skoog (1965) and Grambow and Langenbeck-Schwich (1983) reported that the substitution pattern of phenols affects the rate of IAA degradation. Some monophenolics increased the rate, while some 3-substituted phenols depressed it. Phenols were found to react with hydrogen peroxide produced during IAA degradation, thereby protecting cellular constituents from its toxic effects.

4-chlororesorcinol (**19**), a polyphenol oxidase inhibitor (*i.e.* inhibiting the conversion of monophenols and di-hydric phenols to polyphenols, a process stimulated by ethylene) has been found to improve the rooting and subsequent growth of cuttings (Gad *et al.*, 1988a).

- that morphogenic activity is induced by the products formed when compounds such as phloroglucinol (**20**) and phloridzin (**21**) (see below) are oxidised.

Gur *et al.* (1988) advanced this hypothesis when they found that phloroglucinol only promoted rooting in apple clones with sufficient polyphenol oxidase activity to cause significant oxidation of the compound. Of significance to this proposal is the fact that phloroglucinol and phloridzin can inhibit hyperhydricity, apparently by serving as precursors of lignin synthesis (see Chapter 14).

Correlations with endogenous levels

The natural rate of formation of some phenolic compounds has been observed to depend on the rate of growth of cultured tissues (Barz, 1977) and on auxin/cytokinin levels in the medium (Sargent and Skoog, 1960; Skoog and Montaldi, 1961). Their presence has frequently been correlated with the morphogenic capacity of tissues (Tryon, 1956; Hackett, 1970; Kefeli and Kadyrov, 1971).

Rawal and Mehta (1982) found that shoot formation from haploid tobacco callus occurred as the content of natural phenolic substances declined, while cellular differentiation occurred with increasing phenolic accumulation. Juvenile tissues naturally have high levels of auxin protectors (Stonier 1971; 1972).

Root formation

Some observations on natural levels of auxin protectors might suggest that low endogenous auxin levels are required for root initiation, but high levels for root growth. For example, shoots of apple grown *in vitro* were said to have low phenol contents at the root *induction* phase, but high contents as roots were being *initiated* (Druart *et al.*, 1982); and in *Sequoiadendron giganteum*, phenolic compounds were found to decrease in concentration when shoots were moved to a root induction medium. The activity of peroxidases in the induction medium increased during 7–11 days and then decreased, roots appearing as phenols were decreasing (Monteuuis *et al.*, 1987). In each of these plants, peroxidase activity was the reverse of phenol content.

But in chestnut, rhizogenesis occurred during an increase in the level of auxin protectors, whose basipetal transport was inhibited by applied IBA (Mato and Vieitez, 1986). The best time to explant shoot tips from adult chestnut material to a root-inducing medium, was during one of the first two peaks of growth of shoots in layer beds. These times seemed to coincide with the occurrence of the maximum quantitites of natural phenolics (Chevre and Salesses, 1987).

Exogenous applications of phenols

Phloroglucinol

Workers at East Malling Research Station discovered that in the genera *Malus* and *Prunus*, phloroglucinol (20) (*ca.* 162 mg/l, 1 mM) added to culture media containing growth substances, was able to enhance growth and the rate of axillary shoot production from shoot cultures (Jones, 1976; Jones O.P., 1979). These results have been confirmed in other laboratories; but whether there is any response to phloroglucinol, and the magnitude of the effect, has been demonstrated to vary according to the species or variety of plant (Zimmerman and Broome, 1980). James and Wakerell (1982) found that the compound was without effect on the apple variety 'M26', but promotory on 'M9', while Whiteley and Abbott (1977) reported that the growth of shoot cultures of *Malus* 'Golden Delicious', 'Egremont Russet' and 'Bramley' was completely inhibited by 0.1–10 mM phloroglucinol. Hutchinson (1985) found that 1 mM phloroglucinol more than doubled the number of shoots produced by the apple cultivar 'Northern Spy' during the first two subcultures: there was no increase in shoot number by the fourth subculture.

Root formation. When phloroglucinol is added to rooting media together with auxin, it can increase the number of rooted shoots obtained. This effect has been especially noted in several apple cultivars (Jones *et al.*, 1977, 1979; James and Thurbon, 1979, 1981a,b; Jones and Hatfield, 1976; Zimmerman and Broome, 1981; Zimmerman, 1984b). Welander and Huntrieser (1981) found that IBA plus 0.1 mM phoroglucinol promoted the rooting of adult

(19)　4-chlororesorcinol　MW 144.56

(20)　Phloroglucinol　MW 126.11 (anhydrous)
　　　　　　　　　　　MW 162.14 (.2H₂O)

(21)　Phloridzin　MW 436.41 (anhydrous)
　　　　　　　　　MW 472.44 (.2H₂O)

(22)　Phloretic acid　MW 166.18

shoots: 4.9 μM IBA plus 1 mM phloroglucinol induced the best rooting of juvenile shoots.

The presence of phloroglucinol in media at Stage II of apple shoot cultures can precondition shoots to root at Stage III while they are still multiplying in response to high cytokinin levels (James and Thurbon, 1981b). Phloroglucinol consistently synergised the induction of rooting in 'M9' apple rootstock shoots by IAA, but if rooting was induced by IBA, phloroglucinol was only promotory if present for four days. Longer exposures were inhibitory (James, 1983a).

Phloroglucinol and its analogues (see below) have been shown to promote rooting of *Prunus* (Chancel *et al.*, 1980), strawberry and *Rubus* genotypes in conjunction with IBA (but not NAA) (James, 1979; Sobczykiewicz, 1987).

Analagous compounds. The structurally-related glycoside, phloridzin (21), has the same effect as phloroglucinol (Jones, 1976) but it is heat labile and more expensive (Krikorian *et al.* 1982b). Phloridzin is metabolised into phlorglucinol and phloretic acid (22). Phloretic acid was also found by Jones and Hatfield (1976) to increase the proportion of apple shoots which could be rooted, but it was less active than phlorglucinol (10 mM *vs.* 1 mM). Phloroglucinol has occasionally been found to have inhibitory effects: 162 mg/l inhibited the rooting of sour cherry shoots grown *in vitro* (Snir, 1983).

Phloroglucinol and its analogues have proved to be effective in other plants of the Rosaceae. Added to the medium at 500 μM, phloroglucinol (and catechol — see below) also increased adventitious shoot formation from *Rubus* callus (Compton and Preece, 1988a). Stimulatory effects have also been reported on plants of some other families (*e.g.* on shoot growth and shoot proliferation of *Cinchona* (Rubiaceae) - Hunter, 1979; Krikorian *et al.*, 1982b: and *Ficus carica* (Moraceae) — Pontikis and Melas, 1986). Hyperhydricity is prevented by phlorglucinol in an even wider range of plants (see Chapter $$$). Adding phloridzin and phloroglucinol to the medium, increased the number of somatic embryos produced from embryogenic callus of oil palm (Hanower and Hanower, 1984).

Mode of action. It has been suggested that phloroglucinol acts as a bactericide, increasing shoot regeneration only in shoot cultures carrying concealed bacterial infections. The stimulatory effect of the compound is, however, now thought to be largely independent of this effect (Jones and Hopgood, 1979; Jones and James, 1979). Most probably the compound and its homologues act as auxin synergists (Hess, 1969), or auxin protectors (see above).

Catechol

Catechol (23) is another strong reducing agent which has been reported to regulate the rate of IAA oxidation in plant tissues. Hackett (1970) found that although apices of juvenile *Hedera* shoots would root in an illuminance of 4300–5400 lux when treated with 5–10 mg/l NAA, IAA had very little effect. However, 10 mg/l IAA together with 5.5 mg/l catechol resulted in a rooting response that was almost equal to that produced by the optimum NAA level, suggesting that catechol protected IAA from light-induced degradation (see page 423). In low illumination (540 lux), IAA alone produced almost as many roots as IAA + catechol in high lighting. The rooting response of adult shoot tips in low light was very similar to that of juvenile tips in high light.

(23)   Catechol   MW 110.11

Catechol was much less effective than phloroglucinol for promoting the rooting of apple shoots (Jones and Hatfield, 1976) but promoted the rooting of etiolated *Populus robusta* cuttings in conjunction with IAA and sucrose

(Pal and Nanda, 1981). This last test was not conducted under sterile conditions so that catechol could have acted as an antiseptic. Poor rooting is a feature of contaminated cultures (Lang and Schwartz, 1981).

Catechol (and phloroglucinol, 500 μM), increased the number of adventitious shoots formed from leaf callus of tobacco (Compton and Preece, 1988a).

Chlorogenic acid

Like catechol, chlorogenic acid (24) is a natural constituent of plants. It is a strong reducing agent which has been noted to stimulate callus growth of *Prunus avium* stem segments (Feucht and Johal, 1977; Feucht and Schmid, 1980) and to promote the growth of olive callus (Lavee and Avidan, 1982). Together with 1.6–16.4 mg/l *p*-cou-

(24)   Chlorogenic acid   MW 353.31

maric acid (26), chlorogenic acid has been added routinely to media containing NAA and IBA to promote rooting of *Beta vulgaris* (Margara, 1977a) and *Brassica* (Margara and Leydecker, 1978) shoots *in vitro*. Hammerschlag (1982b) was able to root 100% of *Prunus cerasifera* shoots in the light when chlorogenic acid and IAA were present in the medium, but only 30% formed roots in response to IAA alone. Shoots kept in darkness all rooted in response to IAA alone.

Coumarins

Many natural coumarins are found in plants, but their biochemical or physiological roles are not well understood. Compounds of this kind have been found to affect a wide variety of processes, low levels sometimes exerting a stimulatory role, but higher levels often being inhibitory. This is particularly noticeable in the effect of coumarins on the activity of many classes of enzymes. Scopoletin has been reported to either increase or decrease IAA oxidase activity, according to concentration (Imbert and Wilson, 1970) and in tobacco callus it can inhibit IAA degradation (Skoog and Montaldi, 1961), perhaps by acting as a substrate for peroxidase enzymes.

Coumarin and related compounds, have been found to both stimulate and decrease protein synthesis, respiration and photophosphorylation and decrease carbohydrate metabolism (Brown, 1981), but increased growth in conjunction with IAA has been reported (Neumann, 1960). Adding 90–150 µM coumarin (and no other regulant) to **Murashige and Tucker (1969)** medium induced the formation of roots and shoots from stem sections of *Citrus* 'Swingle Citrumelo' seedlings (Grosser and Chandler, 1986).

Tyrosine

Tobacco pith callus grown on the medium of **Linsmaier and Skoog (1965)** with 2 mg/l IAA and 2 mg/l kinetin is wholly unorganised, but if grown on the same medium supplemented with 100 mg/l tyrosine (25), 106 mg/l adenine sulphate and 340 mg/l $NaH_2PO_4.H_2O$, adventitious shoots are formed (Thorpe and Murashige, 1968b; 1970: Murashige, 1961). Tyrosine is a substrate for the enzyme phenylalanine ammonia lyase (Fig. 109) which converts it to *p*-coumaric acid (26). Perhaps the stimulation of adventitious shoot formation by tyrosine is therefore related to its conversion to phenolic acids which then protect, or interact with, auxin? Auxin requiring callus of tobacco has been found to accumulate more *p*-coumaric and *p*-ferulic acid (28) than callus which is auxin-habituated (*i.e.* auxin autotrophic) (Zador *et al.*, 1985).

Other phenolic compounds

Other compounds which have been suspected to be naturally-occurring inhibitors of IAA oxidase, may increase callus growth in certain circumstances. They include the quinone, juglone (Compton and Preece, 1988a), some diphenolic flavenoids with antioxidant properties such as naringenin (Phillips, 1961, 1962), quercitin and its glycoside quercitrin (Furuya *et al.*, 1962; Thimann, 1963; Feucht and Nachit, 1978), catechin and flavandiols (Feucht and Nachit, 1977; Feucht and Schmid, 1980) and chemicals of the 'β-inhibitor complex' (Bennett-Clark and Kefford, 1953). Examples of the latter are the coumarin (see above), scopoletin (and its glucoside scopolin) (Schaeffer *et al.*, 1967), and various phenolic acids such as caffeic acid (27), chlorogenic acid(see above), and sinapic acid (Thimann, 1963).

In combination with IBA auxin, phenyl propanoid compounds such as chlorogenic acid, phenylalanine and ferulic acid (28), promoted the formation of adventitious root primordia on hypocotyl cuttings of *Pinus* seedlings, but only when the number of roots induced by IBA was low. In experiments where IBA was capable of inducing many roots, the phenolics were ineffective or inhibitory.

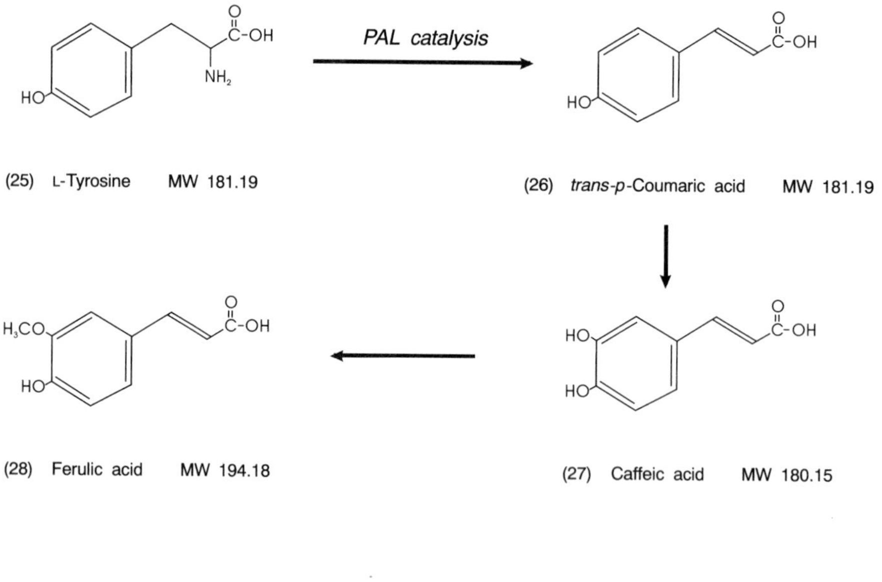

(25) L-Tyrosine   MW 181.19

(26) *trans-p*-Coumaric acid   MW 181.19

(28) Ferulic acid   MW 194.18

(27) Caffeic acid   MW 180.15

Fig. 109. Biosynthetic pathway to simple phenolic compounds

Effect of synthetic auxins on IAA levels

The synthetic auxins which are used exogenously to control the growth and organisation of cultured tissues, may also inhibit IAA oxidase. As is found with callus cultures of many plant species, those of *Arabidopsis thaliana* can be initiated and maintained on a medium containing 2,4-D, but progressively lose their morphogenic capacity the longer they are maintained on it, until after 6–8 months there is no regeneration at all. The loss in regenerative ability was found by Negrutiu *et al.* (1979) to be closely paralleled by a progressive decline in the activity of peroxidase enzymes through successive transfers of the callus. The decline was reversed each time the callus was removed from the presence of 2,4-D and grown on a shoot-inducing medium. Reduction in peroxidase levels would be expected to result in higher endogenous IAA concentrations, but the decrease in peroxidase enzymes appears in this case to have been associated with a decrease in natural auxin biosynthesis.

In cultures of wild cherry, endogenous levels of IAA have also been observed to be considerably *reduced* by the presence of 2,4-D, although the availability of tryptophan (the precursor of IAA biosynthesis) was increased (Sung, 1979). This suggested that 2,4-D interfered directly with IAA synthesis or hastened IAA degradation, or else a phenomenon of auxin self-regulation was operating. 2,4-D inhibition of IAA synthesis has also been noted in sycamore suspension cultures (Elliot *et al.*, 1978). Maeda and Thorpe (1979) suggested that indole-based synthetic auxins might protect IAA from natural destruction by competing with it for IAA oxidase enzymes.

ANTI-AUXINS (AUXIN TRANSPORT INHIBITORS)

In some tissue culture experiments, compounds have been used which, in tests on whole plants or parts of plants, have been thought to act as antiauxins or to inhibit auxin transport or movement. The action of chemicals with activity of this kind is complicated and by no means fully understood. Those which have been most frequently used in tissue cultures are:

TIBA (**29**)	2,3,5-Tri-iodobenzoic acid
PTAA (**30**)	(3-Phenyl-1,2,4- thiadiazol-5-yl)thioacetic acid.
naptalam (**31**) (or NPA)	*N*-1-Naphthylphthalamic acid
2,4,6-T (**32**)	2,4,6-Trichlorophenoxyacetic acid
PCIB (**33**)	*p*-Chlorophenoxy*iso*butyric acid

(29) TIBA   MW 499.81

(30) PTAA   MW 253.32

(31) Naptalam   MW 291.31

(32) 2,4,6-T   MW 255.49

(33) PCIB   MW 214.65

Auxin transport

Auxin is transported in a polar fashion (Chapter 8). Plant cells maintain a pH gradient across the plasma membrane so that the cell wall is more acidic than the cytoplasm. In an acid pH, IAA exists in an undissociated form which can readily enter the cell by diffusion. At the pH of the cytoplasm, the molecule dissociates to the anion IAA⁻, which is unable to pass across the membrane. Movement out of the cell only occurs when IAA⁻ become attached to a carrier molecule. Polar movement of IAA occurs because the carrier is preferentially located at the base of the cell (Jacobs and Gilbert, 1983). Compounds such as TIBA and naphthylthalamic acid become preferentially bound to the auxin carrier, preventing auxin movement. Ethylene is also inhibitory (Van Aartrijk *et al.*, 1985). TIBA acts directly at the auxin receptor site from which it can displace auxins such as IAA and NAA (Thompson *et al.*, 1973). Maan *et al.* (1985a,b) detected two membrane binding sites for auxins in *Nicotiana tabacum*, one exclusively for auxins, the other to which both naptalam and auxins could become attached.

If 'anti-auxins' act only as auxin transport inhibitors, intracellular auxin levels could be expected to increase when both auxin and 'anti-auxin' are presented to tissues. TIBA and PTAA have been found to stimulate IAA uptake into cells in suspension culture, particularly when the pH of the medium is low (pH 4.5) (Rubery, 1979).

Effects *in vitro*

Organogenesis

'Anti-auxins' have been reported to promote or modify morphogenesis and in many instances they do appear to have negated the effect of exogenous or endogenous auxin. Naptalam (or NPA) prevented the growth of tobacco callus when incorporated into the medium at 50 mg/l, but 0.5–5 mg/l promoted growth in conjunction with IAA. The compound seemed to reduce auxin activity or enhance that of cytokinin, because callus cultured with 50 mg/l naptalam plus 2 mg/l IAA and 0.4 mg/l kinetin initiated buds which were not formed if naptalam was not present (Feng and Linck, 1970).

p-Chlorophenoxy*iso*butyric acid (PCIB) counteracted the inhibitory effect of 2,4-D on adventitious bud formation on sections of *Chondrilla juncea* roots (Kefford and Caso, 1972) and together with BAP, it promoted the formation of adventitious shoots from *Solanum melongena* callus, when combinations of IAA and BAP were ineffective. Fiola *et al.* (1978) thought this might be because PCIB overcame excessive endogenous IAA in the tissue.

Work of Cassells (1979; Cassells *et al.*, 1982) similarly suggested that explants of some species may have too high a level of endogenous auxin for shoot buds to be produced directly, or from associated callus. Placing explants of tomato stems on a medium containing 2 mg/l of the cytokinin, zeatin, and 0.01–0.1 mg/l TIBA but no auxin, caused a marked increase in shoot bud formation, probably because the 'anti-auxin' prevented endogenous auxin moving to sites of potential shoot bud formation. In *Pelargonium*, callus that formed on **MS** medium plus zeatin, gave rise to numerous green xylem-containing nodules. These could be induced to develop into shoot buds when TIBA was added to the medium. In the absence of TIBA, the microscopic bud initials of *Pelargonium* seemed to release natural auxin in sufficient concentration to prevent further shoot development.

Callus of *Colocasia esculenta* produced normal shoots when 1 mg/l TIBA was added to the medium whereas shoots produced with combinations of auxin and cytokinin had an abnormal morphology (Nyman and Arditti, 1984). However, although barley callus developed adventitious shoots on a medium with 2,4,5-T auxin, it produced roots on a medium containing TIBA (Jelaska *et al.*, 1984).

Embryogenesis

The effect of 'antiauxins' on somatic embryogenesis or embryo growth have been equivocal. In anther cultures of *Hordeum* (Clapham, 1973) and *Zea mays* (Genovesi and Collins, 1982), TIBA was more effective than normal auxins in inducing callus formation and embryogenesis. 2,4,6-Trichlorophenoxyacetic acid (2,4,6-T) has also been reported to enhance somatic embryo formation in callus cultures (Newcomb and Wetherell, 1970; Smith and Street, 1974), but Stange (1979) found that *p*-chlorophenoxy*iso*butyric acid (PCIB) inhibited meristematic activity, and Fujimura and Komamine (1979a) discovered that 2,4,6-T and PCIB inhibited embryogenesis in carrot suspensions. They took particular care to wash residual auxin from cell clusters and thought that the stimulatory effects of anti-auxins noted by others, were due to their failure to take this precaution.

Other compounds with anti-auxin effect are β-NAA, phenylpropionic acid, and 2-(*o*-chlorophenoxy)-2-methylpropionic acid. These compounds, together with TIBA, prevented the re-callusing of indirectly formed *Sapindus trifoliatus* embryos, but did not permit embryo germination. Germination only occurred when 5-methyltryptophan (34) was added to the medium. The compound seemed to act as an anti-auxin (Desai *et al.*, 1986).

(34)   5-Methyltryptophan   MW 218.26

Use in shoot cultures

Application of two drops of an 1 mg/l solution of TIBA to the apices of cultured rose shoots had the same effect as manually tipping the shoots, and increased the number of axillary shoots subsequently produced. Adding 3 mg/l TIBA to the medium for *Rosa hybrida* shoot cultures increased lateral shoot formation during the first two passages (Voyiatzi and Voyiatzi, 1988). We have not found reports of the beneficial use of antiauxins in shoot cultures of other species.

CYTOKININS

PROPERTIES, DISCOVERY AND OCCURRENCE

Biological activity

Cytokinins comprise a separate class of growth substances and growth regulators. They produce only minor effects when applied to intact plants, but have been noted to stimulate protein synthesis. It is perhaps for this reason that they can promote the maturation of chloroplasts and delay the senescence of detached leaves. Cytokinin application to a single site in the plant (*e.g.* to one leaf) causes the treated organ to become an active sink for amino acids, which then migrate to the organ from surrounding sites. The effect of cytokinins is most noticeable in tissue cultures where they are used, often together with auxins, to stimulate cell division and control morphogenesis. Added to shoot culture media, these compounds overcome apical dominance and release lateral buds from dormancy. In this respect they appear to have an opposite effect to endogenous auxin.

Discovery

As in the case of auxins, there are both naturally-occurring compounds and their synthetic analogues. The first cytokinin to be discovered, kinetin (35), was isolated in

(35)   Kinetin   MW 215.22

Professor Skoog's laboratory at the University of Wisconsin, following experiments to promote continuing growth of the callus which formed on tobacco stem sections on nutrient media. Cells of the explants initially proliferated quickly but although the addition of IAA increased the amount of callus produced, growth soon stopped and was not resumed even if pieces of the newly-formed tissue were subcultured onto a fresh medium. Cell division and callus growth *did* continue however, if either coconut milk or yeast extract were added to the medium and so attempts were made to isolate the active principle. As chromatography of ethanol soluble fractions of yeast extract indicated that the substance was a purine, other

sources of naturally-occurring purines were examined for their ability to promote continued callus growth. Extracts from aged herring DNA yielded a compound with the same sample adsorption peak and chemical behaviour as the one discovered from the yeast extract. It was also isolated in a crystalline form from samples of DNA autoclaved under acidic conditions. The new growth factor was named 'kinetin' because it stimulated cell division in cells that otherwise might have become multinuclear (Miller *et al.*, 1955a,b; Miller, 1961a,b). The general term *cytokinin* was later proposed to cover all compounds having a similar activity (Skoog *et al.*, 1965).

NATURALLY-OCCURRING CYTOKININS

Although kinetin is not now thought to be a naturally-occurring cytokinin, and to have arisen in the original isolates by structural rearrangement of another compound (Hecht, 1980), at least 25 natural cytokinin plant growth substances that are structurally-related to kinetin have been identified, either as free compounds or as glucosides or ribosides (Entsch *et al.*, 1980). Two such compounds used in plant tissue work are:

Zeatin (36)	4-hydroxy-3-methyl-*trans*-2-butenylaminopurine†
	6-(4-hydroxy-3-methylbut-2-enyl)-aminopurine†
	2-methyl-4-(1*H*-purin-6-ylamino)-2-buten-1-ol†
2-iP (37) (or IPA)‡	N^6-(2-isopentyl)adenine*
	N^6-(Δ^2- isopentenyl)adenosine*
	6-(3-methyl-2-butenylamino)purine*
	6-(γ, γ-dimethylallylamino)purine*
Dihydrozeatin (38)	6-(4-hydroxy-3-methyl-*trans*-2-butenyl)aminopurine

† = alternative chemical names for zeatin

* = alternative chemical names for 2-iP

‡ = this abbreviation is not recommended because of possible confusion with indole-3-propionic acid

Because of the presence of a double bond in the side chain, the zeatin molecule has two configurations: the form which occurs in nature is the *trans*-isomer. Syn-

(36) trans-Zeatin   MW 219.25

(37) 2-iP   MW 203.25

(38) dihydro-Zeatin   MW 221.26

(39) Zeatin riboside   MW 363.37

Sites of biosynthesis

Cytokinins occur as free molecules in plants, and are also found in the transfer RNAs (t-RNAs) of the cytoplasm and chloroplast. In whole plants, roots appear to be major sites of natural cytokinin biosynthesis, but some production does take place in other actively dividing tissues, such as the stem cambium (Chen C.-M. *et al.*, 1985). The root apex, and particularly the cells of its 'quiescent centre', could be important sites of synthesis (Short and Torrey, 1972a; Torrey, 1972). It has been suggested that the slow rate of cell division in the root quiescent centre could be the result of a supra-optimal cytokinin concentration. Some experimental evidence that the root tip is a primary site of cytokinin synthesis was obtained by Ochatt and Power (1988c): on the roots, which developed from the callus of *Prunus cerasus*, shoots were only differentiated at the point furthest from the tip; but were formed along the length of a root if its tip was removed. It was thought that cytokinin might have been present in supra-optimal amounts for rhizogenesis, until the tip was removed.

Isolated roots can be cultured without the addition of a cytokinin to the growth medium and Skoog and Tsui (1948) found that although roots, initiated from tobacco calluses, were able to grow indefinitely in White's basic medium without growth substances, shoot buds were incapable of continued growth unless they developed either directly from roots, or from callus immediately adjoining the origin of the adventitious roots. Similar observations have been made by Koda and Okazawa (1980) with asparagus, and by Bollmark *et al.* (1988) with pea cuttings.

Cytokinins produced in roots of plants are normally transported in the xylem to other regions. The bleeding sap of plants is rich in cytokinins and has been shown to promote growth *in vitro* (*e.g.* Skene, 1972b; Zimmer and Pieper 1975; 1976). The cytokinin produced by shoot tissues is only a small proportion of that formed by root apices. That synthesised in shoot apices is insufficient to sustain their prolonged growth *in vitro*.

Nucleotides (compounds composed of D-ribose, phosphoric acid, and a purine) contain iso-pentyladenine groups, characteristic of natural cytokinins. Nucleotides are found in suspension cultured cells, but whether they arise from the degradation of t-RNA or from *de novo* synthesis, is not clear; that they might be a source of cytokinins in cultures is suggested by the finding that their maximum concentration in *Pimpinella anisum* suspensions coincided with the peak occurence of isopentyladenine (2-iP), and isopentyladenosine (2-iP conjugated with D-ribose), in the cells (Ernst and Oesterhelt, 1985).

thetic preparations of the compound often consist of mixed *cis*- and *trans*-isomers, but the *cis*- form does have cytokinin activity. Besides occurring as a free molecule, zeatin also occurs naturally in glycoside (sugar-) and glycotide (sugar-phosphate-) conjugates. Dihydrozeatin (**38**), a natural metabolite of zeatin, has cytokinin activity. Zeatin riboside ((**39**) is highly active as a cytokinin, and has been used in some experimental tissue culture work The riboside of 2-iP [N^6-(2-isopentyl)adenosine], or its 2-methylthio- analogue, can occur in t-RNAs (see below). In *Actinidia* cultures, 2-iP has been shown to be converted to zeatin (Einset, 1986a,b).

Despite the occurrence of endogenous cytokinins in whole plants, many tissues and small organs isolated *in vitro* are unable to synthesize sufficient of these substances to sustain growth. This is particularly the case with dicotyledonous tissues where, a low level of cytokinin is frequently required to be added to the culture medium. The dependence of some callus cultures on cytokinin for cell division has been used as the basis of a sensitive bio-assay for cytokinins (Miller, 1963; Linsmaier and Skoog, 1965; Letham, 1967). However cytokinin-independent callus and cell strains of broad-leafed plants are commonly found, and from some of them, zeatin and 2-iP have been isolated (Dyson and Hall, 1972; Einset and Skoog, 1973). Zeatin and zeatin riboside have been obtained from monocotyledon callus grown in the absence of either auxin or cytokinin (Kemp and Stoltz, 1979). Presumably in tissues that are able to grow without cytokinin being added to the medium, the cells can produce sufficient natural cytokinin for cell division to proceed.

SYNTHETIC CYTOKININ ANALOGUES

Substituted purines

Although used in research, the natural cytokinins 2-iP and zeatin, are not employed by commercial laboratories routinely, because of their cost. Fortunately, several chemical analogues of natural cytokinins apart from kinetin have been prepared which are found to be highly active as cytokinins. Although they are chiefly 6-substituted adenine derivatives, some other slightly less structurally-related compounds also possess cytokinin activity, for example 4- alkylaminopteridines (Iwamura *et al.*., 1980), and 6- benzyloxypurines. Some of these analogues are reported to be more active than kinetin or benzyladenine (BA, or BAP), and particularly effective in promoting morphogenesis (Wilcox *et al.*, 1978, 1981). The 1-deaza analogue of zeatin riboside (Rogozinska *et al.*, 1973; Rodaway and Lutz, 1985; Kamínek *et al.*, 1987) has also been shown to have cytokinin activity.

Only a few of these compounds are available in chemical catalogues, or are expensive and therefore only of interest for research purposes. Synthetic cytokinins most commonly used in micropropagation work are the compounds:

Kinetin **(35)**   6-furfurylaminopurine† *or*

N-(2-furanylmethyl)-1*H*-purin(e)-6-amine†

BAP **(40)**   6-benzylaminopurine* *or*
(or BA)   benzyladenine*

N-(phenylmethyl)-1*H*-purin(e)-6-amine*

† = alternative chemical names for kinetin

* = alternative chemical names for BAP

The synthetic cytokinin:

PBA **(41)**   6-(benzylamino)-9-(2-tetrahydropyranyl)-
or SD 8339   9*H*-purine‡

N-benzyl-9-(2-tetrahydropyranyl)-adenine‡

n-(benzylamino)-9-(2-tetrahydropyranyl)-9*H*- purine‡

‡ = alternative chemical names for PBA

which was a product of Shell Research Ltd., has high physiological activity, but seems only to be have been used experimentally, and not in commercial nicropropagation.

(40) BAP   MW 225.26

(41) PBA   MW 309.37

Several compounds with cytokinin or anticytokinin activity have fungicidal properties (Hecht, 1980). The fungicide benomyl, which has a structure similar to adenine-based cytokinins, has been shown to have the ability to stimulate the growth of soybean and radish callus cultures (Skene, 1972a), but in both species it was a much less efficient cytokinin than kinetin. Benomyl can be damaging to cultures grown in sealed vessels (see page 143): it was, for example, phytotoxic to orchid protocorms at 0.2 mg/l in an agar medium, but stimulated growth at lower levels (Gupta and Hadley, 1977.

The phenylureas

A common way of adding a natural cytokinin to media is by the use of organic supplements such as yeast extract or coconut milk. Coconut milk contains several physiologically-active substances (see Chapter 9); amongst which have been found the natural purine–based cytokinin zeatin, and 1,3-diphenylurea **(42)** (Shantz and Steward, 1955). The latter compound, and many other substituted ureas, have cytokinin activity and can promote the growth of dormant buds (Kefford *et al.*, 1966), and induce cell division in cytokinin-dependent callus tissues (Bruce *et al.* 1965; Bruce and Zwar, 1966). Diphenylureas have not been commonly used in tissue cultures, but there are a few reports. Butenko *et al.* (1972) found 2 mg/l 1,3-diphenylurea facilitated organogenesis in sugar beet callus cultures.

Some N-pyridyl-N′–phenylureas have been discovered to be more active than purines such as BAP and zeatin in promoting callus growth and morphogenesis in tobacco and several other kinds of plants (Okamoto *et al.*, 1978; Takahashi *et al.*, 1978; Kamada and Harada, 1979c; Ohyama and Oka, 1982). Two of the most active of the compounds in this series are:

2Cl-4PU **(43)**   *N*-(2-chloro-4-pyridyl)-*N'*- phenylurea,,
(or CPPU)   and

2,6 Cl-4PU   *N*-(2,6-dichloro-4-pyridyl)-*N'*-phenylurea
  (44)

(42) 1,3-diphenylurea   MW 212.25

(43) 2Cl-4PU   MW 247.69

(44) 2,6 Cl-4PU   MW 282.13

(45) Thidiazuron (TDZ)   MW 220.25

The thiadiazole-substituted phenylurea:

thidiazuron   (*N*-phenyl-*N'*-1,2,3-thiadiazol-5-ylurea
  (TDZ) **(45)**

which was registered as a cotton defoliant (Arndt *et al.*, 1976) and given the product name 'Dropp'®, has similarly been shown to have high cytokinin activity (in Mok *et al.*, 1982a,b and many subsequent tests). In some plants, it is more effective than adenine-based compounds for inducing adventitious shoot regeneration (*e.g.* indirectly in *Vitis vinifera* cvs. — Reisch and Martens, 1988; and directly in *Rhododendron* — Imel and Preece, 1988, and *Malus* — Elobeidy and Korban, 1988). TDZ can also be highly effective for inducing axillary shoot formation in shoot cultures (*e.g.* in *Rorippa* — Gilby and Wainwright, 1989; *Rhodendron* — Fellman *et al.*, 1987; and *Malus domestica* — Fasolo *et al*, 1988a,b), but although many shoots can be formed, they are liable not to elongate sufficiently.

Effective shoot proliferation in the otherwise difficult-to-propagate *Acer × fremanii* (Kerns and Meyer, 1986), and in *Pyrus communis* (Singha and Bhatia, 1988), was achieved using mixtures of BAP and thidiazuron (respecivity 1 μM + 0.01 μM for *Acer* and 5 μM + 0.4 μM for

Pyrus). In both cases there was a significant interaction between the two compounds.

Fellman *et al.* (*loc. cit.*) also found that 0.5 μM 2Cl-4PU was effective for inducing *Rhododendron* shoot proliferation: shoot elongation was inhibited at higher levels.

Mode of action

The mode of action of plant cytokinins is uncertain. Some have been found to be present in transfer-RNA molecules, but it is not yet clear whether incorporation into t-RNA is necessary before typical cytokinin effects can become apparent. In some circumstances, cytokinins have been shown to activate RNA synthesis and to stimulate protein synthesis and enzyme activity (Kulaeva, 1980). But although other workers have recorded a low level of incorporation of a synthetic cytokinin analogue into t-RNA (Burrows *et al.*, 1971; Peaud-Lenoel and Jouanneau, 1980), it could not be correlated with the observed physiological action of the compound.

The action of cytokinins is light-dependent. In blue, far red and white light, the proliferation of shoots of *Prunus* by BAP was strongly dependent on the rate of photon fluence, but the rate of fluence of a red light source was not critical. Baraldi *et al.* (1988a) suggested that shoot proliferation by this cytokinin was promoted by a low energy phytochrome response. In conditions which do not induce shoot proliferation, *viz.* dark, or low fluence far red light, BAP inhibit shoot elongation. Promotion of axillary shoot growth by BAP, and its inhibition of shoot elongation, therefore seem to be two independent processes.

Anti-auxin effect

Kinetin blocks the auxin-stimulated synthesis of a polypeptide (almost certainly a β-1,3-glucanase enzyme) (see above, and Felix and Meins, 1985).

Some aminopurines with cytokinin properties have been shown to act as reductants in a photochemical reaction with riboflavin, and to be oxidised thereby to adenine (Rothwell and Wright, 1967). Part of the biological effects produced by cytokinins could be due to their inhibition of the oxidation of IAA. Kinetin (0.04–1 mg/l) has been noted to alter the activity, distribution, and composition of IAA oxidase isoenzymes within tobacco callus cells (Lee, 1974).

Noting that callus which was induced to form shoots by the addition of cytokinin was more compact than non-shoot-forming callus, Kirkham and Holder (1981) investigated the effect of kinetin on callus water potential; the cytokinin made cell walls more rigid, so that the turgor potential of cells was increased. The water potential of the cells was therefore increased (made less negative), and they became less liable to take up water from the surrounding medium. This was directly opposite to the effect of the auxin *p*-CPA.

Carbohydrate metabolism

Apart from a possible effect on levels of endogenous auxin, cytokinins appear to be implicated in sugar metabolism. Both decreases and increases in the specific activity of enzymes of the glycolytic and oxidative pentose phosphate pathways have been reported. A medium containing adenine sulphate in addition to kinetin, which is conducive to shoot formation in *Nicotiana tabacum*, was noted by Scott *et al.* (1964) to cause a marked *increase* in the activities of two enzymes of the oxidative pentose phosphate pathway (glucose-6-phosphate dehydrogenase and 6-phosphoglucanate dehydrogenase), compared to their activities in a non-shoot-forming medium. Conditions favouring bud formation, including the availability of cytokinins, seem to enhance starch metabolism in tobacco callus (Thorpe and Meier, 1972). Callus which produces shoots has been noted to have high specific activities of enzymes involved in both starch accumulation and breakdown (Thorpe and Meier, 1974). Cytokinins have been noted to reduce the oxygen uptake of cells (Neumann, 1968) and to inhibit the alternative cyanide-resistant respiration pathway which exists in many plants (Miller, 1979; 1980; 1982: Musgrave and Siedow, 1985).

The phenylurea compounds

It is generally assumed that phenyl urea compounds with cytokinin activity act at the same sites as the purine–based cytokinins, *i.e.* that they are active in their own right. This hypothesis was out forward by Kurosaki *et al.* (1981), who suggested that there were structural similarities between the two classes of compound. An alternative hypothesis is that the phenylureas may stimulate the accumulation, or biosynthesis, of natural purine-based cytokinins, or alter the metabolism of these compounds (see below). It is reported that the phenylureas are potent inhibitors of cytokinin oxidase (Laloue, in Horgan, 1987a).

The activity of thidiazuron as a defoliant seems to be associated with its capacity to induce ethylene production in treated leaves (Suttle, 1984). Thidiazuron-induced leaf drop can be inhibited by AVG (see page 454), which prevents ethylene biosynthesis (Elstner *et al.*, 1983), or treatments which prevent ethylene action (Suttle, 1985). How this relates to the marked cytokinin activity of the compound is unclear.

Uptake and metabolism

The uptake of cytokinins into cultured tissues has been found to be rapid (Marino, 1986; Mariano, 1988).

A naturally occurring enzyme, cytokinin oxidase, degrades cytokinins such as zeatin and isopentyl adenine which have a Δ^2- double bond, by cleaving the side chain (Fig. 110) (Horgan, 1987a; Chatfield and Armstrong, 1988); it does not inactivate dihydrozeatin, but rapid degradationof zeatin and 2-iP by the enzyme could explain the ineffectiveness of these compounds on plants, such as *Gerbera*.

In several different kinds of plant tissue, the activity of cytokinin oxidase is enhanced by exogenous application of cytokinins (Palmer and Palni, 1987; Motyka and Kamínek, 1990) suggesting that treating plants with synthetic cytokinins could decrease the level of the natural endogenous compounds. In some other reports treating plant tissues with synthetic homologues caused at least a temporary *increase* in levels of natural zeatin, and zeatin riboside (Thomas and Katterman, 1986; Hansen *et al.*, 1987; Vaňková *et al.*, 1987).

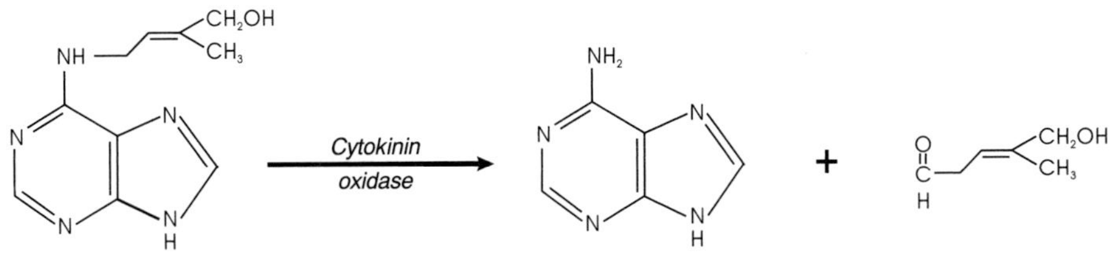

Fig. 110. Cytokinin oxidase degradation of natural cytokinins.

In *Gerbera* callus, free zeatin becomes conjugated with ribose or ribose phosphate within 10 h to produce the physiogically-active compounds, zeatin-9-riboside and zeatin-9-ribotide, but these conjugates then disappear during the next 30 h and adenosine and other products of side- chain cleavage accumulate (Blakesley and Lenton, 1987).

In various plants, BAP has been shown to be initially converted to several metabolites which are probably, mono-, di- and tri-ribotides, the 3- , 7- and 9-glucosides, a 9–riboside, a 9–ribotide, and a 9-riboside-glucoside (Blakesley and Lenton, 1987; Horgan, 1987b; Van der Krieken *et al.*, 1988). The formation of these conjugates does not necessarily mean that BAP is inactivated, as one or more of the conjugates may still have cytokinin activity (Van der Krieken *et al.*, 1988), or may act as storage products.

In some plants, an enzyme other than cytokinin oxidase is thought to be responsible for the degradation of kinetin and benzyladenine to adenine (Forsyth and Van Staden, 1987); a considerable amount of side chain cleavage was found in the shoots from *Gerbera* shoot cultures (Blakesley and Lenton, 1987). In other plants BAP is not broken down in this way; virtually no side chain cleavage was detected after 90 hours of culture with BAP in *Gerbera* callus (Blakesley and Lenton, *loc. cit.*), and adenine or adenosine were not produced from BAP in soybean callus (Van Staden and Mooney, 1988). In *Prunus domestica* shoot cultures, at least some of applied BAP is broken down to CO_2 over 21 days (Mariano, 1988).

EFFECTS IN TISSUE CULTURES

Stimulation of cell division

In tissue cultures, cytokinins appear to be necessary for plant cell division. In their absence, metaphase, but not prophase of mitosis, is considerably protracted, and it has been suggested that cytokinins might be required to regulate the synthesis of proteins involved in the formation and function of the mitotic spindle apparatus (Jouanneau, 1970, 1975). In cultures where cytokinin is limiting, division of cell nuclei becomes arrested at one stage of the cell cycle. Subculture of the tissue onto a medium containing a cytokinin can then cause the cells to divide synchronously after a lag period (Jouanneau, 1971). Callus tissues in which cell division proceeds without the addition of cytokinin to the culture medium (*e.g. Oxalis dispar* — Sunderland and Wells, 1968), are thought to be able to produce their own natural growth substances. Three natural cytokinins could be isolated, for example,

from a cytokinin-independent strain of tobacco callus (Skoog *et al.*, 1973).

Callus proliferation from the tissues of most dicotyledonous plants is usually thought to require the presence of both an auxin and a cytokinin in the growth medium, but Nitsch and Bui Dang Ha (1967) found that proliferation of tobacco pith explants would take place if a synthetic cytokinin and an auxin were supplied sequentially in that order. Thus when grown for one day on a basal medium containing 0.2 mg/l kinetin, before being transferred for 20 days to the same basal medium but with 1.8 mg/l IAA, more callus was produced than when the same quantities of auxin and cytokinin were available together. By contrast, there was practically no growth at all if IAA was provided for only one day, and kinetin for the rest of the time. The sequential promotion of growth was not apparent however when natural cytokinins were employed. Nitsch (1968) interpreted these results to indicate that cytokinins act during the pre-treatment phase at the DNA level (even though no cell divisions occur during this period) and that natural cytokinins were degraded too rapidly to be effective, except when present in the medium continuously.

Dicotyledonous callus, or suspension cultures requiring auxin (*e.g.* 1 mg/l IAA) but not cytokinin for growth, can be cultured for long periods without auxin when a high concentration of cytokinin (*e.g.* 0.1–1 mg/l kinetin) is added to the medium. At this level the cytokinin appears to increase the natural auxin content of the tissues but not to cause auxin-habituation, because after a prolonged period of culture, removal of the cytokinin again causes the cells to become auxin-dependent (Syono and Furuya, 1972a).

Adventitious shoot formation

Cytokinins are very effective in promoting direct or indirect shoot initiation. As mentioned in the previous section, and as shown in the tables of Chapter 12, they are used for this purpose in combination with auxins. A balance between auxin and cytokinin normally gives the most effective organogenesis.

Leaf segments of *Crassula argentea* form callus in response to wounding which then gives rise to roots and later, shoots. Paterson and Rost (1981) found that if cytokinin was added to the medium, shoots were formed from a superficial meristem, and roots were afterwards produced from inside the callus. The normal sequence of organogenesis was therefore reversed.

Embryogenesis

A low concentration of cytokinin (typically 0.5–2.5 μM) is often added to media for the induction of embryogenic callus, especially in broad-leafed plants. There is, however, some evidence to suggest that cytokinins may inhibit embryogenesis in monocotyledons: 0.001 µM exogenous cytokinin was sufficient to prevent it in *Dactylis glomerata*. The presence of endogenous cytokinin may also be responsible for the inability to obtain embryogenesis in some genotypes. Leaf sections of non- embryogenic strains of this grass contained less natural cytokinin than those which were capable of producing embryogenic callus (Wenck *et al.*, 1988). Carman and Campbell (1988) were able to induce embryogenesis in a non-responsive strain of wheat by detaching wheat spikes from the plant some while before culturing immature embryo explants. This was thought to decrease the supply of natural cytokinins from the roots. If zeatin was added to the medium, embryogenesis was suppressed.

Use in shoot cultures

Axillary shoot proliferation. To encourage the growth of axillary buds, and reduce apical dominance in shoot cultures of broad-leafed plants, one or more cytokinins are usually incorporated into the medium at Stage II. A successful treatment induces the growth of several small shoots from each explant over a 4–6 week period. Rates of cytokinin which are too high, cause many small shoots to be produced, which typically fail to elongate; they may also cause the leaves of some species to have an unusual shape, and/or induce shoots to become hyperhydric.

Adventitious shoot bud formation. The formation of adventitious shoots, whether directly from explanted tissues, or indirectly from callus, is regulated by an interaction between auxins and cytokinins.

Inhibition of root formation. High concentrations of cytokinin (0.5–10 mg/l) generally inhibit or delay root formation (Schraudolf and Reinert, 1959; Harris and Hart, 1964; Ben–Jaacov *et al.*, 1991) and also prevent root growth and the promotive effects of auxins on root initiation (Humphries, 1960). For this reason cytokinins are usually omitted from shoot culture media at Stage III when shoots are to be rooted to provide plantlets (see Chapter 14). Sometimes more than one subculture to a cytokinin-free medium may be required until the level of cytokinin within the tissues has been sufficiently reduced.

Despite these observations, there are reports that cytokinins can sometimes induce or promote root growth (Fries, 1960), or adventitious root formation, in the absence of auxins (see review by Nemeth, 1979). In nearly all cases only low rates of cytokinin have been effective, for example, shoots of sugar beet were rooted on **MS** medium containing 0.5 mg/l kinetin and no auxin (Konwar and Coutts, 1990). Boxus and Terzi (1988) advocated the addition of 0.5 mg/l kinetin and auxin to the rooting

medium for strawberries and several woody plants, finding that at this concentration, the cytokinin had a bacteriostatic effect and rooting was not impaired. *Rosa hybrida* 'White Dream' required the addition of 1 mg/l BAP to IBA for root induction and development.

Specificity of action

The effect of cytokinins on tissue or organ cultures can vary according to the particular compound used, the type of culture, the variety of plant from which it was derived and whether the explant is derived from juvenile or mature tissues. In *Corylus avellana*, 5mg/l BAP gave the best rate of shoot multiplication from juvenile explants, but 10 mg/l zeatin was required for nodal sections of plants in the adult phase (Messeguer and Melé, 1987).

A requirement for a particular cytokinin is sometimes noted for the induction of embryogenesis (*e.g.* Fujimura and Komamine, 1975), and for the promotion of direct or indirect adventitious shoot formation; for example, cultures of *Browallia viscosa* required 2-iP for the initiation of adventitious shoots, and kinetin, BAP or zeatin were ineffective (Welsh and Sink, 1981).

Cytokinin specificity in shoot cultures

Most demonstrations of a requirement for a particular cytokinin, have been made with shoot cultures; they are dispersed over many species. BAP promoted axillary bud proliferation of *Castanea* in the experiments of Vieitez and Vieitez (1980b), whereas kinetin was without effect. Zeatin tended to promote the growth of main shoots and gave only a slight increase in the proportion of lateral buds sprouting. Similarly 2-iP and kinetin produced only single shoots from *Prunus* shoot cultures: to obtain multiple shoots, it was necessary to use BAP (Martinelli, 1985).

Elliott (1970) found kinetin to be incapable of promoting the growth of rose shoot tips. On the other hand, *only* 0.5–5 mg/l kinetin (together with gibberellic acid) induced the proliferation of potato shoots, and BAP and 2-iP were not effective. In some cultures, cytokinins tend to produce short rosetted shoots, or shoots which grow only slowly after formation: BAP and kinetin gave shoot rosettes in *Brassica campestris* shoot cultures, whereas axillary shoots induced by 2-iP elongated satisfactorily (Paek *et al.*, 1987): 2-iP and BAP produced many shoots of *Elaeagnus angustifolia*, but unlike those produced on 5 µM kinetin, they failed to grow afterwards (Bertrand and Lalonde, 1985). BAP gives a high rate of shoot proliferation in *Gerbera*, but the best shoot quality is obtained using 5–10 mg/l kinetin (Pierik *et al.*, 1982; Hempel *et al.*, 1985).

Fonnesbech *et al.* (1979) discovered that the natural cytokinins 2-iP and zeatin were better able to promote the growth and survival of shoot cultures of *Asparagus plumosus* than kinetin or BAP, although best results were obtained with PBA. A similar situation is found in plants of the family Ericaceae, where the natural compounds, zeatin and 2-iP, are more effective than other cytokinins for shoot proliferation; 2-iP is most commonly selected because of its lower cost, but in some species, mixtures of the two compounds may give better results than either compound alone (Eccher and Noe, 1989).

In shoot cultures of *Gynura sarmentosa*, BAP, kinetin and 2-iP promoted the formation of buds when used separately, but each in turn produced some abnormality in the shoots obtained. Much faster growth of healthy shoots was obtained by adding all three compounds simultaneously (Cailloux, 1978). A mixture of more than one cytokinin has also been found to give more effective shoot multiplication in some other species (*e.g. Corylus avellana*, Anderson, 1984b; *Cucumis melo*, Kathal *et al.*, 1988)

Plant abnormalities associated with cytokinin use are mentioned in Chapter 15.

Phenylureas

In some tests, some phenylureas are much more effective cytokinins than the adenine-based compounds. 4PU-Cl was, for example, 100 times more active than BAP in the tobacco callus assay (Read *et al.*, 1986) and produced more shoots in azalea shoot cultures than zeatin or 2-iP. In many azalea (*Rhododendron*) cultivars, thidiazuron produced many shoots but these were of poor quality because they were stunted and hyperhydric. Better results were obtained with a mixture of 2-iP and thidiazuron, but there was a tendency for adventitious shoots to be produced, which is not desirable during micropropagation (Briggs *et al.*, 1988a). Thidiazuron was adopted for the micropropagation of woody plants in the family Oleaceae (Einset and Alexander, 1985)

The effect of temperature

Maintaining *in vitro* cultures at abnormally high temperatures is reported to reduce the efficacy of cytokinins, but may enhance auxin activity. Heide (1965b) observed that the ability of cytokinin-dips to either *promote* direct bud formation or *inhibit* direct root formation, was less when begonia leaf cuttings were kept at 27°C after treatment, rather than at 15°C. On a modified **MS** medium containing kinetin, growth and axillary shoot proliferation of

Asparagus plumosus shoot tips was initially rapid at 24°C but stopped after four weeks. The shoot tips grew more slowly at 17°C but their growth was continuous. There was almost no growth at all at either 9°C or 30°C (Fonnesbech *et al.*, 1977a,b). The most effective cytokinin for *A. plumosus* was subsequently found to be PBA. The requirement for this cytokinin increased with temperature. At 17°C, the optimum dose was 0.2 mg/l, at 21°C the optimum was between 0.2 and 2 mg/l, but at 24°C it was 2 mg/l. The best temperature for survival, growth and development was 21°C (Fonnesbech *et al.*, 1979).

ADENINE

A possible growth regulatory effect caused by adenine (**46**) was first noted by Bonner and Haagen-Smit (1939) and Bonner *et al.* (1939), who found that the compound promoted an expansion in the area of leaf discs floated on sugar solutions. Other regulatory properties of the compound were later demonstrated by Skoog and Tsui (1948), Jacquiot (1951) and Miller and Skoog (1953), who discovered that it could induce bud formation in both tobacco stem segments and elm and tobacco callus *in vitro*. The activity of adenine is much less than that of the

Adenine	MW 135.13 (anhydrous)	189.13 (.3H$_2$O)
Adenine sulphate	MW 368.34 (anhydrous)	404.37 (.2H$_2$O)

true cytokinins, and 25–100 times the concentration (*e.g.* 600 μM vs. 20 μM kinetin — Khanna and Chopra, 1977) may be required to produce similar results.

Despite the subsequent discovery of cytokinin activity in adenine derivatives, adenine itself is still often used in cultures from which plant regeneration is required. It seems sometimes to improve growth (Nwankwo and Krikorian, 1983), or to bring about or reinforce responses normally attributed to cytokinin action. Benefits are often only noticed when adenine is administered together with a cytokinin such as kinetin, or BAP. Adenosine and adenylic acid can sometimes act in the same way as adenine (Skoog and Tsui, 1948; Nitsch *et al.*, 1967) but they are generally even less effective. Adenine is known as Vitamin B$_4$. In some papers on tissue culture it is listed amongst the vitamin components of a medium.

Embryogenesis and caulogenesis

Halperin and Wetherell (1964) noted that 2 mg/l adenine or 0.2 mg/l kinetin could be used instead of coconut milk in various media for stimulating embryogenesis in carrot callus. Since then, adenine has been added to media in amounts ranging from 2 to 405 mg/l (but more usually 40– 80 mg/l) to promote somatic embryo formation in other callus cultures (Nag and Johri, 1969; Danilina, 1972; Pareek and Chandra, 1978b; Phillips and Collins, 1980; Reynolds et al., 1980). In the presence of other recognised cytokinins, adenine frequently promotes adventitious shoot formation, indirectly from callus (Plummer and Leopold, 1957; Earle and Torrey, 1965a; Thorpe and Murashige, 1968b; Beach and Smith, 1979; Xiangcan et al., 1989), or directly from explants (Ziv et al., 1970; Start and Cumming, 1976; Seabrook et al., 1976; Nickerson, 1978; Rao and Bapat, 1978). It inhibits root initiation (Doerschug and Miller, 1967) but has been reported to stimulate the growth of preformed roots of *Citrus* embryoids (Kochba et al., 1974) and lupin seedlings (Fries, 1960) in a similar fashion to low levels of cytokinin.

Shoot cultures

Adenine has been used only to a limited extent in meristem or shoot cultures, but has been employed occasionally to enhance the growth of isolated meristem tips (Kassanis, 1957a; Elliott, 1970) and as an aid (or occasionally as an essential component) to induce the proliferation of axillary shoots in shoot cultures (Anderson, 1975; Hennen and Sheehan, 1978; Harris and Stevenson, 1979; Pyott and Converse, 1981; Huang, 1984). Whether improved shoot multiplication will result from adding adenine to the medium can be unpredictable. In peach shoot cultures, a benefit depended on the cultivar being cultured and the nature and rate of the cytokinin used. A stimulation occurred with some rates of BAP, but with others its addition resulted in a decreased rate of propagation (Chiariotti and Antonelli, 1988).

Although the rate of *Brassica campestris* shoot multiplication was not increased, adding 326–434 μM adenine sulphate to a medium containing kinetin and IBA, caused shoot weight to be increased. Leaves were dark green and the cultures more healthy than previously (Paek et al., 1987).

Mode of action

The mode of action of adenine has not been fully explained. Beneficial effects from adenine addition are found in media containing both ammonium nitrate and cytokinins (*e.g.* Ziv et al., 1970; Elliott, 1970; Seabrook et al., 1976; Nickerson, 1978; Pyott and Converse, 1981). Adenine is therefore unlikely to be simply acting as an alternative source of reduced nitrogen, and if it enhances natural cytokinin biosynthesis, the compounds produced must be more effective in causing the required physiological response than cytokinins added to the growth medium. Such a situation was described by Beach and Smith (1979) with callus of red and crimson clover. On **Gamborg et al. (1968) B5** medium, plant regeneration was most effectively achieved when 20 mg/l thiamine, 2.0 mg/l NAA and 2 mg/l adenine were included. Kinetin, 2-iP and BAP were all tested as cytokinins and failed to produce shoot buds. However, in many cultures adenine acts more as a synergist of cytokinins such as kinetin and zeatin (Nitsch et al., 1967). A typical result is that of Start and Cumming (1976), who found that when 125 mg/l adenine was added to a medium in conjunction with 5 mg/l BAP and 0.1 mg/l NAA, it regularly increased direct shoot initiation from African violet leaf sections, whereas in the basal medium with only adenine sulphate, shoot formation was delayed and roots alone were formed.

Both natural and synthetic purine-based cytokinins are degraded in plant tissues to adenine and related nucleotides (Terrine et al., 1972; Entsch et al., 1980; Biondi et al., 1984; McGaw et al., 1984; Forsyth and Van Staden, 1987). Thus one possible method whereby adenine may enhance the growth of cultured plants, could be that an excess of the compound retards the degradation of cytokinins by feed-back inhibition, or by competing for the enzyme systems involved in cytokinin metabolism. Another hypothesis is that, even though adenine is itself a product of cytokinin metabolism, it may act as a substrate for the synthesis of natural cytokinin growth substances. It has been shown that adenine *can* serve as a precursor for zeatin synthesis, but the rate of incorporation is low (McGaw et al., 1984; Dickinson et al., 1986).

Inhibitory effects

The addition of adenine does not always lead to beneficial results; for instance, adenine sulphate in the concentration range 30–300 mg/l was inhibitory for the formation of shoots from cultured tuber discs of potato (Jarret et al., 1980a). The addition of adenine sulphate to shoot cultures of carnation caused axillary shoot formation to be inconsistent; as a smaller number of shoots was produced from each shoot tip, and the main shoots often grew well, Davis et al. (1977) thought that the compound tended to enhance apical dominance. Where adenine is promotory, an excess can have the same consequences as an excess of cytokinin; Nickerson (1978) found that 80 mg/l adenine, enhanced adventitious bud formation in cotyledons and hypocotyl sections of lowbush blueberry, but needed to be withdrawn to promote shoot elongation.

CYTOKININ ANTAGONISTS

Certain chemical analogues of RNA bases can antagonise the action of cytokinins. Blaydes (1966) found that 2,6-diaminopurine, 8-azaguanine and 8-azaadenine inhibited the growth of kinetin-requiring soybean callus. Compounds which reversibly inhibit the growth of cytokinin-dependent and cytokinin-requiring callus cultures were described by Hecht et al. (1971), Skoog et al. (1973, 1975) and Gregorini and Laloue (1980). These authors found that the growth inhibitory effects of compounds such as 7-(3-methylbutylamino)-3-methyl-H- pyrazolo [4,3–d]-pyrimidine (47) and 4–(cyclohexylamino)-2-methylthio-H-pyrrolo[2,3d]pyrimidine (48) were reversed by BAP. Cell death by cytotoxicity was expressed only when the tobacco cells divided. Non-dividing cells in stationary phase were insensitive to either compound which suggests that a specific biochemical event in the cell cycle was affected. Cytokinin-autonomous callus is rendered cytokinin-requiring by these chemicals.

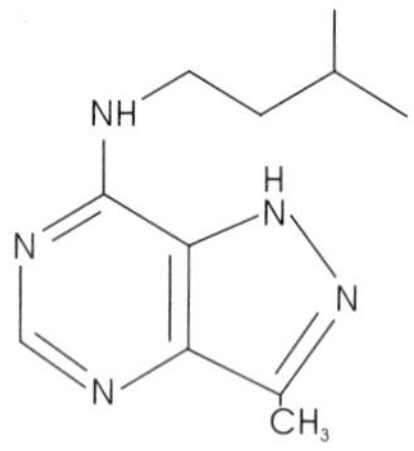

(47) 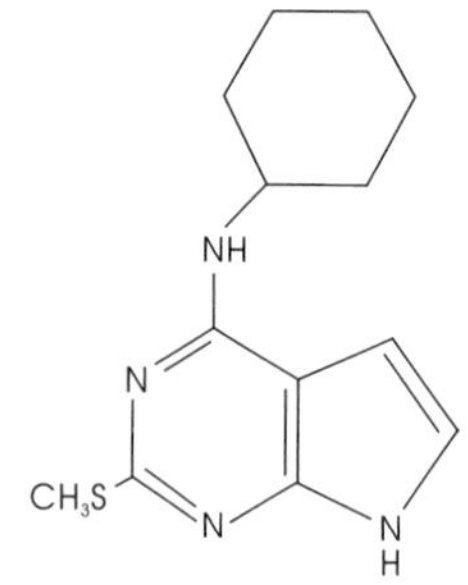　　　　　　　　(48)

Other highly active antagonists of cytokinin-promoted cell division are 4-cyclobutylamino-2-methylpyrrolo [2,3- d]pyrimidine (Iwamura et al., 1979) and its 2-methylthio analogue (49) (Hecht, 1980), and 4-cyclopentylaminopteridine (50) (Iwamura et al., 1980).

Although the compounds mentioned above inhibit cytokinin- promoted cell division, they have not, in all cases

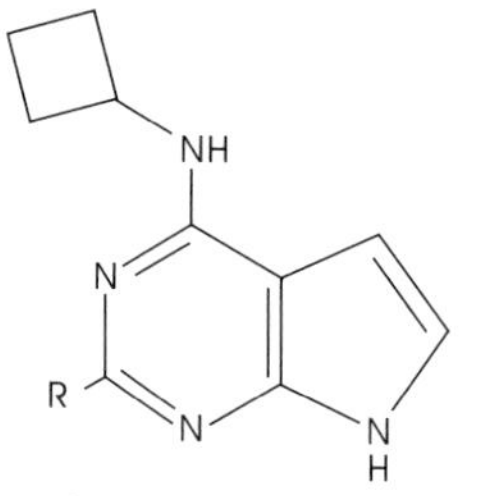

R = CH₃, or R = CH₃S

(49)　　　　　　　　(50)

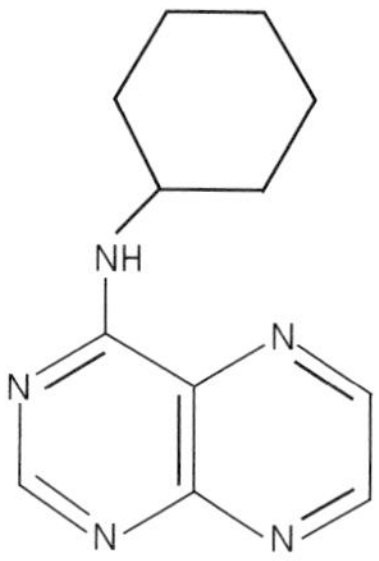

been shown to antagonise other physiological processes normally promoted by cytokinin (such as the stimulation of lateral bud growth, or the initiation of shoot buds in callus tissues). However, Tanimoto and Harada (1982b) used a cytokinin antagonist (4- cyclopentylamino-2-methylpyrrolo[2,3-d]pyrimidine), to overcome the stimulation of adventitious bud formation in Torenia stem segments by both BAP and the phenylurea, 2Cl-4PU. Some compounds which act as anticytokinins in preventing growth of tobacco callus, have been found to promote bud formation in conjunction with an auxin (Skoog et al., 1975; Iwamura et al., 1979). This has led to speculation that there may be separate receptor sites for individual cytokinin-dependent functions (Hecht, 1980).

Anticytokinin activity also exists in compounds structurally related to octopamine (52), such as tyramine (51) and dopamine (53) (Christou and Barton, 1989).

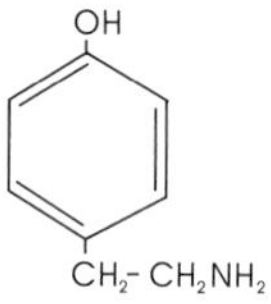

(51)　Tyramine　　MW 137.18

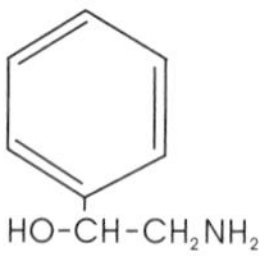

(52)　Octopamine　MW 137.18

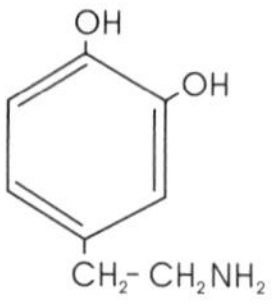

(53)　Dopamine　　MW 153.18

AUXIN-CYTOKININ INTERACTION

Skoog and Miller (1957) found that shoot formation could be induced predictably from tobacco callus using relatively low levels of auxin and a high level of cytokinin in the growth medium. Since this discovery, many aspects of cellular differentiation and organogenesis in tissue and organ cultures have been found to be controlled by an interaction between cytokinin and auxin concentrations. The balance between the two sorts of regulant that is usually required to initiate growth or differentiation in tissue cultures, is illustrated in Fig. 111.

Relative proportions of auxins and cytokinins do not always produce the typical results shown in the figure. For example:

— axillary shoot proliferation in some species may be promoted by the presence of an auxin together with cytokinin;

— tissues from monocotyledons can often be induced to form callus by culture in high levels of auxin alone, and cytokinins may be inessential or unimportant;

— organogenesis in monocotyledons is often promoted by transferring the culture to a medium without auxin, by reducing the concentrations of

a highly active auxin such as 2,4-D, or replacing 2,4-D with another auxin (*e.g.* IAA or NAA).

A balance between auxin and cytokinin growth regulators is most often required for the formation of adventitious shoot and root meristems. The requisite concentration of each type of regulant differs greatly according to the kind of plant being cultured, the cultural conditions and the compounds used; interactions between the two classes of regulant are often complex, and more than one combination of substances is likely to produce optimum results.

Contour diagrams. Results of growth regulator interactions can be difficult to express graphically without resorting to three dimensional graphs. Two dimensional alternatives are island diagrams (Negrutiu *et al.*, 1978a), or contour diagrams (Frett and Smagula, 1983). The latter are a particularly effective means of presentation and can be used to summarize the results of experiments in which several different concentrations of an auxin and a cytokinin (or other combinations of regulants) have been combined. The position of contour lines can be estimated from results, but are most accurately plotted using equations derived from multiple regression. For such statistical analysis to be possible, a properly designed experiment must have been conducted (Beretta and Eccher, 1987). Fig. 112, drawn from results of Saunders and Bingham

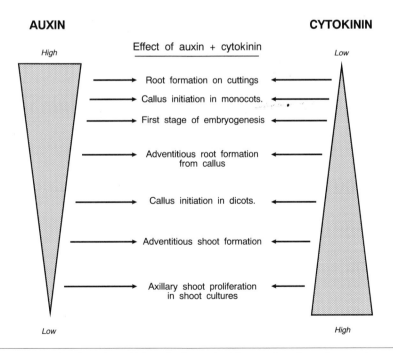

AUXIN   CYTOKININ

High   Effect of auxin + cytokinin   *Low*

Root formation on cuttings

Callus initiation in monocots.

First stage of embryogenesis

Adventitious root formation from callus

Callus initiation in dicots.

Adventitious shoot formation

Axillary shoot proliferation in shoot cultures

Low   *High*

Fig. 111. The relative concentrations of auxin and cytokinin typically required for growth and morphogenesis.

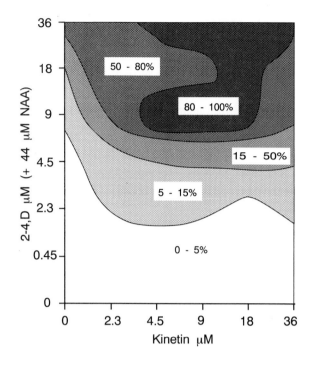

Fig. 112. A contour diagram drawn from the results of Saunders and Bingham (1975).

The diagram shows the percentage of alfalfa calluses producing adventitious shoots when incubated on media containing various combinations of auxin and cytokinin.

often be produced by pretreatment with one regulant, followed by transfer to a second medium containing another. For example, preculturing peach leaf pieces on a medium containing 2,4-D, increased the callus production obtained when explants were placed on a medium with NAA and BAP. If preculture with 2,4-D was followed by subculture to a medium with BAP alone, callus was produced which gave rise to roots (Hammerschlag, 1988).

Despite the frequent need for both an auxin and a cytokinin in tissues cultures, the nature of the interactions between the two types of regulant is seldom commented upon and there is much still to be learned. Although both auxin and cytokinin are usually required for growth or morphogenesis, auxin can inhibit cytokinin accumulation (Hansen *et al.*, 1985) while cytokinins can inhibit at least some of the action of auxin (see above).

Growth regulators and the cell cycle

Cell division seems to be regulated by the joint action of auxins and cytokinins, each of which appears to influence different phases of the cell cycle. Auxins exert an effect on DNA replication, while cytokinin seem to exert some control over the events leading to mitosis (Jouanneau, 1971). Normal cell divisions require synchrony between the *S* phase and cell division, suggesting that auxin and cytokinin levels in cultures need to be carefully matched. Late replication of DNA in cell cultures has been advanced as one cause of chromosome rearrangement (Lee and Phillips, 1988) (see Chapter 3). Cells are thought not to enter mitosis unless cytokinin is present. Where callus or suspension cultures are initiated on media which only contain an auxin, reliance is presumably being placed on endogenous cytokinins for completion of the cell cycle?

(1975), shows how combinations of kinetin and 2,4-D (in conjunction with a constant rate of NAA), influenced the percentage of *Medicago sativa* calluses producing adventitious shoots. Further examples of contour diagrams are given in Chapter 12.

Pretreatments. Similar effects to those produced by having auxin and cytokinin together in the medium, can

GIBBERELLINS

NATURAL OCCURRENCE

Gibberellins form another class of plant growth substance. Over 80 different compounds, related by having a chemical structure based on the 'gibbane' skeleton, have been indentified, from fungi and higher plants and given 'GA' numbers. Only certain of these compounds will occur in any one plant species. Not all gibberellins are biologically active in any given assay: activity of a particular compound may depend on the ability of the tissue to transport it and/or convert it into another truly active compound. Gibberellic acid (GA_3) (**54**), and a mix-

ture of GA_4 and GA_7, are the only gibberellins to have become commercially available. The former has been most frequently used in plant tissue culture experiments.

Gibberellin biosynthesis *in vivo* can be prevented by several synthetic antagonists (see below). The fact that these compounds can influence growth and morphogenesis *in vitro*, shows that gibberellin biosynthesis does occur in plant tissue cultures.

Physiological activity

Applied to whole plants, gibberellins can influence growth and development in a variety of ways (for exam-

(54)　Gibberellic acid (GA$_3$)　　　MW 346.38

ple, by increasing stem length, promoting flowering, or inducing fruit set). Several of the effects of gibberellins on whole plants are caused by selective increases or decreases in the biosynthesis and activity of enzymes (page 448). One possible result is a change in the availabilty of endogenous auxin. Gibberellic acid is found to suppress the synthesis of phosphatase (Zink and Veliky, 1982) and enzymes concerned with the production of some secondary products (see below), but *de novo* synthesis of α-amylase (Thompson *et al.*, 1981) and maltase are stimulated, for example during the germination of cereal seeds.

De la Guardia and Benlloch (1980) proposed that growth promotion by gibberellic acid is also due to the increased transport of potassium ions.

EFFECTS OF GIBBERELLIC ACID ON TISSUE CULTURES

Plant tissue cultures can generally be induced to grow and differentiate without gibberellins, although gibberellic acid may become an essential ingredient of media for culturing cells at low densities (Stuart and Street, 1971). When GA$_3$ is added to culture media, it often produces effects which are of a similar nature to those of auxins. High concentrations of GA$_3$ (*e.g.* greater than *ca.* 5 μM; 1–8 mg/l) induce the growth of undifferentiated callus cells (Schroeder and Spector, 1957; Murashige, 1964; Mehra and Mehra, 1972; Altman and Goren, 1974; Beasley, 1977; Gautam *et al.*, 1983), and can promote the growth of callus in combination with auxin and low rates of cytokinin (Engelke *et al.*, 1973). Growth of *Solanum xanthocarpum* callus was, however, reported to be inhibited by 2 mg/l GA$_3$ (Rao and Narayanaswamy, 1968).

A growth factor, which is probably a gibberellin, is produced by the germinating embryos of some plant species and must be transmitted to the endosperm before this tissue will proliferate to form callus in culture (Brown *et al.*, 1970; Johri and Bhojwani, 1977). Where the presence of both auxin and cytokinin in a growth medium leads to rapid callusing of the cut surfaces of an explant, the further addition of a small amount of GA$_3$ (*e.g.* 0.1 mg/l),

or the replacement of auxin by GA$_3$, usually inhibits callus growth (Sangwan *et al.*, 1976; Kartha *et al.*, 1977).

Morphogenesis

When gibberellic acid is added to plant tissue culture media, it often diminishes or prevents the formation of adventitious roots, shoots or somatic embryos. Thus the prior treatment of callus (Murashige, 1964) or explants (Heide, 1969) with GA$_3$, or the addition of GA$_3$ to the medium together with auxin and cytokinin in concentrations which would normally promote morphogenesis, is usually inhibitory (*e.g.* to shoot formation from callus — Murashige, 1961; Rubluo *et al.*, 1984: or embryogenesis — see later).

Adventitious shoot formation

In tobacco callus, GA$_3$ was particularly inhibitory to shoot formation if present at the time of meristemoid formation, and more repressive during dark incubation than in the light (Thorpe and Meier, 1973). The inhibition has been shown not to be irreversible, but to persist through at least two subcultures on a GA$_3$-free medium. Gibberellins other than GA$_3$ had the same effect (Murashige, 1964). However. the addition of 1.5–3.0 μM GA$_3$ to the medium (which also contained 2-iP and IBA) supporting *Apios americana* internode explants, increased the number of shoots formed from primary callus on each explant, but the number of explants which produced shoots was less (Wickremesinhe *et al.*, 1990a).

In some plants gibberellic acid alone can induce adventitious shoot formation *e.g.* from *Ranunculus scleratus* callus (Konar and Konar, 1973). The compound can also act as a replacement for auxin in the induction of shoot formation (Sekioka and Tanaka, 1981); a precise gibberellin/cytokinin ratio (instead of auxin/cytokinin) may then be required (Pillai and Hildebrandt, 1969; Engelke *et al.*, 1973). Alternatively, gibberellin may simply increase the number of organs formed; shoot regeneration from *Rosa hybrida* callus could be induced by 1–5 mg/l BAP (depending on cv.), but adding 0.3–1 mg/l GA$_3$ increased the number of shoots produced (Valles and Boxus, 1987b). Adding 5–50 μM GA$_3$ to the medium (in conjuction with IBA and BAP), enhanced the formation of vegetative shoots from inflorescence segments of sugar beet (Coumans-Gilles *et al.*, 1981; Coumans *et al.*, 1982).

The combination of GA$_3$ and cytokinin is generally less satisfactory for the induction of shoots than that of auxin and cytokinin, and tissues may have to be transferred to a medium lacking GA$_3$ for further bud development to occur (Kartha *et al.*, 1974d). Shoots formed in the presence of GA$_3$ may be pale and abnormal (see Chapter 12).

Gibberellic acid can also prevent *direct* shoot regeneration, for example in:

Begonia leaf discs	Schraudolf and Reinert (1959)
	Schott and Schraudolf (1967)
	Bigot and Nitsch (1968)
	Heide (1969); Chlyah (1972)
Heloniopsis leaf segments	Kato and Hongo (1974)
Hyacinthus bulb scales	Pierik and Steegmans (1975d)
Sugar beet floral axillary buds	Coumans-Gilles *et al.* (1981)

Some of the differences in the inhibition or promotion of adventitious shoot formation by GA$_3$ might be due to the fact that the compound inhibits meristemoid initiation, but is required for shoot development once meristemoids are formed (Jarrett and Hasegawa, 1981). The timing and duration of treatments will therefore strongly influence the results observed.

Many more established plants could be obtained if petiole explants of *Begonia* × *hiemalis* were placed into liquid culture after adventitious shoots had been initiated on an agar medium. The further addition of 30–60 µM (10–20 mg/l) gibberellic acid increased the number of suitable shoots per explant, but a smaller proportion of the shoots rooted, and their establishment *ex vitro* was not satisfactory (Simmonds and Werry, 1987).

Rhizogenesis

Inhibition. Normally GA$_3$ inhibits root formation, and the local application of relatively high concentrations (1–10 mg/l) of the compound to the base of cuttings, prevents root formation (Brian, 1959), especially if auxins are applied at the same time.

Varga and Humphries (1974) showed that although root formation from the base of the petioles of detached *Phaseolus* bean leaves was inhibited by topical application, it was promoted when GA$_3$ was applied to leaf laminae. Promotion was especially pronounced when tryptophan (a biochemical precursor of IAA) was placed on the leaf surface at the same time as the GA$_3$. This, and other evidence, led to their suggesting that promotion of root formation was in this case due to the gibberellin causing the leaf to produce increased natural auxin which was transported to the base of the petiole. GA$_3$ can slightly stimulate root initiation from tomato leaf discs kept in darkness, and Coleman and Greyson (1977a,b)

concluded that this is because natural auxin biosynthesis is increased.

Nanda *et al.* (1972) found that root formation on cuttings of *Ipomoea fistula* was stimulated if they were dipped into GA$_3$ before being placed in compost. Anand *et al.* (1972) obtained similar results, but found that pre-treatment with IBA was more effective. Gibberellic acid also improved the rooting of shoots from *Coffea arabica* shoot cultures if a 25–50 mg/l solution was applied directly to shoots at the time they were excised for rooting (Sondahl *et al.*, 1985).

The inhibition of rooting caused by GA$_3$ is generally magnified in the presence of auxin, and Coleman and Greyson (1977b) proposed that this might be due to an excessive total auxin concentration. This view is supported by results of Rucker (1982a) who found that gibberellic acid was also able to promote direct root formation on leaf fragments of *Digitalis* when applied with low levels of IAA, but was inhibitory when the concentration of IAA was increased.

Promotion. In some plants however, pre-treating plant material with GA$_3$ enhances root formation when cuttings are afterwards placed on a root-inducing medium. Rooting can sometimes also be promoted by GA$_3$ if it is applied to cuttings in the absence of an auxin, and the plant material (or at least the rooting zone) is subsequently kept in darkness. As in caulogenesis, it has been proposed that the effect of gibberellic acid on root formation is dependent on time of application. If gibberellic acid was applied to *Pinus radiata* cuttings when they were first cut, it inhibited rooting. It did however strongly enhance rooting when given just as there was the first sign of observable root formation, but shortly afterwards it was again inhibitory (Smith and Thorpe, 1975b).

There are, however, examples of root formation occurring in the presence of gibberellic acid and synthetic auxins:

— the number of roots formed by tomato leaf disc explants treated with 20 µM indole-3-lactic acid was further increased by adding 100 µM GA$_3$ (Coleman and Greyson, 1977b);

— the inhibition of direct root and shoot formation on isolated leaves of *Begonia rex* by 1–10 mg/l GA$_3$, was overcome by adding 2,4-D at an equivalent concentration (Schraudolf and Reinert, 1959);

— direct root formation from *Helianthus tuberosus* rhizome pieces was stimulated when 0.35–3500 µg/l GA$_3$ was added to NAA (0.2 mg/l) and the explants were kept in the dark, whereas in the light GA$_3$ was inhibitory (Gautheret, 1969). Six other gibberellins also gave similar results (Tizio *et al.* 1970).

– gibberellic acid was able to promote rooting of *Prunus* shoot cultures at 26°C in conjunction with the auxin IBA; below this temperature it had no effect (Rosati *et al.*, 1980).

By adding 1 mg/l GA₃ to the growth medium, Nemeth (1979) increased the root formation which was unusually induced on *in vitro* shoots of *Prunus myrobalan* by the cytokinin BAP.

Embryogenesis and embryo development

Although occasionally reported to be promotory (Evans *et al.* 1976; Lakshmi Sita *et al.*, 1979), gibberellic acid has generally been found to inhibit somatic embryo formation (Fujimura and Komamine, 1975; Tisserat and Murashige, 1977b,c; Kochba *et al.*, 1978a; Spiegel-Roy and Kochba, 1980). Indeed, the addition of inhibitors of gibberellin biosynthesis increased the number of somatic embryos produced from *Citrus sinensis* callus (Spiegel-Roy and Saad, 1986), although paclobutrazol (an antigibberellin, see page 452) had little effect in *Pennisetum purpureum* (Rajasekaran *et al.*, 1987).

The growth ('germination') of preformed somatic embryos of several different species can be stimulated by the incorporation of GA₃ (*ca.* 0.3–1 mg/l) into the second (post-initiation) medium (*e.g.* in *Citrus* — Ranga Swamy, 1959, 1961; Kochba *et al.*, 1972, 1974; Button and Kochba, 1977; grapevine — Mullins and Srinivasan, 1976; maize and Guinea grass — Lu and Vasil, 1981a, 1982; Lu C. *et al.*, 1982). In some plants embryo root growth is especially promoted, in others (*e.g. Santalum album* — Bapat and Rao (1979): *Panax ginseng* — Chang and Hsing, 1980a,b; Shoyama *et al.*, 1988) shoot regeneration is stimulated. These results accord with the observations of Noma *et al.* (1982) that levels of polar gibberellins (GA₃ is of this type) were high in undifferentiated carrot cells and in a non-embryogenic strain. When somatic embryos were initiated they contained low levels of polar gibberellins and metabolised these compounds rapidly.

In *Citrus* and *Duboisia* (Nwankwo and Krikorian, 1983), once embryos have started to grow, plantlets need to be transferred to a medium lacking gibberellin, otherwise shoots are weak and spindly.

The growth of soybean somatic embryos was promoted by antigibberellins (Gamborg *et al.*, 1983).

Cellular differentiation

Gibberellic acid has little effect on cellular differentiation *in vitro* beyond mediating the action of auxin. In intact plants, xylem formation is observed to be stimulated by

treatment with GA₃ or with auxin and GA₃ combined (Wareing, 1958; Bostrack and Struckmeyer, 1967; Dorley and Leyton, 1968). Auxin is now thought to be mainly responsible for the initial differentiation of phloem and xylem elements in tissue cultures (Aloni, 1980), even though some promotion by GA₃ has been reported (Gautheret, 1961; Roberts and Fosket, 1966; Roberts, 1969; Dalessandro, 1973; Phillips and Dodds, 1977).

In the cactus *Opuntia polyacantha*, axillary meristems became leafy shoots on media with 5–10 mg/l of the cytokinin BAP, but produced spines with 20–100 mg/l GA₃. When 5–50 mg/l NAA was used, roots arose from bud trace procambium (Mauseth and Halperin, 1975).

Enzyme activity. Gibberellins influence the biosynthesis or activity of enzymes and can consequently affect the production of secondary plant products *in vitro e.g.* the synthesis of amaranthine (Laloraya *et al.*, 1976) and anthocyanin (Heinzmann and Seitz, 1977; Mizukami *et al.*, 1988) which are inhibited by the presence of GA₃ in the medium. The failure of carrot cells to produce anthocyanin in these circumstances is apparently due to the absence an *p*-coumaric acid:CoA ligase isoenzyme (Heinzmann *et al.* 1977).

Use in meristem, shoot and node cultures

Although gibberellic acid tends to prevent the formation of organised root and shoot meristems in callus cultures, it may assist the further growth and development of preformed organs. The growth of shoots in meristem and shoot cultures may also be enhanced by its addition.

Meristem cultures

A small amount of GA₃ (typically 0.03–0.1 mg/l) is often added to media for meristem cultures. It may not always be beneficial or absolutely necessary, and there are conflicting results. Mellor and Stace-Smith (1969) for example, found the substance to be without any appreciable effect on meristem tip cultures of potato, but other investigators (*e.g.* Morel *et al.*, 1968; Pennazio and Redolfi, 1973; Novak *et al.*, 1980) have reported that the addition of low concentrations of GA₃ (*e.g.* 0.03 mg/l) to media containing auxin and cytokinin, or cytokinin alone, has improved the growth of meristem tips, inhibited callus proliferation, sometimes encouraged the tips to root more freely, and (Marani and Pisi, 1977), increased the proportion of meristems that developed into shoots. Similar effects have been noted in meristem cultures of some other plants (*e.g.* cassava — Kartha *et al.*, 1974c; Rey and Mroginski, 1978).

Gibberellic acid does not assist in the establishment of the shoot apices of all plants. It was found to be inhibitory to growth of meritem tips of some kinds of geraniums (Theiler, 1977) and flax (Lane, 1979a), and in rose, apices grew rapidly and formed abnormal attenuated leaves, but no roots or new leaves were initiated (Jacobs *et al.*, 1969, 1970; Elliott, 1970).

As mentioned previously, gibberellic acid frequently inhibits root formation, especially in the presence of auxin. When the compound is used to stimulate the growth of isolated meristems or shoot tips therefore, it may prevent eventual root development (Murashige, 1961; Vine and Jones, 1969; Putz, 1971). Plantlets formed on media containing gibberellic acid may need to be moved to a medium containing auxin, but no gibberellin, before they can be rooted (Quak, 1977).

Shoot and node cultures

Gibberellic acid is added to the medium, together with auxin and cytokinin, for Stages I and II of shoot cultures of certain plants. In some genera it is effective when auxins are not (see Chapter 12). At Stage I its presence can improve establishment, for example, De Fossard and de Fossard (1988b) found that the addition of GA$_3$ to the medium was useful to initiate growth in cultures from adult parts of trees of the family Myrtaceae, although thereafter it had a deleterious effect.

Shoot multiplication. At Stage II, GA$_3$ can enhance growth and/or increase the rate of shoot proliferation; adding 1.5 µM GA$_3$ to a medium containing 2-iP and IBA increased the number of shoots produced from seedling and tuber-shoot internodes of *Apios americana*, but reduced the number of explants which produced shoots (Wickremseinhe *et al.*, 1990a).

The benefits of using GA$_3$ at Stage II often vary between closely related plant genotypes. Thus gibberellic acid was antagonistic to shoot proliferation in 'McIntosh' apple shoot cultures (Lane, 1978), but was essential for 'Ottawa 3' apple rootstock, where without the addition of 5 mg/l GA$_3$, shoots had short internodes and small deformed leaves.

Valles and Boxus found that the addition of some gibberellic acid (0.1–1.0 mg/l depending on genotype) to a medium containing 1–5 mg/l BAP, was essential to obtain shoot multiplication of some *Rosa hybrida* cultivars, and an improved rate of proliferation in others. Cultivar 'Goldy' did not proliferate at all unless 1 mg/l GA$_3$ was present (Valles and Boxus, 1987a). Adding 0.7 mg/l GA$_3$ to 2.3 mg/l BAP increased the rate of proliferation in *Camellia saluensis* × *C.japonica* shoot cultures (Beretta and Eccher, 1987). Substituting IAA (0.2 mg/l) for GA$_3$

in *Camellia*, caused only an increase in shoot length; there was no shoot proliferation.

Shoot cultures of the salt-tolerant plant *Atriplex canescens* were found to remain stunted without the application of GA$_3$ (Wochok and Sluis, 1980b). Addition of the growth substance to the agar medium was ineffective and so filter-sterilised solution was flooded onto the plates on which the explants were growing and then decanted away after a few seconds, leaving a residue. This treatment had the effect of first promoting the *multiplication* of adventitious shoots, and then afterwards stimulating their elongation. Similarly, a combination of GA$_3$ (0.01–0.1 mg/l) and kinetin (0.5–5 mg/l) with no auxin, has been found to provide a highly effective growth regulator treatment for the rapid increase of potato shoots in shaken liquid cultures (Goodwin *et al.*, 1980a).

Without the addition of 1 mg/l GA$_3$ to 1 mg/l IBA and 0.2 mg/l BAP at the multiplication stage, shoot cultures of *Humulus lupulus* produced masses of callus at the basal ends of shoots (Vine and Jones, 1969). Necrosis in *Rosa hybrida* shoot cultures was prevented by adding 0.1 mg/l GA$_3$ to the proliferation medium (Valles and Boxus, 1987a).

The use of gibberellic acid in shoot cultures is discussed further in Chapter 12.

Shoot elongation. Shoots are occasionally treated with GA$_3$ to increase the length of shoots during multiplication; or prior to rooting, when it is usually applied at a special elongation stage (Stage IIIa), after shoot multiplication and before shoots are harvested (see Chapter 12). Treatment may be beneficial where a high level of cytokinin has resulted in many short shoots (*e.g.* in rose, Valles and Boxus, 1987a). Some examples of successful use are:

	mg/l	
Malus × *domestica*	0.1	Jones *et al.* (1977; 1979)
	5.0	Pua *et al.* (1983)
	0.1	Doré (1975)
Malus prunifolia	0.1	Aldwinckle and Gustafson (1981)
Rubus caesius	0.1	Babíc and Nesković (1984)
Simmondsia chinensis	2.0	Jacoboni and Standardi (1987)
Fragaria × *ananassa*	0.1	Boxus (1974a,b) Boxus *et al.* (1977)

Apical integrity. Cytokinin treatments used to promote axillary shoot proliferation, can cause shoots to develop with more than one apical meristem (see Chapter 15). In strawberry, gibberellic acid may help to preserve the integrity of apical buds during shoot culture. Anderson H. M. *et al.* (1982) showed that 0.1 mg/l GA$_3$ largely eliminated the formation of abnormal multi-apexed plants which was caused by combinations of BAP and IBA favourable to rapid shoot proliferation.

Detrimental effects. In most plants, the use of gibberellin in shoot culture media is detrimental, producing elongated shoots with narrow leaves. Such was the effect on *Duboisia myoporoides* shoots when 0.1–0.3 mg/l GA$_3$ was introduced into **MS** medium containing 3 mg/l BAP and 1 mg/l IAA (Kukreja and Mathur, 1985). In tree species of the Myrtaceae, adding GA$_3$ to Stage II cultures caused too much shoot elongation, the formation of narrow leaves, and the production of callus at the base of axillary branches (De Fossard and de Fossard (1988b). GA$_3$ inhibited bud formation in *Thuja plicata* shoot cultures (Coleman and Thorpe, 1977) and caused shoot tip explants of *Acer × freemanii* to develop massive basal callus (Kerns and Meyer, 1986).

Shoots treated with GA$_3$ may be difficult to root (page 447 and Chapter 14).

Stage IV treatments

Plantlets of some woody species may become dormant after being transplanted to soil and fail to grow properly unless subjected to a period of cold, or treated with gibberellic acid (Chapter 15). Biosynthesis of gibberellins is often promoted by cold treatment of plant material. Cold treatment of cultured shoots is necessary to promote bulb formation in *Tulipa*, but can be replaced by soaking shoots in 1 mg/l GA$_3$ for 15 h (Wright *et al.*, 1982; Rice *et al.*, 1983).

'ANTI-GIBBERELLINS' AND GROWTH RETARDANTS

As exogenous gibberellic acid is frequently inhibitory to *in vitro* growth and development, chemicals capable of blocking the biosynthesis or action of endogenous gibberellin may have promotory effects on cultures in which natural gibberellin levels are supra–optimal. Although chemicals with both of these kinds of activity are conveniently called anti-gibberellins, those which interfere with gibberellin biosynthesis (which is by far the majority) should not strictly be grouped under this heading, because their effects on plants can usually be reversed by applications of a gibberellin such as GA$_3$.

Several compounds having 'anti-gibberellin' effects have been discovered. Some, such as chlormequat (CCC) (55), AMO 1618 (Carvadan) (57) and ancymidol (58) are known to act by blocking gibberellin synthesis, while the mode of action of other compounds [*e.g.* daminozide (56)] is less clear.

Both chlormequat and daminozide have been noted to stimulate embryogenesis in *Citrus* (inhibited by GA$_3$) (Kochba *et al.* 1978a; Spiegel-Roy and Kochba, 1980). In *Ranunculus scleratus*, direct shoot formation from

(55)   Chlormequat (chloride)   MW 158.07

(56)   Daminozide   MW 160.17

(57)   AMO 1618   MW 354.92

(58)   Ancymidol   MW 269.33

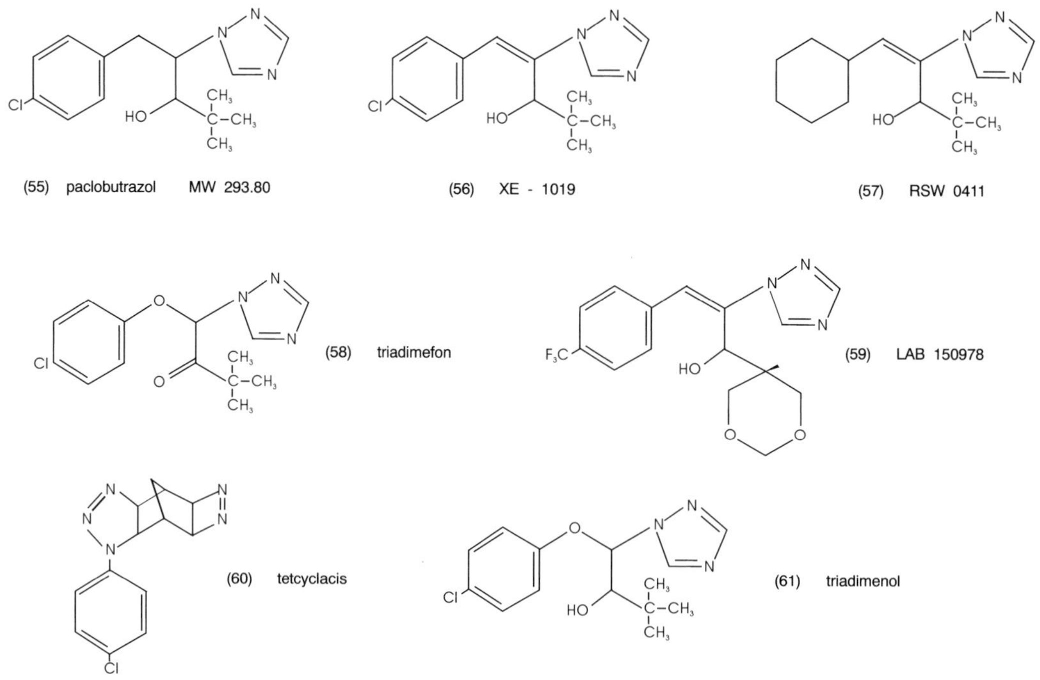

Fig. 113. Structures of some triazole growth retardants.

hypocotyl segments (which was stimulated by GA3) was reduced by 0.01–5 mg/l chlormequat, but chlormequat-induced depression of shoot initiation was counteracted by the simultaneous addition of 1–5 mg/l GA3 (Konar and Konar, 1973). Some workers have added small amounts (0.1 mg/l) of chlormequat to their culture medium believing that it to improve morphogenesis (Blackmon *et al.*, 1981a,b; Blackmon and Reynolds, 1982; Reynolds *et al.*, 1980). In tomato, De Langhe and De Bruijne (1976) found that the addition of chlormequat to the medium was ineffective, but pretreating parent plants with the chemical before explants were removed, did stimulate their shoot-forming capacity in culture. The cytokinin/auxin balance which induced shoot formation in these chlormequat pretreated tomato plants, was not effective on cultures from untreated ones, possibly because there were high amounts of gibberellin in the original tissue; adding GA3 (1–10 µM; or 0.3–3 mg/l) to the medium caused the stem explants to form large amounts of callus and no shoots.

Daminozide [butanedioic acid mono (2,2-dimethyl-hydrazide)] (0.01 mg/l) with no other regulants, increased the production of somatic embryos from *Citrus* 'Marsh' grapefruit (Moore G.A., 1985). According to Stimart

(1986), daminozide is useful for decreasing shoot elongation in shoot cultures of some species.

Ancymidol

When added to **MS** medium containing NAA and kinetin, 0.13 mg/l (0.5 µM) ancymidol (58) enhanced the rate of root and shoot development from single node explants of asparagus. Roots and shoots were also stronger when the retardant was present. Callus growth from the explants was suppressed, and the time required for the production of transplantable plantlets was reduced from 20 to 8 (or even 3) weeks (Chin, 1982). The retardant reduces apical dominance in *Asparagus* shoot cultures and improves the strength of shoots (Khunachak *et al.*, 1987; Desjardins *et al.*, 1987c). Ancymidol acts as an anti-gibberellin and Desjardins *et al.* (1987) thought that it might decrease the activity of invertase enzymes because the rooting of shoots obtained from *Asparagus* single node culture was improved in the presence of 5 µM ancymidol and 7% sucrose. Anymidol overcame the inhibition of rooting caused by gibberellic acid to shoots of *Ceratonia siliqua* (Leguminosae) (Sebastian and McComb, 1986).

Triazole growth inhibitors

Several very effective plant growth retardants have been discovered which include a triazole ring in their structure [Fig. 113, numbers (59–65)]. They are all potent inhibitors of gibberellin synthesis, but can also interfere with sterol and abscisic acid production (Davis *et al.*, 1988). Like other 'anti-gibberellins', these compounds can stimulate embryogenesis where it is inhibited by gibberellic acid (Spiegel-Roy and Saad, 1986). Paclobutrazol (59) (ICI plc) has been the subject of most *in vitro* experimentation.

The addition of 0.5–2 mg/l paclobutrazol, or XE-1019 (60) decreased callus growth of *Vigna aconitifolia* and prevented adventitious shoot formation. The ability of the callus to produced roots or shoots could be restored by adding GA₃ to the medium (Davis *et al.*, 1988).

The length of shoots in shoot cultures of *Prunus avium* was decreased by the addition of 0.2–8 mg/l paclobutrazol to the medium, but below the agar surface, a massive callus was produced which could not be subcultured. Retarded shoots grew normally when transferred to medium containing GA₃ (Snir, 1988).

The triazole growth retardants have been noted to promote adventitious root formation of several different kinds of plants (Chapter 14).

ABSCISIC ACID

OCCURRENCE AND ACTIVITY OF ABA

Abscisic acid (ABA) (66) is another naturally-occurring growth substance. The molecule has two isomeric forms, *cis*- and *trans*-, which depend on the position of the terminal carboxyl group inserted on C-2: the *cis*-isomer is by far the most common in nature, and plants can convert the *trans*- isomer into the *cis*- form. There is also an asymmetric carbon atom at the C-1$'$ ring position which results in there being (+) and (-) enantiomers which are not biologically interconvertible. The (±)-ABA sold by chemical suppliers, is a mixture of both: only the (+) form (which is that found in nature) produces rapid responses in plants. However, responses to ABA which only develop after prolonged exposure can be initiated by the (-) enantiomer.

Abscisic acid is produced by plants directly from mevalonic acid (MVA), or from the breakdown of carotenoid pigments (which are also derived from MVA) (Neill and Horgan, 1984). Biosynthesis occurs in plastids (especially chloroplasts) (Milborrow, 1974). The herbicide 'fluridone' (63), which inhibits the natural production of carotenoids (Bartels and Watson, 1978), can prevent ABA biosynthesis (Moore and Smith, 1984).

Abscisic acid is found ubiquitously in plants and is the most commonly identified of a number of other structurally related natural compounds which have plant growth regulatory activity. It is often regarded as being a plant growth inhibitor, partly because it can control bud and seed dormancy, but more particularly because it inhibits the auxin-promoted cell wall acidification and loosening, which permit cell elongation.

ABA has many other regulatory roles in plants, such as the regulation of stomatal closure, control of water and ion uptake by roots, and of leaf abscission and senescence. In tissue cultures it sometimes promotes morphogenesis or growth. The quantity present in plant cultures can be determined by gas chromatography mass spectrometry or ELISA, following purification by high pressure liquid chromatography (Ryu *et al.*, 1988).

Uptake of ABA into tissues appears to be by simple diffusion of the undissociated molecule, the anions being trapped upon entry into cells. It is decreased at pH levels above 5.5 (Minocha and Nissen, 1985b; Patel *et al.*, 1986).

ABA IN TISSUE CULTURES

Effects on callus growth

ABA is usually inhibitory to callus growth. Sankhla and Sankhla (1968) reported that 1 mg/l was markedly inhibitory to *Ipomoea* callus, but generally, concentrations between 5 and 50 mg/l appear to be necessary to cause a 50% growth inhibition of cell growth (Li *et al.*, 1970; Gamborg and LaRue, 1971; Taylor and Burden, 1972).

(66)　cis-(+) ABA　MW 264.32

Several independent instances have been cited where ABA has been capable of stimulating callus growth, for example:

- on hypocotyl explants of *Cryptomeria* (a gymnosperm tree), 1 mg/l ABA in the culture medium had the same effect as 10 mg/l of the cytokinin BAP in stimulating internal callus or adventitious bud formation (Isikawa, 1974);

- on explants consisting of pieces of *Citrus* leaf and stem, 0.3–2.6 mg/l ABA (1–10 uM) stimulated callus formation specifically on the abscission zone between the petiole and the stem (Altman and Goren, 1971);

- in soybean, ABA stimulated callus growth when 0.05 or 0.5 mg/l kinetin was present in the medium. At lower kinetin levels ABA had no effect or was inhibitory (Blumenfeld and Gazit, 1970);

- haploid tobacco callus was increased in growth by 0.1 mg/l ABA. At 10 mg/l the regulator was completely inhibitory (Kochhar, 1980).

This response is usually only obtained with relatively low ABA concentrations: higher rates bring about corresponding decreases in the weight of callus produced (Torrizo and Zapata, 1986).

Effects on morphogenesis

Adventitious shoots

ABA has been observed to influence morphogenesis in a number of plants. The first report was by Heide (1968) who found that shoot bud formation on isolated *Begonia* × *cheimantha* leaves (not in aseptic culture) was enhanced when the leaves were treated with abscisic acid, and inhibited when either auxin or gibberellin was applied. Seasonal variation in the capacity of *Begonia* leaves to produce shoot buds was thought to be associated with variation in endogenous ABA levels.

Shepard (1980a) found that adding ABA to the growth medium (0.05–0.2 mg/l, depending on variety), caused morphogenesis to occur more rapidly than it otherwise would from potato callus.

Natural ABA levels have been noted to correspond to the maturation state of tissues (Tanimoto *et al.*, 1985). Adding 100 µg/l ABA to the medium on which internode segments of *Torenia* were cultured, stimulated the production of flower buds on previously vegetative explants. The greatest amount of flowering occurred when the ABA within the tissues (*i.e.* the sum of endogenous and exogenous sources) was between 16 and 20 µg/g.

Embryogenesis

ABA is essential for the normal growth of somatic embryos and only in its presence do they closely resemble zygotic embryos in their development and structure. Manipulation of endogenous and/or exogenous ABA levels increases the frequency of embryos reaching maturity and can assist the handling of the large populations of somatic embryos which can be required for mass propagation (Ammirato, 1988).

The slight check to embryo development caused by 0.03 mg/l ABA was found by Ammirato (1973, 1974) to be associated with the elimination of abnormal forms of embryos (such as embryos with fused or multiple cotyledons, mature leaves in place of cotyledons, or other accessory structures — see Chapter 2) that were formed in caraway (*Carum*) suspension cultures, especially in the light. ABA treatment also prevented the formation of accessory embryos in this tissue which were otherwise developed on somatic embryos already in existence. The effectiveness of ABA in decreasing the proportion of abnormal embryos and assisting and synchronising embryo maturation (conversion) has since been confirmed in other species (*e.g.* Kamada and Harada, 1981; Krogstrup *et al.*, 1988; Dunstan *et al.*, 1988).

There are also reports of low concentrations of ABA stimulating somatic embryo initiation or embryo growth:

- embryogenesis was stimulated in growth regulator habituated *Citrus sinensis* (Shamouti orange) callus by 0.01–1 mg/l ABA (Kochba *et al.*, 1978a; Spiegel-Roy and Kochba, 1980);

- embryoids were only developed from suspension cultures of *Pennisetum* when cells were transferred to a medium containing 0.01–0.02 mg/l ABA (Vasil and Vasil, 1981b);

- the addition of 0.1–50 µg/l ABA to media containing 2,4-D, adenine and kinetin, increased the number of embryos which grew from the globular stage to the heart-shaped stage in soybean suspension and callus cultures (Phillips and Collins, 1981).

- adding 0.02–10 mg/l ABA to the medium increased the proportion of *Pennisetum purpureum* leaf explants which produced embryogenic callus, especially from tissues treated with fluridone (0.02–20 mg/l in which, without ABA, embryogenesis was inhibited (Rajasekaran *et al.*, 1987).

Inhibitory effects. Several authors have noticed a growth-inhibiting action of exogenous ABA on embryogenesis and on the growth of both somatic and zygotic embryos, but these reports are rare and often describe the effects of high concentrations of the regulant. Although 0.002–2.6 mg/l ABA had little effect during the development of early globular or heart stages of somatic embryos formed in carrot cultures, it decreased the growth at stages beyond this (Fujimura and Komamine, 1975). Embryo formation in Citrus sinensis is supressed by 11–21 mg/l ABA (Spiegel-Roy and Kochba, 1980), or by even higher concentrations (Tisserat and Murashige, 1977a).

Pre-formed late stage embryos can be completely arrested in growth by 26.4 mg/l ABA; but remain viable (even though they lack chlorophyll), and will continue to develop and grow when the ABA is removed. ABA treatment might therefore be used to facilitate the storage of embryos needed at some future date for plant propagation (Ammirato, 1974). The inhibition of somatic embryos by ABA is very similar to the inhibition of zygotic embryo growth which it induces naturally (LePage-Degivry, 1973; Sondheimer et al., 1968); this serves to keep seed embryos dormant, preventing precocious germination.

Seeds of Dendrocalamus strictus germinated in the presence of 0.1–1.0 μM ABA, but if 2,4-D was also added,

embryogenic callus was produced. However, the number of embryos obtained was finally less than with 2,4-D alone (Rao et al., 1987).

Possible mode of action

The various effects of ABA on cultured plant tissues suggest that it may modify cytokinin synthesis or activity, as has been found in some whole plant tests (Van Overbeek et al., 1967). Instances of ABA having stimulated callus growth or embryogenesis could be due to its having overcome the effect of high natural cytokinin levels. The additive or synergistic effect of ABA with auxins in promoting the rooting of cuttings reported by Basu et al. (1970) could be explained in the same way. Abscisic acid has opposite effects to phenolic substances (Ray et al., 1980) and can, for example, enhance the IAA oxidation which many phenols appear to prevent.

ABA inhibits mitochondrial dark respiration, stimulated by gibberellic acid (Owen et al., 1987).

ETHYLENE

The presence of very low concentrations (e.g. 0.1 v.p.m, i.e. parts per million by volume, or μl/l) of ethylene gas (67) in the atmosphere, has long been known to cause plants to grow abnormally. In more recent years, it has been discovered that ethylene is produced by living plant tissues and regulates their growth. The gas is most obviously involved in fruit ripening, senescence, and the abscission of leaves, but also has many other functions. There is often a self–adjusting balance between natural auxin and ethylene levels (Hayes, 1981).

ETHYLENE BIOSYNTHESIS

Ethylene is produced from the amino acid methionine via 1-aminocylclopropane-1-carboxylic acid (68) (ACC, or 'ethenine' — Yang et al., 1980) (Fig. 114). This process is enhanced by the provision of exogenous carbohydrates, light, auxins, cytokinins and carbon dioxide (Kumar et al., 1987). Adding exogenous ACC to plants usually results in an increase in ethylene production (and thereby engendering physiological effects), indicating it is ACC synthesis which normally limits ethylene formation. The actual conversion of ACC to ethylene is controlled by an ethylene–forming enzyme and requires oxygen, and/or

the presence of a free radical of oxygen (Apelbaum et al., 1981a), probably the superoxide radical (McRae et al., 1982). The superoxide radical and hydroperoxides are thought to be produced in senescing plant tissue through the action of lipoxygenase enzyme on fatty acids (Lynch and Thompson, 1984).

Adding methionine to a medium may increase ethylene biosynthesis, and because methionine can be produced in plants from aspartic acid, asparagine, and cysteine, it has been suggested that their presence may sometimes have the same effect.

Inhibitors of biosynthesis

Several compounds, or groups of compounds, have been found to inhibit steps in natural ethylene production (Fig. 115).

Stage 2 inhibitors

Aminoethoxyvinylglycine (AVG). AVG (69) is a potent inhibitor of ethylene synthesis in many plants. It acts by inhibiting the enzyme which catalyses the formation of ACC from S-adenosyladenine (Step 2 in Fig. 114) (Yang et al., 1980; Kende et al. 1980). AVG is able to block the

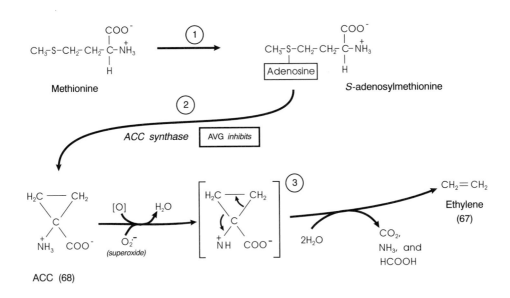

Fig. 114. The biosynthesis of ethylene.

stimulation of ethylene production by IAA and in its presence, ACC levels decrease. In plant tissue cultures, 1–50 mg/l can be effective without causing direct toxicity.

Stage 3 inhibitors

The following compounds, groups of compounds, or factors, inhibit ethylene formation from ACC.

2,5-norbornadiene (NBD) (bicyclo [2,2,1]hepta-2,5-diene. NBD **(70)** partially inhibits the production of ethylene from ACC but is, more importantly, an effective inhibitor of ethylene action. Its effects on tissue cultures are described below.

Cobalt ions. A high concentration of cobalt ions inhibits ethylene production in plant tissues (Lau and Yang, 1976) by preventing the conversion of ACC to ethylene. In the presence of 50–500 µM Co^{2+}, ACC levels increase in tissues treated with IAA (Yu and Yang, 1979). Cobalt chloride (10–100 µM) added to rose shoot cultures increased apical dominance (the opposite of the effect produced by low concentrations of ethylene (Kevers *et al.*, 1992).

Anoxia. Oxygen is required for the conversion of ACC to ethylene, ACC needing to be oxidized to contain a nitrenium ion before the molecule is fragmented. Ethylene production ceases in the absence of oxygen and in some plants, it declines when the partial pressure of oxygen decreases below 15 kPa (see Chapter 7). However in a few plants (*e.g.* barley and maize) production is stimulated at 3–5 kPa (Jackson, 1985a,b). Where oxygen is limiting in waterlogged roots, ACC is transported to the shoots where it is converted to ethylene in the presence of oxygen. An excess of ethylene then frequently causes leaf epinasty. In tissue cultures, ethylene is antagonistic to chlorophyll formation, but in *Spinacia oleracea*, oxygen partial pressures below atmospheric which are still capable of permitting aerobic respiration, were promotive of chloroplast development (Dalton and Street, 1976).

Oxidation inhibitors. The importance of oxygen in the breakdown of ACC is also seen in the inhibition of ethylene production by chemicals which inhibit oxidation. Some compounds which have been found to have this effect are uncouplers of oxidative phosphorylation (Murr and Yang, 1975; Yang *et al*, 1980) and compounds which inactivate cytochrome oxidase (Kende *et al.*, 1980; Yang *et al.*, 1980). However the action of uncouplers of oxidative phosphorylation does not appear to indicate a requirement for ATP in ethylene formation from ACC (Robert *et al.*, 1975), but rather that intact membranes are necessary (Apelbaum *et al.*, 1981a).

Chemicals which can quench free radicals, such as *n*-propyl gallate (73) (Baker *et al.*, 1978; Kende *et al.*, 1980), salicylic acid (71) and acetyl salicylic acid (72) (Leslie and Romani, 1986; 1988); polyamines (Drolet *et al.*, 1986), and compounds reputed to have this property [*e.g.* ioxynil (Robert *et al.*, 1975), bromoxynil, and 3,4,5-trichlorophenol (Apelbaum *et al.*, 1981a], have been found to inhibit the conversion of ACC to ethylene, presumably because they prevent the action of the superoxide radical. Acetyl salicylic acid may have a growth regulatory effect apart from the inhibition of ethylene formation. For example, it inhibits a specific step in the shoot regeneration process of *Convolvulus* (Christianson and Warnick, 1988) and, acting synergistically with 1 mg/l 2,4-D, 30–100 mg/l has been found to promote the formation of callus colonies from maize protoplasts (Carswell *et al.*, 1989): but possibly these are ethylene-mediated events?

Oxidation inhibitors may also prevent the metabolism of ethylene which is necessary for its biological activity (see below).

Acetyl choline (ACH). Red light and ACH are capable of overcoming the ethylene synthesis which is induced by auxin. This may be because red light results in increased acetyl choline (ACH) synthesis: cultures grown under lighting regimes, where far-red light predominates, can be expected to evolve ethylene more rapidly. For a full discussion of ACH action see Parups (1975).

Chelating agents. Like NBD, chelating agents such as EDTA can inhibit the conversion of ACC to ethylene, and also inhibit ethylene action. Ethylene production from apple slices and rose stamens is decreased by 8-hydroxyquinoline sulphate (Parups, 1975). Ethylene synthesis is also blocked by naturally-occurring polyamine compounds, which also have metal complexing capacity.

Gibberellic acid. Up to 2 mM gibberellic acid inhibited ethylene production from ACC in pear fruit suspension cultures. The site of inhibition appeared to be related to the ethylene-forming enzyme (Ben-Arie and Ferguson, 1991).

Solubility and chemical absorption

Ethylene has a solubility of 25.6 cc per 100 cc water at 0°C. For experimental purposes, ethylene in the atmosphere of culture vessels can be be preferentially absorbed on a solution of potassium permanganate or mercuric perchlorate solution (Young *et al.*, 1951). The latter is the most efficient.

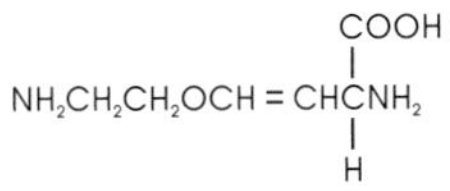

(69) AVG MW 160.17

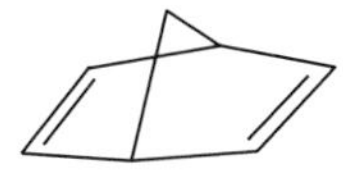

(70) 2,5-Norbordiene MW 92.14

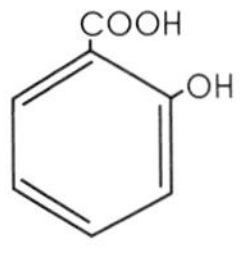

(71) Salicylic acid MW 138.12

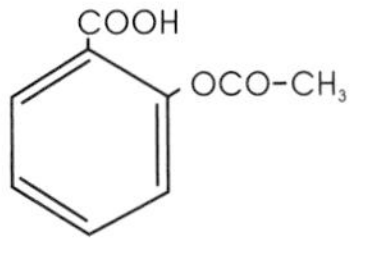

(72) *o*-Acetyl-salicylic acid MW 180.15

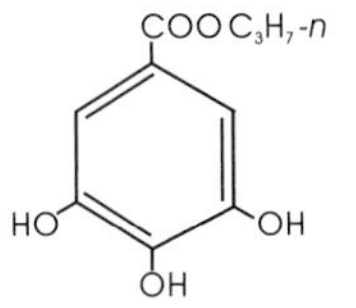

(73) *n*-Propyl gallate MW 212.20

Fig. 115. Some inhibitors of ethylene biosynthesis.

ETHYLENE ACTION

Ethylene is thought to act by binding to an active copper-containing site upon which it becomes oxidized. This seems to result in the stimulation of the activities of specific enzymes. It has been shown, for example, that ripening-related mRNAs are accumulated in tomato fruits in response to ethylene treatment (Maunders *et al.*, 1987).

Inhibitors of ethylene action

Several chemicals and environmental factors are known to inhibit ethylene action. These either prevent the gas binding with its active site, or prevent the cellular metabolism which appears to be essential for biological activity (Beyer and Blomstrom, 1980). Inhibitors of ethylene action have been used experimentally as an alternative to biosynthesis inhibitors, in conditions where ethylene is thought to affect growth or morphogenesis in tissue cultures.

Silver ions. Silver ions are known to overcome the action of ethylene on whole plants (Beyer, 1976a,b). Both silver thiosulphate (AgS_2O_3), and silver nitrate ($AgNO_3$), are therefore effective in preventing ethylene action.

Chelating agents. The use of chelating agents, particularly 8-hydroxyquinoline (8-HQ) and diethyldithiocarbamic acid (DIECA, which has a high affinity for copper ions), inhibit ethylene metabolism in pea seedlings (Beyer and Blomstrom, 1980). 8-HQ, like silver ions, is effective in prolonging the vase-life of cut flowers (thereby overcoming ethylene-induced senescence). Chelating agents (see Chapter 9) probably interfer with the synthesis or activity of the metal-containing enzyme essential for ethylene metabolism.

Carbon dioxide. High concentrations of carbon dioxide can competitively inhibit the association of ethylene with its binding site and may also prevent the oxidation of ethylene which is essential for physiological activity. High concentrations are necessary for this purpose, for example 5–10 per cent CO_2 to overcome the biological action of 5–20 v.p.m. ethylene (Dalton and Street, 1976). The presence of carbon dioxide at atmospheric concentration may however be necessary for some responses to ethylene (Hall *et al.*, 1980). CO_2 has been used in some fruit stores to delay the ripening process. Ethylene action is prevented in the absence of oxygen.

Chemical inhibitors. Some chemical inhibitors of ethylene action are reported, including 3,5-diiodo-4-hydroxybenzoic acid (DIHB) (74) (Jackson, 1985b) and 5-methyl-7-chloro-4-ethoxycarbanylmethoxy-2,1,3-benzothiadiazole (benzothiadiazole, TH 6241) (75) (Van Daalen and Daams, 1970; Parups, 1975), but we have not heard of their use in plant tissue cultures. DIHB is a close analogue of ioxynil which is said to prevent the conversion of ACC to ethylene (see above), and so its mode of action is open to question.

(74) DIHB   MW 389.92   (75) TH 6241   MW 286.74

Cytokinins. Cytokinins are able to block ethylene action. Burg and Burg (1968) found that 0.1 mM (21.5 mg/l) kinetin could even completely reverse the inhibition caused by 1000 v.p.m ethylene to the growth of pea shoots.

Ethylene-releasing chemicals

Several synthetic ethylene-releasing chemicals have been discovered. The one most commonly used in plant tissue culture experiments is ethephon (2-CEPA or 2-chloroethylphosphonic acid) (76). This compound is absorbed into plant tissues where it breaks down to release ethylene at cytoplasmic pH levels. Cultures usually produce more ethylene if the compound from which it is naturally derived, ACC, is added to the medium (Puschmann *et al.*, 1985). Adding methionine may also have the same effect (Druart, 1988).

$$Cl CH_2 CH_2 \overset{\overset{O}{\|}}{P} (OH)_2$$

(76) Ethephon   MW 144.50

ETHYLENE PRODUCTION *IN VITRO*

Ethylene is produced during the culture of all kinds of plant cells, tissues and organs. The rate of biosynthesis is increased if cells are subjected to stress of some kind (*e.g.* high sodium chloride levels — Garcia and Einset, 1982, 1983; toxic levels of ammonium ions — page 276). Some chemicals added to culture media can stimulate ethylene formation. Mannitol, which is commonly used in protoplast and other tissue cultures as an osmoticum, causes ethylene biosynthesis to be increased (Riov and Yang, 1982): polyethylene glycol, which is sometimes used in protoplast fusion experiments, can also have the same effect. Potato protoplasts which had been treated with polyethylene glycol were much more likely to produce microcalli if 100 μg/ml $Ag_2S_2O_3$ was added to the medium (Perl *et al.*, 1988). Ethylene production is also greater during the senescence of cultured plant material: it reaches a maximum in suspension cultures at the start of the stationary phase when nutrients are limiting and most of the cells are senescing (LaRue and Gamborg, 1971a).

Prunus avium shoot cultures produced ethylene at a constant rate over 30 days (19 μg/g dry weight) (Righetti *et al.*, 1988) even when the CO_2 in the culture vessels reached 30% (Righetti *et al.*, 1990).

Suspension cultures of several different kinds of plants were found by Gamborg and LaRue (1968) and LaRue and Gamborg (1971a) to produce ethylene at up to 1220 nmoles/hour/g dry weight of cells. The rate of evolution was greatest as the cells reached stationary phase, was the same in the light or the dark, and varied greatly between species (being especially low in cultures of monocotyledonous plants). Marked differences in the rate of ethylene production in different experiments was attributed to the differing physiological state of the cells. The amount of ethylene produced by callus cultures is also dependent on genotype (Thomas and Murashige, 1979a).

In sunflower suspensions, there appears to be no functional relationship between growth and ethylene synthesis, ethylene being just a by-product of actively dividing cells (Sauerbrey *et al.*, 1987).

As with whole plants or parts of plants, auxins generally increase the production of ethylene by cell and callus cultures but results have not always been predictable. Production of ethylene by suspension cultures is dependent on the level of 2,4-D in the medium, but is independent of the effect of 2,4-D on growth (Mackenzie and Street, 1970; Sauerbrey *et al.*, 1987). Similarly, addition of 2,4-D to suspensions of *Ruta graveolens* promoted ethylene formation, but did not do so in cell cultures of *Rosa*, where only NAA and *p*CPA were stimulatory (Gamborg and LaRue, 1971). IAA increased ethylene production by suspension cultures of pear (Puschmann *et al.*, 1985).

Wulster and Sacalis (1980) observed that ethylene production from callus cultures of *Rosa hybrida* was increased by 1–3 mg/l of the auxins NAA or IBA, but was little affected by 5–15 mg/l of three cytokinins except when they were used in conjunction with auxin. Then the rate of ethylene production could be markedly increased. The concentration of cytokinin at which synergism occurred varied according to whether BAP, 2-iP or zeatin riboside was used. Lau and Yang (1973), who found a similar synergism in mung bean, discovered that ethylene evolution was closely related to the level of free IAA in the tissue. Kinetin promoted ethylene evolution because it prevented added IAA being converted rapidly into indoleacetylaspartic acid. In this conjugated form, the auxin had no effect on ethylene production. The amount of ethylene evolved by *Dahlia* callus was proportional to the concentration of NAA added to the medium (Gavinlertvatana *et al.*, 1982).

The addition of galactose to a medium has been found to increase ethylene levels within tissues (Colclasure and Yopp, 1976).

Accumulation in culture vessels

As ethylene is produced from all kinds of plant cultures, including callus and suspensions, it accumulates in the gas phase within sealed culture vessels. The concentration in the free air space is found to vary according to the type of tissue being grown, the weight of the tissue, the volume of the culture vessel, the manner in which it is sealed, and the culture conditions.

The physiological effects of an ethylene atmosphere within vessels vary according to the concentration of the gas. The desirable and undesirable physiological effects of the concentrations with which cells or tissues are sometimes presented (particularly in containers that are tightly closed), are discussed below. Some of the effects of container size on growth and morphogenesis were described in Chapter 7.

If the suspension cultures of LaRue and Gamborg (1971a) produced ethylene at the same rate in tightly closed flasks as they did in foam-stoppered vessels, the air space in the flasks after 6 days of culture would have contained from only a trace (*Triticum monococcum*); to *ca.* 7.4 v.p.m ethylene (rose). Huxter *et al.* (1981) measured 0.3–1.8 v.p.m ethylene in foam-stoppered flasks containing tobacco callus; Mackenzie and Street (1970), 10 v.p.m in the air space above their sycamore suspensions; De Proft *et al.* (1985), up to 2–3 v.p.m. above tightly stoppered *Magnolia* shoot cultures after 9 weeks.

The retention of ethylene depends of the nature of the closures used on culture vessels, and on the tightness of the seal. Loosely covered flasks, such as those capped with aluminium foil, have been found to lose 50% of their ethylene in 2 hours; the rate of loss thereafter being constant (Gavinlertvatana *et al.*, 1982).

Ethylene can accumulate in flasks in significant quantities if their necks are momentarily flamed with an alcohol or natural gas burner during transfers (Beasley and Eaks, 1979).

Effects on cultures

Some of the physiological effects produced by auxin are identical to those produced by ethylene. Auxin treatment has been found to increase the biosynthesis of the enzyme ACC synthase (which is normally present in very low concentrations in plant tissues), thus increasing the production of ethylene from *S*-adenosylmethionine. This suggests that some of the responses of plants to auxins are ultimately brought about by the ethylene produced in response to an auxin treatment.

Explant isolation

Ethylene production by plant tissues is temporarily increased when they are wounded, and so is significant during explant isolation. Less ethylene was produced during the isolation of potato leaf protoplasts if shoots, from which the leaves were taken, had been previously cultured with silver thiosulphate; the quantity of ethylene decreased still further if acetylsalicylic acid was added during the maceration process (Perl *et al.*, 1988). The effects of wounding on growth and morphogenesis are discussed further on page 470.

Suspension cultures

In the cell cultures of LaRue and Gamborg (1971a) described above, exogenous ethylene could not replace an auxin which was required to induce cell division. Ethylene naturally accumulated within flasks appeared to have little effect, and there was only a 20–30% reduction in cell yield of *Ruta* and *Rosa* suspensions when relatively large amounts of ethylene were artificially added. The addition of ethephon did not stimulate cell division of growth of sycamore cells (Mackenzie and Street, 1970).

Callus initiation and growth

Growth stimulation. It might be expected that the accumulation of ethylene in culture vessels would induce the formation of callus, because in whole plants, undifferentiated callus-like growths (intumescences) have been seen to grow from the stems (Wallace, 1928; Evanari, 1961), or roots (Wilson, 1966), of intact plants which have been kept for prolonged periods in dilute ethylene atmospheres.

Ethylene does seem to stimulate callus growth of some plants *in vitro*. For example, on a hormone-free medium, *Ginkgo biloba* embryos germinated when placed on medium within tubes sealed with cotton plugs, but gave rise to callus if the tubes were covered with Parafilm (Webb *et al.*, 1986). Furthermore, although it has been thought that the increase in ethylene evolution caused by 2,4- D is independent of the effect of the auxin on growth (MacKenzie and Street, 1970), a close correlation has been found between the rate of ethylene production and the growth rate of tobacco (Huxter *et al.*, 1979; Bridgen and Lineberger, 1981a), dahlia (Gavinlertvatana *et al.*, 1982) and tomato (Mukund *et al.*, 1988) calluses. Several chemicals known to inhibit ethylene biosynthesis also reduced growth and ethylene evolution in exact proportion.

Growth inhibition. Contrary indications have also often been obtained: Chalutz and DeVay (1969) showed that ethylene inhibited the formation of callus and suberised cork cells on the injured surfaces of sweet potato roots, and seemed to have little effect on the subsequent division of undifferentiated cells. Similarly, Zobel and Roberts (1978) found that an ethylene concentration above 0.1 v.p.m. prevented the initiation of callus and tracheids from *Lactuca* pith explants and deduced that this was because the gas prevented the cells becoming determined or differentiated. Once the cells became programmed to divide and grow as callus, ethylene had no further effect.

In rice, callus necrosis was most likely to occur in cultivars which produced ethylene at a high rate. Callus growth of these plants was more strongly inhibited by a controlled gas mixture high in ethylene, than was that of necrosis-tolerant cultivars (Adkins *et al.*, 1990).

Other physiological effects. A promotory effect of ethylene on xylogenesis in soybean callus and *Lactuca* pith explants has been reported (Miller and Roberts, 1982; Miller *et al.*, 1985). Chlorophyll synthesis and chloroplast development *in vitro* is depressed by ethylene (Dalton and Street, 1976).

Morphogenesis

The role of ethylene in morphogenesis is by no means clear, although its action in inhibiting polar auxin movement (page 432) must be partly responsible for the observed effects. Besides influencing the determination of cells that will give rise to callus (see above), the gas can influence organ formation *in vitro*. From available results, it appears that there is often a critical concentration at which morphogenesis is stimulated; concentrations below and above this being respectively ineffective, or inhibitory.

Determination. Ethylene appeared to inhibit the capacity of *Helianthus annuus* callus to produce adventitious shoots. The determination was influenced by treatments to the seedlings from which explants were derived. Hypocotyls of dark-grown seedlings of *Helianthus annuus* produced less adventitious shoots than those grown in the light. This seemed to be correlated with an effect of light on the sensitivity of the tissues to ethylene, because treating 3-day-old dark-grown seedlings with 10 μM AVG, inhibited ethylene production for 7 days; providing 4 days elapsed before cultures were initiated, callus from the hypocotyls of these seedlings produced the same number of adventitious shoots as light-grown callus (Robinson and Adams, 1987).

Adventitious shoot formation. Ringe (1972) reported that direct shoot formation on *Begonia* × *richmondensis* stem segments was inhibited by 2–20 mg/l ethephon, and completely prevented by 200 mg/l (although these same concentrations promoted callus proliferation). Adding ethephon to media supporting callus growth of wild or cultivated carrot, has been reported to inhibit root and shoot formation (Wochok and Wetherell, 1971).

Thorpe and co-workers (Thorpe *et al.*, 1981; Huxter *et al.* 1981) concluded that ethylene inhibited shoot formation during the first 5 days of the initiation period, but thereafter it speeded up the formation of primordia.

Callus of wheat and *Nicotiana plumbaginifolia* cultured on **Tran Thanh Van (1973a)** medium with 1 mg/l 2,4-D, formed adventitious shoots when the auxin was omitted.

Shoot formation was inhibited if ethylene (70 µM ethephon) was present from the beginning of the culture period, and was stimulated (and adventitious root formation simultaneously reduced) if 5–50 mg/l silver nitrate was present thoughout the culture period (Purnhauser *et al.*, 1987). Ethylene inhibitors have been found to have a similar effect in other species too. For example, adventitious shoot formation on cotyledons or hypocotyls of *Brassica* spp., was enhanced by adding AVG (1–10 uM), or AgNO₃ (5–30 uM), to **MS** medium containing auxin and cytokinin (Chi *et al.*, 1990).

Ethylene in culture vessels. The ethylene and carbon dioxide which built up in culture flasks during the first 15 days of culture, promoted the formation of shoot buds from *Pinus radiata* cotyledons. The additional ethylene was especially promotory during the first few days of culture, and if flasks were stoppered with foam plugs for 10–15 days, there was only a low frequency of shoot bud formation. Excessive concentrations of ethylene which accumulated after 15 days (*e.g.* 25 µl/l at 25 days) caused a slight dedifferentiation of buds (Kumar *et al.*, 1986, 1987).

Formation of apogamous buds in the fern *Pteridium aquilinum*, was also stimulated most effectively by a certain concentration of ethylene. Gametophytic colonies exposed to air produced only 4 buds per gram of tissue, whereas those exposed to 0.7 v.p.m. ethylene gave rise to 32. Less apogamous buds were formed by colonies in 2.5 and 14.5 v.p.m. ethylene (Elmore and Whittier, 1973).

The number of adventitious buds formed on bulb scale explants of lily was increased if 1–10 v.p.m. ethylene was applied in the gas phase above the cultures during the first 3–7 days of culture (Van Aartrijk *et al.*, 1985). A similar result was obtained by Taeb and Alderson (1987) with sections of the immature floral stems of tulips. Adding 1–10 µM ACC, or 0.1–100 µM ethephon, did not have the same promotory effect.

Bulb formation. The formation of bulbs on tulip shoots was enhanced by increased endogenous ethylene, achieved by adding 0.1–10 mg/l ACC to the medium, or by growing cultures under lights with a low red/far red ratio (Alderson and Taeb, 1990).

Root formation. Ethylene has been reported to have both promotory and inhibitory effects on rooting *in vitro*.

Coleman *et al.* (1980) showed that in conditions where 5 µM IAA promoted the formation of adventitious roots on tomato leaf discs, the simultaneous application of ethylene gas, or ethephon, was inhibitory. Furthermore, although natural ethylene production was stimulated by adding auxin to the medium, lowering its level in the culture flasks by aeration, absorbing it with mercuric perchlorate, or leaf disc pretreatment with AgNO₃ (1.7–17.0 mg/l for 30 min), doubled the number of roots formed.

Although Coleman *et al.* concluded that ethylene was not a rooting hormone *per se*, others have reported contrary indications. Fabijan *et al.* (1981a) suggested that although the initiation of roots from *Helianthus* hypocotyls was blocked by endogenous ethylene on the first day after excision, thereafter the gas was promotory.

Thin cell layers of *Nicotiana tabacum* were found to produce 100-times more ethylene on a root-inducing medium (containing 10 µM IBA and 0.1 µM kinetin) than tissues cultured on other media. The appearance of roots was associated with a further increase in ethylene synthesis, which was maximal at 30°C and only trivial at 15° or 40°C, suggesting an enzyme-mediated process. If silver ions were added to the medium, root formation was blocked and adventitious shoot buds were formed (Le Guyader, 1987).

Providing oxygen was present, the rooting of chrysanthemum cuttings in an experimental mist system was slightly enhanced by adding 10 p.p.m. ethylene in the gas phase (Soffer and Burger, 1988), and extensive wounding (likely to increase endogenous ethylene evolution) also increased rooting of mung bean cuttings except when they were treated with 10 µM AVG (Robbins *et al.*, 1981).

Embryogenesis. Size of culture vessel was found to be most important to obtain optimum rates of embryogenesis from tobacco anthers (Dunwell, 1979), suggesting that a volatile substance was stimulatory at a critical concentration. In embryogenic 'Shamouti' orange cultures, low concentrations of ethephon (0.01–1.0 mg/l) stimulated embryo formation, but levels above these were inhibitory (Kochba *et al.*, 1978a), and excessive levels of ethylene accumulated within closed flasks, have been found to prevent embryogenesis (Spiegel-Roy and Kochba, 1980).

Other evidence also suggests that ethylene, normally produced by tissues, is inhibitory to embryogenesis. The addition of 1–3 mg/l AgNO₃ to anther cultures of many varieties of *Brassica oleracea gemmifera*, increased the production of somatic embryos, and allowed embryos to be obtained from experiments and varieties where there would normally have been very few (Biddington *et al.*, 1988). Similarly, by placing 50–200 µM AgNO₃ in the medium on which maize embryogenic callus was cultured for 21 days (before it was placed on a regeneration medium), the number of plants obtained per unit weight of callus was increased. Acetyl salicylic acid also improved regeneration, but was less effective than AgNO₃ (Duncan and Widholm, 1987).

That ethylene is inhibitory to some early step in embryo initiation was suggested by the results of Duncan and

Widholm (1988). Callus of *Zea mays* derived from immature embryos cultured with 15 μM dicamba (medium **D**) which produced somatic embryos when moved to a regeneration medium without the auxin (medium **H**), tended to regenerate many more plants from somatic embryos if 200 μM silver nitrate had been added to the **D** medium. Tisserat and Murashige (1977c) found that embryogenesis of carrot and *Citrus media* was inhibited if ethephon was added to the medium.

However the inhibitors of ethylene biosynthesis, AVG, amino-oxyacetic acid, 2,4-dinitrophenol and salicylic acid, *prevented* embryogenesis in *Medicago sativa*. Meijer and Brown (1988) suggested that these compounds were possibly blocking a biosynthetic pathway, other than ethylene formation, of crucial importance to embryogenesis.

Shoot growth and axillary bud break

Ethylene in the external atmosphere is generally inhibitory to cell growth in the meristems of seedlings (Fidler, 1960), whole plant shoots (Heck and Pires, 1962a,b), or roots (Chadwick and Burg, 1967; Andreae *et al.*, 1968; Radin and Loomis, 1969). Monocotyledons such as cereals and grasses are less affected than dicotyledons. Many species are extremely sensitive: pea seedlings for instance make noticeably less growth in an atmosphere containing 0.05–0.1 v.p.m ethylene (Fidler, 1960).

It might therefore be expected that concentrations of ethylene found within culture flasks would prevent the normal growth of directly or indirectly regenerated shoots, or of axillary shoots proliferating in shoot cultures. In fact, growth inhibition seldom appears to take place, and there is some evidence that ethylene may often have a stimulatory role. Adding 50–100 mg/l of the ethylene precursor, methionine to the medium together with 1 mg/l BAP, increased the rate of propagation of several woody species through several subcultures (Druart, 1988). Although their quality was poor, more shoots were produced by rose shoot cultures grown in sealed vessels (Horn *et al.*, 1988a,b), and low rates of exogenous ethylene (an injection of which gave an intravessel concentration 5 v.p.m. that declined to zero over 10 days) were found to increase the rate of rose shoot proliferation. Higher concentrations (20 and especially, 100 v.p.m.) were inhibitory (Kevers *et al.*, 1992).

An intriguing experiment of Walker *et al.* (1988) also suggests that ethylene affects the growth of *Rhododendron* shoot cultures. Firstly, the fresh weight and the number of shoots was *reduced* if culture vessels were flushed with a mixture of nitrogen, oxygen and carbon dioxide. Secondly, when cultures were grown in divided vessels with a common atmosphere, the presence in the medium on one side of the partition, of normal growth regulators (4 mg/l IAA and 15 mg/l 2-iP), increased the weight of shoots obtained from the other side when the shoots there were grown without regulants, or with IAA and 2-iP at half the above rates.

Stolon formation. Ethylene appears to be somehow involved in the regulation of stolon formation. Stolons are axillary shoots with the capacity for considerable internode extension. If metal caps covering jars for potato cultures were screwed down too tightly, there was a tendency for stolon-like shoots with small leaves to be produced; but shoots are short and swollen and had only scale leaves if the closures had been further covered with PVC tape or Parafilm. These ethylene—induced effects were eliminated by placing an ethylene- absorbant (a vial containing mercuric perchlorate solution) into sealed jars or by replacing the metal covers with polyurethane foam (Hussey and Stacey, 1981a; Creissen and Karp, 1985). Shoot cultures of *Fragaria* × *ananassa* in covered vessels produced runners if silver nitrate (20 mg/l) and gibberellic acid (20 mg/l) were added to **Boxus (1974a)** medium. Without silver nitrate, gibberellic acid only caused the elongation of normal shoots (Zatyko *et al.*, 1989).

Growth inhibition. Some cases of ethylene-induced inhibition of shoot growth have been reported. That of cultured *Kalanchoe blossfeldiana* shoots was inhibited by the ethylene which built up in sealed tubes. There were less nodes per plant and a higher proportion of yellow leaves (Horn *et al.*, 1988a). Torres *et al.* (1981b) have reported that shoot formation from *in vitro* cultures of *Begonia* × *hiemalis* seemed to be inhibited in sealed flasks, although little difference was observed with Easter lilies or *Exacum*. When carnation shoot cultures were grown in tightly sealed vessels, sufficient ethylene was produced to reduce shoot internode length and cause leaves to become yellowish in colour and more swollen than those of the controls (Mele *et al.*, 1982). Ethylene may normally be prevented from inhibiting the growth (rather than formation) of shoots in shoot cultures, through the presence of cytokinin in the growth medium.

Bud dormancy. Although the dormancy of buds is preserved in the presence of external ethylene, once the plant or plant organ is removed from the gas, dormancy is broken and shoot growth is often more rapid than it might otherwise have been (*e.g.* that of potato tuber sprouts — Elmer, 1936). The dormancy of axillary buds on cuttings of woody plants such as apple, plum, cherry and willow is also broken when shoots which have been kept for some while in an ethylene atmosphere have subsequently been removed (Vacha and Harvey, 1927). For micropropagation purposes, cytokinins are used to promote the growth of axillary shoots, and so in this instance cytokinins and the previous presence of high ethylene have the same final effect.

OTHER VOLATILES

Volatile substances apart from ethylene are produced and evolved from cultured plant tissues. Methane, ethane, acetaldehyde and ethanol have all been detected in the gas phase above tissue cultures (Thomas and Murashige, 1979a,b; Torres *et al.*, 1981b), some of which are the products of inefficient respiration in conditions of oxygen deficiency (page 199): ethane is produced by cells which have been wounded and have suffered membrane damage (Van Aartrijk *et al.*, 1985). Embryogenesis in carrot and date palm callus can be inhibited by ethanol evolved by cultures (Tisserat and Murashige, 1977b; Thomas and Murashige, 1979a,b). Acetaldehyde has been thought to inhibit aerobic respiration, thereby stopping cell division (Laties, 1962).

POSSIBLE SECONDARY MESSENGERS

It is thought that the five 'classical' kinds of growth substance may not be always directly responsible for major regulatory effects, but that other regulants (or *secondary messengers*) may sometomes mediate their action and be finally responsible for gene expression and protein synthesis. Oligosaccharides, sterols, inositol triphosphate and polyamines have been tentatively put into this category: some would argue that polyamines may exert direct regulatory effects.

POLYAMINES

All higher plants contain aliphatic amine compounds which are necessary for growth. The most common of these compounds are putrescine (77) (a diamine), spermidine (78) (a triamine) and spermine (79) (a tetraamine). In solution, at cytoplasmic pH levels, these *polyamines* act as polycations and complexing agents. Polyamines are synthesized by plant cells in culture (Smith *et al.*, 1977).

Polyamines have been found to act as growth stimulants and sometimes to enhance the action of plant growth substances. It has been suggested that they may function as secondary messengers for hormones within cells (Smith, 1985), but this hypothesis is questioned (Fobert and Webb, 1988). Whether they should be regarded as a new class of natural regulants is undecided. Some advantages from their addition to plant culture media are beginning to emerge.

Biosynthesis

The biosynthetic route to polyamines from the precursors arginine and ornithine has been determined (Fig. 116), although the pathways which are operative may vary from one species to another, and according to whether morphogenesis, or growth, is taking place (Feirer *et al.*, 1984; Tiburcio *et al.*, 1987). Ornithine decarboxylase is thought to be chiefly activated during cell division (Heimer *et al*, 1979; Bagni *et al*, 1983), arginine decarboxylase being activated during cell elargement (Galston, 1983).

The biosynthesis of polyamines is influenced by the medium used for *in vitro* culture; that of putrescine has been shown to be much greater on ammonium-based nutrition than when nitrogen is supplied as nitrate ions (Smith and Wiltshire, 1975). This may be in response to the reduction of medium pH which is associated with uptake of NH_4^+, although it has been suggested that putrescine accumulation may result when ammonium competes for potassium at a site of metabolic importance (Le Rudulier and Goas, 1975).

Inhibitors of specific stages in the biosynthetic pathways illustrated in Fig. 116 have been discovered. They are:

DFMA	DL-α-difluoromethylarginine
DFMO	α-difluoromethylornithine
MGBG	methylglyoxal-*bis*(guanylhydrazone)

The cyclohexylammonium ion is also inhibitory: it is commonly made available from one of two compounds, viz:

| DCHA | dicyclohexylammonium sulphate |
| CHAP | cyclohexylammonium phosphate |

Responses obtained from addition of these inhibitors to plant culture media, have been used to indicate the involvement of polyamines in growth and morphogenesis. DFMO has been said to be ineffective in certain plants (Galston, 1983; Flores and Galston, 1984). DFMO re-

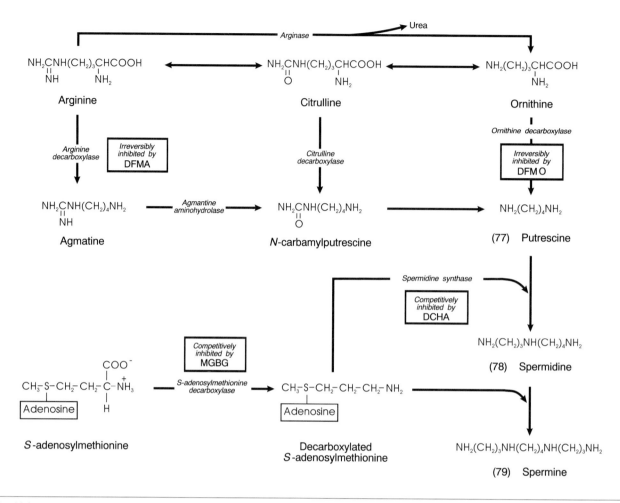

Fig. 116. Biosynthetic pathways to common polyamines.

tards the growth of phytopathogenic fungi and it is claimed that plants treated with this inhibitor are protected from some kinds of fungal attack (Weinstein and Galston, *1988*).

Polyamine conjugates with hydroxylated cinnamic acids also occur in plants. They are thought to have have regulatory properties and to be used by plants to inhibit the multiplication of viral pathogens.

Physiological activity

At physiological pH, polyamines act as cations and bind strongly to nucleic acids and proteins, which carry negatively charged groups. RNA and DNA are stabilized by their association with polyamines, and in the bound form are more resistant to nuclease enzymes and thermal denaturation (Galston *et al.*, 1980). Free polyamines can compensate for ionic deficiencies or stress (Spector,

1989) within plants, and can temporarily substitute for, and sometimes have the same physiological effect as, the cations K^+, Ca^{2+} and Mg^{2+}. Part of their function may be to act as buffers to minimize fluctuations in cellular pH (Slocum *et al.*, 1984). The concentration of putrescine is high in plants grown in conditions which favour the production of H^+ ions, such as acid stress, or where ammonium ions are provided as the major nitrogen source.

The modulation of growth caused by these compounds probably springs from their ability to bind to phospholipid groups and other anionic sites on membranes; cell wall polysaccharides; and nucleic acids such as DNA, tRNA and mRNA. They are thought to modulate enzyme activities, enhance DNA replication and transcription, and to be necessary to convert the structure of tRNA from an inactive to active form (Bagni and Biondi, 1987).

Levels of polyamine compounds tend to be highest in actively growing tissues and organs, such as root tips, buds (Kulpa *et al.*, 1985) and cells and tissues undergoing, or which have just undergone, morphogenesis (Tiburcio *et al.*, 1987; Wang and Faust, 1986; Martin-Tanguy *et al.*, 1988).

Interaction with growth regulators

Auxin activity. Exogenous polyamines have similar effects on plants to auxins, are directly involved in cell division (Bagni, 1966) and cell elongation (Bagni, 1986), and in certain circumstances can be used as a substitute for auxin treatment (Bagni *et al.*, 1978). Both auxins and polyamines are thought to act at cell membranes together with Ca^{2+} ions. The promotion of peroxidase secretion by auxins depends on the presence of calcium but polycations cause a rapid release of Ca^{2+} from the plasma membrane (Kevers *et al.*, 1985).

In *Sideratis* callus, 10 mM spermidine was able to annul the toxic effect of supra-optimal auxin or cytokinin levels (Sánchez-Graz and Segura, 1988a).

The effect of ethylene. Polyamines inhibit ethylene biosynthesis by blocking the conversion of ACC to ethylene (Apelbaum *et al.*, 1981b; Fuhrer *et al.*, 1982), possibly because they can act as free radical scavengers (see page 456). They may also interfere with ethylene action. Ethylene itself can diminish the rate of polyamine synthesis by reducing the activity of arginine decarboxylase (Palavan *et al.*, 1984). This mutual antagonism may have arisen because a common intermediate (*S*-adenosylmethionine) is involved in the biosynthesis of ethylene and spermine and spermidine.

Blocking the formation of ethylene by the inhibitor AVG has been shown to lead to increased spermidine formation (Even-Chen *et al.*, 1982) and using inhibitors to arrest polyamine synthesis may lead to increased (Roberts *et al.*, 1983), or decreased ethylene production. Robie and Minocha (1989) found that carrot embryogenesis occurred in the presence of 0.5–1 mg/l 2,4-D (normally inhibitory levels) if 1–10 mM DFMO had also been added to the medium. They suggested that this might have been due to a reduced rate of ethylene production: polyamine synthesis is increased by DFMO and this might have caused there to be smaller cellular pools of *S*–adenosylmethionine.

Gibberellic acid. In dwarf peas, gibberellic acid enhances the activity of arginine decarboxylase and ornithine decarboxylase, with the result that polyamine levels in tissues are increased (Dai *et al.*, 1982; Galston, 1983; Galston *et al.*, 1983). The quantities of polyamines in genetic lines of peas differing in growth habit from very dwarf to tall, has also been found to be correlated with internode elongation and extractable gibberellin content. Inhibitors of polyamine synthesis also prevent internode elongation of dwarf lines by gibberellic acid (Smith *et al.*, 1985). However polyamines seem to affect only cell division, whereas gibberellin-induced growth involves both cell division and cell elongation. It was therefore concluded that polyamines are involved with only some aspects of these processes.

Cytokinins. Like gibberellins, cytokinins have also been found to increase the polyamine content of several different kinds of plant tissue (Suresh *et al.*, 1978; Cho, 1983; Palavan *et al.*, 1984), apparently because they increase the activity of arginine decarboxylase. Polyamines (and to a lesser extent arginine and lysine) delay leaf senescence in plants, and so have a similar physiological effect as cytokinins (Slocum *et al.*, 1984). Indeed the retardation of senescence by cytokinins may be entirely due to their increasing natural polyamine levels. Polyamines are thought to delay senescence by stabilizing membranes (Altman 1979; Srivasta and Smith, 1982), by interfering with the release or activity of hydrolytic ribonuclease and protease enzymes (Galston *et al.*, 1978), preventing lipid peroxidation, and protecting nucleic acids against nuclease degradation. Some synthetic chelating agents have similar effects (Shoemaker *et al.*, 1983). Polyamines can also prevent senescence because their formation from *S*-adenosylmethionine limits ethylene biosynthesis from this same precursor (Roberts *et al.*, 1983); and because they can neutralise the effect of free radicals *in vitro*, which prevents the conversion of ACC to ethylene (Drolet *et al.*, 1986).

Cadaverine, putrescine (1 mM), spermidine and spermine (0.1 μM), all inhibited the senescence of *Rosa* suspension cultures (Muhitch *et al.*, 1983).

Activity in tissue cultures

Cell division

Putrescine (50–100 μM) and ornithine (25 μM) have been found to stimulate cell division and callus colony formation from *Alnus* protoplasts (Huhtinen *et al.*, 1982); putrescine, spermidine and spermine, improve the plating efficiency of sweet potato protoplasts through interaction with growth regulators (Eilers *et al.*, 1988).

Unconjugated polyamines do not appear to promote callus initiation, but do seem to improve the growth of callus when combined with sub-optimum levels of auxin and cytokinin. Perhaps this is because other growth regulators promote natural polyamine synthesis? If DCHA was added to the medium, callus growth from *Sideratis angustifilium* hypocotyls was decreased in the presence of auxins (Sánchez-Graz and Segura, 1988a).

Spermidine (10 µM) or spermine (100 µM) was found to stimulate the growth of *Helianthus tuberosus* tuber explants and callus in a similar way to 0.05 µM IAA (Bagni, 1966; Bertossi *et al.*, 1965). *Nicotiana sylvestris* callus was stimulated by 90 µM putrescine (Oshmarina *et al.*, 1982), and *Sideritis* callus by spermidine (Sánchez-Graz and Segura, 1988a).

The rapid growth of crown gall tumour tissue is thought to be associated with its high polyamine content (Kulpa *et al.*, 1985).

Conjugates of polyamines. Polyamines conjugated with phenolic acids such as cinnamic, coumaric, caffeic and ferulic derivatives are found in many plants (Smith T.A., 1977). Martin *et al.* (1985) found that putrescine could promote cell division if conjugated with a cinnamic acid. Out of several cinnamoyl derivatives tested, the best was caffeoyl putrescine, where 0.25 mM induced the maximum rate of cell division. Higher concentrations inhibited cell division, but were not toxic. When an hydroxycinnamoylputrescine was added to a medium containing BAP, leaf discs of *N. tabacum* formed undifferentiated callus, instead of direct adventitious buds (Martin-Tanguy *et al.*, 1988).

Adventitious shoot formation

Polyamines may regulate adventitious shoot formation. Inhibitors of polyamine synthesis have been found to reduce the number of adventitious buds formed from chicory roots (Bagni and Biondi, 1987) and cotyledons of *Pinus radiata* (Biondi *et al.*, 1986). Shoot regeneration from apple leaf explants was enhanced by adding 0.1–1 mM putrescine to a medium containing 0.5 mg/l NAA and 2 mg/l BAP (James *et al.*, 1988).

DMFO was ineffective in preventing adventitious bud formation in tobacco, although ornithine decarboxylase appeared to be particularly involved in the production of polyamines required for subsequent growth of the primordia once they had been formed (Tiburcio *et al.*, 1987). In maize, however DMFA promoted indirect shoot formation: embryo-derived calluses of maize were cultured for three months on a modified **MS** medium containing 9 µM 2,4-D and 0.5 mM DMFA, and then moved the cultures to the same medium with 1 µM 2,4-D (and no inhibitor) (Tiburcio *et al.*, 1991). Many more calluses formed adventitious shoots than if the inhibitor had not been present. The number of plants obtained per callus was also four times greater and the plants developed more rapidly than the controls.

Adventitious roots

Inhibitors of polyamine synthesis have been found to prevent the formation of roots by thin cell layers excised

from the floral stems of tobacco (Tiburcio *et al.*, 1989; Torrigiani *et al.*, 1990). Synthesis of endogenous polyamines increased prior to the formation of root primordia and during root growth on cuttings and hypocotyls of *Phaseolus* and *Vigna* treated with IBA (Friedman *et al.*, 1982; 1985: Jarvis *et al*, 1983; 1985). Furthermore, in these plants, rooting was promoted by 50 µM spermine in the presence or absence of IBA, a result confirmed in *Phaseolus* by Fletcher *et al.* (1988) and Kakkar and Rai (1987). Spermidine promoted adventitious root formation on root callus of *Sideratis*, but not on hyopcotyl callus (Sáanchez-Graz and Segura, 1988a).

Light of 60 µmol m^{-2} sec^{-1} flux density is normally inhibitory to the rooting of micropropagated olive shoots, but was found not to be so if 160 mg/l putrescine was added to the rooting medium (Rugini *et al.*, 1988). The compound promoted earlier rooting and increased the proportion of cuttings forming roots.

Flowering

Evidence is accumulating that polyamines are associated with floral development (see review by Evans and Malmberg, 1989). In thin cell layers of tobacco, DFMA diminishes adventitious bud formation, particularly that of floral buds (Tiburcio *et al.*, 1987). Moreover, spermidine is able to induce the formation of flower buds (Kaur-Sawhney *et al.*, 1988), an event which has been said to be associated with the attachment of the compound to a unique protein (Apelbaum *et al.*, 1988).

Embryogenesis

Promotion. That polyamines are required for somatic embryo development was suggested by the discovery of Feirer *et al.*, 1984; 1985) that the number of somatic embryos formed from wild carrot cultures was severely reduced by 1 mM DMFA, but that embryogenesis could be restored if 0.1 mM putrescine, spermidine or spermine were added to the medium. Prevention of embryogenesis by DFMA is accompanied by an inhibition of arginine decarboxylase activity and a reduction in polyamine levels (Robie and Minocha, 1989). DMFO was more effective than DMFA at inhibiting direct embryogenesis on *Solanum melongena* cotyledons; the addition of putrescine restored the incidence of embryo formation to that of the controls (Fobert and Webb, 1988). Altman *et al.* (1990) have observed that MGBG inhibited the growth of embryogenic clumps in suspension cultures of celery. DCHA and CHAP also have some inhibitory effect on carrot embryogenesis (Fienberg *et al.*, 1984; Khan and Minocha, 1991).

Hypocotyl callus of *Sideratis* initiated with NAA, failed to produce somatic embryos when transferred to a medium without regulants, but embryogenesis did occur if the initial medium contained 27 μM NAA and 0.01 mM spermidine (Sáanchez-Graz and Segura, 1988a). This compound also promoted plantlet formation from embryogenic clumps of celery (Altman *et al.*, 1990).

Inhibition, or lack of involvement. Bradley et al. (1984; 1985) found that putrescine and arginine inhibited somatic embryo growth in wild carrot, and could be used experimentally to synchronise embryo development. On a medium containing 40 mg/l arginine, cell suspensions or callus cultures of *D. carota* produced somatic embryos asynchronously approximately 3 weeks after the auxin is withdrawn. But if 0.03 μM putrescine had been added to the induction medium, globular embryos were formed on the second medium (lacking the amine), but failed to develop further. Rapid and synchronous embryo growth of approximately half of these embryos occurred when they were moved to a medium without arginine.

No positive effect of added polyamines on either callus induction, or somatic embryogenesis, was observed from cultured nucelli of mangos (Litz, 1987); or with cotyledon explants of *Solanum melongena* (Fobert and Webb, 1988), although in the latter case DMFO (and to a lesser extent DMFA) caused there to be a reduction in embryogenesis and an increase in adventitious root formation.

PHOSPHATIDYL-INOSITOL CYCLE

The possible existence of the phosphatidylinositol cycle in plants, leading to the formation of *myo*-inositol 1,4,5-triphosphate as a secondary messenger, has been discussed in Chapter 9. Growth of most plant cultures is improved by the addition of inositol to the medium although there are few reports of it having a regulatory role in morphogenesis.

At least in some plants, the majority of exogenous *myo*-inositol is incorporated into phosphatidylinositol, which may be an important factor in the functioning of membranes (Jung *et al.*, 1972; Harran and Dickinson, 1978). The phosphatidylinositol cycle controls various cellular responses in animals and yeasts, but evidence of it playing a similar role in plants is only just being accumulated. Enzymes which are thought to be involved in the cycle have been observed to have activities in plants, and lithium chloride (which inhibits *myo*-inositol-1-phosphatase and decreases the cycle) inhibits callus formation in *Brassica oleracea* (Bagga *et al.*, 1987) and callus growth in *Amaranthus paniculatus* (Das *et al.*, 1987). In both plants the inhibition is reversed by *myo*-inositol.

It is now thought that the phosphatidyl-inositol cycle does exist in plants (Kodama and Komamine, 1988), and that *myo*-inositol- 1,4,5- triphosphate might be a second messenger in plant cells (as it is in animals). This would mean that in binding to a plasma receptor, auxin causes the formation of diacylglycerol and inositol-1,4,5-triphosphate within the cell (Felle, 1988). Auxin applied to *Catharanthus roseus* cells arrested in the *G1* phase, causes there to be an increase in the amount of intracellular inositol-1,4,5-triphosphate and inositol biphosphate within cells (Ettlinger and Lehle, 1988). It is then inositol-1,4,5-triphosphate, acting as a second messenger, which stimulates a release of free Ca^{2+} through which enzymic reactions are initiated. These processes lead to such physiological responses as protein phosphorylation, ion transport and cell division (Rincón *et al.*, 1989).

OLIGOSACCHARIDES

Oligosaccharides are complex sugars composed of two or more different monosaccharides. It has been suggested that these compounds naturally regulate cellular processes when they are released from cell walls by hydrolytic enzymes which are activated by changes in pH, or by the presence of growth regulators such as auxins and cytokinins (Mohen *et al.*, 1985; Mutaftschiev *et al.*, 1987; Tran Thanh Van and Mutaftschiev, 1990). The degree of oligosaccharide polymerisation is critical for determining the biological activity of experimental samples prepared from plant cell walls using an endopolygalacturonase enzyme, or hydrolysis with a base (Tran Thanh Van and Mutaftschiev, 1990).

Synthesis of the enzymes (such as β-1,3-glucanase) which are responsible for the release of oligosaccharides, can be both induced and inhibited by auxin (York *et al.*, 1984; Mutaftshiev *et al.*, 1987), and mixtures of an auxin and a cytokinin (Mohen *et al.*, 1985). Other growth substances may also be involved (Albersheim *et al.*, 1988).

Oligosaccharides have been shown to be capable of inducing cell enlargement and cell division in a similar fashion to IAA (York *et al.*, 1984; Mutaftshiev *et al.*, 1987), and to be capable of regulating morphogenesis (Tran Thanh Van *et al.*, 1985; Mutaftshiev *et al.*, 1987). Cell elongation caused by auxin can be either added to, or inhibited by oligosaccharides. Because it is difficult to explain apical dominance satisfactorily by the translocation of IAA), Martin (1987) suggested that inhibition of lateral bud growth might be due to auxin at the apex inducing the action of β-1,3-glucanase. Oligosaccharides which are consequently released from the walls of apical cells might then be transported to lateral buds, inhibiting their growth.

(80)   Stigmasterol

Vitamins D$_2$ (R = a)   and   D$_3$ (R = b)

(81)   (82)

The effects of exogenous oligosaccahrides are dose and pH dependent, and can depend on the time at which they are introduced to the culture and the relative concentrations of auxin and cytokinin present in the medium (Mutaftschiev *et al.*, 1987; Tran Thanh Van and Mutaftschiev, 1990). Their mode of action is not determined, but they are thought to modulate the transcription of specfic genes (Guern, 1987).

STEROLS

The sterols stigmasterol (**80**) and vitamins D$_2$ (**81**) and D$_3$ (**82**) (which are required in mammals for proper bone structure), have been found to promote adventitious root formation in plants (Pythoud *et al.*, 1986; Talmon *et al.*, 1989). In shoot cultures of some cherry and apple cultivars, 1–10 ml/l of a water soluble formulation of vitamin D$_2$ enhanced the rate of propagation in early subcultures. After many subcultures with 10 ml/l, leaves became yellow (Druart, 1988).

Rooting can be induced by relatively low concentrations of Vitamin D$_3$ (*e.g.* 0.1 mg/l) but yet there is no damage to the plant from relatively high concentrations. Green cuttings of *Populus tremula* rooted best after being pre-dipped for 24 h at room temperature into a 0.25 mM (95.7

mg/l) solution which also contained 50 μM (10.2 mg/l) IBA (Pythoud *et al.*, 1986). The effect of Vitamins D$_2$ and D$_3$ on stimulating root formation has been found to be additive or synergistic with that of auxins such as NAA (Moncousin and Gaspar, 1983), or IBA (Buchala and Schmid, 1979; Pythoud *et al.*, 1986); the number of roots formed depending on the age of the cuttings, the concentration of the compounds and the timing of the treatment. The rooting of cuttings produced by micropropagation has been said to be improved by adding a small amount of one of the D vitamins (*e.g.* 0.1–1 mg/l to an auxin preparation (Pittet and Moncousin, 1982).

In a review of the effect of the D vitamins, Buchala and Pythoud (1988) discuss whether the sterols modulate auxin action, alter the sensitivity of cells to auxin, or influence auxin transport, or auxin oxidation. Some evidence in favour of the latter hypothesis is that provitamin D$_2$ (ergosterol) and vitamins D$_2$, and D$_3$ have been found to reduce calcium-mediated peroxidase secretion (Kevers *et al.*, 1983a). The D vitamins have been shown to induce the *de novo* synthesis of calmodulin in roots of *Phaseolus vulgaris* so that peroxidase secretion may be under the control of the Ca^{2+}– calmodulin messenger system (Vega and Boland, 1986). The natural production of the D vitamins in plants may depend on exposure to ultra-violet light, as it does in vertebrate animals (Zucker *et al.*, 1980).

UNUSUAL REGULANTS

COMPOUNDS WHICH CAN ARREST APICAL GROWTH

In shoot cultures, it is important to encourage the growth of lateral shoots, but genotypes vary in their natural degree of apical dominance: some produce a few long shoots while others have shorter shoots, but many laterals are formed. Perhaps genotypes with strong apical dominance may have a high natural auxin content, or a more sensitive auxin receptor system? (Newbury, 1986).

Although cytokinins are most frequently added to the medium to promote lateral branching, other techniques, can be used to assist the process. Examples are reducing apical dominance by laying explants on their sides, removing the tips of shoots manually (Bressan et al., 1982) and at each harvest subculturing the basal clump of tissue from which shoots have been removed. Some regulants can also help to remove apical dominance.

Dikegulac

Dikegulac (83) is a compound which, when sprayed over entire plants, is capable of arresting the growth of apical buds. Axillary buds are not inhibited and therefore grow out to produce a bushy plant. Dikegulac has been used

(83)   Dikegulac   MW 274.27

(84)   Methyl laurate   MW 214.35
(Methyl dodecanate)

routinely for this purpose on pot azaleas. Adding 500 or 1000 mg/l sodium dikegulac to the medium in which shoot cultures of sweet cherries were grown, caused an increased number of shoots to be developed from axillary buds (Snir, 1982b).

Methyl laurate and OPE

Methyl esters of fatty acids have been applied routinely to field-grown tobacco to prevent the growth of side shoots. Voyiatzi and Voyiatzis (1988) found that 100 mg/l methyl laurate (MELA) (84) added to MS medium containing 0.3 mg/l IAA and 3 mg/l BAP, increased the number of shoots produced by Rosa hybrida shoot cultures. The effect of the compound was initially similar, to manual tipping, but shoot number continued to be increased during further subcultures of the basal clump even though MELA was not then present. TIBA (3mg/l) had an effect similar to manual tipping, but only during the first passage.

When Jackson et al. (1977a) germinated seeds of Colocasia esculenta on Linsmaier and Skoog (1965) medium containing 5 mM of the surfactant octadecyl–polyethoxyethanol (OPE), they found that growth of the seedlings was restricted, but this was followed by the appearance of 5–10 shoots. Trial of this surfactant on shoot cultures is not reported.

Glyphosate

Glyphosate is a general purpose post-emergence weed-killer which is translocated within both xylem and phloem. Winata and Harvey (1980) reported that sub-lethal doses, added to the medium used to induce callus from axillary buds of alfalfa, produced growth responses similar to those of more common growth regulators. In the presence of 0.17 mg/l glyphosate the cultures produced rather more shoots than normal. If mother plants of some clones of lowbush blueberry had been sprayed with 250 or 500 mg/l glyphosate, single bud explants produced more shoots than usual during in vitro culture (Frett and Smagula, 1981a). Scorza et al. (1982; 1984) similarly found that when stem explants of cranberry were dipped in a 102.5 mg/l glyphosate solution for 30 seconds, or a 321.2 mg/l solution for 5 seconds, the development of both axillary and adventitious shoots was greater than usual when the explants were cultured afterwards on Anderson (1975) rhododendron medium containing 2-iP. Lower or higher levels of glyphosate were respectively ineffective, or toxic.

ACTIVATED CHARCOAL

Finely-divided activated charcoal is often added advantageously to media at different stages of tissue cultures. Activated charcoal is not a growth regulator, but a discussion of its properties is conveniently included in this chapter on account of its ability to modify medium composition, and thereby, in some circumstances, improve or regulate plant growth *in vitro*. The properties of activated charcoal vary according to the method by which it has been prepared, and not all brands are equivalent. A clear difference in the effectiveness of charcoal of different origins in promoting androgenesis was reported by Heberle-Bors (1980). As many of the beneficial effects of charcoal depend on its ability to absorb a wide range of compounds, results from even the most effective brands are liable to be unpredictable; inhibition of growth and morphogenesis are frequently observed.

Four kinds of advantageous uses of charcoal have been reported, depending on the type of culture:

1. to absorb compounds secreted from cultured tissues or present in agar that would otherwise inhibit growth;

2. to prevent unwanted callus growth;

3. to promote morphogenesis, particularly embryogenesis;

4. to promote root formation (where some of the beneficial effect seems to be due to its ability to exclude light from the medium).

The use of charcoal for these purposes is described in Chapters 12 and 14.

MODE OF ACTION OF CHARCOAL

Activated charcoal (AC) is prepared by the controlled carbonisation of wood in steam or air: it possesses strong absorptive properties and is used in chemistry to absorb both gases and dissolved solids. Activated charcoal added to tissue culture media, was commonly thought to remove only growth inhibitory substances, exuded by tissues, or present in the ingredients of the medium; but it is now clear that promotory substances can also be absorbed and made unavailable.

Weatherhead *et al.* (1979) pointed out that AC has the potential to absorb some inorganic ions. A sample of fresh unused AC analysed for these authors contained many inorganic impurities, of which iron, aluminium, nickel and magnesium might have had physiological significance, but there was no evidence that these metals were donated to culture media.

Absorption of growth inhibitors

Charcoal can assist in absorbing toxic substances which may be present in media ingredients, produced as a result of autoclaving, or exuded by cultured tissues, particularly when they are first transferred to media (see Chapter 13). Fridborg *et al.* (1978) showed that AC could adsorb some phenols commonly produced by wounded tissues, and this was later confirmed by Weatherhead *et al.* (1979). Extracts of the charcoal that had been incubated in **Bourgin and Nitsch (1969)** agar medium, showed that it had adsorbed 5-hydroxymethyl-furfural (HMF). This compound was thought to have originated from autoclaving sucrose in the medium under mildly acid conditions. Furthermore, HMF was shown to be somewhat inhibitory to embryogenesis in tobacco anther culture, unless activated charcoal was present (Weatherhead *et al.*, 1978).

Charcoal is sometimes used in bacteriological media to remove inhibitory fatty acids present in agar. That some agars can contain substances capable of hindering plant growth and morphogenesis was shown by Kohlenbach and Wernicke (1978). Somatic embryo formation from tobacco anthers on an agar medium was improved when agar was prewashed with water dialysed against activated charcoal. Better results were obtained by using highly purified Difco Noble agar rather than Difco Bacto agar. Tyagi *et al.* (1980) also reported that effective concentrations of charcoal for promoting embryogenesis from *Datura* pollen, varied according to the type of agar employed. The atypical growth of *Pinus radiata* shoots on some brands of agar could be prevented if AC was added (Nairn, 1988).

Adsorption of organic compounds

Growth regulators. Fridborg and Eriksson (1975b) suggested that activated charcoal removed growth regulators, particularly auxin, from the medium and evidence has indeed accumulated to show that this does occur. A protective coating of charcoal is able to protect seeds from herbicides in soil mixtures (Taylor and Warholic (1987). In tissue culture media 0.10% (w/w) AC can effectively absorb 10 μM IAA (1.75 mg/l) and 10 μM IBA (2.03 mg/l) from liquid **MS** medium to the extent that these compounds can no longer be detected by high performance liquid chromatography (limit 0.05 mg/l) (Nissen and Sutter, 1988; 1990).

Examples of growth regulators in culture media which have been rendered ineffective by AC, are shown in Table 56. Note that cytokinins and abscisic acid, as well as auxins, can be made unavailable. Jona and Vigliocco

Table 56. Examples of growth regulators absorbed by activated charcoal.

Growth regulator	AC % w/v	Reference
1 mg/l NAA	1	Fridborg & Eriksson (1975b)
0.01–10 mg/l NAA & IAA	1	Constantin et al. (1976, 1977)
5 mg/l BAP	0.3	Maene and Debergh (1985)
10 mg/l BAP	0.5	Takayama & Misawa (1980)
2,4-D and 0.03 mg/l IAA + 1 mg/l kinetin	0.5	Scholl et al. (1981)
0.002–2 mg/l BAP & 2-iP + up to 300 mg/l NAA	0.3	Weatherhead et al. (1978)
1 mg/l NAA + 10 mg/l BAP	0.5	Steinitz & Yahel (1982)
ABA in cultured anthers	1 & 10	Johansson et al. (1982)
2.64 mg/l ABA	1	Johansson (1983)

(1985) added charcoal (together with GA$_3$) to the medium on which *Prunus persica* shoots were to be elongated, finding that it overcame the negative effect of the high rate of cytokinin previously used in a shoot proliferation medium.

Activated charcoal can make comparatively high concentrations of growth regulators inaccessible to tissue cultures. Nissen and Sutter (1990) recommend that 10–100 times more auxin should be added to a medium if high concentrations of activated charcoal are also introduced. In cultures of palms, where up to 3% AC is added to prevent blackening, it is necessary to add 0.15–0.5 mM 2,4-D to induce embryogenesis (*i.e.* 5–20 times what would normally be required) (Tisserat, 1979; 1984a). To initiate embryogenic callus of oil palm (*Elaeis*), Paranjothy and Rohani (1982) had to use 10 times the level of auxin that would otherwise have been effective, and Nwankwo and Krikorian (1983), using 0.5 g/l AC, increased the concentration of NAA or 2,4-D from 5–10 mg/l to 10–70 mg/l. Activated charcoal is capable of

trapping gases, and so may inactivate ethylene, or other gases, released from cultured tissues (Ernst, 1974; Johansson *et al.*, 1982).

Organic nutrients. AC may not only remove growth regulators from the medium, but also some organic nutrients. Wetherhead *et al.* (1979) found that tobacco anther cultures were deprived of thiamine-HCl and nicotinic acid when 0.3% AC was added to **Bourgin and Nitsch (1967) H** medium. Biotin, folic acid and pyridoxine are also likely to be absorbed, but not *myo*-inositol

Excluding light from the medium

If sufficient AC is added to the medium it can exclude light sufficiently to promote physiological reactions which occur in the dark. The absorptive properties of the substance are incidental, for lamp-black carbon, or graphite, can be used equally effectively.

Altering the pH of the medium

Several authors (Langowska, 1980; Rahbar and Chopra, 1982; Smith and Krikorian, 1990a) have noticed that the presence of activated charcoal causes the pH of culture media to be higher than they would otherwise have been. Owen *et al.* (1991) found that an increase of *ca.* 0.75 units occurred in the pH of **MS** medium in the presence of 0.5% charcoal; the pH change occurred partly during autoclaving, and partly in the the subsequent first 14 days of medium storage. A similar increase in pH occurred with both hydrochloric acid washed, and neutralised activated charcoal (Sigma Chemical Co.), but the final pH of the medium containing the former was *ca.* 6.2; that containing the netralised charcoal was *ca.* 6.7. It has been suggested that increase in pH could be due to the capacity of AC to absorb cations (Langowska, 1980).

As pH can influence culture growth and morphogenesis, it is probable that at least some of the effects of activated charcoal on plant cultures can be attributed to the changes it induces in the pH of the medium.

UNIDENTIFIED GROWTH FACTORS

THE WOUND RESPONSE

Inhibitory effects

Wounding (and a variety of other stresses) temporarily disturbs the ability of adjacent plant cells to regulate the e

xchange of hydrogen and potassium ions across the plasma membrane. Potassium ions are initially lost from injured tissues, increasing (*i.e.* making less negative) the osmotic potential of cells. There is also a rapid and extensive breakdown of the lipids in cell membranes through the action of lipid hydrolase and oxygenase enzymes. These enzymes lead to the generation of damaging free radicals, which according to Thompson *et al.* (1987) can include the following:

$O_2^{-\bullet}$ (the superoxide anion)

$HO_2^{\bullet}$ (the perhydroxy radical)

$OH^{\bullet}$ (the hydroxy radical)

$RO^{\bullet}$ (the alkoxy radical)

$ROO^{\bullet}$ (the peroxy radical)

$ROOH^{\bullet}$ (organic hydroperoxide)

$\left({}^1O_2\right)$ (singlet oxygen)

$\left(RO^*\right)$ (excited carbanyl group)

However, plants also have devices to protect them from some of the injury which might otherwise result. Wounding results in an increase in the activity of peroxidase and catalase enzymes (Salin and Bridges, 1981; Thompson *et al.*, 1987), which act to overcome the effect of oxidizing radicals, and has also been found to induce the production of a translocatable proteinase inhibitor (Makus *et al.*, 1981). Peroxidases are iron-containing proteins. Wounding frequently leads to the oxidation of phenolic compounds.

Superoxide radicals and hydrogen peroxide are produced during protoplast isolation (Ishii, 1987) from cells which have been treated with xylanase or pectin lyase to remove the cell wall. The damage caused by these oxidants can be overcome, and protoplast viabilty and plating efficiency improved, by adding a mixture of superoxide dismutase and catalase enzymes (Ishii, 1988), or 0.25 mM *n*-propyl gallate anti-oxidant (Saleem and Cutler, 1987), to the protoplast isolation medium. Adding glutathione, peroxidase or phospholipase A_2 enzymes to the medium for the culture of rice protoplasts, or *n*-propyl gallate to that used for *Zea* protoplasts, increased the number of cell colonies formed (Ishii, 1988; Saleem and Cutler, 1987). Activated oxygen is thought to initiate lipid peroxidation in plasma membranes, and the protectant chemicals seem to stabilise them by inhibiting lipoxygenase.

Creemers-Molenaar and Van Oort (1990) tried adding anti-oxidants or enzymes to isolated *Lolium* protoplasts to improve plating efficiency. The most effective treatment was a mixture of the anti-oxidant, reduced glutathione, plus glutathione peroxidase enzyme, and phospholipase A2 enzyme. A mixture of superoxide dismutase and catalase, found by Ishii (1988) to improve the plating of rice protoplasts, was also effective. The addition of 0.1 mM *n*-propyl gallate in the media used for the plasmolysis, isolation, purification, and/or initial cul-

ture of maize (Saleem and Cutler, 1987) and sugar beet (Krens *et al.*, 1990) leaf proptoplasts caused the retention of high viability and improved plating. The antioxidant was not required once the protoplasts had been cultured for 12–14 days.

Wounding also stimulates ethylene biosynthesis, and as the conversion of ACC to ethylene is dependent on superoxide, it follows that the antioxidant treatments described above are equally effective in inhibiting the conversion of ACC to ethylene (page 455). Polyamines, which are also able to quench free radicals, similarly inhibit ethylene formation (see page 464).

Wounding is followed by a rapid reduction in cell growth rate, and polarity is temporarily lost (Hanson and Trewavas, 1982). These functions are slowly restored when wounded tissues are washed or incubated.

Promotive effects

Stimulating unorganised growth

Although the substances produced by wounding are usually inhibitory, cases are recorded where growth promotion results (Chapter 13). It is generally agreed that the act of cutting or injuring plant cells eventually produces a stimulus to cell division which, on intact plants or plant organs, can result in the formation of callus tissue (*e.g.* at the base of cuttings) or a wound cambium (*e.g.* in a cut potato tuber). The effect of the wound reaction is also observed when pieces of plant tissue are established in culture media; cell division leading to initial callus formation is favoured if the explant has a high ratio of cut surface to volume. It is often found to be beneficial to wound an explant deliberately before placing it on a nutrient medium (*e.g.* Stewart and Button, 1976; Bornman and Janson, 1980; Mariotti and Arcioni, 1983).

Morphogenesis

Stem explants. Wounding the base of shoots sometimes promotes *in vitro* rooting (Chapter 14). Adventitious shoot formation is also frequently enhanced by deliberately wounding the initial explant. Stem segments of *Torenia fournieri* cultured with BAP cytokinin, mainly produce adventitious buds 0.5 cm from the cut ends, and a few in the middle. If the explants are wounded before culture by small transverse cuts, there is a significant increase in the number of buds produced within 0.5 cm of the site of injury. Longitudinal cuts causes buds to be produced over the entire surface of the explant. Wounding did not increase the uptake of BAP (Norizaku *et al.*, 1985).

Leaves and leaf pieces. Cutting or wounding the surface of leaf explants frequently increases the number of adventitious shoots produced. For this purpose, cuts are usually made across the lamina of the leaves of plants such as *Begonia*, *Saintpaulia* and *Streptocarpus*, or the lamina is cut into smaller pieces. Slashing across the lamina and vasculature of *Liquidamba styracifolia* leaves, significantly increased the number of directly formed adventitious shoots (Brand and Lineberger, 1988). Bud and shoot regeneration from *Vaccinium corymbosum* leaf explants was significantly increased if the leaves were wounded (Callow *et al.*, 1988).

Park and Son (1988a) studied the effect of wounding the leaves of *Populus nigra* × *P. maximowiczii* by pricking them with a pin. Morphogenesis was largely confined to the wounded parts of the explants. On non-punctured leaves this meant that root and shoot formation occurred only on the cut surfaces of leaves and on leaf petioles, but in punctured leaves, morphogenesis occurred around the margin of the perforations. The largest number of adventitious shoots occurred when the abaxial surface was punctured in 5 locations, and the leaves placed with the abaxial surface in contact with the medium.

The growth of axillary buds

Axillary buds (areoles) of the cactus *Opuntia* did not grow *in vitro* and were insensitive to BAP or NAA, but sensitivity was restored and morphogenesis induced, if the explants were wounded when placed on the medium (Mauseth and Halperin, 1975). Splitting the shoot tip explants of some species into two longitudinal halves sometimes increases the total number of shoots which can be obtained from the original explants. This effect was observed in *Yucca glauca*, but not in *Y. elephantipes* (Bentz *et al.*, 1988).

Homogenisation

Zatyko *et al.* (1982) noticed that the formation of globular embryos was enhanced in homogenised callus tissues. A very similar observation was made by Orshinsky *et al.* (1983). If callus of various birdsfoot trefoil genotypes was homogenised and then plated onto a sterile filter paper on the surface of a semisolid medium, the time required for plant regeneration and the number of plants recovered per gram of callus, were consistently increased by comparison with non-homogenised tissue. Orshinsky *et al.* suggested several possible explanations of these results:

- that the macerated cells had better contact with the culture medium;

- that cellular exudates were stimulatory;

- that meristematic regions of the callus were advantageously isolated; or,

- that the observations were due to an unknown wound response.

Causative factors

Pieces of excised plant tissue have been found to have an increased sensitivity to auxin (Hanson and Trewavas, 1982). Is the stimulus caused by wounding simply therefore due to the enhanced response of tissues to growth regulators, or is a wound factor involved? The existence of a 'wound hormone' was first suspected by Haberlandt in 1921. He observed that cell division at the cut surfaces of swede roots and potato tubers was reduced the more the surfaces were washed, while macerated cells placed on the cut surface strongly promoted division. Haberlandt suggested that a wound hormone interacted with another growth regulator present within the potato tissue. Some alternative explanations for the cause of the wound response are discussed below.

Ethylene as a causative agent

Damage to plant tissues results in a short–lived increase in the production of ethylene gas from the wounded cells (Williamson, 1950). Temporary exposure of intact plants to ethylene can cause, amongst many other effects, a stimulation of cell division resulting in gall-like growths within plant tissues (Evanari, 1961). Wallace (1928) thought that such outgrowths resulted from the dissolution of cell walls already showing secondary thickening, followed by cell enlargement and cell multiplication. There is thus reason to suppose that when pieces of plant tissue are transferred to culture media, stimulation of callus growth associated with a wound response, could be induced by localised ethylene liberation.

The loss of polarity in plant tissues which is brought about by wounding (page 471) is thought to be caused by ethylene (page 432). Wounding, treatment with TIBA or NAA, and increased incubation temperature (25°C better than 15° or 20°), all promoted the formation of adventitious buds (and decreased the polarity of regeneration) on *Lilium speciosum* bulb scales. Van Aartrijk *et al.* (1985) conjectured that the common mechanism linking the action of all four factors was their ability to promote ethylene biosynthesis.

Movement of endogenous growth substances

It has been suggested that wounding might cause endogenous growth substances to move preferentially to the damaged sites on an explant (Park and Son, 1988a).

According to this hypothesis, when morphogenesis is caused by an appropriate balance between endogenous hormones and growth regulators supplied exogenously in the medium, wounding would cause tissues to have more suitable levels of growth substances.

Volatile respiration inhibitor

Laties (1962) showed that the respiration of the cells of potato slices decreased down to a constant value, the further they were from the surface. He attributed this phenomenon to acetaldehyde which he thought acted as a volatile inhibitor of cell metabolism and cell division. Laties supposed that the wounding of plant tissues would result in the release of acetaldehyde, thus allowing the surface cells to become capable of increased metabolic activity, and enabled to grow and divide.

Other wound factors

It has been suggested that a 'wound hormone' which gives an initial stimulus to cell division results from the autolysis of damaged cells. There have been several attempts to identify such a compound, but its nature or existence has not been satisfactorily determined. English *et al.* (1939) isolated and identified 1,decene-1,10-dicarboxylic acid (85) as a wound factor which they named traumatic acid. They showed that the compound would promote callus formation on the surfaces of potato and bean pods. Traumatic acid is a product of lipid peroxidation (Thompson *et al*, 1987).

$$OHCO\,CH = CH\,(CH_2)_8\,COOH$$

(85)   Traumatic acid   MW 228.29

Margara (1977a) obtained a considerably increased response of cauliflower curd tissue to IBA and IPA (3-indolepropionic acid) auxins when traumatic acid was also added to the medium. If a wound factor exists, its regulatory effect is most likely to be associated with the modification of auxin levels or auxin activity. The level of naturally-occurring gibberellins (noted to decrease the activity of oxidase enzymes in plant cells — McCune and Galston, 1959) has been reported to increase in wounded tissues (Rappaport and Sachs, 1967).

Alternatively the wound response could be due to auxin inhibitors. Stonier and Yoneda (1967) detected only a low concentration of compounds with such activity in mature tissues but found that they reappeared upon wounding and were then present at a similar level to that found in juvenile tissues. Phenols which act as IAA oxidase inhibitors (see under AUXINS) are commonly present in wounded tissues but are liable to be oxidised to inhibitory quinones.

HABITUATION

As mentioned in Chapter 9, the capacity of cells to change from a state of being dependent on the exogenous supply of a particular substance, to one in which they are wholly- or partly-sufficient, has been termed *habituation*: cells or tissues are said to be *habituated* to substance *X* or substance *Y*. The habituated condition of cultured cells or tissues is usually self-perpetuating from one vegetative generation to another, but can be reversed. Clearly habituation can only occur to organic molecules which can be synthesized by cells, and not to basic nutrients.

Although habituation usually describes a change in the requirement of cultured tissues, from needing an exogenous supply of a substance, to becoming self-sufficient, the definition could be extended to include all cells or tissues capable of self–sufficiency, whether or not the trait was developed in culture. Tissues habituated towards the production of a particular substance or type of substance are *autotrophic* for that compound, while non-habituated tissues are *heterotrophic*.

It has been found that *in vitro* habituation does not necessarily result in complete independence from exogenous growth factors. Meins (1974) showed that cells were capable of shifting into a variety of stable states of cytokinin-habituation and could also undergo changes into states of greater or lesser habituation. Habituated tissues are often differentiated. Highly embryogenic callus (*e.g.* of *Citrus* — Button *et al.*, 1974; Spiegel-Roy and Kochba, 1980) and shoot-forming calluses (*e.g.* of sugar beet — de Greef and Jacobs, 1979; Van Geyt and Jacobs, 1985) have been capable of growth and morphogenesis without the addition of exogenous growth regulants.

Habituation to growth regulators occurs commonly in plant tissue cultures, but plant cells may also become habituated to other organic compounds normally added to culture media to support cell growth. For example, Ikeda *et al.* (1979) record the habituation of soybean cells to thiamine and its precursors, and Savage *et al.* (1979) the recovery of a pantothenate autotroph from a cell line

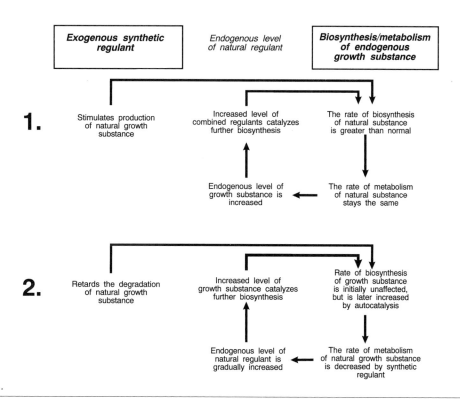

Fig. 117. Two possible explanations for growth regulator habituation in plant cultures.

of *Datura innoxia* which previously required this vitamin for growth.

GROWTH FACTOR DEPENDENCE

Auxin- or *cytokinin-habituations* are found relatively frequently in tissue cultures and are generally very stable. Cells in this condition can remain independent of an exogenous growth factor supply for many generations, although typically the condition is eliminated when plants are regenerated.

Kerbauy *et al.* (1986) found that cytokinin-autotrophic callus could be isolated from tissue explanted directly onto media without cytokinin, and Jackson and Lyndon (1988) have showed that explants removed from the meristematic regions of tobacco are most likely to form cytokinin-autotrophic callus. Thus callus derived from from internode pith of juvenile plants was autotrophic, but that derived from similar regions of a mature plant was not. Pith removed from a few internodes below that which was habituated, gave rise to callus which could become cytokinin-habituated when cultured at 35°C. Cheng (1972) obtained *auxin* autotrophic callus from pith

isolated near the apex of *Nicotiana glauca* × *N. langsdorfii* hybrids, but auxin- requiring (heterotrophic) callus from pith taken from below the 7th node.

Induction of habituation

Meins (1974) showed that a cytokinin-habituated state can be induced in tobacco tissue by incubating explants at 35°C without cytokinin. In subsequent incubation at 25°C, no cytokinin was required for callus initiation or growth, unlike tissue incubated throughout at this temperature. However, cells habituated at 35°C required exogenous cytokinin once again if incubated at 16°C (Binns and Meins, 1979). Presumably endogenous synthesis of cytokinin had decreased at the lower temperature (or there was an accelerated rate of degradation). A reversal of cytokinin habituation by culturing tissue at 16°C, instead of the usual 26°C, was reported by Syono and Furuya (1971); a reversal of habituation is also commonly brought about by the regeneration of complete plants from cell clones autotrophic for cytokinin and/or auxin. Explants from the regenerated plants are unable to grow in culture without addition of the growth factor which was produced endogenously by cells in the original habituated state.

The causes of habituation

Meins (1974) and Meins and Lutz (1980) argued that reversible habituation results from an altered expression of the genes already present in the cell (their repression or derepression) and is epigenetic by nature, because the changes observed:

— are directed rather than random;

— are restricted by the genetic capacity of the cell;

— are potentially reversible;

— involve a large number of cell conversions per generation, and

— do not alter the totipotency of the altered cell.

Meins and Binns (1978) and Meins (1987) have proposed that cell division factors can induce the biosynthesis of naturally-occurring substances of the same kind, through a positive feedback mechanism (Fig. 117). It is not clear whether the rate of biosynthesis is accelerated, or the rate of metabolism increased, and so one could predict either of the two scenarios shown in the figure.

• If according to the first case, kinetin were to cause the natural production of zeatin to be increased, and if this natural cytokinin were not metabolised sufficiently rapidly, the increase in overall cytokinin concentration would cause the level of zeatin biosynthesis to increase even further. Withdrawal of the kinetin trigger to zeatin production, would then leave the tissue in a cytokinin-autonomous state.

• The second hypothesis presumes that biosynthesis of zeatin and/or other natural cytokinins is normally balanced by the metabolism of growth substance which is not required for immediate use. This condition would be disturbed by the presence of an inhibitor of cytokinin metabolism which decreased the rate of biodegradation causing an increase in the level of free natural cytokinin. An elevated level of free growth substance must then be supposed to lead to an autocatalytic increase in biosynthesis.

Case 1 in Fig. 117 is supported by the discovery that kinetin *can* induce the increased accumulation of zeatin riboside in callus tissue (Hansen, reported in Meins, 1987). A similar condition is occasionally noted in shoot cultures of some species, where high endogenous levels of cytokinins are found after several subcultures (Boulay and Francelet, 1986; McCulloch, 1988). That case 2 can also occur, is shown by the findings that thidiazuron can inhibit the cytokinin oxidase enzyme (see page 438), and can induce cytokinin autonomous growth, for example in some *Phaseolus lunatus* genotypes (Mok *et al.*, 1982b).

Genetic control. Although habituation of cultured tissues is usually reversible, it is now known that heterotrophic cells can also become permanently autotrophic as a result of somatic mutation in the genes governing the production of endogenous growth factors. Evidence that this might be the case was discovered by several workers; callus capable of growing on media without the addition of growth substances was, for example, obtained by exposing cultures to gamma radiation (Pandy and Sabharwal, 1979); the ability of some genotypes of *Phaseolus lunatus* to grow *in vitro* without the presence of cytokinin appeared to be under genetic control (Mok and Mok, 1979).

Callus re-initiated from plants derived from habituated sugar beet callus, was again found to be habituated (Coumans *et al.*, 1982), as were plants regenerated from auxin-habituated callus of *Nicotiana bigelovii* var. *quadrivalvis* (Bennici, 1983).

Examples of stable and sexually transmissible 'habituations' are provided by Meins *et al.* (1983) and Meins and Foster (1986).

THE TIMING AND DURATION OF TREATMENTS

GROWTH REGULATOR EXPOSURE

It is common practice to vary the growth regulators to which tissues are exposed *in vitro*; for instance, callus is often initiated on a medium with one set of growth regulators and then moved to a second medium with different regulants for the induction of morphogenesis. Both the nature and the duration of the first and second treatments can be important and, because it is inconvenient to move explants frequently between one medium and another, recommended protocols are often a compromise between the most effective timings and durations of growth regulator exposure, and what is practical. Experimentation is complicated by the difficulty of determining growth regulator carry over from one stage to another (for example, exogenously-applied auxins can become conjugated to other molecules from which they may be released when auxin is withdrawn from the me-

Induction medium	Regeneration medium	Time in induction medium (days) before transfer					
		1	5	8	12	18	Not moved
1 mg/l 2,4-D	0.1 mg/l NAA + 2 mg/l BAP	Callus	Callus	Callus	Callus		Callus
0.04 mg/l 2,4-D	0.1 mg/l NAA + 2 mg/l BAP		Adv. shoots		Adv. shoots	Adv. roots	Adv. roots
0.5 mg/l 2,4-D + 1 mg/l BAP	0.1 mg/l NAA + 2 mg/l zeatin	Adv. shoots	Adv. shoots			Adv. shoots	Callus

Fig. 118. The effect of the growth regulators used for callus induction and the duration of this treatment on subsequent morphogenesis. [From data of Behki and Lesley, 1980 - see text.]

dium), and the difficulty in determining the level of endogenous growth substances, (particularly cytokinins) which may be complementing, or antagonising exogenous treatments (Phillips, 1987).

The effect of the nature of the growth regulators in an induction medium, and the combined effects of concentration and timing, are well illustrated by some of the results of Behki and Lesley (1980). Tomato leaf disc explants were cultured for varying lengths of time with growth regulators which induced callus formation. Small pieces of the callus (or the explant itself when transfer was effected after 1 day) were then moved to a medium containing other regulants known to be capable of inducing shoot formation. The results are illustrated in Fig. 118. Whether there was continued callus growth, or the formation of adventitious shoots or roots, depended on the nature of the the induction medium and the time at which transfer took place. Auxin is necessary early in the culture period to induce cell proliferation (Phillips, 1987).

Pulse treatments

When cultured material is exposed to a substance for only a short period of time, it is frequently said to have been given a *pulse* of that substance or regulant. Sometimes a pulse of a growth regulator at a relatively high rate can be as effective as a lower concentration which is present continuously (Thomas and Tranvan, 1982). Cotyledonary node explants of *Calocedrus decurrens*, for example, produced axillary shoots if exposed to 7–10 µM BAP in the proliferation medium, or to 125 µM BAP for 3 hours

(after which they were moved to a regulant-free medium) (Jelaska, 1987). Adventitious buds of *Picea alba* developed faster after a pulse of 250 µM BAP for 2 h than if placed continually on a medium containing 5 µM BAP (Von Arnold and Eriksson, 1985).

By supplying pulses of a growth regulator for progressively longer periods, it is possible to monitor the gaining of competence and the onset of determination in tissues. These processes can be further studied by the experimental application of metabolic inhibitors at specific times. Explants require to be exposed to a growth regulator for a minimum length of time for a given morphogenic event to be initiated.

Hussey (1977a) showed that morphogenesis in *Freesia* could be determined by the duration of exposure to growth regulators. When explants of soft stem tissue were placed for 12 hours in a liquid culture medium containing 0.12 mg/l NAA and afterwards transferred to another medium without NAA but containing 0.5–1.0 mg/l BAP, meristems were formed which gave rise directly to shoots. Increasing the duration of the preliminary NAA treatment had the same effect as increasing the concentration of NAA during an initial 12 hour period, and induced the formation of callus having the capacity to form only roots. Continuous exposure of explanted tissue to NAA also caused the formation of callus, but its morphogenic capacity was determined by the concentration of the auxin: 0.015–0.03 mg/l NAA induced shoot-forming callus; continuous exposure to higher concentrations caused callus to be produced which mainly gave rise

Table 57. The result of exposing thin cell layers of *Psophocarpus* to IAA and BAP for progressive lengths of time [data of Hahn et al., 1981].

Days on medium with IAA and BAP	Explants forming buds %	Explants forming callus %
0–5	0	0
7	100	0
10	100	0
15	100	100
25	40	100
45	20	100

to roots. Similarly thin cell layers from internodes of 2 week-old *Psophocarpus tetragonolobus* plants needed more than 5 days incubation with 1 μM IAA and 10 μM BAP to become committed to produce adventitious shoots; but when exposed to the regulants for longer than 10 days, the tissues also produced callus and their capacity to form shoot buds declined (Table 57) (Hahn *et al.*, 1981).

James and Wakerell (1982) found that apple shoots rooted optimally if cultured with 3 mg/l IBA for 4 days or 4.9 mg/l IAA for 6 days. Longer exposures decreased final root number and increased callus growth at the cut ends of the shoots. Margara (1969a) found that the best treatment to induce direct adventitious shoots on *Brassica oleracea* var. *botrytis* inflorescence tissue, was to place the explants on a medium with 0.5 μM IBA for one week, and then transfer them to 10 μM for weeks 2 and 3.

Pinus strobus cotyledons required at least 4 days exposure to 4.4 μM BAP for shoot formation to occur: 5 days exposure resulted in 50% of the explants responding, while after 7 days exposure there was an almost 100% response (Flinn and Webb, 1986). Similarly *P. resinosa* embryos, or their cotyledons, needed to be exposed to 10–25 μM BAP for at least 3 days for the stimulation of adventitious shoot formation (Noh *et al.*, 1988). Incubation for only 30–60 minutes on a medium containing 0.17 mg/l GA_3 was sufficient to partly inhibit shoot formation from dark grown tobacco callus. Repression was greatest when this treatment was applied during 6–10 days of incubation on a shoot- inducing medium. Abscisic acid could partly overcome the inhibitory effect, if instead of being placed in GA_3, the tissue was incubated in a GA_3 + ABA mixture for up to 30 minutes; after 30 minutes ABA

failed to prevent the GA_3 repression (Thorpe and Meier, 1973).

Embryogenesis

The duration of auxin requirement has been most clearly determined for the induction of somatic embryogenesis, where it is now well established that an initial application must be withdrawn to permit embryo development. In carrot, 0.05 μM 2,4-D was required to be present for 6 days to induce competent single cells to form somatic embryos. Beyond this stage auxin was inhibitory (Komamine *et al.*, 1990).

Ghazi *et al.* (1986) found that two types of embryogenic callus were produced from immature embryos and young seedling tissues of *Glycine max*:

— a smooth and shiny callus which originated from the cotyledons;

— a rough callus from immature embryos, cotyledon segments and germinated seedlings.

The rough callus took 8–9 weeks to form in the presence of 2–3 mg/l 2,4-D and 3 weeks to form with 5 mg/l 2,4-D. Smooth callus (which was the only kind from which plants were regenerated), was produced in 2 weeks using 10 mg/l 2,4-D.

Over-exposure to regulants

The results above are concerned with cultured tissues gaining competence and becoming determined towards a developmental pathway. Over-exposure to a regulant through excessive concentration, or prolonged treatment, can result in a different developmental outcome to the one desired. The maximum number of adventitious shoots from *Datura innoxia* internodes, was obtained when they were pre-incubated with 1 μM 2,4-D for 6 days (haploid plants) or 12 days (diploid plants), before transfer to a shoot inducing medium (**MS** with 46.5 μM kinetin). Longer periods of pre–incubation resulted in less shoots being produced: there were none at all after 36 days (Forche *et al.*, 1981). Only two days of incubation with 0.1–10 mg/l 2,4-D was necessary to increase the number of buds regenerated from leaves of *Prunus canescens* (Antonelli and Druart, 1990).

Prolonging the exposure of cells to auxin, beyond the time necessary to induce embryogenesis, can result in the production of unregenerative callus, rather than embryogenic tissue.

Table 58. Formula weights of growth regulators used in plant tissue cultures.

Common name or abbreviation	Mol. Wt.	Alternative name	Common name or abbreviation	Mol. Wt.	Alternative name
ABA	264.32	abscisic acid	IAA-pha		indoleacetyl phenylalanine
ACC	102.11	ethinine	IBA	203.24	3-indolebutyric acid
	110.11	(hemihydrate)	Ioxynil	392.9	(M.W. for ioxynil-sodium)
	137.57	(hydrochloride)	2-iP	203.25	IPA (this name not recommended)
Acetylsalicylic acid	180.15		IPA	189.21	indole-3-propionic acid
Adenine	135.13	adenine (anhydrous)	Kinetin	215.22	6-furfurylaminopurine
	189.13	adenine (trihydrate)	MAP	148.15	6-methylaminopurine
	368.34	adenine sulphate (anhydrous)	MCPA	200.62	2-methyl-4-chlorophenoxyacetic acid
	404.37	adenine sulphate (dihydrate)			
Adenosine	267.25		MCPP	214.73	mecoprop
3-aminopyridine	94.11		Methyl dodecanate	214.35	methyl laurate
Ancymidol	269.33		5-methyltryptophan	218.26	
AVG	160.17	aminoethylvinylglycine	MGBG	257.13	(2HCl. xH2O) see Fig. 118
BAP	225.26	BA (6-benzylaminopurine)	NAA	186.21	
BrUR	190.99	5-bromo-uracil	Naptalam	291.31	NPA
BTOA	193.22	2-benzothiazoleacetic acid	NOA	202.21	2-naphthyloxyacetic acid
Caffeic acid	180.15		2,5-Norbordiene	92.14	
Carvadan	354.92	AMO 1618	Octamine	137.38	
Catechol	110.11	catechol	Paclobutrazol	293.80	
Catechin	287.25	catechin	PBA	309.37	SD 8339
CCC	158.07	chlormequat	PCIB	214.65	p-chlorophenoxyisobutyric acid
Chlorogenic acid	353.31				
p-Coumaric acid	181.19		Phloretic acid	166.18	
p-CPA	164.15		Phloridzin	436.41	anhydrous
4-Chlororesorcinol	194.56			472.44	.2H2O
p-Coumaric acid	164.15		PG	126.11	phloroglucinol (anhydrous)
2 Cl-4PU	247.69			162.14	phloroglucinol (dihydrate)
2,6 Cl-4PU	282.13		Picloram	241.46	
Coumarin	146.15	coumarin	n-Propyl gallate	212.20	
CPA	186.16	p-chlorophenoxyacetic acid	Putrescine	88.15	
CPTA	243.80	2-(4-chlorophenyl-thio) triethylamine	Salicylic acid	138.12	
			Spermine	202.35	
2,4-D	221.04	2,4-dichlorophenoxyacetic acid	Spermidine	145.25	
			Stigmasterol	412.70	
Daminozide	160.17		2,4,5-T	255.49	2,4,5-trichlorophenoxyacetic acid
Dicamba	221.04	3,6-dichloroanisic acid			
Dikegulac	274.27		2,4,5-TP	268.50	2,4,5-trichlorophenoxypropionic acid
Dimethyl-aminopurine	162.17				
			2,4,6-T	255.49	
DCHA	181.32	dicyclohexamine (Fig. 118)	Thidiazuron	220.25	TDZ
DFMA		see Fig. 118	Traumatic acid	228.29	
DFMO		see Fig. 118	Tropic acid	166.18	tropic acid
DMPA	212.20	2,3-dimethoxyphenoxyacetic acid	Tryptophan	204.23	
			Tryptophol	161.20	indole-3-ethanol
Dopamine	153.18		Tryptophol arabinoside	308.31	
Ethephon	144.50				
Ethylene	28.05		Tryptophol glucoside	338.33	
Ferulic acid	194.18				
GA3	346.38	gibberellic acid	Tyramine	137.38	
Glyphosate	169.07		Vitamin D2	396.66	ergocalciferol
Hypoxanthine	136.11	6-oxypurine	Vitamin D3	382.65	
IAA	175.19	3-indoleacetic acid	Vitamin E3	430.72	
IAA-ala	246.27	indoleacetyl alanine	Vitamin E3 acetate	472.76	
IAA-gly	232.24	indoleacetyl glycine	Zeatin	219.25	anhydrous
				220.26	dihydrozeatin

Bibliography

ABE T. & SASAHARA T. 1982 Genetical control of callus formation in rice. pp. 419–420 in Fujiwara (ed.) 1982 (q.v.).

ABO EL-NIL M. 1982 Method for asexual reproduction of coniferous trees. U.S. Patent No. 4353184.

ABO EL-NIL M.M. & HILDEBRANDT A.C. 1971b Geranium plant differentiation from anther callus. Am. J. Bot. 58, 475.

ABO EL-NIL M.M. & HILDEBRANDT A.C. 1976 Cell wall regeneration and colony formation from isolated single geranium protoplasts in microculture. Can. J. Bot. 54, 1530–1534.

ABO EL-NIL M.M. & WOCHOK Z. 1977 In vitro developmental responses of wild and full sib families of Douglas fir. Plant Physiol. 59, (Suppl.6) 2 (Abst. 8).

ABO EL-NIL M.M. & ZETTLER F.W. 1976 Callus initiation and organ differentiation from shoot tip cultures of Colocasia esculenta (Taro). Plant Sci. Lett. 6, 401–408.

ABOU-MANDOUR A. 1977b Pharmaceutical-biological studies of the genus Harpagophytum. 2. Communication: Tissue cultures of Harpagophytum procumbens. Planta Med. 31, 238–244.

ABOU-ZEID A. & NEUMANN K.H. 1973 Preliminary investigations on the influence of cotyledons on the development of cherry embryos (Prunus avium L.). Z. Pflanzenphysiol. 69, 299–305.

ABU SALIH H.S., MURANT A.F. & DAFT M.J. 1968a Comparison of the passive haemagglutination and bentonite flocculation tests for serological work with plant viruses. J. Gen. Virol. 2, 155–166.

ABU SALIH H.S., MURANT A.F. & DAFT M.J. 1968b The use of antibody-sensitized latex particles to detect plant viruses. J. Gen. Virol. 3, 299–302.

ABU-QAOUD H., SKIRVIN R.M. & CHEVREAU E. 1990 In vitro separation of chimeral pears into their component genotypes. Euphytica 48, 189–196.

ADAMS A.N. 1972 An improved medium for strawberry meristem culture. J. Hort. Sci. 47, 263–264.

ADAOHA MBANASO E.N. & ROSCOE D.H. 1982 Alginate: an alternative to agar in plant protoplast culture. Plant Sci. Lett. 25, 61–66.

ADATIA M.H. & BESFORD R.T. 1986 The effect of silicon on cucumber plants grown in recirculating nutrient solution. Ann. Bot. 58, 343–351.

ADHIKARI U.K. & BAJRACHARYA D. 1978 Interaction of gibberellic acid and indole-3-acetic acid on root formation in pea (Pisum sativum L.) epicotyl cuttings. Planta 143, 331–332.

ADKINS S.W., SHIRAISHI T. & McCOMB J.A. 1990 Rice callus physiology — identification of volatile emissions and their effects on culture growth. Physiol. Plant. 78, 526–531.

ADRIAN J. & ASSOUMANI M. 1983 Gums and hydrocolloids in nutrition. pp. 301–333 in Rechcigl M. (ed.) 1983 CRC Handbook of Nutritional Supplements Vol. II. Agricultural Use. CRC Press Inc. Baton Rouge.

AHÉE J., ARTHUIS P., CAS G., DUVAL Y., GUENIN G., HANOWER J., HANOWER P., LIEVOUX D., LIORET C., MALAURIE B., PANNETIER C., RAILLOT D., VARECHON C. & ZUCKERMAN L. 1981 La multiplication végétative in vitro du palmier à huile par embryogenèse somatique. Oleagineux 36, 113–118.

AHLOOWALIA B.S. & MARETZKI A. 1983 Plant regeneration via somatic embryogenesis in sugarcane. Plant Cell Rep. 2, 21–25.

AHLOOWALIA B.S. & SHERINGTON J. 1985 Transmission of somaclonal variation in wheat. Euphytica 34, 525–537.

AHUJA M. R. & MUHS H-J. 1982 Control of growth and differentiation in tissues and protoplast derived callus in different genotypes of Aspen. pp. 177–178 in Fujiwara (ed.) 1982 (q.v.).

AHUJA M.R. 1986 Micropropagation of juvenile and mature beech and oak. p. 11 in Abstracts VI Intl. Cong. Plant Tissue and Cell Culture, Minneapolis, Minn.

AITKEN J., HORGAN K.J. & THORPE T.A. 1981 Influence of explant selection on the shoot-forming capacity of juvenile tissues of Pinus radiata. Can. J. Forest Sci. 11, 112–117 (FA 43 1934).

AITKEN-CHRISTIE J. & JONES C. 1987 Towards automation: radiata pine shoot hedges in vitro. Plant Cell Tiss. Organ Cult. 8, 185–196.

AITKEN-CHRISTIE J. & SINGH A.P. 1987 Cold storage in tissue cultures. pp. 285–304 in Bonga and Durzan (eds.) 1987b (q.v.).

AITKEN-CHRISTIE J., JONES C. & BOND S. 1985 Wet and waxy shoots in radiata pine micropropagation. Acta Hort. 166, 93–100.

AKITA M. & TAKAYAMA M. 1988 Mass production of potato tubers using jar fermentor techniques. Acta Hort. 230, 55–61.

AKIYOSHI D.E., KLEE H.J., AMASINO R., NESTER E.W. & GORDON M.P. 1984 T-DNA of Agrobacterium tumefasciens codes an enzyme of cytokinin biosynthesis. Proc. Nat. Acad. Sci. U.S.A. 81, 5994–5998.

AKIYOSHI D.E., MORRIS R.O., HINZ R., MISCHKE B.S., KOSUGE T., GARFINKEL D.J., GORDON M.P. & NESTER E.W. 1983 Cytokinin/auxin balance in crown gall tumours is regulated by specific loci in the T-DNA. Proc. Nat. Acad. Sci. U.S.A. 80, 407–441.

AL-TALIB K.H. & TORREY J.G. 1959 The aseptic culture of isolated buds of Pseudotsuga taxifolia. Plant Physiol. 34, 630-637.

ALBERSHEIM P., DARVILL A.G., DAVIS K.R., DOARES S.H., GOLLIN D.J., O'NEILL R., TOUBART P.R. & YORK W.S. 1988 Oligosaccharins: Regulatory molecules in plants. HortScience 23, 520.

ALBERT A. 1958 Metal-binding agents in chemotherapy: the activation of metals by chelation. pp. 112–138 in Cowan and Rowatt (eds.) The Strategy of Chemotherapy. Soc. for Gen. Microbiol. 8th Symp. Cambridge Univ. Press, Cambridge.

ALBOUY J., FLOUZAT C., KUSIAK C. & TRONCHET M. 1988 Eradication of orchid viruses by chemotherapy from in-vitro cultures of Cymbidium. Acta Hort. 234, 413–420.

ALBRECHT C. 1986 Optimization of tissue culture media. Comb. Proc. Int. Plant Prop. Soc. 1985, 35, 196–199.

ALDERSON P.G. & BARGHCHI M. 1982 The potential for Pistacia propagation through shoot, leaf and callus culture. pp. 739–740 in Fujiwara (ed.) 1982 (q.v.).

ALDERSON P.G. & TAEB A.G. 1990 Influence of cultural environment on shoot growth and bulbing of tulip in vitro. Acta Hort. 266, 91–94.

ALDERSON P.G., HARBOUR M.A. & PATIENCE P.A. 1987 Micropropagation of Prunus tenella cv. Firehill. Acta Hort. 212, 463–468.

ALDERSON P.G., McKINLESS J. & RICE R.D. 1988 Rooting of cultured rose shoots. Acta Hort. 226, 175–182.

ALDWINCKLE H.S. & GUSTAFSON H.L. 1981 In vitro propagation of Malus prunifolia cultivar Xanthocarpa. Env. Exp. Bot. 21, 440 (Abst.).

ALI A.D. 1988 Integrated arthropod part management in plant tissue culture production. Comb. Proc. Int. Plant Prop. Soc. 1987, 37, 104–106.

ALI A.H.N. & JARVIS B.C. 1988 Effects of auxin and boron on nucleic acid metabolism and cell division during adventitious root regeneration. New Phytol. 108, 383–391.

ALLAN E.F. & TREWAVAS A.J. 1987 The role of calcium in metabolic control. pp. 117–149 in Stumpf & Conn (eds.) The Biochemistry of Plants. Vol. 12. Academic Press Inc., London. ISBN 01-12-675412-8.

ALLEN R.N. & DALE J.L. 1981 Application of rapid biochemical methods for detecting avocado sunblotch disease. Ann. Appl. Biol. 98, 451–461.

ALLIATA V. & POLITO V.S. 1982 Growth of calluses derived from adult and juvenile phase meristems of English ivy. HortScience **17**, 25 (Abst.).

ALONI R. 1980 Role of auxin and sucrose in the differentiation of sieve and tracheary elements in plant tissue cultures. Planta **150**, 255–263.

ALPI A. & GARIBALDI M.I. 1969 Propagation by vegetative tip culture in a species of *Cymbidium.* Riv. Ortoflorofruttic. Ital. **53**, 159–167.

ALSKIEF J. & VILLEMUR P. 1978 Greffage *in vitro* d'apex sur des plantules decapitées de Pommier (*Malus pumila* Mill.). Compt. Rend. Acad. Sci. Paris **287D**, 1115–1118.

ALTAMURA M.M., PASQUA G. & MONACELLI B. 1986 *In vitro* floral morphogenesis in a doubled haploid tobacco. Plant Science **46**, 69–75.

ALTMAN A. 1979 Inhibition of senescence of leaves and other plant organs by polyamines: possible modes of action. Israel J. Bot. **28**, 55–63.

ALTMAN A. & GOREN R. 1971 Promotion of callus formation by abscisic acid in citrus bud cultures. Plant Physiol. **47**, 844–846.

ALTMAN A. & GOREN R. 1974 Growth and dormancy cycles in *Citrus* bud cultures and their hormonal control. Physiol. Plant. **30**, 240–245.

ALTMAN A., NADEL B.L., FALASH F. & LEVIN N. 1990 Somatic embryogenesis in celery: induction, control and changes in polyamines and proteins. pp. 454–459 *in* Nijkamp *et al.* (eds.) 1990 (*q.v.*).

ALVAREZ R., NISSEN S.J. & SUTTER E.G. 1989 Relationship between indole-3-acetic acid levels in apple (*Malus pumila* Mill.) rootstocks cultured *in vitro* and adventitious root formation in the presence of indole-3-butyric acid. Plant Physiol. **89**, 439–443.

AMADOR A.M. & STEWART K.A. 1987 Osmotic potential and pH of fluid drilling gels as influenced by moisture loss and incorporation of growth regulators. J. Am. Soc. Hort. Sci. **112**, 26–28.

AMIN M.N. & JAISWAL V.S. 1988 Micropropagation as an aid to rapid cloning of a guava cultivar. Scientia Hort. **36**, 89–95.

AMMIRATO P. V. 1982 Growth and morphogenesis in cultures of the monocot yam, *Dioscorea.* pp. 169–170 *in* Fujiwara (ed.) 1982 (*q.v.*).

AMMIRATO P.V. 1973 Some effects of abscisic acid on the development of embryos from caraway cells in suspension culture. Am. J. Bot. **60**, 4 (Suppl.) 22.

AMMIRATO P.V. 1974 The effects of abscisic acid on the development of somatic embryos from cells of caraway (*Carum carvi* L.). Bot. Gaz. **135**, 328–337.

AMMIRATO P.V. 1976 Hormonal control of tuber formation in cultured axillary buds of *Dioscorea bulbifera* and *D. alata.* Plant Physiol. **57**, (Suppl.) 66.

AMMIRATO P.V. 1987 Organizational events during somatic embryogenesis. pp. 57–81 *in* Green *et al.* (eds.) 1987 (*q.v.*).

AMMIRATO P.V. 1988 Role of ABA in regulation of somatic embryogenesis. HortScience **23**, 520.

AMMIRATO P.V. & STEWARD F.C. 1971 Some effects of the environment on the development of embryos from cultured free cells. Bot. Gaz. **132**, 149–158.

AMMIRATO P.V., EVANS D.A., SHARP W.R. & YAMADA Y. (eds.) 1984 *Handbook of Plant Cell Culture* Vol. 3. Macmillan Publishing Co., New York, London.

AMMIRATO P.V., EVANS D.A., SHARP W.R. & BAJAJ Y.P.S. (eds.) 1990 *Handbook of Plant Cell Culture* Vol. 5. McGraw-Hill Inc., New York.

ANAND V.K., CHIBBAR R.N. & NANDA K.K. 1972 Effects of GA₃ and IBA on rooting and on the sprouting of buds on stem cuttings of *Ipomoea fistulosa.* Plant & Cell Physiol. **13**, 912–917.

ANDERS J., LARRABEE P.L. & FAHEY J.W. 1988 Evaluation of gelrite and numerous agar sources for *in vitro* regeneration of sugarcane. HortScience **23**, 755.

ANDERSEN R. & KASPERBAUER M.J. 1973 Chemical composition of tobacco leaves altered by near-ultraviolet and intensity of visible light. Plant Physiol. **51**, 723–726.

ANDERSON H.M., ABBOTT A.J. & WILTSHIRE S. 1982 Micropropagation of strawberry plants *in vitro* — effect of growth regulators on incidence of multi-apex abnormality. Scientia Hort. **16**, 331-341.

ANDERSON J.O. 1976 Embryogenesis in wild carrot cells. In Vitro **12**, 332 (Abst.155).

ANDERSON P.C. & HIBBERD K.A. 1988 Herbicide resistance in plants. U.S. Patent No. 4761373.

ANDERSON W.C. 1975 Propagation of rhododendrons by tissue culture. I. Development of a culture medium for multiplication of shoots. Comb. Proc. Int. Plant Prop. Soc. **25**, 129–135.

ANDERSON W.C. 1978a Tissue culture propagation of rhododendrons. In Vitro **14**, 334 (Abst. 03).

ANDERSON W.C. 1978b Rooting of tissue cultured rhododendrons. Comb. Proc. Int. Plant Prop. Soc. **28**, 135–139.

ANDERSON W.C. 1980a Tissue culture of red raspberries. pp. 27–34 *in* Anon 1980b (*q.v.*).

ANDERSON W.C. 1980b Tissue culture propagation of red and black raspberries, *Rubus idaeus* and *R. occidentalis.* Acta Hort. **112**, 13–20.

ANDERSON W.C. 1982 Tissue culture propagation of *Lilium.* In Vitro **18**, 293-294 (Abst.82).

ANDERSON W.C. 1984a A revised medium for shoot proliferation of *Rhododendron.* J. Am. Soc. Hort. Sci. **109**, 343–347.

ANDERSON W.C. & CARSTENS J.B. 1977 Tissue culture propagation of broccoli, *Brassica oleracea* (Italica group), for use in F₁ hybrid seed production. J. Am. Soc. Hort. Sci. **102**, 69–73.

ANDREAE W.A., VENIS M.A., JURSIC F. & DUMAS F. 1968 Does ethylene mediate root growth inhibition by indole-3-acetic acid? Plant Physiol. **43**, 1375–1379.

ANGRISH R. & NANDA K.K. 1982a Seasonal culture of dormant reproductive buds of *Salix tetrasperma*: analysis of the flowering process. Plant Cell Tiss. Organ Cult. **1**, 181–193.

ANGRISH R. & NANDA K.K. 1982b Dormancy and flowering process in reproductive buds of *Salix babylonica* cultured *in vitro.* Z. Pflanzenphysiol. **106**, 263–26.

ANKER L. 1974 Auxin-synthesis inhibition by sugars, notably by galactose. Acta Bot. Neerl. **23**, 705–714.

ANON 1978b *Farm Chemicals Handbook,* 1978. Meister Publ.Co. Willoughby, Ohio 44094.

ANON 1979 Proceedings of a meeting on *in vitro* culture techniques for the large-scale propagation of vegetable, ornamental and fruit crops. Pistoia, Oct. 1979. Consiglio Nationale Delle Recerche, Italy.

ANON 1980a Ann. Rep. and Accounts, British Petroleum Co. Ltd. 1979.

ANON 1980b Proceedings of the conference on nursery production of fruit plants — applications and feasibility. U.S.D.A., A.R.S. ARR-NE-11.

ANON 1981a *Plant Tissue Culture.* Proceedings of the Peking Symp. 1978. Pitman, Boston, London, Melbourne.

ANON 1981c Preliminary studies on tissue culture of *Corydalis turtachaninovii* Bess. F. yauhusieo Chou et Hsu. p. 525 *in* Anon 1981a (*q.v.*).

ANON 1983 *Cell and Tissue Culture Techniques for cereal crop improvement.* Science Press Beijing, China. Gordon and Breach, Science Publishers Inc., New York.

ANON (RESEARCH GROUP 301) 1976 A sharp increase of the frequency of pollen plant induction in wheat with potato medium. (Chinese) Acta Genet. Sin. **3**, 25–31.

ANSTIS P.J.P. & NORTHCOTE D.H. 1973 The initiation, growth and characteristics of a tissue culture from potato tubers. J. Exp. Bot. **24**, 425–441.

ANTONELLI M. & DRUART P.H. 1990 The use of a brief 2,4-D treatment to induce leaf regeneration on *Prunus canescens* Bois. Acta Hort. **280**, 45–50.

ANTONIW J.F., KUEH J.S.H., WALKEY D.G.A. & WHITE R.F. 1981 The presence of pathogenesic-related proteins in callus of Xanthi-nc tobacco. Phytopath. Z. **101**, 179– 184.

AOKI S. & ODA M. 1988 Sensing of photosynthetic capacities of seedling lettuce with chlorophyll florescence. Acta Hort. **230**, 363–370.

APAVATJRUT P. & BLAKE J. 1977 Tissue culture of stem explants of coconut (*Cocos nucifera* L.). Oleagineax **32**, 267–271.

APELBAUM A., BURGOON A.C., ANDERSON J.D., LIEBERMAN M., BEN-A-RIE R. & MATTOO A.K. 1981b Polyamines inhibit biosynthesis of ethylene in higher plant tissue and fruit protoplasts. Plant Physiol. **68**, 453–456.

APELBAUM A., CANELLAKIS Z.N., APPLEWHITE .B., KAUR-SAWHNEY R. & GALSTON A.W. 1988 Binding of spermidine to a unique protein in thin-layer tobacco tissue culture. Plant Physiol. **88**, 996–998.

APELBAUM A., WANG S.Y., BURGOON A.C., BAKER J.E. & LIEBERMAN M. 1981a Inhibition of the conversion of 1-aminocyclopropane-1- carboxylic acid to ethylene by structural analogs, inhibitors of electron transfer, uncouplers of oxidative phosphorylation, and free radical scavengers. Plant Physiol. **67**, 74–79.

APPELGREN M. 1976 Regeneration of *Begonia hiemalis in vitro.* Acta Hort. **64**, 31–38.

APPELGREN M. 1984 Tissue culture of ornamental plants with special reference to flowering potted plants. pp. 177–190 in *Micropropagation of selected root crops, palms, citrus and ornamental species.* FAO Plant Production & Protection Paper 59 FAO, Rome. ISBN 92-5-102107-0.

APPELGREN M. & HEIDE O. 1972 Regeneration in *Streptocarpus* leaf discs and its regulation by temperature and growth substances. Physiol. Plant. **27**, 417–423.

ARAI S., ASAO H., KAWABATA R. & KOBATAKE H. 1989 Effects of CO_2 enrichment on the growth of strawberry plantlets regenerated from shoot tip culture. J. Jap. Hort. Sci. **58**, 252–253.

ARCIONI S. & MARIOTTI D. 1983 Tissue culture and plant regeneration in *Onobrychis viciaefolia* Scop. Z. Pflanzenzucht. **90**, 192–197.

ARDITTI J. 1979 Aspects of the physiology of orchids. Adv. Bot. Res. **7**, 421–655.

ARDITTI J. & ERNST R. 1984 Physiology of germinating orchid seeds. pp. 177–222 in Arditti J (ed.) 1984 *Orchid Biology — Reviews and perspectives* III. Comstock Publishing, Cornell Univ. Press, Ithaca, London.

ARDITTI J., BALL E.A. & REISINGER D.M. 1977 Culture of flower-stalk buds: a method for vegetative propagation of *Phalaenopsis.* Am. Orchid Soc. Bull. **46**, 236–240.

ARISUMI T. & FRAZIER L.C. 1968 Cytological and morphological evidence for the single-cell origin of vegetatively propagated shoots in thirteen species of *Saintpaulia* treated with Colchicine. Proc. Am. Soc. Hort. Sci. **93**, 679–685.

ARMSTRONG C.L. & GREEN C.E. 1985 Establishment and maintenance of friable embryogenic maize callus and involvement of L-proline. Planta **164**, 207–214.

ARMSTRONG C.L. & PHILLIPS R.L. 1988 Genetic and cytogenetic variation in plants regenerated from organogenic and friable, embryogenic tissue cultures of maize. Crop Sci. **28**, 363–369.

ARMSTRONG D.W., FLEMING L.P. & GRENZOWSKI D.G. 1990 Cell culture bioreactor. U.S. Patent No. 4906577

ARNDT F., RUSCH R. & STILLFRIED H.V. 1976 SN49537, a new cotton defoliant. Plant Physiol. **57**, 599.

ARNON D.I. & STOUT P.R. 1939 Molybdenum as an essential element for higher plants. Plant Physiol. **14**, 599–602.

ARNOW P., OLESON J.J. & WILLIAMS J.H. 1953 The effect of arginine in the nutrition of *Chlorella vulgaris.* Am. J. Bot. **40**, 100–104.

ARNOZIS P.A., NELEMANS J.A. & FINDENEGG G.R. 1988 Phosphoendpyruvate carboxylase activity in plants grown with either NO_3^- or NH_4^+ as inorganic nitrogen source. J. Plant Physiol. **132**, 23–27.

ASAHIRA T. & KANO Y. 1977 Shoot formation from cultured tissue of strawberry fruits. J. Jap. Soc. Hort. Sci. **46**, 317–324.

ASHER C.J. 1978 Natural and synthetic culture media for spermatophytes. pp. 575–609 in Recheige M. Jr. (ed.). *CRC Handbook Series in Nutrition and Food. Section G. Diets, Culture Media and Food Supplements.* Vol 3.

ASHMORE S.E. & GOULD A.R. 1981 Chromosome number a poor guide to genetic stability. Protoplasma **106**, 297–308.

ASHWOOD-SMITH M.J. 1985 Genetic damage is not produced by normal cryopreservation procedures involving either glycerol or DMSO: A cautionary note however on the possible effects of DMSO. Cryobiology **22**, 427–433.

ASKANI A. & BEIDERBECK R. 1988 Preservation of the differentiated state of mesophyll cells *in vitro.* Ann. Bot. **61**, 393–394.

ASOKAN M.P., O'HAIR S.K. & LITZ R.E. 1983 *In vitro* plant development from bulbil explants of two *Dioscorea* species. HortScience **18**, 702–703.

ASOKAN M.P., O'HAIR S.K. & LITZ R.E. 1984b Rapid multiplication of *Xanthosoma caracu* by *in vitro* shoot tip culture. HortScience **19**, 885–886.

ASOKAN M.P., O'HAIR S.K. & LITZ R.E. 1984c *In vitro* plant regeneration from corm callus of *Amorphophallus rivieri* Durieu. Scientia Hort. **24**, 251–256.

ATANASSOV A. & BROWN D.C.W. 1984 Plant regeneration from suspension culture and mesophyll protoplasts of *Medicago sativa* L. Plant Cell Tiss. Organ Cult. **3**, 149–162.

ATTFIELD E.M. & EVANS P.K. 1991a Developmental pattern of root and shoot organogenesis in cultured leaf explants of *Nicotiana tabacum* cv. Xanthi nc. J. Exp. Bot. **42**, 51–57.

ATTFIELD E.M. & EVANS P.K. 1991b Stages in the initiation of root and shoot organogenesis in cultured leaf explants of *Nicotiana tabacum* cv. Xanthi nc. J. Exp. Bot. **42**, 59–63.

AULT J.R. & BLACKMON W.J. 1985 *In vitro* propagation of selected native cacti species. HortScience **20**, 541.

AVRAMIS T., HUGARD J. & JONARD R. 1982a La multiplication *in vitro* du rosier porte-greffe *Rosa indica* major. Compt. Rend. Acad. Sci. Paris **294 III**, 63–68.

AVRAMIS T., HUGARD J. & JONARD R. 1982b Exaltation des potentialités rhizogènes de pousses feuillées de rosier multipliées *in vitro* a l'aide de trempages avant leur ensemencement direct sur substrat horticole, dans des solutions minérales additionnées ou non de saccharose et d'acide naphthalene-acetique. Compt. Rend. Acad. Sci. Paris **294 III**, 679–682.

AYABE S., UDAGAWA A. & FURUYA T. 1988 Stimulation of chalcone synthase activity by yeast extract in cultured *Glycorrhiza echinata* cells and 5-deoxyflavone formation by isolated protoplasts. Plant Cell Rep. **7**, 35–38.

BABIC V. & NESKOVIC M. 1984 Propagation of three blackberry cultivars from small apical buds *in vitro.* J. Hort. Sci. **59**, 183–185.

BACH A. 1987 The capability of *in vitro* regeneration of various cultivars of *Freesia hybrida.* Acta Hort. **212**, 715–718.

BACH A. & CECOT A. 1988 Micropropagation of *Hyacinthus orientalis* cv. Carnegie in a double-phase culture medium. I. Effect of cytokinins on growth and development. Acta Hort. **226**, 607–610.

BACKS-HÜSEMANN D. & REINERT J. 1970 Embryobildung durch isolierte Einzelzellen aus Gewebkulturen von *Daucus carota.* Protoplasma **70**, 49–60.

BAGGA S., DAS R. & SOPORY S.K. 1987 Inhibition of cell proliferation and glyoxalase-1 activity by calmodulin inhibitors and lithium in *Brassica oleracea.* J. Plant Physiol. **129**, 149–153.

BAGNI N. 1966 Aliphatic amines and a growth factor of coconut milk stimulating cellular proliferation of *Helianthus tuberosus* (Jerusalem artichoke) *in vitro.* Experientia **22**, 732.

BAGNI N. 1986 The function and metabolism of polyamines in plants. Acta Hort. **179**, 95–103.

BAGNI N. & BIONDI S. 1987 Polyamines. pp. 113–124 in Bonga and Durzan (eds.) 1987a (*q.v.*).

BAGNI N., BARBIERI P. & TORRIGIANI P. 1983 Polyamine titer and biosynthetic enzymes during tuber formation in *Helianthus tuberosus.* J. Plant Growth Reg. **2**, 177–184.

BAGNI N., CALZONI G.L. & SPERANZA A. 1978 Polyamines as sole nitrogen sources for *Helianthus tuberosus* explants *in vitro.* New Phytol. **80**, 317–323.

BAJAJ Y.P.S. 1976 Regeneration of plants from cell suspensions frozen at -20, -70 and -196°C. Physiol. Plant. **37**, 263–268.

BAJAJ Y.P.S. 1977a Protoplast isolation, culture and somatic hybridization. pp. 467–496 *in* Reinert and Bajaj (eds.) 1977 (*q.v.*).

BAJAJ Y.P.S. 1979c Technology and prospects of cryopreservation of germplasm. Euphytica **28**, 267–285.

BAJAJ Y.P.S. 1981a Regeneration of plants from ultra-low frozen anthers of *Primula obconica.* Scientia Hort. **14**, 93–95.

BAJAJ Y.P.S. & PIERIK R.L.M. 1974 Vegetative propagation of *Freesia* through callus cultures. Neth. J. Agric. Sci. **22**, 153–159.

BAJAJ Y.P.S. & REINERT J. 1977 Cryobiology of plant cell cultures and establishment of gene-banks. pp. 757–777 *in* Reinert & Bajaj (eds.) 1977 (*q.v.*).

BAKER C.M., WILKINS H.F. & ASCHER P.D. 1990 Comparisons of precultural treatments and cultural conditions on *in vitro* response of tulip. Acta Hort. **266**, 83–90.

BAKER J.E., LIEBERMAN M. & ANDERSON J.D. 1978 Inhibition of ethylene production in fruit slices by a rhizobitoxine analog and free radical scavenger. Plant Physiol. **61**, 886–888.

BALL E. 1953 Hydrolysis of sucrose by autoclaving media, a neglected aspect in the culture of plant tissues. Bull. Torrey Bot. Club **80**, 409–411.

BALL E.A. 1946 Development in sterile culture of stem tips and subjacent regions of *Tropaeolum majus* L. and of *Lupinus albus* L. Am. J. Bot. **33**, 301–318.

BALL E.A. 1969 Histology of mixed callus cultures. Bull. Torrey Bot. Club **96**, 52–59.

BALL E.A. 1978 Cloning *in vitro* of *Sequoia sempervirens.* p. 259 *in* Hughes *et al.* (eds.) 1978 (*q.v.*).

BALL E.A. & ARDITTI J. 1976 Node cultures as a means of clonal propagation for *Dendrobium.* Proc. 8th World Orchid Conf. 367–371.

BALLADE P. 1971 Etude expérimentale de l'organogenèse axillaire chez *Nasturtium officinale* R.Br. Comportement de noeuds isolés cultivés *in vitro.* Compt. Rend. Acad. Sci. Paris **273D**, 2079–2082.

BALLESTER A., SANCHEZ M.C. & VIEITEZ A.M. 1989 Etiolation as a pretreatment for *in vitro* establishment and multiplication of sweet chestnut. Physiol. Plant. **77**, 395–400.

BANDIERA M. & MORPUGO G. 1970 Kinetin/auxin ratio and development of chloroplasts in tissue cultures of *Daucus carota*. Experientia **26**, 558–559.

BANDURSKI R.S. 1980 Homeostatic control of concentrations of indole-3-acetic acid. pp. 37–49 *in* Skoog (ed.) 1980 (*q.v.*).

BANDURSKI R.S. 1984 Metabolism of indole-3-acetic acid. pp. 183–200 *in* Crozier and Hillman (eds.) 1984 (*q.v.*).

BANERJEE N. & DE LANGHE E. 1985 A tissue culture technique for rapid clonal propagation and storage under minimal growth conditions of *Musa* (banana and plantain). Plant Cell Rep. **4**, 351–354.

BANERJEE S. & GUPTA S. 1976 Embryogenesis and differentiation in *Nigella sativa* leaf callus in vitro. Physiol. Plant. **38**, 115–120.

BANKO T.J. & STEFANI M.A. 1989 *In vitro* propagation of *Oxydendron arboreum* from mature trees. HortScience **24**, 683–685.

BANKS M.S. 1979a Plant regeneration from callus from two growth phases of English ivy, *Hedera helix* L. Z. Pflanzenphysiol. **92**, 349–353.

BANKS M.S. 1979b Ploidy changes in cultures of *Hedera helix*. Plant Physiol. **63**, (Suppl.) 138 (Abst. 765)

BANKS-IZEN M.S. & POLITO V.S. 1980 Changes in ploidy level in calluses derived from two growth phases of *Hedera helix L.* the English ivy. Plant Sci. Lett. **18**, 161–167.

BANNIER L.J. & STEPONKUS P.L. 1972 Freeze preservation of callus cultures of *Chrysanthemum morifolium* Ramat. HortScience **7**, 194.

BANNIER L.J. & STEPONKUS P.L. 1976 Cold acclimation of *Chrysanthemum* callus cultures. J. Am. Soc. Hort. Sci. **101**, 409–412.

BAPAT V.A. & RAO P.S. 1977b Shoot apical meristem culture of *Pharbitis nil*. Plant Sci.Lett. **10**, 327–334.

BAPAT V.A. & RAO P.S. 1979 Somatic embryogenesis and plantlet formation in tissue cultures of sandalwood (*Santalum album*). Ann. Bot. **44**, 629–632.

BAPAT V.A. & RAO P.S. 1988 Sandalwood plantlets from 'synthetic seeds'. Plant Cell Rep. **7**, 434–436.

BARALDI R., ROSSI F. & LERCARI B. 1988a *In vitro* shoot development of *Prunus* GF655-2: interaction between light and benzyladenine. Physiol. Plant. **74**, 440–443.

BARBAR S.B. & GUPTA S.C. 1986 Induction of androgenesis and callus formation in *in vitro* cultured anthers of a myrtaceous fruit tree (*Psidium guajava* L.). Bot. Mag. (Tokyo) **99**, 75–83.

BARBARA D.J. & CLARK M.F. 1982 A simple indirect ELISA using F(ab')₂ fragments of immunoglobulin. J. Gen. Virol. **58**, 315–322.

BARBIER M. & DULIEU H. 1983 Early occurrence of genetic variants in protoplast cultures. Plant Sci. Lett. **29**, 201–206.

BARG R. & UMIEL N. 1977a Effects of sugar concentration of growth, greenery and shoot formation in callus cultures of four genetic lines of tobacco. Z.Pflanzenphysiol. **81**, 161–166.

BARGHCHI M. 1986a *In vitro* culture of mature commercial *Pistacia vera* L. cultivars. Comb. Proc. Int. Plant Prop. Soc. 1985 **35**, 331–333.

BARGHCHI M. 1986b *In vitro* micropropagation of *Pistacia* rootstocks. Comb. Proc. Int. Plant Prop. Soc. 1985 **35**, 334–337.

BARGHCHI M. 1988 Micropropagation of *Alnus cordata* (Loisel.) Loisel. Plant Cell Tiss. Organ Cult. **15**, 233–244.

BARKER A.V. & COREY K.A. 1987 Ammonium-induced ethylene evolution by horticultural crops. HortScience **22**, 381 (Abst.).

BARKER P.K., DE FOSSARD R.A. & BOURNE R.A. 1977 Progress toward clonal propagation of *Eucalyptus* species by tissue culture techniques. Comb. Proc. Int. Plant Prop. Soc. **27**, 546–556.

BARLASS M. & SKENE K.G.M. 1978 *In vitro* propagation of grapevine (*Vitis vinifera* L.) from fragmented shoot apices. Vitis **17**, 335–340.

BARLASS M. & SKENE K.G.M. 1980a Studies on the fragmented shoot apex of grapevine. I. The regenerative capacity of leaf primordial fragments *in vitro*. J. Exp. Bot. **31**, 483–488.

BARLASS M. & SKENE K.G.M. 1980b Studies on the fragmented shoot apex of grapevine. II. Factors affecting growth and differentiation *in vitro*. J. Exp. Bot. **31**, 489–495.

BARLASS M. & SKENE K.G.M. 1982a A scanning electron microscope study of adventitious bud formation in the grapevine. pp. 159–160 *in* Fujiwara A. (ed.) 1982 (*q.v.*).

BARLASS M. & SKENE K.G.M. 1982b *In vitro* plantlet formation from *Citrus* species and hybrids. Scientia Hort. **17**, 333–341.

BARLASS M., GRANT W.J.R. & SKENE K.G.M. 1980 Shoot regeneration *in vitro* from native Australian fruit-bearing trees — Quandong and Plum bush. Aust. J. Bot. **28**, 405–409.

BARLASS M., MILLER R.M. & ANTCLIFF A.J. 1986 Development of methods for screening grapevines for resistance to infection by downy mildew. I. Dual culture *in vitro*. Am. J. Enol. Vitic. **37**, 61–66.

BARLASS M., SKENE K.G.M. & CLINGELEFFER P.R. 1981 Studies on the fragmented shoot apex of grapevine. III. A scanning electron microscope study of adventitious bud formation *in vitro*. J. Exp. Bot. **32**, 1079–1083.

BARLASS M., SKENE K.G.M., WOODHAM R.C. & KRAKE L.R. 1982 Regeneration of virus-free grapevines using *in vitro* apical 'culture'. Ann. Appl. Biol. **101**, 291–295.

BARNES L.R. 1979 *In vitro* propagation of water melon. Scientia Hort. **11**, 223–227.

BARNETT O.W., GIBSON P.D. & SEO A. 1975 A comparison of heat treatment, cold treatment and meristem tip culture for obtaining virus-free plants of *Trifolium repens*. Plant Dis. Rep. **59**, 834–837.

BARONCELLI S., BUIATTI M. & BENNICI A. 1973 Genetics of growth and differentiation *in vitro* of *B. oleracea* var. botrytis. I. Differences between 6 inbred lines. Z. Pflanzenzucht. **70**, 99–107.

BARONCELLI S., BUIATTI M., BENNICI A. & PAGLIAI M. 1974 Genetics of growth and differentiation *in vitro* of *Brassica oleracea* var. botrytis. Z. Pflanzenzucht. **72**, 275–282.

BARONCELLI S., BUIATTI M., BENNICI A., FOROUGHI-WEHR G.,MIX B., GAUL H., TAGLIASACCHI A.M., LOIERO M. & GIORGI B. 1978 Genetic control of *in vitro* and *in vivo* growth in hexaploid wheat. I. Behaviour of ditelocentric lines. Z. Pflanzenzucht. **80**, 109–116.

BARROSO M., LEVA A.R. & MURILLO J.M. 1985 La multiplicazione del melo con la tecnica della micropropagazione. Influenza del mezza nutritivo sul contenuto di alcumi elementi minerali nel callo e negli espianti di mela cv. Golden Delicious. Riv. Ortoflorofrutti. Ital. **69**, 123–131.

BARTA A., SUM I. & FOGLEIN F.J. 1981 2-Thiouracil does not inhibit TMV replication in tobacco protoplasts. J. Gen. Virol. **56**, 219–222.

BARTELS P.G. & WATSON C.W. 1978 Inhibition of carotenoid synthesis by fluridone and norflurazon. Weed Sci. **26**, 198–203.

BARTON L.V. 1956 Growth response of physiologic dwarfs of *Malus arnoldiana* Sarg. to gibberellic acid. Contrib. Boyce Thompson Inst. **18**, 311–317.

BARWALE U.B. & WIDHOLM J.M. 1990 Whole plant regeneration via organogenesis and somaclonal variation in *Glycine* species. U.S. Patent No. 4857465

BARWALE U.B., KERNS H.R. & WIDHOLM J.M. 1986 Plant regeneration from callus cultures of several soybean genotypes via embryogenesis and organogenesis. Planta **167**, 473–481.

BARZ W. 1977 Catabolism of endogenous and exogenous compounds by plant cell cultures. pp. 153–171 *in* Barz *et al*. (eds.) 1977 (*q.v.*).

BARZ W., REINHARD E. & ZENK M. H. 1977 *Plant Tissue Culture and its Bio-technological Application.* Springer-Verlag. Berlin, Heidelberg, New York.

BASSUK N. & MAYNARD B. 1987 Stock plant etiolation. HortScience **22**, 749–750.

BASTIAENS L., MAENE L., HARBAOUI Y., VAN SUMERE C., VAN DER CASTEELEK.L. & DEBERGH P.C. 1983 The influence of antibacterial products on plant tissue cultures. Med. Fac. Landbouwwet. Rijsuniv. Gent **48** (1), 13–24.

BASU A., SETH U. & GUHA-MUKHERJEE S. 1989 Regulation of cell proliferation and morphogenesis by amino acids in *Brassica* tissue cultures and its correlation with threonine deaminase. Plant Cell Rep. **8**, 333–335.

BASU R.N., BOSE T.K., ROY B.N. & MUKHOPADHYAY A. 1969 Auxin synergists in rooting of cuttings. Physiol. Plant. **22**, 649–652.

BASU R.N., ROY B.N. & BOSE T.K. 1970 Interaction of abscisic acid and auxins in rooting of cuttings. Plant Cell Physiol. **11**, 681–684.

BATESON J.M., GROUT B.W.W. & LANE S. 1987 The influence of container dimensions on the multiplication rate of regenerating plant cell cultures. pp. 275–277 *in* Ducaté *et al*. (eds.) 1987 (*q.v.*).

BATTEY N.H. & LYNDON R.F. 1988 Determination and differentiation of leaf and petal primordia in *Impatiens balsamina*. Ann. Bot. **61**, 9–16.

BAVIERA J.A., GARCIA J.L. & IBARRA M. 1989 Commercial *in vitro* micropropagation of pear cv. Conference. Acta Hort. **256**, 63–68.

BAWDEN F.C. 1958 Plant Pathology Department. Virus multiplication and inactivation. Rep. Rothamsted Exp. Sta. 1957 106–107.

BAYLEY J.M., KING J. & GAMBORG O.L. 1972a The effect of the source of inorganic nitrogen on growth and enzymes of nitrogen assimilation in soybean and wheat cells in suspension cultures. Planta **105**, 15– 24.

BAYLEY J.M., KING J. & GAMBORG O.L. 1972 b The ability of amino compounds and conditioned medium to alleviate the reduced nitrogen. Planta **105**, 25–32.

BAYLISS M.W. 1973 Origin of chromosome number variation in cultured plant cells. Nature **246**, 529–530.

BAYLISS M.W. 1977 The causes of competition between two cell lines of *Daucus carota* in mixed culture. Protoplasma **92**, 117–127.

BAYLISS M.W. 1980. Chromosomal variation in plant tissues in culture. pp. 113–144 *in* Vasil I.K. (ed.) 1980a (*q.v.*).

BAYLISS M.W. & DUNN S.D.M. 1979 Factors affecting callus formation from embryos of barley (*Hordeum vulgare*). Plant Sci. Lett. **14**, 311–316.

BEACH K.H. & SMITH R.R. 1979 Plant regeneration from callus of red and crimson clover. Plant Sci. Lett. **16**, 231–237.

BEASLEY C.A. 1977 Ovule culture: fundamental and pragmatic research for the cotton industry. pp. 160–178 *in* Reinert and Bajaj (eds.) 1977 (*q.v.*).

BEASLEY C.A. & EAKS I.L. 1979 Ethylene from alcohol lamps and natural gas burners: effects on cotton ovule cultures *in vitro*. In Vitro **15**, 263–269.

BEASLEY C.A., TING I.P., LINKINS A.E., BIRNBAUM E.H. & DELMER D.P. 1974 Cotton ovule culture: A review of progress and a preview of potential. pp. 169–192 *in* Street H.E. (ed.) 1974 (*q.v.*).

BEAUCHESNE G. 1981 Les milieux mineraux utilisés en culture *in vitro* et leur incidence sur l'apparition de boutures d'aspect pathologique. Compt. Rend. Acad. Agric. Paris **67**, 69–74.

BEAUCHESNE G. & POULAIN C. 1966a Influence des éclairements approximativement monochromatiques sur la développement des tissus, de moëlle de tabac cultivés *in vitro* en présence d'auxine et de kinétine. Photochem. Photobiol. **5**, 157–167.

BEAUCHESNE G. & POULAIN C. 1966b Quelques observations sur le développement des cultures *in-vitro* de moëlle de tabac en présence d'auxine et de kinétine, en éclairement relativement monochromatique. Photochem. Photobiol. **5**, 385–389.

BEAUCHESNE G., ALBOUY J., MORAND J.C. & DAGUENET J. 1977 Multiplication de clones de *Pelargonium hortorum* et *Pelargonium peltatum* à partir de culture de meristème pour l'obtention de plants sains. Acta Hort. **78**, 397–402.

BEAUCHESNE G., POULAIN C. & LETOUZÉ R. 1970 Les cultures *in-vitro* de tissu de moëlle de Tabac W.38, en éclairements monochromatiques. Photo-inactivation des auxines indoliques. Physiol. Plant. **23**, 1101–1109.

BECKETT K.A. 1979 Juvenility with a special reference to New Zealand plants. The Plantsman **1**, 81–84.

BECKMANN J.S. & SOLLER M. 1986 Restriction fragment length polymorphisms and genetic improvement of agricultural species. Euphytica **35**, 111–124.

BEHKI R.M. & LESLEY S.M. 1980 Shoot regeneration from leaf callus of *Lycopersicon esculentum*. Z. Pflanzenphysiol. **98**, 83–87.

BEHREND J. & MATELES R.I. 1975 Nitrogen metabolism in plant cell suspension cultures. I. Effect of amino acids on growth. Plant Physiol. **56**, 584–589.

BEHREND J. & MATELES R.I. 1976 Nitrogen metabolism in plant cell suspension cultures. II. Role of organic acids during growth in ammonia. Plant Physiol. **58**, 510–512.

BEHROUZ M. & LINEBERGER R.D. 1981a Influence of light quality on *in vitro* shoot multiplication of *Amelanchier laevis*. HortScience **16**, 406 (Abst.052).

BEHROUZ M. & LINEBERGER R.D. 1981b Interactive influences of auxins and cytokinins on proliferation of cultured *Amelanchier* shoot tips. HortScience **16**, 453 (Abst.398).

BELL P. & COOMBE D. (eds.) 1965 *Strasburger's Textbook of Botany*. English translation. Longman, Green & Co. Ltd., London.

BELLAROSA R. 1988 *In vitro* propagation of oaks (*Q. suber, Q. pubescens, Q. cerris*). Acta Hort. **227**, 433–435.

BELLINCAMPI D., BADURI N. & MORPURGO G. 1985 High plating efficiency with plant cell cultures. Plant Cell Rep. **4**, 155–157.

BEN-ARIE R. & FERGUSON I.B. 1991 Ethylene production by growing and senescing pear fruit cell suspensions in response to gibberellin. Plant Physiol. **95**, 943–947.

BEN-JAACOV J. & DAX E. 1981 *In vitro* propagation of *Grevillea rosmarinifolia*. HortScience **16**, 309–310.

BEN-JAACOV J. & JACOBS G. 1986 Establishing *Protea, Leucospermum* and *Serruria in vitro*. Acta Hort. **185**, 39–52.

BEN-JAACOV J. & LANGHANS R.W. 1972b Rapid multiplication of *Chrysanthemum* plants by stem-tip proliferation. HortScience **7**, 289–290.

BEN-JAACOV J., ACKERMAN A., TAL E. & JACOBS G. 1991 Vegetative propagation of *Alberta magna* by tissue culture and grafting. HortScience **26**, 74.

BEN-ZIONI A., VAADIA Y. & LIPS S.H. 1971 Nitrate uptake by roots as regulated by nitrate reduction products of the shoots. Physiol. Plant. **24**, 288–290.

BENNETT I.J., TONKIN C., WROTH M., DAVISON E. & McCOMB J.A. 1986 A comparison of growth of seedlings and micropropagated *Eucalyptus marginata* (jarrah). For. Ecol. Manag. **14**, 1–12.

BENNET-CLARK T.A. & KEFFORD N.P. 1953 Chromatography of the growth substances in plant extracts. Nature **171**, 645–647.

BENNETT I.J. & McCOMB J.A. 1986 A comparison between the development of seedlings and micropropagated plantlets of *Eucalyptus marginata* (Jarrah). p. 13 *in* Somers *et al.* (eds.) 1986 (*q.v.*).

BENNETT L. 1987 Tissue culture of oaks and redbuds. Comb. Proc. Int. Plant Prop. Soc. 1986 **36**, 421–426.

BENNETT L.K. & DAVIES F.T. 1984b *In vitro* propagation of *Quercus shumardii*. HortScience **19**, 576 (Abst.).

BENNETT L.K. & DAVIES F.T. 1986 *In vitro* propagation of *Quercus shumardii* seedlings. HortScience **21**, 1045–1047.

BENNICI A. 1979 Cytological chimeras in plants regenerated from *Lilium longiflorum* tissues grown *in vitro*. Z.Pflanzenzucht. **82**, 349–353.

BENNICI A. 1983 Expression of hormone-autotrophy in tissues of plantlets regenerated from habituated callus of *Nicotiana bigelovii*. Plant Cell Tiss. Organ Cult. **2**, 355–358.

BENNICI A. & D'AMATO F. 1978 *In vitro* regeneration of Durum wheat plants. 1. Chromosome numbers of regenerated plantlets. Z. Pflanzenzucht. **81**, 305–311.

BENNICI A., CAFFARO L., DAMERI R.M., GASTALDO P. & PROFUMO P. 1988 Callus formation and plantlet regeneration from immature *Triticum darum* Desf. embryos. Euphytica **39**, 255–263.

BENTZ S.E., PARLIMAN B.J., TALBOTT H.-J. & ACKERMAN W.L. 1988 Factors affecting *in vitro* propagation of *Yucca glauca*. Plant Cell Tiss. Organ Cult. **14**, 111–120.

BERETTA D. & ECCHER T. 1987 Determination of optimum level of BAP, GA$_3$ and IAA in micropropagation of *Camellia* by an orthogonal composite design. Acta Hort. **212**, 151–154.

BERGER R.G., DRAWERT F. & KUNZ C. 1988 Isozymes in nutrient medium of suspension-cultured apple cells (*Malus sylvestris* Mill.). Plant Cell Tiss. Organ Cult. **15**, 137–147.

BERGHOEF J. & BRUINSMA J. 1979a Flower development of *Begonia franconis* Liebm. II. Effects of nutrition and growth-regulating substances on the growth of flower buds *in vitro*. Z. Pflanzenphysiol. **93**, 345–357.

BERGHOEF J. & BRUINSMA J. 1979b Flower development of *Begonia franconis* Liebm. III. Effects of growth regulating substances on organ initiation in flower buds *in vitro*. Z. Pflanzenphysiol. **93**, 377–386.

BERGHOEF J. & BRUINSMA J. 1979c Flower development of *Begonia franconis* Liebm. IV. Adventitious flower bud formation in excised inflorescence pedicels *in vitro*. Z. Pflanzenphysiol. **94**, 407– 416.

BERGMANN L. 1967 Wachstum gruner Suspensionskulturen von *Nicotiana tabacum* Var. 'Samsun' mit CO$_2$ als Kohlenstoffquelle. Planta **74**, 243–249.

BERGMANN L. & BALZ A. 1966 Der Einfluss von farblicht auf wachstum und zusammensetzung Pflanzlicher gewebekulturen. Planta **70**, 285–303.

BERGMANN L. & BERGER C.H. 1966 Farblicht und Plastidendifferenzierung in zellkulturen von *Nicotiana tabacum* var. 'Samsun'. Planta **69**, 58–69.

BERLYN M. 1976 Photosynthetic autotrophy in plant tissue culture. In Vitro **12**, 288 (Abst. 12).

BERTHELOT A. 1934 Nouvelles remarques d'ordre chimique sur le choix des milieux de culture maturels et sur la manière de formules des milieux synthétiques. Bull. Soc. Chim. Biol. Paris **16**, 1553– 1557.

BERTOSSI F., BAGNI N., MORUZZI G. & CALDARERA C.M. 1965 Spermine as a new growth-promoting substance for *Helianthus tuberosus* (Jerusalem artichoke) *in vitro*. Experientia **21**, 80–81.

BETZ A. 1963 Ascorbic acid, NADH, cysteine and glutathione inhibit the peroxidase-catalyzed oxidative degradation of β-indoleacetic acid. Z. Botan. **51**, 424– 433.

BEVAN M. & NORTHCOTE D.H. 1981b Some rapid effects of synthetic auxins on messenger RNA levels in cultured plant cells. Planta **152**, 32–35.

BEYER E. Jr. 1975 C_2H_4: its incorporation and metabolism by pea seedlings under aseptic conditions. Plant Physiol. **56**, 273–278.

BEYER E. Jr. 1976a Silver Ion: A potent antiethylene agent in cucumber and tomato. HortScience **11**, 195–196.

BEYER E. Jr. 1976b A potent inhibitor of ethylene action in plants. Plant Physiol. **58**, 268–271.

BEYER E.M. Jr. & BLOMSTROM D.C. 1980 Ethylene metabolism and its possible physiological role in plants. pp. 208–218 in Skoog F.(ed.) 1980 (*q.v.*)

BEYL C.A. & SHARMA G.C. 1983 Picloram induced somatic embryogenesis in *Gasteria* and *Haworthia*. Plant Cell Tiss. Organ Cult. **2**, 123–132.

BEYL C.A., WANG W.C. & SHARMA G.C. 1981 Tissue culture of *Gasteria* and *Haworthia*. HortScience **16**, 406 (Abst. 051).

BHATTACHARYA S., BHATTACHARYA N.C. & MALIK C.P. 1978 Synergistic effect of gibberellic acid and indole-3-acetic acid on rooting in stem cuttings of *Abelmoschus esculentus* Moench. Planta **138**, 111–112.

BHOJWANI S.S. 1981 A tissue culture method for propagation and low temperature storage of *Trifolium repens* cultivar Grasslands huia genotypes. Plant Physiol. **52**, 187–190.

BHOJWANI S.S. & HAYWARD C. 1977 Some observations and comments on tissue culture of wheat. Z. Pflanzenphysiol. **85**, 341–347.

BHOJWANI S.S. & RAZDAN M.K. 1983 Plant *Tissue Culture: Theory and Practice*. Elsevier Science Publishers B. V., Amsterdam.

BHOJWANI S.S., MULLINS K. & COHEN D. 1987 Micropropagation of *Feijoa sellowiana* Berg. Acta Hort. **212**, 69–73.

BIDDINGTON N.L., SUTHERLAND R.A. & ROBINSON H.T. 1988 Silver nitrate increases embryo production in anther culture of Brussels sprouts. Ann. Bot. **62**, 181–185.

BIEDERMANN I.E.G. 1987 Factors affecting establishment and development of *Magnolia* hybrids *in vitro*. Acta Hort. **212**, 625–629.

BIGOT C. 1976 Bourgeonnement *in vitro* à partir d'épiderme séparé de feuille de *Bryophyllum daigremontianum* (Crassulacées). Can. J. Bot. **54**, 852–867.

BIGOT C. 1982 *In vitro* propagation of *Begonia x hiemalis* Fotsch: Plant conformity. pp. 695–696 in Fujiwara (ed.) 1982 (*q.v.*).

BIGOT C. 1983 Multiplication, végétative *in vitro* à partir de plantules d'hybrides F_1 de *Pelargonium x hortorum* Bailey. Acta Hort. **131**, 61–70.

BIGOT C. & NITSCH J.P. 1968 Effet du moment de l'application d'acide gibbérellique ou de 2,6-diaminopurine sur la néoformation des bourgeons chez *Begonia rex* Putz. Compt. Rend. Acad. Sci. Paris **267D**, 619–621.

BIGOT C., OHKI S. & MOUSSEAU J. 1977 Experimental data for a strategy for the improvement of the shoot forming capacity *in vitro*. Acta Hort. **78**, 125–132.

BILDERBACK D.E. 1971 The effects of amino acids upon the development of excised floral buds of *Aquilegia*. Am. J. Bot. **58**, 203–208.

BILKEY P.C. & McCOWN B.H. 1978 Container size as a variable in plantlet growth of *Saintpaulia ionantha* Wendl. (African violet) *in vitro*. pp. 247–248 in Hughes *et al.* (eds.) 1978 (*q.v.*).

BILKEY P.C. & McCOWN B.H. 1979 In vitro culture and propagation of *Episcia* sp. (Flame violets). J. Am. Soc. Hort. Sci. **104**, 109–114.

BILLINGS S. G., CHIN C. K. & JELENKOVIC G. 1988 Regeneration of Blueberry plantlets from leaf segments. HortScience **23**, 763–765.

BINAROVA P. & DOLÉZEL J. 1988 Alfalfa embryogenic cell suspension culture: Growth and ploidy level stability. J. Plant Physiol. **133**, 561–566.

BINDING H. & KOLLMAN R. 1985 pp. 93–99 in Schafer-Menuhr A. (ed.) *In Vitro Techniques. Propagation and Long Term Storage*. Nijhoff/Junk Dordrecht, Boston, Lancaster.

BINDING H., BUNNING D., GORSCHEN E., JORGENSEN J., KOLLMANN R., KRUMBIEGEL-SCHROEREN G., LING H.Q., MONZER J., MORDHORST G., RUDNICK J., SAUER A., WITT D. & ZUBA M. 1988 Uniparental, fusant and chimaeric plants regenerated from protoplasts after streak plating in agarose gels. Plant Cell Tiss. Organ Cult. **12**, 133–135.

BINDING H., NEHLS R.,SCHEIDER O., SOPORY S.K. & WENZEL G. 1978 Regeneration of mesophyll protoplasts isolated from dihaploid clones of *Solanum tuberosum*. Physiol. Plant. **43**, 52–54.

BINGHAM E.T., HURLEY L.V., KAATZ D.M. & SAUNDERS J.W. 1975 Breeding alfalfa which regenerates from callus tissue in culture. Crop Sci. **15**, 719–721.

BINNS A. & MEINS F. Jr. 1979 Cold-sensitive expression of cytokinin habituation by tobacco pith cells in culture. Planta **145**, 365–369.

BINNS A.N. & MEINS F. Jr. 1980 Chromosome number and the degree of cytokinin habituation of cultured tobacco (*Nicotiana tabacum* cultivar Havana 425) pith cells. Protoplasma **103**, 179–188.

BIONDI S. & THORPE T.A. 1981 Requirements for a tissue culture facility. pp. 1–20 in Thorpe T.A. (ed.) 1981 (*q.v.*).

BIONDI S. & THORPE T.A. 1982a Growth regulator effects, metabolite changes, and respiration during shoot initiation in cultured cotyledon explants of *Pinus radiata*. Bot. Gaz. **143**, 20–25.

BIONDI S.,BAGNI N. & SANSOVINI A. 1986 Dicyclohexylamine uptake and effects on polyamine content in cultured cotyledons of radiata pine. Physiol. Plant. **66**, 41–45.

BIONDI S., CANCIANI L. & BAGNI N. 1984 Uptake and translocation of benzyladenine by elm shoots cultured in vitro. Can. J. Bot. **62**, 2385–2390.

BIRNBAUM E.H., BEASLEY C.A. & DUGGER W.M. 1974 Boron deficiency in unfertilized cotton (*Gossypium hirsutum*) ovules grown *in vitro*. Plant Physiol. **54**, 931–935.

BISTER-MIEL F., GUIGNARD J.-L., BURY M. & AGIER C. 1985 Glutamine as an active component of casein hydrolysate: its balancing effect on plant cells cultured in phosphorus deficient medium. Plant Cell Rep. **4**, 161–163.

BJORN L.O. 1976 The state of protochlorophyll and chlorophyll in corn roots. Physiol. Plant. **37**, 183–184.

BLACK C.C. Jr. & HUMPHREYS T.E. 1962 Effects of 2,4- dichlorophenoxyacetic acid on enzymes of glycolysis and pentose phosphate cycle. Plant Physiol. **37**, 66–73.

BLACK R.C., KULECK G.A. & BINNS A.N. 1986 The initiation of auxin autonomy in tissue from tobacco plants carrying the auxin biosynthesizing genes from the T-DNA of *Agrobacterium tumefasciens*. Plant Physiol. **80**, 145–151.

BLACKMON W.J. & REYNOLDS B.D. 1982 *In vitro* shoot regeneration of *Hibiscus acetosella*, muskmelon, watermelon and winged bean. Hortscience **17**, 588–589.

BLACKMON W.J., REYNOLDS B.D. & POSTEK C.E. 1981a Regeneration of shoots from cantaloupe, crepe myrtle, roselle and winged bean explants. Environ. Exp. Bot. **21**, 438–439.

BLACKMON W.J., REYNOLDS B.D. & POSTEK C.E. 1981b Production of somatic embryos from callused cantaloupe hypocotyl explants. HortScience **16**, 451 (Abst. 381).

BLACKWELL S.J., LAETSCH W.M. & HYDE B.B. 1969 Development of chloroplast fine structure in *Aspen* tissue culture. Am. J. Bot. **56**, 457–463.

BLAKE J. 1966 Flower apices cultured *in vitro*. Nature **211**, 990–991.

BLAKE J. 1969 The effect of environmental and nutritional factors on the development of flower apices cultured *in vitro*. J. Exp. Bot. **20**, 113–123.

BLAKE J. 1988 Mites and thrips as bacterial and fungal vectors between plant tissue cultures. Acta Hort. **225**, 163–166.

BLAKE J. & EEUWENS C.J. 1982 Culture of coconut palm tissues with a view to vegetative propagation. pp. 145–148 in Rao A.N. (ed.) 1982 (*q.v.*).

BLAKESLEY D. & LENTON J.R. 1987 Cytokinin uptake and metabolism in relation to shoot multiplication *in vitro*. pp. 87–99 in Jackson *et al.* (eds.) 1987a (*q.v.*).

BLAYDES D.F. 1966 Interaction of kinetin and various inhibitors in the growth of soybean tissue. Physiol. Plant. **19**, 748–753.

BLOMMAERT K.L.J. & KOEN A.P. 1965 The use of thiourea as a rest-breaking spray for controlling prolonged rest of peach trees. S. Afr. J. Agric. Sci. **8**, 1171–1172.

BLUMENFELD A. & GAZIT S. 1970 Interaction of kinetin and abscisic acid in the growth of soybean callus. Plant Physiol. **45**, 535–536.

BOBTELSKY M. & JORDAN J. 1945 The metallic complexes of tartrates and citrates, their structure and behavior in dilute solutions. I. The cupric and nickelous complexes. J. Am. Chem. Soc. **67**, 1824–1831.

BOCCON-GIBOD J., BENBADIS A. & SHORT K.C. 1987 *Cell Culture Techniques Applied to Plant Production and Plant Breeding.* Colloque Franco-Britannique IAPTC, Angers, Oct. 1987.

BOGORAD L. 1950 Factors associated with the synthesis of chlorophyll in the dark in seedlings of *Pinus jeffreyi.* Bot. Gaz. **111**, 221–241.

BOLL W.G. & STREET H.E. 1951 Studies on the growth of excised roots. 1. The stimulatory effect of molybdenum and copper on the growth of excised tomato roots. New Phytol. **50**, 52–75.

BOLLMARK M., KUBAT B. & ELIASSON L. 1988 Variation in endogenous cytokinin content during adventitious root formation in pea cuttings. J. Plant Physiol. **132**, 262–265.

BONGA J.M. 1976 Morphogenesis in cultures of Balsam fir. In Vitro **12**, 333 (Abst. 158).

BONGA J.M. 1982a Vegetative propagation in relation to juvenility, maturity and rejuvenation. pp. 387–412 *in* Bonga and Durzan (eds.) 1982 *(q.v.).*

BONGA J.M. 1982d Tissue Culture Techniques. pp. 4–35 *in* Bonga and Durzan (eds.) 1982 *(q.v.).*

BONGA J.M. 1984 Adventitious shoot formation in cultures of immature female strobili of *Larix decidua.* Physiol. Plant. **62**, 416–421.

BONGA J.M. & DURZAN D.J. (eds.) 1982 *Tissue Culture in Forestry.* Martinus Nijhoff/Dr. W. Junk Publishers, Dordrecht, Boston, Lancaster. ISBN 90-247-2660-3

BONGA J.M. & DURZAN D.J. 1987a *Cell and Tissue Culture in Forestry* Vol. 1. *General Principles and Biotechnology.* Martinus Nijhoff Publishers. Dordrecht, Boston, Lancaster. ISBN 90-247-3430-4

BONGA J.M. & DURZAN D.J. 1987b *Cell and Tissue Culture in Forestry* Vol. 2. *Specific Principles and Methods: Growth and Developments.* Martinus Nijhoff Publishers. Dordrecht, Boston, Lancaster. ISBN 90-247-3431-2

BONGA J.M. & DURZAN D.J. 1987c *Cell and Tissue Culture in Forestry* Vol. 3. *Case Histories: Gymnosperms, Angiosperms and Palms.* Martinus Nijhoff Publishers, Dordrecht, Boston, Lancaster. ISBN 90-247-3432-0

BONNER D.M. & HAAGEN-SMIT A.J. 1939 Leaf growth factors II. The activity of pure substances in leaf growth. Proc. Nat. Acad. Sci. U.S.A. **25**, 184–188.

BONNER D.M., HAAGEN-SMIT A.J. & WENT F.W. 1939 Leaf growth hormones. 1. A bio-assay and source for leaf growth factors. Bot. Gaz. **101**, 128–144.

BONNER J. 1937 Vitamin B$_1$, a growth factor for higher plants. Science **85**, 183–184.

BONNER J. 1938a Thiamin (Vitamin B$_1$) and the growth of roots: the relation of chemical structure to physiological activity. Am. J. Bot. **25**, 543–549.

BONNER J. 1938b Nicotinic acid and the growth of isolated pea embryos. Plant.Physiol. **13**, 865-868.

BONNER J. 1940a Specificity of nicotinic acid as a growth factor for isolated pea roots. Plant Physiol. **15**, 553–557.

BONNER J. 1940b On the growth factor requirements of isolated roots. Am. J. Bot. **27**, 692–701.

BONNER J. & ADDICOTT F. 1937 Cultivation *in vitro* of excised pea roots. Bot. Gaz. **99**, 144–170.

BONNER J. & AXTMAN G. 1937 The growth of plant embryos *in vitro.* Preliminary experiments on the role of accessory substances. Proc. Nat. Acad. Sci. U.S.A. **23**, 453–457.

BONNER J. & DEVIRIAN P.S. 1939 Growth factor requirements of four species of isolated roots. Am. J. Bot. **26**, 661–665.

BONNETT H.T. 1972 Phytochrome regulation of endogenous bud development in root cultures of *Convolvulus arvensis.* Planta **106**, 325–330.

BONNETT H.T. & TORREY J.G. 1965 Chemical control of organ formation in root segments of *Convolvulus* cultured *in vitro.* Plant Physiol. **40**, 1228–1236.

BONNETT H.T. & TORREY J.G. 1966 Comparative anatomy of endogenous bud and lateral root formation in *Convolvulus arvensis* roots cultured *in vitro.* Am. J. Bot. **53**, 496–507.

BOONNOUR K., WAINWRIGHT H. & HICKS R.G.T. 1988 The micropropagation of *Lonicera periclymenum* L. (Honeysuckle). Acta Hort. **226**, 183–189.

BOOTH A. & SATCHUTHANANTHAVALE R. 1974 Regeneration in root cuttting of *Taraxacum officinale.* I. Effects of exogenous hormones on root segments and root callus cultures. New Phytol. **73**, 453–460.

BORKIRD C. & SINK K.C. 1983 Medium components for shoot cultures of chlorophyll-deficient mutants of *Petunia inflata.* Plant Cell Rep. **2**, 1–4.

BORKOWSKA B. & POWELL L.E. 1979 The dormancy status of apple buds as determined by an *in vitro* culture system. J. Am. Soc. Hort. Sci. **104**, 796–799.

BORNMAN C.H. & JANSON E. 1980 Organogenesis in cultured *Pinus sylvestris* tissue. Z. Pflanzenphysiol. **96**, 1–6.

BORNMAN C.H. & VOGELMANN T.C. 1984 Effect of gel medium on benzyladenine-induced adventitious bud formation and vitrification *in vitro* in *Picea abies.* Physiol. Plant. **61**, 505–512.

BORROD G. 1971 Contribution à l'étude des cultures *in vitro* des tissus de Châtaignier. Compt. Rend. Acad. Sci. Paris **272D**, 56–59.

BOSTRACK J.M. & STRUCKMEYER B.E. 1967 Effect of gibberellic acid on growth and anatomy of *Coleus blumei, Antirrhinum majus* and *Salvia splendens.* New Phytol. **66**, 539–544.

BOTTCHER I., ZOGLAUER K. & GORING H. 1988 Induction and reversion of vitrification of plants cultured *in vitro.* Physiol. Plant. **72**, 560–564.

BÖTTGER M. 1986 Proton translocation systems at the plasmalemma and its possible regulation by auxin. Acta Hort. **179**, 83–93.

BOUHARMONT J. 1961 Embryo culture of rice on a sterile medium. Euphytica **10**, 283–293.

BOUILLENNE C. & GASPAR T. 1970 Auxin catabolism and inihibitors in normal and crown gall tissues of *Impatiens balsamina.* Can. J. Bot. **48**, 1159–1163.

BOULAY M. 1987 *In vitro* propagation of tree species. pp. 367–382 in Green *et al.* (eds.) 1987 *(q.v.).*

BOULAY M. & FRANCLET A. 1986 Dégénérescence clonal du douglas (*Pseudotsuga menziesii*) cultivé *in vitro*; relation avec la teneur en éléments mineraux, en auxine, acide abscissique, zéatine et zéatine-riboside. Compt. Rend. Acad. Sci. Paris **303**, ser. 111

BOULAY M., GUPTA P.K., KROGSTRUP P. & DURZAN D.J. 1988 Development of somatic embryos from suspension cultures of Norway spruce (*Picea abies* Karst.). Plant Cell Rep. **7**, 134–137.

BOUNIOLS A. & MARGARA J. 1968 Recherches expérimentales sur la néoformation de bourgeons inflorescentiels ou végétatifs *in vitro* à partir d'explantats d'endive (*Cichorium intybus* L.). Ann. Physiol. Veg. **10**, 69–81.

BOURGIN J.-P. & NITSCH J.P. 1967 Production of haploid *Nicotiana* from excised stamens. Ann. Physiol. Veg. **9**, 377– 382.

BOURGIN J.-P., CHUPEAU Y. & MISSIONIER C. 1979 Plant regeneration from mesophyll protoplasts of several *Nicotiana* species. Physiol. Plant. **45**, 288–292.

BOVÉ J.M., BOVÉ C., WHATLEY F.R. & ARNON D.I. 1963 Chloride requirement for oxygen evolution in photosynthesis. Z. Naturforsch. Teil B **18**, 683–688.

BOVO O.A., MROGINSKI L.A. & REY H.Y. 1986 Regeneration of plants from callus tissue of the pasture legume *Lotononis bainesii.* Plant Cell Rep. **5**, 295–297.

BOWEN J.E. 1979 Boron essentiality and transport in suspension cultured sugarcane cells. Plant Physiol. **63**, (5 Suppl.) 163.

BOWEN M.R., HOWARTH J. & LONGMAN K.A. 1975 Effects of auxins and other factors on the rooting of *Pinus contorta* Dougl. cuttings. Ann. Bot. **39**, 647–656.

BOWES B.G. 1976a *In vitro* morphogenesis of *Crambe maritima* L. Protoplasma **89**, 185–188.

BOWES B.G. 1976b Polar regeneration in excised roots of *T. officinale* Weber. Ann. Bot. **40**, 423–432.

BOWES B.G. 1990 A simple micropropagation technique utilising non-sterile explants and its potential in conservation. Prof. Horticulture **4**, 113–120.

BOWES B.G. & CURTIS E.W. 1991 Conservation of the British national *Begonia* collection by micropropagation. New Phytologist **119**, 169–181.

BOXUS P. 1989 Review on strawberry mass propagation. Acta Hort. **265**, 309–320.

BOXUS Ph. 1974a The production of strawberry plants by *in vitro* micro-propagation. J. Hort. Sci. **49**, 209–210.

BOXUS Ph. 1974b La micropropagation 'in vitro' du fraisier. Proc. Int. Hort. Cong. **19**, (1a) 65.

BOXUS Ph. 1978 The production of fruit and vegetable plants by *in vitro* culture. Actual possibilities and perspectives. pp. 44–58 in Hughes *et al.* (eds.) 1978 *(q.v.).*

BOXUS Ph. 1987 Introductory lecture. pp. 1–6 *in* Boxus and Larvor (eds.) 1987 (*q.v.*).

BOXUS Ph. & LARVOR P. (eds.) 1987 Workshop on strawberry plants issued from tissue culture. Commission of the European Communities Biol. Series. Rep. EUR 10871.

BOXUS Ph. & PLAQUES M. 1986 Propagation of woody plants in a culture medium containing hydrolyzed agar to prevent vitrification. Belgian Patent No. 904661.

BOXUS Ph. & TERZI J.M. 1987 Big losses due to bacterial contaminations can be avoided in mass propagation schemes. Acta Hort. **212**, 91–93.

BOXUS Ph. & TERZI J.M. 1988 Control of accidental contaminations during mass propagation. Acta Hort. **225**, 189–190.

BOXUS Ph., QUOIRIN M. & LAINE J. M. 1977 Large scale propagation of strawberry plants from tissue culture. pp. 130–143 *in* Reinert and Bajaj (eds.) 1977 (*q.v.*).

BOZZINI A. 1980 Plant cell cultures and their possible impact in improving crop production in the developing world. pp. 3–9 *in* Sala *et al.* (eds.) 1980 (*q.v.*).

BRADBURY J.F. 1988 Identification of cultivable bacteria from plants and plant tissue cultures by use of simple classical methods. Acta Hort. **225**, 27–37.

BRADBURY J.P. 1970 Isolation and preliminary study of bacteria from plants. Rev. Plant Path. **49**, 213–218.

BRADLEY P.M., EL-FIKI F. & GILES K.L. 1984 Polyamines and arginine affect somatic embryogenesis of *Daucus carota*. Plant Sci. Lett. **34**, 397–401.

BRADLEY P.M., EL-FIKI F. & GILES K.L. 1985 The effects of putrescine on somatic embryogenesis of *Daucus carota* as examined by two-dimensional electrophoresis. pp. 307–308 *in* Henke *et al.* (eds.) 1985 (*q.v.*).

BRAINERD K.E. & FUCHIGAMI L.H. 1982 Stomatal functioning of *in vitro* and greenhouse apple leaves in darkness, mannitol, ABA and CO_2. J. Exp. Bot. **33**, 388–392.

BRAND A. & BRIDGEN M.P. 1986 Evaluation of a home tissue culture medium. Comb. Proc. Int. Plant Prop. Soc. 1985 **35**, 616–622.

BRAND M.H. & LINEBERGER R.D. 1986 *In vitro* propagation of *Halesia carolina* L. and the influence of explantation timing on initial shoot proliferation. Plant Cell Tiss. Organ Cult. **7**, 103–113.

BRAND M.H. & LINEBERGER R.D. 1988 In vitro adventitious shoot formation on mature-phase leaves and petioles of *Liquidambar styraciflua* L. Plant Science **57**, 173–179.

BRAWLEY S.H., WETHERELL D.F. & ROBINSON K.R. 1984 Electrical polarity in embryos of wild carrot precedes cotyledon differentiation. Proc. Nat. Acad. Sci. U.S.A. **81**, 6064–6067.

BRESSAN P.H., KIM Y-J., HYNDMAN S.E., HASEGAWA P.M. & BRESSAN R.A. 1982 Factors affecting *in vitro* propagation of Rose. J. Am. Soc. Hort. Sci. **107**, 979–990.

BRETTELL R., INGRAM D.S. & THOMAS E. 1980a Selection of maize tissue cultures resistant to *Drechslera* (*Helminthosporium*) *maydis* T-toxin. pp. 233–237 *in* Ingram and Helgeson (eds.) 1980 (*q.v.*).

BRETZLOFF C.W. Jr. 1954 The growth and fruiting of *Sordaria fimicola*. Am. J. Bot. **41**, 58–67.

BRIAN P.W. 1959 Effects of gibberellins on plant growth and development. Biol. Rev. **34**, 37–84.

BRIDGEN M.P. & BARTOK J.W. Jr. 1988 Designing a plant micropropagation laboratory. Comb. Proc. Int. Plant Prop. Soc. 1987 **37**, 462–467.

BRIDGEN M.P. & LINEBERGER R.D. 1981a The effect of hormones on the ethylene production rate of *Nicotiana tabacum* 'KY 10' callus *in vitro*. HortScience **16**, 441 (Abst. 310).

BRIDGEN M.P. & STABY G.L. 1981 Low pressure and low oxygen storage of *N. tabacum* and *Chrysanthemum* × *morifolium* tissue cultures. Plant Sci. Lett. **22**, 177–186.

BRIDGEN M.P. & STABY G.L. 1983 Protocols of low-pressure storage. pp. 816–827 *in* Evans *et al.* (eds.) 1983 (*q.v.*).

BRIDGEN M.P. & VEILLEUX R.E. 1988 A comparison of *in vitro* flowers to *in vivo* flowers of haploid and diploid *Nicotiana tabacum* L. Plant Cell Tiss. Organ Cult. **13**, 3–13.

BRIDSON E.Y. 1978 Diets, culture media and food supplements. pp. 91–281 *in* Rechcigl M. Jr. (ed.) *CRC Handbook Series in Nutrition and Food. Section G.* Vol.3.

BRIGGS B.A. 1975 Nursery understanding of tissue culture. Comb. Proc. Int. Plant Prop. Soc. **25**, 116–118.

BRIGGS B.A., McCULLOCH S.M. & EDICK L.A. 1988a Micropropagation of azaleas using thiadiazuron. Acta Hort. **226**, 205–208.

BRIGGS B.A., McCULLOCH S.M. & EDICK L.A. 1988b Micropropagation of azaleas using thidiazuron. Acta Hort. **227**, 330–333.

BRIGHT S.W.J., NELSON R.S., KARP A, JARRETT V.A., CREISSEN G.P., OOMS G., MIFLIN B.J. & THOMAS E. 1982 Variation in culture-derived potato plants. pp. 413–414 *in* Fujiwara (ed.) 1982 (*q.v.*).

BRINGHURST R.S. & VOTH V. 1965 Strawberry virus transmission by grafting excised leaves. Plant Dis. Rep. **40**, 596–600.

BRINK R.A. 1962 Phase change in higher plants and somatic cell heredity. Q. Rev. Biol. **37**, 1–22.

BRINK R.A., COOPER D.C. & AUSHERMAN L.E. 1944 A hybrid between *Hordeum jubatum* and *Secale cereale*. J. Hered. **35**, 67–75.

BRISSON L., IBRAHIM R.K. & RIDEAU M. 1988 Tissue culture of *Chrysosplenium americanum* and its potential for flavenoid production. Plant Cell Rep. **7**, 130–133.

BRISTOL D.W., GHANUNI A.M. & OLESON A.E. 1977 Metabolism of 2,4-dichlorophenoxyacetic acid by wheat cell suspension cultures. J. Agric. Food Chem. **25**, 1308–1314.

BROERTJES C. 1969 Mutation breeding of *Streptocarpus*. Euphytica **18**, 333–339.

BROERTJES C. 1972a Mutation breeding of *Achimenes*. Euphytica **21**, 48–62.

BROERTJES C. 1972b Use in plant breeding of acute, chronic or fractionated doses of X-rays or fast neutrons as illustrated with leaves of *Saintpaulia*. Thesis, Centr. Agric. Publ. Doc., Wageningen Agric. Res. Rep. No.776.

BROERTJES C. & KEEN A. 1980 Adventitious shoots: do they develop from one cell? Euphytica **29**, 73–87.

BROERTJES C. & LEFFRING L. 1972 Mutation breeding of *Kalanchoe*. Euphytica **21**, 415–423.

BROERTJES C. & VAN HARTEN A.M. 1978 *Application of Mutation Breeding in the Improvement of Vegetatively Propagated Crops.* Elsevier Scientific Publishing Co. Amsterdam, Oxford, New York. I.S.B.N. 0-444- 41618-8

BROERTJES C. & VAN HARTEN A.M. 1985 Single cell origin of adventitious buds. Euphytica **34**, 93–95.

BROERTJES C., HACCIUS B. & WEIDLICH S. 1968 Adventitious bud formation on isolated leaves and its significance for mutation breeding. Euphytica **17**, 321–344.

BROERTJES C., ROEST S. & BOKELMANN G.S. 1976 Mutation breeding of *Chrysanthemum morifolium* using *in vivo* and *in vitro* adventitious bud techniques. Euphytica **25**, 11–19.

BROOKS H.J. & BARTON D.W. 1983 Germplasm maintenance and preservation. pp. 11–20 *in* Moore and Janick (eds.) 1983 *Methods in Fruit Breeding.* Purdue Univ. Press, West Lafayette, Ind.

BROOME O.C. 1986 Laboratory design. pp. 351–364 *in* Zimmerman *et al.* (eds.) 1986 (*q.v.*).

BROOME O.C., BRIGGS B., EVANS R. & HENNEN G. 1986 Summary of panel discussion on laboratory design. pp. 365–366 *in* Zimmerman *et al.* (eds.) 1986 (*q.v.*).

BROWERS M.A. & ORTON T.J. 1982a Transmission of gross chromosomal variability from suspension cultures into regenerated celery plants. J. Hered. **73**, 159–162.

BROWERS M.A. & ORTON T.J. 1982b A factorial study of chromosomal variability in callus cultures of celery (*Apium graveolens*). Plant Sci. Lett. **26**, 65–73.

BROWN C.L. & LAWRENCE R.H. 1968 Culture of pine callus on a defined medium. Forest Sci. **14**, 62–64.

BROWN D.C.W. 1982 The role of osmotic regulation in morphogenesis. In Vitro **18**, 318 (Abst. 179).

BROWN D.C.W. 1988 Germplasm determination of *in vitro* somatic embryogenesis in alfalfa. HortScience **23**, 526–531.

BROWN D.C.W. & ATANASSOV A. 1985 Role of genetic background in somatic embryogenesis in *Medicago*. Plant Cell Tiss. Organ Cult. **4**, 111–122.

BROWN D.C.W. & THORPE T.A. 1980a Changes in water potential and its components during shoot formation in tobacco callus. Physiol. Plant. **49**, 83–87.

BROWN D.C.W., LEUNG D.W.M. & THORPE T.A. 1979 Osmotic requirement for shoot formation in tobacco callus. Physiol. Plant. **46**, 36–41.

BROWN D.D. & DAWID I.B. 1968 Specific gene amplification in oocytes. Science **160**, 272.

BROWN D.H. & SMITH W.E. 1984 Metal ions in biological systems. pp. 162–195 *in* Suckling C.J. (ed.) 1984 *Enzyme Chemistry: Impact and Applications.* Chapman & Hall, London, New York.

BROWN D.J., CANVIN D.T. & ZILKEY B.F. 1970 Growth and metabolism of *Ricinus communis* endosperm in tissue culture. Can. J. Bot. **48**, 2323–2331.

BROWN D.M., GROOM C.L., CVITANIK M., BROWN M., COOPER J.L. & ARDITTI J. 1982 Effects of fungicides and bactericides on orchid seed germination and shoot tip cultures *in vitro*. Plant Cell Tiss. Organ Cult. **1**, 165–180.

BROWN M.S., PEREIRA E.SA.B. & FINKLE B.J. 1974 Freezing of non-woody plant tissues. II. Cell damage and the fine structure of freezing curves. Plant Physiol. **53**, 709–711.

BROWN S., WITHERELL D.F. & DOUGALL D.K. 1976 The potassium requirement for growth and embryogenesis in wild carrot suspension cultures. Physiol. Plant. **37**, 73–79.

BROWN S.A. 1981 Coumarins. pp. 269–300 *in* Conn E.E. (ed.) 1981 (*q.v.*).

BROWNELL P.F. 1979 Sodium as an essential micronutrient element for plants and its possible role in metabolism. Adv. Bot. Res. **7**, 117–224.

BROWNING G., OGNJANOV V., PASSEY A.J. & JAMES D.J. 1987 Multiple shoot and root regeneration from pear embryo cotyledon explants *in vitro*. J. Hort. Sci. **62**, 305–311.

BROWSE P.M. 1980 Propagation of plants from root cuttings. Plantsman **2**, 54–62.

BROYER T.C., CARLTON A.B., JOHNSON C.M. & STOUT P.R. 1954 Chlorine – a micronutrient element for higher plants. Plant Physiol. **29**, 526–532.

BRUCE M.I. & ZWAR J.A. 1966 Cytokinin activity of some ureas and thioureas. Proc. Roy. Soc. (Lond.) Ser. B **165**, 245–265.

BRUCE M.I., ZWAR J.A. & KEFFORD N.P. 1965 Chemical structure and plant kinin activity; the activity of urea and thiourea derivatives. Life Sci. **4**, 461–466.

BRUCK D.K. & WALKER D.B. 1985 Cell determination during embryogenesis in *Citrus jambhiri*. II. Epidermal differentiation as a one time event. Am. J. Bot. **72**, 1602–1609.

BRUMMEL D.A. & HALL J.L. 1987 Rapid cellular responses to auxin and the regulation of growth. Plant Cell & Env. **10**, 523–543.

BUCHALA A.J. & PYTHOUD F. 1988 Vitamin D and related compounds as plant growth substances. Physiol. Plant. **74**, 391–396.

BUCHALA A.J. & SCHMID A. 1979 Vitamin D and its analogues as a new class of plant growth substances affecting rhizogenesis. Nature **280**, 230–231.

BUCHEIM J.A., COLBURN S.M. & RANCH J.P. 1989 Maturation of soybean somatic embryos and the transition to plantlet growth. Plant Physiol. **89**, 768–775.

BUIATTI M., BARONCELLI S. & BENNICI A. 1974b Genetics of growth and differentiation *in vitro* of *Brassica oleracea* var. botrytis. IV. Genotype-hormone interactions. Z. Pflanzenzuchtg. **73**, 298–302.

BUIATTI M., BARONCELLI S., BENNICI A., PAGLIAI M. & TESI R. 1974a Genetics of growth and differentiation *in vitro* of *B. oleracea* var. botrytis. II. An *in vitro* and *in vivo* analysis of a diallel cross. Z. Pflanzenzucht. **72**, 269–274.

BULLOCK W.P., BAENZIGER P.S., SCHAEFFER G.W. & BOTTINO P.J. 1982 Anther culture of wheat (*Triticum aestivum* L.) F₁'s and their reciprocal crosses. Theor. Appl. Genet. **62**, 155–159.

BURG S.P. & BURG E.A. 1968 Ethylene formation in pea seedlings: its relation to the inhibition of bud growth caused by indole-3-acetic acid. Plant Physiol. **43**, 1069–1074.

BURGER D. 1988 Guidelines for autoclaving media used in plant tissue culture. HortScience **23**, 1066–1068.

BURGER D.W. 1985 Micrografting: a tool for the plant propagator. Comb. Proc. Int. Plant Prop. Soc. 1984 **34**, 244–248.

BURGER D.W. & HACKETT W.P. 1986 Gradients of adventitious bud formation on excised epicotyl and root sections of *Citrus*. Plant Science **43**, 229–232.

BURGER D.W., LIU L. & WU L. 1985 Rapid micropropagation of *Paulownia tomentosa*. HortScience **20**, 760–761.

BURK L.G., CHAPLIN J.F., GOODING G.V. & POWELL N.T. 1979 Quantity production of anther-derived haploids from a multiple disease resistant tobacco hybrid. I. Frequency of plants with resistance or susceptibility to tobacco mosaic virus, Potato virus Y and root knot. Euphytica **28**, 201–208.

BURKHOLDER P.R. & NICKELL L.G. 1949 Atypical growth of plants. I. Cultivation of virus tumors of *Rumex* on nutrient agar. Bot. Gaz. **110**, 426–437.

BURNET G. & IBRAHIM R.K. 1973 Tissue culture of *Citrus* peel and its potential for flavonoid synthesis. Z. Pflanzenphysiol. **69**, 152–162.

BURR R.W. 1975 Mass propagation of Boston fern through tissue culture. Comb. Proc. Int. Plant Prop. Soc. **25**, 122–124.

BURR R.W. 1976 Mass propagation of ferns through tissue culture. In Vitro **12**, 309–310 (Abst. 83).

BURR R.W. 1984 Progress and new ideas in tissue culture propagation. Comb. Proc. Int. Plant Prop. Soc. 1983 **33**, 126–129.

BURROWS W.J., SKOOG F. & LEONARD N.J. 1971 Isolation and identification of cytokinins located in the transfer ribonucleic acid of tobacco callus grown in the presence of 6-benzylaminopurine. Biochem. **10**, 2189–2194.

BURSTROM H. 1957 Root surface development, sucrose inversion and free space. Physiol. Plant. **10**, 741–751.

BURSTROM H. 1960 Influence of iron and gibberellic acid on the light sensitivity of roots. Physiol. Plant. **13**, 597–615.

BURSTROM H. 1961 Growth action of EDTA in light and darkness. Physiol. Plant. **14**, 354–377.

BURSTROM H. 1963 Growth regulation by metals and chelates. Adv. Bot. Res. **1**, 73–100.

BUSH S.R., EARLE E.D. & LANGHANS R.W. 1976 Plantlets from petal segments, petal epidermis and shoot tips of the periclinal chimera, *Chrysanthemum morifolium* 'Indianapolis'. Am. J. Bot. **63**, 729– 737.

BUTCHER D.N. & STREET H.E. 1964 Excised root culture. Bot. Rev. **30**, 513–586.

BUTENKO R.G. 1964 pp. 10–24 & 46–47 *in Plant Tissue Culture and Plant Morphogenesis.* Moscow. Israel programme for Scientific Translations 1968.

BUTENKO R.G. & KUCHKO A.A. 1978 Cultivation and plant regeneration studies on isolated protoplasts from two potato species. Abstr. 4th Int. Cong. Plant Tissue Cell Cult. 62.

BUTENKO R.G., ATANASSOV A. & URMANTSEVA W. 1972 Some features of the sugar beet tissue culture. Phytomorph. **22**, 140–143.

BUTENKO R.G., LIPSKY A.K.H., CHERNYAK N.D. & ARYA H.C. 1984 Changes in culture medium pH by cell suspension cultures of *Dioscorea deltoidea*. Plant Sci. Lett. **35**, 207–212.

BUTTON J. & BOTHA C.E.J. 1975 Enzymic maceration of *Citrus* callus and the regeneration of plants from single cells. J. Exp. Bot. **26**, 723–729.

BUTTON J. & KOCHBA J. 1977 Tissue culture in the citrus industry. pp. 70–92 *in* Reinert & Bajaj (eds.) 1977 (*q.v.*).

BUTTON J., KOCHBA J. & BORNMAN C.H. 1974 Fine structure of and embryoid development from embryogenic ovular callus of 'Shamouti' orange (*Citrus sinensis* Osb.). J. Exp. Bot. **25**, 446–457.

BUWALDA F. & GREENWAY H. 1989 Nitrogen uptake and growth of wheat during O_2 deficiency in root media containing NO_3^- only, or NO_3^- plus NH_4^+. New Phytol. **111**, 161–166.

BYANT J.A. & FRANCIS D. (eds.) 1985 *The Cell Division Cycle in Plants.* Soc. for Exp. Biology, Seminar Series 26. Cambridge Univ. Press, London.

CABOCHE M. 1980 Nutritional requirements of protoplast-derived haploid tobacco cells grown at low densities in liquid medium. Planta **149**, 7–18.

CAILLOUX M. 1978 Simultaneous use of 3 cytokinins gives better yields with *Gynura sarmentosa*. p. 248 *in* Hughes *et al.* (eds.) 1978 (*q.v.*).

CALLEBAUT A. & MOTTE J.-C. 1988 Growth of cucumber cells in media with lactose or milk whey as carbon source. Plant Cell Rep. **7**, 162– 165.

CALLOW P., HAGHIGHI K., GIROUX M. & HANCOCK J. 1988 *In vitro* shoot regeneration on leaf tissue from micropropagated highbush blueberry. HortScience **23**, 807–808.

CAMPBELL A.D. & SUTTER E.G. 1986 Changes in IAA concentration in agar during tobacco callus culture. p. 297 *in* Somer *et al.* (eds.) 1986 (*q.v.*).

CAMPBELL R.A. & DURZAN D.J. 1975 Induction of multiple buds and needles in tissue cultures of *Picea glauca*. Can. J. Bot. **53**, 1652–1657.

CAMPBELL R.A. & DURZAN D.J. 1978 The potential for cloning white spruce via tissue culture. 86 Pest Control Section, FOR. Management Br., Min. Nat. Resources, Maple, Ont. Canada. (PBA 48 10115) .

CANAS L.A. & BENBADIS A. 1988 In vitro plant regeneration from cotyledon fragments of the olive tree (*Olea europaea* L.). Plant Science **54**, 65–74.

CAPELLADES QUERALT M., BERUTO M., VANDERSCHAEGHE A. & DEBERGH P.C. 1991 Ornamentals. pp. 215–229 *in* Debergh & Zimmerman (eds.) 1991 (*q.v.*).

CAPLIN S.M. 1959 Mineral oil overlay for conservation of plant tissue cultures. Am. J. Bot. **46**, 324–329.

CAPLIN S.M. & STEWARD F.C. 1948 Effects of coconut milk on the growth of explants from carrot root. Science **108**, 655–657.

CAPONETTI J.D. 1972a Morphogenetic studies on excised leaves of *Osmunda cinnamomea*: developmental capabilities of excised leaf primordial apices in sterile culture. Bot. Gaz. **133**, 331–335.

CAPONETTI J.D. 1972b Morphogenetic studies on excised leaves of *Osmunda cinnamomea*. Morphological and histological effects of sucrose in sterile nutrient culture. Bot. Gaz. **133**, 421–435.

CAPONETTI J.D. & STEEVES I.M. 1963 Morphogenetic studies on excised leaves of *Osmunda cinnamomea* L. Morphological studies of leaf develpment in sterile nutrient culture. Can. J. Bot. **41**, 545–556.

CAPPADOCIA M., CHRETIEN L. & LAUBLIN G. 1988 Production of haploids in *Gerbera jamesonii* via ovule culture: influence of fall versus spring sampling on callus formation and shoot regeneration. Can. J. Bot. **66**, 1107–1110.

CARCELLER M., DAVEY M.R., FOWLER M.W. & STREET H.E. 1971 The influence of sucrose, 2,4-D and kinetin on the growth, fine structure and lignin content of cultured sycamore cells. Protoplasma **73**, 367–385.

CAREW D.P. & PATTERSON B.D. 1970 The effect of antibiotics on the growth of *C. roseus* tissue cultures. Lloydia **33**, 275–277.

CARLSON P. S. & CHALEFF R. S. 1974 Heterogenous associations of cells formed *in vitro*. pp. 245–261 in Ledoux L. (ed.) 1975 (*q.v.*).

CARMAN J.G. 1988 Improved somatic embryogenesis in wheat by partial stimulation of the *in-ovulo* oxygen growth regulator and desiccation environments. Planta **175**, 417–424.

CARMAN J.G. & CAMPBELL W.A. 1988 Factors affecting somatic embryogenesis in wheat. *In* Bajaj Y.P.S. (ed.) 1988. *Biotechnology in Agriculture and Forestry. Crops II*.

CARMAN J.G., JEFFERSON N.E. & CAMPBELL W.F. 1988a Induction of embryogenic *Triticum aestivum* L. calli. I. Quantification of genotype and culture medium effects. Plant Cell Tiss. Organ Cult. **12**, 83–95.

CARMAN J.G., JEFFERSON N.E. & CAMPBELL W.F. 1988b Induction of embryogenic *Triticum aestivum* L. calli. II. Quantification of organic addenda and other culture variable effects. Plant Cell Organ Tiss. Cult. **12**, 97–110.

CARR D.J. (ed.) 1972 *Plant Growth Substances* 1970. Springer Verlag, Berlin, Heidelburg, New York.

CARSWELL G.K., JOHNSON C.M., SHILLITO R.D. & HARMS C.T. 1989 *o*-Acetylsalicylic acid promotes colony formation from protoplasts of an elite maize inbred. Plant Cell Rep. **8**, 282–284.

CARUSO J.L. 1987 The auxin conjugates. HortScience **22**, 1201–1204.

CASE M.W. 1973 Rhubarb. Ann. Rep. Stockbridge House Experimental Hort. Sta., **15**,

CASSELLS A.C. 1979 The effect of 2,3,5-tri-iodobenzoic acid on caulogenesis in callus cultures of tomato and *Pelargonium*. Physiol. Plant. **46**, 159–164.

CASSELLS A.C. & BARLASS M. 1978 A method for the isolation of stable mesophyll protoplasts from tomato leaves throughout the year under standard conditions. Physiol. Plant. **42**, 236–242.

CASSELLS A.C. & LONG R.D. 1980a The regeneration of virus-free plants from cucumber mosaic virus and potato virus Y infected tobacco explants cultured in the presence of virazole. Z. Naturforschung **35c**, 350–351.

CASSELLS A.C. & LONG R.D. 1980b Tobacco explant culture as a screening system for antiviral chemicals. pp. 131–135 *in* Ingram and Helgeson (eds.) 1980 (*q.v.*).

CASSELLS A.C. & MINAS G. 1983 Plant and *in vitro* factors influencing the micropropagation of *Pelargonium* cultivars by bud-tip culture. Scientia Hort. **21**, 53–65.

CASSELLS A.C., HARMEY M.A., CARNEY B.F., McCARTHY E. & McHUGH A. 1988 Problems posed by cultivable bacterial endophpytes in the establishment of axenic cultures of *Pelargonium* × *domesticum*: The use of *Xanthomonas pelargonii* — specific ELISA, DNA probes and culture indexing in the screening of antibiotic treated and untreated donor plants. Acta Hort. **225**, 153–161.

CASSELLS A.C., LONG R.D. & MOUSDALE D.M.A. 1982 Endogenous IAA and morphogenesis in tobacco petiole cultures. Physiol. Plant. **56**, 507–512.

CASSELLS A.C., MINAS G. & LONG R. 1980 Culture of *Pelargonium* hybrids from meristems and explants: chimeral and beneficially-infected varieties. pp. 125–130 *in* Ingram and Helgeson (eds.) 1980 (*q.v.*).

CATHEY H.M. & CAMPBELL L.E. 1980 Light and lighting systems for horticultural plants. Hort. Rev. **2**, 491–537.

CATTOIR-REYNAERTS A., DEGRYSE E., NEGRUTIU I., AERTS M. & JACOBS M. 1981 Effects of aspartate-derived amino acids on growth of barley and *Arabidopsis* plants and callus. Z. Pflanzenphysiol. **101**, 67–74.

CELLÁROVÁ E., GRELAKOVA K., REPCAK M. & HONCARIV R. 1982 Morphogenesis in callus tissue cultures of some *Matricaria* and *Achillea* spp. Biol. Plant. **24**, 430–433.

CERUTTI P.A. 1985 Peroxidant states and tumor promotion. Science **227**, 375–381.

CERVELLI R. 1987 *In vitro* propagation of *Aconitum noveboracense* and *Aconitum napellus*. HortScience **22**, 304–305.

CHADWICK A.V. & BURG S.P. 1967 An explanation of the inhibition of root growth caused by indole-3-acetic acid. Plant Physiol. **42**, 415–420.

CHAILAKHYAN M.Kh. & KHRYANIN V.N. 1980 Hormonal regulation of sex expression in plants. pp. 331–344 *in* Skoog F. (ed.) 1980 (*q.v.*).

CHAILLOU S. & CHAUSSAT R. 1986 Changes in mineral concentration of potato organ fragments. Phytomorph. **36**, 263–270.

CHALEFF R.S. 1981 Genetics of higher plants. Applications of cell culture. Cambridge University Press.

CHALEFF R.S. 1983a Induction, maintenance and differentiation of rice callus cultures on ammonium as sole nitrogen source. Plant Cell Tiss. Organ Cult. **2**, 29–37.

CHALEFF R.S. 1983b Isolation of agronomically useful mutants from plant cell cultures. Science **219**, 676-682.

CHALEFF R.S. & STOLARZ A. 1981 Factors affecting the frequency of callus formation among cultured rice (*Oryza sativa*) anthers. Physiol. Plant. **51**, 201–206.

CHALUPA V. 1979 *In vitro* propagation of some broad-leaved forest trees. Commun. Inst. Forest. Cechoslov. **11**, 159–170.

CHALUPA V. 1981a Clonal propagation of broad-leaved forest trees *in vitro*. Commun. Inst. Forest. Cechoslov. **12**, 255–271.

CHALUPA V. 1983 *In vitro* propagation of Willows (*Salix* spp.), European Mountain ash (*Sorbus aucuparia* L.) and Black Locust (*Robinia pseudoacacia* L.). Biol. Plant. **25**, 305–307.

CHALUPA V. 1984 a *In vitro* propagation of oak (*Quercus robur* L.) and Linden (*Tilia cordata* Mill.). Biol. Plant. **26**, 374–377.

CHALUPA V. 1984b Vegetative propagation of English oak (*Quercus robur* L.), small-leaved Linden (*Tilia cordata* Mill.) and European mountain ash (*Sorbus aucuparia* L.) *in vitro*. Lesnictvi **30**, 1019–1028.

CHALUPA V. 1987 Temperature. pp. 142–151 *in* Bonga and Durzan (eds.) 1987a (*q.v.*).

CHALUTZ E. & DEVAY J.E. 1969 The production of ethylene *in vitro* and *in vivo* by *Ceratocystis fimbriata* in relation to disease development. Phytopath. **59**, 750–755.

CHAMBERS S.M., HEUCH J.H.R. & PIRRIE A. 1991 Micropropagation and *in vitro* flowering of the bamboo *Dendrocalamus hamiltonii* Munro. Plant Cell Tiss. Organ Cult. **27**, 45–48.

CHAMPAGNAT M. & MOREL G. 1972 La culture *in vitro* des tissus de tubercules d'Ophrys. Compt. Rend. Acad. Sci. Paris **274D**, 3379–3380.

CHANCEL L.M., MACHIEX J. & JONARD R. 1980 Les conditions du microbouturage *in vitro* du pêcher (*Prunus persica* Bathsch.): influences combinée des substances de croissance et de divers composés phénoliques. Physiol. Veg. **18**, 597–608.

CHAND S. & ROY S.C. 1980 Effect of different auxins on chromosome behaviour of leaf callus tissues of *Nigella sativa*. Caryologia **33**, 387–392.

CHAND S. & ROY S.C. 1981 Induction of organogenesis in callus cultures of *Nigella sativa* L. Ann. Bot. **48**, 1–4.

CHANDLER F.L. & HAQUE S.Q. 1984 The use of tissue culture in the production of improved yam and sweet potato planting material. pp. 69–87 in *Micropropagation of Selected Root Crops, Palms, Citrus and Ornamental Species*. FAO Plant Production & Protection Paper 59 FAO, Rome. ISBN 92-5-102157-0.

CHANDLER M.T., TANDEAU DE MARSAC N. & KOUCHKOVSKY Y. 1972 Photosynthetic growth of tobacco cells in liquid suspensions. Can. J. Bot. **50**, 2265–2270.

CHANDLER S. F., DODDS J. H. & HENSHAW G. G. 1982 Factors affecting adventitious shoot formation in *Solanum laciniatum* Ait. callus cultures. pp. 133–134 *in* Fujiwara A. (ed.) 1982 (*q.v.*)

CHANDLER S.F., PAEK K.Y., PUA E.-C., RAGOLSKY E., MANDAL B.B. & THORPE T.A. 1988 The effectiveness of selection for salinity tolerance using *in vitro* shoot cultures. Bot. Gaz. **149**, 166–172.

CHANDLER S.F., RAGOLSKY E., PUA E.-C. & THORPE T.A. 1987 Some morphogenic effects of sodium sulphate on tobacco callus. Plant Cell Tiss. Organ Cult. **11**, 141–150.

CHANDRA G.R., GREGORY L.E. & WORLEY J.F. 1971 Studies on the initiation of adventitious roots on mungbean hypocotyl. Plant & Cell Physiol. **12**, 317–324.

CHANG F.Y. & VANDEN BORN W.H. 1971 Dicamba uptake, translocation, metabolism and selectivity. Weed Sci. **19**, 113–117.

CHANG W.-C. & HSING Y.-I. 1980a *in vitro* flowering of embryoids derived from mature root callus of ginseng (*Panax ginseng*). Nature **284**, 341–342.

CHANG W.-C. & HSING Y.-I. 1980b Plant regeneration through somatic embryogenesis in root-derived callus of ginseng (*Panax ginseng* C.A. Meyer). Theor. Appl. Genet. **57**, 133.

CHARNE D.G., PUKACKI P., KOTT L.S. & BEVERSDORF W.D. 1988 Embryogenesis following cryopreservation in isolated microspores of rapeseed (*Brassica napus* L.). Plant Cell Rep. **7**, 407–409.

CHATFIELD J.M. & ARMSTRONG D.J. 1988 Cytokinin oxidase from *Phaseolus vulgaris* callus cultures. Affinity for concanavalin A. Plant Physiol. **88**, 245–247.

CHATTAWAY M.M. 1976 Bud development and lignotuber formation in eucalypts. Aust. J. Bot. **6**, 103–115.

CHATURVEDI H.C. & SHARMA A.K. 1977 Induced flowering in excised shoot apices of *Bougainvillea glabra* cv. 'Magnifica' grown *in vitro*. Ind. J. Exp. Biol. **15**, 402–403.

CHATURVEDI H.C. & SHARMA A.K. 1985 Androgenesis in *Citrus aurantifolia* (Christm.) Swingle. Planta **165**, 142–144.

CHATURVEDI H.C. & SINHA M. 1979b Mass propagation of *Dioscorea floribunda* by tissue culture. Econ. Bot. Inf. Service, Ext. Bull. National Bot. Res. Inst. Lucknow, **6**,

CHATURVEDI H.C., SHARMA A.K. & PRASAD R.N. 1978 Shoot apex culture of *Bougainvillea glabra* 'Magnifica'. HortScience **13**, (1) 36.

CHATURVEDI H.C., SHARMA A.K., SHARMA M. & PRASAD R.N. 1982 b Morphogenesis, micropropagation and germplasm preservation of some economic plants by tissue culture. pp. 687–688 *in* Fujiwara A. (ed.) 1982 (*q.v.*).

CHAUVIN J.E. & SALESSES G. 1988 Advances in chestnut micropropagation (*Castanea* sp.). Acta Hort. **227**, 340–345.

CHEAH K.-T. & CHENG T.-Y. 1978 Histological analysis of adventitious bud formation in cultured Douglas fir cotyledon. Am. J. Bot. **65**, 845–849.

CHEE R. 1986 *In vitro* culture of *Vitis*: The effects of light spectrum, manganese sulfate and potassium iodide on morphogenesis. Plant Cell Tiss. Organ Cult. **7**, 121–134.

CHEE R. & POOL R.M. 1982a The effects of growth substances and photoperiod on the development of shoot apices of *Vitis* cultured *in vitro*. Scientia Hort. **16**, 17–27.

CHEE R. & POOL R.M. 1982b *In vitro* micropropagation of *Vitis*, results with species and cultivars. HortScience **17**, 530 (Abst. 410).

CHEE R. & POOL R.M. 1989 Morphogenic response to propagule trimming, spectral irradiance and photoperiod of grapevine shoots recultured *in vitro*. J. Am. Soc. Hort. Sci. **114**, 350–354.

CHEE R.P., SCHULTHEIS J.R. & CANTCLIFFE D.J. 1990 Plant recovery from sweetpotato somatic embryos. HortScience **25**, 795–797.

CHEN C.-M., ERTL J.R., LEISNER S.M. & CHANG C.-C. 1985 Localization of cytokinin biosynthetic sites in pea plant and carrot roots. Plant Physiol. **78**, 510–513.

CHEN C.H. & GOEDEN-KALLEMEYN Y.C. 1979 *In vitro* induction of tetraploid plants from colchicine-treated diploid daylily callus. Euphytica **28**, 705–710.

CHEN H.-R. & GALSTON A.W. 1967 Growth and development of *Pelargonium* pith cells *in vitro*. II. Initiation of organised development. Physiol. Plant. **20**, 533–539.

CHEN T.H.H. & KARTHA K.K. 1987 Cryopreservation of woody species. pp. 305–319 *in* Bonga and Durzan (eds.) 1987b (*q.v.*).

CHEN T.-H., LAM L. & CHEN S.-C. 1985 Somatic embryogenesis and plant regeneration from cultured young inflorescences of *Oryza sativa* L. (rice). Plant Cell Tiss. Organ Cult. **4**, 51–54.

CHEN Z. 1984 Chapter 19 — Rubber (*Hevea*). pp. 546–571 *in* Sharp (ed.) 1984 (*q.v.*).

CHEN Z., EVANS D.A., SHARP W.R., AMMIRATO P.V. & SONDAHL M.R. 1990 *Handbook of Plant Cell Culture* Vol. 6. *Perennial Crops*. McGraw-Hill Publishing Company. ISBN 0-07-010848-X

CHENG D.S.K. & WANG A. 1989 Process for regenerating corn. U.S. Patent No. 4843005

CHENG T. & SMITH H.H. 1973 The influence of genomes on autonomous growth of pith cultures of *N. glauca-langsdorffii* hybrids. Planta **113**, 29–34.

CHENG T.-Y. 1972 Induction of IAA synthesis in tobacco pith explants. Plant Physiol. **50**, 723–727.

CHENG T.-Y. 1976a Organogenesis in culture from cotyledon explants of Douglas fir. Plant Physiol. **57**, (5 Suppl.) 66 (Abst.342).

CHENG T.-Y. 1977 Factors effecting adventitious bud formation of cotyledon culture of douglas fir. Plant Sci. Lett. **9**, 179–187.

CHENG T.-Y. 1978a Clonal propagation of woody species through tissue culture techniques. Comb. Proc. Int. Plant Prop. Soc. **28**, 139–155.

CHENG T.-Y. & VOQUI T.H. 1977 Regeneration of Douglas fir plantlets through tissue culture. Science **198**, 306–307.

CHENG T.-Y., SAKA H. & VOQUI-DINH T.H. 1980 Plant regeneration from soybean cotyledonary node segments in culture. Plant Sci. Lett. **19**, 91–99.

CHENG Y.W. & CHUA S.E. 1982 The use of air flow system in plant tissue and organ cultures. pp. 210–212 *in* Rao A.N. (ed.) 1982 (*q.v.*).

CHESICK E.E., BILDERBACK D.E. & BLAKE G.M. 1990 *In vitro* multiple bud formation by 20 year-old Western Larch buds and stems. HortScience **25**, 114–116.

CHEVRE A.-M. & SALESSES G. 1987 Choice of explants for chestnut micropropagation. Acta Hort. **212**, 517–523.

CHEVRE A.-M., GILL S.S., MOURAS A. & SALESSES G. 1983 *In vitro* multiplication of chestnut. J. Hort. Sci. **58**, 23—29.

CHEYNE V.A. & DALE P.J. 1980 Shoot tip culture in forage legumes. Plant Sci. Lett. **19**, 303–309.

CHI G.-L., BARFIELD D.G., SIM G.-E. & PUA E.-C. 1990 Effect of AgNO3 and aminoethoxyvinylglycine on *in vitro* shoot and root organogenesis from seedling explants of recalcitrant *Brassica* genotypes. Plant Cell Rep. **9**, 195–198.

CHIARIOTTI A. & ANTONELLI M. 1988 The effect of 6-BAP and adenine sulphate on peach shoot proliferation. Acta Hort. **227**, 418–420.

CHIEN Y.C. & KAO K.N. 1983 Effects of osmolality, cytokinin and organic acids on pollen callus formation in *Triticale* anthers. Can. J. Bot. **61**, 639–641.

CHIN C-K. 1979 Growth behaviour of green and albino plantlets of *Episcia* 'Pink Brocade' in *in vitro* culture. Plant Physiol. **63**, (Suppl.5) 138 (Abs).

CHIN C-K. 1980 Growth behaviour of green and albino plants of *Episcia cupreata* 'Pink Brocade' *in vitro*. In Vitro **16**, 847–850.

CHIN C. & MILLER D. 1982 Some characteristics of the phosphate uptake by *Petunia* cells. HortScience **17**, 488 (Abst. 199).

CHIN C.-K. 1982 Promotion of shoot and root formation in *Asparagus in vitro* by ancymidol. HortScience **17**, 590–591.

CHIN C.-K., KONG Y. & PEDERSEN H. 1988 Culture of droplets containing asparagus cells and protoplasts on polypropylene membrane. Plant Cell Tiss. Organ Cult. **15**, 59–65.

CHLYAH A. 1972 Néoformation caulinaire et radiculaire chez les fragments de feuilles de *Begonia rex Putz: Action de divers facteurs régulateurs trophiques et d'environment. Biol. Plant.* **14**, 204–212.

CHLYAH H. 1974 Inter-tissue correlations in organ fragments: organogenetic capacity of tissues excised from stem segments of *Torenia fournieri* Lind. cultured separately *in vitro*. Plant Physiol. **54**, 341–348.

CHO S.-C. 1983 Effects of cytokinin and several inorganic cations on the polyamine content of lettuce cotyledons. Plant Cell Physiol. **24**, 27–32.

CHONG C. & PUA E.-C. 1985 Carbon nutrition of Ottawa 3 apple rootstock during stages of *in vitro* propagation. J. Hort. Sci. **60**, 285–290.

CHONG C. & TAPER C.D. 1972 *Malus* tissue culture. I. Sorbitol (D-glucitol) as carbon source for callus initiation and growth. Can. J. Bot. **50**, 1399–1404.

CHONG C. & TAPER C.D. 1974a *Malus* tissue cultures. II. Sorbitol metabolism and carbon nutrition. Can. J. Bot. **52**, 2361–2364.

CHONG C. & TAPER C.D. 1974b Influence of light intensity on sorbitol metabolism, growth and chlorophyll content of *Malus* tissue cultures. Ann. Bot. **38**, 359–362.

CHOPRA R.N. & RASHID A. 1969a Auxin-cytokinin interaction in shoot-bud formation of a moss, *Anoectangium thomsonii* Mitt. Z. Pflanzenphysiol. **61**, 192–198.

CHOPRA R.N. & RASHID A. 1969b Induction of shoot buds in *Anoectangium thomsonii* Mitt. by a metal chelate Fe-EDDHA. Z. Pflanzenphysiol. **61**, 199–202.

CHOUREY P.S. & KEMBLE R.J. 1982 Transposition event in tissue cultured cells of maize. pp. 425–426 *in* Fujiwara (ed.) 1982 (*q.v.*).

CHRISTIANSON M., WARNICK D.A. & CARLSON P.S. 1986 Plant generation by cell culture. U.S. Patent No. 4548901

CHRISTIANSON M.L. 1987 Causal effects in morphogenesis. pp. 45–55 *in* Green *et al.*(eds.) 1987 (*q.v.*).

CHRISTIANSON M.L. & WARNICK D.A. 1985 Temporal requirement for phytohormone balance in the control of organogenesis *in vitro*. Dev. Biol. **112**, 494–497.

CHRISTIANSON M.L. & WARNICK D.A. 1988 Organogenesis *in vitro* as a developmental process. HortScience **23**, 515–519.

CHRISTOU P. & BARTON K.A. 1989 Cytokinin antagonist activity of substituted phenethylamines in plant cell culture. Plant Physiol. **89**, 564–568.

CHROBOCZEK-KELKER H. & FILNER P. 1971 Regulation of nitrite reductase and its relationship to the regulation of nitrate reductase in cultured tobacco cells. Biochim. Biophy. Acta **252**, 69–82.

CHU C.-C. 1981 The N_6 medium and its applications to anther culture of cereal crops. pp. 43–50 *in* Anon 1981a (*q.v.*).

CHU C.-C., WANG C.-C., SUN C.-S., HSU C., YIN K.-C., CHU C.-Y. & BI F.-Y. 1975 Establishment of an efficient medium for anther culture of rice, through comparative experiments on the nitrogen sources. Scientia Sinic. **18**, 659–668.

CHU C.C. & HILL R.D. 1988 An improved anther culture method for obtaining higher frequency of pollen embryoids in *Triticum aestivum* L. Plant Science **55**, 175–181.

CHU C.C., WANG Y.X. & SANG J.L. 1987 Long-term plant regeneration from callus cultures of haploid wheat. Plant Cell Tiss. Organ Cult. **11**, 221–226.

CHU P.W.G. & FRANCKI R.I.B. 1982 Detection of lettuce necrotic yellows virus by an enzyme-linked immunosorbent assay in plant hosts and the insect vector. Ann. Appl. Biol. **100**, 149–156.

CHUA B.U., KUNISAKI J.T. & SAGAWA Y. 1981 *In vitro* propagation of *Dracaena marginata* Tricolor. HortScience **16**, p. 494.

CHUA S.E. 1966 Studies on tissue culture of *Hevea brasiliensis*. I. Role of osmotic concentration, carbohydrate and pH value in induction of callus growth in plumule tissue from *Hevea* seedling. J. Rubber Res. Inst. Malaya **19**, 272–276.

CHUANG C.-C., OUYANG T.-W., CHIA H., CHOU S.-M. & CHING C.-K. 1978 A set of potato media for wheat anther culture. pp. 51–56 *in* Anon 1981a (*q.v.*).

CHUN Y.W. & HALL R.B. 1986 Low temperature storage of *in vitro* cultured hybrid poplar, *Populus alba × P. grandidentata* plantlets. p. 13 *in* Abstracts VI Intl. Cong. Plant Tissue & Cell Culture, Minneapolis, Minn.

CHUN Y.W., HALL R.B. & STEPHENS L.C. 1986 Influences of medium consistency and shoot density on *in vitro* shoot proliferation of *Populus alba × P. grandidentata*. Plant Cell Tiss. Organ Cult. **5**, 179–185.

CHUNHE XU, BLAIR L.C., ROGERS S.M.D., GOVINDJEE & WIDHOLM J.M. 1988 Characteristics of five new photoautotrophic suspension cultures including two *Amaranthus* species and a cotton strain growing on ambient CO_2 levels. Plant Physiol. **88**, 1297–1302.

CHUONG P.V. & BEVERSDORF W.D. 1985 High frequency embryogenesis through isolated microspore culture in *Brassica napus* L and *B. carinata* Braun. Plant Science **39**, 219–226.

CHURCHILL M.E., ARDITTI J. & BALL E.A. 1971 Clonal propagation of orchids from leaf tips. Am. Orchid Soc. Bull. **40**, 109–113.

CHURCHILL M.E., BALL E.A. & ARDITTI J. 1973 Tissue culture of orchids. I. Methods for leaf tips. New Phytol. **72**, 161–166.

CIARROCCHI G., CELLA R. & NIELSEN E. 1981 Release of nucleotide- cleaving acid phosphatase from carrot cells grown in suspension culture. Physiol. Plant. **53**, 375–377.

CIONINI P.G., BENNICI A. & D'AMATO F. 1978 Nuclear cytology of callus induction and development *in vitro*. I. Callus from *Vicia faba* cotyledons. Protoplasma **96**, 101–112.

CLAPHAM D. 1973 Haploid *Hordeum* plants from anthers *in vitro*. Z. Pflanzenzucht. **69**, 142–155.

CLAPHAM D.H. 1977 Haploid induction in cereals. pp. 279–298 in Reinert & Bajaj (eds.) 1977 (*q.v.*).

CLARE M.V. & COLLIN H.A. 1974 The production of plantlets from tissue cultures of Brussels sprout (*Brassica oleracea* L. var. gemmifera D.C.). Ann. Bot. **38**, 1067–1076.

CLARK J.R. 1982 Juvenility and plant propagation. Comb. Proc. Int. Plant Prop. Soc. 1981 **31**, 449–453.

CLARK M.F. 1981 Immunosorbent assays in plant pathology. Ann. Rev. Phytopathol. **19**, 83–106.

CLARK M.F. & ADAMS A.N. 1977 Characteristics of the microplate method of enzyme-linked immunosorbent assay for the detection of plant viruses. J. Gen. Virol. **34**, 475–483.

CLARK P.A. & CASIERO B. 1979 A genealogical database for plant propagation records. Euphytica **28**, 785–792.

CLARKSON D.T. & HANSON J.B. 1980 The mineral nutrition of higher plants. Ann. Rev. Plant Physiol. **31**, 239–298.

CLELAND C.F. 1976 Synergistic interaction of red light and cytokinin in promotion of growth in *Lemna gibba* G3. Plant Physiol. **57**, (Suppl.) 75.

CLELAND R. 1977 The control of cell enlargement. pp. 101–115 *in* Jennings D.H. (ed.) S.E.B. Symp. 31. University Press, Cambridge.

CLELAND R.E. & LOMAX T. 1977 Hormonal control of H^+–excretion from oat cells. pp. 161–183 *in* Marre and Ciferri (eds.) 1977 (*q.v.*).

CLEMENTE M., CONTRERAS P., SUSIN J. & PLIEGO-ALFARO F. 1991 Micropropagation of *Artemisia granatensis*. HortScience **26**, 420.

CLOSE K.R. 1987 Process for regenerating corn. U.S. Patent No. 4665030.

CLOSE K.R. 1988 Process for regenerating corn. U.S. Patent No. 4830966.

CODRON H., LATCHE A., PECH J.C., NEBIE B. & FALLOT J. 1979 Control of quiescence and viability in auxin-deprived pear cells in batch and continuous culture. Plant Sci. Lett. **17**, 29–35.

COFFIN R., TAPER C.D. & CHONG C. 1976 Sorbitol and sucrose as carbon source for callus culture of some species of the Rosaceae. Can. J. Bot. **54**, 547–551.

COHEN D. & COOPER P. A. 1982 Micropropagation of babaco — a *Carica* hybrid from Ecuador. pp. 743–744 *in* Fujiwara A. (ed.) 1982 (*q.v.*).

COHEN J.D. & BANDURSKI R.S. 1982 Chemistry and physiology of the bound auxins. Ann. Rev. Plant Physiol. **33**, 403–430.

COLCLASURE G.C. & YOPP J.H. 1976 Galactose-induced ethylene evolution in Mung bean hypocotyls: a possible mechanism for galactose retardation of plant growth. Physiol. Plant. **37**, 298–302.

COLEMAN W.K. & GREYSON R.I. 1977a Analysis of root formation in leaf discs of *Lycopersicon esculentum* Mill. cultured *in vitro*. Ann. Bot. **41**, 307–320.

COLEMAN W.K. & GREYSON R.I. 1977b Promotion of root initiation by gibberellic acid in leaf discs of tomato (*Lycopersicon esculentum*) cultured *in vitro*. New Phytol. **78**, 47–54.

COLEMAN W.K., & THORPE T.A. 1977 *In vitro* culture of Western Red Cedar (*Thuja plicata* Donn). I. Plantlet formation. Bot. Gaz. **138**, 298–304.

COLEMAN W.K., HUXTER T.J., REID D.M. & THORPE T.A. 1980 Ethylene as an endogenous inhibitor of root regeneration in tomato leaf discs cultured *in vitro*. Physiol. Plant. **48**, 519–525.

COLIJN-HOOYMANS C.M., BOUWER R. & DONS J.J.M., 1988a Plant regeneration from cucumber protoplasts. Plant Cell Tiss. Organ Cult. **12, 147–150**.

COLLINS G.B. 1978 Pollen and anther cultures —progress and applications. pp. 179–188 *in* Hughes *et al*. (eds.) 1978 (*q.v.*).

COLLINS G.B. & GROSSER J.W. 1984 Culture of embryos. pp. 241–257 *in* Vasil I.K. (ed.) 1984 *Cell Culture and Somatic Cell Genetics of Plants* Vol. 1. *Laboratory Procedures and their Applications.* Academic Press, New York.

COLMAN B., MAWSON B.T. & ESPIE G.S. 1979 The rapid isolation of photosynthetically active mesophyll cells from *Asparagus* cladophylls. Can. J. Bot. **57**, 1505–1510.

COMPTON M.E. & PREECE J.E. 1988a Effects of phenolic compounds on tobacco callus and blackberry shoot cultures. J. Am. Soc. Hort. Sci. **113**, 160–163.

CONGER B.V. (ed.) 1981a *Cloning Agricultural Plants via* In Vitro *Techniques*. CRC Press Inc., Boca Raton, Florida.

CONGER B.V. & McDANIEL J.K. 1983 Use of callus cultures to screen tall Fescue seed samples for *Acremonium coenophialum*. Crop Sci. **23**, 172–174.

CONN E.E. (ed.) 1981 *The Biochemistry of Plants*. Vol. 7. *Secondary Plant Products*. Academic Press. New York, London, Toronto. ISBN 0-12-675407-1

CONNER A.J. & MEREDITH C.P. 1984 An improved polyurethane support system for monitoring growth in plant cell cultures. Plant Cell Tiss. Organ Cult. **3**, 59–68.

CONRAD P.L., CONRAD J.M., DURBIN R.D. & HELGESON J.P. 1981 Effects of some organic buffers on division of protoplast-derived cells and plant regeneration. Plant Physiol. **67**, (Suppl) 116 (Abst.654).

CONSTABEL F. 1982 Isolation and culture of plant protoplasts. pp. 38–48 *in* Wetter and Constabel (eds.) 1982 (*q.v.*).

CONSTANTIN M.J. 1981 Chromosome instability in cell and tissue cultures and regenerated plants. Env. Exp. Bot. **21**, 359–368.

CONSTANTIN M.J., HENKE R.R. & MANSUR M.A. 1976 Effects of activated charcoal and hormones on growth and organogenesis in tobacco callus. In Vitro **12**, 332–333.

CONSTANTIN M.J., HENKE R.R. & MANSUR M.A. 1977 Effects of activated charcoal on callus growth and shoot organogenesis in tobacco. In Vitro **13**, 293–296.

CONSTANTIN M.J., WEST L.K. & MOKHTARZADEH A. 1978 Effect of continued subculturing of Wisconsin-38 tobacco callus on performance of regenerated plants. p. 255 *in* Hughes *et al.* (eds.) 1978 (*q.v.*).

CONSTANTIN M.J., HENKE R.R., HUGHES K.W. & CONGER B.V. (eds.) 1981 *Propagation of higher plants through tissue culture: Emerging Technologies and Strategies*. Permagon Press, Oxford, New York, Sydney. ISBN 0098-8472

COOKE R.C. 1979 Homogenisation as an aid in tissue culture propagation of *Platycerium* and *Davallia*. HortScience **14**, 21–22.

COOLEY G. & WILCOX A. 1984 Sunflower regeneration through embryogenesis and organogenesis. U.S. Patent No. 4670391

COOMBES A.J., PHIPPS N.W. & LEPP N.W. 1977 Uptake patterns of free and complexed copper in excised roots of barley (*Hordeum vulgare* L. var. Zephyr). Z. Pflanzenphysiol. **82**, 435–439.

COOPER A. 1979 *The ABC of NFT*. Grower Books, London. ISBN 0 901 361224.

COOPER P.A. 1987 Advances in the micropropagation of avacado (*Persea americana* Mill.). Acta Hort. **212**, 571–576.

COOPER V.C. & WALKEY D.G.A. 1978 Thermal inactivation of cherry leaf roll virus in tissue cultures of *Nicotiana rustica* raised from seeds and meristem-tips. Ann. Appl. Biol. **88**, 273–278.

COREY K.A. & BARKER A.V. 1987 Physiology of ethylene evolution by tomato plants under ammmonium-induced stress. HortScience **22**, 381 (Abst.).

CORLEY R.H., WOOI K.C. & WONG C.Y. 1979 Progress with vegetative propagation of oil palm. Planter **55**, 377–380.

CORLEY R.H.V., LEE C.H., LAW L.H. & WONG C.Y. 1986 Abnormal flower development in oil palm clones. Planter **62**, 233–240.

CORNEJO-MARTIN M.J., MINGO-CASTEL A.M. & PRIMO-MILLO E. 1979 Organ redifferentiation in rice callus: effects of C_2H_4, CO_2 and cytokinins. Z. Pflanzenphysiol. **94**, 117–123.

CORNU D. & MICHEL M.F. 1987 Bacteria contaminants in shoot cultures of *Prunus avium* L. Choice and phytotoxicity of antibiotics. Acta Hort. **212**, 83–86.

COUMANS M., COUMANS-GILLÈS M. F., MENARD D., KEVERS C. & CEULEMANS E. 1982 Micropropagation of sugarbeet: possible ways. pp. 689–690 in Fujiwara (ed.) 1982 (*q.v.*).

COUMANS-GILLÈS M.F., KEVERS C., COUMANS M., CEULEMANS E. & GASPAR Th. 1981 Vegetative multiplication of sugarbeet through *in vitro* culture of inflorescence pieces. Plant Cell Tiss. Organ Cult. **1**, 93–101.

COUSSON A. & TRAN THANH VAN K. 1981 In vitro control of *de novo* flower differentiation from tobacco thin cell layers cultured on a liquid medium. Physiol. Plant. **51**, 77–84.

CRANE M.B. & LAWRENCE W.J.C. 1956 *The Genetics of Garden Plants*. Fourth edition. MacMillan & Co. Ltd., London, New York.

CRAVEN G.A., MOTT R.L. & STEWARD F.C. 1972 Solute accumulation in plant cells. IV. Effects of ammonium ions on growth and solute content. Ann. Bot. **36**, 897–914.

CREEMERS-MOLENAAR J., LOEFFEN J.P.M. & VAN DER VALK P. 1988 The effect of 2.4-dichlorophenoxyacetic acid and donor plant environment on plant regeneration from immature inflorescence-derived callus of *Lolium perenne* L. and *Lolium multiflorum* L. Plant Science **57**, 165–172.

CREEMERS-MOLENAAR J. & VAN OORT Y. 1990 Antioxidants influence the plating efficiency and microcallus-growth of protoplasts in *Lolium perenne* L. pp. 44–49 *in* Nijkamp *et al.* (eds.) 1990 (*q.v.*).

CREISSEN G.P. & KARP A. 1985 Karyotypic changes in potato plants regenerated from protoplasts. Plant Cell Tiss. Organ Cult. **4**, 171–182.

CREMIERE L., SBAY H. & PRAT D. 1987 *In vitro* culture of *Alnus* species. Acta Hort. **212**, 543–546.

CRESSWELL R. & NITSCH C. 1975 Organ culture of *Eucalyptus grandis*. Planta **125**, 87–90.

CREVECOUR M., KEVERS C., GREPPIN H. & GASPAR T. 1987 A comparative biochemical and cytological characterization of normal habituated sugarbeet calli. Biol. Plant. **29**, 1–6.

CRISP P. & WALKEY D.G.A. 1974 The use of aseptic meristem culture in cauliflower breeding. Euphytica **23**, 305–313.

CROES A.F. & BARENDSE G.W.M. 1986 Uptake and metabolism of hormones as related to *in vitro* flower bud development in tobacco. p. 299 *in* Somers *et al.* (eds.) 1986 (*q.v.*).

CROES A.F., CREEMERS-MOLENAAR T., VAN DEN ENDE G., KEMP A. & BARENDSE G.W.M. 1985 Tissue age as an endogenous factor controlling *in vitro* bud formation on explants from the inflorescence of *Nicotiana tabacum* L. J. Exp. Bot. **36**, 1771–1779.

CROUCH M.L. 1982 Non-zygotic embryos of *Brassica napus* L. contain embryo-specific storage proteins. Planta **156**, 520–524.

CROZIER A. & HILLMAN J.R. (eds.) 1984 *The Biosynthesis and Metabolism of Plant Hormones*. Soc. for Experimental Biology, Seminar series **23**. Cambridge Univ. Press. ISBN 0 521 26424 3

CRUICKSHANK I.A.M., DUDMAN W.F., PEOPLES M.B. & SMITH M.M. 1987 Elicitation of pisatin in pea (*Pisum sativum* L.) by copper-asparagine complexes. Aust. J. Plant Physiol. **14**, 549–559.

CULAFIC L., BUDIMIR S., VUJICIC R. & NESKOVIC M. 1987b Induction of somatic embryogenesis and embryo development in *Rumex acetosella* L. Plant Cell Tiss. Organ Cult. **11**, 133–139.

CUMMINGS P.D., GREEN C.E. & STUTHMAN D.D. 1976 Callus induction and plant regeneration in oats. Crop Sci. **16**, 465–470.

CURE W.W. & MOTT R.L. 1978 Anatomy of organogenesis in maize, wheat and oats. Physiol. Plant. **42**, 91–96.

CURIR P., DAMIANO C., ESPOSITO P. & RUFFONI B. 1988 *In vitro* propagation of *Ruseus racemosus* Moench. Acta Hort. **226**, 217–222.

CUTTER E.G. 1962 Regeneration in *Zamioculcas*: an experimental study. Ann. Bot. **26**, 55–70.

D'AMATO F. 1975 The problem of genetic stability in plant tissue and all cultures. pp. 333–348 *in* Frankel & Hawkes (eds.) 1975 (*q.v.*).

D'AMATO F. 1977 Cytogenetics of differentiation in tissue and cell cultures. pp. 343–357 *in* Reinert & Bajaj (eds.) 1977 (*q.v.*).

D'AMATO F. 1978 Chromosome number variation in cultured cells and regenerated plants. pp. 287–295 *in* Thorpe T.A. (ed.) 1978 *Frontiers of Plant Tissue Culture* 1978. Int. Assoc. Plant Tiss. Culture, University Calgary Printing Services, Calgary, Canada.

DABIN P. & BEGUIN F. 1987 Somatic embryogenesis in *Fuchsia*. Acta Hort. **212**, 725–726.

DABIN P. & BOUHARMONT J. 1983 Application of *in vitro* cultures in azalea (*Rhododendron simsii* Planch.). Acta Hort. **131**, 89–93.

DAGUIN F. & LETOUZÉ R. 1985 Relations entre hypolignification et état vitreux chez *Salix babylonica* en culture *in vitro*. Role de la nutrition ammoniacale. Can. J. Bot. **63**, 324–326.

DAGUIN F. & LETOUZÉ R. 1986 Ammonium-induced vitrification in cultured tissues. Physiol. Plant. **66**, 94–98.

DAI C., LAMBETH V.N., TAVEN R. & MERTZ D. 1987 Micropropagation of *Rhododendron prinophyllum* by ovary culture. HortScience **22**, 491–493.

DAI J., KAUR-SAWHNEY R. & GALSTON A.W. 1982 Promotion by gibberellic acid of polyamine biosynthesis in internodes of light-grown dwarf peas. Plant Physiol. **69**, 103–105.

DALE P.J., CHEYNE V.A. & DALTON S.J. 1980 Pathogen elimination and *in vitro* plant storage in forage grasses and legumes. pp. 119–124 *in* Ingram & Helgeson (eds.) 1980 (*q.v.*).

DALE P.J., THOMAS E., BRETTELL R.I.S. & WERNICK W. 1981 Embryogenesis from cultured immature inflorescences and nodes of *Lolium multiflorum*. Plant Cell Tiss. Organ Cult. **1**, 47–55.

DALESSANDRO G. 1973 Interaction of auxin, cytokinin and gibberellin on cell division and xylem differentiation in cultured explants of Jerusalem artichoke. Plant Cell Physiol. **14**, 1167–1176.

DALTON C.C. 1980 Photoautotrophy of spinach cells in continuous culture: Photosynthetic development and sustained photoautotrophic growth. J. Exp. Bot. **31**, 791–804.

DALTON C.C. & STREET H.E. 1976 The role of the gas phase in the greening and growth of illuminated cell suspension cultures of spinach (*Spinacea oleracea* L.). In Vitro **12**, 485–494.

DALTON C.C., IQBAL K. & TURNER D.A. 1983 Iron phosphate precipitation in Murashige and Skoog media. Physiol. Plant. **57**, 472–476.

DALTON S.J. & DALE P.J. 1981 Induced tillering of *Lolium multiflorum in vitro*. Plant Cell Tiss. Organ Cult. **1**, 57–64.

DAMANN K.E. Jr. 1983 Evaluation of commercial heat-treatment methods for control of ratoon stunting disease. Plant Disease **67**, 966–967.

DAMIANO C. 1980a Strawberry micropropagation. pp. 11–22 *in* Anon, 1980 (*q.v.*).

DAMIANO C. 1980b Planning and building a tissue culture laboratory. pp. 93–101 *in* Anon, 1980b (*q.v.*).

DAMIANO C., CURIR P. & COSMI T. 1987 Short note on the effects of sugar on the growth of *Eucalyptus gunnii in vitro*. Acta Hort. **212**, 553–556.

DAMM B. & WILLMITZER L. 1991 *Arabidopsis* protoplast transformation and regeneration. Section A7 pp. 1–20 *in* Lindsey (ed.) 1991 (*q.v.*).

DANCKWARDT-LILLIESTROM C. 1957 Kinetin induced shoot formation from isolated roots of *Isatis tinctoria*. Physiol. Plant. **10**, 794–797.

DANDEKAR A.M., MARTIN L.A. & McGRANAHAN G. 1988 Genetic transformation and foreign gene expression in walnut tissue. J. Am. Soc. Hort. Sci. **113**, 945–949.

DANILINA A.N. 1972 Morphogenesis of embryoids from carrot tissue cultures. Phytomorph. **22**, 160–164.

DAS R., BAGGA S. & SOPORY S.K. 1987 Involvement of phosphoinositides, calmodulin and glyoxidase-1 in cell proliferation in callus cultures of *Amaranthus paniculatus*. Plant Sci. **53**, 45–51.

DATTA K. & DATTA S.K. 1984 Rapid clonal multiplication of *Angelonia saricariefolia* through tissue culture. Plant Cell Tiss. Organ Cult. **3**, 215–220.

DAVEY M.R. & POWER J.B. 1988 Aspects of protoplast culture and plant regeneration. Plant Cell Tiss. Organ Cult. **12**, 115–125.

DAVEY M.R., COCKING E.C., FREEMAN J., DRAPER J., PEARCE N., TUDOR I., HERNALSTEENS J.P., DE BEUCKELEER M., VAN MONTAGU M. & SCHELL J. 1980 The use of plant protoplasts for transformation by *Agrobacterium* and isolated plasmids. pp. 425–430 *in* Ferenczy and Farkas (eds.) 1980 (*q.v.*).

DAVEY M.R., FOWLER M.W. & STREET H.E. 1971 Cell clones contrasted in growth, morphology and pigmentation isolated from a callus culture of *Atropa belladonna* var. lutea. Phytochem. **10**, 2559–2575.

DAVID A. 1972 Effets de diverses solutions minérales sur la prolifération des tissus de *Pin maritime* en culture *in vitro*. Compt. Rend. Acad. Sci. Paris **275D**, 2857–2860.

DAVID A., DAVID H. & MATEILLE T. 1982a In vitro adventitious budding on *Pinus pinaster* cotyledons and needles. Physiol. Plant. **56**, 102–107.

DAVIDONIS G.H. & HAMILTON R.H. 1983 Plant regeneration from callus tissue of *Gossypium hirsutum* L. Plant Sci. Lett. **32**, 89–93.

DAVIES D.D. 1980 Anaerobic metabolism and the production of organic acids. pp. 581–611 in *The Biochemistry of Plants* Vol 2. Academic Press Inc., ISBN 0-12-675402-0

DAVIES D.R. 1960 The embryo culture of interspecific hybrids of *Hordeum*. New Phytol. **59**, 9–14.

DAVIES D.R. & ALLEN Y. 1973 In vitro propagation of *Freesia*. Ann. Rep. John Innes Inst. 1973 67–68.

DAVIES M.E. 1972a Polyphenol synthesis in cell suspension cultures of Paul's Scarlet Rose. Planta **104**, 50–65.

DAVIES M.E. & DALE M.M. 1979 Factors affecting *in vitro* shoot regeneration on leaf discs of *Solanum laciniatum*. Z. Pflanzenphysiol. **92**, 51–60.

DAVIS M.J., BAKER R. & HANAN J.J. 1977 Clonal multiplication of carnation by micropropagation. J. Am. Soc. Hort. Sci. **102**, 48–53.

DAVIS T.D., STEFFENS G.L. & SANKHLA N. 1988 Triazole plant growth regulators. Hort. Rev. **10**, 63–105.

DAY A. & ELLIS T.H.N. 1984 Chloroplast DNA deletions associated with wheat plants regenerated from pollen: possible basis for material inheritance of chloroplasts. Cell **39**, 359–368.

DAY A. & ELLIS T.H.N. 1985 Deleted forms of plastid DNA in albino plants from cereal anther culture. Curr. Genet. **9**, 671–678.

DAY D. 1942 Thiamin content of agar. Bull. Torrey Bot. Club **69**, 11–20.

DAY P.R. 1980 Tissue culture methods in plant breeding. pp. 223–231 *in* Ingram and Helgeson (eds.) 1980 (*q.v.*).

DE BRUIJNE E. & DEBERGH P. 1974 Response of cymbidium protocorms to major element deficiency in a culture medium. Med. Fac. Landbouwwet., Rijksuniv. Gent **39**, 210–215.

DE BUYSER J., HARTMAN C., HENRY Y. & RODE A. 1988 Variations in long-term wheat somatic tissue culture. Can. J. Bot. **66**, 1891–1895.

DE CAPITE L. 1948 pH of nutritive solutions and its influence on the development of plants. Ann. facolta agrar. univ. Perugia **5**, 135–145.

DE CAPITE L. 1952a Combined action of p-aminobenzoic acid and indoleacetic acid on the vascular parenchyma of Jerusalem artichoke cultured *in vitro*. Compt. Rend. Soc. Biol. **146**, 863–865.

DE CAPITE L. 1952b Action of *p*-aminophenylsulphonamide and *p*-amino-benzoic acid on the vascular parenchyma of Jerusalem artichoke and of crown-gall tissue of salsify. Compt. Rend. Acad. Sci. Paris **234**, 2478–2480.

DE DONATO M. 1979 Micropropagazione *in vitro* di *Nephrolepis exaltata* var. Bostoniensis. pp. 71–78 *in* Anon 1979 (*q.v.*).

DE FOSSARD R. A. 1976 *Tissue Culture for Plant Propagators*. Dept. Continuing Education, Univ. of New England, NSW 2351, Australia.

DE FOSSARD R.A. 1977 Tissue culture in horticulture —A perspective. Acta Hort. **78**, 455–459.

DE FOSSARD R.A. 1981 Tissue culture propagation of *Eucalyptus ficifolia* F. Muell. pp. 425–438 *in* Anon(1981a) *q.v.*.

DE FOSSARD R.A. 1985 Tissue culture propagation: state of the art. Acta Hort. **166**, 83–92.

DE FOSSARD R.A. 1986 Principles of plant tissue culture. pp. 1–13 *in* Zimmerman *et al.* (eds.) 1986 (*q.v.*).

DE FOSSARD R.A. & BOURNE R.A. 1977 Reducing tissue culture costs for commercial propagation. Acta Hort. **78**, 37–44.

DE FOSSARD R.A. & DE FOSSARD H. 1988a Coping with microbial contaminants and other matters in a small commercial micropropagation laboratory. Acta Hort. **225**, 167–176.

DE FOSSARD R.A. & DE FOSSARD H. 1988b Micropropagation of some members of the Myrtaceae. Acta Hort. **227**, 346–351.

DE FOSSARD R.A., BARKER P.K. & BOURNE R.A. 1977 The organ culture of nodes of four species of *Eucalyptus*. Acta Hort. **78**, 157–165.

DE FOSSARD R.A., BENNETT M.T., GORST J.R. & BOURNE R.A. 1978 Tissue culture propagation of *Eucalyptus ficifolia* F. Muell. Comb. Proc. Int. Plant Prop. Soc. **28**, 427–434.

DE FOSSARD R.A., MYINT A. & LEE E.C.M. 1974a A broad spectrum tissue culture experiment with tobacco (*Nicotiana tabacum*) pith tissue callus. Physiol. Plant. **31**, 125–130.

DE FOSSARD R.A., NITSCH C., CRESSWELL R.J. & LEE E.C.M. 1974b Tissue and organ culture of *Eucalyptus*. N. Z. J. Forest Sci. **4**, 267–278.

DE GREEF W. & JACOBS M. 1979 *In vitro* culture of the sugarbeet: description of a cell line with high regeneration capacity. Plant Sci. Lett. **17**, 55–61.

DE GREEF W., DELON R., DE BLOCK M., LEEMANS J. & BOTTERMAN J. 1989 Evaluation of herbicide resistance in transgenic crops under field conditions. Bio/Technology **7**, 61–64.

DE JONG A.W. & BRUINSMA J. 1974 Pistil development in Cleome flowers III. Effects of growth-regulating substances on flower buds of *Cleome iberidella* Welv. ex Oliv. grown *in vitro*. Z. Pflanzenphysiol. **73**, 142–151.

DE JONG A.W., SMIT A.L. & BRUINSMA J. 1974 Pistil development in Cleome flowers II. Effects of nutrients on flower buds of *Cleome iberidella* Welv. ex Oliv. grown *in vitro*. Z. Pflanzenphysiol. **72**, 227–236.

DE KLERK-KIEBERT Y.M. & VAN DER PLAS L.H.W. 1985 Relationship of respiratory pathways in soybean cell suspensions to growth of the cells at various glucose concentrations. Plant Cell Tiss. Organ Cult. **4**, 225–233.

DE KRUIJFF E. 1906 Composition of coconut water and presence of diastase in coconuts. Bull. Dep. Agric. Indes Neerland. **4**, 1–8.

DE LA GUARDIA M.D. & BENLLOCH M. 1980 Effects of potassium and gibberellic acid on stem growth of whole sunflower plants. Physiol. Plant. **49**, 443–448.

DE LANGHE E. & DE BRUIJNE E. 1976 Continuous propagation of tomato plants by means of callus cultures. Scientia Hort. **4**, 221–227.

DE LANGHE E.A.L. 1984 The role of *in vitro* techniques in germplasm conservation. pp. 131–137 *in* Holden & Williams (eds.) 1984 (*q.v.*).

DE MAGGIO A.E. & WETMORE R.H. 1961 Growth of fern embryos in culture. Nature **191**, 94–95.

DE NETTANCOURT D. & DEVREUX M. 1977 Incompatibility and *in vitro* cultures. pp. 426–441 *in* Reinert & Bajaj (eds.) 1977 (*q.v.*).

DE NETTANCOURT D., DIJKHUIS P., VAN GASTEL A.J.G. & BROERTJES C. 1971 The combined use of leaf irradiation and of the adventitious bud technique for inducing and detecting polyploidy, marker mutations and self-compatability in clonal populations of *Nicotiana alata* Link & Otto. Euphytica **20**, 508–521.

DE PROFT M.P., MAENE M.L. & DEBERGH P. 1985 Carbon dioxide and ethylene evolution in the culture atmosphere of *Magnolia* cultured *in vitro*. Physiol. Plant. **65**, 375–379.

DE ROPP R.S. 1949 The action of antibacterial substances on the growth of *Phytomonas tumefaciens* and of crowngall tumor tissue. Phytopath. **39**, 822–828.

DE WALD F.W. 1982 A small scale tissue culture laboratory. Comb. Proc. Int. Plant Prop. Soc. 1981 **31**, 134–136.

DE WINNAAR W. 1988 Clonal propagation of papaya *in vitro*. Plant Cell Tiss. Organ Cult. **12**, 305–310.

DEATON M., BUXTON J.W. & KEMP T.R. 1980 Senescence studies on *Nicotiana offinis* flowers cultured *in vitro*. HortScience **15**, 433 (Abst. 460).

DEBERGH P. 1975 Intensified vegetative multiplication of *Dracaena deremensis*. Acta Hort. **54**, 83–92.

DEBERGH P. 1976 An *in vitro* technique for the vegetative multiplication of chimaeral plants of *Dracaena* and *Cordyline*. Acta Hort. **64**, 17–19.

DEBERGH P. 1982 Physical properties of culture media. pp. 135–136 *in* Fujiwara A. (ed.) 1982 (*q.v.*).

DEBERGH P. & MAENE L. 1977 Rapid clonal propagation of pathogen- free pelargonium plants starting from shoot tips and apical meristems. Acta Hort. **78**, 449–454.

DEBERGH P. & MAENE L. 1984 Pathological and physiological problems related to the *in vitro* culture of plants. Parasitica **40**, 69–75.

DEBERGH P. & MAENE L. 1985 Some aspects of stock-plant preparation for tissue culture propagation. Acta Hort. **166**, 21–23.

DEBERGH P., HARBAOUI Y. & LEMEUR R. 1981 Mass propagation of globe artichoke (*Cynara scolymus*): evaluation of different hypotheses to overcome vitrification with special reference to water potential. Physiol. Plant. **53**, 181–187.

DEBERGH P.C. 1983 Effects of agar brand and concentration on the tissue culture medium. Physiol. Plant. **59**, 270–276.

DEBERGH P.C. 1986a Micropropagation in Horticulture. Proc. of Inst. Hort. Symposium, Univ. Nottingham, School of Agric. UK.

DEBERGH P.C. 1986b Plant Tissue and Cell Culture. pp. 383–393 in Green C.E. *et al.* (eds.) Alan R. Liss Inc., N.Y.

DEBERGH P.C. 1988 Micropropagation of woody species —state of the art on *in vitro* aspects. Acta Hort. **227**, 287–295.

DEBERGH P.C. & MAENE L.J. 1981 A scheme for the commercial propagation of ornamental plants by tissue culture. Scientia Hort. **14**, 335–345.

DEBERGH P.C. & VANDERSCHAEGHE A.M. 1988 Some symptoms indicating the presence of bacterial contaminants in plant tissue cultures. Acta Hort. **225**, 77–81.

DEBERGH P.C. & ZIMMERMAN R.H. 1991 *Micropropagation. Technology and Application.* Kluwer Academic Publishers. Dordrecht, Boston, London. ISBN 0-7923-0818-2

DEBERGH P.C.A. 1987 Recent trends in the application of tissue culture to ornamentals. pp. 383–393 in Green *et al.* (eds.) 1987 (*q.v.*).

DEBERGH P.C.A. & MAENE L.J. 1990 *Cordyline* and *Dracaena*. pp. 337–351 *in* Ammirato *et al.* (eds.) 1990 (*q.v.*).

DEIMLING S. & MÖLLERS C. 1988 Aseptic handling of potato material during protoplast isolation and regeneration. Acta Hort. **225**, 209–213.

DELARGY J.A. & WRIGHT C.E. 1979 Root formation in cuttings of apple in relation to auxin application and to etiolation. New Phytol. **82**, 341–347.

DELFEL N.E. & SMITH L.J. 1980 The importance of culture conditions and medium component interactions on the growth of *Cephalotaxus harringtonia* tissue cultures. Planta Medica **40**, 237–244.

DENCSO I. 1987 Factors influencing vitrification of carnation and conifers. Acta Hort. **212**, 167–176.

DENNIN K.A. & McDANIEL C.N. 1985 Floral determination in axillary buds of *Nicotiana silvestris*. Dev. Biol. **112**, 377–382.

DENTON I.R., WESTCOTT R.J. & FORD-LLOYD B.V. 1977 Significant morphological differences from control could be due to environmental factors. Potato Res. **20**, 131–136.

DEREUDDRE J. & ENGELMANN F. 1987 The use of cryopreservation for setting up banks of plant germplasm. pp. 48–78 *in* Boccon-Gibod *et al.* (eds.) 1987 (q.v.).

DEREUDDRE J., FABRE J. & BASSAGLIA C. 1988 Resistence to freezing in liquid nitrogen of carnation (*Dianthus caryophyllus* L. var. Eolo) apical and axillary shoot tips excised from different aged *in vitro* plantlets. Plant Cell Rep. **7**, 170–173.

DERRICK K.S. 1973 Quantitative assay for plant viruses using serologically specific electron microscopy. Virology **56**, 652–653.

DESAI H.V., BHATT P.N. & MEHTA A.R. 1986 Plant regeneration of *Sapindus trifoliatus* L. (soapnut) through somatic embryogenesis. Plant Cell Rep. **5**, 190–191.

DESJARDINS Y., LAFORGE F., LUSSIER C. & GOSSELIN A. 1988 Effect of CO_2 enrichment and high photosynthetic photon flux on the development of autotrophy and growth of tissue-cultured strawberry, raspberry and asparagus plants. Acta Hort. **230**, 45–53.

DESJARDINS Y., TIESSEN H. & HARNEY P.M. 1987c The effect of sucrose and ancymidol on the *in vitro* rooting of nodal sections of asparagus. HortScience **22**, 131–133.

DEUS-NEUMANN B. & ZENK M.H. 1984 Instability of indole alkaloid production in *Catharanthus roseus* cell suspension cultures. Planta Med. **50**, 427–431.

DEUTCH B. 1974 Bulblet formation in *Achimenes longiflora*. Physiol. Plant. **30**, 113–118.

DEVLIN R.M. 1975 *Plant Physiology.* 3rd. Edition. Van Nostrand Reinhold Co., New York.

DeWALD M.G., MOORE G.A., SHERMAN W.B. & EVANS M.H. 1988 Production of pineapple plants *in vitro*. Plant Cell Rep. **7**, 535–537.

DIAMANTOGLOU S. & MITRAKOS K. 1979 Sur la culture *in vitro* de l'embryon d'olivier (*Olea europea* L. var. Oleaster). Compt. Rend. Acad. Sci. Paris 288D **288D**, 1537–1540.

DICKENS C.W.S. & VAN STADEN J. 1985 *In vitro* flowering and fruiting of soybean explants. J. Plant Physiol. **120**, 83–86.

DICKINSON J.R., FORSYTH C. & VAN STADEN J. 1986 The role of adenine in the synthesis of cytokinins in tomato plants and in cell-free root extracts. Plant Growth Reg. **4**, 325–334.

DIGBY J. & SKOOG F. 1966 Cytokinin activation of thiamine biosynthesis in tobacco callus cultures. Plant Physiol. **41**, 647–652.

DIJAK M., SMITH K.L., WILSON T.J. & BROWN D.C.W. 1986 Stimulation of direct embryogenesis from mesophyll protoplasts of *Medicago sativa*. Plant Cell Rep. **5**, 468–470.

DIJKEMA C., BOOIJ H., DE JAGER P.A., DE VRIES S.C., SCHAAFSMA T.J. & VAN KAMMEN A. 1990 Aerobic hexose metabolism in embryogenic cell lines of *Daucus carota* studied by ^{13}C NMR using ^{13}C-enriched substrates. pp. 343–348 *in* Nijkamp *et al.* (eds.) 1990 (*q.v.*).

DIJKSTRA J. 1987 Results of experiments with runner plants of tissue cultured strawberry plants (cv. Gorella). pp. 11–14 *in* Boxus and Larvor (eds.) 1987 (*q.v.*).

DIMOCK A.W. 1962 Obtaining pathogen-free stock by cultured cutting techniques. Phytopath. **52**, 1239–1241.

DINNIS S. & ASCHER P.D. 1976 Tissue culture of bulb scale sections for asexual propagation of *Lilium*. HortScience **11**, 311 (Abst. 159).

DIX L. & VAN STADEN J. 1982 Auxin and gibberellin-like substances in coconut milk and malt extract. Plant Cell Tiss. Organ Cult. **1**, 239–245.

DIX P.J. & STREET H.E. 1976 Selection of plant cell lines with enhanced chilling resistance. Ann. Bot. **40**, 903–910.

DIXON N.E., GAZZOLA C., BLAKELEY R.L. & ZERNER B. 1975 Jack bean urease (EC 3.5.1.5). A metalloenzyme. A simple biological role for nickel? J. Am. Chem. Soc. **97**, 4131–4133.

DIXON R.K. & MARX D.H. 1987 Mycorrhizae. pp. 198–215 in Bonga and Durzan (eds.) 1987b (q.v.).

DODDS J. H. (ed.) 1983 *Tissue Culture of Trees.* Croom Helm, Kent, U.K. ISBN 0-7099-0830-X

DODDS J. H. & ROBERTS L. W. 1982 *Experiments in Plant Tissue Culture.* Cambridge University Press, Cambridge, London, New York.

DOERSCHUG M.R. & MILLER C.O. 1967 Chemical control of adventitious organ formation in *Lactuca sativa* explants. Am. J. Bot. **54**, 410–413.

DOLE J. & WILKINS H. 1988 A graft-transmissible factor in *Euphorbia pulcherrima* causing permanent changes in branching and other morphological characteristics. Acta Hort. **226**, 283–288.

DOLEY D. & LEYTON L. 1970 Effects of growth regulating substances and water potential on the development of wound callus in *Fraxinus*. New Phytol. **69**, 87–102.

DOLÉZEL J. & NOVÁK F.J. 1986 Sister chromatid exchanges in garlic (*Allium sativum* L.) callus cells. Plant Cell Rep. **5**, 280–283.

DOMMERGUES P. & GILLOT J. 1973 Obtention de clones génétiquement homogènes dans toutes leur couches ontogénique à partir d'une chimère d'oeillet american. Ann. Amel. Plantes **23**, 83–95.

DOMONEY C. & TIMMINS J.N. 1980 Ribosomal RNA gene redundancy in juvenile and mature ivy. J. Exp. Bot. 31, 1093–1100.

DONKERS J. & EVERS P. 1987 Growth regulator preconditioning of *Platanus × acerifolia* trees for micropropagation. Acta Hort. **212**, 113–116.

DONNELLY D.J. & VIDAVER W.E. 1984 Pigment content and gas exchange of red raspberry *in vitro* and *ex vitro*. J. Am. Soc. Hort. Sci. **109**, 177–181.

DOORBENBOS J. & KARPER J.J. 1975 X-ray induced mutations in *Begonia × hiemalis*. Euphytica **24**, 13–19.

DORÉ C. 1975 La multiplication clonale de l'asperge (*Asparagus officionalis*) par culture *in vitro*: son utilisation en sélection. Ann. Amel. Plantes **25**, 201–224.

DORÉ J. 1955 Studies in the regeneration of horseradish. Ann. Bot. **19**, 127–137.

DORLEY D. & LEYTON L. 1968 Effects of growth regulating substances and water potential on the development of secondary xylem in *Fraxinus*. New Phytol. **67**, 579–594.

DOS SANTOS A.V.P., OUTKA D.E., COCKING E.C. & DAVEY M.R. 1980 Organogenesis and somatic embryogenesis in tissues derived from leaf protoplasts and leaf explants of *Medicago sativa*. Z. Pflanzenphysiol. **99**, 261–270.

DOUGALL D.K. 1964 A method of plant tissue culture giving high growth rates. Exp. Cell Res. **33**, 438–444.

DOUGALL D.K. 1977 Current problems in the regulation of nitrogen metabolism in plant cell cultures. pp. 76–84 in Barz *et al.* (eds.) 1977 (q.v.).

DOUGALL D.K. 1980 Nutrition and metabolism. *Plant Tissue Culture as a Source of Biochemicals*. C.R.C. Press, Boca Raton, Florida.

DOUGALL D.K. 1981 Media factors affecting growth. pp. 277–280 in Constantin *et al.* (eds.) 1981 (q.v.).

DOUGALL D.K. & VERMA D.C. 1978 Growth and embryo formation in wild carrot suspension cultures with ammonium ion as a sole nitrogen source. In Vitro **14**, 180–182.

DOUGALL D.K. & WEYRAUCH K.W. 1980 Abilities of organic acids to support growth and anthocyanin accumulation by suspension cultures of wild carrot cells, using ammonium as the sole nitrogen source. In Vitro **16**, 969–975.

DOUGALL D.K., WEYRAUCH K.W. & ALTON W. 1979 The effects of organic acids on growth and anthocyanin production by wild carrot cells growing on ammonia as a sole nitrogen source. In Vitro **15**, 189–190 (Abst.103).

DOW J.M. & CALLOW J.A. 1979 Leakage of electrolytes from isolated leaf mesophyll cells of tomato induced by glycopeptides from culture filtrates of *Fulvia fulva* (Cooke) Ciferri (syn. *Cladosporium fulvum*). Physiol. Plant Path. **15**, 27–34.

DRAGET K.I., MYHRE S., SKJÅK-BR"K G. & ØSTGAARD K. 1988 Regeneration, cultivation and differentiation of plant protoplasts immobilized in Ca-alginate beads. J. Plant Physiol. **132**, 552–556.

DREW R.A. 1986 The use of tissue culture in the search for Panama disease resistant clones of banana. Comb. Proc. Int. Plant Prop. Soc., 1985 **35**, 44–53.

DREW R.A. 1987 The effects of medium composition and cultural conditions on *in vitro* root initiation and growth of papaya (*Carica papaya* L.). J. Hort. Sci. **62**, 551–556.

DREW R.A. & SMITH N.G. 1986 Growth of apical and lateral buds of pawpaw (*Carica papaya* L.) as affected by nutritional and hormonal factors. J. Hort. Sci. **61**, 535–543.

DREW R.L.K. 1979 The development of carrot (*Daucus carota* L.) embryoids (derived from cell suspension culture) into plantlets on a sugar-free basal medium. Hort. Res. **19**, 79–84.

DRIRA N. & BENBADIS A. 1975 Analyse, par culture d'anthères *in vitro*, des potentialités androgénétiques de deux espèces de citrus (*Citrus medica* L. et *Citrus limon* L. Burm.). Compt. Rend. Acad. Sci. Paris **281D**, 1321–1324.

DRIRA N. & BENBADIS A. 1985 Multiplication végétative du palmier dattier (*Phoenix dactylifera* L.) par révision, en culture *in vitro*, d'ébauches florales de pieds femelles. J. Plant Physiol. **119**, 227–235.

DRIVER J.A. & SUTTLE G.R.L. 1987 Nursery handling of propagules. pp. 320–335 in Bonga and Durzan (eds.) 1987b (q.v.).

DROLET G., DUMBROFF E.B., LEGGE R.L. & THOMPSON J.E. 1986 Radical scavenging properties of polyamines. Phytochem. **25**, 367–371.

DRUART Ph. 1988 Regulation of axillary branching in micropropagation of woody fruit species. Acta Hort. **227**, 369–380.

DRUART Ph., KEVERS Cl., BOXUS Ph. & GASPAR Th. 1982 *In vitro* promotion of root formation by apple shoots through darkness effect on endogenous phenols and peroxidases. Z. Pflanzenphysiol. **108**, 429–436.

DUBLIN P., ENJALRIC F., LARDET L., CARRON M.-P., TROLINDER N. & PANNETIER C. 1990 Estate crops. pp. 337–361 in Debergh and Zimmerman *et al.* (eds.) 1991 (q.v.).

DUCATÉ G., JACOB M. & SIMEON A. 1987 *Plant Micropropagation in Horticultural Industries. Preparation, Hardening and Acclimatization Processes.* Belgian Plant Tissue Culture Group, Symposium Florizel 87; Arlon, Belgium.

DUDITS D., NEMET G. & HAYDU Z. 1975 Study of callus growth and organ formation in wheat (*Triticum aestivum*) tissue cultures. Can. J. Bot. **53**, 957–963.

DUHAMET L. & MENTZER C. 1955 Essais d'isolement des substances excito-formatrices du lait de coco. Compt. Rend. Acad. Sci. Paris **241**, 86–88.

DUHEM K., LE MERCIER N. & BOXUS Ph. 1988 Difficulties in the establishment of axenic *in vitro* cultures of field collected coffee and *Cacao* germplasm. Acta Hort. **225**, 67–75.

DUNCAN D.R. & WIDHOLM J.M. 1987 Improved plant regeneration from maize callus cultures using AgNO₃. Plant Physiol. **83**, Suppl. 35 (Abst. 208).

DUNCAN D.R. & WIDHOLM J.M. 1988 Improved plant regeneration from maize callus cultures using 6-benzyl-aminopurine. Plant Cell Rep. **7**, 452–455.

DUNCAN P.J. & LINEBERGER R.D. 1981 Endophytic bacterial contamination in radish hypocotyl tissue. HortScience **16**, 432 (Abst. 246).

DUNLAP J.R., KRESOVICH S. & McGEE R.E. 1986 The effect of salt concentration on auxin stability in culture media. Plant Physiol. **81**, 934–936.

DUNSTAN D.I. 1982 Transplantation and post-transplantation of micropropagated tree-fruit rootstocks. Comb. Proc. Int. Plant Prop. Soc., 1981 **31**, 39–44.

DUNSTAN D.I. & SHORT K.C. 1977a Improved growth of tissue cultures of the onion *Allium cepa*. Physiol. Plant. **41**, 70–72.

DUNSTAN D.I. & SHORT K.C. 1977b *In vitro* studies on organogenesis and growth in *Allium cepa* tissue cultures. Acta Hort. **78**, 139–148.

DUNSTAN D.I. & SHORT K.C. 1979a Shoot production from the flower head of *Allium cepa* L. Scientia Hort. **10**, 345–356.

DUNSTAN D.I., BEKKAOUI F., PILON M., FOWKE L.C. & ABRAMS S.R. 1988 Effects of abscisic acid and analagues on the maturation of white spruce (*Picea glauca*) somatic embryos. Plant Science **58**, 77–84.

DUNSTAN D.I., SHORT K.C. & THOMAS E. 1978 The anatomy of secondary morphogenesis in cultured scutellum tissues of *Sorghum bicolor*. Protoplasma **97**, 251–260.

DUNSTAN W.R. 1906 Report on a sample of coconut "water" from Ceylon. Trop. Agric. (Ceylon) **26**, 377–378.

DUNWELL J.M. 1979 Anther culture in *Nicotiana tabacum*: The role of the culture vessel atmosphere in pollen embryo induction and growth. J. Exp. Bot. **30**, 419–428.

DUNWELL J.M. 1981a *In vitro* regeneration from excised leaves of three *Brassica* species. J. Exp. Bot. **32**, 789–799.

DUNWELL J.M. 1981b Influence of genotype and environment on growth of barley *Hordeum vulgare* embryos *in vitro*. Ann. Bot. **48**, 535–542.

DUNWELL J.M. 1985 Anther and ovary culture. pp. 1–44 in Bright and Jones (eds) 1985 *Cereal Tissue and Cell Culture*. Martinus Nijhoff, Dortrecht.

DUNWELL J.M. & CORNISH M. 1980 Regeneration of plants from immature embryos of *Secale cereale*. Ann. Rep. John Innes Inst., 1979 59–60.

DUNWELL J.M. & PERRY M.E. 1973 The influence of *in vivo* growth conditions of *N. tabacum* plants on the *in vitro* embryogenic potential of their anthers. Ann. Rep. John Innes Inst. **64**, 69–70.

DUNWELL J.M. & ROBERTS M. 1975 Influence of culture vessel size on embryo induction in anthers of *Nicotiana tabacum*. Ann. Rep. John Innes Inst., 1975 61–62.

DURAND J. 1979 High and reproducible plating efficiencies of protoplasts isolated from *in vitro* grown haploid *Nicotiana sylvestris* Spegaz. et Comes. Z. Pflanzenphysiol. **93**, 283–296.

DURAND R. & DURAND B. 1984 Sexual differentiation in higher plants. Physiol. Plant. **60**, 267–274.

DURAND-CRESSWELL R. & NITSCH C. 1977 Factors affecting the regeneration of *Eucalyptus grandis* by organ culture. Acta Hort. **78**, 149–155.

DURAND-CRESSWELL R., BOULAY M. & FRANCLET A. 1982 Vegetative propagation of *Eucalyptus*. pp. 150–181 in Bonga & Durzan (eds.) 1982 (*q.v.*).

DURBIN R.D. (ed.) 1979 *Nicotiana: Procedures for experimental use*. U.S. Dept. Agric., Technical Bulletin 1586.

DURZAN D.J. 1976 Biochemical changes during gynosperm development. Acta Hort. **56**, 183–194.

DURZAN D.J. 1982 Nitrogen metabolism and vegetative propagation of forest trees. pp. 256–324 in Bonga and Durzan (eds.) 1982a (*q.v.*).

DURZAN D.J. 1987 Ammonia: Its analogues, metabolic products and site of action in somatic embryogenesis. pp. 92–136 in Bonga and Durzan (eds.) 1987b (*q.v.*).

DURZAN D.J. 1988 Rooting in woody perennials: problems and opportunities with somatic embryos and artificial seeds. Acta Hort. **227**, 121–125.

DURZAN D.J. & GUPTA P.K. 1987 Somatic embryogenesis and polyembryogenesis in Douglas fir cell suspension cultures. Plant Sci. **1952**, 229–235.

DURZAN D.J., CHAFE S.C. & LOPUSHANSKI S.M. 1973 Effects of environmental changes on sugars, tannins and organised growth in cell suspension cultures of white spruce. Planta **113**, 241–249.

DYCHDALA G.R. 1977 pp. 167–195 in Block S.S. (ed.) *Disinfection, Sterilisation and Preservation*. Lea and Febiger, Philadelphia.

DYSON W.H. & HALL R.H. 1972 N^6-$(\Delta^2$-isopentenyl) adenosine: its occurrence as a free nucleoside in an autonomous strain of tobacco tissue. Plant Physiol. **50**, 616–621.

EAPEN S. & RAO P.S. 1985 Plant regeneration from immature inflorescence callus cultures of wheat, rye and triticale. Euphytica **34**, 153–159.

EAPEN S., ABRAHAM V., GERDEMANN M. & SCHIEDER O. 1989 Direct somatic embryogenesis, plant regeneration and evaluation of plants obtained from mesophyll protoplasts of *Brassica juncea*. Ann. Bot. **63**, 369–372.

EARLE E.D. 1983 The use of phytotoxins for *in vitro* selection of disease-resistant plants. pp. 265–278 in Anon (1983) q.v.

EARLE E.D. & LANGHANS R.W. 1974a Propagation of *Chrysanthemum in vitro* . I. Multiple plantlets from shoot tips and the establishment of tissue cultures. J. Am. Soc. Hort. Sci. **99**, 128–132.

EARLE E.D. & LANGHANS R.W. 1974b Propagation of carnation *in vitro*. HortScience **9**, 270–271.

EARLE E.D. & LANGHANS R.W. 1974c Propagation of *Chrysanthemum in vitro*. II. Production growth and flowering of plantlets from tissue cultures. J. Am. Soc. Hort. Sci. **99**, 352–358.

EARLE E.D. & LANGHANS R.W. 1975 Carnation propagation from shoot tips cultured in liquid medium. HortScience **10**, 608–610.

EARLE E.D. & TORREY J.G. 1965a Morphogenesis in cell colonies grown from *Convolvulus* cell suspensions plated on synthetic media. Am. J. Bot. **52**, 891–899.

EARLE E.D. & TORREY J.G. 1965b Colony formation by isolated *Convolvulus* cells plated on defined media. Plant Physiol. **40**, 520–528.

EARNSHAW B.A. & JOHNSON M.A. 1985 The effect of glutathione on development in wild carrot suspension cultures. Biochem. Biophys. Res. Comm. **133**, 988–993.

EARNSHAW B.A. & JOHNSON M.A. 1986 The role of antioxidants in the growth and development of wild carrot suspension cultures. p. 340 in Somers *et al.* (eds.) 1986 (*q.v.*).

EATON F.M. 1940 Interrelations in the effects of boron and indoleacetic acid on plant growth. Bot. Gaz. **101**, 700–705.

ECCHER T. & NOÈ N. 1989 Comparison between 2iP and zeatin in the micropropagation of highbush blueberry (*Vaccinium corymbosum*). Acta Hort. **241**, 185–190.

ECCHER T., NOÈ N., PIAGNANI C. & CASTELLI S. 1986 Effects of increasing concentrations of BAP and 2iP on *in vitro* culture of *Vaccinium cormbosum*. Acta Hort. **179**, 879–881.

ECONOMOU A. & READ P.E. 1980 Effect of benzyladenine pretreatments on shoot proliferation from petunia leaf segments. Proc. Plant Growth Reg. Working Group, U.S.A. **7**, 96–103.

ECONOMOU A. & READ P.E. 1986a Influence of light duration and irradiance on micropropagation of a hardy deciduous azalea. J. Am. Soc. Hort. Sci. **111**, 146–149.

ECONOMOU A.S. 1986 Effect of red and far-red light on azalea microcutting production in vitro and rooting *in vivo*. p.431 in Somers *et al.* (eds.) 1986 (*q.v.*).

ECONOMOU A.S. & READ P.E. 1984 *In vitro* shoot proliferation of Minnesota deciduous azaleas. HortScience **19**, 60–61.

ECONOMOU A.S. & SPANOUDAKI M.J. 1988 Regeneration *in vitro* of oleaster (*Elaeagnus angustifolia* L.) from shoot tips of mature tree. Acta Hort. **227**, 363–368.

EDELMAN J. & HANSON A.D. 1972 Sucrose suppression of chlorophyll synthesis in carrot-tissue cultures. J. Exp. Bot. **23**, 469–478.

EDRISS M.H. & BURGER D.W. 1984a *In vitro* propagation of 'Troyer' citrange from epicotyl segments. Scientia Hort. **23**, 159–162.

EDRISS M.H. & BURGER D.W. 1984b Micro-grafting shoot-tip culture of *Citrus* on three trifoliate rootstocks. Scientia Hort. **23**, 255–259.

EDWARDS K.L. & GOLDSMITH M.H.M. 1980 pH-dependent accumulation of indoleacetic acid by corn coleoptile sections. Planta **147**, 457–466.

EEUWENS C.J. 1976 Mineral requirements for growth and callus initiation of tissue explants excised from mature coconut palms (*Cocos nucifera*) and cultured *in vitro*. Physiol. Plant. **36**, 23–28.

EEUWENS C.J. & BLAKE J. 1977 Culture of coconut and date palm tissue with a view to vegetative propagation. Acta Hort. **78**, 277–281.

EICHHOLTZ D.A., ROBITAILLE H.A. & HASEGAWA P.M. 1979 Adventive embryony in apple. HortScience **14**, 699–700.

EICHHORN G.L. 1980 The function of metal ions in genetic regulation. pp. 1–21 in Sigel H. (ed.) 1980 *Metal Ions in Biological Systems* **10**. Marcel Dekker Inc. New York, Basel.

EILERS R.J., SULLIVAN J.C. & SKIRVIN R.M. 1988 Analyzing the effects of exogenous polyamines and growth regulators on plating efficiency of sweet potato protoplasts using a central composite test design. Plant Cell Rep. **7**, 216–219.

EINSET J.W. 1978 *Citrus* tissue culture — stimulation of fruit explant cultures with orange juice. Plant Physiol. **62**, 885–888.

EINSET J.W. 1986a Zeatin biosynthesis from N^6- $(\Delta^2$-isopentenyl)adinine in *Actinidia* and other woody plants. Proc. Nat. Acad. Sci. U.S.A. **83**, 972–975.

EINSET J.W. 1986b Role of cytokinin in shoot cultures of woody species. p. 298 in Somers *et al.* (eds.) 1986 (*q.v.*).

EINSET J.W. & ALEXANDER J.H. (III) 1985 Multiplication of *Syringa* species and cultivars in tissue culture. Comb. Proc. Int. Plant Prop. Soc. 1984 **34**, 628–636.

EINSET J.W. & SKOOG F. 1973 Biosynthesis of cytokinins in cytokinin-autotrophic tobacco callus. Proc. Nat. Acad. Sci. U.S.A. **70**, 658–660.

EL HINNAWIY E. 1974 Effect of some growth regulating substances and carbohydrates on chlorophyll production in *Melilotus alba* (Desr.) callus tissue cultures. Z. Pflanzenphysiol. **74**, 95–105.

EL-MANSY H.I. & SALISBURY F.B. 1971 Biochemical responses of *Xanthium* leaves to ultraviolet light. Rad. Bot. **11**, 325–328.

ELENA E.B. & GINZO H.D. 1988 Effect of auxin levels on shoot formation with different embryo tissues from a cultivar and a commercial hybrid of wheat (*Triticum aestivum* L.). J. Plant Physiol. **132**, 600–603.

ELLIOT M.C., MALONEY M.M. & HALL J.F. 1978 Auxin relations in *Sycamore* cell suspension cultures. Plant Physiol. **61**, (Suppl.) 45 (Abst. 244).

ELLIOT M.C., O'SULLIVAN A.M., HALL J.F., XING T. & BARKER R.D.J. 1986 The roles of IAA and IAA binding proteins in the regulation of *Acer pseudoplatanus* L. cell division. p. 23 *in* Somers *et al.* (1986) *q.v.*

ELLIOTT R.F. 1970 Axenic culture of meristem tips of *Rosa multiflora*. Planta **95**, 183–186.

ELMER O.H. 1936 Growth inhibition in the potato caused by a gas emanating from apples. J. Agric. Res. **52**, 609–626.

ELMORE H.W. & WHITTIER D.P. 1973 The role of ethylene in the induction of apogamous buds in *Pteridium gametophytes*. Planta **111**, 85–90.

ELOBEIDY A. & KORBAN S.S. 1988 The effect of thadiazuron on shoot regeneration from apple leaf discs. HortScience **23**, 755.

ELSHENNAWY O.A. & BLACKMON W.J. 1988 *In vitro* screening for stem rot (*Phytophthora cactorum*) resistance in Easter lily (*Lilium longiflorum*). HortScience **23**, 758.

ELSTNER E.F., KELLER G. & PARADIES I. 1983 Contrasting effects of the cotton defoliant thidiazuron and aminoethoxyvinylglycine, an inhibitor of ethylene formation, on stomatal aperture and on ethylene formation in bean (*Phaseolus vulgaris*) leaves. Ber. Deutsch. Bot. Ges. **96**, 459–467.

ELTINGE E.T. & REED H.S. 1940 The effect of zinc deficiency upon the root of *Lycopersicon esculentum*. Am. J. Bot. **27**, 331–335.

EMBREE G.G. & HICKS G.S. 1985 Field performance and micropropagation of a hardy apple rootstock candidate KSC-3. Can. J. Plant Sci. **65**, 459–464.

EMERY A.E.H. 1955 The formation of buds on the roots of *Chamaenerion angustifolium* (L.) Scop. Phytomorph. **5**, 139–145.

ENGELKE A.L., HAMZI H.Q. & SKOOG F. 1973 Cytokinin-gibberellin regulation of shoot development and leaf form in tobacco plantlets. Am. J. Bot. **60**, 491–495.

ENGELMANN F. & BAUBAULT C. 1986 La cryoconservation des embryons somatiques polliniques et zygotiques. Actual. Bot. **133**, 89–103.

ENGELMANN F., DUVAL Y. & DEREUDDRE J. 1985 Survie et prolifération d'embryons somatiques de palmier àhuile (*Elaesis guinensis* Jacq) après congélation dans l'azote liquide. Compt. Rend. Acad. Sci. Paris **301 III**, 111–116.

ENGELMANN F., GODIN G., LEBOEUF J. & BIGOT C. 1987 *In vitro* propagation of juvenile and adult clones of *Cunninghamia lanceolata* (Lamb.) Hook. Acta Hort. **212**, 479–487.

ENGLISH J., BONNER J. & HAAGEN-SMIT A.J. 1939 The wound hormones of plants. IV Structure and synthesis of a traumatin. J. Am. Chem. Soc. **61**, 3434–3436.

ENJALRIC F., CARRON M.P. & LARDET L. 1988 Contamination of primary cultures in tropical areas: the case of *Hevea brasiliensis*. Acta Hort. **225**, 57–65.

ENTSCH B., LETHAM D.S., PARKER C.W., SUMMONS R.E. & GOLLNOW B.I. 1980 Metabolites of cytokinins. pp. 109–118 *in* Skoog (ed.) 1980 (*q.v.*).

ENZMANN-BECKER G. 1973 Plating efficiency of protoplasts of tobacco in different light conditions. Z. Naturf. **28**, 470–471.

EPSTEIN E. 1971 *Mineral Nutrition of Plants. Principles and Perspectives*. John Wiley and Sons Inc., New York, London, Sydney, Toronto.

EREZ A., COUVILLON G.A. & KAYS S.J. 1980 The effect of oxygen concentration on the release of peach leaf buds from rest. HortScience **15**, 39–41.

ERIKSSON T. 1965 Studies on the growth requirements and growth measurements of cell cultures of *Happlopapus gracilis*. Physiol. Plant. **18**, 976–993.

ERNER Y. & REUVENI O. 1981 Promotion of citrus tissue culture by citric acid. Plant Physiol. **67**, (Suppl.) 27 (Abst. 146).

ERNST D. & OESTERHELT D. 1985 Changes of cytokinin nucleotides in an anise cell culture (*Pimpinella anisum* L.) during growth and embryogenesis. Plant Cell Rep. **4**, 140–143.

ERNST R. 1967 Effects of carbohydrate selection on the growth rate of freshly germinated *Phalaenopsis* and *Dendrobium* seed. Am. Orchid Soc. Bull. **36**, 1068–1073.

ERNST R. 1974 The use of activated charcoal in asymbiotic seedling culture of *Paphiopedilum*. Am. Orchid Soc. Bull. **43**, 35–38.

ERNST R., ARDITTI J. & HEALEY P.L. 1971 Carbohydrate physiology of orchid seedlings. II. Hydrolysis and effects of oligosaccharides. Am. J. Bot. **58**, 827–835.

ESAN E.B. 1973 A detailed study of adventive embryogenesis in the Rutaceae. Ph. D. Thesis. Univ. California, Riverside Diss. Abst. 34 (07) 3128–3129B .

ESKEW D.L., WELCH R.M. & CARY E.E. 1983 Nickel: an essential micronutrient for legumes and possibly all higher plants. Science **222**, 621–623.

ESPINASSE A. & LAY C. 1989 Shoot regeneration of callus derived from globular to torpedo embryos from 59 sunflower genotypes. Crop Sci. **29**, 201–205.

ESTRADA R., TOVAR P. & DODDS J.H. 1986 Induction of *in vitro* tubers in a broad range of potato genotypes. Plant Cell Tiss. Organ Cult. **7**, 3–10.

ETTLINGER C. & LEHLE L. 1988 Auxin induces rapid changes in phosphatidylinositol metabolites. Nature **331**, 176–178.

EVALDSSON I.E. & WELANDER N.T. 1985 The effects of medium composition on *in vitro* propagation and *in vivo* growth of *Cordyline terminalis* cv. Atoom. J. Hort. Sci. **60**, 525–530.

EVANARI M. 1961 Chemical influences of other plants (allelopathy). pp. 691–736 *in* Ruhland W. (ed.) *Encyclopedia of Plant Physiology* 16. Springer Verlag, Berlin.

EVANS D.A. & BRAVO J.E. 1983 Plant protoplast isolation and culture. Int. Rev. Cytol. Suppl. **16**, 33–53.

EVANS D.A. & GAMBORG O.L. 1980 Chromosome stability of plant cell suspension cultures. Plant Physiol. **65**, (Suppl) 35 (Abst.190).

EVANS D.A. & MORRISON R. 1988 Tomato anther culture. U.S. Patent No. 4835339

EVANS D.A. & SHARP W.R. 1982 Application of tissue culture technology in the agricultural industry. pp. 209–231 *in* Tomes *et al.* (eds.) 1982 (*q.v.*).

EVANS D.A. & SHARP W.R. 1988 Tissue cultures of *Lycopersica* spp. U.S. Patent No. 4734369

EVANS D.A., CHU I.Y.E., HARTMAN R.D. & SWARTZ H.J. 1986 Summary of panel discussion on phenotypic and genotypic stability of tissue cultured plants. pp. 95–96 *in* Zimmerman *et al.* (eds.) 1986 (*q.v.*).

EVANS D.A., FLICK C. & SHARP W. 1988a Generation of somaclonal non-Mendelian variants. U.S. Patent No. 4818699

EVANS D.A., FLICK C.E. & SHARP W. 1988b Generation of somaclonal non-Mendelian variants. U.S. Patent No. 4827079

EVANS D.A., SHARP W.R. & FLICK C.E. 1981a Growth and behaviour of cell cultures: embryogenesis and organogenesis. pp. 45–113 *in* Thorpe T.A. (ed.) 1981 (*q.v.*).

EVANS D.A., SHARP W.R. & MEDINA-FILHO H.P. 1984 Somaclonal and gametoclonal variation. Am. J. Bot. **71**, 759–774.

EVANS D.A., SHARP W.R. & PADDOCK E.F. 1976 Variation in callus proliferation and root morphogenesis in leaf tissue cultures of *Glycine max* strain T 219. Phytomorph. **26**, 379–384.

EVANS D.A., SHARP W.R., AMMIRATO P.V. & YAMADA Y. (eds.) 1983 *Handbook of Plant Cell Culture*. Vol. 1. *Techniques for Propagation and Breeding*. Macmillan Publishing Co., New York, London.

EVANS P.K. & COCKING E.C. 1977 Isolated plant protoplasts. pp. 103–135 *in* Street H.E. (ed.) 1977 (*q.v.*).

EVANS P.T. & MALMBERG R.L. 1989 Do polyamines have roles in plant development? Ann. Rev. Plant Physiol. Mol. Biol. **40**, 235–269.

EVEN-CHEN Z., MATTOO A.K. & GOREN R. 1982 Inhibition of ethylene biosynthesis by aminoethoxyvinylglycine and by polyamines shunts label from 3,4-^{14}C -methionine into spermidine in aged orange peel discs. Plant Physiol. **69**, 385–388.

EVERETT N. 1982 The determination phase of differentiation. pp. 93–94 *in* Fujiwara (ed.) 1982 (*q.v.*).

EVERETT N.P. 1986 Plant growth medium. U.S. Patent 4552844.

EVERETT N.P., WACH M.J. & ASHWORTH D.J. 1985 Biochemical markers of embryogenesis in tissue cultures of the maize inbred B73. Plant Science **41**, 133–140.

EVERS P.W. 1984 Growth and morphogenesis of shoot initials of Douglas fir, *Pseudotsuga mensiesii* (Mirb.) Franco, *in vitro*. Diss., Agric. Univ. Wageningen.

EVERT D.R. & HOLT M.A. 1975 Aseptic culture of chrysanths in the plant propagation class. Comb. Proc. Int. Plant Prop. Soc. **25**, 444–447.

FABIJAN D., TAYLOR J.S. & REID D.M. 1981a Adventitious rooting in hypocotyls of sunflower (*Helianthus annuus*) seedlings. II. Action of gibberellins, cytokinins, auxins and ethylene. Physiol. Plant. **53**, 589–597.

FAHY G.M., MacFARLANE D.R., ANGELL C.A. & MERYMAN H.T. 1984 Vitrification as an approach to cryopreservation. Cryobiology **21**, 407.

FAKHRAI F. & EVANS P.K. 1990 Morphogenic potential of cultured floral explants of *Crocus sativus* L. for the *in vitro* production of saffron. J. Exp. Bot. **41**, 47–52.

FAKHRAI H., FAKHRAI F. & EVANS P.K. 1989 *In vitro* culture and plant regeneration in *Vicia faba* subsp. *equina* (var. Spring Blaze). J. Exp. Bot. **40**, 813–817.

FALAVIGNA A., HUSSEY G. & HILTON J. 1980 The effect of colchicine on proliferating adventitious shoots in *Allium cepa*. Ann. Rep. John Innes Inst., 1979, p. 58.

FALKINER F.R. 1988 Strategy for the selection of antibiotics for use against common bacterial pathogens and endophytes of plants. Acta Hort. **225**, 53–56.

FALKINER F.R. 1990 The criteria for choosing an antibiotic for control of bacteria in plant tissue culture. pp. 13–23 *in* Newsletter No. 60, International Assoc. Plant Tiss. Cult. March 1990.

FARI M. & CZAKO M. 1981 Relationship between position and morphogenetic response of pepper hypocotyl explants cultured *in vitro*. Scientia Hort. **15**, 207–213.

FARKAS R., VIGH L.H.I. (née NAGY V.A.F.F.), MESZAROS A., TOTH I. & HUNGARY S. 1986 Plant tissue cultivation process. U.S. Patent No. 4554252

FASOLO F., ZIMMERMAN R. H., FORDHAM I. & FALBO L. 1988a Adventitious shoot formation on excised leaves of *in vitro* cultured apples: effects of cytokinin, auxin, and leaf age. HortScience **23**, 755.

FASOLO F., ZIMMERMAN R.H. & FORDHAM I. 1988b Adventitious shoot formation on excised leaves *in vitro* cultured apple cultivars. HortScience **23**, 676.

FAVRE J.-M. 1977 Premiers résultats concernant l'obtention *in vitro* néoformations culinaires chez la vigne. Ann. Amel. Plant. **27**, 151–169.

FAVRE J.M. & GRENAN S. 1979 Sur la production de vrille, de fleurs et de baies chez la vigne cultivée *in vitro*. Ann. Amelior. Plantes **29**, 247–252.

FAYE M., DAVID A. & LAMANT A. 1986 Nitrate reductase activity and nitrate accumulation in *in vitro* produced axillary shoots, plantlets and seedlings of *Pinus pinaster*. Plant Cell Rep. **5**, 368–371.

FEIERABEND J. 1969 Der Einfluss von Cytokinen auf die Bildung von Photosyntheseenzymen in Roggenkeimlingen. Planta **84**, 11–29.

FEIRER R., MIGNON G. & LITVAY J. 1984 Arginine decarboxylase and polyamines required for embryogenesis in the wild carrot. Science **223**, 1433–1435.

FEIRER R.P., WANN S.R. & EINSPHAR D.W. 1985 The effects of spermidine synthesis inhibitors on *in vitro* plant development. Plant Growth Reg. **3**, 319–327.

FELIX G. & MEINS F. Jr. 1985 Purification, immunoassay and characterization of an abundant cytokinin-regulated polypeptide in cultured tobacco tissues. Planta **164**, 423–428.

FELLE H. 1988 Short-term pH regulation in plants. Physiol. Plant. **74**, 583–591.

FELLMAN C.D., READ P.E. & HOSIER M.A. 1987 Effects of thidiazuron and CPPU on meristem formation and shoot proliferation. HortScience **22**, 1197–1200.

FENG G.H. & OUYANG J. 1988 The effects of KNO₃ concentration in callus induction medium for wheat anther culture. Plant Cell Tiss. Organ Cult. **12**, 3–12.

FENG K. & LINCK A.J. 1970 Effects of N-1-naphthylphthalamic acid on the growth and bud formation of tobacco callus grown *in vitro*. Plant Cell Physiol. **11**, 589–598.

FERENCZY L. & FARKAS G.L. (eds.) 1980 *Advances in Protoplast Research*. Proc. 5th Int. Protoplast Symposium, Szeged, Hungary 1979. Permagon Press. Oxford, New York, Toronto.

FERGUSON I.B. & DRØBAK B.K. 1988 Calcium, mineral nutrition and salinity. HortScience **23**, 262–269.

FERGUSON J.D. & McEWAN J.M. 1970 The chemical induction of supernumerary shoots in the developing embryos of wheat. Physiol. Plant. **23**, 18–28.

FERGUSON J.D., McEWAN J.M. & CARD K.A. 1979 Hormonally-induced polyembryos in wheat. Physiol. Plant. **45**, 470–474.

FERGUSON J.D., STREET H.E. & DAVID S.B. 1958 The carbohydrate nutrition of tomato roots. V. The promotion and inhibition of excised root growth by various sugars and sugar alcohols. Ann. Bot. **22**, 513–524.

FERREIRA C.M. & HANDRO W. 1988 Micropropagation of *Stevia rebaudiana* through leaf explants from adult plants. Planta Med. **54**, 157–162.

FEUCHT W. & JOHAL C.S. 1977 Effect of chlorogenic acids on the growth of excised young stem segments of *Prunus avium*. Acta Hort. **78**, 109–114.

FEUCHT W. & NACHIT M. 1977 Flavolans and growth-promoting catechins in young shoot tips of *Prunus* species and hybrids. Physiol. Plant. **40**, 230–234.

FEUCHT W. & NACHIT M. 1978 Flavenol glycosides of different species and hybrids from the *Prunus* section *Eucerasus* and the growth-promoting activity of quercetin derivatives. Scientia Hort. **8**, 51–56.

FEUCHT W. & SCHMID P.P.S. 1980 Effect of ortho-dihydroxyphenols on growth and protein pattern of callus cultures. Physiol. Plant. **50**, 309–313.

FIDLER J.C. 1960 Naturally occurring volatile organic compounds. pp. 347–359 in *Encyclopaedia of Plant Physiology* **12** (2) Spring-Verlag, Berlin.

FIECHTER A. (ed.) 1980a *Advances in Biochemical Engineering*. **16**. Springer-Verlag, Berlin, Heidelberg, N.York.

FIECHTER A. (ed.) 1980b *Advances in Biochemical Engineering*. **18**. Springer-Verlag, Berlin, Heidelberg, N.York.

FIENBERG A.A., CHOI J.H., LUBICH W.P. & SUNG Z.R. 1984 Developmental regulation of polyamine metabolism in growth and differentiation of carrot culture. Planta **162**, 532–539.

FILLATTI J. & COMAI L. 1988 Transformation and foreign gene expression with woody species. U.S. Patent No. 4795855

FILNER P. 1965 Semi-conservative replication of DNA in a higher plant cell. Exp. Cell Res. **39**, 33–39.

FINDENEGG G.R., VAN BEUSICHEM M.L. & KELTJENS W.G. 1986 Proton balance of plants: physiological, agronomical and economical implications. Neth. J. Agric. Sci. **34**, 371–379.

FINER J.J. 1988b Plant regeneration from somatic embryogenic suspension cultures of cotton (*Gossypium hirsutum* L.). Plant Cell Rep. **7**, 399–402.

FINER J.J. & NAGASAWA A. 1988 Development of an embryogenic suspension culture of soybean (*Glycine max* Merrill.). Plant Cell Tiss. Organ Cult. **15**, 125–136.

FINK C.V.M., STICKLEN M.B., LINEBERGER R.D. & DOMIR S.C. 1986 In vitro organogenesis from shoot tip, internode and leaf explants of *Ulmus* × 'Pioneer'. Plant Cell Tiss. Organ Cult. **7**, 237–245.

FINKELSTEIN R.R. & CROUCH M.C. 1986 Rapeseed embryo development on high osmoticum is similar to that in seeds. Plant Physiol. **81**, 907–912.

FINKLE B. & ULRICH J. 1983 Protocols of cryopreservation. pp. 806–815 in Evans *et al.* (eds.) 1983 (*q.v.*).

FINKLE B.J. & ULRICH J.M. 1979 Effects of cryoprotectants in combination on the survival of frozen sugarcane cells. Plant Physiol. **63**, 598–604.

FIOLA J.A., CHIN C. & POLLACK B.L. 1978 Effect of α-(*p*-chlorophenoxy) isobutyric acid on regeneration of eggplant from callus tissue. HortScience **13**, 354 (Abst. 125).

FIORINO P. & LORETI F. 1987 Propagation of fruit trees by tissue culture in Italy. HortScience **22**, 353–358.

FISH N. & JONES M.G.K. 1988 A comparison of tissue culture response between related tetraploid and dihaploid *S. tuberosum* genotypes. Plant Cell Tiss. Organ Cult. **15**, 201–210.

FISHER F.J.F. 1954 Effect of temperature on leaf-shape in *Ranunculus*. Nature **173**, 406–407.

FISSE J., BATTLE A. & PERA J. 1987 Endogenous bacteria elimination in ornamental explants. Acta Hort. **212**, 87–90.

FLAMÉE M. & BOESMAN G. 1977 Clonal multiplication of *Phalaenopsis* hybrids by means of sections of the flower stalk. Med. Fac. Landbouwwet. Rijksuniv. Gent **42**, 1865–1868.

FLASHMAN S.M. 1981 Genotypic and karyotypic stability of plants regenerated from tobacco callus culture. Env. Exp. Bot. **21**, 429 (Abst.).

FLASHMAN S.M. 1982 A study of genetic instability in tobacco callus cultures. pp. 411–412 in Fujiwara (ed) 1982 (*q.v.*).

FLEGMANN A.W. & WAINWRIGHT H. 1981 Shoot doubling time: a quantitative parameter for characterizing shoot cultures *in vitro*. Plant Cell Tiss. Organ Cult. **1**, 85–92.

FLEMION F. 1959 Effect of temperature, light and gibberellic acid on stem elongation and leaf development in physiologically dwarfed seedlings of peach and *Rhodotypos*. Contrib. Boyce Thompson Inst. **20**, 57–70.

FLETCHER J.S. 1980 Influence of nitrate and sucrose supply on the growth and senescence of Paul's Scarlet rose cells. Plant Physiol. **65**, (Suppl.) 37 (Abst. 199).

FLETCHER R.A., ASARE-BOAMAH N.K., KRIEG L.C., HOFSTRA G. & DUMBROFF E.B. 1988 Triadimefon stimulates rooting in bean hypocotyl. Physiol. Plant. **73**, 401–405.

FLINN B. & WEBB D.T. 1986 Effects of media components and the timing of cytokinin application on caulogenesis from *Pinus strobus* embryonic explants. p. 36 *in* Abstracts VI Intl. Cong. Plant Tissue & Cell Culture. Minneapolis, Minn.

FLINN B.S., WEBB D.T. & NEWCOMB W. 1988 The role of cell clusters and promeristemoids in determination and competence for caulogenesis by *Pinus strobus* cotyledons *in vitro*. Can. J. Bot. **66**, 1556–1565.

FLORES H.E. & GALSTON A.W. 1984 Osmotic stress-induced polyamine accumulation in cereal leaves. Plant Physiol. **75**, 102–113.

FOBERT P.R. & WEBB D.T. 1988 Effects of polyamines, polyamine precursors and polyamine biosynthetic inhibitors on somatic embryogenesis from eggplant (*Solanum melongena*) cotyledons. Can. J. Bot. **66**, 1734–1742.

FONNESBECH A. & FONNESBECH M. 1978 Clonal *in vitro* propagation of *Monstera deliciosa* Limb. Proc. Int. Hort. Congr. **20**, Abst. 1890.

FONNESBECH A., FONNESBECH M. & BREDMOSE N. 1977a Growth and development of *Asparagus plumosus* shoot tips *in vitro*. Acta Hort. **78**, 287.

FONNESBECH A., FONNESBECH M. & BREDMOSE N. 1979 Influence of cytokinins and temperature on development of *Asparagus plumosus* shoot tips *in vitro*. Physiol. Plant. **45**, 73–76.

FONNESBECH M. 1972b Organic nutrients in the media for propagation of *Cymbidium in vitro*. Physiol. Plant. **27**, 360–364.

FONNESBECH M. 1974a The influence of NAA, BA and temperature on shoot and root development from *Begonia* × *cheimantha* petiole segments grown *in vitro*. Physiol. Plant. **32**, 49-54.

FONNESBECH M. 1974c The influence of naphthyl acetic, benzyl ademine and temperature on plantlet development from petiole segments of *Begonia* × *cheimantha* grown *in vitro*. Proc. Int. Hort. Cong. **19**, 66.

FONNESBECH M., FONNESBECH A. & BREDMOSE N. 1977b Development of *Asparagus plumosus* shoot tips grown *in vitro*. Physiol. Plant. **40**, 73–76.

FORCHE E., KIBLER R. & NEUMANN K.-H. 1981 The influence of developmental stages of haploid and diploid callus cultures of *Datura innoxia* on shoot initiation. Z. Pflanzenphysiol. **101**, 257–262.

FOROUGHI-WEHR B. & WENZEL G. 1989 Androgenetic haploid production. pp. 11–18 *in* I.A.P.T.C. Newsletter No. 58 July 1989.

FOROUGHI-WEHR B., FRIEDT W. & WENZEL G. 1982 On the genetic improvement of androgenetic haploid formation in *Hordeum vulgare* L. Theor. Appl. Genet. **62**, 233–239.

FORSYTH C. & VAN STADEN J. 1987 Cytokinin metabolism in tomato plants. II. Metabolites of kinetin and benzyladenine in decapitated roots. Plant Growth Reg. **6**, 277–292.

FORWARD D.F. 1965 The respiration of bulky organs. pp. 311–376 *in* Steward F.C. (ed.) 1965 *Plant Physiology —A Treatise*. Vol. IVA. Academic Press, New York.

FOSKET D.E. 1972 pp. 33–50 *in* Miller and Kuehnert (eds.) 1972 *The Dynamics of Meristem Cell Populations*. Plenum Press, N. York, London.

FOSKET D.E. & TORREY J.G. 1969 Hormonal control of cell proliferation and xylem differentiation in cultured tissues of *Glycine max* var. Biloxi. Plant Physiol. **44**, 871–880.

FOWKE L.C. 1982a Isolation and culture of protoplasts from green algae. pp. 57–61 *in* Wetter and Constabel (eds.) 1982 (*q.v.*).

FOWKE L.C. 1982b Fusion of carrot and algal protoplasts. pp. 63–65 *in* Wetter and Constabel (eds.) 1982 (*q.v.*).

FOX J.E. & MILLER C. 1959 Factors in corn steep water promoting growth of plant tissues. Plant Physiol. **34**, 577–579.

FOX J.L. 1980 Plants thrive in ultrasonic nutrient mists. Bio/Technology **6**, 361.

FOYER C., ROWELL J. & WALKER D. 1983 Measurement of the ascorbate content of spinach leaf protoplasts and chloroplasts during illumination. Planta **157**, 239–244.

FRANCLET A. 1987 Exposé introductif. pp. 23–40 *in* Ducaté *et al*. (eds.) 1987 (*q.v.*).

FRANCO E.O. & SWARTZ O.J. 1985 Micropropagation of two tropical conifers: *Pinus oocarpa* Schiede and *Cupressus lusitanica* Miller. pp. 195–213 *in* Henke *et al*. (eds.) 1985 (*q.v.*).

FRANK H. & RENNER O. 1956 Uber verjungung bei *Hedera helix* L. Planta **47**, 105–114.

FRANKEL O.H. & HAWKES J.G. (eds.) 1975 *Crop Genetic Resources for Today and Tomorrow*. Cambridge University Press.

FRANKENBERGER E.A. & TIGCHELAAR E.C. 1980 Genetic analysis of shoot formation from excised leaf discs of tomato. In Vitro **16**, 217 (Abst. 53).

FRANKENBERGER E.A., HASEGAWA P.W. & TIGCHELAAR E.C. 1981 Influence of environment and developmental state on the shoot-forming capacity of tomato genotypes. Z. Pflanzenphysiol. **102**, 221–232.

FRANKLIN C.I. 1989 Plant regeneration through somatic embryogenesis in the forage grass *Biothriochloa caucasia*. Plant Physiol. **89**, (Suppl.) 8 (Abst. 48).

FRASER R.S.S. & WHENHAM R.J. 1978 Chemotherapy of plant virus disease with methylbenzimidazol-2-yl carbamate: effects on plant growth and multiplication of tobacco mosaic virus. Physiol. Plant Path. **13**, 51–67.

FRASER R.S.S., LOENING U.E. & YEOMAN M.M. 1967 Effect of light on cell division in plant tissue cultures. Nature **215**, 873.

FRETT J.J. & SMAGULA J.M. 1981a Effect of stock plant pretreatment on lowbush blueberry explant shoot multiplication. HortScience **16**, 418 (Abst. 138).

FRETT J.J. & SMAGULA J.M. 1981b The effect of 2iP, IAA and explant bud position of lowbush blueberry shoots produced *in vitro*. HortScience **16**, 459 (Abst. 442).

FRETT J.J. & SMAGULA J.M. 1983 *In vitro* shoot production of lowbush blueberry. Can. J. Plant Sci. **63**, 467–472.

FREYSSINET G. & FREYSSINET M. 1991 Process for regenerating sunflowers by embryogenesis. U.S. Patent No. 5017491.

FREYSSINET M. & FREYSSINET G. 1988 Fertile plant regeneration from sunflower (*Helianthus annuus* L.) immature embryos. Plant Science **56**, 177–181.

FREYTAG A.H., ANAND S.C., RAO-ARELLA P. & OWENS L.D. 1988 An improved medium for adventitious shoot formation and callus induction in *Beta vulgaris* L. *in vitro*. Plant Cell Rep. **7**, 30–34.

FRIDBORG G. & ERIKSSON T. 1975a Partial reversal by cytokinin and (2-chloroethyl)-trimethylammonium chloride of near-ultraviolet inhibited growth and morphogenesis in callus cultures. Physiol. Plant. **34**, 162–166.

FRIDBORG G. & ERIKSSON T. 1975b Effects of activated charcoal on growth and morphogenesis in cell cultures. Physiol. Plant. **34**, 306–308.

FRIDBORG G., PEDERSEN M., LANDSTROM M. & ERIKSSON T. 1978 The effect of activated charcoal on tissue cultures: absorbtion of metabolites inhibiting morphogenesis. Physiol. Plant. **43**, 104–106.

FRIEDMAN R., ALTMAN A. & BACHRACH U. 1982 Polyamines and root formation in mung bean hypocotyl cuttings. I. Effect of endogenous compounds on endogenous polyamic content. Plant Physiol. **70**, 844–848.

FRIEDMAN R., ALTMAN A. & BACHRACH U. 1985 Polyamines and root formation in mung bean hypocotyl cuttings. II. Incorporation of precursors into polyamines. Plant Physiol. **79**, 80–83.

FRIES L. 1962 Vitamin B$_{12}$ *in Pisum sativum* (L.). Physiol. Plant. **15**, 566–571.

FRIES N. 1960 The effect of adenine and kinetin on growth and differentiation of *Lupinus*. Physiol. Plant. **13**, 468–481.

FROBERG C.A. 1986 Tissue culture propagation of *Sophora secundiflora*. Comb. Proc. Int. Plant Prop. Soc. 1985 **35**, 750–754.

FUCHIGAMI L.H. & NEE C.-C. 1987 Degree growth stage model and rest-breaking mechanisms in temperate woody perennials. HortScience **22**, 836–845.

FUGGI A., RUGANO V.M., VONA V. & RIGANO C. 1981 Nitrate and ammonium assimilation in algae cell-suspensions and related pH variations in the external medium, monitored by electrodes. Plant Sci. Lett. **23**, 129–138.

FUHRER J., KAUR-SAWHNEY R., SHIH L.-M. & GALSTON A.W. 1982 Effects of exogenous 1,3-diaminopropane and spermidine on senescence of oat leaves. Plant Physiol. **70**, 1597–1600.

FUJII J., SLADE D. & REDENBAUGH K. 1989 Maturation and greenhouse planting of alfalfa artificial seed. In Vitro Cell Dev. Biol. **25**, 1179–1182.

FUJIMURA T. & KOMAMINE A. 1975 Effects of various growth regulators on the embryogenesis in a carrot cell suspension culture. Plant Sci. Lett. **5**, 359–364.

FUJIMURA T. & KOMAMINE A. 1979a Involvement of endogenous auxin in somatic embryogenesis in a carrot cell suspension culture. Z. Pflanzenphysiol. **95**, 13–19.

FUJIMURA T. & KOMAMINE A. 1980 The serial observation of embryogenesis in a carrot cell suspension culture. New Phytol. **86**, 213–218.

FUJIWARA A. (ed.) 1982 *Plant Tissue Culture 1982*. Proc. 5th Int.Cong.Plant Tiss. Cell Cult., Japan. Jap. Assoc. Plant Tissue Culture; Tokyo.

FUJIWARA K., KOZAI T. & WATANABE I. 1987 Fundamental studies on environments in plant tissue culture vessels. (3) Measurements of carbon dioxide gas concentration in closed vessels containing tissue-cultured plantlets and estimates of net photosynthetic rates of the plantlets. J. Agric. Met. **43**, 21–30.

FUJIWARA K., KOZAI T. & WATANABE I. 1988 Development of a photoautotrophic tissue culture system for shoots and/or plantlets at rooting and acclimatization stages. Acta Hort. **230**, 153–158.

FUKAMI T. & HILDEBRANDT A.C. 1967 Growth and chlorophyll formation in edible green plant callus tissues *in vitro* on media with limited sugar supplements. Bot. Mag. Tokyo **80**, 199–212.

FUKUI K. & NIIZEKI H. 1982 Artificial reduction of chromosome number in *Fragaria ananasa* following treatment with *p*-fluorophenylalanine. pp. 427–428 in Fujiwara A. (ed.) 1982 (*q.v.*).

FUKUNAGA Y., KING J. & CHILD J.J. 1978 The differential effects to TCA-cycle acids on the growth of plant cells cultured in liquid media containing various nitrogen sources. Planta **139**, 199–202.

FURGUSON J.D. 1967 The nutrition of excised wheat roots. Physiol. Plant. **20**, 276–284.

FURNER I.J., KING J. & GAMBORG O.L. 1978 Plant regeneration from protoplasts isolated from a predominantly haploid suspension culture of *Datura innoxia* (Mill.). Plant Sci. Lett. **11**, 169–176.

FURUHASHI K. F& TAKAHASHI Y. 1982 Glutamate dehydrogenase of green tobacco callus tissue. pp. 241–242 in Fujiwara (ed.) 1982 (*q.v.*).

FURUYA M. & TORREY J.G. 1964 The reversible inhibition by red and far-red light of auxin-induced lateral root initiation in isolated pea roots. Plant Physiol. **39**, 987–991.

FURUYA M., GALSTON A.W. & STOWE B.B. 1962 Isolation from peas of co-factors and inhibitors of indole-3-acetic acid oxidase. Nature **193**, 456–457.

GABRYSZEWSKA E. & SANIEWSKI M. 1983 Auxin control of tulip stalk elongation *in vitro*. Scientia Hort. **19**, 153–159.

GAD A.E., BEN-EFRAIM I., YAVZURY M., WEINBERG C. & FRIEDMAN G. 1988a Improvement of cutting quality by 4-chlororesorcinol. Comb. Proc. Int. Plant Prop. Soc. 1987 **37**, 119–123.

GAISER M.S., LAZARTE J.E. & BROWN O.R. 1981 *In vitro* propagation of *Epiphyllum chrysocardium*. HortScience **16**, 425 (Abst.194).

GALIBA G. & ERDEI L. 1986 Dependence of wheat callus growth, differentiation and mineral content on carbohydrate supply. Plant Science **45**, 65–70.

GALIBA G. & YAMADA Y. 1988 A novel method for increasing the frequency of somatic embryogenesis in wheat tissue culture by NaCl and KCl supplementation. Plant Cell Rep. **7**, 55–58.

GALSTON A.W. 1983 Polyamines as modulators of plant development. Bioscience **33**, 382–388.

GALSTON A.W. & HILLMAN W.S. 1961 The degradation of auxin. Encyclopedia of Plant Physiology **14**, 647–670.

GALSTON A.W., ALTMAN A. & KAUR-SAWHNEY R. 1978 Polyamines, ribonuclease and the improvement of oat leaf protoplasts. Plant Sci. Lett. **11**, 69–79.

GALSTON A.W., DAI Y.-R., FLORES H. & YOUNG N.D. 1983 The control of arginine decarboxylase activity in higher plants. pp. 381–393 in Bachrach *et al.* (eds.) 1983 *Advances in Polyamine Research* **4**.

GALSTON A.W., SAWHNEY R.K., ALTMAN A. & FLORES H. 1980 Polyamines, macromolecular syntheses and the problem of cereal protoplast regeneration. pp. 485–497 in Ferenczy and Farkas (eds.) 1980 (*q.v.*).

GALUN E., JUNG Y. & LANG A. 1962 Culture and sex modification of male cucumber buds *in vitro*. Nature **194**, 596–598.

GALZY R. 1969 Recherches sur la croissance de *Vitis rupestris* Scheele sain et court noue cultivé *in vitro* à différentes températures. Ann. Phytopath. **1**, 149–166.

GALZY R. & COMPAN D. 1988 Growth and nutrition of grapevine during *in vitro* long-term storage. Plant Cell Tiss. Organ Cult. **13**, 229–237.

GAMBORG O.L. 1966 Aromatic metabolism in plants. II. Enzymes of the shikimate pathway in suspension cultures of plant cells. Can. J. Biochem. **44**, 791–799.

GAMBORG O.L. 1970 The effects of amino acids and ammonium on the growth of plant cells in suspension culture. Plant Physiol. **45**, 372–375.

GAMBORG O.L. 1982a Callus and cell culture. pp. 1–9 in Wetter and Constabel (eds.) 1982 (*q.v.*).

GAMBORG O.L. 1991 Media preparation. *Plant Tissue Culture Manual* **A1** 1–24. Kluwer Acad. Publ., The Netherlands.

GAMBORG O.L. & EVELEIGH D.E. 1968 Culture methods and detection of glucanases in suspension cultures of wheat and barley. Can. J. Biochem. **46**, 417–421.

GAMBORG O.L. & LARUE T.A.G. 1968 Ethylene produced by plant cells in suspension cultures. Nature **220**, 604–605.

GAMBORG O.L. & LARUE T.A.G. 1971 The effect of auxins, abscisic acid and kinetin on ethylene production in suspension cultures of rose and *Ruta* cells. Plant Physiol. **48**, 399–401.

GAMBORG O.L. & SHYLUK J.P. 1970 The culture of plant cells with ammonium salts as a sole nitrogen source. Plant Physiol. **45**, 598–600.

GAMBORG O.L. & SHYLUK J.P. 1981 Nutrition, media and characteristics of plant cell and tissue cultures. pp. 21–44 in Thorpe T.A. (ed.) 1981 (*q.v.*).

GAMBORG O.L., CONSTABEL F. & SHYLUK J.P. 1974 Organogenesis in callus from shoot apices of *Pisum sativum*. Physiol. Plant. **30**, 125–128.

GAMBORG O.L., DAVIS B.P. & STAHLUT R.W. 1983 Somatic embryogenesis in cell cultures of *Glycine* species. Plant Cell Rep. **2**, 209–212.

GAMBORG O.L., MILLER R.A. & OJIMA K. 1968 Nutrient requirements of suspension cultures of soybean root cells. Exp. Cell Res. **50**, 151–158.

GAMBORG O.L., MURASHIGE T., THORPE T.A. & VASIL I.K. 1976 Plant tissue culture media. In Vitro **12**, 473–478.

GAMBORG O.L., SHYLUK J.P. & SHAHIN E.A. 1981 Isolation, fusion and culture of plant protoplasts. pp. 115–153 in Thorpe T.A. (ed.) 1981 (*q.v.*).

GARCIA F. & EINSET J.W. 1982 Ethylene and ethane production in salt-stressed or 2,4-D stressed tobacco tissue cultures. In Vitro **18**, 275 (Abst. 2).

GARCIA F.G. & EINSET J.W. 1983 Ethylene and ethane production in 2,4-D-treated and salt-treated tobacco tissue cultures. Ann. Bot. **51**, 287–295.

GARTON S. & MOSES M.S. 1986 Production of native plants in tissue culture. Comb. Proc. Int. Plant Prop. Soc. 1985 **35**, 306–315.

GARTON S., READ P.E. & FARNHAM R.S. 1983 Effect of stock plant nutrition on macro- and micro-propagability of *Salix*. Acta Hort. **131**, 141–151.

GARVE R., LUCKNER M., VOGEL E., TEWES A. & NOVER L. 1980 Growth, morphogenesis and cardenolide formation in long-term cultures of *Digitalis lanata*. Planta Med. **40**, 92–103.

GASPAR Th. & KEVERS C. 1985 Cobalt prevention of vitrification process in carnation. Plant Physiol. **77**, Suppl. 13 (Abst. 65).

GATHERCOLE R.W.E., MANSFIELD K.J. & STREET H.E. 1976 Carbon dioxide as an esssential requirement for cultured sycamore cells. Physiol. Plant. **37**, 213–217.

GAUTAM V.K., MITTAL A., NANDA K. & GUPTA S.C. 1983 *In vitro* regeneration of plantlets from somatic explants of *Matthiola incana*. Plant Sci. Lett. **29**, 25–32.

GAUTHERET R.J. 1939 Sur la possibilité de réaliser la culture indéfinie des tissus tubercule de carotte. Compt. Rend. Acad. Sci. Paris **208**, 118.

GAUTHERET R.J. 1942 *Manuel Technique de Culture des Tissue Végétaux*. Masson et Cie, Paris.

GAUTHERET R.J. 1945 *Une voie nouvelle en biologie végétale: la culture des tissus*. Gallimard, Paris.

GAUTHERET R.J. 1948 Sur la culture indéfinie des tissus de *Salix caprea*. Compt. Rend. Soc. Biol. **142**, 807.

GAUTHERET R.J. 1959 *La Culture des Tissus Végétaux*. Masson et Cie, Paris.

GAUTHERET R.J. 1961 Action conjuguée de l'acide gibbérellique, de la cinétine et de l'acide indole-acétique sur les tissus cultivés *in vitro*, particulièrement sur ceux de Tropinambour. Compt. Rend. Acad. Sci. Paris **253**, 1381–1385.

GAUTHERET R.J. 1969 Investigations on the root formation in the tissues of *Helianthus tuberosus* cultured *in vitro*. Am. J. Bot. **56**, 702–717.

GAVAZZI G., TONELLI C., TODESCO G., ARREGHINI E., RAFFALID F., VECCHIO F., BARBUZZI G., BIASINI M.G. & SALA F. 1987 Somaclonal variation versus chemically induced mutagenesis in tomato (*Lycopersicon esculentum* L.). Theor. Appl. Genet. **74**, 733–738.

GAVINLERTVATANA P., READ P.E., WILKINS H.F. & HEINS R. 1979 Influence of photoperiod and danienozide stock plant pretreatments on ethylene and CO$_2$ levels and callus formation from *Dahlia* leaf segment cultures. J. Am. Soc. Hort. Sci. **104**, 849–852.

GAVINLERTVATANA P., READ P.E., WILKINS H.F. & HEINS R. 1982 Ethylene levels in flask atmospheres of *Dahlia pinata* Cav. leaf segments and callus cultured *in vitro*. J. Am. Soc. Hort. Sci. **107**, 3–6.

GAWEL N.J., RAO A.P. & ROBACKER C.D. 1986 Somatic embryogenesis from leaf and petiole callus cultures of *Gossypium hirsutum* L. Plant Cell Rep. **5**, 457–459.

GE KOULIN, WANG YUNZHU, YUAN XUNMEI & HUANG PEIMING 1990 Method of regenerating plantlets from mesophyll protoplasts of *Phaseolus angularis*. U.S. Patent No. 4977087

GEIER T. 1977 Morphogenesis and plant regeneration from cultured organ fragments of *Cyclamen persicum*. Acta Hort. **78**, 167–174.

GEIER T. 1978 Development of isolated rudimentary anthers from somatic anther callus of *Cyclamen persicum* Mill. Z. Pflanzenphysiol. **90**, 245–256.

GEIER T. 1986 Factors affecting plant regeneration from leaf segments of *Anthurium scherzerianum* Schott (Araceae) cultured *in vitro*. Plant Cell Tiss. Organ Cult. **6**, 115–125.

GEIER T. 1987 Micropropagation of *Anthurium scherzerianum*: propagation schemes and plant conformity. Acta Hort. **212**, 439–443.

GEIER T. 1988 Ploidy variation in callus and regenerated plants of *Anthurium scherzerianum* Schott. Acta Hort. **226**, 293–298.

GEIER T. & KOHLENBACH H.W. 1973 Entwicklung von Embryonen und embryogenem Kallus aus Pollenkörnern von *Datura meteloides* und *Datura innoxia*. Protoplasma **78**, 381–396.

GEILE W. & WAGNER E. 1980 Rapid development of cell suspension cultures from leaf sections of *Chenopodium rubrum* L. Plant Cell & Env. **3**, 141–148.

GELVIN S. 1988 Transcription in plants and bacteria. U.S. Patent No. 4771002

GENEVE R.L., KESTER S.T. & EL-SHALL S. 1990 *In vitro* shoot initiation in Kentucky coffee tree. HortScience **25**, p. 578.

GENOVESI A.D. & COLLINS G.B. 1982 *In vitro* production of haploid plants of corn via anther culture. Crop Sci. **22**, 1137–1144.

GEORGE E.F. (ed.) 1979 *Differentiation and the Control of Development in Plants —Potential for Chemical Modification*. British Plant Growth Reg. Group. Monograph No. 3. ISBN 0-906673-01-0

GEORGE E.F. & SHERRINGTON P.D. 1984 *Plant Propagation by Tissue Culture*. Exegetics Ltd., Basingstoke, England.

GEORGE E.F., PUTTOCK D.J.M. & GEORGE H.J. 1987 *Plant Culture Media* Vol.1. Exegetics Ltd., Westbury, England.

GEORGE E.F., PUTTOCK D.J.M. & GEORGE H.J. 1988 *Plant Culture Media* Vol.2. Exegetics Ltd., Westbury, England.

GEORGE J., HOFER E., LEIKE H., DAUTZENBERG H.F & LOTH F. 1983 The use of a novel stabilizing substrate for the *in vitro* cultivation of cauliflower (*Brassica oleracea* L. var. botrytis). Plant Cell Rep. **2**, 189–191.

GEORGE L., BAPAT V.A. & RAO P.S. 1987 In vitro multiplication of sesame (*Sesamum indicum*) through tissue culture. Ann. Bot. **60**, 17–20.

GERACI G. & TUSA N. 1988 Calli and plants from *Citrus limon* Burn cv. 'Femminello' ovules in vitro. Acta Hort. **227**, 381–383.

GERTSSON U.E. 1988a Large-scale *in vitro* propagation of *Senecio × hybridus* Hyl. J. Hort. Sci. **63**, 131–136.

GERTSSON U.E. 1988b Development of micropropagated plants from different clones of *Senecio × hybridus* in relation to BAP concentration and temperature *in vitro*. J. Hort. Sci. **63**, 489–496.

GERTSSON U.E. 1988c Influence of macronutrient composition, TIBA and dark treatment on shoot formation and nitrogen content in petiole explants of *Senecio × hybridus*. J. Hort. Sci. **63**, 497–502.

GHARYAL P.K. & MAHESHWARI S.C. 1981 *In vitro* differentiation of somatic embryoids in a leguminous tree — *Albizzia lebeck* L. Naturwiss. **68**, 379–380.

GHAZI T.D., CHEEMA H.V. & NABORS M.W. 1986 Somatic embryogenesis and plant regeneration from embryogenic callus of soybean, *Glycine max* L. Plant Cell Rep. **5**, 452–456.

GILBY A.C. & WAINWRIGHT H. 1989 Use of tissue culture in improvement of watercress (*Rorippa nasturtium aquaticum* L. Hayek). Acta Hort. **244**, 105–113.

GILES K.K. & PRAKASH J. 1987 Pollen: cytology and development. Int. Rev. Cytology **107**, 1–455.

GILL B.S., KAM L.N.W. & SHEPARD J.F. 1982 Cytogenetic basis of phenotypic variation in potato protoclones regenerated from mesophyll cells. HortScience **17**, 531 (Abst.421).

GIROD P.-A. & ZYRD J.P. 1987 Clonal variability and light induction of betalin synthesis in red beet cell cultures. Plant Cell Rep. **6**, 27–30.

GIULIANO G., ROSELLINI D. & TERZI M. 1983 A new method for the purification of the different stages of carrot embryoids. Plant Cell Rep. **2**, 216–218.

GLASSTONE S. 1946 *Textbook of Physical Chemistry*. Second edition. MacMillan, London.

GLASSTONE V.F.C. 1947 Inorganic micronutrients in tomato root tissue culture. Am. J. Bot. **34**, 218–224.

GLIMELIUS K. 1988 Potentials of protoplast fusion in plant breeding programmes. Plant Cell Tiss. Organ Cult. **12**, 163–172.

GOLDBACH H. & AMBERGER A. 1986 Influence of boron deficiency on ^{3}H indole-3yl-acetic acid uptake and efflux in cell cultures of *Daucus carota* L. Plant Growth Reg. **4**, 81–86.

GOLDSCHMIDT E.E. 1976 Edogenous growth substances of citrus tissues. HortScience **11**, 95–99.

GOLOSIN B. & RADOJEVIC L. 1987 Micropropagation of apple rootstocks. Acta Hort. **212**, 589–594.

GONCALVES A.N., MACHADO M.A., CALDAS L.S., SHARP W.R. & MELLO H.D.A. 1979 Tissue culture of *Eucalyptus*. pp. 509–526 *in* Sharp *et al.* (eds.) 1979 (*q.v.*).

GOODENOUGH U. 1978 *Genetics*. Holt-Saunders. ISBN 0-03-050886-X

GOODWIN P.B. 1966 An improved medium for the rapid growth of isolated potato buds. J. Exp. Bot. **17**, 590–595.

GOODWIN P.B., KIM Y.C. & ADISARWANTO T. 1980a Propagation of potato by root-tip culture. 1. Shoot multiplication. Potato Res. **23**, 9–18.

GOODWIN T.W. (ed.) 1976 *Chemistry and Biochemistry of Plant Pigments*. Academic Press, London, New York, San Francisco.

GOODWIN T.W. & MERCER E.I. 1972 *Introduction to Plant Biochemistry*. Pergamon Press. Oxford, New York.

GÓRECKA K. 1987 In vitro propagation of horse-radish (*Cochlearia armoracia* L.). Acta Hort. **212**, 671–674.

GORST J.R., BOURNE R.A., HARDAKER S.E., RICHARDS A.E., DIRCKS S. & DE FOSSARD R.A. 1978 Tissue culture propagation of two *Grevillea* hybrids. Comb. Proc. Int. Plant Prop. Soc. **28**, 435–446.

GORTER C.J. 1965 Vegatative propagation of *Asparagus officinalis* by cuttings. J. Hort. Sci. **40**, 177–179.

GOSCH-WACKERLE G., AVIVI L. & GALUN E. 1979 Induction, culture and differentiation of callus from immature rachises, seeds and embryos of *Triticum*. Z. Pflanzenphysiol. **91**, 267–278.

GOTO N. 1981 Organogenetic capacity of mutant lines and their hybrids in *Arabidopsis thaliana*. Bot. Mag. Tokyo **94**, 77–82.

GOUGH K.H. & SHUKLA D.D. 1980 Further studies on the use of Protein A in immune electron microscopy for detecting virus particles. J. Gen. Virol. **51**, 415–419.

GOULD A.R. 1978 Diverse pathways of morphogenesis in tissue cultures of the composite *Brachycome lineariloba* (2n=4). Protoplasma **97**, 125–135.

GOULD A.R. 1979 Chromosomal and phenotypic stability during regeneration of whole plants from tissue cultures of *Brachycome dichromosomatica* (2n=4). Aust. J. Bot. **27**, 117–121.

GOULD A.R. 1982 Chromosome instability in plant tissue cultures studied with banding techniques. pp. 431–432 *in* Fujiwara A. (ed.) 1982 (*q.v.*).

GOYAL Y., BINGHAM R.L. & FELKER P. 1985 Propagation of the tropical tree, *Leucaena leucocephala* K67, by in vitro bud culture. Plant Cell Tiss. Organ Cult. **4**, 3–10.

GRAMBOW H.J. & LANGENBECK-SCHWICH B. 1983 The relationship between oxidase activity, peroxidase activity, hydrogen peroxide, and phenolic compounds in the degradation of indole-3-acetic acid *in vitro*. Planta **157**, 131–137.

GRANATEK C.H. & COCKERLINE A.W. 1978 Callus formation versus differentiation of cultured barley embryos: hormonal osmotic interactions. In Vitro **14**, 212–217.

GRANATEK C.H. & COCKERLINE A.W. 1979 Callus formation of cultured early differentiating barley embryos. Bull. Torrey Bot. Club **106**, 85–96.

GRAVES R.H., REID R.H. & MATHES M.C. 1978 Tissue culture of the monocots *Lilium, Hemerocallis* and *Hippeastrum*. p. 248 *in* Hughes *et al.* (eds.) 1978 (*q.v.*).

GRAY D.J. 1987a Introduction to the symposium "Synthetic seed technology for the mass cloning of crop plants: problems and perspectives". HortScience **22**, 796–797.

GRAY D.J. 1987b Quiescence in monocotyledonous and dicotyledonous somatic embryos induced by dehydration. HortScience **22**, 810–814.

GRAY D.J. 1989 Effects of dehydration and exogenous growth regulators on dormancy, quiescence and germination of grape somatic embryos. In Vitro Cell Dev. Biol. **25**, 1173–1178.

GRAY D.J. & BENTON C.M. 1991 *In vitro* micropropagation and plant establishment of muscadine grape cultivars (*Vitis rotundifolia*). Plant Cell Tiss. Organ Cult. **27**, 7–14.

GRAY D.J. & CONGER B.V. 1985 Influence of dicamba and casein hydrolysate on somatic embryo number and culture quality in cell suspensions of *Dactylis glomerata* (Gramineae). Plant Cell Tiss. Organ Cult. **4**, 123–133.

GRAY D.J., CONGER B.V. & HANNING G.E. 1984 Somatic embryogenesis in suspension and suspension-derived callus cultures of *Dactylis glomerata*. Protoplasma **122**, 196–202.

GRECO B., TANZARELLA O.A., CARROZZO G. & BLANCO A. 1984 Callus induction and shoot regeneration in Sunflower (*Helianthus annuus*). Plant Sci. Lett. **36**, 73–77.

GREEN C.E. 1977 Prospects for crop improvement in the field of cell culture. HortScience **12**, 131–134.

GREEN C.E. 1982 Somatic embryogenesis and plant regeneration from the friable callus of *Zea mays*. pp. 107–108 *in* Fujiwara A. (ed.) 1982 (*q.v.*).

GREEN C.E. & PHILLIPS R.L. 1975 Plant regeneration from tissue cultures of maize. Crop Sci. **15**, 417–427.

GREEN C.E., PHILLIPS R.L. & KLEESE R.A. 1974 Tissue culture of maize (*Zea mays* L.): Initiation, maintenance and organic growth factors. Crop Sci. **14**, 54–58.

GREEN C.E., SOMERS D.A., HACKETT W.P. & BIESBOER D.D. (**eds.**) 1987 *Plant Tissue and Cell Culture*. Alan R. Liss, Inc., New York.

GREENWOOD M.S. 1987 Rejuvenation of forest trees. Plant Growth Reg. **6**, 1–12.

GREENWOOD N.N. 1973 *The Chemistry of Boron*. Pergamon texts in inorganic chemistry Vol. 8. Pergamon Press, Oxford, New York, Toronto.

GREGORINI G. & LALOUE M. 1980 Biological effects of cytokinin antagonists 7-(pentylamino) and 7-(benzylamino)-3-methylpyrazolo (4,3- *d*) pyrimidines on suspension-cultured tobacco cells. Plant Physiol. **65**, 363–367.

GRENO V., NAVARRO L. & DURAN-VILAN N. 1988 Influence of virus and virus-like agents on the development of citrus buds cultured *in vitro*. Plant Cell Tiss. Organ Cult. **15**, 113–124.

GRESSHOFF P.M. & DOY C.H. 1972a Haploid *Arabidopsis thaliana* callus and plants from anther culture. Aust. J. Biol. Sci. **25**, 259–264.

GRESSHOFF P.M. & DOY C.H. 1972b Development and differentiation of haploid *Lycopersicon esculentum* (tomato). Planta **107**, 161–170.

GREWAL S., KOUL S., AHUJA A. & ATAL C.K. 1979 Hormonal control of growth, organogenesis and alkaloid production in *in vitro* cultures of *Hyoscyamus muticus* Linn. Ind. J. Exp. Biol. **17**, 558–561.

GREWAL S., KOUL S., SACHDEVA U. & ATAL C.K. 1977 Regeneration of plants of *Dioscorea deltoides* Wall. by apical meristem cultures. Ind. J. Exp. Biol. **15**, 201–203.

GRIESBACH R. & SINK K.C. 1982 Griseofulvin-induced chromosome instability. HortScience **17**, 489 (Abst. 120).

GRIESBACH R.J. 1983 The use of indoleacetyl amino acids in the *in vitro* propagation of *Phalaenopsis* orchids. Scientia Hort. **19**, 363–366.

GRIESBACH R.J. 1986 Orchid tissue culture. pp. 343–349 *in* Zimmerman *et al.* (eds.) 1986 (*q.v.*).

GRIESBACH R.J. 1989 Selection of a dwarf *Hemerocallis* through tissue culture. HortScience **24**, 1027–1028.

GRIESBACH R.J., SEMENIUK P., ROH M. & LAWSON R.H. 1988 Tissue culture in the improvement of *Eustoma*. HortScience **23**, 658 & 791.

GRIMES H.D. & HODGES T.K. 1990 The inorganic NO_3^-: NH_4^+ ratio influences plant regeneration and auxin sensitivity in primary callus derived from immature embryos of Indica rice (*Oryza sativa* L.). J. Plant Physiol. **136**, 362–367.

GROOSE R.W. & BINGHAM E.T. 1984 Variation in plants regenerated from tissue culture of tetraploid alfalfa heterozygous for several traits. Crop Sci. **24**, 655–658.

GROOSE R.W. & BINGHAM E.T. 1986a An unstable anthocyanin mutation recovered from tissue culture of alfalfa (*Medicago sativa*). 1. High frequency of reversion upon reculture. Plant Cell Rep. **5**, 104–107.

GROOSE R.W. & BINGHAM E.T. 1986b An unstable anthocyanin mutation recovered from tissue culture of alfalfa (*Medicago sativa*). 2. Stable nonrevertants derived from reculture. Plant Cell Rep. **5**, 108–110.

GROOTAARTS H., SCHEL J.H.N. & PIERIK R.L.M. 1981 The origin of bulblets formed on excised twin scales of *Nerine bowdenii* W. Watts. Plant Cell Tiss. Organ Cult. **1**, 39–46.

GROSSER J.W. & CHANDLER J.L. 1986 In vitro multiplication of Swingle citrumelo rootstock with coumarin. HortScience **21**, 518–520.

GROUT B.W.W. 1988 Wax development on leaf surfaces of *Brassica oleracea* var. Currawong regenerated from meristem culture. Acta Hort. **230**, 129–135.

GROUT B.W.W. 1990 Genetic preservation *in vitro*. pp. 13–22 *in* Nijkamp *et al.* (eds.) 1990 (*q.v.*).

GROUT B.W.W. & ASTON M.J. 1978 Transplanting of cauliflower plants regenerated from meristem culture. II. Carbon dioxide fixation and the development of photosynthetic ability. Hort. Res. **17**, 65–71.

GROUT B.W.W. & CRISP P. 1977 Practical aspects of the propagation of cauliflower by meristem culture. Acta Hort. **78**, 289–296.

GROUT B.W.W. & CRISP P. 1980 The origin and nature of shoots propagated from cauliflower roots. J. Hort. Sci. **55**, 65–70.

GROUT B.W.W. & DONKIN M.E. 1987 Photosynthetic activity of cauliflower meristem cultures *in vitro* and at transplanting into soil. Acta Hort. **212**, 323–327.

GROUT B.W.W. & HENSHAW G.G. 1978 Freeze preservation of potato shoot tip cultures. Ann. Bot. **42**, 1227–1229.

GROUT B.W.W. & HENSHAW G.G. 1980 Structural observations on the growth of potato shoot-tip cultures after thawing from liquid nitrogen. Ann. Bot. **46**, 243–248.

GROUT B.W.W. & PRICE F. 1987 The establishment of photosynthetic independence in strawberry cultures prior to transplanting. pp. 55–60 *in* Ducaté *et al.* (eds.) 1987 (*q.v.*).

GROUT B.W.W., WESTCOTT R.J. & HENSHAW G.G. 1977 Scanning electron microscope studies of multiple shoot tip production by meristem tip cultures of *Solanum × curtilobum*. Ann. Bot. **41**, 1113–1116.

GRUMET R. 1990 Genetically engineered plant virus resistance. HortScience **25**, 508–513.

GRUNEWALDT J. 1977 Adventivknospenbildung und Planzenregeneration bei Gesneriaceae *in vitro*. Gartenbauwiss. **42**, 171–175.

GRUNEWALDT J. 1988a *In vitro* selection and propagation of temperature tolerant *Saintpaulia*. Acta Hort. **226**, 271–275.

GUAN Y.-Q., GRAY L.E. & WIDHOLM J.M. 1990 *In vitro* screening for and selection of *Glycine max* resistant to *Phialophora gregata*. U.S. Patent No. 4937970

GUERN J. 1987 Regulation from within: The hormone dilemma. Ann. Bot. **60**, (Suppl. 4) 75–102.

GUERRA M.P. & HANDRO W. 1988 Somatic embryogenesis and plant regeneration in embryo cultures of *Euterpe edulis* Mart. (Palmae). Plant Cell Rep. **7**, 550–552.

GUHA S. & JOHRI B.M. 1966 *In vitro* development of overy and ovule of *Allium cepa* L. Phytomorph. **16**, 353–364.

GUHA S. & MAHESHWARI S.C. 1964 *In vitro* production of embryos from anthers of *Datura*. Nature **204**, 497.

GUHA S. & MAHESHWARI S.C. 1967 Development of embryoids from pollen grains of *Datura in vitro*. Phytomorph. **17**, 454–461.

GUI Y.-L. 1979 Induction of callus and regeneration of plantlets in stem segment culture of Chinese gooseberry. Acta Bot. Sin. **21**, 339–344.

GUIDERDONI E. & DEMARLY Y. 1988 Histology of somatic embryogenesis in cultured leaf segments of sugarcane plantlets. Plant Cell Tiss. Organ Cult. **14**, 71–88.

GUNAY A.L. & RAO A.S. 1978 *In vitro* plant regeneration from hypocotyl and cotyledon explants of red pepper. Plant Sci. Lett. **11**, 365–372.

GUNNING B.E.S. & STEER M.W. 1975 *Ultrastructure and the Biology of Plant Cells*. Arnold, London.

GUNNING J. & LAGERSTEDT H.B. 1986 Long-term storage techniques for *in vitro* plant germplasm. Comb. Proc. Int. Plant Prop. Soc. 1985 **35**, 199–205.

GUPTA G.R.P., GUHA S. & MAHESHWARI S.C. 1966 Differentiation of buds from leaves of *Nicotiana tabacum* Linn. in sterile culture. Phytomorph. **16**, 175–182.

GUPTA P. & PULLMAN G.S. 1991 Method for reproducing coniferous plants by somatic embryogenesis using abscisic acid and osmotic potential variation. U.S. Patent No. 5036007

GUPTA P.K. & DURZAN D.J. 1985 Shoot multiplication from mature trees of Douglas-fir (*Pseudotsuga menziesii*) and sugar pine (*Pinus lambertiana*). Plant Cell Rep. **4**, 177–179.

GUPTA P.K. & DURZAN D.J. 1986a Somatic embryogenesis from callus of mature sugar pine embryos. Bio/Technology **4**, 643–645.

GUPTA P.K. & DURZAN D.J. 1986b Isolation and cell regeneration of protoplasts from sugar pine (*Pinus lambertiana*). Plant Cell Rep. **5**, 346–348.

GUPTA P.K. & DURZAN D.J. 1987a Micropropagation and phase specificity in mature, elite Douglas fir. J. Am. Soc. Hort. Sci. **112**, 969–971.

GUPTA P.K., DANDEKAR A.M. & DURZAN D.J. 1988 Somatic proembryo formation and transient expression of a luciferase gene in Douglas fir and loblolly pine protoplasts. Plant Science **58**, 85–92.

GUPTA P.K., MASCARENHAS A.F. & JAGANNATHAN V. 1981 Tissue culture of forest trees — clonal propagation of mature trees of *Eucalyptus citriodora* Hook. by tissue culture. Plant Sci. Lett. **20**, 195–200.

GUPTA P.K., NADGIR A.L., MASCARENHAS A.F. & JAGANNATHAN V. 1980 Tissue culture of forest trees: clonal multiplication of *Tectona grandis* L. (Teak) by tissue culture. Plant Sci. Lett. **17**, 259–268.

GUPTA P.K., TIMMIS R., PULLMAN G., YANCY M., KREITINGER M., CARLSON W. & CARPENTER C. 1991 Development of a embryogenic system for automated propagation of forest trees. pp. 75–93 *in* Vasil I.K. (ed.) 1991 (*q.v.*).

GUPTA P.P. 1985 Plant regeneration and variabilities from tissue cultures of cocoyams (*Xanthosoma sagittifolium* and *X.violaceum*). Plant Cell Rep. **4**, 88–91.

GUPTA S., SEN B. & BHATTACHARYA S. 1987 Embryogenesis and differentiation in two species of *Trigonella*. Phytomorph. **37**, 95–101.

GUPTA S.D. & HADLEY G. 1977 Phytotoxicity of benomyl on orchid seedlings. Am. Orchid Soc. Bull. **46**, 905–907.

GUR A., GAD A.E. & HAAS E. 1988 Rooting of apple rootstock clones as related to phenols and their oxidation. Acta Hort. **227**, 160–166.

GUTMAN T.S. & SHIRYAEVA G.A. 1980 New method for growing cultures of isolated tissues of higher plants. Rastit. Resur. **16**, 601–606.

HABERLACH G.T., COHEN B.A., REICHERT N.A., BAER M.A., TOWELL L.E. & HELGESON J.P. 1985 Isolation culture and regeneration of protoplasts from potato and several related *Solanum* species. Plant Science **39**, 67–74.

HACCIUS B. 1978 Question of unicellular origin of non-zygotic embryos in callus cultures. Phytomorph. **28**, 74–81.

HACCIUS B. & HAUSNER G. 1976 A transplantable embryogenic callus from nucellar tissue of *Cynanchum vincetoxicum* and the significance of a globular proembryonal cell complex in the non-zygotic embryo development. Protoplasma **90**, 265–282.

HACCIUS B. & LAKSHMANAN K.K. 1965 Adventive embryogenesis in callus culture of *Nicotiana* under high light intensity. Planta **65**, 102–104.

HACCIUS B., BHANDARI N.N. & HAUSNER N.N. 1974 In vitro transformation of ovules into rudimentary pistils in *Nicotiana tabacum* L. J. Exp. Bot. **25**, 695–704.

HACKETT D.P. 1952 The osmotic change during auxin-induced water uptake by potato tissue. Plant Physiol. **27**, 279–284.

HACKETT W.P. 1969b Aseptic multiplication of lily bulblets from bulb scales. Comb. Proc. Int. Plant Prop. Soc. **19**, 105–108.

HACKETT W.P. 1970 The influence of auxin, catechol and methanolic tissue extracts on root initiation in aseptically cultured shoot apices of the juvenile and adult forms of *Hedera helix*. J. Am. Soc. Hort. Sci. **95**, 398–402.

HACKETT W.P. 1976 Control of phase change in woody plants. Acta Hort. **56**, 143–154.

HACKETT W.P. 1985 Juvenility, maturation and rejuvenation in woody plants. Hort. Rev. **7**, 109–155.

HACKETT W.P. & ANDERSON J.M. 1967 Aseptic multiplication and maintenance of differentiated carnation shoot tissue derived from shoot apices. Proc. Am. Soc. Hort. Sci. **90**, 365–369.

HAGA K.I. & SODEK L. 1987 Utilization of nitrogen sources by immature soybean cotyledons in culture. Ann. Bot. **59**, 597–601.

HAGEN C.E. & HOPKINS H.T. 1955 Ionic species in orthophosphate absorption by barley roots. Plant Physiol. **30**, 193–199.

HAHLBROCK K. 1974 Correlation between nitrate uptake, growth and changes in metabolic activities of cultured plant cells. p. 363 *in* Street H.E. (ed.) 1974 (*q.v.*).

HAHLBROCK K. 1977 Regulatory aspects of phenylpropanoid biosynthesis in cell cultures. pp. 95–111 *in* Barz, Reinhard and Zenk (eds.) 1977 (*q.v.*).

HAHLBROCK K., EBEL J. & OAKS A. 1974 Determination of specific growth stages of plant cell suspension cultures by monitoring conductivity changes in the medium. Planta **118**, 75–85.

HAHLBROCK K., SCHRODER I. & VIEREGGE J. 1980b Enzyme regulation in parsley and soybean cell cultures. pp. 39–60 *in* Fiechter A. (ed.) 1980 q.v.).

HAHN T.T., SCHRICKE H.L. & VAN K.T.T. 1981 Direct *in vitro* bud formation from fragments and thin cell layers of different organs of the winged bean (*Psophocarpus tetragonolobus* L. DC.). Z. Pflanzenphysiol. **102**, 127–139.

HAHNE G. & HOFFMAN F. 1984 Dimethyl sulphoxide can initiate cell divisions of arrested callus protoplasts by promoting cortical microtubule assembly. Proc. Nat. Acad. Sci. U.S.A. **81**, 5449–5453.

HAHNE G., MAYER J.E. & LÖRZ H. 1988 Embryogenic and callus-specific proteins in somatic embryogenesis of the grass *Dactylis glomerata* L. Plant Science **55**, 267–279.

HAINES R.J. & DE FOSSARD R.A. 1977 Propagation of Hoop pine (*Araucaria cunninghamii*) by organ culture. Acta Hort. **78**, 297–301.

HAKKAART F.A. & VERSLUIJS J.M.A. 1983 Some factors affecting glassiness in carnation meristem tip cultures. Neth. J. Plant Path. **89**, 47–53.

HALDEMAN J.H., THOMAS R.L. & McKAMY D.L. 1987 Use of benomyl and rifampicin for *in vitro* shoot tip culture of *Camellia sinensis* and *C. japonica*. HortScience **22**, 306–307.

HALL M.A., ACASTER M.A., BENGOCHEA T., DODDS J.H., EVANS D.E., JONES J.F., JERIE P.H., MUTUMBA G.C., NIEPEL B. & SHAARI A.R. 1980 Ethylene and seeds. pp. 199–207 *in* Skoog F. (ed.) 1980 (*q.v.*).

HALL P.J. & BANDURSKI R.S. 1986 3H Indole-3-acetyl-*myo*- inositol hydrolysis by extracts of *Zea mays* L. vegetative tissue. Plant Physiol. **80**, 374–377.

HALPERIN W. 1966 Alternative morphogenetic events in cell suspensions. Am. J. Bot. **53**, 443–453.

HALPERIN W. 1967 Population density effects on embryogenesis in carrot cell cultures. Exp. Cell Res. **48**, 170–173.

HALPERIN W. & MINOCHA S. 1973 Benzyladenine effects on cell separation and wall metabolism. Can. J. Bot. **51**, 1347–1354.

HALPERIN W. & WETHERELL D.F. 1964 Adventive embryony in tissue cultures of the wild carrot, *Daucus carota*. Am. J. Bot. **51**, 274–283.

HALPERIN W. & WETHERELL D.F. 1965 Ammonium requirement for embryogenesis *in vitro*. Nature **205**, 519–520.

HAMA I. 1986 Artificial seeds. Japanese Patent Application no. 40708/1986

HAMID A. & LOCKE S.B. 1961 Heat inactivation of leafroll virus in potato tuber tissues. Am. Pot. J. **38**, 304–310.

HAMILL J.D., AHUJA P.S., DAVEY M.R. & COCKING E.C. 1986 Protoplast-derived streptomycin resistant plants of the forage legume *Onobrychis viciifolia* Scop. (sainfoin). Plant Cell Rep. **5**, 439–441.

HAMMATT H., NELSON R.S. & DAVEY M.R. 1987 Plant regeneration from seedling explants of perennial *Glycine* species. Plant Cell Tiss. Organ Cult. **11**, 3–11.

HAMMERSCHLAG F. 1980 Peach micropropagation. pp. 48–52 *in* Anon 1980b (*q.v.*).

HAMMERSCHLAG F. 1982a Factors affecting establishment and growth of peach shoots *in vitro*. HortScience **17**, 85–86.

HAMMERSCHLAG F. 1982b Factors influencing *in vitro* multiplication and rooting of the plum rootstock myrobalan (*Prunus cerasifera* Ehrh.). J. Am. Soc. Hort. Sci. **107**, 44–47.

HAMMERSCHLAG F. & BOTTINO P. 1981 Effect of plant age on callus growth, plant regeneration and anther culture of geranium. J. Am. Soc. Hort. Sci. **106**, 114–116.

HAMMERSCHLAG F.A. 1978 Influence of light intensity and date of explantation on growth of geranium callus. HortScience **13**, 153–154.

HAMMERSCHLAG F.A. 1981a Factors affecting the culturing of peach shoots *in vitro*. HortScience **16**, 282 (Abst.).

HAMMERSCHLAG F.A. 1988 Callus and root formation from leaves of mature peach plants propagated *in vitro*. HortScience **23**, 756.

HAMMERSLEY-STRAW D.R.H. & THORPE T.A. 1988 Use of osmotic inhibition in studies of shoot formation in tobacco callus cultures. Bot. Gaz. **149**, 303–310.

HAN B. & LIU S. 1990 Walnut. pp. 431–439 *in* Chen *et al.* (eds.) 1990 (*q.v.*).

HAN H., ZIYING X., JIANKANG J. & XINGZHI W. 1982 Production of aneuploids and heteroploids of pollen-derived plants. pp. 421–424 *in* Fujiwara A. (ed.) 1982 (*q.v.*).

HANDLEY L.W. & CHAMBLISS O.L. 1979 *In vitro* propagation of *Cucumis sativus* L. HortScience **14**, 22–23.

HANDLEY L.W. & SINK K.C. 1985a Plant regeneration of *Solanum lycopersicoides* Dun. from stem explants, callus and suspension cultures. Plant Cell Tiss. Organ Cult. **5**, 129–138.

HANDLEY L.W. & SINK K.C. 1985b Plant regeneration of protoplasts isolated from suspension cultures of *Solanum lycopersicoides*. Plant Science **42**, 201–207.

HANDRO W. 1983 Effects of some growth regulators on *in vitro* flowering of *Streptocarpus nobilis*. Plant Cell Rep. **2**, 133–136.

HANGARTER R., PETERSON M. & GOOD N. 1980 Biological activities of indolacetylamino acids and their use as auxins in tissue culture. Plant Physiol. **65**, 761–767.

HANNAY J.W. & STREET H.E. 1954 Studies on the growth of excised roots. III. The molybdenum and manganese requirement of excised tomato roots. New Phytol. **53**, 68–80.

HANNAY J.W. 1956 A study of the micronutrient requirements of excised roots. Ph.D. Thesis, Univ. Manchester [from Street, 1966 (*q.v.*)].

HANNINGS D.W. & LANGHANS R.W. 1974 *In vitro* propagation of the Rieger Elatior begonia. HortScience **9**, 271.

HANOWER J. & HANOWER P. 1984 Inhibition et stimulation en culture *in vitro* de l'embryogenèse des souches issues d'explant foliaires de palmier a huile. Compt. Rend. Acad. Sci. Paris **298**, ser. III 45–48.

HANSEN C.E., MEINS F. Jr. & AEBI R. 1987 Hormonal regulation of zeatin-riboside accumulation by cultured tobacco cells. Planta **172**, 520–525.

HANSEN C.E., MEINS F. Jr. & MILANI A. 1985 Clonal and physiological variation in the cytokinin content of tobacco cell lines differing in cytokinin requirement and capacity for neoplastic growth. Differentiation **29**, 1–6.

HANSEN J. 1975 Light dependent promotion and inhibition of adventitious root formation by gibberellic acid. Planta **123**, 203–205.

HANSEN J. 1976 Adventitious root formation induced by gibberellic acid and regulated by the irradiance to the stock plants. Plant Physiol. **36**, 77–81.

HANSEN J. 1978 Light-dependent promotion and inhibition of adventitious root formation by gibberellic acid. Planta **123**, 203–205.

HANSEN J. 1987 Stock plant lighting and adventitious root formation. HortScience **22**, 746–749.

HANSEN J. & ERIKSEN E.N. 1974 Root formation of pea cuttings in relation to the irradiance of the stock plants. Physiol. Plant. **32**, 170–173.

HANSEN K.C. & LAZARTE J.E. 1984 *In vitro* propagation of pecan seedlings. HortScience **19**, 237–239.

HANSON J. & READ P.E. 1981 A comparison of *in vitro* culture and whole plant performance of four *Petunia hybrida* cultivars and their inbred parents. HortScience **16**, 426 (Abst.198).

HANSON J.B. & TREWAVAS A.J. 1982 Regulation of plant cell growth: the changing perspective. New Phytol. **90**, 1–18.

HANUS D. & ROHR R. 1987 *In vitro* plantlet regeneration from juvenile and mature sycamore maple. Acta Hort. **212**, 77–82.

HARADA H. & IMAMURA J. 1983 Factors that stimulate pollen embryogenesis. pp. 145–158 *in* Anon 1983 (*q.v.*).

HARAMAKI C. 1971 Tissue culture of *Gloxinia*. Comb. Proc. Int. Plant Prop. Soc. **21**, 442–448.

HARAMAKI C. & MURASHIGE T. 1972 *In vitro* culture of *Gloxinia*. HortScience **7**, 339 (Abst. 206).

HARDER R., SCHUMACHER W., FIRBAS F. & VON DENFFER D. 1965 *Strasburger's Textbook of Botany*. New English Edition. Longmans, Green & Co. Ltd. London.

HARDING H.G. & TREBLER H.A. 1947 Detergents for dairy plants and methods for their evaluation. Food Technol. **1**, 478–493.

HARI V. 1980 Effect of cell density changes and conditioned media on carrot cell embryogenesis. Z. Pflanzenphysiol. **96**, 227–231.

HARNEY P.M. 1982 Tissue culture propagation of some herbaceous horticultural plants. pp. 187–208 *in* Tomes *et al.* (eds.) 1982 (*q.v.*).

HARNEY P.M. & KNAP A. 1979 A technique for the *in vitro* propagation of African violets using petioles. Can. J. Plant Sci. **59**, 263–266.

HARRAN S. & DICKINSON D.B. 1978 Metabolism of *myo*-inositol and growth in various sugars of suspension cultured cells. Planta **141**, 77–82.

HARRINGTON H.M. & HENKE R.R. 1981 Amino acid transport into cultured tobacco cells. I. Lysine transport. Plant Physiol. **67**, 373–378.

HARRIS G.P. 1956 Amino acids as sources of nitrogen for the growth of isolated oat embryos. New Phytol. **55**, 253–268.

HARRIS G.P. & HART E.M.H. 1964 Regeneration from leaf squares of *Peperomia sandersii* A, DC: a relationship between rooting and budding. Ann. Bot. **28**, 509–526.

HARRIS R.E. & MASON E.B.B. 1983 Two machines for *in vitro* propagation of plants in liquid media. Can. J. Plant Sci. **63**, 311–316.

HARRIS R.E. & STEVENSON J.H. 1979 Virus elimination and rapid propagation of grapes *in vitro*. Comb. Proc. Int. Plant Prop. Soc. **29**, 95–108.

HARRIS R.V. & KING M.E. 1942 Studies in strawberry virus diseases. V. The use of *Fragaria vesca* L. as an indicator of yellow edge and crinkle. J. Pomol. & Hort. Sci. **19**, 227–242.

HARTMANN H.T. & KESTER D.E. 1983 *Plant Propagation: Principles and Practices*. 4th edition. Prentice-Hall Inc., Englewood Cliffs, New Jersey.

HARTNEY V.J. & KABAY E.D. 1985 From tissue culture to forest trees. Comb. Proc. Int. Plant Prop. Soc. 1984 **34**, 93–99.

HARVAIS G. 1982 An improved medium for growing the orchid *Cypripedium reginae* axenically. Can. J. Bot. **60**, 2547–2555.

HASEGAWA P.M. 1979 *In vitro* propagation of Rose (*Rosa hybrida* L.). HortScience **14**, 610–612.

HASEGAWA P.M., MURASHIGE T. & TAKATORI F.H. 1973 Propagation of aparagus through shoot apex culture. II. Light and temperature requirements, transplantability of plants, and cyto-histological characteristics. J. Am. Soc. Hort. Sci. **98**, 143–148.

HATANO K., KAMURA K., SOYAMA Y. & NISHIOKA I. 1988 Clonal multiplication of *Aconitum carmichaeli* by tip culture and alkaloid contents of clonally propagated plant. Planta Med. **54**, 152–155.

HAUPTMANN R.M., WIDHOLM J.M. & PAXTON J.D. 1985 Benomyl: a broad spectrum fungicide for use in plant cell and protoplast culture. Plant Cell Rep. **4**, 129–132.

HAUZINSKA E. 1974 L'organogénèse dans le tissu de cal de l'oeillet (*Dianthus caryophyllus* L.) dans le conditions de culture *in vitro*. Proc. Int. Hort. Congr. **19**, 60.

HAVEL L.F & NOVÁK F.J. 1988 Regulation of somatic embryogenesis and organogenesis in *Allium carinatum* L. J. Plant Physiol. **132**, 373–377.

HAYASHI M. & KOZAI T. 1987 Development of a facility for accelerating the acclimatization of tissue-cultured plantlets and the performance of test cultivations. pp. 123–134 *in* Ducaté *et al.* (eds.) 1987 (*q.v.*).

HAYES A.B. 1981 The interaction of auxin and ethylene in the maintenance of leaf blade form in *Phaseolus vulgaris* L. var Pinto. Am. J. Bot. **68**, 733–740.

HE D.G., YANG Y.M. & SCOTT K.J. 1988 A comparison of scutellum callus and epiblast callus induction in wheat: the effect of genotype, embryo age and medium. Plant Science **57**, 225–233.

HE G.G., TANNER G. & SCOTT K.J. 1986 Somatic embryogenesis and morphogenesis in callus derived from the epiblast of immature embryos of wheat (*Triticum aestivum*). Plant Science **45**, 119–124.

HEATH O.V.S. & CLARK J.E. 1956a Chelating agents as plant growth substances. A possible clue to the mode of action of auxin. Nature **177**, 1118–1121.

HEATH O.V.S. & CLARK J.E. 1956b Chelating agents as growth substances. Nature **178**, 600–601.

HEATH O.V.S. & CLARK J.E. 1960 Chelation in auxin action. J. Exp. Bot. **11**, 167–187.

HEATH-PAGLIUSO S. & RAPPAPORT L. 1988 Horticultural evaluation of celery lines derived from cell suspension cultures. HortScience **23**, 812.

HEBERLE-BORS E. 1980 Interaction of activated charcoal and iron chelates in anther cultures of *Nicotiana* and *Atropa belladonna*. Z. Pflanzenphysiol. **99**, 339–347.

HEBERLE-BORS E. 1985 In vitro haploid formation from pollen: a critical review. Theor. Apl. Genet. **71**, 361–374.

HECHT S.M. 1980 Probing the cytokinin receptor site(s). pp. 144–160 *in* Skoog F. (ed.) 1980 (*q.v.*).

HECHT S.M., BOCK R.M., SCHMITZ R.Y., SKOOG F. & LEONARD N.J. 1971 Cytokinins: Development of a potent antagonist. Proc. Nat. Acad. Sci. U.S.A. **68**, 2608–2610.

HECK W.W. & PIRES E.G. 1962a Growth of plants fumigated with saturated and unsaturated hydrocarbon gases and their derivatives. Texas Agr. Exp. Sta. Misc. Pub., MP-603

HECK W.W. & PIRES E.G. 1962b Growth of plants fumigated with saturated and unsaturated hydrocarbon gases. Texas Agr. Exp. Sta. Misc. Pub., MP-613 3–12.

HEDTRICH C.M. 1977 Differentiation of cultivated leaf discs of *Prunus mahaleb*. Acta Hort. **78**, 177–183.

HEGEDUS P. & PHAN C.T. 1983a Malformation chez le pommier M-26 cultivé *in vitro*: action de la phloridzin. Annales ACFAS **49**, 35.

HEGEDUS P. & PHAN C.T. 1983b Action de phenols sur les malformations observées chez les parte-greffes de pommiers M-26 et O-3 cultivés *in vitro*. Rev. Can. Biol. Exptl. **42**, 33–38.

HEGEDUS P. & PHAN C.T. 1987 Activities of 5 enzymes of the phenolic metabolism on rooted and acclimated vitreous plants in relation with phenolic treatments. Acta Hort. **212**, 211–216.

HEIDE O.M. 1964 Effects of light and temperature on regenerative ability of *Begonia* leaf cuttings. Physiol. Plant. **17**, 789–804.

HEIDE O.M. 1965 Interaction of temperature, auxins and kinins in the regeneration ability of *Begonia* leaf cuttings. Physiol. Plant. **18**, 891–920.

HEIDE O.M. 1968 Stimulation of adventitious bud formation in *Begonia* leaves by abscisic acid. Nature **219**, 960–961.

HEIDE O.M. 1969 Non-reversibility of gibberellin-induced inhibition of regeneration in *Begonia* leaves. Physiol. Plant. **22**, 671–679.

HEIMER Y., MIZRAHI Y. & BACHRACH U. 1979 Ornithine decarboxylase activity in rapidly dividing plant cells. FEBS Lett. **104**, 146–149.

HEIMER Y.M. & FILNER P. 1971 Regulation of the nitrate assimilation pathway in cultured tobacco cells. Biochim. Biophys. Acta **230**, 362–372.

HEINZ D.J. & MEE G.W.P. 1969 Plant differentiation from callus tissue of *Saccharum* species. Crop Sci. **9**, 346–348.

HEINZ D.J. & MEE G.W.P. 1971 Morphologic, cytogenetic and enzymatic variation in *Saccharum* species hybrid clones, derived from callus tissue. Am. J. Bot. **58**, 257–262.

HEINZ D.J., KRISHNAMURTHI M., NICKELL L.G. & MARETZKI A. 1977 Cell, tissue and organ culture in sugarcane improvement. pp. 3–17 *in* Reinert & Bajaj (eds.) 1977 (*q.v.*).

HEINZMANN U. & SEITZ U. 1977 Synthesis of phenylalanine ammonia-lyase in anthocyanin-containing and anthocyanin-free callus cells of *Daucus carota* L. Planta **135**, 63–67.

HEINZMANN U., SEITZ U. & SEITZ U. 1977 Purification and substrate specificities of hydroxycinnamate: CoA ligase from anthocyanin-containing and anthocyanin-free carrot cells. Planta **135**, 313–318.

HELGESON J.P. 1979 Tissue and cell suspension culture. pp. 52–59 *in* Durbin (ed.) 1979 (*q.v.*).

HELGESON J.P. 1980 Plant tissue and cell suspension culture. pp. 19–25 *in* Ingram and Helgeson (eds.) 1980 (*q.v.*).

HELGESON J.P. & HABERLACH G.T. 1980 Disease resistance studies with tissue cultures. pp. 179–184 *in* Ingram and Helgeson (eds.) 1980 (*q.v.*).

HELGESON J.P., UPPER C.D. & HABERLACH G.T. 1972 Medium and tissue sugar concentrations during cytokinin-controlled growth of tobacco callus tissues. pp. 484–492 *in* Carr D.J. (ed.) 1972 (*q.v.*).

HELLER R. 1953 Researches on the mineral nutrition of plant tissues. Ann. Sci. Nat. Bot. Biol. Vég., 11th Ser. **14**, 1–223.

HELLER R. 1955 Les besoins mineraux des tissus en culture. pp. 1–21 in *La Physiologie des Cultures de Tissus végétaux*. Union Internationale des Sciences Biol. Series B (Colloques) 20 (1954).

HELLER R. & GAUTHERET R.J. 1949a Sur l'emploi d'un ruban de verre comme support pour les cultures de tissus végétaux. Compt. Rend. Seance Soc. Biol., Paris **141**, 662–665.

HELLER R. & GAUTHERET R.J. 1949b Sur l'emploi de papier filtre sans cendres commes support pour les cultures de tissues végétaux. Compt. Rend. Seance Soc. Biol., Paris **143**, 335–337.

HEMBERG T. 1951 Rooting experiments with hypocotyles of *Phaseolus vulgaris* L. Physiol. Plant. **4**, 358–369.

HEMPEL M. 1988 Microcomputers in micropropagation. Acta Hort. **226**, 699–702.

HEMPEL M., PETOS-WITKOWSKA B. & TYMOSZUK J. 1985 The influence of cytokinins on multiplication and subsequent rooting of *Gerbera in vitro*. Acta Hort. **167**, 301–305.

HEMPHILL J.K. & EIKENBERRY E.J. 1987 Process for regenerating soybeans. U.S. Patent No. 4684612

HENDERSON W.E. & KINNERSLEY A.M. 1988 Corn starch as an alternative gelling agent for plant tissue culture. Plant Cell Tiss. Organ Cult. **15**, 17–22.

HENDRICKSON C.E. 1954 The flowering of sunflower explants in aseptic culture. Plant Physiol. **29**, 536–538.

HENKE R.R., HUGHES K.W., CONSTANTIN M.J., HOLLAENDER A. & WILSON C.M. (eds.) 1985 *Tissue culture in Forestry and Agriculture*. Plenum Press. New York, London.

HENNEN G.R. & SHEEHAN T.J. 1978 *In vitro* propagation of *Platycerium stemaria*. HortScience **13**, 245 (No.3).

HENNERTY M.J., UPTON M.E., FURLONG P.A., HARRIS D.P., JAMES D.J. & EATON R.A. 1988 Microbial contamination of *in vitro* cultures of apple rootstocks M26 and M9. Acta Hort. **225**, 129–137.

HENRICH J.E., STIMART D.P. & ASCHER P.D. 1981 Terrestrial orchid seed germination *in vitro* on a defined medium. J. Am. Soc. Hort. Sci. **106**, 193–196.

HENSHAW G.G. 1975 Technical aspects of tissue culture storage for genetic conservation. pp. 349–357 *in* Frankel & Hawkes (eds.) 1975 (*q.v.*).

HENSHAW G.G. 1982 Tissue culture methods and germplasm storage. pp. 789–792 *in* Fujiwara (ed.) 1982 (*q.v.*).

HENSHAW G.G., O'HARA J.F. & WESTCOTT R.J. 1980 Tissue culture methods for the storage and utilisation of potato germplasm. pp. 71–76 *in* Ingram and Helgeson (eds.) 1980 (*q.v.*).

HENSON N. 1979 The aseptic culture of ferns at Kew. The Plantsman **1**, 74–80.

HEPHER A., BOULTER M.E., HARRIS N. & NELSON R.S. 1988 Development of a superficial meristem during somatic embryogenesis from immature cotyledons of soybean (*Glycine max* L.). Ann. Bot. **62**, 513–519.

HEPLER P.K. & WAYNE R.O. 1985 Calcium and plant development. Ann. Rev. Plant Physiol. **36**, 397–439.

HERBER B., ULBRICH B. & JACOBSEN H-J., 1988 Modulation of soluble auxin-binding proteins in soybean cell suspensions. Plant Cell Rep. **7**, 178–181.

HERVEY A. & ROBBINS W.J. 1978 Development of plants from leaf discs of variegated *Coleus* and its relation to patterns of leaf chlorosis. In Vitro **14**, 294–300.

HESS C.E. 1969 Internal and external factors regulating root initiation. pp. 42–53 *in* Whittingham W.J. (ed.) 1969 *Root Growth*. Butterworths, London.

HESS D., LEIPOLDT G. & ILLG R.D. 1979 Investigations on the lactose induction of β-galactosides activity in callus tissue cultures of *Nemesia strumosa* and *Petunia hybrida*. Z. Pflanzenphysiol. **94**, 45–53.

HEUSER C.W. 1983 *In vitro* propagation of *Lythrum virgatum*. HortScience **18**, p. 303.

HEW C.S., TING S.K. & CHIA T.F. 1988 Substrate utilization by *Dendrobium* tissues. Bot. Gaz. **149**, 153–157.

HEWITT E.J. 1948 Relation of manganese and some other metals to the iron status of plants. Nature **161**, 489.

HEWITT E.J. 1963 Mineral nutrition of plants in culture media. pp. 97–133 *in* Steward F.C. (ed.) *Plant Physiology — A Treatise* Vol. 3. *Inorganic Nutrition of Plants*. Academic Press, New York, London.

HEWITT E.J. & SMITH T.A. 1975 *Plant Mineral Nutrition*. English University Press.

HEYSER J.W., DYKES T.A., DEMOTT K.J. & NABORS M.W. 1983 High frequency, long-term regeneration of rice from callus culture. Plant Sci. Lett. **29**, 175–182.

HIATT A.J. 1978 Critique of absorbtion and utilization of ammonium nitrogen by plants. pp. 191–199 in *Nitrogen in the Environment* Vol.2. *Soil-Plant-Nitrogen Relationships*. Academic Press, New York, San Francisco, London. ISBN 0-12-518402-6 (v.2).

HICKS G.S. 1975 Carpelloids on tobacco stamen primordia *in vitro*. Can. J. Bot. **53**, 77–81.

HICKS G.S. 1980 Patterns of organ development in plant tissue culture and the problem of organ determination. Bot. Rev. **46**, 1–23.

HICKS G.S. & McHUGHEN A. 1974 Altered morphogenesis of placental tissues of tobacco *in vitro*: stigmatoid and carpelloid outgrowths. Planta **121**, 193–196.

HICKS G.S. & SAND S.A. 1977 *In vitro* culture of the stamen primordia from a male sterile tobacco. Plant Sci. Lett. **10**, 257–263.

HICKS G.S. & SUSSEX I.M. 1970 Development *in vitro* of excised flower primordia of *Nicotiana tabacum*. Can. J. Bot. **48**, 133–139.

HICKS R.G.T., NGAMYEESOON N. & PERKINS C.J. 1988 Double-stranded RNA analysis as a method for detecting viruses in woody ornamentals. Acta Hort. **226**, 417–424.

HIGUCHI H. & AMAKI W. 1989 Effects of 6-benzylaminopurine on the organogenesis of *Asplenium nidus* L. through *in vitro* propagation. Scientia Hort. **37**, 351–359.

HILDEBRANDT A.C. 1962 Tissue and single cell cultures of higher plants as a basic experimental method. pp. 383–421 in Linskens and Tracey (eds.) *Modern Methods of Plant Analysis* Vol. 5.

HILDEBRANDT A.C. 1977 Single cell culture, protoplasts and plant viruses. pp. 581–597 in Reinert and Bajaj (eds.) 1977 (*q.v.*).

HILDEBRANDT A.C., RIKER A.J. & DUGGAR B.M. 1946 The influence of the composition of the medium on growth *in vitro* of excised tobacco and sunflower tissue cultures. Am. J. Bot. **33**, 591–597.

HILDEBRANDT A.C., WILMAR J.C., JOHNS H. & RIKER A.J. 1963 Growth of edible chlorophyllous plant tissues *in vitro*. Am. J. Bot. **50**, 248–254.

HILDEBRANDT V. & HARNEY P.M. 1983 In vitro propagation of *Syringa vulgaris* 'Vesper'. HortScience **18**, 432–434.

HILDING A. & WELANDER T. 1976 Effects of some factors on propagation of *Begonia × hiemalis in vitro*. Swedish J. Agric. Res. **6**, 191–199.

HILL M. 1988 The specifications for Neo Plants' new propagation unit. Comb. Proc. Int. Plant Prop. Soc., 1987, **37**, 306–313.

HILL-COTTINGHAM D.G. & LLOYD-JONES C.P. 1961 Absorption and breakdown of iron EDTA by tomato plants. Nature **189**, 312.

HILLMAN W.S. 1959 Experimental control of flowering in *Lemna*. I. General methods. Photoperiodism in *L. pepusilla* 6746. Am. J. Bot. **46**, 466–473.

HILLMAN W.S. 1961 Experimental control of flowering in *Lemna*. III. A relationship between medium composition and the opposite photoperiodic responses of *L. perpusilla* 6746 and *L. gibba* G3. Am. J. Bot. **48**, 413–419.

HILLMAN W.S. & GALSTON A.W. 1961 The effect of external factors on auxin content. Encyclopedia of Plant Physiology **14**, 683–702.

HIMENO H. & SANO K. 1987 Synthesis of crocin, picrocrocin and safranal by saffron stigma-like structures proliferated *in vitro*. Agric. Biol. Chem. **51**, 2395–2400.

HIRAOKA N. & KODAMA T. 1982 Effects of non-frozen cold storage on the growth, organogenesis, and secondary metabolite production of callus cultures. pp. 359–360 in Fujiwara A. (ed.) 1982 (*q.v.*).

HIRATSUKA S. & KATAGIRI M. 1988 Shoot and callus formation in explants from immature seeds of Japanese pear. Scientia Hort. **34**, 193–199.

HIRSCH P. & CONTI S.F. 1964 Biology of budding bacteria. II. Growth and nutrition of *Hyphomicrobium* spp. Arch. Mikrobiol. **48**, 358–368.

HISAJIMA S. 1981 Multiple shoot formation from various kinds of plant seeds. Plant Physiol. **67**, (Suppl.) 28 (Abst. 147).

HISAJIMA S. 1982a Multiple shoot formation from almond seeds and an excised single shoot. Agric. Biol. Chem. **46**, 1091–1093.

HISAJIMA S. 1982b Multiple shoot formation from almond embryos. Biol. Plant. **24**, 235–238.

HISAJIMA S. 1982c Microplant propagation through multiple shoot formation from seeds and embryos. pp. 141–142 in Fujiwara (ed.) 1982 (*q.v.*).

HISAJIMA S. & CHURCH L. 1981 Multiple shoot formation from soybean embryo. Plant Physiol. **67**, (Suppl.) 28 (Abst. 148).

HO W.-J. & VASIL I.K. 1983 Somatic embryogenesis in sugarcane (*Saccharum officinarum* L.): Growth and plant regeneration from embryogenic cell suspension cultures. Ann. Bot. **51**, 719–726.

HOAGLAND D.R. 1920 Optimum nutrient solutions for plants. Science **52**, 562–564.

HOAGLAND D.R. & ARNON D.I. 1938 The water-culture method for growing plants without soil. Univ. Calif. Coll. Agric. Exp. Sta. Circ.347.

HOAGLAND D.R. & SNYDER W.C. 1933 Nutrition of strawberry plant under controlled conditions. Proc. Am. Soc. Hort. Sci. **30**, 288–296.

HODGE M.H. 1986 Propagation of herbaceous perennials by root cuttings. Comb. Proc. Int. Plant Prop. Soc. 1985 **35**, 548–554.

HODGMAN C.D., WEAST R.C., SHANKLAND R.S. & SELBY S.M. 1962 *Handbook of Chemistry and Physics*. Chemical Rubber Publishing Co., Cleveland, Ohio.

HODGSON J. 1990 Growing plants and growing companies. Bio/Technology **8**, 624–628.

HOHTOLA A. 1988 Seasonal changes in explant viability and contamination of tissue cultures from mature Scots pine. Plant Cell Tiss. Organ Cult. **15**, 211–222.

HOLDEN J.H.W. & WILLIAMS J.T. (eds.) 1984 *Crop Genetic Resources: Conservation and Evaluation*. George Allen and Unwin, London.

HOLDGATE D.P. 1977 Propagation of ornamentals by tissue culture. pp. 18–43 in Reinert and Bajaj (eds.) 1977 (*q.v.*).

HOLDGATE D.P. & AYNSLEY J.S. 1977 The development and establishment of a commercial tissue culture laboratory. Acta Hort. **78**, 31–36.

HOLLIDAY P. 1989 *A Dictionary of Plant Pathology*. Cambridge Univ. Press, Cambridge, New York. ISBN 0 521 33117X

HOLLIDAY R. 1989 A different kind of inheritance. Scientific American **260**, 40–48.

HOLLINGS M. 1965 Disease control through virus-free stock. Ann. Rev. Phytopath. **3**, 367–396.

HOLLINGS M. & STONE O.M. 1964 Investigation of carnation viruses. I. Carnation mottle. Ann. Appl. Biol. **53**, 103–118.

HOLLINGS M. & STONE O.M. 1965 Investigation of carnation viruses. II. Carnation ringspot. Ann. Appl. Biol. **56**, 73.

HOLM-HANSEN O., GERLOFF G.C. & SKOOG F. 1954 Cobalt as an essential element for blue-green algae. Physiol. Plant. **7**, 665–675.

HOLMES F.O. 1948 Elimination of spotted wilt from a stock of dahlia. Phytopath. **38**, 314.

HOLMES F.O. 1955 Elimination of Spotted Wilt from dahlias by propagation of tip cuttings. Phytopath. **45**, 224–226.

HOMÈS J. & VANSÉVEREN-VAN ESPEN N. 1973 Effets du saccharose et de la lumière sur le développement *et al* morphologie de protocormes d'Orchidées cultivés *in vitro*. Bull. Soc. Roy. Bot. Belg. **106**, 89–106.

HOMÈS J., LEGROS M. & JAZIRI M. 1987 *In vitro* multiplication of *Crocus sativus* L. Acta Hort. **212**, 675–676.

HOOD J.V. & LIBBY W.J. 1978 Continuing effects of maturation state in radiata pine and a general maturation model. pp. 220–232 in Hughes K.W. *et al.* 1978 (*q.v.*).

HORAK J. 1972 Ploidy chimeras in plants regenerated from the tissue cultures of *Brassica oleracea* L. Biol. Plant. **14**, 423–426.

HORAK J., LUSTINEC J., MESICEK J., KAMINEK M. & POLACKOVA D. 1975 a Regeneration of diploid and polyploid plants from the stem pith explants of diploid marrow stem kale (*Brassica oleracea* L.). Ann. Bot. **39**, 571–577.

HORGAN K. & AITKEN J. 1981 Reliable plantlet formation from embryos and seedling shoot tips of radiata pine. Physiol. Plant. **53**, 170–175.

HORGAN R. 1987a Plant growth regulators and the control of growth and differentiation in plant tissue cultures. pp. 135–149 in Green *et al*.(eds.) 1987 (*q.v.*).

HORGAN R. 1987b Cytokinin genes. pp. 119–130 in Hoad G.V., Lenton J.R., Jackson M.B. and Atkin R.K. (eds.) 1987 *Hormone Action in Plant Development —A Critical Appraisal*. Butterworths, London, Boston.

HORN M.E. 1991 Transformation and regeneration of orchard grass protoplasts. Section B3 pp. 1–15 in Lindsey (ed.) 1991 (*q.v.*).

HORN M.E., CONGER B.V. & HARMS C.T. 1988c Plant regeneration from protoplasts of embryogenic suspension cultures of orchard grass (*Dactylis glomerata* L.). Plant Cell Rep. **7**, 371–374.

HORN W. 1988 Micropropagation of *Pelargonium* × *domesticum* (*P. grandiflorum* hybrids). Acta Hort. **226**, 53–58.

HORN W., SCHLEGEL G. & HAUFT B. 1988a *In vitro* stock plant culture of *Kalanchoe* hybrids. Acta Hort. **226**, 627–630.

HORN W., SCHLEGEL G. & JOHN K. 1988b Micropropagation of roses (*Rosa* hybr.). Acta Hort. **226**, 623–626.

HORNER M., McCOMB J.A., McCOMB A.J. & STREET H.E. 1977 Ethylene production and plantlet formation by *Nicotiana* anthers cultured in the presence and absence of charcoal. J. Exp. Bot. **28**, 1365–1372.

HORSCH R.B. & KING J. 1983 A covert contaminant of cultured plant cells: elimination of a hyphomicrobium sp. from cultures of *Datura innoxia* (Mill.). Plant Cell Tiss. Organ Cult. **2**, 21–28.

HORST R.K. 1988 Production of plants free of virus and prevention of reinfection. Acta Hort. **234**, 393–402.

HORST R.K. & COHEN D. 1980 Amantadine supplemented tissue culture medium: a method for obtaining chrysanthemums free of *Chrysanthemum* stunt viroid. Acta Hort. **110**, 315–319.

HOSEMANS D. & BOSSOUTROT D. 1983 Induction of haploid plants from *in vitro* culture of unpollinated beet ovules (*Beta vulgaris* L.). Z. Pflanzenzucht. **91**, 74–77.

HOVENKAMP-HERMELINK J.H.M., JACOBSEN E., PIJNACKER L.P., DE VRIES J.N., WITHOLT B. & FEENSTRA W.J. 1988 Cytological studies on adventitious shoots and minitubers of a monoploid potato clone. Euphytica **39**, 213–219.

HOWARD B. 1990 Rooting potential in cuttings. The Garden **115**, 608–611.

HOWARD B.H. & MARKS T.R. 1987 The *in vitro* — *in vivo* interface. pp. 101–111 *in* Jackson *et al.* (eds.) 1987a (*q.v.*).

HOWARD B.H. & OEHL V.H. 1981 Improved establishment of *in vitro*-propagated plum micropropagules following treatment with GA₃ or prior chilling. J. Hort. Sci. **56**, 1–7.

HOWLAND A.K. 1976 A rapid multiplication technique. pp. 42–44 *in* Terry and MacIntyre (eds.) 1976 (*q.v.*).

HU C.-Y. 1977 Advances in *Ilex* embryo culture. Proc. 54th Meeting of the Holly Soc. of America 5–6 (HA 48 10780).

HU C.-Y. & SUSSEX I. 1986 Suspensor and *in vitro* culture of immature soybean embryos. p. 41 *in* Somers *et al.* (eds.) 1986 (*q.v.*).

HU C.-Y. & SUSSEX I.M. 1972 *In vitro* development of embryoids on cotyledons of *Ilex aquifolium*. Phytomorph. **21**, 103–107.

HU C.-Y., OCHS J.D. & MANCINI F.M. 1978 Further observations on *Ilex* embryoid production. Z. Pflanzenphysiol. **89**, 41–49.

HU H. & YANG H. (eds.) 1986 *Haploids of Higher Plants* in vitro. Springer-Verlag, Heidelberg.

HUANG L.-C. 1984 Alternative media and method for *Cattleya* propagation by tissue culture. Am. Orchid Soc. Bull. **53**, 167–170.

HUANG S.-C. & MILLIKAN D.F. 1979 Disease-free plants through micropropagation. Comb. Proc. Int. Plant Prop. Soc. **29**, 393–398.

HUANG S.-C. & MILLIKAN D.F. 1980 *In vitro* micrografting of apple shoot tips. HortScience **15**, 741–743.

HUDSON J.P. & WILLIAMS I.H. 1955 Juvenility phenomena associated with crown gall. Nature **175**, 814.

HUGHES K. W., HENKE R. & CONSTANTIN M. (eds.) 1978 *Propagation of Higher Plants through Tissue Culture*. Technical Inf. Center, U.S. Dept. Energy, Springfield, Va. CONF-7804111.

HUHTINEN O., HONKANEN J. & SIMOLA L.K. 1982 Ornithine- and putrescine-suppoorted divisions and cell colony formation in leaf protoplasts of alders (*Alnus glutinosa* and *A. incana*). Plant Sci. Lett. **28**, 3–9.

HUMPHRIES E.C. 1960 Kinetin inhibited root formation on leaf petioles of detached leaves of *Phaseolus vulgaris* (dwarf bean). Physiol. Plant. **13**, 659–663.

HUNAULT G. 1979 Recherches sur le comportement des fragments d'organes et des tissus de monocotyledones cultivés *in vitro*. V. Discussion. Rev. Cytol. Biol. Vég. – Bot. **2**, 259–287.

HUNAULT G. 1985 Organic acids, pH, ammonium and nitrate interactions on the growth of *Asparagus* tissues cultivated *in vitro*. Ann. Sci. Nat., Bot. **13**, 63–75.

HUNTER C.P. 1989 Plant generation method. U.S. Patent No. 4840906.

HUNTER C.S. 1979 In vitro culture of *Cinchona ledgeriana* L. J. Hort. Sci. **54**, 111–114.

HUNTER C.S., CHAMPION L.N. & SAUL J. 1986 Photosynthesis by *Chichona* shoots *in vitro*: Effects of CO₂ concentration. p. 410 *in* Somers *et al.* (eds.) 1986 (*q.v.*).

HÜSEMANN W. & REINERT J. 1976 Regulating growth and morphogenesis of cell cultures of *Crepis capillaris* by light and phytohormones. Protoplasma **90**, 353–367.

HÜSEMANN W., AMINO S., FISCHER K., HERZBECK H. & CALLIS R. 1990 Light dependent growth and differentiation processes in photoautotrophic cell cultures. pp. 373–378 *in* Nijkamp *et al.* (eds.) 1990 (*q.v.*).

HUSSEY G. 1975b Totipotency in tissue explants and callus of some members of the Liliaceae, Iridaceae and Amaryllidaceae. J. Exp. Bot. **26**, 253–262.

HUSSEY G. 1975c Propagation of hyacinths by tissue culture. Scientia Hort. **3**, 21–28.

HUSSEY G. 1976b Plant regeneration from callus and parent tissue in *Ornithogallum thyrsoides*. J. Exp. Bot. **27**, 375–380.

HUSSEY G. 1976c *In vitro* release of axillary shoots from apical dominance in monocotyledonous plantlets. Ann. Bot. **40**, 1323–1325.

HUSSEY G. 1977a *In vitro* propagation of some members of the Liliaceae, Iridaceae and Amaryllidaceae. Acta Hort. **78**, 303–309.

HUSSEY G. 1977b *In vitro* propagation of *Gladiolus* by precocious axillary shoot formation. Scientia Hort. **6**, 287–296.

HUSSEY G. 1978a *In vitro* propagation of the onion *Allium cepa* by axillary and adventitious shoot proliferation. Scientia Hort. **9**, 227-236.

HUSSEY G. 1978b The application of tissue culture to the vegetative propagation of plants. Science Prog. **65**, 185–208.

HUSSEY G. 1982 *In vitro* propagation of *Narcissus*. Ann. Bot. **49**, 707–719.

HUSSEY G. 1983 *In vitro* propagation of horticultural and agricultural crops. pp. 111–138 *in* Mantell & Smith (eds.) *Plant Biotechnology*. Soc. Exp. Biol. seminar series 18 1983. C.U.P.

HUSSEY G. & FALAVIGNA A. 1980 Origin and production of *in vitro* adventitious shoots in the onion *Allium cepa* L. J. Exp. Bot. **31**, 1675–1686.

HUSSEY G. & GUNN H. 1983 Shoot regeneration *in vitro* in *Pisum*. Ann. Rep. John Innes Inst. 1981/1982. 127–128.

HUSSEY G. & GUNN H.V. 1984 Plant production in pea (*Pisum sativum* L. cvs. Puget and Upton) from long-term callus with superficial meristems. Plant Sci. Lett. **37**, 143–148.

HUSSEY G. & HARGREAVES J. 1974 Multiplication of *in vitro* plantlets in bulbous species. Ann.Rep. John Innes Inst. 1974 58–59.

HUSSEY G. & HEPHER A. 1978a Clonal propagation of sugar beet plants and the formation of polyploids by tissue culture. Ann. Bot. **42**, 477–479.

HUSSEY G. & HILTON J. 1978a *In vitro* propagation of *Narcissus*. Ann. Rep. John Innes Inst. 1977 45–46.

HUSSEY G. & HILTON J. 1980a Sustained proliferation of adventitious shoots in bulbous genera. Ann. Rep. John Innes Inst. 1979 55–56.

HUSSEY G. & HILTON J. 1980b *In vitro* propagation of *Tulipa*. Ann. Rep. John Innes Inst. 1979 56–58.

HUSSEY G. & STACEY N.J. 1981a *In vitro* propagation of potato (*Solanum tuberosum* L.) Ann. Bot. **48**, 787–796.

HUSSEY G. & STACEY N.J. 1981b *In vitro* propagation of potato (*Solanum tuberosum* L.). Ann. Rep. John Innes Inst. 1980 57–59.

HUSSEY G., HILTON J. & LUMSDEN P. 1980 *In vitro* propagation of *Alstroemeria*. Ann. Rep. John Innes Inst. 1979 56.

HUTCHINSON J.F. 1982a *In vitro* propagation of apple using organ culture. pp. 729–730 *in* Fujiwara (ed.) 1982 (*q.v.*).

HUTCHINSON J.F. 1985 Effect of explant type on shoot proliferation and physical support on root initiation for a range of horticultural species. pp. 327–328 *in* Henke *et al.* (eds.) 1985 (*q.v.*).

HUXTER T.J., REID D.M. & THORPE T.A. 1979 Ethylene production by tobacco (*Nicotiana tabacum*) callus. Physiol. Plant. **46**, 374–380.

HUXTER T.J., THORPE T.A. & REID D.M. 1981 Shoot initiation in light- and dark-grown tobacco callus: the role of ethylene. Physiol. Plant. **53**, 319–326.

HWANG L.S., SKIRVIN R.M. & BOUWKAMP J. 1981 Shoot formation from sweet potato (*Ipomoea batatas* Lam.) tuberous discs *in vitro*. HortScience **16**, 433 (Abst. 250).

HWANG S.C. 1986 Variation in banana plants propagated through tissue culture. J. Chin. Soc. Hort. Sci. **32**, 117–125.

HWANG S.C. & KO W.H. 1984 *In vitro* somaclonal variation in banana and its applications for screening for resistance to fusarial wilt. Tech. Bull. 107 Food and Fertilizer Technol. Center, Taipei City, Taiwan.

HYNDMAN S.E., HASEGAWA P.M. & BRESSAN R.A. 1982b The role of sucrose and nitrogen in adventitious root formation on cultured rose shoots. Plant Cell Tiss. Organ Cult. **1**, 229-238.

ICHI T., KODA T., ASAI I., HATANAKA A. & SEKIYA J. 1986 Effects of gelling agents on *in vitro* culture of plant tissues. Agric. Biol. Chem. **50**, 2397–2399.

ICHIHASHI S. 1978 Studies on the media for orchid seed germination. II. The effects of anionic and cationic combinations relevent to seeding populations and culture periods on the growth of *Bletilla striata* seedlings. J. Jap. Soc. Hort. Sci. **46**, 521–529.

ICHIHASHI S. 1979 Studies on the media for orchid seed germination. III. The effects of total ionic concentration, cation/anion ratio, NH_4^+/NO_3^- ratio, and minor elements on the growth of *Bletilla striata*. J. Jap. Soc. Hort. Sci. **47**, 524–536.

ICHIHASHI S. & KAKO S. 1973 Studies on clonal propagation of *Cattleya* through tissue culture method. I. Factors affecting survival and growth of shoot meristem of *Cattleya in vitro*. J. Jap. Soc. Hort. Sci. **42**, 264–270.

ICHIHASHI S. & KAKO S. 1977 Studies in clonal proopagation of *Cattleya* by tissue culture. II. Browning of *Cattleya*. J. Jap. Soc. Hort. Sci. **46**, 325–330.

ICHIHASHI S. & YAMASHITA M. 1977 Studies of the media for orchid germination. I. The effects of balances inside each cation and anion group for the germination and seedling development of *Bletilla striata* seeds. J. Jap. Soc. Hort. Sci. **45**, 407–413.

IKEDA M., OJIMA K. & OHIRA K. 1979 Habituation in suspension- cultured soybean cells to thiamine and its precursors. Plant Cell Physiol. **20**, 733–740.

IMBERT M.P. & WILSON L.A. 1970 Stimulatory and inhibitory effects of scopoletin on IAA oxidase preparations from sweet potato. Phytochem. **9**, 1787–1794.

IMEL M.R. & PREECE J.E. 1988 Adventitious shoot formation from recultured leaves of rhododendron. HortScience **23**, 760.

INGRAM D.S. 1977 Applications in plant pathology. pp. 463–500 *in* Street H.E. (ed.) 1977 (*q.v.*).

INGRAM D.S. & HELGESON J.P. (eds.) 1980 *Tissue Culture Methods for Plant Pathologist*. Blackwell Scientific Publications.

INOUE M. & MAEDA E. 1982 Control of organ formation in rice callus using two-step culture method. pp. 183–184 *in* Fujiwara A. (ed.) 1982 (*q.v.*).

IRVINE J.E., FITCH M. & MOORE P.H. 1983 The induction of callus in sugarcane tissue cultures by selected chemicals. Plant Cell Tiss. Organ Cult. **2**, 141–149.

ISHIHARA A. & KATANO M. 1982 Propagation of apple cultivars and rootstocks by shoot-tip culture. pp. 733–734 *in* Fujiwara A. (ed.) 1982 (*q.v.*).

ISHII K. 1986 *In vitro* plantlet formation from adventitious buds on juvenile seedlings of Hinoki cypress (*Chamaecyparis obtusa*). Plant Cell Tiss. Organ Cult. **7**, 247–255.

ISHII S. 1987 Generation of active oxygen species during enzymic isolation of protoplasts from oat leaves. In Vitro Cell Dev. Biol. **23**, 653–658.

ISHII S. 1988 Factors influencing protoplast viability of suspension-cultured rice cells during isolation process. Plant Physiol. **88**, 26–29.

ISIKAWA H. 1974 In vitro formation of adventitious buds and roots on the hypocotyl of *Cryptomeria japonica*. Bot. Mag. (Tokyo) **87**, 73–77.

ISKANDER S.R. & BROSSARD-CHRIQUI D. 1980 Potentialités organogènes des disques foliaires du *Datura innoxia* Mill. cultivés *in vitro*. Z. Pflanzenphysiol. **98**, 245–254.

IVANICKA J. 1987 *In vitro* micropropagation of mulberry, *Morus nigra* L. Scientia Hort. **32**, 33–39.

IWAI S., KISHI C., NAKATA K. & KUBO S. 1985 Production of a hybrid *Nicotiana repanda* Willd. × *N. tabacum* L. by ovule culture. Plant Science **41**, 175–178.

IWAMURA H., MASUDA N., KOSHIMIZU K. & MATSUBARA S. 1979 Cytokinin-agonist and antagonist activities of 4-substituted-2-methylpyrrolo 2.3-*d* pyrimidines, 7-deaza analogs of cytokinin-active adenine derivatives. Phytochem. **18**, 217–222.

IWAMURA H., MASUDA N., KOSHIMIZU K. & MATSUBARA S. 1980 Effects of 4-alkylaminopteridines on tobacco callus growth. Plant Sci. Lett. **20**, 15–18.

IZHAR S. & POWER J.B. 1977 Genetical studies with *Petunia* leaf protoplasts. 1. Genetic variation to specific growth hormones and possible genetic control on stages of protoplast development in culture. Plant Sci. Lett. **8**, 375–383.

JACKSON G.V.H., BALL E.A. & ARDITTI J. 1977a Seed germination and seedling proliferation of taro, *Colocasia esculenta* (L.) Schott. *in vitro*. J. Hort. Sci. **52**, 169–171.

JACKSON G.V.H., BALL E.A. & ARDITTI J. 1977b Tissue culture of taro, *Colocasia esculenta* (L.) Schott. J. Hort. Sci. **52**, 373–382.

JACKSON J.A. & DALE P.J. 1988 Callus induction, plant regeneration and an assessment of cytological variation in regenerated plants of *Lolium multiflorum* L. J. Plant Physiol. **132**, 351–355.

JACKSON J.A. & LYNDON R.F. 1988 Cytokinin habituation in juvenile and flowering tobacco. J. Plant Physiol. **132**, 575–579.

JACKSON M.B. 1985a Ethylene and responses of plants to soil waterlogging and submergence. Ann. Rev. Plant Physiol. **36**, 145–174.

JACKSON M.B. 1985b Ethylene and the responses of plants to excess water in their environment — a review. pp. 241–265 *in* Roberts and Tucker (eds.) 1985 *Ethylene and Plant Development*. Butterworths, London. ISBN 0-407-00902-5

JACKSON M.B. (ed.) 1986 *New Root Formation in Plants and Cuttings*. Martinus Nijhoff Publishers, Dordrecht, Boston, Lancaster. ISBN 90-247-3260-3

JACKSON M.B., ABBOTT A.J., BELCHER A.R. & HALL K.C. 1987b Gas exchange in plant tissue cultures. pp. 57–71 *in* Jackson *et al.* (eds.) 1987a (*q.v.*).

JACKSON M.B., MANTELL S.H. & BLAKE J. 1987a *Advances in the Chemical Manipulation of Plant Tissue Cultures*. Monograph 16, British Plant Growth Regulator Group, Bristol.

JACOBONI A. & STANDARDI A. 1987 Tissue culture of jojoba (*Simmondsia chinensis* Link.). Acta Hort. **212**, 557–560.

JACOBS G., ALLAN P. & BORNMAN C.H. 1969 Tissue culture studies on rose: use of shoot tip explants. I. Auxin: cytokinin effects. II. Cytokinin: gibberellin effects. Agroplantae **1**, 179–187.

JACOBS G., ALLAN P. & BORNMAN C.H. 1970 Tissue culture studies on rose: use of shoot tip explants. III. Auxin: gibberellin effects. Agroplantae **2**, 45–49.

JACOBS M. & GILBERT S.F. 1983 Basal localization of the presumptive auxin transport carrier in pea stem cells. Science **220**, 1297–1300.

JACOBSEN L., HANNAPEL R.J. & MOORE D.P. 1958 Non-metabolic uptake of ions by barley roots. Plant Physiol. **33**, 278–282.

JACOBSON L. 1951 Maintenance of iron supply in nutrient solutions by a single addition of ferric potassium ethylenediamine tetra-acetate. Plant Physiol. **26**, 411–413.

JACOBSON L., COOPER B.R. & VOLZ M.G. 1971 The interaction of pH and aeration in Cl uptake by barley roots. Physiol. Plant. **25**, 432–435.

JACQUIOT C. 1950 *In vitro* culture of the cambial tissue of *Castanea vesca* Gaertn. Compt. Rend. Acad. Sci. Paris **231**, 1080–1081.

JACQUIOT C. 1951 Action of meso-inositol and of adenine on bud formation in the cambium tissue of *Ulmus campestris* cultivated *in vitro*. Compt. Rend. Acad. Sci. Paris **233**, 815–817.

JAGADISH CHANDRA K.S. & SREENATH H.L. 1982 *In vitro* culture and morphogenetic studies in some species of *Cymbopogon* Spreng. (aromatic grasses). pp. 703–705 *in* Fujiwara (ed.) 1982 (*q.v.*).

JAGANNATHAN L. & MARCOTRIGIANO M. 1986 Phenotypic and ploidy status of *Paulownia tomentosa* trees regenerated from cultured hypocotyls. Plant Cell Tiss. Organ Cult. **7**, 227–236.

JAIN R.K., CHOWDHURY J.B., SHARMA D.R. & FRIEDT W. 1988b Genotypic and media effects on plant regeneration from cotyledon explant cultures of some *Brassica* species. Plant Cell Tiss. Organ Cult. **14**, 197–206.

JAIN S.M., SHAHIN E.A. & SUN S. 1988a Interspecific protoplast fusion for the transfer of atrazine resistance from *Solanum nigrum* to tomato (*Lycopersicon esculentum* L.). Plant Cell Tiss. Organ Cult. **12**, 189–192.

JAISWAL S.K., BHOJWANI S.S. & BHATNAGAR S.P. 1987 *In vitro* regeneration potentialities of seedling explants of *Brassica carinata* A. Braun. Phytomorph. **37**, 235–241.

JAKOBEK J.L., BACKHAUS R.A. & HERMAN K. 1986 Micropropagation of candellila, *Euphorbia antisyphilitica* Zucc. Plant Cell Tiss. Organ Cult. **7**, 145–148.

JAMES D.J. 1979 The role of auxins and phloroglucinol in adventitious root formation in *Rubus* and *Fragaria* grown *in vitro*. J. Hort. Sci. **54**, 273–277.

JAMES D.J. 1983a Adventitious root formation *in vitro* in apple rootstocks (*Malus pumila*). I. Factors affecting the length of the auxin sensitive phase in M.9. Physiol. Plant. **57**, 149–153.

JAMES D.J. & DANDEKAR A.M. 1991 Regeneration and transformation of apple (*Malus pumila* Mill.). Section B8 pp. 1–18 *in* Lindsey (ed.) 1991 (*q.v.*).

JAMES D.J. & THURBON I.J. 1979 Rapid *in vitro* rooting of the apple rootstock M.9. J. Hort. Sci. **54**, 309–311.

JAMES D.J. & THURBON I.J. 1981a Shoot and root initiation *in vitro* in the apple rootstock M.9 and the promotive effect of phloroglucinol. J. Hort. Sci. **56**, 15–20.

JAMES D.J. & THURBON I.J. 1981b Phenolic compounds and other factors controlling rhizogenesis *in vitro* in the apple rootstocks M.9 and M.26. Z. Pflanzenphysiol. **105**, 11–20.

JAMES D.J. & WAKERELL I.J. 1982 The control of rhizogenesis *in vitro* in difficult-to-root apple rootstocks. pp. 187–188 *in* Fujiwara A. (ed.) 1982 (*q.v.*).

JAMES D.J., PASSEY A.J. & MALHOTRA S.B. 1984 Organogenesis in callus derived from stem and leaf tissues of apple and cherry rootstocks. Plant Cell Tiss. Organ Cult. **3**, 333–341.

JAMES D.J., PASSEY A.J. & RUGINI E. 1988 Factors affecting high frequency plant regeneration from apple leaf tissues cultured *in vitro*. J. Plant Physiol. **132**, 148–154.

JAMESON R.F. 1981 Coordination chemistry of copper with regard to biological systems. pp. 1–30 *in* Sigel H. (ed.) *Metal Ions in Biological Systems* **12**. Marcel Dekker Inc., New York, Basel.

JANES H.W., CHIN C.-K. & BACHMANSKY J. 1988 Growth and metabolism of tomato roots grown in tissue cultures held at various temperatures. HortScience **23**, 773.

JANICK J.P., SKIRVIN R.M. & JANDERS R.B. 1977 Comparison of *in vitro* and *in vivo* tissue culture systems in scented geranium. J. Hered. **68**, 62–64.

JANSSON E. & BORNMAN C.H. 1981 *In vitro* initiation of adventitious structures in relation to the abscission zone in needle explants of *Picea abies*: anatomical considerations. Physiol. Plant. **53**, 191–197.

JARRET R.L. & FLORKOWSKI W.J. 1990 *In vitro* active vs. field genebank maintenance of sweet potato germplasm: major costs and considerations. HortScience **25**, 141–146.

JARRET R.L. & HASEGAWA P.M. 1981 An analysis of the effect of gibberellic acid on adventitious shoot formation and development from tuber discs of potato. Env. Exp. Bot. **21**, 436 (Abst.).

JARRET R.L., FISHER J.B. & LITZ R.E. 1985b Organ formation in *Musa* tissue cultures. J. Plant Physiol. **121**, 123–130.

JARRET R.L., HASEGAWA P.M. & ERICKSON H.T. 1980a Effects of medium components on shoot formation from cultured tuber discs of potato. J. Am. Soc. Hort. Sci. **105**, 238–242.

JARVIS B.C. 1986 Endogenous control of adventitious rooting in non-woody cuttings. pp. 191–222 *in* Jackson M.B. (ed.) 1986 (*q.v.*).

JARVIS B.C., SHANNON P.R.M. & YASMIN S. 1983 Involvement of polyamines with adventitious root development in stem cuttings of mung bean. Plant Cell Physiol. **24**, 677–683.

JARVIS B.C., YASMIN S. & COLEMAN M. 1985 RNA and protein metabolism during adventitious root formation in stem cuttings of *Phaseolus aureus* cultivar Berkin. Plant Physiol. **64**, 53–59.

JARVIS S.C. 1984 The effects of nitrogen supply on the absorption and distribution of copper in Red clover (*Trifolium pratense* L.) grown in flowing solution with a low, maintained concentration of copper. Ann. Bot. **53**, 153–161.

JEFFS R.A. & NORTHCOTE D.H. 1967 The influence of IAA and sugar on the pattern of induced differentiation in plant tissue culture. J. Cell Sci. **2**, 77–88.

JELASKA S. 1987 Micropropagation of juvenile *Calocedrus decurrens*. Acta Hort. **212**, 449–456.

JELASKA S. & JELENCIC B. 1980 Plantlet regeneration from shoot tip culture of *Pelargonium zonale* hybrid. Acta Bot. Croat. **39**, 59–64.

JELASKA S., MAGNUS V., SERETIN M. & LACAN G. 1985 Induction of embryogenic callus in *Cucurbita pepo* hypocotyl explants by indole-3-ethanol and its sugar conjugates. Physiol. Plant. **64**, 237–242.

JELASKA S., RENGEL Z. & CESAR V. 1984 Plant regeneration from mesocotyl callus of *Hordeum vulgare* L. Plant Cell Rep. **3**, 125–129.

JENNY H. 1966 Pathways of ions from soil into root according to diffusion models. Plant and Soil **25**, 265–289.

JENSEN C.J. 1974 Production of monoploids in barley: A progress report. pp. 153–190 *in* Kasha K.J. (ed.) 1974 *Haploids in Higher Plants: Advances and Potential*. Univ. Guelph.

JENSEN C.J. 1977 Monoploid production by chromosome elimination. pp. 299–330 *in* Reinert and Bajaj (eds.) 1977 (*q.v.*).

JHA T.B. & ROY S.C. 1982 Effect of different hormones on *Vigna* tissue culture and its chromosomal behaviour. Plant Sci. Lett. **24**, 219–224.

JHA T.B., ROY S.C. & MITRA G.C. 1983 *In vitro* culture of *Cuminum cyminum* regeneration of flowering shoots from calli of hypocotyl and leaf explants. Plant Cell Tiss. Organ Cult. **2**, 11–14.

JOHANSSON L. 1983 Effects of activated charcoal in anther cultures. Physiol. Plant. **59**, 397–403.

JOHANSSON L. 1986 Improved method for induction of embryogenesis in anther cultures of *Solanum tuberosum*. Potato Res. **29**, 179–190.

JOHANSSON L. & ERIKSSON T. 1984 Effects of carbon dioxide in anther cultures. Physiol. Plant. **60**, 26–30.

JOHANSSON L., ANDERSSON B. & ERIKSSON T. 1982 Improvement of anther culture: activated charcoal bound in agar medium in combination with liquid medium and elevated CO_2 concentration. Physiol. Plant. **54**, 24–30.

JOHN A. 1986 Vitrification in Sitka spruce cultures. pp. 167–174 *in* Withers L.A. & Alderson P.G. (eds.). *Plant Tissue Culture and its Agricultural Applications*. Butterworths.

JOHNSON B.B. & MITCHELL E.D. 1978c The effect of temperature on *in vitro* propagation of Broccoli from leaf rib and leaf explants. In Vitro **14**, 334 (Abst. 01).

JOHNSON C.M., STOUT P.R., BROYER T.C. & CARLTON A.B. 1957 Comparative chlorine requirements of different plant species. Plant & Soil **8**, 337–353.

JOHNSON J.L. & EMINO E.R. 1979 *In vitro* propagation of *Mammillaria elongata*. HortScience **14**, 605–606.

JOHNSON L.B., STUTEVILLE D.L. & SKINNER D.Z. 1980 Phenotypic variants in progeny of selfed alfalfa regenerated from calli. Plant Physiol. **65**, (Suppl.) 36 (Abst. 193).

JOHNSON M.A. & CARLSON J.A. 1977a Attempts to induce embryogenesis in conifer suspension cultures: biochemical aspects. Tappi Forest Biol. Wood Chem. Conf. 25–29.

JOHNSON R., GUDERIAN R.H., EDEN F., CHILTON M.-D., GORDON M.P. & NESTER E.W. 1974 Detection and quantitation of octopine in normal plant tissue and in crown gall tumors. Proc. Nat. Acad. Sci. U.S.A. **71**, 536–539.

JOHRI B.M. & BHOJWANI S.S. 1977 Triploid plants through endosperm culture. pp. 398–411 *in* Reinert and Bajaj (eds.) 1977 (*q.v.*).

JOHRI B.M. & GUHA S. 1963 In vitro development of onion plants from flowers. pp. 215–223 *in* Maheshwari and Ranga Swamy (eds.) 1963 (*q.v.*).

JONA R. & GRIBAUDO I. 1987 Adventitious bud formation from leaf explants of *Ficus lyrata*. HortScience **22**, 651–653.

JONA R. & VIGLIOCCO R. 1985 Axillary bud culture of peach. Acta Hort. **173**, 223–228.

JONA R. & VIGLIOCCO R. 1987 Genotypical differences in response to micropropagation technics in *Prunus domestica*. Acta Hort. **212**, 139–142.

JONARD R., HUGARD J., MACHEIX J.-J., MARTINEZ J., MOSELLA-CHANCEL L., POESSEL J.L. & VILLEMUR P. 1983 *In vitro* micrografting and its application to fruit science. Scientia Hort. **20**, 147–159.

JONES A.M. & PETOLINO J.F. 1988 Effects of support medium on embryo and plant production from cultured anthers of soft-red winter wheat (*Triticum aestivum* L.). Plant Cell Tiss. Organ Cult. **12**, 253–261.

JONES J.B. & MURASHIGE T. 1974 Tissue culture propagation *Aechmea fasciata* Baker and other Bromeliads. Comb. Proc. Int. Plant Prop. Soc. **24**, 117–126.

JONES J.D., HULME A.C. & WOOLTORTON L.S.C. 1965 The use of polyvinylpyrrolidone in the isolation of enzymes from apple fruits. Phytochem. **4**, 659–676.

JONES L.H. 1974b Long-term survival of embryoids of carrot (*Daucus carota* L.). Plant Sci. Lett. **2**, 221–224.

JONES L.H. 1988 Commercial development of oil palm clones. Fat Sci. Technol. **2**, 58–61.

JONES O.P. 1976 Effect of phloridzin and phloroglucinol on apple shoots. Nature **262**, 392–393; 724.

JONES O.P. 1979 Propagation *in vitro* of apple trees and other woody fruit plants: methods and applications. Scientific Hort. **30**, 44–48.

JONES O.P. & HATFIELD S.G.S. 1976 Root initiation in apple shoots cultured *in vitro* with auxins and phenolic compounds. J. Hort. Sci. **51**, 495–499.

JONES O.P. & HOPGOOD M.E. 1979 The successful propagation *in vitro* of two rootstocks of *Prunus*: the plum rootstock Pixy (*P. institia*) and the cherry rootstock F.12/1 (*P. avium*). J. Hort. Sci. **54**, 63–66.

JONES O.P. & JAMES D.J. 1979 Propagation *in vitro* of apple and other woody fruit plants. In Vitro **15**, 210 (Abst.195).

JONES O.P., HOPGOOD M.E. & O'FARRELL D. 1977 Propagation *in vitro* of M.26 apple root stocks. J. Hort. Sci. **52**, 235–238.

JONES O.P., PONTIKIS C.A. & HOPGOOD M.E. 1979 Propagation *in vitro* of five apple scion cultivars. J. Hort. Sci. **54**, 155–158.

JONES O.P., WALLER B.J. & BEECH M.G. 1988 The production of strawberry plants from callus cultures. Plant Cell Tiss. Organ Cult. **12**, 235–241.

JONES O.P., ZIMMERMAN R.H., FORDHAM I.M. & HOPGOOD M.E. 1985 Propagation *in vitro* of some dwarf apple trees. J. Hort. Sci. **60**, 141–144.

JONES T.J. & ROST T.L. 1989 The developmental anatomy and ultrastructure of somatic embryos from rice (*Oryza sativa* L.) scutellum epithelial cells. Bot. Gaz. **150**, 41–49.

JORDAN D.B. & FLETCHER J.S. 1979 The relationship between NO_2^- accumulation, nitrate reductase and nitrite reductase in suspension cultures of Paul's Scarlet rose. Plant Sci. Lett. **17**, 95–99.

JORDAN M., ITURRIAGA L. & FEUCHT W. 1982 Effects of nitrogenous bases on root formation of hypocotyls from *Prunus avium* L. 'Mericier' and 'Bing' grown *in vitro*. Gartenbauwiss. **47**, 46–48.

JORDAN M.C. & LARTER E.N. 1985 Somaclonal variation in triticale (× *Triticosecale* Wittmack) cv. Carman. Can. J. Genet. Cytol. **27**, 151–157.

JORDAN R.L. 1986 Diagnosis of plant viruses using double-stranded RNA. pp. 125–134 *in* Zimmerman *et al.* (eds.) 1986 (*q.v.*).

JOSHI M.K., SINGH U.S. & GARG G.K. 1988 Use of *Brassica* callus cultures to induce sporulation in *Alternarra brassicae* (Berk.) Sacc. Plant Cell Tiss. Organ Cult. **14**, 59–62.

JOUANNEAU J.-P. 1970 Renouvellement des protéines et effet spécifique de la kinétine sur des cultures de cellules de Tabac. Physiol. Plant. **23**, 232–244.

JOUANNEAU J.P. 1971 Côntrole par les cytokinines de la synchronisation des mitoses dans les cellules de tabac. Exp. Cell Res. **67**, 329–337.

JOUANNEAU J.P. 1975 Protein synthesis requirement for the cytokinin effect upon tobacco cell division. Exp. Cell Res. **91**, 184–190.

JOUNG H., KORBAN S.S. & SKIRVIN R.M. 1987 Screening shoot cultures of *Malus* for Cedar-apple rust infection. Plant Disease **71**, 1119–1122.

JOY R.W. IV, PATEL K.R. & THORPE T.A. 1988 Ascorbic acid enhancement of organogenesis in tobacco callus. Plant Cell Tiss. Organ Cult. **13**, 219–228.

JULLIEN M. 1974 La culture *in vitro* de cellules du tissu foliaire d'*Asparagus officinalis* L.: obtention de souches à embryogenèse permanente et régénération de plantes entières. Compt. Rend. Acad. Sci. Paris **279D**, 747–750.

JULLIEN M. & ROSSINI L. 1977 Isolation of mesophyll cells from higher plant leaves: advantages and potentialities of a mechanical method. Ann. Amel. Plantes **27**, 87–104.

JUNG P., TANNER W. & WOLTER K. 1972 The fate of *myo*-inositol in *Fraximus* tissue cultures. Phytochem. **11**, 1655–1659.

KADKADE P. & SEIBERT M. 1977 Phytochrome-regulated organogenesis in lettuce tissue culture. Nature **270**, 49–50.

KADKADE P.G. & JOPSON H.A. 1977 *In vitro* studies of adventitious bud formation in Douglas fir and pine embryo cultures. Plant Physiol. **59**, (6 Suppl.) 62.

KAHL G., ROSENSTOCK G. & LANGE H. 1969 Die Trennung von Zellteilung und Suberinsynthese in dereprimiertem pflanzlichem Speichergewebe durch Tris-(hydroxymethyl-) aminomethan. Planta **87**, 365–371.

KAHN R.P. 1978 International exchange of genetic stocks. pp. 233–245 *in* Hughes *et al.* (eds.) 1978 (*q.v.*).

KAHN R.P. 1986 Plant quarantine and international shipment of tissue culture plants. pp. 147–166 *in* Zimmerman *et al.* (eds.) 1986 (*q.v.*).

KAKKAR R.K. & RAI V.R. 1987 Effects of spermine and IAA on carbohydrate metabolism during rhizogenesis in *Phaseolus vulgaris*. India J. Exp. Biol. **25**, 476–478.

KAMADA H. & HARADA H. 1977 Influence of several growth regulators and amino acids on *in vitro* organogenesis of *Torenia* and *Daucus*. Acta Hort. **78**, 175.

KAMADA H. & HARADA H. 1979b Studies on the organogenesis in carrot tissue cultures. II. Effects of amino acids and inorganic nitrogenous compounds on somatic embryogenesis. Z. Pflanzenphysiol. **91**, 453–463.

KAMADA H. & HARADA H. 1979c Influence of several growth regulators and amino acids on *in vitro* organogenesis of *Torenia fournieri*. J. Exp. Bot. **30**, 27–36.

KAMADA H. & HARADA H. 1981 Changes in the endogenous levels and effects of abscisic acid during somatic embryogenesis of *Daucus carota* L. Plant Cell Physiol. **22**, 1423–1429.

KAMADA H. & HARADA H. 1982 Studies on nitrogen metabolism during somatic embryogenesis in carrot. pp. 115–116 *in* Fujiwara (ed.) 1982 (*q.v.*).

KAMADA H., KIYOSUE T. & HARADA H. 1988 New methods for somatic embryo induction and their use for synthetic seed production. In Vitro Cell Dev. Biol. **24**, 71A (Abst. 237).

KAMAT M.G. & RAO P.S. 1978 Vegetative multiplication of eggplants (*Solanum melongena*) using tissue culture techniques. Plant Sci. Lett. **13**, 57–65.

KAMÍNEK M., VANĚK T., KALENDOVA-KULASOVA A. & PILAR J. 1987 The effect of two cytokinins on production of stem cuttings by stock plants of *Euphorbia pulcherrima* Willd. and *Gerbera jamesonii* Hook. Scientia Hort. **33**, 281–289.

KAMISAKA S. & SHIBATA K. 1977 Anticotyledon factor: competitive inhibitors of the action of dihydroconiferyl alcohol in stimulating gibberellic acid-induced lettuce hypocotyl elongation. Plant Cell Physiol. **18**, 1057–1066.

KAMIYA A., IKEGAMI I. & HASE E. 1981 Effects of light on chlorophyll formation in cultured tobacco cells. I. Chlorophyll accumulation and phototransformation of protochlorophyll (ide) in callus cells under blue and red light. Plant & Cell Physiol. **22**, 1385–1396.

KAMO K.K., BECWAR M.R. & HODGES T.K. 1985 Regeneration of *Zea mays* L. from embryogenic callus. Bot. Gaz. **146**, 327–334.

KANABUS J., BRESSAN R.A. & CARPITA N.C. 1986 Carbon assimilation in carrot cells in liquid culture. Plant Physiol. **82**, 363–368.

KANG K.S., VEEDER G.T., MIRRASOUL P.J., KANEKO T. & COTTRELL W. 1982 Agar-like polysaccharide produced by a *Pseudomonas* species: Production and basic properties. Appl. Environ. Microbiol. **43**, 1086–1091.

KANTA K., RANGASWAMY N.S. & MAHESHWARI P. 1962 Test tube fertilisation in a flowering plant. Nature **194**, 1214–1217.

KAO K.N. 1977 Chromosomal behaviour in somatic hybrids of soybean-*Nicotiana glauca*. Mol. Gen. Genet. **150**, 225–230.

KAO K.N. 1981 Plant formation from barley anther cultures with Ficoll media. Z. Pflanzenphysiol. **103**, 437–443.

KAO K.N. 1982 Plant protoplast fusion and isolation of heterokaryocytes. pp. 49–56 *in* Wetter and Constabel (eds.) 1982 (*q.v.*).

KAO K.N. & MICHAYLUK M.R. 1975 Nutritional requirements for growth of *Vicia hajastana* cells and protoplasts at a very low population density in liquid media. Planta **126**, 105–110.

KAO K.N. & MICHAYLUK M.R. 1980 Plant regeneration from mesophyll protoplasts of alfalfa. Z. Pflanzenphysiol. **96**, 135–141.

KAPIK R.H., EARNSHAW B.A., CARLSON J.A. & JOHNSON M.A. 1986 The promotion of somatic embryogenesis by exogenous hydrogen peroxide. p. 372 *in* Somers *et al.* (eds.) 1986 (*q.v.*).

KARNOSKY D.F. & DINER A.M. 1987 Method for clonal propagation of coniferous trees. U.S. Patent No. 4607378

KARTEL N.A. & MANESHINA T.V. 1978 Regeneration of barley plants in a culture of callus tissue. Soviet Plant Physiol. **25**, 223–226.

KARTHA K.K. 1981a Meristem culture and cryopreservation – Methods and applications. pp. 181–211 *in* Thorpe (ed.) 1981 (*q.v.*).

KARTHA K.K. 1981b Cryogenic preservation of meristems as a method of germplasm preservation. HortScience **16**, 460 (Abst. 448).

KARTHA K.K. 1982c Genepool conservation through tissue culture. pp. 213–218 *in* Rao A. N. (ed.) 1982 (*q.v.*).

KARTHA K.K. 1984 Cassava tissue culture. pp. 50–68 *in Micropropagation of Selected Rootcrops, Palms, Citrus and Ornamental Species*. FAO Plant Production & Protection Paper 59 FAO, Rome. ISBN 92- 5-102157-0.

KARTHA K.K. (ed.) 1985a *Cryopreservation of Plant Cells and Organs*. CRC Press Inc., Boca Raton, Florida.

KARTHA K.K. 1985b Meristem culture and germplasm preservation. pp. 115–134 *in* Kartha K.K. (ed.) 1985a (q.v.).

KARTHA K.K. & GAMBORG O.L. 1975a Elimination of cassava mosaic disease by meristem culture. Phytopath. **65**, 826–828.

KARTHA K.K. & GAMBORG O.L. 1975b Potential value of a tissue culture technique for producing mosaic symptom-free Cassava plants. pp. 45–50 *in* Nestel and MacIntyre (eds.) 1977 *The International Exchange and Testing of Cassava Germplasm.* Int. Dev. Res. Centre, Ottawa.

KARTHA K.K., CHAMPOUX S., GAMBORG O.L. & PAHL K. 1977 *In vitro* propagation of tomato by shoot apical meristem culture. J. Am. Soc. Hort. Sci. **102**, 346–349.

KARTHA K.K., FOWKE L.C., LEUNG N.L., CASWELL K.L. & HAKMAN I. 1988 Induction of somatic embryos and plantlets from cryopreserved cell cultures of white spruce (*Picea glauca*). J. Plant Physiol. **132**, 529–539.

KARTHA K.K., GAMBORG O.L. & CONSTABEL F. 1974a *In vitro* plant formation from stem explants of rape (*Brassica napus* cv. Zephyr). Physiol. Plant. **31**, 217–220.

KARTHA K.K., GAMBORG O.L., CONSTABEL F. & KAO K.N. 1974d Fusion of rape seed and soybean protoplasts and subsequent division of heterokaryocytes. Can. J. Bot. **52**, 2435–2436.

KARTHA K.K., GAMBORG O.L., CONSTABEL F. & SHYLUK J.P. 1974c Regeneration of cassava plants from apical meristems. Plant Sci. Lett. **2**, 107–113.

KARTHA K.K., LEUNG N. & PAHL K. 1980 Cryopreservation of strawberry meristems and mass propagation of plantlets. J. Am. Soc. Hort. Sci. **105**, 481–484.

KARTHA K.K., LEUNG N.L. & GAMBORG O.L. 1979 Freeze-preservation of pea meristems in liquid nitrogen and subsequent plant regeneration. Plant Sci. Lett. **15**, 7–15.

KARTHA K.K., LEUNG N.L. & MROGINSKI L.A. 1982 *In vitro* growth responses and plant regeneration from cryopreserved meristems of cassava (*Manihot esculenta* Crantz). Z. Pflanzenphyiol. **107**, 133–140.

KARTHA K.K., MROGINSKI L.A., PAHL K. & LEUNG N.L. 1981 Germplasm preservation of coffee (*Coffea arabica*) by *in vitro* culture of shoot apical meristems. Plant Sci. Lett. **22**, 301–307.

KASPERBAUER M.J. & COLLINS G.B. 1972 Reconstitution of diploids from leaf tissue of anther-derived haploids in tobacco. Crop Sci. **12**, 98–101.

KASPERBAUER M.J. & REINERT R.A. 1967 Photometrically assayable phytochrome *in vivo* in callus tissue cultured from *Nicotiana tabacum*. Physiol. Plant. **20**, 977–981.

KASPERBAUER M.J., SUTTON T.G., ANDERSEN R.A. & GUPTON C.L. 1981 Tissue culture of plants from a chimeral mutation of tobacco *Nicotiana tabacum*. Crop Sci. **21**, 588–590.

KASSANIS B. 1957a The use of tissue cultures to produce virus-free clones from infected potato varieties. Ann. Appl. Biol. **45**, 422–427.

KATAEVA N.V. & BUTENKO R.G. 1987 Clonal micropropagation of apple trees. Acta Hort. **212**, 585–588.

KATHAL R., BHATNAGAR S.P. & BHOJWANI S.S. 1988 Regeneration of plants from leaf explants of *Cucumis melo* cv. Pusa Shaibati. Plant Cell Rep. **7**, 449–451.

KATO M. & TOKUMASU S. 1983 Characteristics of F_1 hybrids produced by ovule-culture in ornamental *Pelargonium*. Acta Hort. **131**, 247–252.

KATO Y. 1974 Bud formation on excised *Heloniopsis* leaf fragments: effects of leaf age and the midrib. Plant Cell Physiol. **15**, 363–372.

KATO Y. 1976 Induced budding in root-tips and attached leaves of *Heloniopsis orientalis* (Liiliaceae). Plant Sci. Lett. **6**, 431–436.

KATO Y. 1978a Induction of adventitious buds on undetached leaves, excised leaves, and leaf fragments of *Heloniopsis orientalis*. Physiol. Plant. **42**, 39–44.

KATO Y. 1978b The involvement of photosynthesis in inducing bud formation on excised leaf segments of *Heloniopsis orientalis* (Liliaceae). Plant Cell Physiol. **19**, 791–799.

KATO Y. & HONGO M. 1974 Regulation of bud and root formation in excised leaf segments of *Heloniopsis orientalis* (Liliaceae). Phytomorph. **24**, 273–279.

KATO Y. & OZAWA N. 1979 Adventitious bud formation on leaf and stem segments of *Heloniopsis orientalis* grown at various temperatures. Plant Cell Physiol. **20**, 491–497.

KATOH K. & HIROSE Y. 1982 Photoautotrophic and synchronous growth of *Marchantia polymorpha* cells in suspension culture. pp. 55–56 *in* Fujiwara A. (ed.) 1982 (q.v.).

KAUL B. & STABA E.J. 1968 *Dioscorea* tissue cultures. 1. Biosynthesis and isolation of diesgenin from *Dioscorea deltoidea* callus and suspension cells. Lloydia **31**, 171–179.

KAUL K. 1985 Seasonal variation in callus proliferation from explants of mature *Pinus strobus* trees. p. 330 *in* Henke *et al.* (eds.) 1985 (q.v.).

KAUL K. 1986 Establishment of long-term callus cultures from mature white pine (*Pinus strobus*, Pinaceae). Am. J. Bot. **73**, 242–245.

KAUL K. & KOCHHAR T.S. 1985 Growth and differentiation of callus cultures of *Pinus*. Plant Cell Rep. **4**, 180–183.

KAUL K. & SABHARWAL P.S. 1971 Effects of sucrose and kinetin on growth and chlorophyll synthesis in tobacco tissue cultures. Plant Physiol. **47**, 691–695.

KAUL K. & SABHARWAL P.S. 1972 Morphogenetic studies on *Haworthia*: Establishment of tissue culture and control of differentiation. Am. J. Bot. **59**, 377–385.

KAUL K. & SABHARWAL P.S. 1975 Morphogenetic studies on *Haworthia*: Effects of inositol on growth and differentiation. Am. J. Bot. **62**, 655–659.

KAUR-SAWHNEY R., TIBURCIO A.F. & GALSTON A.W. 1988 Spermidine and flower-bud differentiation in thin-layer explants of tobacco. Planta **173**, 282–284.

KAVATHEKAR A.K., GANAPATHY P.S. & JOHRI B.M. 1977 Chilling induces development of embryoids into plantlets in *Eschscholzia*. Z. Pflanzenphysiol. **81**, 358–363.

KAVATHEKAR A.K., GANAPATHY P.S. & JOHRI B.M. 1978 *In vitro* responses of embryoids of *Eschscholzia californica*. Biol. Plant. **20**, 98–106.

KAVI KISHOR P.B. & MEHTA A.R. 1982 Some aspects of carbohydrate metabolism in organ-differentiating tobacco and non-differentiating cotton callus cultures. pp. 143–144 *in* Fujiwara A. (ed.) 1982 (q.v.).

KAVI KISHOR P.B. & REDDY G.M. 1986 Regeneration of plants from long-term cultures of *Oryza sativa* L. Plant Cell Rep. **5**, 391–393.

KAWARABAYASHI W., MATSUBARA K., YOSHIOKA T., YAMAGATA H., TAKAHASHI S., HIRATA Y. & SHIRANE Y. 1991 Culturing apparatus. U.S. Patent No. 4951415

KEE K.K. 1983 An overview of a commercial plant tissue culture laboratory in Hawaii. Comb. Proc. Int. Plant Prop. Soc., 1982, **32**, 315–322.

KEFELI V.I. & KADYROV C.Sh. 1971 Natural growth inhibitors, their chemical and physiological properties. Ann. Rev. Plant Physiol. **22**, 185–196.

KEFFORD N.P. & CASO O.H. 1972 Organ regeneration on excised roots of *Chondrilla juncea* and its chemical regulation. Aust. J. Biol. Sci. **25**, 691–706.

KEFFORD N.P., BRUCE M.I. & ZWAR J.A. 1966 Cytokinin activities of phenylurea derivatives — bud growth. Planta **68**, 292–296.

KELLER J. 1990 Haploids from unpollinated ovaries of *Allium cepa* — single plant screening, haploid determination, and long term storage.

KELLER W. A. & STRINGAM G. R. 1978 Production and utilisation of microspore-derived plants. pp. 113–122 *in* Thorpe T.A. (ed.) 1978 (q.v.)

KELLER W.A., SETTERFIELD G., DOUGLAS G., GLEDDIE S. & NAKAMURA C. 1982 Production, characterization and utilization of somatic hybrids of higher plants. pp. 81–114 *in* Tomes *et al.* (eds.) 1982 (q.v.).

KEMP T.R. & STOLTZ L.P. 1979 Cytokinins from growth regulator autonomous callus tissue. Plant Sci. Lett. **16**, 403–408.

KENDE H., KONZE J.R. & BOLLER T. 1980 Enzymes of ethylene biosynthesis. pp. 230–238 *in* Skoog F. (ed.) 1980 (q.v.).

KENTON R.H. 1955 The oxidation of β-(3-indolyl)propionic acid and γ-(3-indolyl)-*n*-butyric acid by peroxidase and Mn^{2+}. Biochem. J. **61**, 353–354.

KERBAUY G.B. 1984a Regeneration of protocorm-like bodies through *in vitro* culture of root tips of *Catasetum* (Orchidaceae). Z. Pflanzenphysiol. **113**, 287–291.

KERBAUY G.B. 1984b Plant regeneration of *Oncidium varicosum* (Orchidaceae) by means of root tip culture. Plant Cell Rep. **3**, 27–29.

KERBAUY G.B. 1984c *In vitro* flowering of *Oncidium varicosum* mericlones (Orchidaceae). Plant Sci. Lett. **35**, 73–75.

KERBAUY G.B., PETERS J.A. & HELL K.G. 1986 Cytokinin autotrophy and differentiation in tissue cultures of haploid *Nicotiana tabacum* L. Plant Science **45**, 125–132.

KERMODE A., BEWLEY J.D., DASGUPTA J. & MISRA S. 1986 The transition from seed development to germination: a key role for desiccation? HortScience **21**, 1113–1118.

KERNS H.R. & MEYER M.M. Jr. 1986 Tissue culture propagation of *Acer × freemanii* using thidiazuron to stimulate shoot tip proliferation. HortScience **21**, 1209–1210.

KERNS H.R. & MEYER M.M. Jr. 1988 Micropropagation of selected *Acer* sp. and cultivars. HortScience **23**, 452.

KERTZ H.G. 1990 Integument and method for micropropagation and tissue culturing. U.S. Patent No. 4908315

KESSELL R.H.L. & CARR A.H. 1972 The effect of dissolved oxygen concentrations on growth and differentiation of carrot (*Daucus carota*) tissue. J. Exp. Bot. **23**, 996–1007.

KETELLAPPER H.J. 1953 The mechanism of the action of indole-3- acetic acid on the water absorption by *Avena coleoptile* sections. Acta Bot. Neerl. **2**, 387–444.

KEVERS C. & GASPAR T. 1985 Vitrification of carnation *in vitro*: Changes in ethylene production, ACC level and capacity to convert ACC to ethylene. Plant. Cell Tiss. Organ Cult. **4**, 215–223.

KEVERS C., BOYER N., COURDUROUX J.-C. & GASPAR Th. 1992 The influence of ethylene on proliferation and growth of rose shoot cultures. Plant Cell Tiss. Organ Cult. **28**, 175–181.

KEVERS C., COUMANS M., COUMANS-GILLÈS M-F. & GASPAR Th. 1984 Physiological and biochemical events leading to vitrification of plants cultured *in vitro*. Physiol. Plant. **61**, 69–74.

KEVERS C., COUMANS M., DE GREEF W., HOFINGER M. & GASPAR Th. 1981a Habituation in sugar beet callus: auxin content, auxin protectors, peroxidase pattern and inhibitors. Physiol. Plant. **51**, 281–286.

KEVERS C., COUMANS M., DE GREEF W., JACOBS M. & GASPAR Th. 1981b Organogenesis in habituated sugarbeet callus: auxin content and protectors, peroxidase pattern and inhibitors. Z. Pflanzenphysiol. **101**, 79–87.

KEVERS C., GASPAR Th., PENEL C. & GREPPIN H. 1985 Auxin-polyamine interaction with the calcium-controlled secretion of peroxidase by sugar beet cells. Plant Cell Rep. **4**, 120–122.

KEVERS C., STICHER L., PENEL C., GREPPIN H. & GASPAR Th. 1982 Calcium-controlled peroxidase secretion by sugarbeet cell suspensions in relation to habituation. Plant Growth Reg. **1**, 61–66.

KEVERS C., STICHER L., PENEL C., GREPPIN H. & GASPAR Th. 1983a The effect of ergosterol, ergocalciferol and cholecaleiferol on calcium- controlled peroxidase secretion by sugarbeet cells. Physiol. Plant. **57**, 17–20.

KEY J.L. 1969 Hormones and nucleic acid metabolism. Ann. Rev. Plant Physiol **20**, 449–474.

KEYES G.J. & BINGHAM E.T. 1979 Heterosis and ploidy effects on the growth of alfalfa callus. Crop Sci. **19**, 473–476.

KEYES G.J., DEATON W.R., COLLINS G.B. & LEGG P.D. 1981 Hybrid vigour in callus tissue cultures and seedlings of *Nicotiana tabacum* L. J. Hered. **72**, 172–174.

KHALID N., DAVEY M.R. & POWER J.B. 1989 An assessment of somaclonal variation in *Chrysanthemum morifolium*: the generation of plants of potential commercial value. Scientia Hort. **38**, 287–294.

KHAN A.A. 1966 Breaking of dormancy in *Xanthium* seeds by kinetin mediated by light and DNA-dependent RNA synthesis. Physiol. Plant. **19**, 869–874.

KHAN A.J. & MINOCHA S.C. 1991 Polyamines and somatic embryogenesis in carrot. II. The effects of cyclohexglammonium phosphate. J. Plant Physiol. **137**, 446–452.

KHAN M.R.I., HEYES J.K. & COHEN D. 1988 Plant regeneration from oca (*Oxalis tuberosa* M.): The effect of explant type and culture media. Plant Cell Tiss. Organ Cult. **14**, 41–50.

KHANNA R. & CHOPRA R.N. 1977 Regulation of shoot-bud and root formation from stem explants of *Lobularia maritima*. Phytomorph. **27**, 267–274.

KHODER M., VILLEMUR P. & JONARD R. 1979 Micropropagation et bouturage *in vitro* chez le jasmin (*Jasminum officinale* L.). Compt. Rend. Acad. Sci. Paris **288D**, 323–326.

KHOSH-KHUI M. & SINK K.C. 1982a Micropropagation of new and old world rose species. J. Hort. Sci. **57**, 315–319.

KHUNACHAK A., CHIN C.-K., LÊ T. & GIANFAGNA T. 1987 Promotion of asparagus shoot and root growth by growth retardants. Plant Cell Tiss. Organ Cult. **11**, 97–110.

KIBLER R. & NEUMANN K.-H. 1980 On cytogenetic stability of cultured tissue and cell suspensions of haploid and diploid origin. pp. 59–65 *in* Sala *et al.* (eds.) 1980 (*q.v.*).

KIM S.-G., CHANG J.-R., CHA H.C. & LEE K.-W. 1988 Callus growth and plant regeneration in diverse cultivars of cucumber (*Cucumis sativus* L.). Plant Cell Tiss. Organ Cult. **12**, 67–84.

KIM S.H., WOODWARD W.A. & FAUL S.K. 1984 Effects of oxytetracycline on geranium fasciation. Phytopath. **74**, 822 (Abst. A260).

KIM Y.-H. & JANICK J. 1989a ABA and polyox-encapsulation or high humidity increases survival of desiccated somatic embryos of celery. HortScience **24**, 674–676.

KIM Y.-H. & JANICK J. 1989b Somatic embryogenesis and organogenesis in cucumber. HortScience **24**, p. 702.

KIMBALL S.L. & BINGHAM E.T. 1973 Adventitious bud development of soybean hypocotyl sections in culture. Crop Sci. **13**, 758–760.

KIMBALL S.L., BEVERSDORF W.D. & BINGHAM E.T. 1975 Influence of osmotic potential on the growth and development of soybean tissue cultures. Crop Sci. **15**, 750–752.

KINET J.M. & PARMENTIER A. 1989 The flowering behaviour of micropropagated strawberry plants cv. 'Gorella': The influence of the number of sub-cultures on the multiplication medium. Acta Hort. **265**, 327–334.

KING P. & SHIMAMOTO K. 1984 Chapter 3 — Maize. pp. 69–91 *in* Sharp *et al.* (eds.) 1984 (*q.v.*).

KING P.J. 1977 Studies on the growth in culture of plant cells, growth limitiation by nitrate and glucose in a chemostat culture of *Acer pseudoplatanus*. J. Exp. Bot. **28**, 142–155.

KING P.J. & STREET H.E. 1977 Growth patterns in cell cultures. pp. 307–387 *in* Street H.E. (ed.) 1977 (*q.v.*).

KING P.J., POTRYKUS I. & THOMAS E. 1978 *In vitro* genetics of cereals. Problems and perspectives. Phyiol. Veg. **16**, 381–399.

KINNERSLEY A.M. & HENDERSON W.E. 1988 Alternative carbohydrates promote differentiation of plant cells. Plant Cell Tiss. Organ Cult. **15**, 3–16.

KINNERSLEY A.M., SCOTT T.C., YOPP J.H. & WHITTEN G. 1988 Method for regulating plant growth. U.S. Patent No. 4813997

KIRBY E.G. 1982 The effects of organic nitrogen sources on growth of cell cultures of Douglas fir. Physiol. Plant. **56**, 114–117.

KIRBY E.G. & CHENG T-Y. 1979 Colony formation from protoplasts derived from Douglas-fir cotyledons. Plant Sci. Lett. **14**, 145–154.

KIRBY E.G., LEUSTEK T. & LEE M.S. 1987 Nitrogen nutrition. pp. 67–88 *in* Bonga and Durzan (eds.) 1987a (*q.v.*).

KIRKHAM M.B. & HOLDER P.L. 1981 Water osmotic and turgor potentials of kinetin-treated callus. HortScience **16**, 306–307.

KISHORE G.M. & SHAH D. 1990 Glyphosate-tolerant 5-enolpyruvyl 3- phosphoshikimate synthase. U.S. Patent No. 4971908

KITTO S.L. & JANICK J. 1981 Testing artificial seed coats for asexual embryos. HortScience **16**, 452 (Abst. 388).

KITTO S.L. & JANICK J. 1982 Polyox as an artificial seed coat for asexual embryos. HortScience **17**, 488 (Abst. 113).

KITTO S.L. & JANICK J. 1983 ABA and chilling increase survival of asexual carrot embryos encapsulated with artificial seed coats. HortScience **18**, 618 (Abst.).

KITTO S.L. & JANICK J. 1985a Production of synthetic seeds by encapsulating asexual embryos of carrot. J. Am. Soc. Hort. Sci. **110**, 277–282.

KITTO S.L. & JANICK J. 1985b Hardening treatments increase survival of synthetically-coated asexual embryos of carrot. J. Am. Soc. Hort. Sci. **110**, 283–286.

KIYOSUE T., KAMADA H. & HARADA H. 1989a Induction of somatic embryogenesis from carrot seed by hypochlorite treatment. Plant Tiss. Cult. Lett. **6**, 138–143.

KIYOSUE T., KAMADA H. & HARADA H. 1989b Induction of somatic embryogenesis by salt stress in carrot. Plant Tiss. Cult. Lett. **6**, 162–164.

KIYOSUE T., TAKANO K., KAMADA H. & HARADA H. 1990 Induction of somatic embryogenesis in carrot by heavy metal ions. Can. J. Bot. **68**, 2301–2303.

KLAPHECK S., GROSSE W. & BERGMANN L. 1982 Effect of sulphur deficiency on protein synthesis and amino acid accumulation in cell suspension cultures of *Nicotiana tabacum*. Z. Pflanzenphysiol. **108**, 235–245.

KLEIN R.M. 1964 Repression of tissue culture growth by visible and near visible radiation. Plant Physiol. **39**, 536–539.

KLEIN R.M. & MANOS G.E. 1960 Use of metal chelates for plant tissue cultures. Ann. New York Acad. Sci. **88**, 416–425.

KLEIN R.M., CAPUTO E.M. & WITTERHOLT B.A. 1962 The role of zinc in the growth of plant tissue cultures. Am. J. Bot. **49**, 323–327.

KLEIN T.M., WOLF E.D., WU R. & SANFORD J.C. 1987 High velocity microprojectiles for delivering nucleic acids into living cells. Nature **327**, 70–73.

KLEIN T.M., FROMM M., WEISSINGER A., TOMES D., SCHAAF S., SLETTEN M. & SANFORD J.C. 1988 Transfer of foreign genes into intact maize cells with high-velocity microprojectiles. Proc. Nat. Acad. Sci. U.S.A. **85**, 4305–4309.

KLIMASZEWSKA K. 1979 The regenerative potential of two species of *Peperomia* in tissue cultures and biological activity of endogenous growth regulators. Acta Hort. **91**, 281–286.

KLOCKE J.A. & MYERS P. 1984 Chemical control of thrips on cultured *Simmondsia chinensis* (jojoba) shoots. HortScience **19**, 400.

KNAUSS J.F. 1976a A tissue culture method for producing *Diffenbachia picta* cv. 'Perfection' free of fungi and bacteria. Proc. Fla. State Hort. Soc. **89**, 293–295.

KNAUSS J.F. 1976b A partial tissue culture method of pathogen- free propagation of selected ferns from spores. Proc. Fla. State Hort. Soc. **89**, 363–365.

KNAUSS J.F. & KNAUSS M.E. 1980 Contamination in plant tissue cultures. Proc. Fla. State Hort. Soc. **92**, 341–343.

KNAUSS J.F. & MILLER J.W. 1978 A contaminant, *Erwinia carotovora*, affecting plant tissue cultures. In Vitro **14**, 754–756.

KNOP W. 1865 Quantitative Untersuchungen über die Ernahrungsprozesse der Pflanzen. Landwirtsch. Vers. Stn. **7**, 93–107.

KNUDSON L. 1922 Non-symbiotic germination of orchid seeds. Bot. Gaz. **73**, 1–25.

KNUDSON L. 1943 Nutrient solutions for orchid seed germination. Am. Orchid Soc. Bull. **12**, 77–79.

KNUDSON L. 1946 A new nutrient solution for the germination of orchid seed. Am. Orchid Soc. Bull. **15**, 214–217.

KO C.J. 1986 The effect of temperature on *in vitro* bulblet formation of *Hyacinthus orientalis* L. M.S. Thesis, Univ. of Minnesota.

KOBLITZ H. & SCHUMANN U. 1976 Tissue cultures of alkaloid plants. V. Some morphogenetic abilities of long-term callus cultures of *Macleaya microcarpa*. Biochem. Physiol. Pflanz. **169**, 289–297.

KOBLITZ H., KOBLITZ D., SCHMAUDER H.- P. & GRÖGER D. 1983a Studies on tissue cultures of the genus *Cinchona* L. *In vitro* mass propagation through meristem-derived plants. Plant Cell Rep. **2**, 95–97.

KOCHBA J. & BUTTON J. 1974 The stimulation of embryogenesis and embryoid development in habituated ovular callus from the 'Shamouti' orange (*Citrus sinensis*) as affected by tissue age and sucrose concentration. Z. Pflanzenphysiol. **73**, 415–421.

KOCHBA J., BUTTON J., SPIEGEL-ROY P., BORNMAN C.H. & KOCHBA M. 1974 Stimulation of rooting of citrus embryoids by gibberellic acid and adenine sulphate. Ann. Bot. **38**, 795–802.

KOCHBA J., SPIEGEL-ROY P. & SAFRAN H. 1972 Adventive plants from ovules and nucelli in *Citrus*. Planta **106**, 237–245.

KOCHBA J., SPIEGEL-ROY P., NEUMANN H. & SAAD S. 1978a Stimulation of embryogenesis in *Citrus* ovular callus by ABA, ethephon, CCC and Alar and its suppression by GA$_3$. Z. Pflanzenphysiol. **89**, 427–432.

KOCHBA J., SPIEGEL-ROY P., SAAD S. & NEUMANN H. 1978b Stimulation of embryogenesis in *Citrus* tissue culture by galactose. Naturwiss. **65**, 261–262.

KOCHHAR T., BHALLA P. & SABHARWAL P. 1970 Formation de bourgeons végétatifs par des cals de tabac sous l'influence d'un agent de chélation: l'acide 1,3-diamino-2-hydroxypropane- N,N′,N′,N′,-tetracétique (DNPTA). Compt. Rend. Acad. Sci. Paris **271D**, 1619–1622.

KOCHHAR T.S. 1980 Effect of abscisic acid and auxins on the growth of tobacco callus. Z. Pflanzenphysiol. **97**, 1–4.

KOCHHAR T.S., BHALLA P.R. & SABHARWAL P.S. 1971 Induction of vegetative buds in tobacco callus by chelating agents. Am. J. Bot. **58**, 453.

KODA Y. & OKAZAWA Y. 1980 Cytokinin production by asparagus shoot apex cultured *in vitro*. Physiol. Plant. **49**, 193–197.

KODAMA H. & KOMAMINE A. 1988 Regulation and gene expression in the cell cycle of higher plants. Oxford Surveys of Plant Mol. & Cell Biol. **5**, 185–193.

KOENIG R. 1981 Indirect ELISA methods for the broad specificity detection of plant viruses. J. Gen. Virol. **55**, 53–62.

KOETJE D.S., GRIMES H.D., WANG Y.-C. & HODGES T.K. 1989 Regeneration of indica rice (*Oryza sativa* L.) from primary callus from immature embryos. J. Plant Physiol. **13**, 184–190.

KOEVARY K., RAPPAPORT L. & MORRIS L.L. 1978 Tissue culture propagation of head lettuce. HortScience **13**, 39–41.

KOHLENBACH H.W. 1965 Uber organisierte bildungen aus *Macleaya cordata* kallus. Planta **64**, 37–40.

KOHLENBACH H.W. 1966 Die entwick lungspotengen explantierter und isolierter Dauerzellen. 1. Das Streckungt und Teilungswachstum isolierter Mesophyllzellen von *Macleaya cordata*. Z. Pflanzenphysiol. **55**, 142–147.

KOHLENBACH H.W. 1967 The potentialities for development of explanted and isolated permanent cells. IV. The organogenic growth of *Macleaya cordata* calli. Z. Pflanzenphysiol. **57**, 305–309.

KOHLENBACH H.W. 1977 Basic aspects of differentiation and plant regeneration from cell and tissue cultures. pp.355–366 *in* Barz, Reinhard and Zenk (eds.) 1977 (*q.v.*).

KOHLENBACH H.W. & SCHMIT B. 1975 Cytodifferentiation in the form of a direct change of isolated mesophyll cells to tracheids. Z. Pflanzenphysiol. **75**, 369–374.

KOHLENBACH H.W. & WERNICKE W. 1978 Investigations on the inhibitory effect of agar and the function of active carbon in anther culture. Z. Pflanzenphysiol. **86**, 463–472.

KOLAR Z., BARTEK J. & VYSKOT B. 1976 Vegetative propagation of the cactus *Mamillaria woodsii* Craig through tissue cultures. Experientia **32**, 668-669.

KOLTHOFF I.M. & AUERBACH C. 1952 Studies on the system iron-ethylenediamine tetraacetate. J. Am. Chem. Soc. **74**, 1452–1456.

KOMAMINE A., MATSUMOTO M., TSUKAHARA M., FUJIWARA A., KAWAHARA R., ITO M., SMITH J., NOMURA K. & FUJIMURA T. 1990 Mechanisms of somatic embryogenesis in cell cultures — physiology, biochemistry and molecular biology. pp. 307–313 *in* Nijkamp *et al.* (eds.) 1990 (*q.v.*).

KOMOR E., ROTTER M. & TANNER W. 1977 A proton-cotransport system in a hgher plant: sucrose transport in *Ricinus communis*. Plant Sci. Lett. **9**, 153–162.

KOMOR E., THOM M. & MARETZKI A. 1981 The mechanism of sugar uptake by sugarcane suspension cells. Planta **153**, 181–192.

KOMOSZYNSKI M. & BANDURSKI R.S. 1986 Transport and metabolism of indole-3-acetyl-*myo*-inositol-galactoside in seedlings of *Zea mays*. Plant Physiol. **80**, 961–964.

KONAR R.N. & KONAR A. 1973 Interaction of CCC and gibberellic acid in the morphogenesis of *Ranunculus sceleratus* tissue *in vitro*. Phytomorph. **23**, 105–109.

KONAR R.N. & NATARAJA K. 1965a Experimental studies in *Ranunculus sceleratus* L. Development of embryos from the stem epidermis. Phytomorph. **15**, 132–137.

KONAR R.N. & NATARAJA K. 1965b Experimental studies in *Ranunculus sceleratus* L. plantlets from truly suspended cells and cell groups. Phytomorph. **15**, 206–211.

KONAR R.N. & OBEROI Y.P. 1965 *In vitro* development of embryoids on the cotyledons of *Biota orientalis*. Phytomorph. **15**, 137–140.

KONAR R.N., THOMAS E. & STREET H.E. 1972a Origin and structure of embryoids arising from epidermal cells of the stem of *Ranunculus sceleratus* L. J. Cell Sci. **11**, 77–93.

KONINGS H. & JACKSON M.B. 1979 A relationship between rates of ethylene production by roots and the promoting or inhibiting effects of exogenous ethylene and water on root elongation. Z. Pflanzenphysiol. **92**, 385–397.

KONISHI T., HAYASHI M. & IKAMI M. 1982 Induction of flower buds in tissue culture of perianth of *Haworthia arachnoidea* and *H. cymbiformis*. pp. 145–146 *in* Fujiwara A. (ed.) 1982 (*q.v.*).

KONONOWICZ H. & JANICK J. 1984a *In vitro* propagation of *Vanilla planifolia*. HortScience **19**, 58–59.

KONWAR B.K. & COUTTS R.H.A. 1990 Rapid regeneration of sugar beet (*Beta vulgaris* L.) plants from in vitro cultures. pp. 114–118 *in* Nijkamp *et al.* (eds.) 1990 (*q.v.*).

KOOP H.U., WEBER G. & SCHWEIGER H.G. 1983 Individual culture of selected single cells and protoplasts of higher plants in microdroplets of defined media. Z. Pflanzenphysiol. **112**, 21–34.

KORBAN S.S. & SKIRVIN R.M. 1985 *In vitro* shoot regeneration from an intact and a sectioned embryo-axis of apple seeds. Plant Science **39**, 61–66.

KORDAN H.A. 1959 Proliferation of excised juice vesicles of Lemon *in vitro*. Science **129**, 779–780.

KORHONEN P., TÕRMÄLÄ T. & BANSEMA J. 1988 Model for minimisation of contamination costs in micropropagation by computer simulation. Acta Hort. **225**, 177–182.

KOTH P. 1974 Aenderungen in Enzymmuster ergruender Kalluskulturen von *Nicotiana tabacum* var. 'Samsun'. Planta **120**, 207–211.

KOTTE W. 1922 Wurzelmeristem in Gewebekultur. Ber. der Deutschen Bot. Gesell. **40**, 269–272.

KOUADIO J.Y. & PHAN C.T. 1987 Heterogeneity of progeny in meristem culture. Acta Hort. **212**, 411–417.

KOUIDER M., KORBAN S.S., SKIRVIN R.M. & YOUNG H. 1985 The relationship of apple embryos and their cotyledons to maturity, dormancy, and the potential to form shoots *in vitro*. J. Am. Soc. Hort. Sci. **110**, 93–96.

KOUIDER M., SKIRVIN R.M., SALADIN K.P., DAWSON J.O. & JOKELA J.J. 1984b A method to culture immature embryos of *Populus deltoides in vitro*. Can. J. For. Res. **14**, 956–958.

KOYAMA A., OHMORI Y., FUJIOKA N., MIYAGAWA K., YAMAZAKI K. & KOHDA H. 1987 Formation of stigma-like structures and pigments in cultured tissue of *Crocus sativus*. Shoyakugaku Zasshi **41**, 226–229.

KOZAI T. 1989 Autotrophic (sugar-free) micropropagation for a significant reduction in production costs. Chronica Hort. **29**, 19–20.

KOZAI T. 1991 Micropropagation under photoautotrophic conditions. pp. 447–469 *in* Debergh and Zimmerman (eds.) 1991 (*q.v.*).

KOZAI T. & IWANAMI Y. 1987 Effects of CO_2 enrichment and sucrose concentration under high photon fluxes on plantlet growth of carnation (*Dianthus caryophyllus* L.) in tissue culture during the preparation stage. J. Jap. Soc. Hort. Sci. **57**, 255–264.

KOZAI T. & IWANAMI Y. 1988 Effects of CO_2 enrichment and sucrose concentration under high photon fluxes on plant growth of carnation (*Dianthus caryophyllus* L.) in tissue culture during the preparation stage. J. Jap. Soc. Hort. Sci. **57**, 279–288.

KOZAI T. & SEKIMOTO K. 1988 Effects of the number of air changes per hour of the stoppered vessel and the photosynthetic photon flux on the carbon dioxide concentration inside the vessel and the growth of strawberry plantlets *in vitro*. Environment Control Biol. **26**, 21–29.

KOZAI T., IWANAMI Y. & FUJIWARA K. 1987a Effects of CO_2 enrichment on the plantlet growth during the multiplication stage. Plant Tiss. Cult. Lett. **4**, (1) 22–26.

KOZAI T., KUBOTA C. & WATANABE I. 1988 Effects of basal medium composition on the growth of carnation plantlets in auto- and mixo-trophic tissue culture. Acta Hort. **230**, 159–166.

KOZAI T., OKI H. & FUJIWARA K. 1987b Effects of CO_2 enrichment and sucrose concentration under high photosynthetic photon fluxes on growth of issue-cultured *Cymbidium* plantlets during the preparation stage. pp. 135–141 *in* Ducaté *et al.* (eds.) 1987 (*q.v.*).

KRATZ K.A. & LANGHANS R.W. 1978 Tissue culture propagation and dormancy studies on *Clematis* cultivars. HortScience **13**, 356 (Abst.137).

KRENS F.A., JAMAR D., ROUWENDAL G.J.A. & HALL R.D. 1990 Transfer of cytoplasm from new *Beta* CMS sources to sugar beet by asymetric fusion. 1. Shoot regeneration from mesophyll protoplasts and characterisation of regenerated plants. Theor. Appl. Genet. **79**, 390–396.

KREUTMEIER C., GEBHARDT K., PAUL L. & FEUCHT W. 1984 The effect of $MgSO_4$ and $CaCl_2$ on regeneration of shoot tip cultures of *Prunus cerasus in vitro*. Gartenbauwiss. **49**, 204–212.

KRIEG N.R. & GERHARDT P. 1981 pp. 143–156 *in* Gerhardt *et al.* (eds.) 1981 *Manual of Methods for General Bacteriology*. American Soc. for Microbiol. Washington D.C.

KRIEG N.R. & HOLT J.G. (eds.) 1984 *Bergey's Manual of Systematic Bacteriology* Vol.1. Williams & Wilkins, Baltimore. ISBN 0-683-04108-8.

KRIKORIAN A.D. & KANN R.P. 1979 Clonal micropropagation of daylilies. pp. 835–836 *in* Sharp *et al.*(eds.) 1979 (*q.v.*).

KRIKORIAN A.D. & KANN R.P. 1981 Plantlet production from morphogenetically competent cell suspensions of daylilies. Ann. Bot. **47 (5)**, 679–686 (BA 72 41049).

KRIKORIAN A.D. & KANN R.P. 1987 Aseptic multiplication of chinese tallow *Sapium sebiferum* (L.) Roxb. pp. 357–369 *in* Bonga and Durzan (eds.) 1987c (*q.v.*).

KRIKORIAN A.D., O'CONNOR S.A., FITTER M.S. & KANN R.P. 1982a Karyotype analysis of daylily plants clonally derived from a long term totipotent suspension culture. pp. 429–430 *in* Fujiwara (ed.) 1982 (*q.v.*).

KRIKORIAN A.D., SINGH M. & QUINN C.E. 1982b Aseptic micropropagation of *Cinchona*: Prospects and problems. pp. 167–174 *in* Rao A.N. (ed.) 1982b (*q.v.*).

KRISHNAMURTHI M. 1982 Sugarcane improvement through tissue culture and review of progress. pp. 70–77 *in* Rao A.N. (ed.) 1982 (*q.v.*).

KRISHNAMURTHY M. & TLASKAL J. 1974 Fiji disease resistant *Saccharum officinarum* var. Pindar sub-clones from tissue cultures. Proc. Int. Soc. Sug. Cane Tech. **15**, 130–137.

KRISTENSEN H.R. 1984 Potato tissue culture. pp. 25–49 *in Micropropagation of selected root crops, palms, citrus and ornamental species*. FAO Plant Production and Protection Paper 59 FAO, Rome. ISBN 92-5-102157-0.

KROGSTRUP P., ERIKSEN E.N., MØLLER J.D. & ROULUND H. 1988 Somatic embryogenesis in Sitka spruce (*Picea sitchensis* Bong. Carr.). Plant Cell Rep. **7**, 594–597.

KROMER K. & KUKULCZANKA K. 1985 *In vitro* cultures of meristem tips of *Canna indica* L. Acta Hort. **167**, 279–285.

KROSING M. 1978 Tissue culture under conditions of boron deficiency. Z. Pflanzenernaehr Bodenkd. **141**, 523–534.

KRUL W. 1990 *In vitro* propagation of grape via leaf disk culture. U.S. Patent No. 4931394

KRUL W.R. 1986 *In vitro* propagation of grape. U.S. Patent No. 4532733.

KRUL W.R. 1988 *In vitro* propagation of grape. U.S. Patent No. 4714679.

KRUL W.R. & COLCLASURE G.C. 1977 Effect of galactose and other monosaccharides on IAA movement in bean hypocotol segments. Physiol. Plant. **41**, 249–253.

KRUL W.R. & WORLEY J.F. 1977a Formation of adventitious embryos in callus cultures of 'Seyval', a French hybrid grape. J. Am. Soc. Hort. Sci. **102**, 360–363.

KRUL W.R. & WORLEY J.F. 1977b Formation of adventitious embryos in callus cultures of 'Seyval', a French hybrid grape. HortScience **12**, 411 (Abst. 258).

KRUSE P.F. & PATTERSON M.K. Jr. (eds.) 1973 *Tissue Culture Methods and Applications*. Academic Press, New York.

KUKREJA A.K. & MATHUR A.K. 1985 Tissue culture studies in *Duboisia myoporoides*; 1. Plant regeneration and clonal propagation by stem node cultures. Planta Med. **51**, 93–96.

KUKULCZANKA K. & CZASTKA B. 1988 *In vitro* cultures of *Drosera* sp. Acta Hort. **226**, 631–634.

KUKULCZANKA K., KLIMASZEWSKA K. & PLUTA H. 1977 Regeneration of entire plants of *Peperomia scandens* from different parts of leaves *in vitro*. Acta Hort. **78**, 365–371.

KULAEVA O.N. 1980 Cytokinin action on enzyme activities in plants. pp. 119–128 *in* Skoog F. (ed.) 1980 (*q.v.*).

KULPA J.M., GALSKY A.G., LIPETZ P. & STEPHENS R. 1985 Polyamines and crown gall tumour growth. Plant Cell Rep. **4**, 81–83.

KUMAR A.S., GAMBORG O.L. & NABORS M.W. 1988 Plant regeneration from suspension cultures of *Vigna aconitifolia*. Plant Cell Rep. **7**, 138–141.

KUMAR P.P., REID D.M. & THORPE T.A. 1986 Ethylene and carbon dioxide accumulation and morphogenesis in excised cotyledons of *Pinus radiata*. p. 11 *in* Abstracts VI Intl. Cong. Plant Tissue & Cell Culture, Minneapolis, Minn.

KUMAR P.P., REID D.M. & THORPE T.A. 1987 The role of ethylene and carbon dioxide in differentiation of shoot buds in excised cotyledons of *Pinus radiata in vitro*. Physiol. Plant. **69**, 244–252.

KUNISAKI J.T. 1975 *In vitro* propagation of *Cordyline terminalis* L. Kunth. HortScience **10**, 601–602.

KUNISAKI J.T. 1980 *In vitro* propagation of *Anthurium andreanum* Lind. Hort-Science **15**, 508–509.

KUNISAKI J.T. 1990 Micropropagation of *Leucospermum*. Acta Hort. **264**, 45–48.

KUNNEMANN B.P.A.M. & FAAIJ-GROENEN G.P.M. 1988 Elimination of bacterial contaminants: a matter of detection and transplanting procedures. Acta Hort. **225**, 183–188.

KUNZE R., STARLINGER P. & SCHWARTZ D. 1988 DNA methylation of the maize transposable element Ac interferes with its transcription. Mol. Gen. Genet. **214**, 325–327.

KURAISHI S. & OKUMURA F.S. 1961 A new green-leaf growth stimulating factor, phyllococosine, from coconut milk. Nature **189**, 148–149.

KURKDJIAN A. & GUERN J. 1989 Intracellular pH: Measurement and importance in cell activity. Ann. Rev. Plant Physiol. Mol. Biol. **40**, 271–303.

KURKDJIAN A., MATHIEU Y. & GUERN J. 1982 Evidence for an action of 2,4-dichlorophenoxyacetic acid on the vacuolar pH of *Acer pseudoplatanus* cells in suspension culture. Plant Sci. Lett. **27**, 77–86.

KUROSAKI F., TAKAHASHI S., SHUDO K., OKAMOTO T. & ISOGAI Y. 1981 Structure and biological links between urea and purine cytokinins. Chem. Pharm. Bull. **29 (12)**, 3751–3753.

KURZ M.L. 1986 Tissue culture of conifers. Comb. Proc. Int. Plant Prop. Soc. 1985 **35**, 206–216.

KUSEY W.E., HAMMER P.A. & WEILER T.C. 1980 *In vitro* propagation of *Gypsophila paniculata* 'Bristol Fairy'. HortScience **15**, 600–601.

KYOZUKA J. & SHIMAMOTO K. 1991 Transformation and regeneration of rice protoplasts. Section B2 pp. 1–17 *in* Lindsey (ed.) 1991 (*q.v.*).

KYTE L. 1983 *Plants from Test Tubes. An Introduction to Micropropagation.* The Timber Press, Beaverton, Oregon. ISBN 0-917304-50-0.

KYTE L. & BRIGGS B. 1979 A simplified entry into tissue culture production of rhododendrons. Comb. Proc. Int. Plant Proc. Soc. **29**, 90–95.

LA RUE C.D. 1936 The growth of plant embryos in culture. Bull. Torrey Bot. Club **63**, 365–382.

LA RUE C.D. 1949 Cultures of the endosperm of maize. Am. J. Bot. **36**, 798.

LA RUE C.D. 1954 p. 187 *in* Brookhaven Symp. Biol. 6. Brookhaven National Laboratory, New York.

LAKSHMANA RAO P.V. & DE D.N. 1987 Haploid plants from *in vitro* anther culture of the leguminous tree, *Peltophorum pterocarpum* (DC) K. Hayne (Copper pod). Plant Cell Tiss. Organ Cult. **11**, 167–177.

LAKSHMI SITA G. & SHOBHA RANI B. 1985 *In vitro* propagation of *Eucalyptus grandis* L. by tissue culture. Plant Cell Rep. **4**, 63–65.

LAKSHMI SITA G., RAGHAVA RAM N.V. & VAIDYANATHAN C.S. 1979 Differentiation of embryoids and plantlets from shoot callus of sandalwood. Plant Sci. Lett. **15**, 265–270.

LAL M. 1963 Experimental induction of apogamy and the control of differentiation in gametophytic callus of the moss *Physcomitrium coorgense* Broth. pp. 363–381 *in* Maheshwari & Ranga Swamy (eds.) 1963 (*q.v.*).

LALORAYA M.M., SRIVASTAN H.N. & GURUPRASAD K.N. 1976 Recovery of gibberellic acid inhibition of betacyanin biosynthesis by pigment precursors. Planta **128**, 275–276.

LAMOTTE C.E. 1960 The effects of tyrosine and other amino acids on the formation of buds in tobacco callus. Dissertation Abstracts **21**, 31–32.

LAMOTTE C.E. & LERSTEN N.R. 1971 An attempt to induce bacteria-free plants of *Psychotria punctata* (Rubiaceae) in tissue culture. Am. J. Bot. **58**, 476.

LANDRY L.G. & SMYTH D.A. 1988 Characterization of starch produced by suspension cultures of Indica rice (*Oryza sativa* L.). Plant Cell Tiss. Organ Cult. **15**, 23–32.

LANE B.H. & STILL S.M. 1981 Influence of extended photoperiod and fertilization on rooting of *Acer rubrum* 'Red Sunset'. HortScience **16**, 408 (Abst. 68).

LANE W.D. 1978 Regeneration of apple plants from shoot meristem tips. Plant Sci. Lett. **13**, 281–285.

LANE W.D. 1979a Influence of growth regulators on root and shoot initiation from flax meristem tips and hypocotyls *in vitro*. Physiol. Plant. **45**, 260–264.

LANE W.D. 1979b Regeneration of pear plants from shoot meristem tips. Plant Sci. Lett. **16**, 337–342.

LANE W.D. 1982 Plant manipulation *in vitro* with hormones. Comb. Proc. Int. Plant Prop. Soc. 1981 **31**, 101–108.

LANG A.R.G. 1967 Osmotic coefficients and water potentials of sodium chloride solutions from 0 to 40°C. Austr. J. Chem. **20**, 2017–2023.

LANG G.A. & SCHWARTZ R.F. 1981 Effects of a bacterial contamination on rooting and growth of *in vitro Nephrolepsis* cultures, and isolation and identification of causal organism. HortScience **16**, 463 (Abst. 471).

LANG W.H. (ed.) 1921 *Strasburger's Text Book of Botany.* 5th English Edition. MacMillan & Co. Ltd. London.

LANGFORD P.J. & WAINWRIGHT H. 1987 Effects of sucrose concentration on the photosynthetic ability of rose shoots *in vitro*. Ann. Bot. **60**, 633–640.

LANGFORD P.J. & WAINWRIGHT H. 1988 Influence of sucrose concentration on the photosynthetic ability of *in vitro* grown rose shoots. Acta Hort. **227**, 305–310.

LANGHANS R.W., HORST R.K. & EARLE E.D. 1977 Disease-free plants via tissue culture propagation. HortScience **12**, 149–150.

LANGOWSKA T. 1980 Effect of activated carbon and brown coal suspensions for growth and development of *Scenedesmus obliquus* (SC. 449). Pol. Arch. Hydrobiol. **27**, 125–136.

LANGRIDGE J. & BROCK R.D. 1961 A thiamine-requiring mutant of the tomato. Aust. J. Biol. Sci. **14**, 66–69.

LAPEÑA L., PÉREZ-BERMÚDEZ P. & SEGURA J. 1988 Morphogenesis in hypocotyl cultures of *Digitalis obscura*; influence of carbohydrate levels and sources. Plant Science **57**, 247–252.

LARKIN P.J. 1982 Sugarcane tissue and protoplast culture. Plant Cell Tiss. Organ Cult. **1**, 149–164.

LARKIN P.J. & SCOWCROFT W.R. 1981 Somaclonal variation – a novel source of variability from cell cultures for plant improvement. Theor. Appl. Genet. **60**, 197–214.

LARKIN P.J. & SCOWCROFT W.R. 1983 Somaclonal variation and eyespot toxin tolerance in sugarcane. Plant Cell Tiss. Organ Cult. **2**, 111–121.

LARKIN P.J., DAVIES P.A. & TANNER G.J. 1988 Nurse culture of low numbers of *Medicago* and *Nicotiana* protoplasts using calcium alginate beads. Plant Science **58**, 203–210.

LARKIN P.J., SPINDLER L.H. & BANKS P.M. 1990 Cell culture of alien chromosome addition lines to induce somatic recombination and gene introgression. pp. 163–168 *in* Nijkamp *et al.* (eds.) 1990 (*q.v.*).

LAROSA P.C., HASEGAWA P.M. & BRESSAN R.A. 1981 Initiation of photoautotrophic potato cells. HortScience **16**, 433 (Abst. 249).

LARUE T.A.G. & GAMBORG O.L. 1971a Ethylene production by plant cell cultures. Variations in production during growing cycle and in different plant species. Plant Physiol. **48**, 394–398.

LASSOCINSKI W. 1985 Chlorophyll-deficient cacti in tissue cultures. Acta Hort. **167**, 287–293.

LATIES G.G. 1962 Controlling influence of thickness on development and type of respiratory activity in potato slices. Plant Physiol. **37**, 679–690.

LATUNDE-DADA A.O. & LUCAS J.A. 1983 Somaclonal variation and reaction to *Verticillium* wilt in *Medicago sativa* L. plants regenerated from protoplasts. Plant Sci. Lett. **32**, 205–211.

LATUNDE-DADA A.O. & LUCAS J.A. 1988 Somaclonal variation and resistance to *Verticillium* wilt in lucerne, *Medicago sativa* L., plants regenerated from callus. Plant Science **58**, 111–119.

LAU O.-L. & YANG S.F. 1973 Mechanism of a synergistic effect of kinetin on auxin-induced ethylene production. Plant Physiol. **51**, 1011–1014.

LAU O.-L. & YANG S.F. 1976 Stimulation of ethylene production in the mung bean hypocotyls by cupric ion, calcium ion, and kinetin. Plant Physiol. **57**, 88–92.

LAVARDE F. 1987 Apex tissue culture of alder (*Alnus glutinosa* Gaertn.). Preliminary results. Acta Hort. **212**, 547–550.

LAVEE S. & AVIDAN N. 1982 Growth responses of tree callus to chlorogenic acid and related phenolic substances. pp. 165–168 *in* Fujiwara A. (ed.) 1982 (*q.v.*).

LAVEE S. & HOFFMAN M. 1971 The effect of potassium ions on peroxidase activity and its isoenzyme composition as related to apple callus growth *in vitro*. Bot. Gaz. **132**, 232–237.

LAWSON G.M. & GOODWIN P.P. 1986 Commercial production of Kangaroo Paws. Comb. Prop. Int. Plant Prop. Soc. 1985 **35**, 57–65.

LAWSON R.H. 1974 Virus transmission may occur through developing protocorms and produce a population of uniformly infected plants. pp. 247–253 *in* Ospina H.M. (ed.) 1974 (*q.v.*).

LAWSON R.H. 1986 Pathogen detection and elimination. pp. 97–117 *in* Zimmerman *et al.* (eds.) 1986 (*q.v.*).

LAWSON R.H. & HEARON S.S. 1973 Symptomatology of cattleya mericlones infected with cymbidium mosaic virus. Am. Orchid Soc. Bull. **42**, 1071–1074.

LAWSON R.H. & HEARON S.S. 1974a Ultrastructure of carnation etched ring virus-infected *Saponaria vaccaria* and *Dianthus caryophyllus*. J. Ultrastruct. Res. **48**, 201–215.

LAWSON R.H. & HEARON S.S. 1974 b Distribution and staining properties of *Cymbidium* mosaic virus in buds of *Cattleya* orchids. Acta Hort. **36**, 195–206.

LAZAR M.D. & COLLINS G.B. 1981 Comparative glutamine metabolism in tobacco callus and leaf tissues. Env. Exp. Bot. **21**, 425 (Abst.).

LAZAR M.D., BAENZIGER P.S. & SCHAEFFER G.W. 1984 Combined abilities and heritability of callus formation and plantlet regeneration in wheat (*Triticum aestivum* L.) anther cultures. Theor. Appl. Genet. **68**, 131–134.

LAZAR M.D., COLLINS G.B. & VIAN W.E. 1983 Genetic and environmental effects on the growth and differentiation of wheat somatic cell cultures. J. Heredity **74**, 353–357.

LAZARTE J.E. 1984a Tissue culture of pecan, oak and other woody plant species. Comb. Proc. Int. Plant Prop. Soc. 1983 **33**, 614–618.

LAZZERI P.A. & DUNWELL J.M. 1986a *In vitro* regeneration from seedling organs of *Brassica oleracea* var. italica Plenck cv. Green Comet. I. Effect of plant growth regulators. Ann. Bot. **58**, 689–697.

LAZZERI P.A. & DUNWELL J.M. 1986b *In vitro* regeneration from seedling organs of *Brassica oleracea* var. italica cv. Green Comet. II. Effect of light conditions and explant size. Ann. Bot. **58**, 699–710.

LAZZERI P.A., HILDEBRAND D.F., SUNEGA J., WILLIAMS E.G. & COLLINS G.B. 1988 Soybean somatic embryogenesis: interactions between sucrose and auxin. Plant Cell Rep. **7**, 517–520.

LE GUYADER H. 1987 Ethylène et différenciation de racines par des cultures de couches cellulaires minces de tabac. Compt. Rend. Acad. Sci. Paris **305**, Ser. III 591–594.

LE ROUX J.J. & VAN STADEN J. 1991 Micropropagation of *Eucalyptus* species. HortScience **26**, 199–200.

LE RUDULIER D. & GOAS G. 1975 Effect of ammonium and potassium ions on the accumulation of putrescine in young decotylized *Soja hispida* plants. Physiol. Veg. **13**, 125–136.

LEA P.J., HUGHES J.S. & MIFLIN B.J. 1979 Glutamine- and asparagine-dependent protein synthesis in maturing legume cotyledons cultured *in vitro*. J. Exp. Bot. **30**, 529–537.

LEACH G.N. 1979 Growth in soil of plantlets produced by tissue culture, – loblolly pine. Tappi **62**, (4) 59–61.

LEDOUX L. (ed.) 1975 *Genetic Manipulations with Plant Material*. NATO Advanced Study Institutes Series. Life Sciences Vol. 3. Plenum Publishing Corp. New York.

LEE B.T., MURDOCH K., TOPPING J., DE BOTH M.T.J., WU Q.S., KARP A., STEELE S., SYMONDS C., KREIS M.F & JONES M.G.K. 1988 Isolation, culture and morphogenesis from wheat protoplasts, and study of expression of DNA constructs by direct gene transfer. Plant Cell Tiss. Organ Cult. **12**, 223–226.

LEE C.H. & POWER J.B. 1988 Intra- and interspecific gametosomatic hybridisation within the genus *Petunia*. Plant Cell Tiss. Organ Cult. **12**, 197–200.

LEE H.S., LIU J.R., YANG S.G., LEE Y.H. & LEE K.-W. 1990 *In vitro* flowering of plantlets regenerated from zygotic embryo- derived somatic embryos of ginseng. HortScience **25**, 1652–1654.

LEE M. & PHILLIPS R.L. 1988 The chromosomal basis of somaclonal variation. Ann. Rev. Plant Physiol. **39**, 413–417.

LEE N., WETZSTEIN H.Y. & SOMMER H.E. 1988 Quantum flux density effects on the anatomy and surface morphology of *in vitro*- and *in vivo*-developed sweetgum leaves. J. Am. Soc. Hort. Sci. **113**, 167–171.

LEE S.K. & RAO A.N. 1986 *In vitro* regeneration of plantlets in *Fagraea fragrans* Roxb. — a tropical tree. Plant Cell Tiss. Organ Cult. **7**, 43–51.

LEE T.T. 1971a Cytokinin-controlled indoleacetic acid oxidase isoenzymes in tobacco callus cultures. Plant Physiol. **47**, 181–185.

LEE T.T. 1971b Increase of indoleacetic acid oxidase isoenzymes by gibberellic acid in tobacco callus cultures. Can. J. Bot. **49**, 687–693.

LEE T.T. 1971c Promotion of indoleacetic acid oxidase isoenzymes in tobacco callus cultures by indoleacetic acid. Plant Physiol. **48**, 56–59.

LEE T.T. 1974 Cytokinin control in subcellular localization of indoleacetic acid oxidase and peroxidase. Phytochem. **13**, 2445–2453.

LEE T.T. 1980 Effects of phenolic substances on metabolism of exogenous indole-3-acetic acid in maize stems. Physiol. Plant. **50**, 107–112.

LEE T.T. & SKOOG F. 1965 Effects of hydroxybenzoic acids on indoleacetic acid inactivation by tobacco callus extracts. Physiol. Plant. **18**, 577–585.

LEGGATT I.V., WAITES W.M., LEIFERT C. & NICHOLAS J. 1988 Characterisation of micro-organisms isolated from plants during micropropagation. Acta Hort. **225**, 93–102.

LEGRAND B. 1972 Influence des conditions initiales d'éclairement sur le bourgeonnement et la polarité de tissus de feuilles d'endive cultivés *in vitro*. Compt. Rend. Acad. Sci. Paris **275D**, 31–32.

LEGRAND B. 1974 Influence of the lighting conditions on the neoformation of shoots by leaf tissues of endive cultivated *in vitro* and on the peroxidase activity of the tissues. Compt. Rend. Acad. Sci. Paris **278D**, 2425–2428.

LEGRAND B. 1975 Action of iron and EDTA on the neoformation of buds, by the leaf fragments of endive cultivated *in vitro*. Compt. Rend. Acad. Sci. Paris **280D**, 2215–2218.

LEIFERT C. & WAITES W.M. 1990 Contaminants of plant tissue cultures. pp. 2–13 *in* Newsletter No. 60, International Assoc. Plant Tiss. Cult. March 1990.

LEIFERT C., WAITES W.M. & NICHOLAS J.R. 1989a Bacterial contaminants of micropropagated plant cultures. J. Appl. Bacteriol. **67**, 353–361.

LEIFERT C., WAITES W.M., CAMOTTA H. & NICHOLAS J.R. 1989b *Lactobacillus plantarum*; a deleterious contaminant of plant tissue culture. J. Appl. Bacteriol. **67**, 363–370.

LEIFERT C., WAITES W.M., NICHOLAS J.R. & KEETLEY J.W. 1990 Yeast contaminants of micropropagated plant cultures. J. Appl. Bact. **69**, 471–476.

LELLIOTT R.A. & STEAD D.E. 1987 *Methods for the Diagnosis of Bacterial Diseases of Plants*. Blackwell Scientific Publications Ltd. ISBN 0-632-01233-1.

LENEE P. & CHUPEAU Y. 1989 Development of nitrogen assimilating enzymes during growth of cells derived from protoplasts of sunflower and tobacco. Plant Science **59**, 109–117.

LEPAGE-DEGIVRY M.-T. 1973 Étude en culture *in vitro* de la dormance embryonnaire de *Taxus baccata* L. Biol. Plant. **15**, 264–269.

LERCH B. 1977 Inhibition of the biosynthesis of potato virus by ribavirin. Phytopathologische Zeitschrift. **89**, 44–49.

LERCH K. 1981 Copper monooxygenases: tyrosine and dopamine β-monooxygenase. pp. 143–186 *in* Sigel H. (ed.) 1981 *Metal Ions in Biological Systems* **13** Marcel Dekker Inc. New York, Basel.

LEROUX R. 1968 Action de l'acide gibberéllique sur la rhizogénèse de fragments de tiges de pois (*Pisum sativum* L.) cultivés *in vitro* en presence d'auxine à l'obscurité ou à la lumière. Compt. Rend. Acad. Sci. Paris **266D**, 106–108.

LESHEM B. 1983 Growth of carnation meristems *in vitro*: anatomical structure of abnormal plantlets and the effect of agar concentration in the medium on their formation. Ann. Bot. **52**, 413–415.

LESHEM B. & SACHS T. 1985 Vitrified *Dianthus* — teratomata *in vitro* due to growth factor imbalance. Ann. Bot. **56**, 613–617.

LESHEM B., LILIEN-KIPNIS H. & STEINITZ B. 1982 The effect of light and of explant orientation on the regeneration and subsequent growth of bulblets on *Lilium longiflorum* Thunb. bulb-scale sections cultured *in vitro*. Scientia Hort. **17**, 129–136.

LESHEM B., SHALEY D.P. & IZHAR S. 1988a Cytokinin as an inducer of vitrification in melon. Ann. Bot. **61**, 255–260.

LESHEM B., WERKER E. & SHALEV D.P. 1988 The effect of cytokinins and vitrification in melon and carnation. Ann. Bot. **62**, 271–276.

LESLIE C.A. & ROMANI R.J. 1986 Salicylic acid: A new inhibitor of ethylene biosynthesis. Plant Cell Rep. **5**, 144–146.

LESLIE C.A. & ROMANI R.J. 1988 Inhibition of ethylene biosynthesis by salicylic acid. Plant Physiol. **88**, 833–837.

LETHAM D.S. 1966 Regulation of cell division in plant tissues. II. A cytokinin in plant extracts: isolation and interaction with other growth regulators. Phytochem. **5**, 269–286.

LETHAM D.S. 1967 Chemistry and physiology of kinetin-like compounds. Ann. Rev. Plant Physiol. **18**, 349–364.

LETHAM D.S. 1968 A new cytokinin bioassay and the naturally occurring cytokinin complex. pp. 19–31 *in* Wightman and Setterfield (eds.) *Biochemistry and Physiology of Plant Growth Substances*. Runge Press, Ottawa.

LETHAM D.S. 1974 Regulators of cell division in plant tissues. XX. The cytokinins of coconut milk. Physiol. Plant. **32**, 66–70.

LETHAM D.S. 1982 A compound in coconut milk which actively promoted radish cotyledon expansion, but exhibited negligible activity in tissue culture bioassays for cytokinins, was identified as the 6 oxypurine, 2-(3-methylbut-2-enylamino)-purin-6-one. Plant Sci. Lett. **26**, 241–249.

LETOUZÉ R. 1970 Maintien de la dominance apicale après décapitation d'une bouture de saule (*Salix babylonica* L.) en culture *in vitro*. Influence de la lumière bleue-violette. Compt. Rend. Acad. Sci. Paris. **271**, 2309–2312.

LETOUZÉ R. 1974 The growth of the axillary bud of a willow cutting cultured *in vitro*: apical dominance and light quality. Physiol. Veg. **12**, 397–412.

LETOUZÉ R. 1975 Growth of axillary buds of *Salix babylonica* and action of phenylalanine ammonia-lyase (PAL). Planta **123**, 155–162.

LETOUZÉ R. & BEAUCHESNE G. 1969 Action d'éclairements monochromatiques sur la rhizogen se de tissus de Topinambour. Compt. Rend. Acad. Sci. Paris **269**, 1528–1531.

LETOUZÉ R. & DAGUIN F. 1987 Control of vitrification and hypolignification. Acta Hort. **212**, 185–191.

LEVA A.R., BARROSO M. & MURILLO J.M. 1984 La moltiplicazione del melo con la tecnica della micropropagazione. Vriazione del pH in substrati diversi durante la fase di multiplicazione. Riv. Ortoflorofrutti. Ital. **68**, 483–492.

LEVIN R. 1989 Process for plant tissue culture propagation. U.S. Patent No. 4855236

LEVY D. 1988 Propagation of potato by the transfer of transplants of *in vitro* proliferated shoot cuttings into the field. Scientia Hort. **36**, 165–171.

LEWIS D.H. 1980 Boron, lignification and the origin of vascular plants — a unified hypothesis. New Phytol. **84**, 209–229.

LI H.C., RICE E.L., ROHRBAUGH L.M. & WENDER S.H. 1970 Effects of abscisic acid on phenolic content and lignin biosynthesis in tobacco tissue culture. Physiol. Plant. **23**, 928–936.

LIAU D.F. & BOLL W.G. 1970 Callus and cell suspension culture of bush bean (*Phaseolus vulgaris*). Can. J. Bot. **48**, 1119–1130.

LICHTER R. 1981 Anther culture of *Brassica napus* in a liquid culture medium. Z. Pflanzenphysiol. **103**, 229–237.

LIDE D.R. (ed.) 1991 *CRC Handbook of Chemistry and Physics.* CRC Press, Boca Raton.

LIM-HO C. L. 1982 Tissue culture of local orchid hybrids at the Singapore Botanic Gardens. pp. 295–300 *in* Rao A. N. (ed.) 1982 (*q.v.*)

LIMBERG M., CRESS D. & LARK K.G. 1979 Variants of soybean cells which can grow in suspension with maltose as a carbon-energy source. Plant Physiol. **63**, 718–721.

LIN K.C., CHEN F.C. & WANG P.J. 1978 J. Chinese Soc. Hort. Sci. **24**, p. 260.

LIN M.-L. & STABA E.J. 1961 Peppermint and spearmint tissue cultures. I. Callus formation and submerged culture. Lloydia **24**, 139–145.

LINDEMANN E.G.P., GUNCKEL J.E. & DAVIDSON O.W. 1970 Meristem culture of *Cattleya*. Am. Orchid Soc. Bull. **39**, 1002–1004.

LINDSEY K. (ed.) 1991 *Plant Tissue Culture Manual.* Kluwer Academic Publishers. Dordrecht, Netherlands.

LINDSEY K. & YEOMAN M.M. 1983 Novel experimental systems for studying the production of secondary metabolites by plant tissue culture. pp. 39–66 *in* Mantell and Smith (eds.) 1983 (*q.v.*).

LINEBERGER R.D. & DRUCKENBROD M. 1985 Chimeral nature of the pinwheel flowering African violets (*Saintpaulia*, Gesneriaceae). Am. J. Bot. **72**, 1204–1212.

LINK G.K.K. & EGGERS V. 1946 Mode, site and time of initiation of hypocotyledonary bud primordia in *Linum usitatissimum* L. Bot. Gaz. **107**, 441–454.

LINSMAIER E.M. & SKOOG F. 1965 Organic growth factor requirements of tobacco tissue cultures. Physiol. Plant. **18**, 100–127.

LINSMAIER-BEDNAR E.M. & SKOOG F. 1967 Thiamine requirement in relation to cytokinin in 'normal' and 'mutant' strains of tobacco callus. Planta **72**, 146–154.

LIPETZ J. & GALSTON A.W. 1959 Indole acetic acid oxidase and peroxidase activities in normal and crown gall tissue cultures of *Parthenocissus tricuspidata*. Am. J. Bot. **46**, 193–196.

LIPPMANN B. & LIPPMANN G. 1984 Induction of somatic embryos in cotyledonary tissue of soybean, *Glycine max* L. Merr. Plant Cell Rep. **3**, 215–218.

LISO R., INNOCENI A.M., BITONTI M.B. & ARRIGONI O. 1988 Ascorbic acid-induced progression of quiescent centre cells from G_1 to S phase. New Phytol. **110**, 469–471.

LIST A. 1963 Some observations on DNA content and cell and nuclear volume growth in the developing xylem cells of certain higher plants. Am. J. Bot. **50**, 320–329.

LITVAY J.D., JOHNSON M.A., VERMA D., EINSPAHR D. & WEYRAUCH K. 1981 Conifer suspension culture medium development using analytical data from developing needs. IPC Technical paper series, no.115.

LITZ R.E. 1987 Application of tissue culture to tropical fruits. pp. 407–418 *in* Green *et al.* (eds.) 1987 (*q.v.*).

LITZ R.E. 1988 Somatic embryogenesis from cultured leaf explants of the tropical tree *Euphoria longan* Stend. J. Plant Physiol. **132**, 190–193.

LITZ R.E. & CONOVER R.A. 1977 Tissue culture propagation of some foliage plants. Proc. Fla. State Hort. Soc. **90**, 301–303.

LITZ R.E. & CONOVER R.A. 1981a *In vitro* polyembryony in *Carica papaya* ovules. HortScience **16**, 459 (Abst. 444).

LITZ R.E. & CONOVER R.A. 1981b *In vitro* polyembryony in *Carica papaya* L. ovules. Z. Pflanzenphysiol. **104**, 285–288.

LITZ R.E. & CONOVER R.A. 1981c Effect of sex type, season, and other factors on *in vitro* establishment and culture of *Carica papaya* L. explants. J. Am. Soc. Hort. Sci. **106**, 792–794.

LIU J.R. & CANTLIFFE D.J. 1984 Somatic embryogenesis and plant regeneration in tissue cultures of sweet potato (*Ipomoea batatas* Poir.). Plant Cell Rep. **3**, 112–115.

LIU L. & BURGER D.W. 1986 *In vitro* propagation of Easter lily from pedicels. HortScience **21**, 1437–1438.

LIU M.-C. & CHEN W.-H. 1976 Tissue and cell culture as aids to sugar cane breeding. I. Creation of genetic variability through callus culture. Euphytica **25**, 393–403.

LIU M.-C. & CHEN W.-H. 1978 Tissue and cell culture as aids to sugarcane breeding. II. Performance and yield potential of callus derived lines. Euphytica **27**, 273–282.

LIU M.-C., SHANG K.C., CHEN W.H. & SHIH S.C. 1977 Tissue and cell culture as aids to sugar cane breeding. III. Aneuploid cells and plants induced by treatment of cell suspension culture with colchicine. Proc. Int. Soc. Sug. Cane Tech. **16**, 1–13.

LLOYD D., ROBERTS A.V. & SHORT K.C. 1988 The induction *in vitro* of adventitious shoots in *Rosa*. Euphytica **37**, 31–36.

LLOYD G. & McCOWN B. 1980 Use of microculture for production and improvement of *Rhododendron* spp. HortScience **15**, 416 (Abst. 321).

LLOYD G. & McCOWN B. 1981 Commercially-feasible micropropagation of Mountain laurel, *Kalmia latifolia*, by use of shoot tip culture. Int. Plant Prop. Soc. Proc. **30**, 421–427.

LO SCHIAVO F. 1984 A critical review of the procedures for embryo purification. Plant Mol. Biol. Rep. **2 (3)**, 15–18.

LO SCHIAVO F., PITTO L., GIULIANO G., TORTI G., NUTI-RONCHI V., MARAZZITI D., VERGARA R., ORSELLI S. & TERZI M. 1989 DNA methylation of embryogenic carrot cell cultures and its variations as caused by mutation, differentiation, hormones and hypomethylating drugs. Theor. Appl. Genet. **77**, 325–331.

LOEWUS F.A. 1974 The biochemistry of *myo*-inositol in plants. Recent Adv. Phytochem. **8**, 179–207.

LOEWUS F.A. & LOEWUS M.W. 1980 *Myo*-inositol: Biosynthesis and metabolism. pp. 43–76 *in* Stumpf and Conn (eds.): *The Biochemistry of Plants* 3. Academic Press N.Y. 43–76.

LOEWUS F.A., KELLY S. & NEUFELD E.F. 1962 Metabolism of *myo*-inositol in plants: Conversion to pectin hemicellulose, D-xylose and sugar acids. Proc. Nat. Acad. Sci. U.S.A. **48**, 421–425.

LOGAN A.E. & ZETTER F.W. 1985 Rapid *in vitro* propagation of virus indexed gladioli. Acta Hort. **164**, 169–180.

LONG C. (ed.) 1961 *Biochemists Handbook.* E. & F.N. Spon Ltd., London.

LONG R.D., CURTIN T.F. & CASSELLS A.C. 1988 An investigation of the effects of bacterial contamination on potato nodal cultures. Acta Hort. **225**, 83–91.

LOO S.-W. 1945 Cultivation of excised stem tips of *Asparagus in vitro*. Am. J. Bot. **32**, 13–17.

LOO S.-W. 1946a Further experiments on the culture of excised asparagus tips *in vitro*. Am. J. Bot. **33**, 156–159.

LOO S.-W. 1946b Cultivation of excised stem tips of dodder *in vitro*. Am. J. Bot. **33**, 295–300.

LORETI F. & PASQUALETTO P.L. 1986 Vitrification of plants cultured *in vitro*. Comb. Proc. Int. Plant Prop. Soc. **36**, 66–71.

LORETI F., MORINI S. & CONCETTI S. 1988 Effect of potassium and nitrogen concentration on growth of peach shoots cultured *in vitro*. Acta Hort. **227**, 311–317.

LORETI F., MULEO R. & MORINI S. 1991 Effect of light quality on growth of *in vitro* cultured organs and tissues. Comb. Proc. Int. Plant Prop. Soc. 1990 **40**, 615–623.

LÖRZ H., LARKIN P.J., THOMSON J. & SCOWCROFT W.R. 1983 Improved protoplast culture and agarose media. Plant Cell Tiss. Organ Cult. **2**, 217–226.

LOVELL P.H., ILLSLEY A. & MOORE K.G. 1972 The effects of light intensity and sucrose on root formation, photosynthetic ability, and senescence in detached cotyledons of *Sinapis alba* L. and *Raphanus sativus* L. Ann. Bot. **36**, 123–134.

LOZOYA-SALDANA G., DAWSON W.O. & MURASHIGE T. 1984 Effect of ribavirin and adenosine arabinoside on tobacco mosaic virus in *Nicotiana tabacum* L. var. Xanthi tissue cultures. Plant Cell. Tiss. Organ Cult. **3**, 41–48.

LU C., VASIL I.K. & OZIAS-AKINS P. 1982 Somatic embryogenesis in *Zea mays*. Theor. Appl. Genet. **62**, 109–112.

LU C.-Y. & VASIL I.K. 1981a Somatic embryogenesis and plant regeneration from leaf tissues of *Panicum maximum* Jacq. Theor. Appl. Genet. **59**, 275–280.

LU C.-Y. & VASIL I.K. 1981b Somatic embryogenesis and plant regeneration from freely-suspended cells and cell groups of *Panicum maximum*. Ann. Bot. **48**, 543–548.

LU C.-Y. & VASIL I.K. 1982 Somatic embryogenesis and plant regeneration in tissue cultures of *Panicum maximum* Jacq. Am. J. Bot. **69**, 77–81.

LUMSDEN P.J., PRYCE S. & LEIFERT C. 1990 Effect of mineral nutrition on the growth and multiplication of *in vitro* cultured plants. pp. 108–113 *in* Nijkamp *et al.* (eds.) 1990 (*q.v.*).

LUNDERGAN C. & JANICK J. 1979 Low temperature storage of *in vitro* apple shoots. HortScience **14**, 514.

LUPI M.C., BENNICI A., LOCCI F. & GENNAI D. 1987 Plantlet formation from callus and shoot-tip culture of *Helianthus annuus* (L.). Plant Cell Tiss. Organ Cult. **11**, 47–55.

LUPOTTO E. 1986 The use of single somatic embryo culture in propagating and regenerating lucerne (*Medicago sativa* L.). Ann. Bot. **57**, 19–24.

LUTZ A. 1971 Morphogenetic aptitudes of tissue cultures of unicellular origin. pp. 163–168 in *Les Cultures de Tissus de Plantes*. Coll. Int. C.N.R.S. Paris 193.

LUTZ J.D., WONG J.R., ROWE J., TRICOLI D.M. & LAWRENCE R.H. Jr. 1985 Somatic embryogenesis for mass cloning of crop plants. pp. 105–116 *in* Henke *et al.* (eds.) 1985 (*q.v.*).

LUYET B.J. 1937 The vitrification of organic colloids and of protoplasms. Biodynamica **1**, 1–14.

LYMAN G. & MATHUS G. 1990 Tissue culture flask. U.S. Patent No. 4927764

LYNCH D.V. & THOMPSON J.E. 1984 Lipoxygenase-mediated production of superoxide anion in senescing plant tissue. FEBS Lett. **173**, 251–254.

LYRENE P.M. 1980 Micropropagation of rabbit-eye blueberries (*V. ashei*). HortScience **15**, 80–81.

LYRENE P.M. 1981 Juvenility and production of fast-rooting cuttings from blueberry shoot cultures. J. Am. Soc Hort. Sci. **106**, 396–398.

MA S.S. & SHII C.T. 1974 Growing banana plantlets from adventitious buds. J. Hort. Soc. China **20**, 6–12.

MA S.S. & WANG S.O. 1977 Clonal multiplication of azaleas through tissue culture. Acta Hort. **78**, 209–215.

MAAN A.C., KUHNEL B., BEUKERS J.J.B. & LIBBENGA K.R. 1985a Naphthylphthalamic acid-binding sites in cultured cells from *Nicotiana tabacum*. Planta **164**, 69–74.

MAAN A.C., VAN DER LINDE P.C.G., HARKES P.A.A. & LIBBENGA K.R. 1985b Correlation between the presence of membrane-bound auxin binding and root regeneration in cultured tobacco cells. Planta **164**, 376–378.

MACCARTHY J.J., RATCLIFFE D. & STREET H.E. 1980 The effect of nutrient composition on the growth cycle of *Catharanthus roseus* G.Don cells grown in batch culture. J. Exp. Bot. **31**, 1315–1325.

MACCHIA F., SCARAMUZZI F. & PORCELLI S. 1983 Organogenesis and propagation *in vitro* of F₁ hybrid of *Solanum melongena* L. from vegetative segments. Acta Hort. **131**, 117–124.

MACHIN B. 1978 Maintaining varietal character. Grower **89**, 857, 859–860.

MACKAY W.A. & KITTO S.L. 1988 Factors affecting *in vitro* shoot proliferation of French tarragon. J. Am. Soc. Hort. Sci. **113**, 282–287.

MACKAY W.A. & NG T.J. 1988 Regeneration of *Cucumis melo* L. from cotyledon culture. HortScience **23**, 753.

MACKENZIE I.A. & STREET H.E. 1970 Studies on the growth in culture of plant cells. VIII. Production of ethylene by suspension cultures of *Acer pseudoplatanus* L. J. Exp. Bot. **21**, 824–834.

MACKLON A.E.S. & SIM A. 1976 Cortical cell fluxes and transport to the stele in excised root segments of *Allium cepa* L. III. Magnesium. Planta **128**, 5–9.

MACLACHLAN G.A. & WAYGOOD E.R. 1956 Catalysis of indoleacetic acid oxidation by manganic ions. Physiol. Plant. **9**, 321–330.

MACLEOD R.D. 1968 Changes in the mitotic cycle in lateral root meristems of *Vicia faba* following kinetin treatment. Chromosoma **24**, 177–187.

MACVICAR R. & STRUCKMEYER B.E. 1946 The relation of photoperiod to the boron requirement of plants. Bot. Gaz. **107**, 454–461.

MADDOCK S.E., LANCASTER V.A., RISIOTT R. & FRANKLIN J. 1983 Plant regeneration from cultured immature embryos and inflorescences of 25 cultivars of wheat (*Triticum aestivum*). J. Exp. Bot. **34**, 915–926.

MADDOCK S.E., RISIOTT R., PARMAR S., JONES M.G.K. & SHEWRY P.R. 1985 Somaclonal variation in the gliadin patterns of grains of regenerated wheat plants. J. Exp. Bot. **36**, 1976–1984.

MADDOX A.D., CONSALVES F. & SHIELDS R. 1983 Successful preservation of suspension cultures of three *Nicotiana* species at the temperature of liquid nitrogen. Plant Sci. Lett. **28**, 157–162.

MAEDA E. & SAKA H. 1973 Light microscopy of cell organelles in shoot-forming rice callus tissues. (In Japanese) Proc. Crop Sci. Jap. **42**, 442–453.

MAEDA E. & THORPE T.A. 1979 Effects of various auxins on growth and shoot formation in tobacco callus. Phytomorph. **29**, 146–155.

MAEDA E., CHEN M.-H., NAKANO H. & SETHI M. 1982b Cytodifferentiation in *in vitro* cells of rice and *Amaryllis* and studies on protoplasts of wheat. pp. 43–44 *in* Fujiwara A. (ed.) 1982 (*q.v.*).

MAEDA E., INOUE M. & CHEN M-H. 1982a Regulatory mechanism of shoot formation in rice callus. pp. 1–6 *in* Rao A.N. (ed.) 1982 (*q.v.*).

MAENE L. & DEBERGH P. 1985 Liquid medium additions to established tissue cultures to improve elongation and rooting *in vivo*. Plant Cell Tiss. Organ Cult. **5**, 23–33.

MAENE L.J. & DEBERGH P.C. 1982 Stimulation of axillary shoot development of *Cordyline terminalis* 'Celestine Queen' by foliar sprays of 6-benylamino purine. HortScience **17**, 344–34.

MAENE L.J. & DEBERGH P.C. 1987 Optimalisation of the transfer of tissue cultured shoots to *in vivo* conditions. Acta Hort. **212**, 335–348.

MAGGS D.H. & ALEXANDER D.McE. 1967 A topophysic relation between regrowth and pruning in *Eucalyptus cladocalyx* F. Muell. Aust. J. Bot. **15**, 1–9.

MAGNUS V. 1979 Tryptophol β-D-glucopyranoside: chemical synthesis, metabolism and growth promoting activity. Carbohydrate Res. **76**, 261–264.

MAGNUS V., ISKRIC S. & KVEDER S. 1973 The formation of tryptophol glucoside in the tryptamine metabolism of pea seedlings. Planta **110**, 57–62.

MAHESHWARI P. 1950 *An Introduction to the Embryology of Angiosperms*. McGraw-Hill, New York.

MAHESHWARI P. & BALDEV B. 1961 Artificial production of buds from the embryos of *Cuscuta reflexa*. Nature **191**, 197–198.

MAHESHWARI P. & RANGA SWAMY N.S. (eds.) 1963 *Plant Tissue and Organ Culture*. Int. Soc. Plant Morphologists, Delhi, India.

MAHESHWARI S.C. & CHAUHAN O.S. 1963 *In vitro* control of flowering in *Wolffia microscopica*. Nature **198**, 99–100.

MAHESHWARI S.C. & SETH P.N. 1966 Induction of flowering in *Wolffia microscopica* by the iron salt of ethylene- di-*o*-hydroxyphenylacetic acid (Fe-EDDHA). Z. Pflanzenphysiol. **55**, 89–91.

MAHESHWARI S.C., RASHID A. & TYAGI A.K. 1980 Physiology of pollen haploid formation — the current status. pp. 393–398 *in* Sala *et al.* (eds.) 1980 (*q.v.*).

MAHESHWARI S.C., RASHID A. & TYAGI A.K. 1982 Haploids from pollen grains — retrospect and prospect. Am. J. Bot. **69**, 865–879.

MAHESWARAN G. & WILLIAMS E.G. 1984 Direct somatic embryoid formation on immature embryos of *Trifolium repens, T. pratense* and *Medicago sativa*, and rapid clonal propagation of *T. repens*. Ann. Bot. **54**, 201–211.

MAHESWARAN G. & WILLIAMS E.G. 1985 Origin and development of somatic embryoids formed directly on immature embryos of *Trifolium repens in vitro*. Ann. Bot. **56**, 619–630.

MAHESWARAN G. & WILLIAMS E.G. 1987 Uniformity of plants regenerated by direct somatic embryogenesis from zygotic embryos of *Trifolium repens*. Ann. Bot. **59**, 93–97.

MAHLBERG P.G., MASI P. & PAUL D.R. 1980 Use of polypropylene film for capping tissue culture containers. Phytomorph. **30**, 397–399.

MAHOTIERE S., HERNER R.C. & DENNIS F.G. 1976a Effects of applied growth substances on growth of shoot apices excised from onion in rest. J. Am. Soc. Hort. Sci. **101**, 211–213.

MAHOTIERE S., HERNER R.C. & DENNIS F.G. 1976b Effect of temperature on growth of shoot apices excised from onions in rest. HortScience **11**, 154–155.

MAKUS D.J., ZUROSKE G. & RYAN C.A. 1981 Evidence that the transport of the proteinase inhibitor inducing factor out of wounded tomato leaves is phloem-mediated. HortScience **16**, 454 (Abst. 408).

MALIGA P., SZ.-BREZNOVITS A. & MARTON L. 1973 Streptomycin- resistant plants from callus culture of haploid tobacco. Nature, New Biol. **244**, 29–30.

MALIGA P., SZ.-BREZNOVITS A. & MARTON L. 1975 Non-Mendelian streptomycin-resistant tobacco mutant with altered chloroplasts and mitochondria. Nature **255**, 401–402.

MANDAL S. & GADGIL V.N. 1979 Differentiation of shoot buds and roots in fruit callus of *Solanum nigrum* L. Ind. J. Exp. Biol. **17**, 876–878.

MANGAT B.S. & ROY M.K. 1986 Tissue culture and plant regeneration of okra (*Abelmoschus esculentus*). Plant Science **47**, 57–61.

MANN M.L., SKIRVIN R.M. & CHU M.C. 1982 Effects of autoclaving on the pH of tissue culture media. HortScience **17**, 534 (Abst.436).

MANNONEN L., TOIVONEN L. & KAUPPINEN V. 1990 Effect of long-term preservation on growth and productivity of *Panax ginseng* and *Catharanthus roseus* cell cultures. Plant Cell Rep. **9**, 173–177.

MANTELL S.H. & SMITH H. 1983 *Plant Biotechnology*. Soc. Exp. Biology Seminar Series 18. Cambridge Univ. Press. Cambridge, London, New York.

MANTELL S.H., MATTHEWS J.A. & McKEE R.A. 1985 *Principles of Plant Biotechnology. An Introduction to Genetic Engineering in Plants*. Blackwell Scientific Publications, Oxford. ISBN 0-632-01215-3

MAPES M.O. 1973 Tissue culture of bromeliads. Comb. Proc. Int. Plant Prop. Soc. **23**, 47–55.

MAPES M.O. & ZAERR J.B. 1981 The effect of the female gametophyte on the growth of cultured Douglas fir embryos. Ann. Bot. **48**, 577–582.

MAPSON L.W. & BURTON W.G. 1962 Terminal oxidases of the potato tuber. Biochem. J. **82**, 19–25.

MARANI F. & PISI A. 1977 Meristem-tip culture and vegetative propagation in potato. Acta Hort. **78**, 415–422.

MARCKER K., JENSEN J.S. & IGIHCO T. 1990 Method for the expression of genes in plants, parts of plants, and plant cell cultures, and DNA fragments, plasmids and transformed microorganisms to be used when carrying out the method as well as the use thereof for the expression of genes in plants. U.S. Patent No. 4886753

MARCOTRIGIANO M. 1986 Synthesing plant chimeras as a source of new phenotypes. Comb. Proc. Int. Plant Prop. Soc. **35**, 582–586.

MARCOTRIGIANO M. & GOUIN F.R. 1984a Experimentally synthesized plant chimeras. 1. In vitro recovery of *Nicotiana tabacum* L. chimeras from mixed callus cultures. Ann. Bot. **54**, 503–511.

MARCOTRIGIANO M. & GOUIN F.R. 1984b Experimentally synthesized plant chimaeras. 2. A comparison of *in vitro* and *in vivo* techniques for the production of interspecific *Nicotiana* chimaeras. Ann. Bot. **54**, 513–521.

MARCOTRIGIANO M. & STIMART D.P. 1981 *In vitro* organogenesis and shoot proliferation of *Paulownia tomentosa* Steud. (Empress tree). HortScience **16**, 405 (Abst. 48).

MARCOTRIGIANO M., MORGAN P.A., SWARTZ H.J. & RUTH J. 1987 Histogenic instability in tissue culture-proliferated strawberry plants. J. Am. Soc. Hort. Sci. **112**, 583–587.

MARCOTRIGIANO M., SWARTZ H.J., GRAY S.E., TOKARCIK D. & POPENOE J. 1984 The effect of benzylamino purine on the *in vitro* multiplication rate and subsequent field performance of tissue-culture propagated strawberry plants. Adv. Strawberry Prod. **3**, 23–25.

MARETZKI A. 1987 Tissue culture: Its prospects and problems. pp. 343–384 *in* Heinz D.J. (ed.) 1987 *Sugarcane Improvement through breeding*. Dev. in Crop Science **11**. Elsevier Amsterdam, Oxford, New York, Tokyo.

MARETZKI A., DELA-CRUZ A. & NICKELL L.G. 1971 Extracellular hydrolysis of starch in sugarcane cell suspensions. Plant Physiol. **48**, 521–525.

MARETZKI A., THOM A. & NICKELL L.G. 1972 Influence of osmotic potentials on the growth and chemical composition of sugarcane cell cultures. Hawaii Plant Res. **58**, 183–199.

MARETZKI A., THOM M. & NICKELL L.G. 1974 Utilisation and metabolism of carbohydrates in cell and callus cultures. pp. 329–361 *in* Street H.E. (ed.) 1974 (*q.v.*).

MARGARA J. 1969a Étude des facteurs de la néoformation de bourgeons en culture *in vitro* chez le chou-fleur (*Brassica oleracea* L. var. *botrytis*). Ann. Physiol. Veg. **11**, 95–112.

MARGARA J. 1969b Étude prliminaire des facteurs de la néoformations de bourgeons chez le chou-fleur (*Brassica oleracea* L. var. *botrytis*). Compt. Rend. Acad. Sci. Paris **268D**, 686–688.

MARGARA J. 1969c Sur l'aptitude de tissus au bourgeonnement et a l'initiation florale *in vitro*. Compt. Rend. Acad. Sci. Paris **268D**, 803–805.

MARGARA J. 1977a Effets d'auxines et d'antiauxines sur la néoformation de bourgeons *in vitro* chez le Chou-fleur (*Brassica oleracea* L. var. botrytis). Compt. Rend. Acad. Sci. Paris **284D**, 1883–1885.

MARGARA J. 1977b La multiplication végétative de la betterave (*Beta vulgaris* L.) en culture *in vitro*. Compt. Rend. Acad. Sci. Paris **285D**, 1041–1044.

MARGARA J. 1978 Mise au point d'une gamme de milieux minéraux pour les conditions de la culture '*in vitro*'. Compt. Rend. Seances Acad. Agric. France **64**, 654–661.

MARGARA J. & LEYDECKER M.-T. 1978 Différents types d'organogenèse observés chez le Colza, *Brassica napus* L. var. oleifera Metzg. Compt. Rend. Acad. Sci. Paris **287D**, 17–20.

MARGARA J. & RANCILLAC M. 1966 Observations préliminaires sur le rôle du milieu nutritif dans l'initiation florale des bourgeons néoformés *in vitro* chez *Cichorium intybus* L. Compt. Rend. Acad. Sci. Paris **263D**, 1455–1458.

MARGARA J., RANCILLAC M. & BOUNIOLS A. 1966 Recherches expérimentales sur la néoformation de bougeons inflorescentiels ou végétatifs *in vitro* à partir d'explantats d'endive (*Cichorium intybus* L). Ann. Physiol. Veg. **8**, 285–305.

MARIANO G. 1988 *In vitro* ^{14}C-labelled 6-benzyladenine uptake and CO_2 evolution in two Japanese plum cultivars. Plant Cell Tiss. Organ Cult. **13**, 49–59.

MARIN J.A. & GELLA R. 1987 Aclimatization of the micropropagated cherry rootstock 'Masto de Montanana' (*Prunus cerasus* L.). Acta Hort. **212**, 603–606.

MARIN M.L. & DURAN-VILA N. 1988 Survival of somatic embryos and recovery of plants of sweet orange (*Citrus sinensis* L. Osb.) after immersion in liquid nitrogen. Plant Cell Tiss. Organ Cult. **14**, 51–57.

MARINO G. 1986 *In vitro* 6-benzylaminopurine purine uptake in two Japanese plums. Acta Hort. **179**, 871–872.

MARINO G., ROSATI P. & SAGRATI F. 1985 Storage of *in vitro* cultures of *Prunus rootstocks*. Plant Cell Tiss. Organ Cult. **5**, 73–78.

MARINUS J. 1983 Some aspects of the *in vitro* multiplication of potatoes. Pot. Res. **26**, 85–86.

MARIOTTI D. & ARCIONI S. 1983 *Coronilla varia* L. (Crown vetch): plant regeneration through somatic embryogenesis. Plant Cell Tiss. Organ Cult. **2**, 103–110.

MARKS T.R., SIMPSON S.E., BECKHAM C.F. & DOBSON H.E. 1987 Micropropagation of hardy ornamentals. East Malling Res. Sta. Rep. 1986 pp. 31–34.

MARONEK D.M., HENDRIX J.W. & KIERNAN J. 1981 Mycorrhizal fungi and their importance in horticultural crop production. Hort. Rev. **3**, 172–213.

MARQUES D.V. 1986 Study of some factors involved on *in vitro* callus growth and somatic embryogenesis of coffee tissues. p. 42 *in* Somers *et al.* (eds.) 1986 (q.v.).

MARRÉ E. 1977 Effects of fusicoccin and hormones on plant cell membrane activities: observations and hypotheses. pp. 185–202 *in* Marré and Ciferri (eds.) 1977 (q.v.).

MARRÉ E. 1979 Fusicoccin: a tool in plant physiology. Ann. Rev. Plant Physiol. **30**, 273–288.

MARRÉ E. & CIFERRI O. (eds.) 1977 *Regulation of Cell Membrane Activities in Plants*. Elsevier/North Holland, Amsterdam.

MARSOLAIS A.A., WILSON D.P.M., TSUJITA M.J. & SENARATNA T. 1991 Somatic embryogenesis and artificial seed production in Zonal (*Pelargonium horterum*) and Regal (*Pelargonium domesticum*) geranium. Can. J. Bot. **69**, 1188–1193.

MARTIN C., KUNESCH G., MARTIN-TANGUY J., NEGREL J., PAYNOT M. & CARRÉ M. 1985 Effect of cinnamoyl putrescines on *in vitro* cell multiplication and differentiation of tobacco explants. Plant Cell Rep. **4**, 158–160.

MARTIN G.C. 1987 Apical dominance. HortScience **22**, 824–833.

MARTIN R.B. 1979 Complexes of a-amino acids with chelatable side chain donor atoms. pp. 1–39 *in* Sigel H. (ed.) 1979 *in Metal Ions in Biological Systems* **9** Marcel Dekker Inc., New York and Basel.

MARTIN S.M. & ROSE D. 1976 Growth of plant cell (*Ipomoea*) suspension cultures at controlled pH levels. Can. J. Bot. **54**, 1264–1270.

MARTIN S.M., ROSE D. & HUI V. 1977 Growth of plant cell suspensions with ammonium as the sole nitrogen source. Can. J. Bot. **55**, 2838–2843.

MARTIN-TANGUY J., MARTIN C., PAYNOT M. & ROSSIN N. 1988 Effect of hormone treatment on growth bud formation and free amine and hydroxycinnamoyl putrescine levels in leaf explant of *Nicotiana tabacum* cultivated *in vitro*. Plant Physiol. **88**, 600–604.

MARTINELLI A. 1985 Factors affecting *in vitro* propagation of the peach almond hybrids 'Hansen 536'. Acta Hort. **173**, 237–244.

MARTINELLI A. 1988 Use of *in vitro* techniques for selection and cloning of different *Pistacia* species. Acta Hort. **227**, 436–437.

MARTINEZ E.A. & TIZIO R. 1989 Grapevine micropropagation through shoot tips and minicuttings from *in vitro* cultured one-node cuttings. HortScience **24**, p. 513.

MASCARENHAS A. F., GUPTA P. K., KULKARNI V. M., MEHTA U., IYER R. S., KHUSPE S. S. & JAGANNATHAN V. 1982b Propagation of trees by tissue culture. pp. 175–179 *in* Rao A.N. (ed.) 1982 (*q.v.*).

MASIREVEC S.N., SECOR G.A. & GULYA T.J. 1988 Use of cell culture to screen sunflower germplasm for resistance to *Phomopsis* brown/gray stem spot. Plant Cell Rep. **7**, 528–530.

MATHES M.C., MORSELLI M. & MARVIN J.W. 1973 Use of various carbon sources by isolated maple callus cultures. Plant & Cell Physiol. **14**, 797–801.

MATHEWS H. 1987 Morphogenetic responses from *in vitro* cultured seedling explants of mung bean (*Vigna radiata* L. Wilczek). Plant Cell Tiss. Organ Cult. **11**, 233–240.

MATHEWS H. 1988 *In vitro* responses of *Brassica juncea* and *Vigna radiata* to the antibiotic kanomycin. Ann. Bot. **62**, 671–675.

MATHIAS P.J., ALDERSON P.G. & LEAKEY R.R.B. 1987 Bacterial contamination in tropical hardwood cultures. Acta Hort. **212**, 43–48.

MATHIAS R.J. & BOYD L.A. 1986 Cefotaxime stimulates callus growth, embryogenesis and regeneration in hexaploid bread wheat (*Triticum aestivum* L. em. Thell.). Plant Science **46**, 217–223.

MATHIAS R.J. & FUKUI K. 1986 The effect of specific chromosome and cytoplasmic substitutions on the tissue culture response of wheat (*Triticum aestivum*) callus. Theor. Appl. Genet. **71**, 797–800.

MATHIAS R.J. & SIMPSON E.S. 1986 The interaction of genotype and culture medium on the tissue culture responses of wheat (*Triticum aestivum* L. em.thell) callus. Plant Cell Tiss. Organ Cult. **7**, 31–37.

MATHIAS R.J., FUKUI K. & LAW C.N. 1986 Cytoplasmic effects on the tissue culture reponse of wheat (*Triticum aestivum*) callus. Theor. Appl. Genet. **72**, 70–75.

MATHUR J. 1991 Enhanced somatic embryogenesis in *Selinum candolii* DC. under a mineral oil overlay. Plant Cell Tiss. Organ Cult. **27**, 23–26.

MATO M.C. & VIEITEZ A.M. 1986 Changes in auxin protectors and IAA oxidase during the rooting of chestnut shoots *in vitro*. Physiol. Plant. **66**, 491–494.

MATSUBARA S. 1973 Population effect in lateral bud culture of asparagus and promotion of root formation by transplanting. J. Jap. Soc. Hort. Sci. **42**, 142–146.

MATSUBARA S. & CLORE W.J. 1974 Vegetative propagation of asparagus from lateral buds. Sci. Rep., Fac. Agr., Okayama Univ., Jap. **43**, 19–26.

MATSUOKA H. & HINATA K. 1979 NAA-induced organogenesis and embryogenesis in hypocotyl callus of *Solanum melongena* L. J. Exp. Bot. **30**, 363–370.

MATSUZAKI T., KOIWAI A., IWAI S. & YAMADA Y. 1984 *In vitro* proliferation of stigma-like, style-like structures of *Nicotiana tobacum* and its fatty acid composition. Plant Cell Physiol. **25**, 197–203.

MAUNDERS M.J., HOLDSWORTH M.J., SLATER A., KNAPP J.E., BIRD C.R., SCHUCH W. & GRIERSON D. 1987 Ethylene stimulates the accumulation of ripening-related mRNAs in tomatoes. Plant Cell & Env. **10**, 177–184.

MAUNEY J.R., CHAPPELL J. & WARD B.J. 1967 Effects of malic acid salts on growth of young cotton embryos *in vitro*. Bot. Gaz. **128**, 198–200.

MAURO M.C., NEF C. & FALLOT J. 1986 Stimulation of somatic embryogenesis and plant regeneration from anther culture of *Vitis vinifera* cv. Cabernet-Sauvignon. Plant Cell Rep. **5**, 377–380.

MAUSETH J.D. 1979 Cytokinin-elicited formation of the pith-rib meristem and other effects of growth regulators on the morphogenesis of *Echino cereus* (Cactaceae) seedling shoot apical meristems. Am. J. Bot. **66**, 446–451.

MAUSETH J.D. & HALPERIN W. 1975 Hormonal control of organogenesis in *Opuntia polyacantha* (Cactaceae). Am. J. Bot. **62**, 869–877.

MAZÉ P. 1914 Recherche de physiologie végétale. Influence respective des éléments de la solution minérale sur le développement du mais. Ann. Inst. Pasteur **28**, 21–46.

MAZÉ P. 1919 Recherche d'une solution purément minérale capable d'assurer l'évolution complète du mais culturé à l'abri des microbes. Ann. Inst. Pasteur **33**, p. 139.

McCANCE R.A. & WIDDOWSON E.M. 1940 *The Chemical Composition of Foods.* British M.R.C. Spec. Rep. Serv. No. 235.

McCLELLAND M.T. & SMITH M.A.L. 1990 Vessel type, closure and explant orientation influence *in vitro* performance of five woody species. HortScience **25**, 797–800.

McCLENDON J.H. 1976 Elemental abundance as a factor in the origins of mineral nutrient requirements. J. Mol. Evol. **8**, 175–195.

McCOMB J.A. & BENNETT I.J. 1982 Vegetative propagation of *Eucalyptus* using tissue culture and its application to forest improvement in Western Australia. pp. 721–722 *in* Fujiwara (ed.) 1982 (*q.v.*).

McCOMB J.A. & NEWTON S. 1981 Propagation of Kangaroo paws using tissue culture. J. Hort. Sci. **56**, 181–183.

McCORMICK S. 1991 Transformation of tomato with *Agrobacterium tumefaciens*. Section B6 pp. 1–9 *in* Lindsey (ed.) 1991 (*q.v.*).

McCOWN B. & AMOS R. 1979 Initial trials with commercial micropropagation of birch selections. Comb. Proc. Int. Plant Prop. Soc. **29**, 387–393.

McCOWN B.H. 1986 Woody ornamentals, shade trees and conifers. pp. 333–342 Zimmerman *et al.* (eds.). 1986 (*q.v.*).

McCOWN B.H. & AMOS R. 1982 A survey of the response of gymnosperms to microculture. HortScience **17**, 489 (Abst. 123).

McCOWN B.H. & LLOYD G. 1981 Woody plant medium (WPM) — a mineral nutrient formulation for microculture of woody plant species. HortScience **16**, 453 (Abst. 394).

McCOWN B.H. & SELLMER J.C. 1987 General media and vessels suitable for woody plant culture. pp. 4–16 *in* Bonga and Durzan (eds.) 1987a (*q.v.*).

McCOWN D.D. & McCOWN B.H. 1987 North American hardwoods. pp. 247–271 *in* Bonga and Durzan (eds.) 1987c (*q.v.*).

McCOY R.J., PHILLIPS R.L. & RINES H.W. 1982 Cytogametic analysis of plants regenerated from oat (*Avena sativa*) tissue cultures; high frequency of partial chromosome loss. Can. J. Genet. Cytol. **24**, 37–50.

McCOY T.J. & BINGHAM E.T. 1977 Regeneration of diploid alfalfa plants from cells grown in suspension culture. Plant Sci. Lett. **10**, 59–66.

McCOY T.J. & BINGHAM E.T. 1979 Breeding and selection of diploid alfalfa (*Medicago sativa* L.) that regenerates plants from cells grown in suspension culture. p. 851 *in* Sharp *et al.* (eds.) 1979 (*q.v.*).

McCULLOCH S.M. 1988 Commercial micropropagation of *Kalmia*. Comb. Proc. Int. Plant Prop. Soc. 1987 **37**, 107–109.

McCULLOCH S.M. & BRIGGS B.A. 1983 Preparation of plants for micropropagation. Comb. Proc. Int. Plant Prop. Soc. 1982 **32**, 297–304.

McCUNE D.C. & GALSTON A.W. 1959 Inverse effects of gibberellin on peroxidase activity and growth in dwarf strains of peas and corn. Plant Physiol. **34**, 416–418.

McGAW B.A., SCOTT I.M. & HORGAN R. 1984 Cytokinin biosynthesis and metabolism. pp. 105–133 *in* Crozier and Hillman (eds.) 1984 (*q.v.*).

McGRANAHAN G., LESLIE C.A. & DRIVER J.A. 1988a *In vitro* propagation of mature persian walnut cultivars. HortScience **23**, 220.

McGRANAHAN G.H., DRIVER J.A. & TULECKE W. 1987 Tissue culture of *Juglans*. pp. 261–271 *in* Bonga and Durzan (eds.) 1987c (*q.v.*).

McGRANAHAN G.H., LESLIE C.A., URATSU S.L., MARTIN L.A. & DANDEKAR A.M. 1988b *Agrobacterium*-mediated transformation of walnut somatic embryos and regeneration of transgenic plants. Bio/Technology **6**, 800–804.

McGREW J.R. 1967 A sensitive strawberry virus indicator clone of *Fragaria vesca* from the U.S.S.R. Plant Dis. Rep. **51**, 288–290.

McGREW J.R. 1980 Meristem culture for production of virus-free strawberries. pp. 80–85 *in Proc. of Conf. on Nursery Production of Fruit Plants through Tissue Culture: Applications and Feasibility*. USDA-SEA, Agric. Res. Results. ARR-NE-11. Beltsville, Maryland.

McHUGHEN A.G. 1987 Production of improved plants having an increased tolerance to the presence of a normally deleterious concentration of a plurality of inorganic salts. U.S. Patent No. 4616100

McKEAND S.E. & ALLEN H.L. 1984 Nutritional and root developmental factors affecting growth of tissue culture plantlets of loblolly pine. Physiol. Plant. **61**, 523–528.

McKENZIE B.L. 1983 Development of a tissue culture laboratory in New Zealand. Comb. Proc. Int. Plant Prop. Soc. 1982 **32**, 311–314.

McKERSIE B.D., SENARATNA T., BOWLEY S.R., BROWN D.C.W., KROCHKO J.E. & BEWLEY J.D. 1989 Application of artificial seed technology in the production of hybrid alfalfa (*Medicago sativa* L.). In Vitro Cell Dev. Biol. **25**, 1183–1188.

McPHEETERS K. & SKIRVIN R.M. 1981 *In vitro* development of a pure thornless form of chimeral 'Thornless Evergreen' blackberry. HortScience **16**, 426–427 (Abst. 203).

McPHEETERS K. & SKIRVIN R.M. 1982 Cane and fruiting characteristics of micropropagated 'Thornless Evergreen' blackberry. HortScience **17**, 530 (Abst. 412).

McPHEETERS K. & SKIRVIN R.M. 1983 Histogenic layer manipulation in chimeral 'Thornless Evergreen' trailing blackberry. Euphytica **32**, 351–360.

McRAE D.G., BAKER J.E. & THOMPSON J.E. 1982 Evidence for involvement of the superoxide radical in the conversion of 1-amino-1- carboxylic acid to ethylene by pea microsomal membranes. Plant & Cell Physiol. **23**, 375–383.

McWILLIAM A.A., SMITH S.M. & STREET H.E. 1974 The origin and development of embryoids in suspension cultures of carrot (*Daucus carota*). Ann. Bot. **38**, 243–250.

MEDEROS S. & RODRÍGUEZ ENRÍQUEZ M.J. 1987 *In vitro* propagation of 'Golden Times' roses. Factors affecting shoot tips and axillary bud growth and morphogenesis. Acta Hort. **212**, 619–624.

MEHRA A. & MEHRA P.N. 1972 Differentiation in callus cultures of *Mesembryanthemum floribundum*. Phytomorph. **22**, 171–176.

MEHRA P.N. & CHEEMA G.S. 1980b Clonal multiplication *in vitro* of Himalayan poplar (*Populus ciliata*). Phytomorph. **30**, 336–343.

MEHRA P.N. & JAIDKA K. 1985 Experimental induction of embryogenesis in pear. Phytomorph. **35**, 1–10.

MEHTA A.R. 1966 *In vitro* initiation and growth of root callus of *Phaseolus vulgaris* L. Ind. J. Exp. Biol. **4**, 187–188.

MEHTA A.R. 1982 Comparative studies on some physiological aspects in organ forming (diploid as well as haploid) tobacco and non-organ forming cotton callus tissues. pp. 125–126 *in* Fujiwara *et al.* (ed.) 1982 (*q.v.*).

MEIJER E.G.M. & BROWN D.C.W. 1988 Inhibition of somatic embryogenesis in tissue cultures of *Medicago sativa* by aminoethoxyvinylglycine, amino-oxyacetic acid, 2,4-dinitrophenol and salicylic acid at concentrations which do not inhibit ethylene biosynthesis and growth. J. Exp. Bot. **39**, 263–270.

MEINS F. 1974 Mechanisms underlying the persistence of tumour autonomy in crown gall disease. pp. 233–264 *in* Street H.E. (ed.) 1974 (q.v.).

MEINS F. Jr. 1987 Hormones and the molecular basis of determination in plants. pp. 19–28 *in* Jackson *et al.* (eds.) 1987a (*q.v.*).

MEINS F. Jr. & BINNS A.N. 1978 Epigenetic clonal variation in the requirement of plant cells for cytokinins. Symp. Soc. Dev. Biol. **36**, 188–201.

MEINS F. Jr. & FOSTER R. 1986 A cytokinin mutant derived from cultured tobacco cells. Dev. Genet. **7**, 159–165.

MEINS F. Jr. & LUTZ J. 1980 Epigenetic changes in tobacco cell culture: studies of cytokinin habituation. pp. 220–236 *in* Rubenstein *et al.* (eds.) 1980 (*q.v.*).

MEINS F. Jr., FOSTER R. & LUTZ J.D. 1983 Evidence for a Mendelian factor controlling the cytokinin requirement of cultured tobacco cells. Dev. Genet. **4**, 129–141.

MEKERS O. 1977 *In vitro* propagation of some Tillansoideae (Bromeliaceae). Acta Hort. **78**, 311–320.

MELÉ E., MESSEGUER J. & CAMPRUBI P. 1982 Effect of ethylene on carnation explants grown in sealed vessels. pp. 69–70 *in* Fujiwara (ed.) 1982 (*q.v.*)

MELLOR F.C. & STACE-SMITH R. 1969 Development of excised potato buds in nutrient medium. Can. J. Bot. **47**, 1617–1621.

MELLOR F.C. & STACE-SMITH R. 1977 Virus-free potatoes by tissue culture. pp. 616–635 *in* Reinert and Bajaj (eds.) 1977 (*q.v.*).

MENCZEL L. & WOLFE K. 1984 High frequency of fusion induced in freely suspended protoplast mixtures by polyethylene glycol and dimethylsulfoxide at high pH. Plant Cell Rep. **3**, 196–198.

MENGEL K. & KIRKBY E.A. 1982 *Principles of Plant Nutrition*. 3rd Edition. Internat. Potash Institute, Bern, Switzerland.

MENON M.K.C. & LAL M. 1972 Influence of sucrose on the differentiation of cells with zygote-like potentialities in a moss. Naturwissenschaften **59**, 514.

MERYL SMITH M. & STONE B.A. 1973 Studies on *Lolium multiflorum* endosperm in tissue culture. 1. Nutrition. Aust. J. Biol. Sci. **26**, 123–133.

MESSEGUER J. & MELÉ E. 1987 *In vitro* propagation of adult material and seedlings of *Corylus avellana*. Acta Hort. **212**, 499–503.

MEYER H.J. & VAN STADEN J. 1988 The *in vitro* culture of *Gerbera aurantica*. Plant Cell Tiss. Organ Cult. **14**, 25–30.

MEYER M.M. Jr. 1974 Propagation of tall bearded Iris by *in vitro* techniques. HortScience **9**, 271 (Abst. 22).

MEYER M.M. Jr. 1980 *In vitro* propagation of *Hosta sieboldiana*. HortScience **15**, 737–738.

MEYER M.M. Jr. 1982 *In vitro* propagation of *Rhododendron catawbiense* from flower buds. HortScience **17**, 891–892.

MEYER M.M. Jr. 1984 Clonal propagation of perennial plants from flowers by tissue culture. Comb. Proc. Int. Plant Prop. Soc. 1983 **33**, 402–407.

MEYER M.M. Jr. 1986 Semiportable laminar flow hood for tissue culture and microscope use for research and teaching. HortScience **21**, 1064–1065.

MEYER Y. & ABEL W.O. 1975a Importance of the cell wall for cell division and in the activity of the cytoplasm in cultured tobacco protoplasts. Planta **123**, 33–40.

MEYER Y. & ABEL W.O. 1975b Budding and cleavage division of tobacco mesophyll protoplasts in relation to pseudo-wall and wall formation. Planta **125**, 1–13.

MEYNET J. & SIBI M. 1984 Haploid plants from *in vitro* culture of unfertilized ovules in *Gerbera jamesonii*. Z. Pflanzenzucht. **93**, 78–85.

MICHLER C.H. & LINEBERGER R.D. 1981 Survival determination of *Nicotiana* callus cultures following ultrarapid cooling. HortScience **16**, 441 (Abst. 306).

MICHLER C.H. & LINEBERGER R.D. 1987 Effects of light on somatic embryo development and abscisic levels in carrot suspension cultures. Plant Cell Tiss. Organ Cult. **11**, 189–207.

MIDDLETON W., JARVIS B.C. & BOOTH A. 1978 The boron requirement for root development in stem cuttings of *Phaseolus aureus* Roxb. New Phytol. **81**, 287–297.

MIKAMI T. & KINOSHITA T. 1988 Genotypic effects on the callus formation from different explants of rice *Oryza sativa* L. Plant Cell Tiss. Organ Cult. **12**, 311–314.

MIKKELSEN E.P. & SINK K.C. Jr. 1978a Histology of adventitious shoot and root formation on leaf-petiole cuttings of *Begonia × hiemalis* Forsch 'Aphrodite Peach'. Scientia Hort. **8**, 179–192.

MIKKELSEN E.P. & SINK K.C. Jr. 1978b *In vitro* propagation of Rieger Elatior begonias. HortScience **13**, 242–244.

MIKSCH U. & BEIDERBECK R. 1976 Mechanical isolation of single cells from leaves of higher plants. Biochem. Biophys. Pflanzen. **169**, 191–196.

MILBORROW B.V. 1974 The chemistry and physiology of abscisic acid. Ann. Rev. Plant Physiol. **25**, 259–307.

MILLER A.R. & ROBERTS L.W. 1982 Regulation of tracheary element differentiation by exogenous L-methionine in callus of soya bean cultivars. Ann. Bot. **50**, 111–116.

MILLER A.R., CRAWFORD D.L. & ROBERTS L.W. 1985 Lignification and xylogenesis in *Lactuca* pith explants cultured *in vitro* in the presence of auxin and cytokinin: a role for endogenous ethylene. J. Exp. Bot. **36**, 110–118.

MILLER C. & SKOOG F. 1953 Chemical control of bud formation in tobacco stem segments. Am. J. Bot. **40**, 768–773.

MILLER C.O. 1954 The influence of cobalt and sugar upon the elongation of etiolated pea stem segments. Plant Physiol. **29**, 79–82.

MILLER C.O. 1956 Similarity of some kinetin and red light effects. Plant Physiol. **31**, 318–319.

MILLER C.O. 1958 The relationship of the kinetin and red light promotions of lettuce seed germination. Plant Physiol. **33**, 115–117.

MILLER C.O. 1961a A kinetin-like compound in maize. Proc. Nat. Acad. Sci. U.S.A. **47**, 170–174.

MILLER C.O. 1961b Kinetin related compounds in plant growth. Ann. Rev. Plant Physiol. **12**, 395–408.

MILLER C.O. 1963 Kinetin and kinetin-like compounds. pp. 194–202 *in* Linskens & Tracey (eds.). *Modern Methods of Plant Analysis*. Vol. 6. Springer-Verlag, Berlin.

MILLER C.O. 1979 Cytokinin inhibition of respiration by cells and mitochondria of soybean. Planta **146**, 503–511.

MILLER C.O. 1980 Cytokinin inhibition of respiration in mitochondria from six plant species. Proc. Nat. Acad. Sci. U.S.A. **77**, 4731–4735.

MILLER C.O. 1982 Cytokinin modification of mitochondrial function. Plant Physiol. **69**, 1274–1277.

MILLER C.O., SKOOG F., OKUMURA F.S., VON SALTZA M.H. & STRONG F.M. 1955b Structure and synthesis of kinetin. J. Am. Chem. Soc. **77**, 2662–2663.

MILLER C.O., SKOOG F., OKUMURA F.S., VON SALZA M. & STRONG F.M. 1956 Isolation, structure and synthesis of kinetin, a substance promoting cell division. J. Am. Chem. Soc. **78**, 1375.

MILLER C.O., SKOOG F., VON SALTZA M. & STRONG F.M. 1955a Kinetin, a cell division factor from deoxyribonucleic acid. J. Am. Chem. Soc. **77**, 1392.

MILLER E.C. 1931 *Plant Physiology with Reference to the Green Plant*. McGraw-Hill.

MILLER J.H. 1968 Fern gametophytes as experimental material. Bot. Rev. **34**, 361–426.

MILLER L.R. & MURASHIGE T. 1976 Tissue culture propagation of tropical foliage plants. In Vitro **12**, 797–813.

MILLER M.W. & KUEHNERT C.C. 1972 *The Dynamics of Meristem Cell Populations*. Plenum Press, N. York, London.

MILLERD A., SPENCER D., DUDMAN W.F. & STILLER M. 1975 Growth of immature pea cotyledons in culture. Aust. J. Plant Physiol. **2**, 51–59.

MILO G.E. & SRIVASTAVA S.B.I. 1969a Effects of cytokinins on tobacco mosaic virus production in local lesion and systemic hosts. Virol. **38**, 26–31.

MILO G.E. & SRIVASTAVA S.B.I. 1969b Effect of cytokinins on tobacco mosaic virus production in tobacco pith tissue cultures. Virol. **39**, 621–623.

MINOCHA S.C. 1987 pH of the medium and the growth and metabolism of cells in culture. pp. 125–141 *in* Bonga and Durzan (eds.) 1987a (*q.v.*).

MINOCHA S.C. & HALPERIN W. 1974 Hormones and metabolites which control tracheid differentiation with or without concomitant effects on growth in cultured tuber tissue of *Helianthus tuberosus* L. Planta **116**, 319–331.

MINOCHA S.C. & NISSEN P. 1985a Uptake of abscisic acid in tuber slices of Jerusalem artichoke and potato. J. Plant Physiol. **120**, 313–320.

MINOCHA S.C. & NISSEN P. 1985b Uptake of 2,4-dichlorophenoxyacetic acid and indole acetic acid in tuber slices of Jerusalem artichoke and potato. J. Plant Physiol. **120**, 351–362.

MISHRA D. & KAR M. 1975 Nickel in plant growth and metabolism. Bot. Rev. **40**, 395–452.

MISRA P. & CHATURVEDI H.C. 1984 Micropropagation of *Rosmarinus officinalis* L. Plant Cell Tiss. Organ Cult. **3**, 163–168.

MISSON J.P., COUMANS M., GIOT-WIRGOT P. & GASPAR TH. 1982 Inductions de bourgeons adventifs sur bougeons de *Picea pungens* en culture *in vitro*. Z. Pflanzenphysiol. **107**, 161–167.

MITRA G.C., PRASAD R.N. & ROYCHOWDHURY A. 1976 Inorganic salts and differentiation of protocorms in seed-callus of an orchid and correlated changes in its free amino acid content. Ind. J. Exp. Biol. **14**, 350–351.

MIURA Y. & HIRATA K. 1990 Use of an organ culture of *Catharanthus roseus* to produce vincristine and vinblastine. U.S. Patent No. 4910138

MIURA Y. & TABATA M. 1986 Direct somatic embryogenesis from protoplasts of *Foeniculum vulgare*. Plant Cell Rep. **5**, 310–313.

MIX G. 1981 Kartoffelsorten aus dem Reagenzglas-Bedingungen zur Langzeitlagerung. Der Kartoffelbau **32**, 198–199.

MIYAGAWA H., FUJIOKA N., KOHDA H., YAMASAKI K., TANIGUCHI K. & TANAKA R. 1986 Studies on the tissue culture of *Stevia rebaudiana* and its components; II. Induction of shoot primordia. Planta Med. **52**, 321–323.

MIZUKAMI H., TOMITA K., OHASHI H. & HIRAOKA N. 1988 Anthocyanin production in callus cultures of roselli (*Hibiscus sabdariffa* L.). Plant Cell Rep. **7**, 553–556.

MOHAMMED G.H. & VIDAVER W.E. 1988 Root production and plantlet development in tissue-cultured conifers. Plant Cell Tiss. Organ Cult. **14**, 137–160.

MOHANTY B. & FLETCHER J.S. 1978 Influence of ammonium on the growth and development of suspension cultures of Paul's Scarlet rose. Physiol. Plant. **42**, 221–225.

MOHANTY B. & FLETCHER J.S. 1980 Ammonium influence on nitrogen assimilating enzymes and protein accumulation in suspension cultures of Paul's Scarlet rose. Physiol. Plant. **48**, 453–459.

MOHAPATRA D. & BAJAJ Y.P.S. 1988 Hybridization in *Brassica juncea* × *Brassica campestris* through ovary culture. Euphytica **37**, 83–88.

MOHEN D., SHINSHI H., FELIX G. & MEINS F. 1985 Hormonal regulation of β-1,3 glucanase messenger RNA levels in cultured tobacco tissues. The Embo Journal **4**, 1631–1635.

MOHR H. 1987 Regulation from without: Darkness and light. Ann. Bot. **60**, (Suppl. 4) 139–155.

MOK M.C. & MOK D.W. 1977 Genotypic responses to auxins in tissue culture of *Phaseolus*. Physiol. Plant. **40**, 261–264.

MOK M.C. & MOK D.W.S. 1979 Cytokinin independence in tissue cultures of *Phaseolus*: A genetic trait. In Vitro **15**, 190 (Abst. 105).

MOK M.C., CAPELLE S.C., KIRCHNER S.C., MOK D.W.S. & ARMSTRONG D.J. 1982b The effects of N-phenyl-N′-1,2,3-thiadiazol-5-ylurea (thidiazuron) on cytokinin autonomy and the metabolism of ^{14}C-N^6- (Δ^2 -isopentenyl) adenosine (^{14}C-6Ado) in callus cultures of *Phaseolus lunatus* L. In Vitro **18**, 275–276 (Abst. 4).

MOK M.C., GABELMAN W.H. & SKOOG F. 1976 Carotenoid synthesis in tissue cultures of *Daucus carota* L. J. Am. Soc. Hort. Sci. **101**, 442–449.

MOK M.C., MOK D.W.S., ARMSTRONG D.J., SHUDO K., ISOGAI Y. & OKAMOTO T. 1982a Cytokinin activity of N-phenyl-N′-1,2,3-thiadiazol-5-ylurea (thiadiazuron). Phytochem. **21**, 1509–1511.

MØLLER I.M. & PALMER J.M. 1981 The inhibition of exogenous NAD(P)H oxidation in plant mitochondria by chelators and mersalyl as a function of pH. Physiol. Plant. **53**, 413–420.

MOLNAR G., TETENYI P., DOBOS E. & BERNATH J. 1986 Process for the sterile micropropagation of plant material. U.S. Patent No. 4569914.

MOLNAR G.Y. 1987 A new patented method for mass propagation of shoot cultures. Acta Hort. **212**, 125–130.

MOLNAR S.J. 1988a High frequency of stable 5-methyl-DL-tryptophan resistance in *Brassica nigra* cell suspension cultures. Plant Cell Tiss. Organ Cult. **15**, 245–256.

MOLNAR S.J. 1988b Nutrient modifications for improved growth of *Brassica nigra* cell suspension cultures. Plant Cell Tiss. Organ Cult. **15**, 257–267.

MONCOUSIN C. 1982 Peroxidase as a tracer for rooting improvement and expressing rejuvenation during *in vitro* multiplication of *Cynara cardunculus scolymus* L. pp. 147–148 *in* Fujiwara A. (ed.) 1982 (*q.v.*).

MONCOUSIN Ch. & GASPAR Th. 1983 Peroxidase as a marker for rooting improvement of *Cynara scolymus* L. cultured *in vitro*. Biochem. Physiol. Pflanz. **178**, 263–271.

MONDAL H., MANDAL R.K. & BISWAS B.B. 1972 RNA polymerase from eukaryotic cells. Isolation and purification of enzymes and factors from chromatin of coconut nuclei. Eur. J. Biochem. **25**, 463–470.

MONETTE P.L. 1983 Influence of size of culture vessel on *in vitro* proliferation of grape in a liquid medium. Plant Cell Tiss. Organ Cult. **2**, 327–332.

MONETTE P.L. 1986a Micropropagation of kiwi fruit using non-axenic shoot tips. Plant Cell Tiss. Organ Cult. **6**, 73–82.

MONETTE P.L. 1986c Cold storage of kiwi fruit shoot tips *in vitro*. HortScience **21**, 1203–1205.

MONETTE P.L. 1987 Organogenesis and plantlet regeneration following *in vitro* cold storage of kiwi fruit shoot tip cultures. Scientia Hort. **31**, 101–106.

MONNIER M. 1976 Culture *in vitro* de l'embryon immature de *Capsella bursa-pastoris* Moench (L.). Rev. Cytol. Biol. Vég. **39**, 1–120.

MONNIER M. 1978 Culture of zygotic embryos. pp. 277–286 *in* Thorpe T. A. (ed.) 1978 (*q.v.*).

MONNIER M. 1990 Zygotic embryo culture. *in* Bhojwani S.S. (ed.) 1990 *Plant Tissue Culture: Applications and Limitations*. Elsevier, Amsterdam.

MONNIER M. & LEDDET C. 1978 Sur l'acquisition de la résistance au froid des embryons immatures de *Capsella bursa- pastoris*. Compt. Rend. Acad. Sci., Paris. **287D**, 615–618.

MONNIER M. & LEDDET C. 1980 Action du saccharose sur la résistance au gel des embryons immatures de capselle. Bull. Soc. Bot. France **127**, 71–77.

MONSION M. & DUNEZ J. 1971 Obtention de jeunes plantes de *Prunus mariana* à partir de boutures cultivées *in vitro*. Compt. Rend. Acad. Sci., Paris **272D**, 1861–1864.

MONTAGUE M.J., ENNS R.K., SIEGEL N.R. & JAWORSKI E.G. 1981a A comparison of 2,4-D metabolism in cultured soybean cells and in embryogenic carrot cells. Plant Physiol. **67**, 603–607.

MONTAGUE M.J., ENNS R.K., SIEGEL N.R. & JAWORSKI E.G. 1981b Inhibition of 2,4-D conjugation to amino acids by treatment of cultured soybean cells with cytokinins. Plant Physiol. **67**, (4) 701.

MONTEUUIS O., BON M.C. & BERTHON J.Y. 1987 Micropropagation aspects of *Sequoiadendron giganteum* juvenile and mature clones. Acta Hort. **212**, 489–497.

MOORE G.A. 1985 Factors affecting *in vitro* embryogenesis from undeveloped ovules of mature *Citrus* fruit. J. Am. Soc. Hort. Sci. **110**, 66–70.

MOORE G.M. 1985 Mechanisms of hormone action in plants. Comb. Proc. Int. Plant Prop. Soc. 1984 **34**, 79–90.

MOORE G.M., HALL R.G. & JAMES E.A. 1983 Pausteurization of growing media by microwave radiation. Comb. Proc. Int. Plant Prop. Soc., 1982 **32**, 45–55.

MOORE H.M. & HIRSCH A.M. 1981 DNA synthesis and mitosis in boron-deficient and control sunflower root tips. Plant Physiol. **67**, (Suppl.) 12 (Abst. 66).

MOORE R. & SMITH J.D. 1984 Growth, graviresponsiveness and abscisic acid content of *Zea mays* seedlings treated with fluridone. Planta **162**, 342–344.

MOREL G. 1946 Action de l'acid pantothénique sur la croissance de tissus d'Aubépine cultivés *in vitro*. Compt. Rend. Acad. Sci., Paris **223**, 166–168.

MOREL G. 1960 Producing virus-free *Cymbidium*. Am. Orchid Soc. Bull. **29**, 495–497.

MOREL G. 1964 Tissue culture — a new means of clonal propagation in orchids. Am. Orchid Soc. Bull. **33**, 473–478.

MOREL G. 1975 Meristem culture techniques for the long-term storage of cultivated plants. pp. 327–332 *in* Frankel & Hawkes (eds.) 1975 (*q.v.*).

MOREL G. & MARTIN C. 1952 Guérison de dahlias atteints d'une maladie à virus. Compt. Rend. Acad. Sci., Paris **235**, 1324–1325.

MOREL G. & MARTIN C. 1955 Curing potatoes infected with virus. C. R. hebd. Seance Acad. Agric. Fr. **41**, 472–473.

MOREL G. & MÜLLER J.-F. 1964 *In vitro* culture of the apical meristem of the potato. Compt. Rend. Acad. Sci., Paris **258**, 5250–5252.

MOREL G. & WETMORE R.H. 1951a Tissue culture of monocotyledons. Am. J. Bot. **38**, 138–140.

MOREL G., MARTIN C. & MÜLLER J.F. 1968 La guérison des pommes de terre atteintes de maladies à virus. Ann. Physiol. Veg. **10**, 113–139.

MORENO V.O.A., VAZQUEZ-DUHALT R. & NOLASCO H. 1990 Extracellular accumulation of high specific-activity peroxidase by cell suspension cultures of cowpea. Plant Cell Rep. **9**, 147–150.

MORI K., HOSOKAWA D. & YAMASHITA T. 1982 Regeneration of virus-free plants from protoplasts isolated from dark green areas of tobacco mosaic virus-infected tobacco leaves. pp. 803–804 *in* Fujiwara A. (ed.) 1982 (*q.v.*).

MORIGUCHI T. & YAMAKI S. 1989 Prolonged storage of grape nodal culture using a low concentration of ammonium nitrate. HortScience **24**, 372–373.

MORIGUCHI T., KOZAKI I., MATSUTA N. & YAMAKI S. 1988 Plant regeneration from grape callus stored under a combination of low temperature and silicone treatment. Plant Cell Tiss. Organ Cult. **15**, 67–71.

MORRIS G.J. 1980 Plant Cells. pp. 253–284 *in* Ashwood-Smith and Farrant (eds.) *Low Temperature Preservation in Medicine and Biology*. Pitman, London.

MORRIS S.C., GRAHAM D. & LEE T.H. 1979 Phytochrome control of chlorophyll synthesis in potato tubers. Plant Sci. Lett. **17**, 13–19.

MORRIS T.J. & DODDS J.A. 1979 Isolation and analysis of double-stranded RNA from virus infected plant and fungal tissue. Phytopath. **69**, 854–858.

MORRISON R.A. & EVANS D.A. 1988 Haploid plants from tissue culture: new plant varieties in a shortened time frame. Bio/Technology **6**, 684–690.

MOTT R.L. 1981 Trees. pp. 217–254 *in* Conger B.V. (ed.) 1981a (*q.v.*).

MOTT R.L., AMERSON H.V. & FRAMPTON L.J. 1986 Clonal propagation of *Pinus taeda* L. from juvenile and mature stock plants. p. 10 *in* Abstracts VI Intl. Cong. Plant Tissue & Cell Culture, Minneapolis, Minn.

MOTT R.L., CORDTS J.M. & LARSON A.M. 1985 Nitrogen and growth regulator effects on shoot and root growth of soybean *in vitro*. pp. 336–337 *in* Henke *et al.* (eds.) 1985 (*q.v.*).

MOTYKA V. & KAMINEK M. 1990 Regulation of cytokinin catabolism in tobacco callus cultures. pp. 492–497 *in* Nijkamp *et al.* (eds.) 1990 (*q.v.*).

MOYER B.G. & GUSTINE D.L. 1984 Regeneration of *Coronilla varia* L. (Crown-vetch) plants from callus culture. Plant Cell Tiss. Organ Cult. **3**, 143–148.

MSIKITA W., WILKINSON H.T. & SKIRVIN R.M. 1990a Resistance of *in vitro*-derived cucumber plants to *Pythium aphanidermatum*. HortScience **25**, 967–969.

MUDGE K.W., BORGMAN C.A., NEAL J.C. & WELLER H.A. 1986 Present limitations and future prospects for commercial micropropagation of small fruits. Comb. Proc. Int. Plant Prop. Soc. **36**, 538–543.

MUHITCH M.J. & FLETCHER J.S. 1984 Isolation and identification of the phenols of Paul's Scarlet rose stems and stem derived suspension cultures. Plant Physiol. **75**, 572–575.

MUHITCH M.J., EDWARDS L.A. & FLETCHER J.S. 1983 Influence of diamines and polyamines on the senescence of plant suspension cultures. Plant Cell Rep. **2**, 82–84.

MUKUND S., ROBACKER C. & SHEWFELT R. 1988 Callus and suspension cultures of tomato fruits for postharvest studies. HortScience **23**, 754.

MÜLLER A.J. & GRAFE R. 1978 Isolation and characterization of cell lines of *Nicotiana tabacum* lacking nitrate reductase. Mol. Gen. Genet. **161**, 67–76.

MÜLLER A.J. & MENDEL R.R. 1982 Nitrate reductase-deficient tobacco mutants and the regulation of nitrate assimilation. pp. 233–234 *in* Fujiwara (ed.) 1982 (*q.v.*).

MÜLLER J.F., MISSIONIER C. & CABOCHE M. 1983 Low density growth of cells derived from *Nicotiana* and *Petunia* protoplasts: Influence of the source of protoplasts and comparison of the growth- promoting activity of various auxins. Physiol. Plant. **57**, 35–41.

MULLIN R.H. & SCHLEGEL D.E. 1976 Cold maintenance of strawberry meristem explants. HortScience **11**, 100–101.

MULLIN R.H., SMITH S.H., FRAZIER N.W., SCHLEGEL D.E. & McCALL S.R. 1974 Meristem culture frees strawberries of mild yellow edge, pallidosis and mottle diseases. Phytopath. **64**, 1425–1429.

MULLINS K.V. 1987 Micropropagation of chestnut (*Castanea sativa* Mill.). Acta Hort. **212**, 525–530.

MULLINS M.G. 1980 Regulation of flowering in the grapevine (*Vitis vinifera* L.). pp. 323–330 *in* Skoog F. (ed.) 1980 (*q.v.*).

MULLINS M.G. 1982 Tissue culture and plant propagation: coming down to earth. Comb. Proc. Int. Plant Prop. Soc. 1981 **31**, 162–165.

MULLINS M.G. 1985 Regulation of adventitious root formation in microcuttings. Acta Hort. **166**, 53–61.

MULLINS M.G. & SRINIVASAN C. 1976 Somatic embryos and plantlets from an ancient clone of the grapevine (cv. Cabernet-Sauvignon) by apomixis *in vitro*. J. Exp. Bot. **27**, 1022–1030.

MULLINS M.G., NAIR Y. & SAMPET P. 1979 Rejuvenation *in vitro*: Induction of juvenile characters in an adult clone of *Vitis vinifera* L. Ann. Bot. **44**, 623–627.

MULLINS M.G., SRISKANDARAJAH S. & NOITON D. 1986 Enhanced capacity for adventitious root formation in apple microcuttings by conditioning of mother cuttings. Acta Hort. **179**, 873.

MURAKISHI H.H. & CARLSON P.S. 1979 Regeneration of virus-free *Petunia*, tobacco and *Brassica* plants from green islands of mosaic-infected leaves. In Vitro **15**, 192 (Abst. 114).

MURALIDHAR C.E. & MEHTA A.R. 1982 Clonal propagation of three ornamental plants through tissue culture methods. pp. 693–694 *in* Fujiwara (ed.) 1982 (*q.v.*).

MURASAKI K. & TSURUSHIMA H. 1988 Improvement on clonal propagation of *Cyclamen in vitro* by the use of etiolated petioles. Acta Hort. **226**, 721–724.

MURASHIGE T. 1961 Supression of shoot formation in cultured tobacco cells by gibberellic acid. Science **134**, 280.

MURASHIGE T. 1964 Analysis of the inhibition of organ formation in tobacco tissue culture by gibberellin. Physiol. Plant. **17**, 636–643.

MURASHIGE T. 1974 Plant propagation through tissue cultures. Ann. Rev. Plant Physiol. **25**, 135–166.

MURASHIGE T. 1978 Principles of rapid propagation. pp. 14–24 *in* Hughes K.W. *et al.* (eds.) 1978 (*q.v.*).

MURASHIGE T. & JONES J.B. 1974 Cell and organ culture methods in virus disease therapy. Acta Hort. **36**, 207–221.

MURASHIGE T. & NAKANO R. 1965 Morphogenetic behavior of tobacco tissue cultures and implication of plant senescence. Am. J. Bot. **52**, 819–827.

MURASHIGE T. & NAKANO R. 1966 Tissue culture as a potential tool in obtaining polyploid plants. J. Hered. **57**, 114–118.

MURASHIGE T. & NAKANO R. 1967 Chromosome complement as a determinant of the morphogenic potential of tobacco cells. Am. J. Bot. **54**, 963–970.

MURASHIGE T. & NAKANO R.T. 1968 The light requirement for shoot initiation in tobacco callus culture. Am. J. Bot. **55**, 710 (Abst.).

MURASHIGE T. & SKOOG F. 1962 A revised medium for rapid growth and bio-assays with tobacco tissue cultures. Physiol. Plant. **15**, 473–497.

MURASHIGE T. & TUCKER D.P.H. 1969 Growth factor requirements of citrus tissue culture. pp. 1155–1161 *in* Chapman H. D. (ed.) Proc. 1st Int. Citrus Symp. Vol. 3, Univ. Calif., Riverside Publication.

MURASHIGE T., BITTERS W.P., RANGAN T.S., ROISTACHER C.N. & HOLLIDAY B.P. 1972a A technique of shoot apex grafting and its utilization towards recovering virus-free *Citrus* clones. HortScience **7**, 118–119.

MURASHIGE T., SERPA M. & JONES J.B. 1974 Clonal multiplication of *Gerbera* through tissue culture. HortScience **9**, 175–180.

MURASHIGE T., SHABDE M.N., HASEGAWA P.M., TAKATORI F.H. & JONES J.B. 1972b Propagation of asparagus through shoot apex culture. I. Nutrient media for formation of plantlets. J. Am. Soc. Hort. Sci. **97**, 158–161.

MURATA M. & ORTON T.J. 1983 Chromosome structural changes in cultured celery cells. In Vitro **19**, 83–89.

MURR D.P. & YANG S.F. 1975 Inhibition of *in vivo* conversion of methionine to ethylene by L-canaline and 2,4-dinitrophenol. Plant Physiol. **55**, 79–82.

MURRAY B.E., HANDYSIDE R.J. & KELLER W.A. 1977 *In vitro* regeneration of shoots on stem explants of haploid and diploid flax (*Linum usitatissimum*). Can. J. Genet. Cytol. **19**, 177–186.

MUSGRAVE M.E. & SIEDOW J.N. 1985 A relationship between plant responses to cytokinins and cyanide resistant respiration. Physiol. Plant. **64**, 161–166.

MUTAFTSCHIEV S., COUSSON A. & TRAN THANH VAN K. 1987 Modulation of cell growth and differentiation by pH and oligosaccharides. pp. 29–42 *in* Jackson *et al.* (eds.) 1987a (*q.v.*).

MYERSON J. & KRUL W.R. 1982 Stability of growth and morphological changes in *Gynura aurantiaca* plants regenerated from callus. HortScience **17**, 80–82.

NABORS M.W., HEYSER J.W., DYKES T.A. & DE MOTT K.J. 1983 Long-duration, high-frequency plant regeneration from cereal tissue cultures. Planta **157**, 385–391.

NADGAUDA R.S., PARASHARAMI V.A. & MASCARENHAS A.F. 1990 Precocious flowering and seeding behaviour in tissue cultured bamboos. Nature **344**, 335–336.

NAG K.K. & JOHRI B.M. 1969 Organogenesis and chromosomal constitution in embryo callus of *Nuytsia floribunda*. Phytomorph. **19**, 405–408.

NAG K.K. & JOHRI B.M. 1976 Experimental morphogenesis of the embryo of *Dendrophthoe, Taxillus* and *Nuytsia*. Bot. Gaz. **137**, 378–390.

NAG K.K. & STREET H.E. 1973 Carrot embryogenesis from frozen cultured cells. Nature **245**, 270–272.

NAG K.K. & STREET H.E. 1975a Freeze preservation of cultured plant cells. I. The pretreatment phase. Physiol. Plant. **34**, 254–260.

NAG K.K. & STREET H.E. 1975b Freeze preservation of cultured plant cells. II. The freezing and thawing phases. Physiol. Plant. **34**, 361–365.

NAGATA T. & TAKEBE I. 1970 Cell wall regeneration and cell division in isolated tobacco mesophyll protoplasts. Planta **92**, 301–308.

NAGATA T. & TAKEBE I. 1971 Plating of isolated tobacco mesophyll protoplasts on agar medium. Planta **99**, 12–20.

NAGL W. 1974 The *Phaseolus* suspensor and its polytene chromosomes. Z. Pflanzenphysiol. **73**, 1–44.

NAGMANI R. & BONGA J.M. 1985 Embryogenesis in subcultured callus of *Larix decidua*. Can. J. For. Res. **15**, 1088–1091.

NAGMANI R., BECWAR M.R. & WANN S.R. 1987 Single-cell origin and development of somatic embryos in *Picea abies* (L.) Karst. (Norway spruce) and *P. glauca* (Moench) Voss (White spruce). Plant Cell Rep. **6**, 157–159.

NAIR S., GUPTA P.K. & MASCARENHAS A.F. 1983 Haploid plants from *in vitro* anther culture of *Annona squamosa* Linn. Plant Cell Rep. **2**, 198–200.

NAIRN B.J. 1988 Significance of gelling agents in a production tissue culture laboratory. Comb. Proc. Int. Plant Prop. Soc. 1987 **37**, 200–205.

NAKAGAWA K., MIURA Y., FUKUI H. & TABATA M. 1982 Clonal propagation of medicinal plants through the induction of somatic embryogenesis from the cultured cells. pp. 701–702 *in* Fujiwara (ed.) 1982 (*q.v.*).

NAKAMURA C., NAKATA M., SHIOJI M. & ONO H. 1985 2,4-D resistance in a tobacco cell culture variant: cross-resistance to auxins and uptake, efflux and metabolism of 2,4-D. Plant Cell Physiol. **26**, 271–280.

NAMERA A., KOYAMA A., FUJIOKA N., YAMAZAKI Y. & KOHDA H. 1987 Formation of stigma-like structures and pigments in cultured tissue of *Crocus sativus* (2). Shoyakugaku Zasshi **41**, 260–262.

NANDA K.K., ANAND V.K. & CHIBBAR R.N. 1972 The promotive effect of gibberellic acid on the production of adventitious roots on stem cuttings of *Ipomoea fistulata*. Planta **105**, 360–363.

NANDA K.K., PUROHIT A.N. & BALA A. 1967 Effect of photoperiod, auxins and gibberellic acid on rooting of stem cuttings of *Bryophyllum tubiflorum*. Physiol. Plant. **20**, 1096–1102.

NARASIMHULU S.B. & CHOPRA V.L. 1988 Species specific shoot regeneration response of cotyledonary explants of *Brassicas*. Plant Cell Rep. **7**, 104–106.

NARASIMHULU S.B., PRAKASH S. & CHOPRA V.L. 1988 Comparative shoot regeneration responses of diploid brassicas and their synthetic amphidiploid products. Plant Cell Rep. **7**, 525–527.

NARAYANASWAMI S. & LARUE C.D. 1955 The morphogenic effects of various physical factors on the gemmae of *Lunaria*. Phytomorph. **5**, 99–109.

NARAYANASWAMY S. 1977 Regeneration of plants from tissue cultures. pp. 179–206 *in* Reinert & Bajaj (eds.) 1977 (*q.v.*).

NASIR F.R. & MILES N.W. 1981 Histological origin of EMLA 26 apple shoots generated during micro propagation. HortScience **16**, 417 (Abst. 131).

NATO A., LAVERGNE D., FLIPO V. & HOARAU J. 1990 Are two localization sites of nitrate reductase responsible for the differential expression in tobacco cells during the growth cycle? pp. 349–354 *in* Nijkamp *et al.* (eds.) 1990 (*q.v.*).

NAVARRO L. 1984 *Citrus* tissue culture. pp. 113–154 in *Micropropagation of Selected Root Crops, Palms, Citrus and Ornamental Species.* FAO Plant Production and Protection Paper 59, FAO, Rome. ISBN 92-5-102157-0.

NAVARRO L. 1988 Application of shoot-tip grafting *in vitro* to woody species. Acta Hort. **227**, 43–55.

NAVARRO L. & JUAREZ J. 1977 Tissue culture techniques used in Spain to recover virus-free citrus plants. Acta Hort. **78**, 425–435.

NAVARRO L., ORTIZ J.M. & JUAREZ J. 1985 Aberrant *Citrus* plants obtained by somatic embryogenesis of nucelli cultured *in vitro*. HortScience **20**, 214–215.

NAVARRO L., ROISTACHER C.N. & MURASHIGE T. 1975 Improvement of shoot-tip grafting *in vitro* for virus-free citrus. J. Am. Soc. Hort. Sci. **100**, 471–479.

NEAL C.A. & TOPOLESKI L.D. 1983 Effects of the basal medium on growth of immature tomato embryos *in vitro*. J. Am. Soc. Hort. Sci. **108**, 434–438.

NEALES T.F. 1959 The boron requirement of flax roots grown in sterile culture. J. Exp. Bot. **10**, 426.

NEALES T.F. 1964 A comparison of the boron requirements of intact tomato plants and excised tomato roots grown in sterile culture. J. Exp. Bot. **15**, 647–653.

NEGRUTIU I. & JACOBS M. 1978a Factors which enhance *in vitro* morphogenesis of *Arabidopsis thaliana*. Z. Pflanzenphysiol. **90**, 423–430.

NEGRUTIU I., JACOBS M. & CACHITA D. 1978a Some factors controlling *in vitro* morphogenesis of *Arabidopsis thaliana*. Z. Pflanzenphysiol. **86**, 113–124.

NEGRUTIU I., JACOBS M. & GASPAR Th. 1979 Leaf formation and peroxidases from *Arabidopsis* callus. Z. Pflanzenphysiol. **91**, 119–126.

NEHRA N.S. & STUSHNOFF C. 1988 Regeneration of plants from immature leaf-derived callus of strawberry. HortScience **23**, p. 756.

NEHRA N.S., STUSHNOFF C. & KARTHA K.K. 1988 Direct shoot regeneration from leaf discs in strawberry. HortScience **23**, 808.

NEILL S.J. & HORGAN R. 1984 Biosynthesis of abscisic acid. pp. 43–70 *in* Crozier and Hillman (eds.) 1984 (*q.v.*).

NELSON C., STRICKLAND S., DAVIS R. & REDENBAUGH K. 1988 Method for the preparation of hydrated, pregerminated seeds in gel capsules. U.S. Patent No. 4780987

NEMETH G. 1979 Benzyladenine-stimulated rooting in fruit-tree rootstocks cultured *in vitro*. Z. Pflanzenphysiol. **95**, 389–396.

NEMETH G. 1981 Adventitious root induction by substituted 2-chloro-3-phenyl-propionitriles in apple rootstocks cultured *in vitro*. Scientia Hort. **14**, 253–259.

NERNST W. 1904 Theorie der Reaktionsgeschwindigkeit in heterogenen Systemen. Phys. Chem. **47**, 52–55.

NESIUS K.K. & FLETCHER J.S. 1973 Carbon dioxide and pH requirement of non-photosynthetic tissue culture cells. Physiol. Plant. **28**, 259–263.

NESIUS K.K. & FLETCHER J.S. 1975 Contribution of non-autotrophic carbondioxide to protein synthesis in suspension cultures of Paul's Scarlet rose. Plant Physiol. **55**, 643–645.

NESTEL B. & COCK J. 1976 Cassava: The Development of an International Research Network. Int. Dev. Res. Centre, Ottawa.

NEUMANN J. 1960 The nature of the growth-promoting action of coumarin. Physiol. Plant. **13**, 328–341.

NEUMANN K.H. 1968 Untersuchungen uber Beziehungen zwischen Zellteilung und Morphogenese bei Gewebekulturen von *Daucus carota*. II. Respiration von Gewebekulturen in Abhangigkeit von der Zellteilungsintensitat. Physiol. Plant. **21**, 519–524.

NEWBURY H.J. 1986 Multiplication of *Antirrhinum majus* L. by shoot-tip culture. Plant Cell Tiss. Organ Cult. **7**, 39–42.

NEWCOMB W. & WETHERELL D.F. 1970 The effects of 2,4,6-trichlorophenoxyacetic acid on embryogenesis in wild carrot tissue cultures. Bot. Gaz. **131**, 242–245.

NEWHART S.R., ROMAINE C.P. & CRAIG R. 1980 A rapid method for virus-indexing the florists' geranium. HortScience **15**, 811–813.

NG S.Y.C. 1988 *In vitro* tuberization in white yam (*Dioscorea rotundata* Poir.). Plant Cell Tiss. Organ Cult. **14**, 121–128.

NICHOL J.W., SLADE D., VISS P. & STUARD D.A. 1991 Effect of organic acid pretreatment on the regeneration and development (conversion) of whole plants from callus cultures of alfalfa, *Medicago sativa* L. Plant Sci. **79**, 181–192.

NICKELL L.G. 1952 Stimulation of plant growth by antibiotics. Proc. Soc. Exp. Biol. & Med. **80**, 615–617.

NICKELL L.G. 1977 Crop improvement in sugarcane: studies using *in vitro* methods. Crop Sci. **17**, 717–719.

NICKELL L.G. & BURKHOLDER P.R. 1950 Atypical growth of plants. II. Growth *in vitro* of virus tumors of *Rumex* in relation to temperature, pH and various sources of nitrogen, carbon and sulfur. Am. J. Bot. **37**, 538–547.

NICKELL L.G. & MARETZKI A. 1969 Growth of suspension cultures of sugarcane cells in chemically defined media. Physiol. Plant. **22**, 117–125.

NICKERSON N.L. 1978 *In vitro* shoot formation in lowbush Blueberry seedling explants. HortScience **13**, 698.

NIEDERWIESER J.G. & VCELAR B.M. 1990 Regeneration of *Lachenalia* species from leaf explants. HortScience **25**, 684–687.

NIIMI Y. & ONOZAWA T. 1979 *In vitro* bulblet formation from leaf segments of lilies, especially *Lilium rubellum*. Scientia Hort. **11**, 379–390.

NIJKAMP H.J.J., VAN DER PLAS L.H.W. & VAN AARTRIJK (eds.) 1990 *Progress in Plant Cellular and Molecular Biology*. Proc. VIIth Int. Cong. on Plant Tissue & Cell Culture. Amsterdam, The Netherlands. 24–29 June 1990. Kluwer Academic Publishers, Dortrecht, Netherlands.

NISHIUCHI Y. 1979 Studies on the vegetative propagation of tulip. II. Formation and development of adventitious buds on excised scales cultured *in vitro*. J. Jap. Soc. Hort. Sci. **48**, 99–105.

NISSEN S.J. & SUTTER E.G. 1988 Stability of IAA and IBA in nutrient medium after autoclaving and after storage under various environmental conditions. HortScience **23**, 758.

NISSEN S.J. & SUTTER E.G. 1990 Stability of IAA and IBA in nutrient medium to several tissue culture procedures. HortScience **25**, 800–802.

NITSCH C. 1968 Induction *in vitro* de la floraison chez une plante de jours courts: *Plumbago indica* L. Ann. Sci. Nat. Bot. Paris, 12th Series **9**, 1–91.

NITSCH C. 1977 Culture of isolated microspores. pp. 268–278 *in* Reinert & Bajaj (eds.) 1977 (*q.v.*).

NITSCH C. 1981 Production of isogenic lines: basic technical aspects of androgenesis. pp. 241–252 *in* Thorpe T.A. (ed.) 1981 (*q.v.*).

NITSCH C. 1983 Progress in anther and pollen culture techniques. pp. 1–10 *in* Anon (1983) q.v.

NITSCH J.P. 1951 Growth and development *in vitro* of excised ovaries. Am. J. Bot. **38**, 566–577.

NITSCH J.P. 1963 The *in vitro* culture of flowers and fruits. pp. 198–214 *in* Maheshwari & Ranga Swamy (eds.) 1963 (*q.v.*).

NITSCH J.P. 1969 Experimental androgenesis in *Nicotiana*. Phytomorph. **19**, 389–404.

NITSCH J.P. & BUI DANG HA D. 1967 Effet de l'ordre d'application de l'acide indolyl-3-acetique et de la kinetine sur la division cellulaire. Compt. Rend. Acad. Sci. Paris **264D**, 288–291.

NITSCH J.P. & NITSCH C. 1956 Auxin-dependent growth of excised *Helianthus* tissues. Am. J. Bot. **43**, 839–851.

NITSCH J.P. & NITSCH C. 1965 Néoformation de fleurs *in vitro* chez une espèce de jours courts: *Plumbaga indica* L. Ann. Phys. Veg. **7**, 251–256.

NITSCH J.P. & NITSCH C. 1969 Haploid plants from pollen grains. Science **163**, 85–87.

NITSCH J.P., ASHIRA T., ROSSINI L.M.E. & NITSCH C. 1970 Bases physiologique de la production de chair de pomme et de poire *in vitro*. Bull. Soc. Bot. Fr. **117**, 479–492.

NITSCH J.P., NITSCH C., ROSSINI L.M.E. & BUI DANG HA D. 1967 The role of adenine in bud differentiation. Phytomorph. **17**, 446–453.

NITZSCHE W. 1978 Conservation of viability in dried callus. Z. Pflanzenphysiol. **87**, 469–472.

NITZSCHE W. 1980 One year storage of dried carrot callus. Z. Pflanzenphysiol. **100**, 269–272.

NITZSCHE W. 1983 Germplasm preservation. pp. 782–805 *in* Evans *et al.* (eds.) 1983 (*q.v.*).

NITZSCHE W. & WENZEL G. 1977 *Haploids in Plant Breeding*. Suppl. 8 to Z. Pflanzenzucht. Parey. Berlin and Hamburg.

NOBÉCOURT P. 1937 Culture en serie des tissus végétaux sur milieux artificial. Compt. Rend. Acad. Sci. Paris **205**, 521–523.

NOBUHARU G. 1980 Organogenetic capacity and its heritability. Arabidopsis Inf. Serv. **0** (17), 49–58 (BA **71**, 6607).

NOH E.W., MINOCHA S.C. & RIEMENSCHNEIDER D.E. 1988 Adventitious shoot formation from embryonic explants of red pine (*Pinus resinosa*). Physiol. Plant. **74**, 119–124.

NOMA M., HUBER J., ERNST D. & PHARIS R. 1982 Quantitation of gibberellins and the metabolism of [^{3}H] gibberellin A$_1$ during somatic embryogenesis in carrot and aniseed cell cultures. Planta **155**, 369–376.

NOMURA K. & KOMAMINE A. 1985 Identification and isolation of single cells that produce somatic embryos at a high frequency in a carrot suspension culture. Plant Physiol. **79**, 988–991.

NOMURA K. & KOMAMINE A. 1986a Polarized DNA synthesis and cell division in cell clusters during somatic embryogenesis from single carrot cells. New Phytol. **104**, 25–32.

NOMURA K. & KOMAMINE A. 1986b Embryogenesis from microinjected single cells in a carrot cell suspension culture. Plant Science **44**, 53–58.

NORIZAKU T., TANIMOTO S. & HARADA H. 1985 Effects of wounding on adventitous bud formation in *Torenia fournieri* stem segments cultured *in vitro*. J Exp. Bot. **36**, 841–847.

NORRIS D. 1953 Reconstitution of virus X–saturated potato varieties with malachite green. Nature **172**, 816.

NORRIS R.E. & SMITH R.H. 1981 Regeneration of variegated African violet (*Saintpaulia ionantha* Wendl.) leaf chimeras in culture. Plant Physiol. **67**, 117 (Abst. 661).

NORRIS R.F. & BUKOVAK M.J. 1972 Effect of pH on penetration of naphthaleneacetic acid and naphtheleneacetamide through isolated pea leaf cuticle. Plant Physiol. **49**, 615–618.

NORSTOG K. 1961 The growth and differentiation of cultured barley embryos. Am. J. Bot. **48**, 876–884.

NORSTOG K. 1965a Development of cultured barley embryos. I. Growth of 0.1–0.4 mm embryos. Am. J. Bot. **52**, 538–546.

NORSTOG K. 1965b Induction of apogamy in megagametophytes of *Zamia integrifolia*. Am. J. Bot. **52**, 993–999.

NORSTOG K. 1967 Studies on the survival of very small barley embryos in culture. Bull. Torrey Bot. Club **94**, 223–229.

NORSTOG K. 1970 Induction of embryo-like structures in cultured barley embryos. Dev. Biol. **23**, 665–670.

NORSTOG K. 1973 New synthetic medium for the culture of premature barley embryos. In Vitro **8**, 307–308.

NORSTOG K. 1979 Embryo culture as a tool in the study of comparative and developmental morphology. pp. 179–202 *in* Sharp *et al.* (eds.) 1979 (*q.v.*).

NORSTOG K. & KLEIN R.M. 1972 Development of cultured barley embryos. II. Precocious germination and dormancy. Can. J. Bot. **50**, 1887–1894.

NORSTOG K. & RHAMSTINE E. 1967 Isolation and culture of haploid and diploid Cycad tissues. Phytomorph. **17**, 374–381.

NORSTOG K. & SMITH J. 1963 Culture of small barley embryos on defined media. Science **142**, 1655–1656.

NORTHCOTE D.H. 1979 Biochemical mechanisms involved in plant morphogenesis. pp. 11–20 *in* George E.F. (ed.) 1979 (*q.v.*).

NORTON C.R. 1988 Metabolic and non-metabolic gas treatments to induce shoot proliferation in woody ornamental plants *in vitro*. Acta Hort. **227**, 302–304.

NORTON C.R. & NORTON M.E. 1986 Light quality and shoot proliferation in micropropagated *Prunus*, *Spiraea* and *Rhododendron*. p. 434 *in* Somers *et al.* (eds.) 1986 (*q.v.*).

NORTON C.R. & NORTON M.E. 1988b Induced dormancy of *Spiraea* cultured *in vitro* by low temperature and anoxic stresses. HortScience **23**, 760.

NORTON C.R. & NORTON M.E. 1988c Manipulation of differentiation in *Spiraea in vitro*. Acta Hort. **226**, 191–194.

NORTON C.R., NORTON M.E., HERRINGTON T. & PHILLIPS D. 1988a Light quality and light pipe in the micropropagation of woody ornamental plants. Acta Hort. **226**, 413–416.

NORTON J.P. & BOLL W.G. 1954 Callus and shoot formation from tomato roots *in vitro*. Science **119**, 220–221.

NORTON M.E. & NORTON C.R. 1988a A comparative study of *in* and *ex vitro* rhizogenesis on micropropagated shoots in the plant families Rosaceae and Ericaceae. HortScience **23**, 739.

NORTON M.E. & NORTON C.R. 1988d Stock plant conditioning, the generation of propagative material and propagule selection in *Spiraea*. Acta Hort. **226**, 369–374.

NOVÁK F.J. 1980 a Chromosomal instabilities in callus tissue from haploid barley (*Hordeum vulgare* L.). Biol. Plant. **22**, 303–305.

NOVÁK F.J. & VYSKOT B. 1975 Karyology of callus cultures from *Nicotiana tabacum* L. haploids. Z. Pflanzenchtg. **75**, 62–70.

NOVÁK F.J., ZADINA J., HORACKOVA V. & MASKOVA I. 1980 The effect of growth regulators on meristem tip development and *in vitro* multiplication of *Solanum tuberosum* L. plants. Potato Res. **23**, 155–160.

NOVÁK P.J. 1980b Phenotype and cytological status of plants regenerated from callus cultures of *Allium sativum* L. Z. Pflanzenzucht. **84**, 250–260.

NOWACKI J. & BANDURSKI R.S. 1980 *Myo*-inositol esters of indole-3-acetic acid as seed auxin precursors of *Zea mays* L. Plant Physiol. **65**, 422–427.

NOZERAN R. 1978a Multiple growth correlations. pp. 423–443 *in* Tomlinson & Zimmerman (eds.). *Tropical Trees as Living Systems*. Cambridge Univ. Press.

NOZERAN R., BANCILHON-ROSSIGNOL L. & GRENAN S. 1977 Nouvelles possibilités d'obtention et de multiplication rapide de clones de pommes de terre (*Solanum tuberosum* L.). Compt. Rend. Acad. Sci. Paris **285D**, 37–40.

NUTI RONCHI V., CALIGO M.A., NOZZOLINI M. & LUCCARINI G. 1984 Stimulation of carrot somatic embryogenesis by proline and serine. Plant Cell Rep. **3**, 210–214.

NUTI RONCHI V., NOZZOLINI M. & AVANZI L. 1981 Chromosomal variation on plants regenerated from two *Nicotiana* spp. Protoplasma **109**, 433–444.

NWANKWO B.A. & KRIKORIAN A.D. 1983 Morphogenetic potential of embryo- and seedling-derived callus of *Elaeis guineensis* Jacq. var. *pisifera* Becc. Ann. Bot. **51**, 65–76.

NYMAN L.P. & ARDITTI J. 1984 Effects of 2,3,5-triodobenzoic acid on plantlet formation from cultured tissues of Taro, *Colocasia esculenta* L. Schott. (Araceae). Ann. Bot. **54**, 459–466.

O'NEILL G. 1981 *Somaclones — A New Frontier in Plant Breeding.* Rural Research CSIRO Australia June 1981 4–7.

O'RÍORDÁIN F. 1988 Final discussion and conclusions. Acta Hort. **225**, 223–225.

O'RÍORDÁIN F. & GRANT J. 1984 A computer program that allows easy comparison of the constituents of different plant tissue culture media. Laboratory Practice **33**, 114–115.

OBATA-SASAMOTO H., BEAUDOIN-EAGAN L. & THORPE T.A. 1984 C-metabolism during callus induction in tobacco. Plant Cell Tiss. Organ Cult. **3**, 291–299.

OCHATT S.J. & CASO O.H. 1982 Red-leaf peach micropropagation. Plant Physiol. **69**, (Suppl.) 34 (Abst. 188).

OCHATT S.J. & CASO O.H. 1986 Shoot regeneration from leaf mesophyll protoplasts of wild pear (*Pyrus communis* var. *pyraster* L.). J. Plant Physiol. **122**, 243–249.

OCHATT S.J. & POWER J.B. 1988a Rhizogenesis in callus from conference pear (*Pyrus communis* L.) protoplasts. Plant Cell Tiss. Organ Cult. **13**, 159–164.

OCHATT S.J. & POWER J.B. 1988b Plant regeneration from mesophyll protoplasts of Williams' Bon Chretien (syn. Bartlett) pear (*Pyrus communis* L.). Plant Cell Rep. **7**, 587–589.

OCHATT S.J. & POWER J.B. 1988c An alternative approach to plant regeneration from protoplasts of sour cherry (*Prunus cerasus* L.). Plant Science **56**, 75–79.

ODHNOFF C. 1957 Boron deficiency and growth. Physiol. Plant. **10**, 984–1000.

OERTLI J.J. & GRGUREVIC E. 1974 Effect of pH on the absorption of boron by excised embryos. Agron. J. **67**, 278–280.

OERTLI J.J. & GRGUREVIC E. 1975 Effect of pH on the absorption of boron by excised embryos. Agron. J. **67**, 278–280.

OGIHARA Y. 1982 Characterization of chromosomal changes of calluses induced by callus cloning and para-fluorophenylalanine (PFP) treatment and regenerates from them. pp. 439–440 *in* Fujiwara (ed.) 1982 (*q.v.*).

OGIHARA Y. & TSUNEWAKI K. 1979 Tissue culture in *Haworthia setata* 3. Occurrence of callus variants during sub cultures and its mechanism. Jap. J. Genet. **54**, 271–294.

OGLESBY R.P. 1978 Tissue cultures of ornamentals and flowers: Problems and perspectives. pp. 59–61 *in* Hughes *et al.* (eds.) 1978 (*q.v.*).

OGLESBY R.P. & STRODE R.E. 1978 Commercial tissue culturing at Oglesby Nursery. Comb. Proc. Int. Plant Prop. Soc. **28**, 341–344.

OGURA H. 1976 The cytological chimeras in original regenerates from tobacco tissues and their offspring. Jap. J. Genet. **51**, 161–174.

OGURA H. 1982 Studies on the genetic instability of cultured tissues and the regenerated plants — effects of auxins and cytokinins on mitosis of *Vicia faba* cells. pp. 433–434 *in* Fujiwara A. (ed.) 1982 (*q.v.*).

OGURA H. & TSUJI S. 1977 Differential responses of *Nicotiana tabacum* L. and its putative progenitors to de- and re-differentiation. Z. Pflanzenphysiol. **83**, 419–426.

OHIRA K., OJIMA K. & FUJIWARA A. 1973 Studies on the nutrition of rice cell culture. I. A simple defined medium for rapid growth in suspension culture. Plant & Cell Physiol. **14**, 1113–1121.

OHKI S., BIGOT C. & MOUSSEAU J. 1978 Analysis of shoot-forming capacity *in vitro* in two lines of tomato (*Lycopersicon esculentum* Mill.) and their hybrids. Plant Cell Physiol. **19**, 27–42.

OHYAMA K. & OKA S. 1982 Multiple shoot formation from Mulberry (*Morus alba* L.) hypocotyls by N-(2-chloro-4-pyridyl)-N'-phenylurea. pp. 149–150 *in* Fujiwara A. (ed.) 1982 (*q.v.*).

OJIMA K. & OHIRA K. 1980 The exudation and characterization of iron-solubilizing compounds in a rice cell suspension culture. Plant Cell Physiol. **21**, 1151–1161.

OKA S. & OHYAMA K. 1981 In vitro initiation of adventitious buds and modification by high concentrations of benzyladenine in leaf tissues of mulberry (*Morus alba*). Can. J. Bot. **59**, 68–74.

OKA S. & OHYAMA K. 1982 Sugar utilization in mulberry (Morus alba L.) bud culture. pp. 67–68 *in* Fujiwara A. (ed.) 1982 (*q.v.*).

OKAMOTO T., SHUDO K., TAKAHASHI S., YATSUNAMI T., ISOGAI Y. & YAMADA K. 1978 Shoot formation of tobacco callus by varous cytokinin-active ureas and pyrimidines. Chem. Pharm. Bull. **26**, 3250–3252.

OKI G. 1978 Setting up a tissue culture system. Comb. Proc. Int. Plant Prop. Soc. **28**, 344–348.

OKI L.R. 1981 The modification of research procedures for commercial propagation of Boston ferns. Env. Exp. Bot. **21**, 397–400.

OKKELS F.T. & PEDERSEN M.G. 1988 The toxicity to plant tissue and to *Agrobacterium tumefaciens* of some antibiotics. Acta Hort. **225**, 199–207.

OLESEN P.O. 1978 On cyclophysis and topophysis. Silvae Genet. **27**, 173–178.

OLIPHANT J.L. 1988 Micropropagation of *Lavendula* species. Comb. Proc. Int. Plant Prop. Soc. 1987 **37**, 158–160.

OONO K. 1978 Test tube breeding of rice and tissue culture. Trop. Agric. Res. Ser. **11**, 109–124.

OONO K. 1982 Characteristics of mutation in cultured rice tissue. pp. 409–410 *in* Fujiwara (ed.) 1982 (*q.v.*).

ORCHARD J.E., COLLIN H.A. & HARDWICK K. 1979 Culture of shoot apices of *Theobroma cacao*. Physiol. Plant. **47**, 207–210.

ORCZYK W. & MALEPSZY S. 1985 *In vitro* culture of *Cucumis sativus* L. V. Stabilizing effect of glycine on leaf protoplasts. Plant Cell Rep. **4**, 269–273.

ORSHINSKY B.R., SWANSON E.B. & TOMES D.T. 1983 Enhanced shoot regeneration from homogenized callus cultures of birdsfoot trefoil (*Lotus corniculatus* L.) Plant Cell Tiss. Organ Cult. **2**, 341–347.

ORTON T.J. 1980 Chromosome variability in tissue cultures and regenerated plants of *Hordeum*. Theor. Appl. Genet. **56**, 101–112.

ORTON T.J. 1985 Genetic instability during embryogenic cloning of celery. Plant Cell Tiss. Organ Cult. **4**, 159–169.

OSBORNE R. & VAN STADEN J. 1987 *In vitro* regeneration of *Stangeria eriopus*. HortScience **22**, 1326.

OSHIMA N. & LIVINGSTON C.H. 1961 The effects of antiviral chemicals on potato virus X-1. Am. Potato J. **38**, 294–299.

OSHMARINA V.I., SHEVYAKOVA N.I. & SHAMINA Z.B. 1982 Dynamics of free amino acids and amides in *Nicotiana sylvestris* cell cultures at different concentrations of putrescine in the medium. Sov. Plant Physiol. **29**, 477–481.

OSIFO E.O. 1988 Somatic embryogenesis in *Dioscorea*. J. Plant Physiol. **133**, 378–380.

OSIFO E.O., WEBB J.K. & HENSHAW G.C. 1989a Variation amongst callus-derived potato plants, *Solanum brevidens*. J. Plant Physiol. **134**, 1–4.

OSPINA H.M. (ed.) 1974 Proc. World Orchid Conf. 7. Medellin, Columbia.

OSWALD T.H., NICHOLSON R.L. & BAUMAN L.F. 1977a Cell suspension and callus culture from somatic tissue of maize. Physiol. Plant. **41**, 45–50.

OSWALD T.H., SMITH A.E. & PHILLIPS D.V. 1977b Herbicide tolerance developed in cell suspension cultures of perennial white clover. Can. J. Bot. **55**, 1351–1358.

OSWALD T.H., SMITH A.E. & PHILLIPS D.V. 1977c Callus and plantlet regeneration from cell cultures of Ladino clover and soybean. Physiol. Plant. **39**, 129–134.

OWEN H.R. & MILLER A.R. 1992 An examination and correction of plant tissue culture basal medium formulations. Plant Cell Tiss. Organ Cult. **28**, 147–150.

OWEN H.R., WENGERD D. & MILLER A.R. 1991 Culture medium pH influenced by basal medium, carbohydrate source, gelling agent, activated charcoal, and medium storage method. Plant Cell Rep. **10**, 583–586.

OWEN J.H., LAYBOURN-PARRY J.E.M. & WELLBURN A.R. 1987 Influences of light quality, growth regulators and inhibitors of protein synthesis on respiration of protoplasts from meristematic cells in barley seedlings. Ann. Bot. **59**, 99–105.

OWENS L.D. 1979a Kanamycin stimulates shoot differentiation from tobacco tissues — protoplast transformation studies. Plant Physiol. **63**, 683–686.

OWENS L.D. 1979b Kanamycin promotes morphogenesis of plant tissues. Plant Sci. Lett. **16**, 225–230.

OZANNE P.G. 1958 Chlorine deficiency in soils. Nature **182**, 1172–1173.

OZANNE P.G., WOOLLEY J.T. & BROYER T.C. 1957 Chlorine and bromine in the nutrition of higher plants. Austr. J. Biol. Sci. **10**, 66–79.

OZIAS-AKINS P. & VASIL I.K. 1982 Plant regeneration from cultured immature embryos and inflorescences of *Triticum aestivum* L. (wheat): evidence for somatic embryogenesis. Protoplasma **110**, 95–105.

PADUCH-CHICAL E. & KRYCZYNSKI S. 1987 A low temperature therapy and meristem-tip culture for eliminating four viroids from infected plants. J. Phytopath. **118**, 341–346.

PAEK K.Y. 1982 Studies on the clonal propagation by the culture of bulb scale segments, inflorescence stems and flower buds in hyacinth. pp. 713–714 *in* Fujiwara A. (ed.) 1982 (*q.v.*).

PAEK K.Y., CHANDLER S.F. & THORPE T.A. 1987 *In vitro* propagation of Chinese cabbage from seedling shoot tips. J. Am. Soc. Hort. Sci. **112**, 841–845.

PAFFEN A.M.G., AGUETTAZ P., DELVALLEE I., DE KLERK G.J. & BOGERS R.J. 1990 The development of dormancy in lily bulblets generated *in vitro*. Acta Hort. **266**, 51–66.

PAIS M.S.S. & CASAL M. 1987 Propagation of the fern *Adiantum copillas-veneris* through tissue culture of the circinate part of young leaves. Acta Hort. **212**, 651–654.

PAL M. & NANDA K.K. 1981 Rooting of etiolated stem segments of *Populus robusta* — interaction of temperature, catechol and sucrose in the presence of IAA. Physiol. Plant. **53**, 540–542.

PALAVAN N., GOREN R. & GALSTON A.W. 1984 Effects of some growth regulators on polyamine biosynthetic enzymes in etiolated pea seedlings. Plant Cell Physiol: **25**, 541–546.

PALMER M.V. & PALNI L.M.S. 1987 Substrate effects on cytokinin metabolism in soybean callus tissue. J. Plant Physiol. **126**, 365–371.

PALUDAN N. 1980 *Chrysanthemum* stunt and chlorotic mottle. Establishment of healthy chrysanthemum plants and storage at low temperature of chrysanthemum, carnation, campanula and pelargonium in tubes. Acta Hort. **110**, 303–313.

PALUKAITIS P. & SYMONS R.H. 1979 Hybridization analysis of *Chrysanthamum* stunt viroid with complementary DNA and the quantitation of viroid RNA sequences in extracts of infected plants. Virology **98**, 238–245.

PALUKAITIS P., RAKOWSKI A.G., ALEXANDER D.M. & SYMONS R.H. 1981 Rapid indexing of the sunblotch disease of avocados using a complementary DNA probe to avocado sunblotch viroid. Ann. Appl. Biol. **98**, 439–449.

PAMPLIN E.J. & CHAPMAN J.M. 1975 Sucrose suppression of chlorophyll synthesis in tissue cultures. J. Exp. Bot. **26**, 212–220.

PANDEY K.N. & SABHARWAL P.S. 1979 *In vitro* neoplastic transformation of plant callus tissue by γ - radiation. Mutation Res. **62**, 459–465.

PAPACHATZI M., HAMMER P.A. & HASEGAWA P.M. 1981 *In vitro* propagation of *Hosta decorata* 'Thomas Hogg' using cultured shoot tips. J. Am. Soc. Hort. Sci. **106**, 232–236.

PAQUES M. & BOXUS Ph. 1987b A model to learn 'vitrification', the rootstock apple M.26. Present results. Acta Hort. **212**, 193–210.

PARANJOTHY K. & ROHANI O. 1982 *In vitro* propagation of oil palm. pp. 747–749 *in* Fujiwara A. (ed.) 1982 (*q.v.*).

PAREEK L.K. & CHANDRA N. 1978b Differentiation of shoot buds *in vitro* in tissue cultures of *Sisymbrium irio*. J. Exp. Bot. **29**, 239–244.

PARFITT D.E., ALMEHDI A.A. & BLOKSBERG L.N. 1988 Use of organic buffers in plant tissue-culture systems. Scientia Hort. **36**, 157–163.

PARIS D. & DUHAMET L. 1953 Action d'un mélange d'acides aminés et vitamines sur la prolifération des cultures de croun-gall de Scorsonère; comparison avec l'action du lait de coco. Compt. Rend. Acad. Sci. Paris **236**, 1690–1692.

PARK H-B., KIM Y-H., WHIPKEY A. & JANICK J. 1988 Proline and ABA increase survival of desiccated somatic embryos of celery. HortScience **23**, 754.

PARK Y.G. & SON S.H. 1988a *In vitro* organogenesis and somatic embryogenesis from punctured leaf of *Populus nigra* × *P. maximowiezii*. Plant Cell Tiss. Organ Cult. **15**, 95–105.

PARLIMAN B.J. 1986 Tissue culture techniques and plant introduction/quarantine procedures. pp. 271–292 *in* Zimmerman *et al.* (eds.) 1986 (*q.v.*).

PARLIMAN B.J. & DAUBENY H.A. 1988 Considerations for effective exchange of clonally propagated plant germplasm. HortScience **23**, 67–73.

PARR A.J., ROBBINS R.J. & RHODES M.J.C. 1984 Permeabilization of *Chinchona ledgeriana* cells by dimethylsulphoxide. Effects on alkaloid release and long-term membrane integrity. Plant Cell Rep. **3**, 262–265.

PARUPS E.V. 1975 Chemical modification of ethylene responses in plants. Acta Hort. **41**, 143–158.

PASQUALETTO P.-L., ZIMMERMAN R.H. & FORDHAM I. 1986 Gelling agent and growth regulator effects on shoot vitrification of 'Gala' apple *in vitro*. J. Am. Soc. Hort. Sci. **111**, 976–980 & **112**, 407.

PASQUALETTO P.-L., WERGIN W.P. & ZIMMERMAN R.H. 1988a Changes in structure and elemental composition of vitrified leaves of 'Gala' apple *in vitro*. Acta Hort. **227**, 352–357.

PASQUALETTO P.-L., ZIMMERMAN R.H. & FORDHAM I. 1988b The influence of cation and gelling agent concentrations on vitrification of apple cultivars *in vitro*. Plant Cell Tiss. Organ Cult. **14**, 31–40.

PATEL B.N., CATTELL K.J. & HOCKING T.J. 1986 Uptake of abscisic acid by isolated mesophyll protoplast from *Vicia faba*. Plant Science **45**, 195–199.

PATEL K.R. & BERLYN G.P. 1983 Cytochemical investigations on multiple bud formation in tissue cultures of *Pinus coulteri*. Can. J. Bot. **61**, 575–585.

PATENA L., SUTTER E.G. & DANDEKAR A.M. 1988 Root induction by *Agrocbacterium rhizogenes* in a difficult-to-root woody species. Acta Hort. **227**, 324–329.

PATERSON K.E. & ROST T.L. 1981 Callus formation and organogenesis from cultured leaf segments of *Crassula argentea*: cytokinin-induced developmental pattern changes. Am. J. Bot. **68**, 965–972.

PATTON D.A. & MEINKE D.W. 1988 High-frequency plant regeneration from cultured cotyledons of *Arabidopsis thaliana*. Plant Cell Rep. **7**, 233–237.

PAUL J. 1959 *Cell and Tissue Culture*. E. & S. Livingstone. Edinburgh, London.

PAULET P. & KETATA S. 1969 La régulation de l'organogenèse sur des cultures *in vitro* de fragments d'entre-noeuds de tiges de *Nicotiana glauca* Grah. Compt. Rend. Acad. Sci. Paris **268D**, 1604–1606.

PAVLOVA M.K. 1986 Experimental gynogenesis *in vitro*. p. 94 *in* Somers *et al.* (eds.) 1986 (*q.v.*).

PEAUD-LENOEL C. & JOUANNEAU J.-P. 1980 Presence and possible functions of cytokinins in RNA. pp. 129–143 *in* Skoog F. (ed.) 1980 (*q.v.*).

PECH J.C. & ROMANI R.J. 1979 Senescence of pear fruit cells cultured in a continuously renewed auxin-deprived medium. Plant Physiol. **64**, 814–817.

PÉLISSIER B., BOUCHEFRA O., PEPIN R. & FREYSSINET G. 1990 Production of isolated somatic emmbryos from sunflower thin cell layers. Plant Cell Rep. **9**, 47–50.

PELLETIER G., PRIMARD C., VEDEL F., CHETRIT P., REMY R., ROUSSELLE & RENARD M. 1983 Intergeneric cytoplasmic hybridization in Cruciferae by protoplast fusion. Mol. Gen. Genet. **191**, 244–250.

PENCE V.C. & CARUSO J.L. 1984 Effects of IAA and four IAA conjugates on morphogenesis and callus growth from tomato leaf discs. Plant Cell Tiss. Organ Cult. **3**, 101–110.

PENCE V.C. & SOUKUP V.G. 1986 Plant regeneration from *Trilium* spp. *in vitro*. HortScience **21**, 1211–1213.

PENCE V.C., HASEGAWA P.M. & JANICK J. 1980a Initiation and development of asexual embryos of *Theobroma cacao in vitro*. Z. Pflanzenphysiol. **98**, 1–14.

PENCE V.C., PETRETIC N.L., HASEGAWA P.M. & JANICK J. 1980b Regulation of fatty acid synthesis in asexual embryos of *Cacao*. Plant Physiol. **65**, (Suppl.) 38 (Abst. 205).

PENNELL D. 1987 *Micropropagation in Horticulture*. Grower Books, London. ISBN 0 901361 83 6

PERCIVAL F.W., PURVES W.K. & VICKERY L.E. 1973 Indole-3-ethanol oxidase. Kinetics, inhibition and regulation by auxins. Plant Physiol. **51**, 739–743.

PÉREZ C., RODRÍGUEZ R. & TAMES R.S. 1985 Embryonic axis control in filbert cotyledon rhizogenesis *in vitro*. Phyton. **45**, 129–134.

PERINET P. & LALONDE M. 1983 In vitro propagation and nodulation of the actinorhizal host plant *Alnus glutinosa* L. Gaertn. Plant Sci. Lett. **29**, 9–17.

PERINET P., VALLEE G. & TREMBLAY F.M. 1988 *In vitro* propagation of mature trees of *Alnus incana* (L.) Moench. Plant Cell Tiss. Organ Cult. **15**, 85–89.

PERL A., AVIV D. & GALUN E. 1988 Ethylene and *in vitro* culture of potato: suppression of ethylene generation vastly improves protoplast yield, plating efficiency and transient expression of an alien gene. Plant Cell Rep. **7**, 403–406.

PESCHKE V.M., PHILLIPS R.L. & GEGENBACH B.G. 1987 Discovery of transposable element activity among tissue culture-derived maize plants. Science **238**, 804–807.

PETERS G.A. & MAYNE B.C. 1974 The *Azolla, Anabaena azollae* relationship. I. Initial characterization of the association. Plant Physiol. **53**, 813–819.

PETERSON W.D. Jr. & STULBERG C.S. 1964 Freeze preservation of cultured animal cells. Cryobiology **1**, 80–86.

PETIARD V. & YVERNEL D. 1991 Process for cultivating plant cells *in vitro*. U.S. Patent No. 5030573.

PETRÙ E. 1970 Development of embryoids in carrot root callus culture (*Daucus carota* L.). Biol. Plant. **12**, 1–5.

PEVALEK-KOZLINA B. & JELASKA S. 1987 Microclonal propagation of *Prunus avium* L. Acta Hort. **212**, 599–602.

PFEFFER W. 1900 *The Physiology of Plants. A Treatise upon the Metabolism and Sources of Energy in Plants*. Vol. I. Trans. and ed. by A. J. Ewart. 2nd Edition. Clarendon Press, Oxford.

PHAN C.T. & HEGEDUS P. 1986 Possible metabolic basis for the developmental anomaly observed in *in vitro* culture, called 'vitreous plants'. Plant Cell Tiss. Organ Cult. **6**, 83–94.

PHARIS R.P. & KING R.W. 1985 Gibberellins and reproductive development in seed plants. Ann. Rev. Plant Physiol. **36**, 517–568.

PHARIS R.P. & KUO C.G. 1977 Physiology of gibberellins in conifers. Can. J. For. Res. **7**, 299–325.

PHARIS R.P., ROSS S.D. & McMULLAN E. 1980 Promotion of flowering in the Pinaceae by gibberellins. Physiol. Plant. **50**, 119–126.

PHARIS R.P., ROSS S.D., WAMPLE R.L. & OWENS J.N. 1976 Promotion of flowering in conifers of the Pinaceae by certain of the gibberellins. Acta Hort. **56**, 155–162.

PHILIP V.J. & NAINAR S.A.Z. 1986 Clonal propagation of *Vanilla planifolia* (Salisb.) Ames using tissue culture. J. Plant Physiol. **122**, 211–215.

PHILLIPS D.J. 1961 Induction of a light requirement for the germination of lettuce seed by naringenin, and its removal by gibberellic acid. Nature **192**, 240–241.

PHILLIPS D.J. 1962 Control of carnation streak virus by shoot tip culture. Phytopath. **52**, 747.

PHILLIPS D.V. & SMITH A.E. 1974 Soluble carbohydrates in soybean. Can. J. Bot. **52**, 2447–2452.

PHILLIPS G.C. & COLLINS G.B. 1979a *In vitro* tissue culture of selected legumes and plant regeneration from callus cultures of red clover. Crop Sci. **19**, 59–64.

PHILLIPS G.C. & COLLINS G.B. 1979b Virus symptom-free plants of red clover using meristem culture. Crop Sci. **19**, 213–216.

PHILLIPS G.C. & COLLINS G.B. 1980 Somatic embryogenesis from cell suspension cultures of red clover. Crop Sci. **20**, 323–326.

PHILLIPS G.C. & COLLINS G.B. 1981 Induction and development of somatic embryos from cell suspension cultures of soybean. Plant Cell Tiss. Organ Cult. **1**, 123–129.

PHILLIPS G.C. & HUBSTENBERGER J.F. 1985 Organogenesis in pepper tissue cultures. Plant Cell Tiss. Organ Cult. **4**, 261–269.

PHILLIPS R. 1987 Effects of sequential exposure to auxin and cytokinin on xylogenesis in cultured explants of Jerusalem artichoke (*Helianthus tuberosus* L.). Ann. Bot. **59**, 245–250.

PHILLIPS R. & DODDS J.H. 1977 Rapid differentiation of tracheary elements in cultured explants of Jerusalem artichoke. Planta **135**, 207–212.

PHILLIPS R. & TORREY J.G. 1973 DNA synthesis, cell division and specific cytodifferentiation in cultured pea root cortical explants. Dev. Biol. **31**, 336–347.

PHILLIPS R., ARNOTT S.M. & KAPLAN S.E. 1981 Antibiotics in plant tissue culture: rifampicin effectively controls bacterial contaminants without affecting the growth of short-term explant cultures of *Helianthus tuberosus*. Plant Sci. Lett. **21**, 235–240.

PHILLIPS R.L., KAEPPLER S.M., & PESCHKE V.M. 1990 Do we understand somaclonal variation? pp. 131–141 *in* Nijkamp *et al.* (eds.) 1990 (*q.v.*).

PIAGNANI C. & ECCHER T. 1988 Factors affecting the proliferation and rooting of chestnut *in vitro*. Acta Hort. **227**, 384–386.

PIEPER M.A. & SMITH M.A.L. 1988 A whole plant microculture selection system for Kentucky bluegrass. Crop Sci. **28**, 611–614.

PIERIK R.L.M. 1967 Regeneration, vernalization and flowering in *Lunaria annua in vivo* and *in vitro*. Meded. Landbouwhogeschool, Wageningen **67**, 1–71.

PIERIK R.L.M. 1969 Factors affecting adventitious root formation in isolated stem segments of *Rhododendron*. Neth. J. Agric. Sci. **17**, 203–208.

PIERIK R.L.M. 1987 Plant Cell Culture Technology — a book review. Scientia Hort. **33**, 308–309.

PIERIK R.L.M. 1988 *In vitro* culture of higher plants as a tool in the propagation of horticultural crops. Acta Hort. **226**, 25–40.

PIERIK R.L.M. 1990a Rejuvenation and micropropagation. pp. 91–101 *in* Nijkamp *et al.* (eds.) 1990 (*q.v.*).

PIERIK R.L.M. 1990b Rejuvenation and micropropagation. Newsletter Int. Ass. Plant Tiss. Cult. **62**, 11–21.

PIERIK R.L.M. & STEEGMANS H.H. 1972 The effect of 6-benzylamino- purine on growth and development of *Cattleya* seedlings grown from unripe seeds. Z. Pflanzenphysiol. **68**, 228–234.

PIERIK R.L.M. & STEEGMANS H.H.M. 1975a *Freesia* plantlets from flower-buds cultivated *in vitro*. Neth. J. Agric. Sci. **23**, 334–337.

PIERIK R.L.M. & STEEGMANS H.H.M. 1975c Analysis of adventitious root formation in isolated stem explants of *Rhododendron*. Scientia Hort. **3**, 1–20.

PIERIK R.L.M. & STEEGMANS H.H.M. 1983 Vegatative propagation of a chimerical *Yucca elephantipes* Regel *in vitro*. Scientia Hort. **21**, 267–272.

PIERIK R.L.M., SPRENKELS P.A., VAN DER HARST B. & VAN DER MEYS Q.G. 1988a Seed germination and further development of plantlets of *Paphiopedilum ciliolare* Pfitz. *in vitro*. Scientia Hort. **34**, 139–153.

PIERIK R.L.M., STEEGMANS H.H.M. & MOLENBERG H. 1986 Vegetative propagation of *Syringa vulgaris* L. *in vitro*. p. 434 *in* Somers *et al.* (eds.) 1986 (*q.v.*).

PIERIK R.L.M., STEEGMANS H.H.M. & VAN DER MEYS J.A.J. 1974b Plantlet formation in callus tissues of *Anthurium andraeanum* Lind. Scientia Hort. **2**, 193–198.

PIERIK R.L.M., STEEGMANS H.H.M., ELIAS A.A., STIEKEMA O.T.J. & VAN DER VELDE A.J. 1988c Vegetative propagation of *Syringa vulgaris* L. *in vitro*. Acta Hort. **226**, 195–204.

PIERIK R.L.M., STEEGMANS H.H.M., VERHAEGH J.A.M. & WOUTERS A.N. 1982 Effect of cytokinin and cultivar on shoot formation of *Gerbera jamesonii in vitro*. Neth. J. Agric. Sci. **30**, 341–346.

PIERIK R.L.M., VAN VOORST A., BOOY G., VAN ACKER C.A.M., LELIVELT C.L.C. & DE WIT J.C. 1988b Vegetative propagation of *Alstroemeria* hybrids *in vitro*. Acta Hort. **226**, 81–89.

PILLAI S.K. & HILDEBRANDT A.C. 1969 Induced differentiation of geranium plants from undifferentiated callus *in vitro*. Am. J. Bot. **56**, 52–58.

PITTET H. & MONCOUSIN C. 1982 La micropropagation *in vitro* du rosier. Rev. Hort. Suisse **55**, 67–69.

PLATT R.S. 1954 The inactivation of auxin in normal and tumerous tissue. Ann. Biol. **30**, 349–359.

PLIEGO-ALFARO F. 1988 Development of an *in-vitro* rooting bioassay using juvenile-phase stem cuttings of *Persea american* Mill. J. Hort. Sci. **63**, 295–301.

PLIEGO-ALFARO F. & MURASHIGE T. 1987 Possible rejuvenation of adult Avocado by graftage onto juvenile rootstocks *in vitro*. HortScience **22**, 1321–1324.

PLUMB-DHINDSA P.L., DHINDSA R.S. & THORPE T.A. 1979 Non- autotrophic CO_2 fixation during shoot formation in tobacco callus. J. Exp. Bot. **30**, 759–767.

PLUMMER T.H. & LEOPOLD A.C. 1957 Chemical treatment for bud formation in *Saintpaulia*. Proc. Am. Soc. Hort. Sci. **70**, 442–444.

PODWYSZYNSKA M. & HEMPEL M. 1987 Identification and elimination of 'slowly growing' bacteria from a micropropagated *Gerbera*. Acta Hort. **212**, 112.

POGANY M.E. & LINEBERGER R.D. 1991 Considerations for micropropagation of plant chimeras. Comb. Proc. Int. Plant Prop. Soc. 1990 **40**, 576–580.

POIRIER-HAMON S., RAO P.S. & HARADA H. 1974 Culture of mesophyll protoplasts and stem segments of *Antirrhinum majus* (snapdragon): growth and organization of embryoids. J. Exp. Bot. **25**, 752–760.

POLACCO J.C. 1977a Is nickel a universal component of plant ureases? Plant Sci. Lett. **10**, 249–255.

POLACCO J.C. 1977b Nitrogen metabolism in soybean tissue culture. II. Urea utilisation and urease synthesis require Ni^{2+}. Plant Physiol. **59**, 827–830.

POLEVAJA V.S. 1967 The effect of light of various spectral compositions on some aspects of auxin metabolism in cultures of isolated carrot tissues. Fiziol. Rast. **14**, 582–591.

POLIKARPOCHKINA R.T., GAMBURG K.Z. & KHAVIN E.E. 1979 Cell- suspension culture of Maize (*Zea mays* L.). Z. Pflanzenphysiol. **95**, 57–67.

POLITO V.S. & ALLIATA V. 1981 Growth of calluses derived from shoot apical meristems of adult and juvenile English ivy (*Hedera helix* L.). Plant Sci. Lett. **22**, 387–393.

POLLARD A.S., PARR A.J. & LOUGHMAN C.L. 1977 Boron in relation to membrane function in higher plants. J. Exp. Bot. **28**, 831–841.

POLLARD J.K., SHANTZ E.M. & STEWARD F.C. 1961 Hexitols in coconut milk: their role in the nurture of dividing cells. Plant Physiol. **36**, 492–501.

POLLE E.O. & JENNY H. 1971 Boundary layer effects in ion absorption by roots and storage organs of plants. Physiol. Plant. **25**, 219–224.

POLLOCK K., BARFIELD D.G. & SHIELDS R. 1983 The toxicity of antibiotics to plant cell cultures. Plant Cell Rep. **2**, 36–39.

PONTIKIS C.A. & MELAS P. 1986 Micropropagation of *Ficus carica* L. HortScience **21**, 153.

POOVAIAH B.W. 1988 Molecular and cellular aspects of calcium action in plants. HortScience **23**, 267–271.

POSPISILOVA J., CATSKY J., SOLAROVA J. & TICHA I. 1987 Photosynthesis of plant regenerants: Specificity of *in vitro* conditions and plant response. Biol. Plant. **29**, 415–421.

POULSEN G.B. 1988 Elimination of contaminating micro-organisms from meristem culture of apple rootstock M26. Acta Hort. **225**, 193–197.

POW J.J. 1969 Clonal propagation *in vitro* from cauliflower curd. Hort. Res. **9**, 151–152.

POWELL L.E., BORKOWSKA B. & SINGHA S. 1980 Dormancy status of apple buds and abscisic acid relationships. Plant Physiol. **65**, (Suppl.) 92 (Abst. 502).

POWELL W. & UHRIG H. 1987 Anther culture of *Solanum* gemotypes. Plant Cell Tiss. Organ Cult. **11**, 13–24.

POWELL W., BORRINO E.M. & GOODALL V. 1988 The effect of anther orientation on microspore-derived plant production in barley (*Hordeum vulgare* L.). Euphytica **38**, 159–163.

POWER C.J. & FIROOZABADY E. 1991 Sunflower regeneration from cotyledons. U.S. Patent No. 5030572

POWER J.B., FREARSON E.M., GEORGE D., EVANS P.K., BERRY S.F., HAYWARD C. & COCKING E.C. 1976 The isolation, culture and regeneration of leaf protoplasts in the genus *Petunia*. Plant Sci. Lett. **7**, 51–55.

POWLING A. & HUSSEY G. 1981 Establishment of aseptic cultures of sugar beet. Ann. Rep. John Innes Inst. 1980, p. 60.

PRAKESH J. 1988 Plant health. A useful service for large scale propagation of ornamental plants through micropropagation. Acta Hort. **226**, 115–120.

PREDIERI S., INFANTE R., FASOLO F. & RIGHETTI B. 1991 CO_2 enrichment effect on *in vitro* grown apple and kiwi fruit. Acta Hort. **300**, 107–110.

PREECE J.E. 1987 Treatment of the stock plant with plant growth regulators to improve propagation success. HortScience **22**, 754–759.

PREECE J.E. & SUTTER E.G. 1991 Acclimatization of micropropagated plants to the greenhouse and field. pp. 71–93 *in* Debergh and Zimmerman (eds.) 1991 (*q.v.*).

PREIL W. 1991 Application of bioreactors in plant propagation. pp. 425–445 *in* Debergh and Zimmerman (eds.) 1991 (*q.v.*).

PREIL W. & ENGELHARDT M. 1982 *In vitro* separation of chimera by suspension cultures of *Euphorbia pulcherrima* Willd. Gartenbauwiss. **47**, 241–244.

PREIL W., FLOREK P., WIX U. & BECK A. 1988 Towards mass propagation by use of bioreactors. Acta Hort. **226**, 99–106.

PRETOVA A. & WILLIAMS E.G. 1986 Direct somatic embryogenesis from immature zygotic embryos of flax (*Linum usitatissimum* L.). J. Plant Physiol. **126**, 155–161.

PRICE H.J. & SMITH R.H. 1979a Somatic embryogenesis in suspension cultures of *Gossypium klotzschianum* Anderss. Planta **145**, 305–307.

PRICE H.J. & SMITH R.H. 1979b Somatic embryogenesis in *Gossypium*. In Vitro **15**, 177 (Abst.45).

PRING D.R., CONDE M.F. & GENGENBACH B.G. 1981 Cytoplasmic genome variability in tissue culture-derived plants. Env. Exp. Bot. **21**, 369–377.

PRITCHARD H.W., GROUT B.W.W. & SHORT K.C. 1986 Osmotic stress as a pregrowth procedure for cryopreservation. 1. Growth and ultrastructure of sycamore suspensions. Ann. Bot. **57**, 41–48.

PROFUMO P., GASTALDO P., BEVILACQUA L. & CARLI S. 1991 Plant regeneration from cotyledonary explants of *Aesculus hippocastanum*. Plant Science **76**, 139–142.

PUA E.-C., CHONG C. & ROUSSELLE G.L. 1983 *In vitro* propagation of Ottowa 3 apple rootstock. Can. J. Plant Sci. **63**, 183–188.

PUA E.-C., RAGOLSKY E. & THORPE T.A. 1985b Retention of shoot regeneration capacity of tobacco callus by Na₂SO₄. Plant Cell Rep. **4**, 225–228.

PUA E.-C., RAGOLSKY E., CHANDLER S.F. & THORPE T.A. 1985a Effect of sodium sulfate on *in vitro* organogenesis of tobacco callus. Plant Cell Tiss. Organ Cult. **5**, 55–62.

PUHLER A., REILAENDER H. & WEBER G. 1988 Nitrogen fixation regulator genes. U.S. Patent No. 4782022

PULLMAN G.S. & GUPTA P. 1991 Method for reproducing coniferous plants by somatic embryogenesis using adsorbent materials in the development stage media. U.S. Patent No. 5034326

PURCELL A.H. 1977 Cold therapy of Pierce's disease of grapevines. Plant Dis. Rep. **61**, 514–518.

PURNHAUSER L., MEDGYESY P., CZAKO M., DIX P.J. & MARTON L. 1987 Stimulation of shoot regeneration in *Triticum aestivum* and *Nicotiana plumbaginifolia* Viv. tissue cultures using the ethylene inhibitor AgNO₃. Plant Cell Rep. **6**, 1–4.

PUSCHMANN R., KE D. & ROMANI R. 1985 Ethylene production by suspension-cultured pear fruit cells as related to their senescence. Plant Physiol. **79**, 973–976.

PUTZ C. 1971 Obtention de framboisiers (var. Bois blanc) sans virus par la technique des cultures de méristèmes. Phytopath. **3**, 493–501.

PYOTT J.L. & CONVERSE R.H. 1981 *In vitro* propagation of heat-treated red raspberry clones. HortScience **16**, 308–309.

PYTHOUD F., BUCHALA A.J. & SCHMID A. 1986 Adventitious root formation in green cuttings of *Populus tremula* L., characterisation of the effect of Vit. D₃ and indolylbutyric acid. Physiol. Plant. **68**, 93–99.

QUAK F. 1961 Heat treatment and substances inhibiting virus multiplication in meristem culture to obtain virus-free plants. Advan. Hort. Sci. Appl. **1**, 144–148.

QUAK F. 1977 Meristem culture and virus-free plants. pp. 598–615 *in* Reinert and Bajaj (eds.) 1977 (*q.v.*).

QUEMADA H., ROTH E.J. & LARK K.G. 1987 Changes in methylation of tissue cultured soybean cells detected by digestion with the restriction enzymes HpaII and MspI. Plant Cell Rep. **6**, 63–66.

QUERFURTH G. & PAUL H.L. 1979 Protein A-coated latex-linked antisera (PAL-LAS): new reagents for a sensitive test permitting the use of antisera unsuitable for the latextest. Phytopathol. Z. **94**, 282–285.

QUOIRIN M. & LEPOIVRE P. 1977 Improved media for *in vitro* culture of *Prunus* sp. Acta Hort. **78**, 437–442.

QUOIRIN M., BOXUS Ph. & GASPAR Th. 1974 Root initiation and isoperoxidases of stem tip cuttings from mature *Prunus* plants. Physiol. Veg. **12**, 165–174.

QUOIRIN M., GASPAR T. & BOXUS Ph. 1975 Substances de croissance endogènes liées à la reprise de méristèmes de *Prunus Accolade* en culture *in vitro*. Compt. Rend. Acad. Sci. Paris **281D**, 1309–1312.

RADIN J.W. & LOOMIS R.S. 1969 Ethylene and carbon dioxide in the growth and development of cultured radish roots. Plant Physiol. **44**, 1584–1589.

RADLEY M. & DEAR E. 1958 Occurrence of gibberellin-like substances in coconut. Nature **182**, 1098.

RADOJEVIC L. 1988 Plant regeneration of *Aesculus hippocastanum* L. (Horse Chestnut) through somatic embryogenesis. J. Plant Physiol. **132**, 322–326.

RADOJEVIC Lj., SOKIC O. & TUCIC B. 1987b Somatic embryogenesis in tissue culture of iris (*Iris pumila* L.). Acta Hort. **212**, 719–723.

RAGGIO M., RAGGIO N. & TORREY J.G. 1957 The nodulation of isolated leguminous roots. Am. J. Bot. **44**, 325–334.

RAGHAVA RAM N.V. & NABORS M.W. 1985 Plant regeneration from tissue cultures of Pokkali rice is promoted by optimizing callus to medium volume ratio and by a medium-conditioning factor produced by embryogenic callus. Plant Cell Tiss. Organ Cult. **4**, 241–248.

RAGHAVAN V. 1967 pp. 413 *in* Wilt & Wessels (eds.) 1967 *Methods in Developmental Biology*. Thomas Y. Crowell, New York.

RAGHAVAN V. 1977a Applied aspects of embryo culture. pp. 375–397 *in* Reinert and Bajaj (eds.) 1977 (*q.v.*).

RAGHAVAN V. 1977b Diets and culture media for plant embryos. pp. 361–413 *in* Recheigl M. Jr. (ed.) 1977 *CRC Handbook Series in Nutrition & Food* Vol. 4. CRC Press, Baton Rouge, Florida.

RAGHAVAN V. 1980 Embryo culture. pp. 209–240 *in* Vasil I.K. (ed.) 1980b (*q.v.*).

RAGHAVAN V. 1990 From microspore to embryoid: faces of the angiosperm pollen grain. pp. 213–221 *in* Nijkamp *et al*. (eds.) 1990 (*q.v.*).

RAHMAN M.A. & BLAKE J. 1988a Factors affecting *in vitro* proliferation and rooting of shoots of jack fruit (*Artocarpus heterophyllus* Lam.). Plant Cell Tiss. Organ Cult. **13**, 179–187.

RAHMAN M.A. & BLAKE J. 1988b The effects of medium composition and culture conditions on *in vitro* rooting and *ex vitro* establishment of jackfruit (*Artocarpas heterophyllus* Lam.). Plant Cell Tiss. Organ Cult. **13**, 189–200.

RAINS D.W. 1976 Mineral metabolism. pp. 561–597 *in* Bonner J. and Varner J.L. (eds.) 1976 *Plant Biochemistry*. Academic Press, New York.

RAINS D.W., VALENTINE R.C. & HOLLAENDER A. (eds.) 1980 *Genetic Engineering of Osmoregulation*. Plenum Press, New York, London.

RAJASEKARAN K. & MULLINS M.G. 1979 Embryos and plantlets from cultured anthers of hybrid grapevines. J. Exp. Bot. **30**, 399–407.

RAJASEKARAN K. & MULLINS M.G. 1982 Regeneration of grapevines by aseptic methods. Comb. Proc. Int. Plant Prop. Soc. 1981 **31**, 213–218.

RAJASEKARAN K., HEIN M.B. & VASIL I.K. 1987 Endogenous abscisic acid and indole-3-acetic acid and somatic embryogenesis in cultured leaf explants of *Pennisetum purpureum* Schum. Effects *in vivo* and *in vitro* of glyphosate, fluridone and paclobutrazol. Plant Physiol. **84**, 47–51.

RAJASEKARAN K., MULLINS M.G. & NAIR Y. 1983 Flower formation *in vitro* by hypocotyl explants of cucumber (*Cucumis sativus* L.). Ann. Bot. **52**, 417–420.

RAJASEKARAN K., VINE J. & MULLINS M.G. 1982 Dormancy in somatic embryos and seeds of *Vitis*: changes in endogenous abscisic acid during embryogeny and germination. Planta **154**, 139–144.

RAJU B.C. & TROLINGER J.C. 1986 Pathogen indexing in large-scale propagation of florist crops. pp. 135–138 *in* Zimmerman *et al*. (eds.) 1986 (*q.v.*).

RAJU M.V.S. & MANN H.E. 1970 Regenerative studies on the detached leaves of *Echeveria elegans*. Anatomy and regeneration of leaves in sterile culture. Can. J. Bot. **48**, 1887–1891.

RAJU M.V.S. & MANN H.E. 1971 Regeneration studies on the detached leaves of *Echeveria elegans*. Patterns of regeneration of leaves in sterile culture. Can. J. Bot. **49**, 2015–2021.

RAMMING D.W. 1990 The use of embryo culture in fruit breeding. HortScience **25**, 393–398.

RAMMING D.W., EMERSHAD R.L., SPIEGEL-ROY P., SAHAR N. & BARON I. 1990 Embryo culture of early ripening seeded grape (*Vitis vinifera*) genotypes. HortScience **25**, 339–342.

RANCH J. & WIDHOLM J. 1980 Studies on the use of toxic metabolic analogs for the isolation of nutritional variants from plant cell cultures. Plant Physiol. **65**, (Suppl.) 37 (Abst.201).

RANCH J.P. & BUCHEIM J. 1991 Propagating multiple whole fertile plants from immature leguminous plants. U.S. Patent No. 5008200

RANCH J.P., OGLESBY L. & ZIELINSKI A.C. 1986 Plant regeneration from tissue cultures of soybean by somatic embryogenesis. pp. 97–109 *in* Vasil I.K. (ed.) 1986 *Cell Culture and Somatic Cell Genetics of Plants* Vol. 3. Academic Press.

RANCILLAC K.J. & NOURISSEAU J.G. 1989 Micropropagation and strawberry plant quality. HortScience **265**, 343–348.

RANCILLAC M., NOURRISSEAU J.G., NAVATEL J.C. & ROUDEILLAC P. 1987 Incidence de la multiplication *in vitro* sur le comportement du plant de fraisier en France. pp. 55–73 *in* Boxus and Larvor (eds.) 1987 (*q.v.*).

RANGA SWAMY N.S. 1958 Culture of nucellar tissue of *Citrus in vitro*. Experientia **14**, 111–112.

RANGA SWAMY N.S. 1959 Morphogenetic response of *Citrus* ovules to growth adjuvants in culture. Nature **183**, 735–736.

RANGA SWAMY N.S. 1961 Experimental studies on female reproductive structures of *Citrus microcarpa* Bunge. Phytomorph. **11**, 109–127.

RANGA SWAMY N.S. 1963 Studies on culturing seeds of *Orobanche aegyptiaca*. pp. 345–354 *in* Maheshwari and Ranga Swamy (eds.) 1963 (*q.v.*).

RANGAN T.S. 1974 Morphogenic investigations on tissue cultures of *Panicum miliaceum*. Z. Pflanzenphysiol. **72**, 456–459.

RANGASWAMY N.S. 1977 Applications of *in vitro* pollination and *in vitro* fertilization. pp. 412–425 *in* Reinert & Bajaj (eds.) 1977 (*q.v.*).

RANGASWAMY N.S. 1982 Nucellus as an experimental system in basic and applied tissue culture research. pp. 269–286 in Rao A.N. (ed.) 1982 (*q.v.*).

RANJIT M. & KESTER D.E. 1988 Micropropagation of cherry rootstocks: II. Invigoration and enhanced rooting of '46-1 Mazzard' by co- culture with 'Colt'. J. Am. Soc. Hort. Sci. **113**, 150–154.

RANJIT M., KESTER D.E. & MICKE W.C. 1988 Micropropagation of cherry rootstocks: I. Response to culture. J. Am. Soc. Hort. Sci. **113**, 146–149.

RAO A.N. (ed.) 1982 *Tissue Culture of Economically Important Plants.* Proc. of Int. Symp., Singapore 1981. COSTED and ANBS, Pubs.

RAO P.S. & BAPAT V.A. 1978 Vegetative propagation of sandalwood plants through tissue culture. Can. J. Bot. **56**, 1153–1156.

RAO P.S. & NARAYANASWAMI S. 1972 Investigations in callus cultures of *Tylophora indica*. Physiol. Plant. **27**, 271–276.

RAO P.S. & NARAYANASWAMY S. 1968 Induced morphogenesis in tissue cultures of *Solanum xanthocarpum*. Planta **81**, 372–375.

RAO P.S., HANDRO W. & HARADA H. 1973a Hormonal control of differentiation of shoots, roots and embryos in leaf and stem cultures of *Petunia inflata* and *P. hybrida*. Physiol. Plant. **28**, 458–463.

RAO P.S., HANDRO W. & HARADA H. 1973b Bud formation and embryo differentiation in *in vitro* cultures of *Petunia*. Z. Pflanzenphysiol. **69**, 87–90.

RAO U., NARANG V. & RAO R. 1987 Plant regeneration from somatic embryos of bamboo and their transplantation to soil. pp. 101–107 in Ducaté *et al.* (eds.) 1987 (*q.v.*).

RAPPAPORT L. & SACHS M. 1967 Wound-induced gibberellins. Nature **214**, 1149.

RAQUIN C. 1983 Utilization of different sugars as carbon sources for *in vitro* anther culture of petunia. Z. Pflanzenphysiol. **111**, (Suppl.) 453–457.

RAQUIN C. 1986 Induction of haploid and "haploid plus" *Petunias* by combining gametophyte irradiation and *in vitro* ovary culture. p. 123 in Somers *et al.* (eds.) 1986 (*q.v.*).

RASHID A. & REINERT J. 1983 Factors affecting high-frequency embryo formation in *ab initio* pollen cultures of *Nicotiana*. Protoplasma **116**, 155–160.

RASHID A. & STREET H.E. 1973 The development of haploid embryoids from anther cultures of *Atropa belladonna* L. Planta **113**, 263–270.

RASTOGI R. & SAWHNEY V.K. 1988a *In vitro* culture of stamen primordia of the normal and a male sterile stamenless-2 mutant of tomato (*Lycopersicon esculentum* Mill.). J. Plant Physiol. **133**, 349–352.

RASTOGI R. & SAWHNEY V.K. 1988b Suppression of stamen development by CCC and ABA in tomato floral buds cultured *in vitro*. J. Plant Physiol. **133**, 620–624.

RATNAMBA S.P. & CHOPRA R.N. 1974 *In vitro* induction of embryoids from hypocotyls and cotyledons of *Arethum graveolens* seedlings. Z. Pflanzenphysiol. **73**, 452–455.

RAVEH D., HUBERMANN E. & GALUN E. 1973 *In vitro* culture of tobacco protoplasts: Use of feeder techniques to support division of cells plated at low densities. In Vitro **9**, 216–222.

RAVEN J.A. 1979 The possible role of membrane electrophoresis in the polar transport of IAA and other solutes in plant tissues. New Phytol. **82**, 285–291.

RAVEN J.A. 1986 Biochemical disposal of excess H^+ in growing plants? New Phytol. **104**, 175–206.

RAVEN J.A. & SMITH F.A. 1976 Cytoplasmic pH regulation and electrogenic H^+ extrusion. Curr. Adv. Plant Sci. **8**, 649–660.

RAWAL S.K. & MEHTA A.R. 1982 Changes in enzyme activity and isoperoxidases in haploid tobacco callus during organogenesis. Plant Sci. Lett. **24**, 67–77.

RAY S.D., GURUPRASAD K.N. & LALORAYA M.M. 1980 Antagonistic action of phenolic compounds on abscisic acid -induced inhibition of hypocotyl growth. J. Exp. Bot. **31**, 1651–1656.

RAYLE D.L. & CLELAND R. 1977 Control of plant enlargement by H ions. pp. 187–211 in *Current Topics in Developmental Biology* Vol.II. Moscona & Monroy (eds.).

RAYLE D.L. & PURVES W.K. 1967 Conversion of indole-3-ethanol to indole-3-acetic acid in cucumber seedling shoots. Plant Physiol. **42**, 1091–1093.

READ P.E. 1988 Stock plants influence micropropagation success. Acta Hort. **226**, 41–52.

READ P. & ECONOMOU A.S. 1983 Supplemental lighting in the propagation of deciduous azaleas. Comb. Proc. Int. Plant Prop. Soc. 1982 **32**, 639–645.

READ P. & ECONOMOU A. 1987 Stock plant influence on tissue culture success. Acta Hort. **212**, 111.

READ P.E. & YANG Q. 1987 Novel plant growth regulator delivery systems for *in vitro* culture of horticultural plants. Acta Hort. **212**, 55–58.

READ P.E., FELLMAN C.D. & ZIMMERMAN E. 1986 New plant growth regulators for cuttings and for tissue culture. Comb. Proc. Int. Plant Prop. Soc. 1985 **35**, 78–84.

READ P.E., GARTON S. & LOUIS K. 1983 Use of recirculating hydroponic systems for macro- and micropropagation studies. Acta Hort. **150**, 405–414.

READ P.E., GAVINLERTVATANA P., SURIYAJANTRATONG P., GARTON S. & BRENNER M.I. 1978a Stock plants affect tissue culture success. p. 249 in Hughes *et al.* (eds.) 1978 (*q.v.*).

READ P.E., GAVINLERTVATANA P., SURIYAJANTRATONG P., GARTON S. & BRENNER M.I. 1978b Influence of stock-plant treatments on the response of explants cultured *in vitro*. p. 154 Abst. 4th Int. Cong. IAPTC, Calgary, Canada.

REDENBAUGH K. & WALKER K. 1990 Role of artificial seeds in alfalfa breeding. In Bhojwani S. (ed.) 1990 *Plant Tissue Culture: Applications and Limitations*. Elsevier Science Publications, Amsterdam.

REDENBAUGH K., FUJII J.A. & SLADE D. 1991 Synthetic seed technology. pp. 35–74 in Vasil I.K. (ed.) 1991 (*q.v.*).

REDENBAUGH K., PAASCH B.D., NICHOL J.W., KOSSLER M.E., VISS P.R. & WALKER K.A. 1986 Somatic seeds: encapsulation of asexual plant embryos. Bio/Technology **4**, 797–801.

REDENBAUGH K., SLADE D., VISSE P. & FUJII J.A. 1987a Encapsulation of somatic embryos in synthetic seed coats. HortScience **22**, 803–809.

REDENBAUGH K., VISS P., SLADE D. & FUJII J.A. 1987b Scale-up: artificial seeds. pp. 473–493 in Green *et al.* (eds.) 1987 (*q.v.*).

REDENBAUGH M.K. 1986 Analogs of botanic seed. U.S. Patent 4562663.

REDENBAUGH M.K. & REYES Z. 1988 Artificial seed coat for botanic seed analogs. U.S. Patent 4715143.

REDENBAUGH M.K., SLADE D. & FUJII J. 1988 Desiccated analogs of botanic seed. U.S. Patent No. 4777762.

REED B.M. 1989 The effect of cold hardening and cooling rate on the survival of *Vaccinium* species frozen in liquid nitrogen. Cryo- Letters **10**, 315–322.

REED B.M. & LAGERSTEDT H.B. 1987 Freeze preservation of apical meritems of *Rubus* in liquid nitrogen. HortScience **22**, 302–303.

REILLEY C.N. & SCHMID R.W. 1958 Chelometric titrations with potentiometric end point detection. Anal. Chem. **30**, 947–953.

REINERT J. & BACKS D. 1968 Control of totipotency in plant cells growing *in vitro*. Nature **220**, 1340–1341.

REINERT J. & BAJAJ Y. P. S. (eds.) 1977 *Plant Cell, Tissue and Organ Culture*. Springer-Verlag, Berlin.

REINERT J. & WHITE P.R. 1956 The cultivation *in vitro* of tumor tissues and normal tissues of *Picea glauca*. Physiol. Plant. **9**, 177–189.

REINERT J., BACKS-HÜSEMANN D. & ZERMAN H. 1971 Determination of embryo and root formation in tissue cultures from *Daucus carota*. pp. 261–268 in *Les Cultures de Tissus de Plantes*. Coll. Int. CNRS 193 Paris.

REINERT J., BAJAJ Y.P.S. & ZBELL B. 1977 Aspects of organization — organogenesis, embryogenesis, cytodifferentiation. pp. 389–427 in Street H.E. (ed.) 1977a (*q.v.*).

REINERT J., TAZAWA M. & SEMENOFF S. 1967 Nitrogen compounds as factors of embryogenesis *in vitro*. Nature **216**, 1215–1216.

REISCH B. & BINGHAM E.T. 1980 The genetic control of bud formation from callus cultures of diploid alfalfa. Plant Sci. Lett. **20**, 71–77.

REISCH B.I. & MARTENS M.-H.R. 1988 Shoot regeneration from grape leaf, petiole and tendril tissues. HortScience **23**, 807.

REUFF I., SEITZ U., ULBRICH B. & REINHARD E. 1988 Cryopreservation of *Coleus blumei* suspension and callus cultures. J. Plant Physiol. **133**, 414–418.

REUSTLE G., MANN M. & HEINTZ C. 1988 Experience and problems with infections in tissue culture of grapevine. Acta Hort. **225**, 119–127.

REUTHER G. 1977 Adventitious organ formation and somatic embryogenesis in callus of *Asparagus* and *Iris* and its possible application. Acta Hort. **78**, 217–224.

REUTHER G. 1988a Problems of transmission and identification of bacteria in tissue culture propagated geraniums. Acta Hort. **225**, 139–152.

REUTHER G. 1988c Variability of *Pelargonium peltatum* cultivar in long-term *in vitro* culture of disease-free nucleus stocks. Acta Hort. **226**, 647–654.

REUTHER G. & BECKER U. 1987 Relationships between ploidy variations and organogenic potency in long-term callus cultures of *Asparagus officinalis*. Acta Hort. **212**, 143–149.

REUVENI O. & ISRAELI Y. 1990 Measures to reduce somaclonal variation in *in vitro* propagated bananas. Acta Hort. **275**, 307–313.

REUVENI O. & SHLESINGER D.R. 1990 Rapid vegetative propagation of papaya plants by cuttings. Acta Hort. **275**, 301–306.

REUVENI O., ISRAELI Y., DEGANI H. & ESHDUT Y. 1984 Genetic variability in banana plants multiplied via *in vitro* techniques. pp. 1–8 *in* Int. Board for Plant Genetic Resources Meeting, Leuren Univ., Belgium.

REUVENY Z., DOUGALL D.K. & TRINITY P.M. 1980 Regulatory coupling of nitrate and sulfate assimilation pathways in cultured tobacco cells. Proc. Nat. Acad. Sci. U.S.A. **77**, 6670–6672.

REVILLA M.A. & POWER J.B. 1988 Morphogenetic potential of long- term callus cultures of *Actinidia deliciosa*. J. Hort. Sci. **63**, 541–545.

REY H.Y. & MROGINSKI L.A. 1978 *In vitro* culture of caulinary apices of manioc (*Manihot esculenta*). Phyton Rev. Int. Bot. Exp. **36** (2), 171–176.

REYNOLDS B.D., BLACKMON W.J. & POSTEK C.E. 1980 Production of somatic embryos from *Roselle* callus. HortScience **15**, 432 (Abst.447).

RHODES C.A., GREEN C.E. & PHILLIPS R.L. 1986a Factors affecting tissue culture initiation from maize tassels. Plant Science **46**, 225–232.

RICE R.D., ALDERSON P.G. & WRIGHT N.A. 1983 Induction of bulbing of tulip shoots *in vitro*. Scientia Hort. **20**, 377–390.

RICE T.B. & CARLSON P.S. 1975 Genetic analysis and plant improvement. Ann. Rev. Plant Physiol. **26**, 279–308.

RICE T.B., REID R.K. & GORDON P.N. 1979 Morphogenesis in field crops. pp. 262–277 *in* Hughes K.W. *et al.* (eds.) 1979 (*q.v.*).

RICHTER G. & WESSEL K. 1985 Red light inhibits blue light-induced chloroplast development in cultured plant cells at the mRNA level. Plant Mol. Biol. **5**, 175–182.

RICHTER G., DANNHAUER I., KALDENHOFF R. & OTTERSBACH N. 1990 Blue-light effects on gene expression in plant-cell cultures. pp. 366–372 *in* Nijkamp *et al.* (eds.) 1990 (*q.v.*).

RIER J.P. & BESLOW D.T. 1967 Sucrose concentration and the differentiation of xylem in callus. Bot. Gaz. **128**, 73–77.

RIER J.P. & CHEN P.K. 1964 Pigment induction in plant tissue cultures. Plant Physiol. **39**, Suppl.

RIER J.P. & HENDERSON J.H.M. 1956 Effect of bacitracin on sunflower tissue cultures contaminated with bacteria. J. Nat. Cancer Inst. **16**, 981–984.

RIGHETTI B., MAGNANINI E. & MACCAFERRI M. 1988 Ethylene and other volatile substances produced by *in vitro*-cultured *Prunus avium*. Acta Hort. **227**, 402–404.

RIGHETTI B., MAGNANINI E., INFANTE R. & PREDIERI S. 1990 Ethylene, ethanol, acetaldehyde and carbon dioxide released by *Prunus avium* shoot cultures. Physiol. Plant. **78**, 507–510.

RINCÓN M., CHEN Q. & BOSS W.F. 1989 Characterization of inositol phosphates in carrot (*Daucus carota* L.) cells. Plant Physiol. **89**, 126–132.

RINGE F. 1972 Forderung der Zellproliferation unter der Einwirkung von 2-Chlorathylphosphorsaure bei Explantaten von *Begonia* × *richmondensis* in steriler Kultur. Z. Pflanzenphysiol. **67**, 45–48.

RIOV J. & YANG S.F. 1982 Stimulation of ethylene production in *Citrus* leaf discs by mannitol. Plant Physiol. **70**, 142–146.

RISSER P.G. & WHITE P.R. 1964 Nutritional requirements of Spruce tumour cells *in vitro*. Physiol. Plant. **17**, 620–635.

RITCHIE G.A. & LONG A.J. 1986 Field performance of micropropagated Douglas fir. N. Z. J. Forest Sci. **16**, 343–356.

ROBB S.M. 1957 The culture of excised tissue from bulb scales of *Lilium speciosum*. J. Exp. Bot. **8**, 348–352.

ROBBINS J.A., KAYS S.J. & DIRR M.A. 1981 Ethylene and its role in the rooting of wounded Mung Bean cuttings. HortScience **16**, 401 (abst.).

ROBBINS W.J. 1922a Cultivation of excised root tips and stem tips under sterile conditions. Bot. Gaz. **73**, 376–390.

ROBBINS W.J. 1922b Effect of autolized yeast and peptone in growth of excised corn root tips. Bot. Gaz. **74**, 59–79.

ROBBINS W.J. & BARTLEY M.A. 1937 Vitamin B, and the growth of excised tomato roots. Science **85**, 246–247.

ROBBINS W.J. & HERVEY A. 1970 Tissue culture of callus from seedling and adult stages of *Hedera helix*. Am. J. Bot. **57**, 452–457.

ROBBINS W.J. & SCHMIDT M.B. 1939a Vitamin B$_6$, a growth substance for isolated tomato roots. Proc. Nat. Acad. Sci. Wash. **25**, 1–3.

ROBBINS W.J. & SCHMIDT M.B. 1939b Further experiments on excised tomato roots. Am. J. Bot. **26**, 149–159.

ROBERT M.L., ROBLES M. & LOYOLA-VARGAS V.M. 1986 Growth promoting activity of certain penicillins on cultured cells of *Bouvardia ternifolia*. p. 300 *in* Somers *et al.* (eds.) 1986 (*q.v.*).

ROBERT N.L., TAYLOR H.F. & WAIN R.L. 1975 Ethylene production by cress roots and excised cress root segments and its inhibition by 3,5-diiodo-4-hydroxybenzoic acid. Planta **126**, 273–284.

ROBERTS D.R., FLINN B.S. & SUTTON B.C.S. 1989a Desiccation promotes and synchronizes the germination of white spruce somatic embryos. Plant Physiol. **89**, (Suppl.) 9 (Abst.).

ROBERTS D.R., FLINN B.S., WEBB D.T., WEBSTER F.W. & SUTTON B.C.S. 1989b The role of abscisic acid and indole-butyric acid in the differentiation and quality of somatic embryos of white spruce. Plant Physiol. **89**, (Suppl.) 9 (Abst.).

ROBERTS D.R., WALKER M.A., THOMPSON J.E. & DUMBROFF E.B. 1983 The effects of inhibitors of polyamine and ethylene biosynthesis on senescence, ethylene production and polyamine levels in cut carnations. Plant Cell Physiol. **25**, 315–322.

ROBERTS L.W. 1969 The initiation of xylem differentiation. Bot. Rev. **35**, 201–250.

ROBERTS L.W. & FOSKET D.E. 1966 Interaction of gibberellic acid and indoleacetic acid in the differentiation of wound vessel members. New Phytol. **65**, 5–8.

ROBERTSON D. & EARLE E.D. 1986 Plant regeneration from leaf protoplasts of *Brassica oleracea* var. italica cv. Green Comet broccoli. Plant Cell Rep. **5**, 61–64.

ROBIE C.A. & MINOCHA S.C. 1989 Polyamines and somatic embryogenesis in carrot. I. The effects of difluoromethylornithine and difluoromethylarginine. Plant Science **65**, 45–54.

ROBINSON K.E.P. & ADAMS D.O. 1987 The role of ethylene in the regeneration of *Helianthus annuus* (sunflower) plants from callus. Physiol. Plant. **71**, 151–156.

ROCA W.M., BRYAN J.E. & ROCA M.R. 1979 Tissue culture for the international transfer of potato genetic resources. Am. Pot. J. **56**, 1–10.

ROCA W.M., ESPINOZA N.O., ROCA M.R. & BRYAN J.E. 1978 A tissue culture method for the rapid propagation of potatoes. Am. Pot. J. **55**, 691–701.

ROCA W.M., RODRÍGUEZ J., BELTRAN J., ROA J. & MAFLA G. 1982 Tissue culture for the conservation and international exchange of germplasm. pp. 771–772 *in* Fujiwara (ed.) 1982 (*q.v.*).

RODAWAY S. & LUTZ A.W. 1985 Nitroguanidines: a new class of synthetic cytokinins. Plant Physiol. **77**, Suppl. 21 (Abst. 109).

RODRÍGUEZ G. & LORENZO MARTIN J.R. 1987 *In vitro* propagation of Canary Island banana (*Musa acuminata* Colla AAA var. Dwarf Cavendish). Studies of factors affecting culture obtention, preservation and conformity of the plants. Acta Hort. **212**, 577–583.

RODRÍGUEZ R. 1982 b Stimulation of multiple shoot-bud formation in walnut seeds. HortScience **17**, 592.

RODRÍGUEZ R., DIAZ-SALA C., CUOZZO L. & ANCORA G. 1991 Pear *in vitro* propagation using a double-phase culture system. HortScience **26**, 62–64.

ROEST S. 1977 Vegetative propagation *in vitro* and its significance for mutation breeding. Acta Hort. **78**, 349–359.

ROEST S. & BOKELMANN G.S. 1975 Vegetative propagation of *Chrysanthemum morifolium* Ram. *in vitro*. Scientia Hort. **3**, 317–330.

ROGLER C.E. & DAHMUS M.E. 1974 Gibberellic acid-induced phase change in *Hedera helix* as studied by deoxyribonucleic acid-ribonucleic acid hybridization. Plant Physiol. **54**, 88–94.

ROGOZINSKA J.H., KROON C. & SALEMINK C.A. 1973 Influence of alterations in the purine ring on biological activity of cytokinins. Phytochem. **12**, 2087–2092.

ROH M.S. & WOCIAL M. 1989 *In vitro* production of *Achimenantha* 'Inferno' as influenced by season and the source of explants. Acta Hort. **252**, 129–136.

ROMBERGER J.A. & TABOR C.A. 1971 The *Picea abies* shoot apical meristem in culture. I. Agar and autoclaving effects. Am. J. Bot. **58**, 131–140.

ROMBERGER J.A., VARNELL R.J. & TABOR C.A. 1970 Culture of apical meristems and embryonic shoots of *Picea abies* — approach and techniques. U.S.D.A. Technical Bull. **1409**, 1–30.

RÖMHELD V. & MARSCHNER H. 1983 Mechanism of iron uptake by peanut plants. Plant Physiol. **71**, 949–954.

RÖMHELD V. & MARSCHNER H. 1986 Evidence for a specific uptake system for iron phytosiderophores in roots of grasses. Plant Physiol. **80**, 175–180.

ROSATI P., MARINO G. & SWIERCZEWSKI C. 1980 *In vitro* propagation of Japanese plum (*Prunus salicina* Lindl. cv. Calita). J. Am. Soc. Hort. Sci. **105**, 126–129.

ROSCOE D.H. & BELL G.M. 1981 Use of an indicator in protoplast culture medium. Plant Sci. Lett. **21**, 275–279.

ROSE D. & MARTIN S.M. 1975 Effect of ammonium on growth of plant cells (*Ipomoea* sp.) in suspension cultures. Can. J. Bot. **53**, 1942–1949.

ROSE R.J., LOWELL B., JOHNSON L.B. & KEMBLE R.J. 1986a Restriction endonuclease studies on the chloroplast and mitochondrial DNAs of alfalfa (*Medicago sativa* L.) protoclones. Plant Molec. Biol. **6**, 331–338.

ROSNER A., GRESSEL J. & JAKOB K.M. 1977 Discoordination of ribosomal RNA metabolism during metabolic shifts of *Spirodela* plants. Biochim. Biophy. Acta **474**, 386–397.

ROSS S.D., PIESCH R.F. & PORTLACK F.F. 1981 Promotion of cone and seed production in rooted ramets and seedlings of western hemlock by gibberellins and adjunct cultural treatments. Can. J. For. Res. **1**, 90–98.

ROSSIGNOL M., SANTONI V., SZPONARSKI W. & VANSUYT G. 1990 Differential sensitivity to auxin at the plasma membrane level. pp. 498–503 in Nijkamp *et al.* (eds.) 1990 (*q.v.*).

ROTHWELL K. & WRIGHT S.T.C. 1967 Phytokinin activity in some new 6-substituted purines. Proc. Roy. Soc. **167B**, 202–223.

ROUAN D. & GUERCHE P. 1991 Transformation and regeneration of oil seed protoplasts. Section B4 pp. 1–24 in Lindsey (ed.) 1991 (*q.v.*).

ROY S.C. 1980 Chromosomal variations in the callus tissues of *Allium tuberosum* and *A. cepa*. Protoplasma **102**, 171–176.

RUBENSTEIN L., GENGENBACH B., PHILLIPS R.L. & GREEN C.E. 1980 *Genetic Improvement of Crop Plants — Emergent Techniques.* Univ. Minnesota Press, Minneapolis.

RUBERY P.H. 1979 The effects of (3-phenyl-1,2,4-thiadiazol-5- yl)thio acetic acid, a systemic growth regulator, on auxin uptake by tobacco stem segments and crown gall suspension culture cells. Plant Sci. Lett. **14**, 365–371.

RUBERY P.H. 1980 The mechanism of transmembrane auxin transport and its relation to the chemiosmotic hypothesis of the polar transport of auxin. pp. 50–60 in Skoog F. (ed.) 1980 (*q.v.*).

RUBLUO A., KARTHA K.K., MROGINSKI L.A. & DYCK J. 1984 Plant regeneration from pea leaflets cultured *in vitro* and genetic stability of regenerants. J. Plant Physiol. **117**, 119–130.

RÜCKER W. 1982a Combined influence of indoleacetic acid, gibberellic acid and benzylaminopurine or callus and organ differentiation in *Digitalis purpurea* leaf explants. Z. Pflanzenphysiol. **107**, 141–151.

RUDDAT M., KOKONTIS J. & SHOUP J.R. 1979 *In vitro* culture of isolated male and female flower buds from *Silene alba*. Plant Physiol. **63**, (Suppl. 5) Abst. 759.

RUGINI E. 1986 Olive. pp. 253–266 in Bajaj Y.P.S. (ed.) 1986 *Biotechnology in Agriculture and Forestry* Vol 1., Springer-Verlag.

RUGINI E. & FONTANAZZA G. 1981 *In vitro* propagation of 'Dolce Agogia' olive. HortScience **16**, 492–493.

RUGINI E. & VERMA D.C. 1982 Micropropagation and cell suspensions of a difficult to propagate almond (*Prunus amygdalus* Batch) cultivar. pp. 741–742 in Fujiwara (ed.) 1982 (*q.v.*).

RUGINI E. & VERMA D.C. 1983 Micropropagation of difficult-to-propagate Almond (*Prunus amygdalus*) cultivar. Plant Sci. Lett. **28**, 273–281.

RUGINI E., BAZZOFFIA A. & JACOBONI A. 1988 A simple *in vitro* method to avoid the initial dark period and to increase rooting in fruit trees. Acta Hort. **227**, 438–440.

RUGINI E., TARINI P. & ROSSODIVITA M.E. 1987 Control of shoot vitrification of almond and olive grown *in vitro*. Acta Hort. **212**, 177–183.

RUPERT E.A., SEO A., BROWNE W.C. & GIBSON P.B. 1976 Differentiation in callus and cell suspension cultures of *Trifolium* species and hybrids. Agronomy Abstracts, Am. Soc. Agron.

RUSSELL J.A. & McCOWN B.H. 1986a Culture and regeneration of *Populus* leaf protoplasts isolated from non-seedling tissue. Plant Science **46**, 133–142.

RUSSELL J.A. & McCOWN B.H. 1988a Recovery of plants from leaf protoplasts of hybrid-poplar and aspen clones. Plant Cell Rep. **7**, 59–62.

RUTE T.N., BUTENKO R.G. & MAURINYA Kh.A. 1978 Effect of growth conditions on morphogenesis of apical meristem tissues from cucumber plants cultivated *in vitro*. Soviet Plant Physiol. **25**, 432–438.

RYAN J. & JULIEN D. 1988 Crosslinked silicone coatings for botanical seeds. U.S. Patent No. 4753 035.

RYU S.B., LI P.H. & BRENNER M.L. 1988 Purification and estimation of ABA from potato cell suspension. HortScience **23**, 754.

SAALBACH G. & KOBLITZ H. 1978 Attempts to initiate callus formation from barley leaves. Plant Sci. Lett. **13**, 165–169.

SACHAR R.C. & IYER R.D. 1959 Effect of auxin, kinetin and gibberellin on the placental tissue of *Opuntia dillenii* Haw. cultured *in vitro*. Phytomorph. **9**, 1–3.

SACHS T. & THIMANN K.V. 1964 Release of lateral buds from apical dominance. Nature **201**, 939–940.

SACRISTÁN M.D. 1967 Auxin-autotrophie and chromosomenzahl-Untersuchungen an alten, spontan habituierten and crowngall-kallus-kulturen von *Nicotiana tabacum* aus dem Laboratorium Gautherets. Mol. Gen. Genet. **99**, 311–321.

SACRISTÁN M.D. & LUTZ A.M. 1970 Etude du nombre chromosomique sur de plantes de tabac d'origine unicellulaire. Compt. Rend. Acad. Sci. Paris **270D**, 1334–1336.

SACRISTÁN M.D. & MELCHERS G. 1969 The caryological analysis of plants regenerated from tumorous and other callus cultures of tobacco. Mol. Gen. Genet. **105**, 317–333.

SADASIVAN V. 1951 The phosphatases in coconut (*Cocos nucifera*). Arch. Biochem. **30**, 159–164.

SAGAWA Y. & KUNISAKI J.T. 1982 Clonal propagation of orchids by tissue culture. pp. 683–684 in Fujiwara A. (ed.) 1982 (*q.v.*).

SAGAWA Y. & SHOJI T. 1967 Clonal propagation of *Dendrobiums* through shoot meristem culture. Am. Orchid Soc. Bull. **36**, 856–859.

SAGLIO P., L'HOPITAL D., LAFLECHE G., DUPONT J.M., BOVÉ J.G. & TULLEY F.E.A. 1973 *Spiroplasma citri* gen. and sp. n: a mycoplasma-like organism associated with 'stubborn' disease of *Citrus*. Int. J. Syst. Bacteriol. **23**, 191–204.

SAGLIO P.H., RANCILLAC M., BRUZAN F. & PRADET A. 1984 Critical oxygen pressure for growth and respiration of excised and intact roots. Plant Physiol. **76**, 151–154.

SAHAVACHARIN O. 1982 Rapid propagation of *Caladium* through tissue culture. pp. 699–700 in Fujiwara (ed.) 1982 (*q.v.*).

SAID A.G.E. & MURASHIGE T. 1979 Continuous cultures of tomato and citron roots *in vitro*. In Vitro **15**, 593–602.

SAKAI A. 1984 Cryopreservation of apical meristems. Hort. Rev. **6**, 357–372.

SAKAI A. 1985 Cryopreservation of shoot tips of fruit trees and herbaceous plants. pp. 135–158 in Kartha K.K. (ed.) 1985a (*q.v.*).

SAKAI A. & SUGAWARA Y. 1973 Survival of poplar callus at super low temperatures after cold acclimation. Plant Cell Physiol. **14**, 1201–1204.

SALA F., PARISI B., CELLA R. & CIFERRI O. (eds.) 1980 *Plant Cell Cultures: Results and Perspectives*. Elsevier/North-Holland, Amsterdam, New York. ISBN 0-444-80204-5

SALEEM M. & CUTLER A.J. 1987 Stabilizing corn leaf protoplasts with n-propyl gallate. J. Plant Physiol. **128**, 479–484.

SALIN M.L. & BRIDGES S.M. 1981 Chemiluminescence in wounded root tissue. Plant Physiol. **67**, 43–46.

SALISBURY F.B. 1959 Growth regulators and flowering. II. The cobaltous ion. Plant Physiol. **34**, 598–604.

SAMARTIN A. 1989 A comparative study of effects of nutrient media and cultural conditions on shoot multiplication of *in vitro* cultures of *Camellia japonica* explants. J. Hort. Sci. **64**, 73–79.

SANCHEZ-GRAS M.C. & SEGURA J. 1988a Morphogenesis *in vitro* of *Sideritis angustifolia*: effect of auxins benzyladenine and spermidine. Plant Science **57**, 151–158.

SANDERS M.E. & ZIEBUR N.K. 1958 Artificial culture of embryos. pp. 297–325 *in* Maheshwari P. (ed.) *Recent Advances in Embryology of Angiosperms.* Univ. of Delhi: Int. Soc. for Plant Morphology.

SANDSTEDT R. & SKOOG F. 1960 Effects of amino acid components of yeast extract on the growth of tobacco tissue *in vitro.* Physiol. Plant. **13**, 250–256.

SANGWAN R.S. & HARADA H. 1975 Chemical regulation of callus growth, organogenesis, plant regeneration and somatic embryogenesis in *Antirrhinum majus* tissue and cell cultures. J. Exp. Bot. **26**, 868–881.

SANGWAN R.S. & SANGWAN-NORREEL B.S. 1990 Anther and pollen culture. *in* Bhojwani S.S. (ed.) 1990 *Plant Tissue Culture: Applications and Limitations.* Elsevier, Amsterdam.

SANGWAN R.S., NORREEL B. & HARADA H. 1976 Effects of kinetin and gibberellin A_3 on callus growth and orange formation in *Limnophila chinensis* tissue culture. Biol. Plant. **18**, 126–131.

SANGWAN-NORREEL B.S. 1977 Androgenic stimulating factors in the anther and isolated pollen grain culture of *Datura innoxia* Mill. J. Exp. Bot. **28**, 843–852.

SANKARA RAO K. & VENKATESWARA R. 1985 Tissue culture of forest trees: clonal multiplication of *Eucalyptus grandis.* Plant Science **40**, 51–55.

SANKHLA N. & SANDHLA D. 1968 Abscisin II-kinetin antagonism in growth of *Ipomaea* cotyledonary callus. Naturwiss. **55**, 91–92.

SANO K. & HIMENO H. 1987 *In vitro* proliferation of saffron (*Crocus sativus* L.) stigma. Plant Cell Tiss. Organ Cult. **11**, 159–166.

SANTOS I. & SALEMA R. 1989 Penicillins and activity of nitrogen metabolism emzymes in plant tissue cultures. Plant Science **59**, 119–125.

SARGENT J.A. & SKOOG F. 1960 Effects of indoleacetic acid and kinetin on scopoletin and scopolin levels in relation to growth of tobacco tissue *in vitro.* Plant Physiol. **35**, 934–941.

SARGENT P.A. & KING J. 1974 Investigations of growth-promoting factors in conditioned soybean root cells and in the liquid medium in which they grow: cytokinin-like compounds. Can. J. Bot. **52**, 2459–2463.

SARMA K.S., MAESATO K., HARA T. & SONADA Y. 1990 Effect of method of agar addition on post-autoclave pH of the tissue culture media. Ann. Bot. **65**, 37–40.

SATTER R.L. & GALSTON A.W. 1976 The physiological functions of phytochrome. pp. 680–735 *in* Goodwin T.W. (ed.) *The Chemistry & Biochemistry of Plant Pigments* 1. Academic Press, London, New York, San Francisco.

SAUERBREY P., GROSSMANN K. & JUNG J. 1987 Is ethylene involved in the regulation of growth of sunflower cell suspension cultures? J. Plant Physiol. **127**, 471–479.

SAUNDERS J.W. & BINGHAM E.T. 1972 Production of alfalfa plants from callus tissue. Crop Sci. **12**, 804–808.

SAUNDERS J.W. & BINGHAM E.T. 1975 Growth regulator effects on bud initiation in callus cultures of *Medicago sativa.* Am. J. Bot. **62**, 850–855.

SAUNDERS J.W., HOSFIELD G.L. & LEVI A. 1987 Morphogenetic effects of 2,4-dichlorophenoxyacetic acid on pinto bean (*Phaseolus vulgaris* L.) leaf explants *in vitro.* Plant Cell Rep. **6**, 46–49.

SAUNDERS M.J. & HEPLER P.K. 1981 Localization of membrane-associated calcium following cytokinin treatment in *Funaria* using chlorotetracycline. Planta **152**, 272–281.

SAUTON A., MOURAS A. & LUTZ A. 1982 Plant regeneration from citrus root meristems. J. Hort. Sci. **57**, 227–231.

SAVAGE A.D., KING J. & GAMBORG O.L. 1979 Recovery of a pantothenate auxotroph from a cell suspension culture of *Datura innoxia* Mill. Plant Sci. Lett. **16**, 367–376.

SCARAMUZZI F. & DE GAETANO A. 1974 Studies on the rooting of shoot explants of *O. europea* cv. Ogliarola di monopoli grown *in vitro.* Ortoflorofrutticoltura Ital. **58**, 419–436.

SCHAAD N.W. 1980 *Laboratory Guide for the Identification of Plant Pathogenic Bacteria.* The American Phytopathological Society, 3340 Pilot Knob Road, St. Paul, Minnesota 55121. ISBN 0-89054-028-4.

SCHAEFFER G.W. *et al.* 1980 Transcription of panel discussion on genetic stability of tissue cultured propagated plants. pp. 64–79 *in* Anon 1980.

SCHAEFFER G.W., BUTA J.G. & SHARPE F. 1967 Scopoletin and polyphenol-induced lag in peroxidase catalyzed oxidation of indole-3-acetic acid. Physiol. Plant. **20**, 342–347.

SCHAFER E., BRUNS B., FROHNMEYER H., HAALBROCK K., HARTER K., MERKLE T & OHL S. 1990 Phytochrome in plant cell cultures. pp. 355–365 *in* Nijkamp *et al.* (eds.) 1990 (*q.v.*).

SCHENK R.U. & HILDEBRANDT A.C. 1972 Medium and techniques for induction and growth of monocotyledonous and dicotyledonous plant cell cultures. Can. J. Bot. **50**, 199–204.

SCHERER P.A. 1988 Standardization of plant micropropagation by usage of a liquid medium with polyurethane foam plugs or a solidified medium with the gellan gum Gelrite instead of agar. Acta Hort. **226**, 107–114.

SCHERER R.A., MÜLLER E., LIPPERT H. & WOLFF G. 1988 Multielement analysis of agar and Gelrite impurities investigated by inductively coupled plasma emission spectrometry as well as physical properties of tissue culture media prepared with agar or the gellan gum Gelrite. Acta Hort. **226**, 655–658.

SCHIEDER O. & VASIL I.K. 1980 Protoplast fusion and somatic hybridization. pp. 21–46 *in* Vasil I.K. (ed.) 1980b (*q.v.*).

SCHILDE-RENTSCHLER L., ESPINOZA N., ESTRADA R. & LIZARRAGA R. 1982 *In vitro* storage and distribution of potato germplasm. pp. 781–782 *in* Fujiwara (ed.) 1982 (*q.v.*).

SCHMITZ R.Y. & SKOOG F. 1970 The use of dimethylsulfoxide as a solvent in the tobacco bioassay for cytokinins. Plant Physiol. **45**, 537–538.

SCHNAPP S.R. & PREECE J.E. 1986 *In vitro* growth reduction of tomato and carnation microplants. Plant Cell Tiss. Organ Cult. **6**, 3–8.

SCHOLL R.L., KEATHLEY D.E. & BARIBAULT T.J. 1981 Enhancement of root formation and fertility in shoots regenerated from anther– and seedling–derived callus cultures of *Arabidopsis thaliana.* Z. Pflanzenphysiol. **104**, 225–231.

SCHÖNER S. & REINHARD E. 1982 Clonal multiplication of *Digitalis lanata* by meristem culture. Planta Med. **45**, 155.

SCHÖNER S. & REINHARD E. 1986 Long-term cultivation of *Digitalis lanata* clones propagated *in vitro*: cardenolide content of the regenerated plants. Planta Med. **52**, 478–481.

SCHOTT H.-H. & SCHRAUDOLF H. 1967 Die wirkung einiger derivate der 9-fluorenol-9-carbonsaure auf die regeneration von begonienblattscheiben (*Begonia rex*). Z. Pflanzenphysiol. **56**, 387–396.

SCHRAUDOLF H. & REINERT J. 1959 Interaction of plant growth regulators in regeneration processes. Nature **184**, 465–466.

SCHROEDER C.A. & SPECTOR C. 1957 Effect of gibberellic acid and indoleacetic acid on growth of excised fruit tissue. Science **126**, 701–702.

SCHUBERT S. & MATZKE H. 1985 Influence of phytohormones and other effectors on proton extrusion by isolated protoplasts from rape leaves. Physiol. Plant. **64**, 285–289.

SCHULZE D. 1988 *Saintpaulia ionantha* H. Wendl. — *In vitro* propagation and acclimatization in a commercial laboratory. Acta Hort. **226**, 619–622.

SCHWAIGER G. & HORN W. 1988 Somaclonal variations in micropropagated *Kalanchoe* hybrids. Acta Hort. **226**, 695–698.

SCHWENK F.W. 1981 Callus formation from mechanically isolated mesophyll cells of soybean and sweet potato. Plant Sci. Lett. **23**, 147–151.

SCHWENK F.W., PEARSON C.A. & ROTH M.R. 1981 Soybean *Glycine max* cultivar Columbus mesophyll protoplasts. Plant Sci. Lett. **23**, 153–156.

SCHWENK F.W.A 1980 Callus formation from mechanically isolated soybean cotyledonary cells. Plant Sci. Lett. **17**, 437–442.

SCORTICHINI M. & CHIARIOTTI A. 1988 *In vitro* culture of *Prunus persica* var. laevis Gray (nectarine): detection of bacterial contaminants and possibility of decontamination by means of antibiotics. Acta Hort. **225**, 109–118.

SCORZA R. 1982 *In vitro* flowering. Hort. Rev. **4**, 106–127.

SCORZA R., WELKER W.V. & DUNN L.J. 1982 Effect of glyphosate N-(phosphonomethyl)glycine on *in vitro* shoot regeneration and development in cranberry (*Vaccinium macrocarpon* Ait.). HortScience **17**, 530 (Abst. 413).

SCORZA R., WELKER W.V. & DUNN L.J. 1984 The effects of glyphosate, auxin and cytokinin combinations on *in vitro* development of cranberry node explants. HortScience **19**, 66–68.

SCOTT J. & BREEN P. 1988 Sugar uptake by strawberry fruit discs and protoplasts. HortScience **23**, 756.

SCOTT K.J., DALY J. & SMITH H.H. 1964 Effects of indoleacetic acid and kinetin on activities of enzymes of the hexose monophosphate shunt in tissue cultures of *Nicotiana.* Plant Physiol. **39**, 709–712.

SCOTT-PEARSE F. 1991 Method of producing plant cell lines and plant hybrids. U.S. Patent No. 5043282

SCOWCROFT W.R. & ADAMSON J.A. 1976 Organogenesis from callus cultures of the legume *Stylosanthes hamata*. Plant Sci. Lett. **7**, 39–42.

SCOWCROFT W.R. & LARKIN P.J. 1980 Isolation, culture and plant regeneration from protoplasts of *Nicotiana debneyi*. Aust. J. Plant Physiol. **7**, 635–644.

SCULLY R.M. Jr. 1967 Aspects of meristem culture in *Cattleya* Alliance. Am. Orchid Soc. Bull. **36**, 103–108.

SEABROOK J.E.A. 1987 Changing the growth and morphology of potato plantlets *in vitro* by varying the illumination source. Acta Hort. **212**, 401–410.

SEABROOK J.E.A., CUMMING B.G. & DIONNE L.A. 1976 The *in vitro* induction of adventitious shoot and root apices on *Narcissus* (daffodil and narcissus) cultivar tissue. Can. J. Bot. **54**, 814–819.

SEARS R.G. & DECKARD E.L. 1982 Tissue culture variability in wheat: callus induction and plant regeneration. Crop Sci. **22**, 546–550.

SEBASTIAN K.T. & McCOMB J.A. 1986 A micropropagation system for carob (*Ceratonia siliqua* L.). Scientia Hort. **28**, 127–131.

SEELIGER I. 1956 Uber die Kultur isolierter Wurzeln de Robinie (*Robinia pseudoacacia* L.). Flora **144**, 47–83.

SEGRETAIN G. & HIRTH L. 1953 Action de substances azotées sur la multiplication du virus de la mosaique du tabac en culture de tissus. Compt. Rend. Seanc. Soc. Biol. **147**, 1042–1043.

SEIBERT M. 1976 Shoot initiation from carnation shoot apices frozen to -196°C. Science **191**, 1178–1179.

SEIBERT M. & WETHERBEE P.J. 1977 Increased survival and differentiation of frozen herbaceous plant organ cultures through cold treatment. Plant Physiol. **59**, 1043–1046.

SEIBERT M., WETHERBEE P. & JOB D. 1975 The effects of light intensity and spectral quality on growth and shoot initiation in tobacco callus. Plant Physiol. **56**, 130–139.

SEKIOKA T.T. & TANAKA J.S. 1981 Differentiation in callus cultures of cucumber (*Cucumis sativus* L.). HortScience **16**, 451 (Abst.386).

SEMAL J. (ed.) 1985 *Somaclonal Variation and Crop Improvement*. Martinus Nijhoff, Dordrecht.

SENARATNA T., McKERSIE B. & ECCLESTONE S. 1989b Germination of desiccated somatic embryos of alfalfa (*Medicago sativa* L.). Plant Physiol. **89**, 135 (Suppl.).

SENARATNA T., McKERSIE B., BOWLEY S., BEWLEY J. & BROWN D. 1987 Process to induce desiccation tolerance in somatic embryos. Europ. Patent Application No. 88306589 8.

SENARATNA T., McKERSIE B.D. & BOWLEY S. 1990 Artificial seeds of Alfalfa (*Medicago sativa* L.). Induction of desiccation tolerance in somatic embryos. In Vitro Cell Dev. Biol. **26**, 85–90.

SEO B.-B. & KIM H.-H. 1988 Regeneration of amphidiploid plants from tissue cultures of *Allium wakegi*. Plant Cell Rep. **7**, 297–300.

SERRES R.A. 1988 Effects of sucrose and basal medium concentration on *in vitro* rooting of American chestnut. HortScience **23**, 739.

SERVAITES J.C. & OGREN W.L. 1977 Rapid isolation of mesophyll cells from leaves of soybean for photosynthetic studies. Plant Physiol. **59**, 587–590.

SHA L., McCOWN B.H. & PETERSON L.A. 1985 Occurrence and cause of shoot-tip necrosis in shoot cultures. J. Am. Soc. Hort. Sci. **110**, 631–634.

SHAH D.M., ROGERS S., HORSCH R. & FRALEY R. 1990 Glyphosate-resistant plants. U.S. Patent No. 4940835

SHAH R.R. & DALAL K.C. 1980 *In vitro* multiplication of *Glycyrrhiza*. Current Sci. **49**, 69–71.

SHAH R.R. & DALAL K.C. 1982 *Glycyrrhiza glabra* (liquorice): from test tube to field. pp. 685–686 *in* Fujiwara (ed.) 1982 (*q.v.*).

SHAH V.C. 1976 Effects of some antibiotics on cell cycles and chromosomes. J. Cell Biol. **70**, 405a (Abs. 1215).

SHANNON J.C. & BATEY J.W. 1973 Inbred and hybrid effects on establishment of *in vitro* cultures of *Zea mays* L. endosperm. Crop Sci. **13**, 491–493.

SHANTZ E.M. & STEWARD F.C. 1952 Coconut milk factor: the growth-promoting substances in coconut milk. J. Am. Chem. Soc. **74**, 6133.

SHANTZ E.M. & STEWARD F.C. 1955 The identification of compound A from coconut milk as 1,3-diphenylurea. J. Am. Chem. Soc. **77**, 6351–6353.

SHANTZ E.M. & STEWARD F.C. 1956 The general nature of some nitrogen free growth-promoting substances from *Aesculus* and *Cocos*. Plant Physiol. **30**, Suppl. XXXV.

SHANTZ E.M. & STEWARD F.C. 1964 Growth-promoting substances from the environment of the embryo. II. The growth-stimulating complexes of coconut milk, corn and *Aesculus*. pp. 59–75 *in* Actes du Coll. Int. C.N.R.S. No. 123.

SHARMA A.K., PRASAD R.N. & CHATURVEDI H.C. 1981a Clonal propagation of *Bougainvillea glabra* 'Magnifica' through shoot apex culture. Plant Cell Tiss. Organ Cult. **1**, 33–38.

SHARMA C.P. & SINGH S. 1990 Sodium helps overcome potassium deficiency effects on water relations of cauliflower. HortScience **25**, 458–459.

SHARMA D.R., CHOWDHURY J.B., AHUJA U. & DHANKHAR B.S. 1980 Interspecific hybridization in genus *Solanum*, a cross between *S. melongena* and *S. khasianum* through embryo culture. Z. Pflanzenzuchtg. **85**, 248–253.

SHARP W.R. & EVANS D.A. 1982 Application of somatic embryogenesis to crop improvement. pp. 759–762 *in* Fujiwara A. (ed.) 1982 (*q.v.*).

SHARP W.R., EVANS D.A., AMMIRATO P.V. & YAMADA Y. (eds.) 1984 *Handbook of Plant Cell Culture* Vol 2. *Crop Species*. Macmillan Publishing Co., New York, London.

SHARP W.R., LARSEN P.O., PADDOCK E.F. & RAGHAVAN V. (eds.) 1979 *Plant Cell and Tissue Culture*. Ohio State Univ. Press, Colombus.

SHARP W.R., SONDAHL M.R., CALDAS L.S. & MARAFFA S.B. 1980 The physiology of *in vitro* asexual embryogenesis. Hort. Rev. **2**, 268–310.

SHARROCK R.A. & QUAIL P.H. 1989 Novel phytochrome sequences in *Arabidopsis thaliana*: structure, evolution and differential expression of a plant regulatory photoreceptor family. Genes and Development **3**, 1745–1757.

SHEA E.M., SKARIA A. & CARPITA N.C. 1988 Growth of carrot cell suspension cultures in medium containing amino acid conjugates of indoleacetic acid. J. Plant Physiol. **132**, 298–302.

SHEAT D.E.G., FLETCHER B.H. & STREET H.E. 1959 Studies on the growth of excised roots. VIII. The growth of excised tomato roots supplied with various inorganic sources of nitrogen. New Phytol. **58**, 128–141.

SHEERMAN S. & BEVAN M.W. 1988 A rapid tansformation method for *Solanum tuberosum* using binary *Agrobacterium tumefaciens* vectors. Plant Cell Rep. **7**, 13–16.

SHEKHAWAT N.S. & GALSTON A.W. 1983b Mesophyll protoplasts of fenugreek (*Trigonella foenumgraecum*): Isolation, culture and shoot regeneration. Plant Cell Rep. **2**, 119–121.

SHELTON B.B., EVANS G.F. & BOSS W.F. 1981 During embryogenesis, do cells exhibit polarity prior to morphological differentiation? Env. Exp. Bot. **21**, 426 (Abst.).

SHEPARD J.F. 1975 Regeneration of plants from protoplasts of potato virus X infected tobacco leaves. Virology **66**, 492–501.

SHEPARD J.F. 1977a Regeneration of plants from protoplasts of potato virus X infected leaves. II. Influence of Virazole on the frequency of infection. Virology **78**, 261–266.

SHEPARD J.F. 1980a Abscisic acid-enhanced shoot initiation in protoplast-derived calli of potato. Plant Sci. Lett. **18**, 327–333.

SHEPARD J.F. 1980b Mutant selection and plant regeneration from potato mesophyll protoplasts. pp. 185–219 *in* Rubenstein *et al.* (eds.) 1980 (*q.v.*).

SHEPARD J.F. & TOTTEN R.E. 1977 Mesophyll cell protoplasts of potato: isolation, proliferation and plant regeneration. Plant Physiol. **60**, 313–316.

SHEPHERD N., SCHWARZ Z., WIENAND U., SOMMER H., SAEDLER H., HAHLBROCK K., KREUZALER F., RAGG H. & PETERSON P.A. 1982 Genomic DNA clones of *Zea mays*. pp. 217–219 *in* Sheridan W.F. (ed.) 1982 *Maize for Biological Research*, Plant Mol. Biol. Association, Charlottesville, U.S.A. ISBN 0-9608758-0-8

SHERIDAN W.F. 1974 A long term callus culture of *Lilium*: relative stability of the karyotype. J. Cell Biol. **63**, 313a (Abst. 625).

SHERIDAN W.F. 1975 Plant regeneration and chromosome stability in tissue cultures. pp. 263–295 *in* Ledoux L. (ed.) 1975 (*q.v.*).

SHIELDS R., ROBINSON S.J. & ANSLOW P.A. 1984 Use of fungicides in plant tissue culture. Plant Cell Rep. **3**, 33–36.

SHILLITO R.D., PASZKOWSKI J. & POTRYKUS I. 1983 Agarose plating and a bead type culture technique enable and stimulate development of protoplast-derived colonies in a number of plant species. Plant Cell Rep. **2**, 244–247.

SHIMADA N., TANAKA F. & KOZAI T. 1988 Effects of low O_2 concentration on net photosynthesis of C_3 plantlets *in vitro*. Acta Hort. **230**, 171–175.

SHIMADA T. & MAKINO T. 1975 In vitro culture of wheat. III.Anther culture of the A genome aneuploids in common wheat. Theor. Appl. Genet. **46**, 407–410.

SHININGER T.L. 1979 The control of vascular development. Ann. Rev. Plant Physiol. **30**, 313–337.

SHKOLNIK M. YA. 1984 *Trace Elements in Plants.* Developments in Crop Science 6. Elsevier Amsterdam, Oxford, New York, Tokyo.

SHOEMAKER N.P. & SWARTZ H.J. 1985 Cultivar dependent variation in pathogen resistance due to tissue culture propagation of strawberries. HortScience **20**, 253–254.

SHOEMAKER R.C., ATHERLY A.G. & PALMER R.G. 1983 Inhibition of deoxyribonuclease activity associated with soybean chloroplasts. Plant Cell Rep. **2**, 98–100.

SHOLTO DOUGLAS J. 1976 *Advanced Guide to Hydroponics.* Pelham Books, London. ISBN 0 7207 08303.

SHORT K.C. & TORREY J.G. 1972a Cytokinins in seedling roots of pea. Plant Physiol. **49**, 155–160.

SHORT K.C. & TORREY J.G. 1972b Cytokinin production in relation to the growth of pea-root callus tissue. J. Exp. Bot. **23**, 1099–1105.

SHORT K.C., WARBURTON J. & ROBERT A.V. 1987 *In vitro* hardening of cultured cauliflower and chrysanthemum plantlets to humidity. Acta Hort. **212**, 329–334.

SHOYAMA Y., KAMURA K. & NISHIOKA I. 1988 Somatic embryogenesis and clonal multiplication of *Panax ginseng.* Planta Med. **54**, 155–156.

SHU O. WANG & SU SHIEN MA 1978 Clonal multiplication of *Chrysanthemum in vitro.* J. Agric. Assoc. China **101**, 64–73.

SHVETSOV S.G. & GAMBURG K.Z. 1981 Uptake of 2,4-D by corn cells in a suspension culture. Dokl. Akad. Nank S.S.S.R. **257**, 765–768.

SIBI M. 1976 La notion de programme génétiques chez les végétaux superieur. II. Aspect expérimental. Obtention de variants par culture de tissus *in vitro* sur *Lactuca sativa* L. Apparition de vigeur chez les croisement. Ann. Amel. Plantes **26**, 523–547.

SIEGEL S.M. & PORTO F. 1961 Oxidants, antioxidants and growth regulation. pp. 341–353 in *Plant Growth Regulation.* Iowa State University Press, Ames, Iowa.

SIEVERT R.C. & HILDEBRANDT A.C. 1965 Variations within single cell clones of tobacco tissue cultures. Am. J. Bot. **52**, 742–750.

SIHACHAKR D., HAICOUR R., SERRAF I., BARRIENTOS E., HERBRETEAU C., DUCREUX G. ROSSIGNOL L. & SOUVANNAVONG V. 1988 Electrofusion for the production of somatic hybrid plants of *Solanum melongena* L. and *Solanum khasianum* C.B. Clark. Plant Science **57**, 215–223.

SIM G.-E., LOH C.-H. & GOH C.-J. 1988 Direct somatic embryogenesis from protoplasts of *Citrus mitis* Blanco. Plant Cell Rep. **7**, 418–420.

SIM G.E., GOH C.J. & LOH C.S. 1989 Micropropagation of *Citrus mitis* Blanco — multiple bud formation from shoot and root explants in the presence of 6-benzylaminopurine. Plant Science **59**, 203–210.

SIMMONDS J. 1981 *In vitro* flower bud production on leaf explants of *Streptocarpus nobilis.* Plant Physiol. **67**, (Suppl.) 27 (Abst. 143).

SIMMONDS J. 1982 *In vitro* flowering on leaf explants of *Streptocarpus nobilis.* The influence of culture medium components on vegetative and reproductive development. Can. J. Bot. **60**, 1461–1468.

SIMMONDS J.A. & CUMMING B.G. 1976b Propagation of *Lilium* hybrids. II. Production of plantlets from bulb scale callus cultures for increased propagation rates. Scientia Hort. **5**, 161–170.

SIMMONDS J.A. & NELSON S.D. 1989 Improved micropagation of *Begonia × hiemalis* by maintaining donor plants in long- day conditions. HortScience **24** 831–832.

SIMMONDS J.A. & WERRY T. 1987 Liquid-shake culture for improved micropropagation of *Begonia × hiemalis.* HortScience **22**, 122–124.

SIMON P.W. & PELOQUIN S.J. 1977 The influence of paternal species on the origin of callus in anther culture of *Solanum* hybrids. Theor. Appl. Genet. **50**, 53–56.

SIMONSON J. & HILDEBRANDT A.C. 1971 *In vitro* growth and differentiation of *Gladiolus* plants from callus cultures. Can. J. Bot. **49**, 1817–1819.

SIMPKINS I., WALKEY D.G.A. & NEELY H.A. 1981 Chemical suppression of virus in cultured plant tissues. Ann. Appl. Biol. **99**, 161–169.

SINGH B.D. & HARVEY B.L. 1975 Selection for diploid cells in suspension cultures of *Haplopappus gracilis.* Nature **253**, 453.

SINGH B.D., HARVEY B.L., KAO K.N. & MILLER R.A. 1975 Karyotypic changes and selection pressure in *Haplopappus gracilis* suspension cultures. Can. J. Genet. Cytol. **17**, 109–116.

SINGH F. & PRAKASH D. 1984 *In vitro* propagation of *Thunia alba* (Wall.) Reichb.F. through flower stalk cuttings. Scientia Hort. **24**, 385–390.

SINGH J.P. 1978 Effect of nitrogen sources on shoot bud differentiation of *Dioscorea deltoidea* Wall. callus culture. Biol. Plant. **20**, 436–439.

SINGH M. & KRIKORIAN A.D. 1980 Chelated iron in culture media. Ann. Bot. **46**, 807–809.

SINGH M. & KRIKORIAN A.D. 1981 White's standard nutrient solution. Ann. Bot. **47**, 133–139.

SINGH M.N., KONAR R.N. & BHATNAGAR S.P. 1981 Haploid plantlet formation from female gametophytes of *Ephedra foliata* Boiss. *in vitro.* Ann. Bot. **48**, 215–220.

SINGHA S. 1982a Effect of agar concentrations on shoot proliferation of pear and crabapple *in vitro.* HortScience **17**, 531 (Abst.416).

SINGHA S. 1982c Influence of agar concentration on *in vitro* shoot proliferation of *Malus* sp. 'Almey' and *Pyrus communis* 'Seckel'. J. Am. Soc. Hort. Sci. **107**, 657–660.

SINGHA S. 1984 Influence of two commercial agars on *in vitro* shoot proliferation of 'Almey' crabapple and 'Seckel' pear. HortScience **19**, 227–228.

SINGHA S. & BHATIA S.K. 1988 Shoot proliferation of pear cultures on medium containing thidiazuron and benzylamino purine. HortScience **23**, 803.

SINGHA S., BISSONNETTE G.K. & DOUBLE M.L. 1987a Methods for sterilising instruments contaminated with *Bacillus* sp. from plant tissue cultures. HortScience **22**, 659.

SINGHA S., OBERLEY G.H. & TOWNSEND E.C. 1987b Changes in nutrient composition and pH of the culture medium during *in vitro* shoot proliferation of crab apple and pear. Plant Cell Tiss. Organ Cult. **11**, 209–220.

SINGHA S., TOWNSEND E.C. & OBERLY G.H. 1985 Agar induced variations in the nutritional composition of pear and crabapple shoots *in vitro.* p. 351 *in* Henke *et al.* (eds.) 1985 (*q.v.*).

SIRIWARDANA S. & NABORS M.W. 1983 Tryptophan enhancement of somatic embryogenesis in rice. Plant Physiol. **73**, 142–146.

SITBON M. 1981 Production of haploid *Gerbera jamesonii* plants by *in vitro* culture of unfertilized ovules. Agronomie **1**, 807-812.

SKELLERN G.G. 1989 Thiocarbamides. pp. 49–89 *in* Damani L.A. (ed.) 1989 *Sulphur-containing Drugs and Related Organic Compounds: Chemistry, Biochemistry and Toxicology.* Vol. 1. Part B. *Metabolism of Sulphur Functional Groups.* Ellis Horwood Ltd. Chichester.

SKENE K.G.M. 1972a Cytokinin like properties of the systemic fungicide benomyl. J. Hort. Sci. **47**, 179–182.

SKENE K.G.M. 1972b Cytokinins in the bleeding sap of the grape vine. pp. 476–483 *in* Carr D.J. (ed.) 1972 (*q.v.*).

SKENE K.G.M. & BARLASS M. 1981 Micropropagation of grapevine. Comb. Proc. Int. Plant Prop. Soc. 1980 **30**, 564–570.

SKIDMORE D.I., SIMMONS A.J. & BEDI S. 1988 *In vitro* culture of shoots of *Pinus caribala* on a liquid medium. Plant Cell Tiss. Organ Cult. **14**, 129–136.

SKINNER J.C. & STREET H.E. 1954 Studies on the growth of excised roots. II. Observations on the growth of excised groundsel roots. New Phytol. **53**, 44–67.

SKIRM G.W. 1942 Embryo culturing as an aid to plant breeding. J. Hered. **33**, 211–215.

SKIRVIN R.M. 1977 Natural and induced variation in tissue culture. Euphytica **27**, 241–266.

SKIRVIN R.M. 1981 Fruit crops. pp. 51–139 *in* Conger B.V. (ed.) 1981 (*q.v.*).

SKIRVIN R.M. & CHU M.C. 1978a *Rubus* tissue culture. p. 253 *in* Hughes et al. (eds.) 1978 (*q.v.*).

SKIRVIN R.M. & CHU M.C. 1978b Tissue culture of peach shoot tips. HortScience **13**, 349 (Abst.81).

SKIRVIN R.M. & JANICK J. 1976a 'Velvet Rose' *Pelargonium,* a scented geranium. HortScience **11**, 61-62.

SKIRVIN R.M., CHU M.C., MANN M.L., YOUNG H., SULLIVAN J. & FERMANIAN T. 1986 Stability of tissue culture medium pH as a function of autoclaving, time, and cultured plant material. Plant Cell Rep. **5**, 292–294.

SKOKUT T.A. & FILNER P. 1980 Slow adaptive changes in urease levels of tobacco cells cultured on urea and other nitrogen sources. Plant Physiol. **65**, 995–1003.

SKOOG F. 1940 Relationship between zinc and auxin in the growth of higher plants. Am. J. Bot. **27**, 939–951.

SKOOG F. 1944 Growth and organ formation in tobacco tissue cultures. Am. J. Bot. **31**, 19–24.

SKOOG F. 1980 *Plant Growth Substances.* Proc. 10th Int. Conf. Plant Growth Substances, Madison, Wisconsin, 1979. Springer-Verlag, Berlin, Heidelberg.

SKOOG F. & MILLER C.O. 1957 Chemical regulation of growth and organ formation in plant tissues cultured *in vitro.* Symp. Soc. Exp. Biol. **11**, 118–131.

SKOOG F. & MONTALDI E. 1961 Auxin-kinetin interaction regulating the scopoletin and scopolin levels in tobacco tissue cultures. Proc. Nat. Acad. Sci. U.S.A. **47**, 36–49.

SKOOG F. & TSUI C. 1948 Chemical control of growth and bud formation in tobacco stem segments and callus cultured *in vitro.* Am. J. Bot. **35**, 782–787.

SKOOG F., SCHMITZ R.Y., BOCK R.M. & HECHT S.M. 1973 Cytokinin antagonists: synthesis and physiological effects of 7-substituted 3-methyepyrazolo (4;3-*d*) pyrimidines. Phytochem. **12**, 25–37.

SKOOG F., SCHMITZ R.Y., HECHT S.M. & FRYE R.B. 1975 Anticytokinin activity of substituted pyrrolo 2,3-*d* pyrimidines. Proc. Nat. Acad. Sci. U.S.A. **72**, 3508–3512.

SKOOG F., STRONG F.M. & MILLER C.O. 1965 Cytokinins. Science **148**, 532–533.

SLOCUM R.D., KAUR-SAWHNEY R. & GALSTON A.W. 1984 The physiology and biochemistry of polyamines in plants. Archiv. Biochem. Biophys. **235**, 283–303.

SMAGULA J. M. & LYRENE P. M. 1984 Chapter 15 — Blueberry. pp. 383–401 *in* Ammirato *et al.* (eds.) 1984 (*q.v.*).

SMITH C.W. 1967 A study of the growth of excised embryo shoot apices of wheat *in vitro.* Ann. Bot. **31**, 593–605.

SMITH D.L. 1968 The growth of shoot apices and inflorescences of *Carex flacca* Schreb. in aseptic culture. Ann. Bot. **32**, 361–370.

SMITH D.L. & KRIKORIAN A.D. 1988 Production of somatic embryos from carrot tissues in hormone-free medium. Plant Science **58**, 103–110.

SMITH D.L. & KRIKORIAN A.D. 1989 Release of somatic embryogenic potential from excised zygotic embryos of carrot and maintenance of polyembryonic cultures in hormone-free medium. Am. J. Bot. **76**, 1832–1843.

SMITH D.L. & KRIKORIAN A.D. 1990a Somatic proembryo production from excised wounded zygotic carrot embryos on hormone-free medium; evaluation of the effects of pH, ethylene and activated charcoal. Plant Cell Rep. **9**, 34–37.

SMITH D.L. & KRIKORIAN A.D. 1990b pH control of carrot somatic embryogenesis. pp. 449–453 *in* Nijkamp *et al.* (eds.) 1990 (*q.v.*).

SMITH D.R. & THORPE T.A. 1975a Root initiation in cuttings of *Pinus radiata* seedlings. J. Exp. Bot. **26**, 184–192.

SMITH D.R. & THORPE T.A. 1975b Root initiation in cuttings of *Pinus radiata.* II. Growth regulation interactions. J. Exp. Bot. **26**, 193–202.

SMITH D.R., HORGAN K. J. & AITKEN-CHRISTIE J. 1982 Micropropagation of *Pinus radiata* for afforestation. pp. 723–724 *in* Fujiwara A. (ed.) 1982 (*q.v.*).

SMITH F.A. & RAVEN J.A. 1979 Intercellular pH and its regulation. Ann. Rev. Plant Physiol. **30**, 289–311.

SMITH H. & KENDRICK R.E. 1976 The structure and properties of phytochrome. pp. 377–424 *in* Goodwin T. W. (ed.) 1976 (*q.v.*).

SMITH M.A., DAVIES P.J. & REID J.B. 1985 Role of polyamines in gibberellin-induced internode growth in peas. Plant Physiol. **78**, 92–99.

SMITH M.M. & STONE B.A. 1973 Studies on *Lolium multiflorum* endosperm in tissue culture. I. Nutrition. Aust. J. Biol. **26**, 123–133.

SMITH R.H. 1981a Phytohormone and primordial leaf effects on *Coleus blumei* apical domes. Plant Physiol. **67**, (Suppl) 118 (Abst.665).

SMITH R.H. & MURASHIGE T. 1970 *In vitro* development of the isolated shoot apical meristem of angiosperms. Am. J. Bot. **57**, 562–568.

SMITH S.M. & STREET H.E. 1974 The decline of embryogenic potential as callus and suspension cultures of carrot are serially subcultured. Ann. Bot. **38**, 223–241.

SMITH T.A. 1977 Recent advances in the biochemistry of plant amines. Prog. Phytochem. **4**, 27–81.

SMITH T.A. 1985 Polyamines. Ann. Rev. Plant Physiol. **36**, 117–143.

SMITH T.A. & WILTSHIRE G. 1975 Distribution of cadaverine and other amines in higher plants. Phytochem. **14**, 2341–2346.

SMITH T.A., ABBOTT A.J., BEST G.R. & CLEMENTS E. 1977 Polyamines in Paul's Scarlet rose cell suspensions. p. 62 *in* Long Ashton Annual Rep. 1976.

SNEATH P.H.A., MAIR N.S. & SHARPE E. (eds.) 1986 *Bergey's Manual of Systematic Bacteriology* Vol. 2. Williams and Wilkins, Baltimore. ISBN 0-683-07893-3.

SNEEP J. & HENDRIKSEN A.J.T. 1979 *Plant Breeding Perspectives.* Centre for Agric. Publ. and Documentation, Wageningen, The Netherlands.

SNIR I. 1981 Micropropagation of red raspberry. Scientia Hort. **14**, 139–143.

SNIR I. 1982a *In vitro* propagation of sweet cherry cultivars. HortScience **17**, 192–193.

SNIR I. 1982b *In vitro* micropropagation of sweet cherry cultivars. pp. 735–736 *in* Fujiwara (ed.) 1982 (*q.v.*).

SNIR I. 1983 A micropropagation system for sour cherry. Scientia Hort. **19**, 85–90.

SNIR I. 1984 *In vitro* propagation of 'Canino' apricot. HortScience **19**, 229–230.

SNIR I. 1988 Influence of paclobutrazol on *in vitro* growth of sweet cherry shoots. HortScience **23**, 304–305.

SNIR I. & EREZ A. 1980 *In vitro* propagation of Malling Merton apple rootstocks. HortScience **15**, 597–598.

SOBCZYKIEWICZ D. 1987 Mass propagation of raspberry plants by meristem culture. Acta Hort. **212**, 607–609.

SOCZEK U. & HEMPEL M. 1988 The influence of some organic medium compounds on multiplication of gerbera *in vitro.* Acta Hort. **226**, 643–646.

SOFFER H. & BURGER D.W. 1988 Studies on plant propagation using the aero-hydroponic method. Acta Hort. **230**, 261–269.

SOLOMON B. 1950 Inhibiting effect of autoclaved malt preventing the *in vitro* growth of *Datura* embryos. Am. J. Bot. **37**, 1–5.

SOMERS D.A., GENGENBACH B.G., BIESBOER D.D., HACKETT W.P. & GREEN C.E. (eds.) 1986 Abstracts VI Intl. Cong. Plant Tissue and Cell Culture, Internat. Assoc. Plant Tiss. Cult., Minneapolis, Minn.

SOMMER A.L. 1931 Copper as an essential for plant growth. Plant Physiol. **6**, 339–345.

SOMMER A.L. & LIPMAN C.B. 1926 Evidence on the indispensable nature of zinc and boron for higher green plants. Plant Physiol. **1**, 231–249.

SOMMER H.E., BROWN C.L. & KORMANIK P.P. 1975 Differentiation of plantlets in Longleaf pine (*Pinus palustris*) tissue cultured *in vitro.* Bot. Gaz. **136**, 196–200.

SONDAHL M. & EVANS D. 1987 Controlled regeneration of corn plants and breeding strategies therewith. U.S. Patent No. 4659668.

SONDAHL M.R. 1982 Tissue culture of morphological mutants of coffee. pp. 417–418 *in* Fujiwara A. (ed.) 1982 (*q.v.*).

SONDAHL M.R. & SHARP W.R. 1977a High frequency induction of somatic embryos in cultured leaf explants of *Coffea arabica* L. Z. Planzenphysiol. **81**, 395–408.

SONDAHL M.R. & SHARP W.R. 1977b Growth and embryogenesis in leaf tissues of *Coffea.* Plant Physiol. **59**, (6) Abstr. 3.

SONDAHL M.R. & SHARP W.R. 1977c High frequency initiation of somatic embryos in cultured leaf explants of *Coffea arabica* L. In Vitro **13**, 146 (Abst. 14).

SONDAHL M.R. & SHARPE W.R. 1979 Research in *Coffea* spp. and applications of tissue culture methods. pp. 527–584 *in* Sharpe *et al.* (eds.) 1979 (*q.v.*).

SONDAHL M.R., EVANS D.A. & PRIOLI L. 1988 Controlled regeneration of *Zea diploperennis* hybrids and breeding strategies therewith. U.S. Patent No. 4810649.

SONDAHL M.R., NAKAMURA T. & SHARP W.R. 1985 Propagation of coffee. pp. 215–232 *in* Henke *et al.* (eds.) 1985 (*q.v.*).

SONDAHL M.R., SALISBURY J.L. & SHARP W.R. 1979a S.E.M. characterization of embryogenic tissue and globular embryos during high frequency somatic embryogenesis in coffee callus cells. Z. Pflanzenphysiol. **94**, 185–188.

SONDAHL M.R., SPAHLINGER D.A. & SHARP W.R. 1979b A histological study of high frequency and low frequency induction of somatic embryos in cultured leaf explants of *Coffea arabica* L. Z. Pflanzenphysiol. **94**, 101–108.

SONDHEIMER E., TZOU D.S. & GALSON E.C. 1968 Abscisic acid levels and seed dormancy. Plant Physiol. **43**, 1443–1447.

SOPORY S.K. & MAHESHWARI S.C. 1976a Development of pollen embryoids in anther cultures of *Datura innoxia* I. General observations and effects of physical factors. J. Exp. Bot. **27**, 49–57.

SOPORY S.K., JACOBSEN E. & WENZEL G. 1978 Production of monohaploid embryoids and plantlets in cultured anthers of *Solanum tuberosum.* Plant Sci. Lett. **12**, 47–54.

SORVARI S. 1986a The effect of starch gelatinized nutrient media in barley anther cultures. Ann. Agric. Fenn. **25**, 127–133.

SORVARI S. 1986 b Differentiation of potato discs in barley starch gelatinized nutrient media. Ann. Agric. Fenn. **25**, 135–138.

SORVARI S. 1986c Comparison of anther cultures of barley cultivars in barley-starch and agar gelatinized media. Ann. Agric. Fenn. **25**, 249–254.

SPANGENBERG G., KOOP H.-U., LICHTER R. & SCHWEIGER H.G. 1986 Micro-culture of single protoplasts of *Brassica napus.* Physiol. Plant. **66**, 1–8.

SPECTOR M. 1989 Method for protecting plants and plant matter from stress. U.S. Patent No. 4802905

SPENCER D.F. & KIMMINS W.C. 1969 Presence of plasmodesmata in callus cultures of tobacco and carrot. Can. J. Bot. **47**, 2049–2050.

SPENCER S.J., THURSTON K.C., JOHNSON J.A., PERERA R.G. & ARDITTI J. 1980 Media which do not require sterilization for the culture of orchid seedlings and *Phalaenopsis* flower stalks. Malay. Orchid Rev. **14**, (1) 44–53.

SPIEGEL-ROY P. & KOCHBA J. 1980 Role of polyembryony and apomixis in *Citrus* propagation and breeding. pp. 28–48 *in* Fiechter A. (ed.) 1980a (*q.v.*).

SPIEGEL-ROY P. & SAAD S. 1986 Effect of carbohydrates and inhibitors of GA$_3$ biosynthesis on embryogenic potential of salt tolerant and non-tolerant callus lines of orange (*Citrus sinensis* Osbeck). Plant Sci. **47**, 215–220.

SQUIRES W.M. & LANGTON F.A. 1990 Potential and limitations of narcissus micropropagation: an experimental evaluation. Acta Hort. **266**, 67–76.

SREE RAMULU K. & DIJKHUIS P. 1986 Flow cytometric analysis of polysomaty and *in vitro* genetic instability in potato. J. Plant Physiol. **5**, 234–237.

SREE RAMULU K., DEVREUX M. & DE MARTINIS P. 1976a Origin and genetic analysis of plants regenerated *in vitro* from periclinal chimeras of *Lycopersicon peruvianum.* Z. Pflanzenzucht. **77**, 112–120.

SREE RAMULU K., DEVREUX M., ANCORA G. & LANERI V. 1976b Chimerism in *Lycopersicon peruvianum* plants regenerated from *in vitro* cultures of anthers and stem internodes. Z. Pflanzenzucht. **77**, 299–319.

SREE RAMULU K., DIJKHUIS P., ROEST S., BOKELMANN G.S. & DE GROOT B. 1984 Early occurrence of genetic instability in protoplast cultures of potato. Plant Sci. Lett. **36**, 79–86.

SRISKANDARAJAH S. & MULLINS M.G. 1982 Micropropagation of apple scion cultivars. Comb. Proc. Int. Plant Prop. Soc. 1981 **31**, 209–213.

SRIVASTA S.K. & SMITH T.A. 1982 The effect of some oligo-amines and guanidi-nes on membrane permiability in higher plants. Phytochem. **21**, 997–1008.

SROGA G.E. 1983 Callus and sususpension culture of *Lupinus angustifolius* cv. Turkus. Plant Sci. Lett. **32**, 183–192.

STAMP J.A. & HENSHAW G.G. 1982 Somatic embryogenesis in cassava. Z. Pflanzenphysiol. **105**, 183–187.

STAMP J.A. & MEREDITH C.P. 1988a Proliferative somatic embryogenesis from zygotic embryos of grapevine. J. Am. Soc. Hort. Sci. **113**, 941–945.

STANDARDI A. 1979 In dagine preliminare sull'influenza della luce nella micro-propagazione di alcune specie legnose. pp. 107–118 *in* Anon, 1979 (*q.v.*).

STANDARDI A. 1982 Effetti di sobcolture ripetute in germogli di *Actinidia sinensis* (Pl.) coltivati *in vitro.* Riv. Ortoflorofrutti. Ital. **66**, 419–429.

STANDARDI A. & CATALANO F. 1985 Tissue culture propagation of kiwi fruit. Comb. Proc. Int. Plant Prop. Soc. 1984 **34**, 236–243.

STANDARDI A. & MICHELI M. 1988 Control of vitrification in proliferating shoots of M-26. Acta Hort. **227**, 425–427.

STANGE L. 1979 Reversible blockage of the cell cycle in the meristem of *Riella helicophylla* (Bory et Mont.) Mont. by *p*-chlorophenoxyisobutyric acid (PCIB). Planta **145**, 347–350.

STAPFER R.E. & HEUSER C.W. 1985 *In vitro* propagation of periwinkle. Hort-Science **20**, 141–142.

STARRANTINO A. & CARUSO A. 1987 Experiences of the '*in vitro*' propagation of some citrus rootstocks. Acta Hort. **212**, 471–478.

STARRANTINO A. & CARUSO A. 1988 The shoot-tip grafting technique applied to citriculture. Acta Hort. **227**, 101–103.

STARRANTINO A. & RUSSO F. 1983 Reproduction of seedless orange cultivars from undeveloped ovules raised '*in vitro*'. Acta Hort. **131**, 253–258.

START N.G. & CUMMING B.G. 1976 *In vitro* propagation of *Saintpaulia ionantha* Wendl. HortScience **11**, 204–206.

STAUDT G. 1984 The effect of *myo*-inositol on the growth of callus tissue in *Vitis.* J. Plant Physiol. **116**, 161–166.

STEAD D.E. 1988 Identification of bacteria by computer-assisted fatty acid profil-ing. Acta Hort. **225**, 39–46.

STECK W., BAILEY B.K., SHYLUK J.P. & GAMBORG O.L. 1971 Coumarins and alkaloids from cell cultures of *Ruta graveolens.* Phytochem. **10**, 191–198.

STEEVES T.A. & SUSSEX T.A. 1957 Studies on the development of excised leaves in sterile culture. Am. J. Bot. **44**, 665–673.

STEFFEN J.D., SACHS R.M. & HACKETT W.P. 1988 Growth and development of reproductive and vegetative tissues of *Bougainvillea* cultured *in vitro* as a function of carbohydrate. Am. J. Bot. **75**, 1219–1224.

STEFFENSEN D.M. 1961 Chromosome structure with special reference to the role of metal ions. Int. Rev. Cytol. ,**12**, 163–197.

STEHSEL M.L. & CAPLIN S.M. 1969 Sugars: autoclaving versus sterile filtration and the growth of carrot root tissue. Life Sci. **8**, 1255–1259.

STEINER A.A. & VAN WINDEN H. 1970 Recipe for ferric salts of ethyle-nediaminetetraacetic acid. Plant Physiol. **46**, 862–863.

STEINER S. & LESTER R.L. 1972 Studies on the diversity of inositol-containing yeast phospholipids: incorporation of 2-deoxyglucose into lipid. J. Bacteriol. **109**, 81–88.

STEINER S., SMITH S., WAECHTER C.J. & LESTER R.L. 1969 Isolation and partial characterization of a major inositol-containing yeast phospholipid in baker's yeast, mannosyl-diinositol, diphosphorylceramide. Proc. Nat. Acad. Sci. U.S.A. **64**, 1042–1048.

STEINITZ B. & YAHEL H. 1982 *In vitro* propagation of *Narcissus tazetta.* Hort-Science **17**, 333–334.

STEPONKUS P.L. 1985 Cryopreservation of isolated protoplasts: applications to plant cell cryopreservation. pp. 49–60 *in* Kartha K.K. (ed.) 1985a (*q.v.*).

STETLER D.A. & LAETSCH W.M. 1968 Prolamellar body-like structures in tobacco tissue cultured on a medium lacking kinetin. Am. J. Bot. **55**, 709 (Abst.).

STEUTER A.A., MOZAFAR A. & GOODIN J.R. 1981 Water potential of aqueous glycol. Plant Physiol. **67**, 64–67.

STEVENSON J.H. & HARRIS R.E. 1980 *In vitro* plantlet formation from shoot tip explants of *Fuchsia hybrida* cv. Swingtime. Can. J. Bot. **58**, 2190–2192.

STEVENSON J.H. & MONETTE P.L. 1983 Delay of onset of leafroll symptom expression in *Vitis vinifera* 'Liemberger' from Ribavirin- treated *in vitro* cultures. Can. J. Plant Sci. **63**, 557–560.

STEWARD F.C. 1963 Carrots and coconuts: Some investigations on growth. pp. 178–197 *in* Maheshwari and Ranga Swamy (eds.) 1963 (*q.v.*).

STEWARD F.C. & CAPLIN S.M. 1951 A tissue culture from potato tuber: the synergistic action of 2,4-D and of coconut milk. Science **113**, 518–520.

STEWARD F.C. & CAPLIN S.M. 1952 Investigations on growth and metabolism of plant cells. IV. Evidence on the role of the coconut milk factor. Ann. Bot. **16**, 491–504.

STEWARD F.C. & MOHAN RAM H.Y. 1961 Determining factors in cell growth: some implications for morphogenesis in plants. Adv. Morph. **1**, 189–265.

STEWARD F.C. & RAO K.V.N. 1970 Investigations on the growth and metabolism of cultured explants of *Daucus carota.* III. The range of responses induced in carrot explants by exogenous growth factors and by trace elements. Planta **91**, 129–145.

STEWARD F.C. & SHANTZ E.M. 1956 The chemical induction of growth in plant tissue cultures. pp. 165–186 *in* Wain and Wightman (eds.) 1956 *The Chemistry and Mode of Action of Plant Growth Substances.* Butterworth Scientific Publica-tions Ltd., London.

STEWARD F.C. & SHANTZ E.M. 1959 The chemical regulation of growth: Some substances and extracts which induce growth and morphogenesis. Ann. Rev. Plant Physiol. **10**, 379–404.

STEWARD F.C., CAPLIN S.M. & MILLAR F.K. 1952 Investigations on growth and metabolism of plant cells. I. New techniques for the investigation of metabolism, nutrition, and growth in undifferentiated cells. Ann. Bot. **16**, 57–77.

STEWARD F.C., MAPES M.O. & AMMIRATO P.V. 1969 Growth and morphogenesis in tissue and free cell cultures. pp. 329–376 in Steward F.C. (ed.) 1969 *Plant Physiology – A Treatise* Vol. VB. Academic Press, New York, London.

STEWARD F.C., MAPES M.O., KENT A.E. & HOLSTEN R.D. 1964 Growth and development of cultured plant cells. Science **143**, 20–27.

STEWARD F.C., SHANTZ E.M., POLLARD J.K., MAPES M.O. & MITRA J. 1961 Growth induction in explanted cells and tissues: Metabolic and morphogenetic manifestations. pp. 193–246 in Rudnick D. (ed.) *Synthesis of Molecular and Cellular Structure*. Ronald Press, New York.

STEWARD J.McD. & HSU C.L. 1977 *In ovulo* embryo culture and seedling development of cotton (*Gossypium hirsutum* L.). Planta **137**, 113–117.

STEWART J. & BUTTON J. 1976 Rapid vegetative multiplication of *Epidendrum O'brienianum in vitro* and in the greenhouse. Ann. Orchid Soc. Bull. **45**, 922–930.

STEWART J. & BUTTON J. 1978 Development of callus and plantlets from *Epidendrum* root tips cultured *in vitro*. Am. Orchid Soc. Bull. **47**, 607–612.

STEWART R.N., SEMENIUK P. & DERMEN H. 1974 Competition and accommodation between apical layers and their derivatives in the ontogeny of chimeral shoots of *Pelargonium × hortorum*. Am. J. Bot. **61**, 54–67.

STICKLAND R.G. & SUNDERLAND N. 1972a Production of anthocyanins, flavonols and chlorogenic acids by cultured callus tissues of *Haplopappus gracilis*. Ann. Bot. **36**, 443–457.

STICKLAND R.G. & SUNDERLAND N. 1972b Photocontrol of growth, and of anthocyanin and chlorogenic acid production in cultured callus tissues of *Happlopappus gracilis*. Ann. Bot. **36**, 671–685.

STIEKEMA W.J., HEIDEKAMP F., LOUWERS J.D., VERHOEVEN H.A. & DIJKHUIS P. 1988 Introduction of foreign genes into potato cultivars Bintje and Desiree using an *Agrobacterium tumefaciens* binary vector. Plant Cell Rep. **7**, 47–50.

STIMART D.P. 1986 Commercial micropropagation of florist flower crops. pp. 301–315 in Zimmerman *et al.*(eds.) 1986 (*q.v.*).

STIMART D.P. & ASCHER P.D. 1978a Foliar emergence and growth of *in vitro* generated bulblets from bulb scale explants of *Lilium longiflorum*. HortScience **13**, 356 (Abstr. 140).

STIMART D.P. & ASCHER P.D. 1981a Foliar emergence from bulblets of *Lilium longiflorum* Thunb. as related to *in vitro* generation temperatures. J. Am. Soc. Hort. Sci. **106**, 446–450.

STIMART D.P. & ASCHER P.D. 1981b Developmental responses of *Lilium longiflorum* bulblets to constant or alternating temperatures *in vitro*. J. Am. Soc. Hort. Sci. **106**, 450–454.

STIMART D.P. & ASCHER P.D. 1982 Plantlet regeneration and stability from callus cultures of *Freesia × hybrida* Bailey cultivar 'Royal'. Scientia Hort. **17**, 153–157.

STIMART D.P., ASCHER P.D. & WILKINS H.F. 1983 Axis elongation from tissue cultured generated bulblets of *Lilium longiflorum* Thunb. J. Am. Soc. Hort. Sci. **108**, 99–101.

STIMART D.P., ASCHER P.D. & ZAGORSKI J.S. 1980 Plants from callus of interspecific hybrid of *Lilium* 'Black Beauty'. HortScience **15**, 313–315.

STOKES M.J. 1974a Plant propagation by means of aseptic techniques. Comb. Proc. Int. Plant Prop. Soc. **24**, 196–206.

STOLTZ L.P. 1979b Getting started in tissue culture — equipment and costs. Comb. Proc. Int. Plant Prop. Soc. **29**, 375–381.

STONE O.M. 1963 Factors affecting the growth of carnation plants from shoot apices. Ann. Appl. Biol. **52**, 199–209.

STONE O.M. 1973 The elimination of viruses from *Narcissus tazetta* cv. Grand Soleil d'Or, and rapid multiplication of virus-free clones. Ann. Appl. Biol. **73**, 45–52.

STONE O.M. 1978 The production and propagation of disease free plants. pp. 25–33 in Hughes *et al.* (eds.) 1978 (*q.v.*).

STONE O.M. 1982 The elimination of four viruses from *Ullucus tuberosus* by meristem-tip culture and chemotherapy. Ann. Appl. Biol. **101**, 79–83.

STONE O.M., HOLLINGS M. & PAWLEY R.R. 1979 Production of virus-free plants. Ann. Rep. Glasshouse Crops Res. Inst. 1978 151–152.

STONIER T. 1969 Studies on auxin protectors. VII. Association of auxin protectors with crown gall development in sunflower stems. Plant Physiol. **44**, 1169–1174.

STONIER T. 1971 The role of auxin protectors in autonomous growth. pp. 423–435 in *Les Cultures de Tissus de Plantes*. Coll. Int. C.N.R.S. No. 193, Paris.

STONIER T. 1972 The role of auxin protectors in autonomous growth. pp. 423–435 in *Les Cultures de Tissus de Plantes*. Proc. 2nd Int. Conf. Plant Tissue Cult. Strasbourg 1970.

STONIER T. & YONEDA Y. 1967 Stem internode elongation in the Japanese Morning Glory (*Pharbitis nil* Choisy) in relation to an inhibitor system of auxin destruction. Physiol. Plant. **20**, 13–19.

STONIER T., HUDEK J., VANDE-STOUWE R. & YANG H.-M. 1970 Studies of auxin protectors. VIII. Evidence that auxin protectors act as cellular poisers. Physiol. Plant. **23**, 775–783.

STOUTEMEYER V.T. & BRITT O.K. 1961 Effect of temperature and grafting on vegetative phases of Algerian ivy. Nature **189**, 854–855.

STOUTEMYER V.T. & BRITT O.K. 1965 The behaviour of tissue cultures from English and Algerian ivy in different growth phases. Am. J. Bot. **52**, 805–810.

STRAUB P.F., DECKER D.M. & GALLAGHER J.L. 1988 Tissue culture and long-term regeneration of *Phragmites australis* (Cav.) Trin. ex Steud. Plant Cell Tiss. Organ Cult. **15**, 73–78.

STRAUS J. & LA RUE C.D. 1954 Maize endosperm tissue grown *in vitro*. 1. Culture requirements. Am. J. Bot. **41**, 687–694.

STREET H.E. 1954 Growing roots without plants. Discovery **15**, 286–292.

STREET H.E. 1957 Excised root culture. Biol. Rev. **32**, 117–155.

STREET H.E. 1966 The nutrition and metabolism of plant tissue and organ cultures. pp. 533–629 in Willmer E. N. (ed.) 1966 (*q.v.*).

STREET H.E. 1969 Growth in organised and unorganised systems — knowledge gained by culture of organs and tissue explants. pp. 3–224 in Steward F. C. (ed.) 1969. *Plant Physiology — a Treatise*. 5B. Academic Press, New York.

STREET H.E. (ed.) 1977a *Plant Tissue and Cell Culture*. Bot. Monographs Vol.11 Blackwell Scientific Publications. Oxford, London.

STREET H.E. 1977b Laboratory organization. pp. 11–30 in Street H.E. (ed.) 1977a (*q.v.*).

STREET H.E. 1977c Cell (suspension) cultures — techniques. pp. 61–102 in Street H.E. (ed.) 1977a (*q.v.*).

STREET H.E. 1977d Single cell clones — derivation and selection. pp. 207–222 in Street H.E. (ed.) 1977a (*q.v.*).

STREET H.E. 1977e The anatomy and physiology of morphogenesis. Studies involving tissue and cell cultures. pp. 20–33 in Gautheret R.J. (ed.) 1977 *La Culture de Tissus des Végétaux. Résultat généraux et réalisations practiques*. Masson, Paris.

STREET H.E. 1979 Embryogenesis and chemically induced organogenesis. pp. 123–153 in Sharp *et al.* (eds.) 1979 (*q.v.*).

STREET H.E. (ed.) 1974 *Tissue Culture and Plant Science*. Academic Press, London, New York and San Francisco.

STREET H.E. & HENSHAW G.G. 1966 Introduction and methods employed in plant tissue culture. pp. 459–532 in Willmer E.N. (ed.) 1966 (*q.v.*).

STREET H.E. & McGREGOR S.M. 1952 The carbohydrate nutrition of tomato roots. III. The effects of external sucrose concentration on the growth and anatomy of excised roots. Ann. Bot. **16**, 185–205.

STREET H.E. & WITHERS L.A. 1974 The anatomy of embryogenesis in culture. pp. 71–100 in Street H.E. (ed.) 1974 (*q.v.*).

STREET H.E. (ed.) 1977 *Plant Tissue and Cell Culture*. Bot. Monographs Vol.11 Blackwell Scientific Publications.

STREET H.E., McGONAGLE M.P. & LOWE J.S. 1951 Observations on the 'staling' of White's medium by excised tomato roots. Physiol. Plant. **4**, 592–616.

STREET H.E., McGONAGLE M.P. & McGREGOR S.M. 1952 Observations on the 'staling' of White's medium by excised tomato roots. II. Iron availability. Physiol. Plant. **5**, 248–276.

STRICKLAND S.G., NICHOL J.W., McCALL C.M. & STUART D.A. 1987 Effect of carbohydrate source on alfalfa embryogenesis. Plant Science **48**, 113–121.

STRODE R.A. & ABNER G. 1986 Large scale tissue culture production for horticultural crops. pp. 367–371 in Zimmerman *et al.* (eds.) 1986 (*q.v.*).

STRULLU D.G., GRELLIER B., MARCINIAK D. & LETOUZÉ R. 1986 Micropropagation of chestnut and conditions of mycorrhizal synthesis *in vitro*. New Phytol. **102**, 95–101.

STUART D.A. & NELSEN J. 1988 Isolation and characterisation of alfalfa 7 S and 11 S seed storage protein. J. Plant Physiol. **132**, 129–133.

STUART D.A. & STRICKLAND S.G. 1987 Methods and media for enhanced somatic embryogenesis. Int. Patent Application No. WO 87/02701

STUART D.A., NELSEN J. & NICHOL J.W. 1988 Expression of 7 S and 11 S alfalfa seed storage proteins in somatic embryos. J. Plant Physiol. **132**, 134–139.

STUART D.A., STRICKLAND S.G. & NICHOL J.W. 1986 Enhanced somatic embryogenesis using maltose. U.S. Patent No. 4801545 ,

STUART D.A., STRICKLAND S.G. & WALKER K.A. 1987 Bioreactor production of alfalfa somatic embryos. HortScience **22**, 800–803.

STUART R. & STREET H.E. 1969 The initiation of division in suspensions of stationary-phase cells of *Acer pseudoplatanus* L. J. Exp. Bot. **20**, 556–571.

STUART R. & STREET H.E. 1971 Studies on the growth in culture of plant cells. J. Exp. Bot. **22**, 96–106.

SUDARSONO & GOLDY R.G. 1991 Growth regulator and axillary bud position effects on *in vitro* establishment of *Vitis rotundifolia*. HortScience **26**, 304–307.

SUEZAWA K., MATSUTA N., OMURA M. & YAMAKI S. 1988 Plantlet formation from cell suspensions of kiwi fruit (*Actinidia chinensis* Planch. var. *hispida*). Scientia Hort. **37**, 123–128.

SUGAWARA Y. & SAKAI A. 1974 Survival of suspension-cultured Sycamore cells coded to the temperature of liquid nitrogen. Plant Physiol. **54**, 722–724.

SUGIURA A., TAO R., MURAYAMA H. & TOMANA T. 1986 *In vitro* propagation of Japanese persimmon. HortScience **21**, 1205–1207.

SUNBLADE T.M. & MEYER M.M. Jr. 1982 *In vitro* culture of variegated *Saintpaulia* and *Episcia* plants. HortScience **17**, 532 (Abst. 426).

SUNDERLAND N. 1974 Anther culture as a means of haploid induction. pp. 91–122 in Kasha K.J. (ed.) *Haploids in Higher Plants: Advances and Potential*. University of Guelph, Guelph, Canada.

SUNDERLAND N. 1977 Nuclear cytology. pp. 177–205 in Street H.E. (ed.) 1977 (*q.v.*).

SUNDERLAND N. 1979 Comparative studies of anther and pollen culture. pp. 203–219 in Sharp *et al.* (eds.) 1979 (*q.v.*).

SUNDERLAND N. & DUNWELL J.M. 1977 Anther and pollen culture. pp. 223–265 in Street H.E. (ed.) 1977 (*q.v.*).

SUNDERLAND N. & ROBERTS M. 1977 New approach to pollen culture. Nature **270**, 236–238.

SUNDERLAND N. & WELLS B. 1968 Plastid structure and development in green callus tissues of *Oxalis dispar*. Ann. Bot. **32**, 327–346.

SUNDQVIST C., BJORN L.O. & VIRGIN H.I. 1980 pp. 201–224 in Reinert J. (ed.) 1980 *Results and Problems in Cell Differentiation: 10. Chloroplasts*. Springer-Verlag Berlin, Heidelberg, New York.

SUNG Z.R. 1979 Relationship of indole-3-acetic acid and tryptophan concentrations in normal and 5-methyltryptophan-resistant cell lines of wild carrots. Planta **145**, 339–345.

SUNG Z.R., SMITH J.M., CHOI J.H., KRAUSS M., BORKIRD C. & LIU L.-S. 1988 Gene expression in embryogenesis. HortScience **23**, 513–515.

SURESH M.R., RAMAKRISHNA S. & ADIGA P.R. 1978 Regulation of arginine decarboxylase and putrescine level in *Cucumis sativus* cotyledons. Phytochem. **17**, 57–63.

SURIYAJANTRATONG P. 1979 The influence of *Petunia hybrida* stock plants on growth and differentiation of explants *in vitro*. Ph. D. Diss. Univ. Minnesota Diss. Abs. Int. 40/06 p. 2464-B.

SUTTER E. 1984 Chemical composition of epicuticular wax in cabbage plants grown *in vitro*. Can. J. Bot. **62**, 74–77.

SUTTER E. 1988 Stomatal and cuticular water loss from apple cherry and sweet-gum plants after removal from *in vitro* culture. J. Am. Soc. Hort. Sci. **113**, 234–238.

SUTTER E. & BARKER P. 1984 Tissue culture propagation of selected mature clones of *Liquidambar styraciflua*. Comb. Proc. Int. Plant Prop. Soc. 1983 **33**, 113–117.

SUTTER E. & LANGHANS R.W. 1978a Tissue culture propagation of *Anemone coronaria*. HortScience **13**, 348 (Abst. 74).

SUTTER E. & LANGHANS R.W. 1979 Epicuticular wax formation on carnation plantlets regenerated from shoot tip culture. J. Am. Soc. Hort. Sci. **104**, 493–496.

SUTTER E. & LANGHANS R.W. 1980 Formation of epicuticular wax and its effect on water loss in cabbage plants regenerated from shoot tip culture. HortScience **15**, 429 (Abst. 428).

SUTTER E. & LANGHANS R.W. 1981 Abnormalities in *Chrysanthemum* regenerated from long-term cultures. Ann. Bot. **48**, 559–568.

SUTTLE J.C. 1984 Effect of the defoliant thidiazuron on ethylene evolution from mung bean hypocotyl segments. Plant Physiol. **75**, 902–907.

SUTTLE J.C. 1985 Involvement of ethylene in the action of the defoliant thidiazuron. Plant Physiol. **78**, 272–276.

SUZUKI A. & NATO A. 1982 Glutamate synthase isoforms in tobacco cultured cells. Immunological studies. pp. 239–240 in Fujiwara A. (ed.) 1982 (*q.v.*).

SWANSON E.B. & TOMES D.T. 1980 *In vitro* responses of tolerant and susceptible lines of *Lotus corniculatus* L. to 2,4-D. Crop Sci. **20**, 792–795.

SWARTZ H.J. 1991 Post culture behaviour: genetic and epigenetic effects and related problems. pp. 95–121 in Debergh and Zimmerman (eds.) 1991 (*q.v.*).

SWEDLUND B. & LOCY R.D. 1988 Somatic embryogenesis and plant regeneration in two-year old cultures of *Zea diploperennis*. Plant Cell Rep. **7**, 144–147.

SWEET H.C. & BOLTON W.E. 1979 The surface decontamination of seeds to produce axenic seedlings. Am. J. Bot. **66**, 692–698.

SYONO K. 1979 Correlation between induction of auxin-nonrequiring tobacco calluses and increase in inhibitor(s) of IAA-destruction activity. Plant Cell Physiol. **20**, 29–42.

SYONO K. & FURUYA T. 1971 Effects of temperature on the cytokinin requirement of tobacco calluses. Plant Cell Physiol. **12**, 61–71.

SYONO K. & FURUYA T. 1972a Effects of cytokinins on the auxin content of tobacco calluses. Plant Cell Physiol. **13**, 843–856.

SYONO K. & FURUYA T. 1972b The differentiation of *Coptis* plants *in vitro* from callus cultures. Experientia **28**, p. 236.

SYONO K. & FURUYA T. 1974 Induction of auxin-non-requiring tobacco calluses and its reversal by treatments with auxins. Plant & Cell Physiol. **15**, 7–17.

SZAKACS E., KOVACS G., JANOS P. & BARNABAS B. 1988 Substitution analysis of callus induction and plant regeneration from anther culture in wheat (*Triticum aestivum* L.). Plant Cell Rep. **7**, 127–129.

TABATA M. & MOTOYOSHI F. 1965 Hereditary control of callus formation in maize endosperm cultured *in vitro*. Jap. J. Genet. **40**, 343–355.

TAEB A.G. & ALDERSON P.G. 1987 Micropropagation of tulip: optimising shoot production from floral stem explants. Acta Hort. **212**, 677–681.

TAIARIOL V., OAKLEY R. & VENTURA P. 1991 Method for *in vitro* reproduction and growth of cells in culture medium. U.S. Patent 5017490

TAIRA T., HASKINS F.A. & GORZ H.J. 1977 Callus and suspension cultures of *Melilotus alba* tissues and cells. Crop Sci. **17**, 407–411.

TAKAHASHI S., SHUDO K., OKAMOTO T., YAMADA K. & ISOGAI Y. 1978 Cytokinin activity of N-phenyl-N'-(4-pyridyl) urea derivatives. Phytochem. **17**, 1201–1207.

TAKATORI F.H., MURASHIGE T. & STILLMAN J.I. 1968 Vegetative propagation of asparagus through tissue culture. HortScience **3**, 20–22.

TAKAYAMA S. & AKITA M. 1991 Method for propagation of potatoes. U.S. Patent No. 5034327.

TAKAYAMA S. & MISAWA M. 1979 Differentiation in *Lilium* bulb scales grown *in vitro* — effect of various cultural conditions. Physiol. Plant. **46**, 184–190.

TAKAYAMA S. & MISAWA M. 1980 Differentiation in *Lilium* bulb scales *in vitro*. Effects of activated charcoal, physiological age of bulbs and sucrose concentration on differentiation and scale leaf formation *in vitro*. Physiol. Plant. **48**, 121–125.

TAKAYAMA S. & MISAWA M. 1981 Mass propagation of *Begonia × hiemalis* plantlets by shake culture. Plant & Cell Physiol. **22**, 461–467.

TAKAYAMA S. & MISAWA M. 1982b Factors affecting differentiation and growth *in vitro*, and a mass propagation scheme for *Begonia × hiemalis* Scientia Hort. **16**, 65–75.

TAKAYAMA S. & MISAWA M. 1982c Mass propagation of ornamental plants through tissue culture. pp. 681–682 in Fujiwara (ed.) 1982 (*q.v.*).

TAKAYAMA S. & MISAWA M. 1983b A scheme for mass propagation of *Lilium in vitro*. Scientia Hort. **18**, 353–362.

TAKAYAMA S., MISAWA M., TAKASHIGE Y., TSUMORI H. & OHKAWA K. 1982 Cultivation of *in vitro*-propagated *Lilium* bulbs in soil. J. Am. Soc. Hort. Sci. **107**, 830–834.

TAKEBE I., LABIB G. & MELCHERS G. 1971 Regeneration of whole plants from isolated mesophyll protoplasts of tobacco. Naturwiss. **58**, 318–320.

TAKEBE I., OTSUKI Y. & AOKI S. 1968 Isolation of tobacco mesophyll cells in intact and active state. Plant Cell Physiol. **9**, 115–124.

TALMON L., VEGA M., MUJICA B. & BOLAND B. 1989 Cytohistological studies on the action of vitamin D_3 and stigmasterol on *Phaseolus vulgaris* growing *in vitro*. Plant Science **59**, 183–190.

TANADA T. 1978 Boron — key element in the actions of phytochrome and gravity? Planta **143**, 109–111.

TANAKA M. & SAKANISHI Y. 1978 Factors affecting the growth of *in vitro* cultured lateral buds from *Phalaenopsis* flower stalks. Scientia Hort. **8**, 169–178.

TANAKA M., GOI M. & HIGASHIURA T. 1988a A novel disposable culture vessel made of fluorocarbon polymer films for micropropagation. Acta Hort. **226**, 663–670.

TANAKA M., HASEGAWA A. & GOI M. 1975 Studies on the clonal propagation of monopodial orchids by tissue culture: 1. Formation of protocorm-like bodies (PLB) from leaf tissue in above sp. J. Jap. Soc. Hort. Sci. **44**, 47–58.

TANAKA M., HIRANO T., GOI M., HIGASHIURA T., SASAHARA H. & MURASAKI K. 1991 Practical application of a novel disposable film culture vessel in micropropagation. Acta Hort. **300**, 77–84.

TANAKA M., JINNO K., GOI M. & HIGASHIURA T. 1988b The use of disposable fluorocarbon polymer film culture vessel in micropropagation. Acta Hort. **230**, 73–80.

TANAKA M., KUMURA M. & GOI M. 1988c Optimal conditions for shoot production from *Phalaenopsis* flower-stalk cuttings cultured *in vitro*. Scientia Hort. **35**, 117–126.

TANDEAU DE MARSAC N. & PEAUD-LENOEL C. 1972a Cultures photosynthétique de lignées clonales de cellules de tabac. Compt. Rend. Acad. Sci. Paris **274D**, 1800–1802.

TANDEAU DE MARSAC N. & PEAUD-LENOEL C. 1972b Exchanges d'oxygène et assimilation de gaz carbonique de tissus de tabac en culture photosynthétique. Compt. Rend. Acad. Sci. Paris **274D**, 2310–2313.

TANIMOTO S. & HARADA H. 1979 Influence of environmental and physiological conditions on floral bud formation of *Torenia* stem segments cultured *in vitro*. Z. Pflanzenphysiol. **95**, 33–41.

TANIMOTO S. & HARADA H. 1980 Hormonal control of morphogenesis in leaf explants of *Perilla frutescens* Britton var. crispa, Decaisnef. viridi-crispa Makino. Ann. Bot. **45**, 321–327.

TANIMOTO S. & HARADA H. 1981a Chemical factors controlling floral bud formation of *Torenia* stem segments cultured *in vitro*. I. Effects of mineral nutrients and sugars. Plant Cell Physiol. **22**, 533–541.

TANIMOTO S. & HARADA H. 1981c Effects of IAA, zeatin, ammonium nitrate and sucrose on the initiation and development of floral buds in *Torenia* stem segments cultured *in vitro*. Plant Cell Physiol. **22**, 1553–1560.

TANIMOTO S. & HARADA H. 1982b Effects of cytokinin and anticytokinin on the initial stage of adventitious bud differentiation in the epidermis of *Torenia* stem segments. Plant Cell Physiol. **23**, 1371–1376.

TANIMOTO S. & HARADA H. 1982c Studies on floral initiation and development in *Torenia* stem segments cultured *in vitro*. pp. 155–156 *in* Fujiwara (ed.) 1982 (*q.v.*).

TANIMOTO S. & HARADA H. 1986 Involvement of calcium in adventitious bud initiation in *Torenia* stem segments. Plant Cell Physiol. **27**, 1–10.

TANIMOTO S., MIYAZAKI A. & HARADA H. 1985 Regulation by abscisic acid of *in vitro* flower formation in *Torenia* stem segments. Plant Cell Physiol. **26**, 675–682.

TANNO N. 1977 Dormancy in *Laportea* bulbils: experiments with buds cultured *in vitro*. Plant Cell Physiol. **18**, 869–874.

TAUBÖCK K. 1942 Ueber die Lebensnotwendigkeit des Aluminiums fur Pteridophyten. Bot. Arch. **43**, 291–295.

TAUSSON W.O., PROKOFIEV A.A. & PONTOVICH W.E. 1944 Sterile cultures as a method for studying metabolism in higher plants. Compt. Rend. Acad. Sci. USSR. **42**, 131–134.

TAUTORUS T.E., FOWKE L.C. & DUNSTAN D.I. 1991 Somatic embryogenesis in conifers. Can. J. Bot. **69**, 1873–1899.

TAYLOR A.G. & WARHOLIC D.T. 1987 Protecting fluid drilled lettuce from herbicides by incorporating activated carbon into gels. J. Hort. Sci. **62**, 31–37.

TAYLOR B.H., AMASINO R.M., WHITE F.F., NESTER E.W. & GORDON M.P. 1985 T-DNA analysis of plants regenerated from hairy root cultures. Mol. Gen. Genet. **201**, 554–557.

TAYLOR H.F. & BURDEN R.S. 1972 Xanthoxin, a recently discovered plant growth inhibitor. Proc. Roy. Soc. Lond. **180B**, 317–346.

TAYLOR R.M. 1972 Germination of cotton (*Gossypium hirsutum* L.) pollen on an artificial medium. Crop Sci. **12**, 243–244.

TAZZARI L., PESTELLI P., FIORINO P. & PARRI G. 1990 Propagation techniques for *Annona cherimola* Mill. Acta Hort. **275**, 315–321.

TEASDALE R.D. 1987 Micronutrients. pp. 17–49 *in* Bonga and Durzan (eds.) 1987a (*q.v.*).

TEASDALE R.D., DAWSON P.A. & WOOLHOUSE H.W. 1986 Mineral nutrient requirements of a loblolly pine (*Pinus taeda*) cell suspension culture. Plant Physiol. **82**, 942–945.

TEJOVATHI G. & ANWAR S.Y. 1984 *In vitro* induction of capitula from cotyledons of *Carthamus tinctorius* (Safflower). Plant Sci. Lett. **36**, 165–168.

TELLE J. & GAUTHERET R.J. 1947 Sur la culture indéfinie des tissus de la racine de jusquiame (*Hyascyamus niger*). Compt. Rend. Acad. Sci. Paris **224**, 1653–1654.

TEO C.K.H. & TEO F.S. 1974 Are orchid mericlones true to type? Planter **50**, 234–236.

TEPFER D. 1984 Transformation of several species of higher plants by *Agrobacterium rhizogenes*: sexual transmission of the transformed genotype and phenotype. Cell **37**, 959–967.

TEPFER D.A. & BONNETT H.T. 1972 The role of phytochrome in the geotropic behavior of roots of *Convolvulus arvensis*. Planta **106**, 311–324.

TERRINE C. & LALOUE M. 1980 Kinetics of N^6-(Δ^2- isopentenyl) adenosine degradation in tobacco cells. Plant Physiol. **65**, 1090–1095.

TERRINE C., DOREE M., GUERN J. & HALL R.H. 1972 Uptake of cytokinins by *Acer pseudoplatanus* cells: enzymes of the adenosine deaminase type as possible regulators of the cytokinin level inside the cell. pp. 467–475 *in* Carr D.J. (ed.) 1972 7th Int. Conf. on Plant Growth Subs. 1970 Springer-Verlag.

TERRY E. & MACINTYRE R. (eds.) 1976 *The International Exchange and Testing of Cassava Germplasm in Africa*. Proc. of workshop at IITA, Ibadan, Nigeria 1975.

TERRY N. 1977 Photosynthesis, growth and the role of chloride. Plant Physiol. **60**, 69–75.

TERZI M. & LO SCHIAVO F. 1990 Developmental mutants in carrot. pp. 391–397 *in* Nijkamp *et al.* (eds.) 1990 (*q.v.*).

THAKUR S. & GANAPATHY P.S. 1978 Morphogenesis of organ differentiation in *Bacopa monnieri*: stem cultures. Ind. J. Exp. Biol. **16**, 514–516.

THEILER R. 1977 *In vitro* culture of shoot tips of *Pelargonium* species. Acta Hort. **78**, 403–409.

THENGANE S., PARANJPE S.V., KHUSPE S.S. & MASCARENHAS A.F. 1986 Hybridization of *Gossypium* species through *in ovulo* embryo culture. Plant Cell Tiss. Organ Cult. **6**, 209–219.

THEVENOT C. & CÔME D. 1973 Inhibition de la germination de l'axe embryonnaire par les cotyledons chez le pommier (*Prunus malus* L.). Compt. Rend. Acad. Sci. Paris **277D**, 1873–1876.

THIMANN K.V. 1963 Plant growth substances, present and future. Ann. Rev. Plant Physiol. **14**, 1–18.

THIMANN K.V. & TAKAHASHI N. 1958 The action of chelating agents on growth of *Avena*. Plant Physiol. **33**, (Suppl.) 33 (Abst.).

THOM M., MARETZKI A., KOMOR E. & SAKAI W.S. 1981 Nutrient uptake and accumulation by sugarcane cell cultures in relation to the growth cycle. Plant Cell Tiss. Organ Cult. **1**, 3–14.

THOMALE H. 1954 *Die Orchideen*. Eugen Ulmer, Verlag, Stuttgart.

THOMAS B.J. 1980 The detection by serological methods of viruses infecting the rose. Ann. Appl. Biol. **94**, 91–101.

THOMAS D. des S. & MURASHIGE T. 1979a Volatile emissions of plant tissue cultures. I. Identification of the major components. In Vitro **15**, 654–658.

THOMAS D. des S. & MURASHIGE T. 1979b Volatile emissions of plant tissue cultures. II. Effects of the auxin 2,4-D on production of volatiles in callus cultures. In Vitro **15**, 659–663.

THOMAS E. & STREET H.E. 1972 Factors influencing morphogenesis in excised roots and suspension cultures of *Atropa belladonna*. Ann. Bot. **36**, 239–247.

THOMAS E., BRIGHT S.W.J., FRANKLIN J., LANCASTER V.A., MIFLIN B.J. & GIBSON R. 1982 Variation amongst protoplast-derived potato plants (*Solanum tuberosum* cv. 'Maris Bard'). Theor. Appl. Genet. **62**, 65–68.

THOMAS E., HOFFMANN F., POTRYKUS I. & WENZEL G. 1976 Protoplast regeneration and stem embryogenesis of haploid androgenetic rape. Mol. Gen. Genet. **145**, 245–247.

THOMAS E., KING P.J. & POTRYKUS I. 1979 Improvement of crop plants via single cells *in vitro* — an assessment. Z. Pflanzenzuchtg. **82**, 1–30.

THOMAS J.C. & KATTERMAN F.R. 1986 Cytokinin activity induced by thidiazuron. Plant Physiol. **81**, 681–683.

THOMAS M.J. & TRANVAN H. 1982 Influence relative de la BAP et de l'IBA sur la néoformation de bourgeons et de racines sur les plantules du *Biota orientalis* (Cupressacées). Physiol. Plant. **56**, 118–122.

THOMPSON B.L., SINK K.C. & DENNIS F.G. Jr. 1981 A non-destructive assay for gibberellin production *in vitro* and its application to callus cultures of *Phaseolus*. HortScience **16**, 432 (Abst. 247).

THOMPSON J.E., LEGGE R.L. & BARBER R.F. 1987 The role of free- radicals in senescence and wounding. New Phytol. **105**, 317–344.

THOMPSON J.F., MADISON J.T. & MUENSTER A.-M.E. 1977 *In vitro* culture of immature cotyledons of soya bean (*Glycine max* L.). Ann. Bot. **41**, 29–39.

THOMPSON M.R. & THORPE T.A. 1981 Mannitol metabolism in cell cultures.. Plant Physiol. **67**, (Suppl.) 27 (Abst. 142).

THOMPSON P.A. 1977 *Orchids from seed.* Royal Botanic Gardens, Kew.

THOMPSON P.W. & WOOD L. 1990 Anti-lift fermenter. U.S. Patent No. 4943535.

THOMSON A.D. 1956a Heat treatment and tissue culture as a means of freeing potatoes from Virus Y. Nature **177**, 709.

THOMSON A.D. 1956b Studies on the effect of malachite green on potato viruses X and Y. Aust. J. Agric. Res. **7**, 428–434.

THORPE T.A. (ed.) 1978a *Frontiers of Plant Tissue Culture.* Int. Assoc. for Plant Tissue Culture. Distrib. by The Bookstore, Univ. of Calgary, Calgary, Alberta T2N 1N4, Canada.

THORPE T.A. 1978b Physiological and biochemical aspects of organogenesis *in vitro*. pp. 47–58 in Thorpe T.A. (ed.) 1978a (*q.v.*).

THORPE T.A. 1980 Organogenesis *in vitro*: structural, physiological, and biochemical aspects. pp. 71–111 in Vasil I.K. (ed.) 1980a (*q.v.*).

THORPE T.A. (ed.) 1981 *Plant Tissue Culture. Methods and Applications in Agriculture.* Academic Press, New York, London, Toronto, Sydney.

THORPE T.A. 1982 Physiological and biochemical aspects of organogenesis *in vitro*. pp. 121–124 in Fujiwara A. (ed.) 1982 (*q.v.*).

THORPE T.A. & LAISHLEY E.J. 1973 Glucose oxidation during shoot initiation in tobacco callus cultures. J. Exp. Bot. **24**, 1082–1089.

THORPE T.A. & MEIER D.D. 1972 Starch metabolism, repiration and shoot formation in tobacco callus cultures. Physiol. Plant. **27**, 365–369.

THORPE T.A. & MEIER D.D. 1973 Effects of gibberellic acid and abscisic acid on shoot formation in tobacco callus cultures. Physiol. Plant. **29**, 121–124.

THORPE T.A. & MEIER D.D. 1974 Starch metabolism in shoot-forming tobacco callus. J. Exp. Bot. **25**, 288–294.

THORPE T.A. & MEIER D.D. 1975 Effect of gibberellic acid on starch metabolism in tobacco callus cultured under shoot-forming conditions. Phytomorph. **25**, 238–245.

THORPE T.A. & MURASHIGE T. 1968a Some histochemical changes underlying shoot initiation in tobacco callus culture. Am. J. Bot. **55**, 710 (Abst.).

THORPE T.A. & MURASHIGE T. 1968b Starch accumulation in shoot-forming tobacco callus cultures. Science **160**, 421–422.

THORPE T.A. & MURASHIGE T. 1970 Some histochemical changes underlying shoot initiation in tobacco callus cultures. Can. J. Bot. **48**, 277–285.

THORPE T.A., HUXTER T.J. & REID D.M. 1981 The role of ethylene in shoot formation in tobacco callus. Plant Physiol. **67**, (Suppl.) 27 (Abst. 141).

THORPE T.A., JOY R.W. IV & LEUNG W.M. 1986 Starch turnover in shoot-forming tobacco callus. Physiol. Plant. **66**, 58–62.

THORPE T.A., VAN T.T. & GASPAR Th. 1978 Isoperoxidases in epidermal layers of tobacco and change during organ formation *in vitro*. Physiol. Plant. **44**, 388–394.

THURSTON K.C., SPENCER S.J. & ARDITTI J. 1979 Phytotoxicity of bactericides and fungicides in orchid culture media. Am. J. Bot. **66**, 825–835.

TIBURCIO A.F., FIGUERAS X., CLAPAROLS T., SANTOS M. & TORNÉ J.M. 1991 Improved plant regeneration in maize callus cultures after pretreatment with DL-α-difluoromethylarginine. Plant Cell Tiss. Organ Cult. **27**, 27–32.

TIBURCIO A.F., GENDY C.A. & TRAN THANH VAN K. 1989 Morphogenesis in tobacco subepidermal cells: putrescine as a marker of root differentiation. Plant Cell Tiss. Organ Cult. **19**, 43–54.

TIBURCIO A.F., KAUR-SAWHNEY R. & GALSTON A.W. 1987 Polyamines and organogenesis in thin layer tobacco tissue cultures. pp. 43–56 in Jackson *et al.* (eds.) 1987a (*q.v.*).

TIDEMAN J. & HAWKER J.S. 1982 *In vitro* propagation of latex-producing plants. Ann. Bot. **49**, 273–279.

TIFFIN L.O., BROWN J.C. & KRAUSS R.W. 1960 Differential absorption of metal chelate components by plant roots. Plant Physiol. **35**, 362–367.

TILNEY-BASSETT R.A.E. 1986 *Plant chimeras.* Edward Arnold (Publishers) Ltd. London. ISBN 0-7131-2936-0

TISSERAT B. & MURASHIGE T. 1977a Effects of ethephon, ethylene and 2,4-dichlorophenoxyacetic acid on asexual embryogenesis *in vitro*. Plant Physiol. **60**, 437–439.

TISSERAT B. & MURASHIGE T. 1977b Probable identity of substances in citrus that repress asexual embryogenesis. In Vitro **13**, 785–789.

TISSERAT B. & MURASHIGE T. 1977c Repression of asexual embryogenesis *in vitro* by some plant growth regulators. In Vitro **13**, 799–805.

TISSERAT B., ESAN E.B. & MURASHIGE T. 1979a Somatic embryogenesis in angiosperms. Hort. Rev. **1**, 1–78.

TISSERAT B., ULRICH J.M. & FINKLE B.J. 1981 Cryogenic preservation and regeneration of date palm tissue. HortScience **16**, 47–48.

TIZIO R., SAUSSAY R. & GAUTHERET R. 1970 Action de quelques gibbérellines sur la rhizogenèse de fragments de Topinambour cultivés *in vitro*. Compt. Rend. Acad. Sci. Paris **270D**, 2088–2092.

TOIVONEN P.M.A. & KARTHA K.K. 1988 Regeneration of plantlets from *in vitro* cultured cotyledons of white spruce (*Picea glauca* Moench Voss). Plant Cell Rep. **7**, 318–321.

TOMAR U.K. & GUPTA S.C. 1988a Somatic embryogenesis and organogenesis in callus cultures of a tree legume — *Albizia richardiana* King. Plant Cell Rep. **7**, 70–73.

TOMAR U.K. & GUPTA S.C. 1988b In vitro plant regeneration of leguminous trees (*Albizia* spp.). Plant Cell Rep. **7**, 385–388.

TOMES D. 1979 A tissue culture procedure for propagation and maintenance of *Lotus corniculatus* genotypes. Can. J. Bot. **57**, 137–140.

TOMES D.T., ELLIS B.E., HARNEY P.M., KASHA K.J. & PETERSON R.L. 1982 *Application of Plant Cell and Tissue Culture to Agriculture and Industry.* Plant Cell Culture Centre, University of Guelph, Ontario, Canada.

TOPPING J.F. & LINDSEY K. 1991 Shoot cultures and root cultures of tobacco. Section A4 pp. 1–13 in Lindsey K. (ed.) 1991 (*q.v.*).

TÖRMÄLÄ T. 1990 Genotype-phenotype interplay in micropropagation. pp. 102–107 in Nijkamp *et al.* (eds.) 1990 (*q.v.*).

TORRANCE L. 1980a Use of Protein A to improve sensitisation of latex particles with antibodies to plant viruses. Ann. Appl. Biol. **96**, 45–50.

TORRANCE L. 1980b Use of bovine C1q to detect plant viruses in an enzyme-linked immunosorbent-type assay. J. Gen. Virol. **51**, 229–232.

TORRANCE L. 1981 Use of C1q enzyme-linked immunosorbent assay to detect plant viruses and their serologically different strains. Ann. Appl. Biol. **99**, 291–299.

TORRANCE L. & JONES R.A.C. 1981 Recent developments in serological methods suited for use in routine testing for plant viruses. Plant Pathology **30**, 1–24.

TORRES K. & CARLISI J.A. 1986 Shoot and root organogenesis of *Camellia sasanqua*. Plant Cell Rep. **5**, 381–384.

TORRES K., TORRES J. & NATARELLA N.J. 1981b The production of gases by various plant species grown *in vitro*. HortScience **16**, 441.

TORREY J.G. 1956 Chemical factors limiting lateral root formation in isolated pea roots. Physiol. Plant. **9**, 370–388.

TORREY J.G. 1958a Differential mitotic response of diploid and polyploid nuclei to auxin and kinetin treatment. Science **128**, 1148.

TORREY J.G. 1958b Endogenous bud and root formation by isolated root of *Convolvulus* grown *in vitro*. Plant Physiol. **33**, 258–263.

TORREY J.G. 1961 Kinetin as a trigger for mitosis in mature endomitotic plant cells. Exp. Cell Res. **23**, 281–299.

TORREY J.G. 1963 Cellular patterns in developing roots. pp. 285–314 *in* Symp. XVII Soc. Exp. Biol., Cambridge University Press.

TORREY J.G. 1966 The initiation of organized development in plants. Adv. Morphogenesis **5**, 39–91.

TORREY J.G. 1967 Morphogenesis in relation to chromosomal constitution in long-term plant tissue cultures. Physiol. Plant. **20**, 265–275.

TORREY J.G. 1972 On the initiation of organisation in the root apex. pp. 1–13 *in* Miller and Kuehnert (eds.) 1972 (*q.v.*).

TORREY J.G. 1973 Plant embryo. pp. 166–170 *in* Kruse and Patterson (eds.) 1973 (*q.v.*).

TORREY J.G. & REINERT J. 1961 Suspension cultures of higher plant cells in synthetic media. Plant Physiol. **36**, 483–491.

TORRIGIANI P., ALTAMURA M.M., CAPITANI F., FALASCA G., BAGNI N. & SERAFINI-FRACASSINI D. 1990 Inhibition of polyamine biosynthsis affects the rhizogenic response in tobacco thin cell layers. pp. 480–485 *in* Nijkamp *et al.* (eds.) 1990 (*q.v.*).

TORRIZO L.B. & ZAPATA F.J. 1986 Anther culture in rice: IV. The effect of abscisic acid on plant regeneration. Plant Cell Rep. **5**, 136–139.

TOSHINORI A. & FUTSUHARA Y. 1985 Efficient plant regeneration by somatic embryogenesis from root callus tissues of rice (*Oryza sativa* L.). J. Plant Physiol. **121**, 111–118.

TOURAINE B., GRIGNON N. & GRIGNON C. 1988 Charge balance in NO_3^--fed soybean. Estimation of K^+ and carboxylate recirculation. Plant Physiol. **88**, 605–612.

TOWILL L.E. 1981 *Solanum etuberosum*: a model for studying the cryobiology of shoot tips in the tuber-bearing *Solanum* species. Plant Sci. Lett. **20**, 315–324.

TOWILL L.E. 1988 Genetic considerations for germplasm preservation of clonal materials. HortScience **23**, 91–95.

TRAN THANH VAN K. 1977 Regulation of morphogenesis. pp. 367–385 *in* Barz *et al.* (eds.) 1977 (*q.v.*).

TRAN THANH VAN K. 1980 Control of morphogenesis by inherent and exogenously applied factors in thin cell layers. pp. 175–194 *in* Vasil I.K. (ed.) 1980a (*q.v.*).

TRAN THANH VAN K. & MUTAFTSCHIEV S. 1990 Signals influencing cell elongation, cell enlargment, cell division and morphogenesis. pp. 514–519 *in* Nijkamp *et al.* (eds.) 1990 (*q.v.*).

TRAN THANH VAN K. & TRINH H. 1978 Plant propagation: non- identical and identical copies. pp. 134–158 *in* Hughes *et al.* 1978 (*q.v.*).

TRAN THANH VAN K., TOUBART P., COUSSON A., DARVILL A.G., GOLLIN D.J., CHELF P. & ALBERSHEIM P. 1985 Manipulation of the morphogenetic pathways of tobacco explants by oligosaccharins. Nature **314**, 615–617.

TRAN THANH VAN K., YILMAZ-LENTZ D. & TRINH T.H. 1987 *In vitro* control of morphogenesis in conifers. pp. 168–182 *in* Bonga and Durzan (eds.) 1987b (*q.v.*).

TRAN THANH VAN M. 1973a Direct flower neoformation from superficial tissue of small explants of *Nicotiana tabacum* L. Planta **115**, 87–92.

TRAN THANH VAN M. 1973b *In vitro* control of *de novo* flower, bud, root and callus differentiation from excised epidermal tissues. Nature **246**, 44-45.

TRAN THANH VAN M., DIEN N.T. & CHLYAH A. 1974 Regulation of organogenesis in small explants of superficial tissue of *Nicotiana tabacum* L. Planta **119**, 149–159.

TRAYNOR P.L. & FLASHMAN S.M. 1981 Hormone-induced caulogenesis in long-term tobacco cell lines and its effect on nuclear DNA content. Theor. Appl. Genet. **60**, 31–36.

TRELEASE S.F. & TRELEASE H.M. 1933 Physiologically balanced culture solutions with stable hydrogen-ion concentration. Science **78**, 438–439.

TREMBLAY F.M. & LALONDE M. 1984 Requirements for *in vitro* propagation of seven nitrogen-fixing *Alnus* species. Plant Cell Tiss. Organ Cult. **3**, 189–199.

TREMBLAY F.M., NESME X. & LALONDE M. 1984 Selection and micropropagation of nodulating and non-nodulating clones of *Alnus crispa* (Ait.) Pursh. Plant & Soil **78**, 171–179.

TREWAVAS A. 1968 Relationship between plant growth hormones and nucleic acid metabolism. pp. 113–161 *in* Reinhold and Liwschitz (eds.) *Progress in Phytochemistry* 1, Wiley, New York, London.

TRIGIANO R.N., GRAY D.J., CONGER B.V. & McDANIEL J.K. 1989 Origin of direct somatic embryos from cultured leaf segments of *Dactylis glomerata*. Bot. Gaz. **150**, 72–77.

TRIMBOLI D.S., PRAKASH N. & DE FOSSARD R.A. 1977 The initiation, rooting and establishment of cortical buds in cauliflower. Acta Hort. **78**, 243–248.

TRINH T.H. & TRAN THANH VAN K. 1981 *In vitro* flower formation from diploid and haploid thin layer of epidermal and subepidermal cells of *N. tabacum* L. and of *N. plumbaginifolia* Viv. Z. Pflanzenphysiol. **101**, 1–8.

TRIPPI V.S. 1963 Studies on ontogeny and senility of plants. III. Changes in the proliferative capacity *in vitro* during ontogeny in *Robinia pseudoacacia* and *Castanea vulgaris* and in adult and juvenile clones of *R. pseudoacacia*. Phyton **20**, 153–159.

TROLINDER N.L. & GOODIN J.R. 1987 Somatic embryogenesis and plant regeneration in cotton (*Gossypium hirsutum* L.). Plant Cell Rep. **6**, 231–234.

TROLINDER N.L. & GOODIN J.R. 1988b Somatic embryogenesis in cotton (*Gossypium*). II. Requirements for embryo development and plant regeneration. Plant Cell Tiss. Organ Cult. **12**, 43–53.

TRUONG-ANDRE I. & DEMARLY Y. 1984 Obtaining plants by *in vitro* culture of unfertilised maize ovaries (*Zea mays* L.) and preliminary studies on the progeny of a gynogenetic plant. Z. Pflanzenzucht. **92**, 309–320.

TRYON K. 1956 Scopoletin in differentiating and non-differentiating cultured tobacco tissue. Science **123**, 590.

TSAY H.S. & SU C.Y. 1985 Anther culture of papaya (*Carica papaya* L.). Plant Cell Rep. **4**, 28–30.

TSUI C. 1948 The role of zinc in auxin synthesis in the tomato plant. Am. J. Bot. **35**, 172–178.

TUCKER D.J. 1976 Effects of far-red light on the hormonal control of side shoot growth in the tomato. Ann. Bot. **40**, 1033–1042.

TUCKER D.J. & MANSFIELD T.A. 1972 Effects of light quality on apical dominance in *Xanthium strumarium* and the associated changes in endogenous levels of abscisic acid and cytokinins. Planta **102**, 140–151.

TUKEY H.B. 1933 Artificial culture of sweet cherry embryos. J. Hered. **24**, 7–12.

TUKEY H.B. 1934 Artificial culture methods for isolated embryos of deciduous fruits. Proc. Am. Soc. Hort. Sci. **32**, 313–322.

TULECKE W. & McGRANAHAN G. 1985 Somatic embryogenesis and plant regeneration from cotyledons of walnut, *Juglans regia* L. Plant Science **40**, 57–63.

TULECKE W., WEINSTEIN L.H., RUTNER A. & LAURENCOT H.J. 1961 The biochemical composition of coconut water as related to its use in plant tissue culture. Contrib. Boyce Thompson Inst. **21**, 115–128.

TUMANOV I.I., BUTENKO R.G. & OGOLEVETS I.V. 1968 Application of isolated tissue culture technique for studying hardening process in plant cells. Fiziol. Rast. **15**, 749–756.

TUMER N.E. 1990 Virus resistant plants. U.S. Patent No. 4970168

TUR-KASPA Y., HARTMAN R.D., HORNACEK K.J. & BRENDEL K.J. 1970 Automated plant culture proliferation system. U.S. Patent No. 4910146.

TURNER S.R. & SINGHA S. 1990 Vitrification of crabapple, pear and geum on gellan gum-solidified culture medium. HortScience **25**, 1648–1650.

TYAGI A.K., BHARAL S., RASHID A. & MAHESHWARI N. 1985 Plant regeneration from tissue cultures initiated from immature inflorescences of a grass, *Echinochloa colonum* (L.) Link. Plant Cell Rep. **4**, 115–117.

TYAGI A.K., RASHID A. & MAHESHWARI S.C. 1980 Enhancement of pollen embryo formation in *Datura innoxia* by charcoal. Physiol. Plant. **49**, 296–298.

UCHIMIYA H. & MURASHIGE T. 1974 Evaluation of parameters in the isolation of viable protoplasts from cultured tobacco cells. Plant Physiol. **54**, 936–944.

UEDA H. & TORIKATA H. 1972 Effects of light and culture medium on adventitious root formation by *Cymbidiums* in aseptic culture. Am. Orchid Soc. Bull. **41**, 322–327.

UESATO K. 1973 Effect of different forms of nitrogen in the culture media on the growth of young *Cattleya* seedlings. Sci. Bull. Coll. Agric. Univ. Ryukyus **20**, 1–12.

UHRING J. 1982 *In vitro* propagation of *Scutellaria costericana*. HortScience **17**, 533 (Abst. 429).

UKAJI T. & ASHIHARA H. 1987 Effect of inorganic phosphate on the levels of amino-acids in suspension-cultured cells of *Catharanthus roseus*. Ann. Bot. **60**, 109–114.

ULRYCHOVA M. & PETRÙ E. 1975 Elimination of mycoplasma in tobacco callus tissues (*Nicotiana glauca* Grah.) cultured *in vitro* in the presence of 2,4-D in the nutrient medium. Biol. Plant. **17**, 103–108.

UMBECK P., JOHNSON G., BARTON K. & SWAIN W. 1987 Genetically transformed cotton (*Gossypium hirsutum* L.) plants. Bio/Technology **5**, 263–266.

UMBECK P.F. & NORSTOG K. 1979 Effects of abscisic acid and ammonium ion on morphogenesis of cultured barley embryos. Bull. Torrey Bot. Club **106**, 110–116.

UMIEL N. & GOLDNER R. 1976 Effect of streptomycin on diploid tobacco callus cultures and the isolation of resistant mutants. Protoplasma **89**, 83–89.

UNO S. & PREECE J.E. 1987 Micro- and cutting propagation of 'Crimson Pygmy' barberry. HortScience **22**, 488–491.

URAGAMI U., SAKAI A., NAGAI M. & TAKAHASHI T. 1990 Cryopreservation by vitrification of cultured cells and somatic embryos from mesophyll tissue of asparagus. Acta Hort. **271**, 109–116.

USHA RAO I., RAMANUJA RAO V. & NARANG V. 1985 Somatic embryogenesis and regeneration of plants in the bamboo *Dendrocalamus strictus*. Plant Cell Rep. **4**, 191–194.

VACHA G.A. & HARVEY R.B. 1927 The use of ethylene, propylene and similar compounds in breaking the rest period of tubers, bulbs, cuttings, and seeds. Plant Physiol. **2**, 187–192.

VACIN E.F. & WENT F.W. 1949 Some pH changes in nutrient solutions. Bot. Gaz. **110**, 605–613.

VAJRABHAYA T. 1977 Variation in clonal propagation. pp. 178–201 *in* Arditti J. (ed.) *Orchid Biology: Reviews and Perspectives*, 1. Cornell University Press, Ithaca.

VALDOVINOS J.G., ERNEST L.C. & HENRY E.W. 1967 Effect of ethylene and gibberellic acid on auxin synthesis in plant tissues. Plant Physiol. **42**, 1803–1806.

VALLES M. & BOXUS Ph. 1987a Micropropagation of several *Rosa hybrida* L. cultivars. Acta Hort. **212**, 611–617.

VALLES M. & BOXUS Ph. 1987b Regeneration from *Rosa* callus. Acta Hort. **212**, 691–696.

VAN AARTRIJK J. & VAN DER LINDE P.C.G. 1986 *In vitro* propagation of flower-bulb crops. pp. 317–331 *in* Zimmerman *et al.* (eds.) 1986 (*q.v.*).

VAN AARTRIJK J., BLOM-BARNHOORN G.J. & BRUINSMA J. 1982 Interactions between NAA, wounding, temperature, and TIBA in their effects on adventitious sprout formation on *Lilium* bulb tissue.

VAN AARTRIJK J., BLOM-BARNHOORN G.J. & BRUINSMA J. 1985 Adventitious bud formation from bulb-scale explants of *Lilium speciosum* Thunb. *in vitro*. Effects of aminoethoxyvinyl-glycine, 1-aminocyclopropane-1-carboxylic acid, and ethylene. J. Plant Physiol. **117**, 401–410.

VAN DAALEN J.J. & DAAMS J. 1970 Substituted alkoxycarbonylmethoxy-2,1,3-benzothiadiazoles. New group of synthetic plant growth regulators. Naturwiss. **8**, 395.

VAN DEN ENDE G., CROES A.F., KEMP A. & BARENDSE G.W.M. 1984a Development of flower buds in thin-layer cultures of floral stalk tissue from tobacco: role of hormones in different stages. Physiol. Plant. **61**, 114–118.

VAN DER KRIEKEN W.M., CROES A.F., BARENDSE G.W.M. & WULLEMS G.J. 1988 Uptake and metabolism of benzyladenine in the early stage of flower bud development *in vitro* in tobacco. Physiol. Plant. **74**, 113–118.

VAN DER LINDE P.C.G., HOL G.M.G.M., BLOM-BARNHOORN G.J., VAN AARTRIJK J. & DE KLERK G.J. 1988 *In vitro* propagation of *Iris hollandica* Tub. cv. Prof. Blaauw. I. Regeneration of bulb-scale explants. Acta Hort. **226**, 121–128.

VAN DER PLAS L.H.W. & WAGNER M.J. 1986 Effect of oxygen on growth and respiration of potato tuber callus. Plant Cell Tiss. Organ Cult. **7**, 217–225.

VAN GEYT J.P.C. & JACOBS M. 1985 Suspension cultures of sugarbeet (*Beta vulgaris* L.). Induction and habituation of dedifferentiated and self-regenerating cell lines. Plant Cell Rep. **4**, 66–69.

VAN HOOF P. & GASPAR Th. 1976 Peroxidase and isoperoxidase changes in relation to root initiation of *Asparagus* cultured *in vitro*. Scientia Hort. **4**, 27–31.

VAN HUYSTEE R.B. 1977 Porphyrin metabolism in peanut cells cultured in sucrose containing medium. Acta Hort. **78**, 83–87.

VAN OVERBEEK J. 1942 Water uptake by excised root systems of the tomato due to non-osmotic forces. Am. J. Bot. **29**, 677–683.

VAN OVERBEEK J., CONKLIN M.E. & BLAKESLEE A.F. 1941 Factors in coconut milk essential for growth and development of very young *Datura* embryos. Science **94**, 350–351.

VAN OVERBEEK J., CONKLIN M.E. & BLAKESLEE A.F. 1942 Cultivation *in vitro* of small *Datura* embryos. Am. J. Bot. **29**, 472–477.

VAN OVERBEEK J., LOEFFLER J.E. & MASON M.I.R. 1967 Dormin (Abscisin II), inhibitor of plant DNA synthesis? Science **156**, 1497–1499.

VAN OVERBEEK J., SIU R. & HAAGEN-SMIT A.J. 1944 Factors affecting the growth of *Datura* embryos *in vitro*. Am. J. Bot. **31**, 219–224.

VAN REGENMORTEL M.H.V. & BURCKARD J. 1980 Detection of a wide spectrum of tobacco mosaic virus strains by indirect enzyme-linked immunosorbent assays (ELISA). Virology **106**, 327–334.

VAN REGENMORTEL M.H.V., DEKKER E.L., DORÉ I., PORTA C., WEISS E. & BURCKARD J. 1988 Recent advances in seradiagnosis of plant virus diseases. Acta Hort. **234**, 175–183.

VAN STADEN J. 1976 The identification of zeatin glucoside from coconut milk. Physiol. Plant. **36**, 123–126.

VAN STADEN J. & DREWES S.E. 1975 Identification of zeatin and zeatin riboside in coconut milk. Physiol. Plant. **34**, 106–109.

VAN STADEN J. & MOONEY P.A. 1988 The effect of cytokinin preconditioning on the metabolism of adenine derivatives in soybean callus. J. Plant Physiol. **133**, 466–469.

VAN'T HOF J. 1985 Control points within the cell cycle. pp. 1–13 *in* Byant and Francis (eds.) 1985 (*q.v.*).

VAN'T HOF J. & KOVACS C.J. 1972 Principal control point hypothesis. pp. 15–32 *in* Miller and Keuhnert (eds.) 1972 (*q.v.*).

VAN WAES J.M. & DEBERGH P.C. 1986 *In vitro* germination of some Western European orchids. Physiol. Plant. **67**, 253–261.

VANDENBELT J.M. 1945 Nutritive value of coconut. Nature **156**, 174–175.

VANDERHOVEN C. & ZYRD J.P. 1978 Changes in malate content and enzymes involved in dark CO_2 fixation during growth of *Acer pseudoplatanus* cells in suspension culture. Physiol. Plant. **43**, 93–103.

VANDERSCHAEGHE A.M. & DEBERGH P.C. 1987 Technical aspects of the control of the relative humidity in tissue culture containers. pp. 68–76 *in* Ducaté *et al.* (eds.) 1987 (*q.v.*).

VANDERSCHAEGHE A.M. & DEBERGH P.C. 1988 Automation of tissue culture manipulations in the final stages. Acta Hort. **227**, 399–401.

VAŇKOVÁ R., KAMINEK M., EDER J. & VANÉK T. 1987 Dynamics of production of trans-zeatin and trans-zeatin riboside by immobilized cytokinin-autonomous and cytokinin-dependent tobacco cells. J. Plant Growth Reg. **6**, 147–157.

VANNINI G.L. & POLI F. 1983 Binucleation and abnormal chromosome distribution in *Euglena gracilis* cells treated with dimethyl sulfoxide. Protoplasma **114**, 62–66.

VANSÉVEREN-VAN ESPEN N. 1973 Effets du saccharose sur le contenu en chlorophylles de protocormes de *Cymbidium* Sw. (Orchidaceae) cultivés *in vitro*. Bull. Soc. Roy. Bot. Belg. **106**, 107–115.

VARGA M. & HUMPHRIES E.C. 1974 Root formation on petioles of detached primary leaves of dwarf bean (*Phaseolus vulgaris*) pretreated with gibberellic acid, triodobenzoic acid, and cytokinins. Ann. Bot. **38**, 803–807.

VASIL I.K. (ed.) 1980a *Perspectives in Plant Cell and Tissue Culture.* Int. Rev. Cytology Suppl. 11A Academic Press.

VASIL I.K. (ed.) 1980b *Perspectives in Plant Cell and Tissue Culture.* Int. Rev. Cytology Suppl. 11B Academic Press.

VASIL I.K. 1980c Androgenetic haploids. pp. 195–223 *in* Vasil I.K. (ed.) 1980a (*q.v.*).

VASIL I.K. 1983 Towards the development of a single cell system for grasses. pp. 131–144 *in* Anon (1983) q.v.

VASIL I.K. (ed.) 1991 Scale-up and automation in plant propagation. *Cell Culture and Somatic Cell Genetics of Plants* Vol. 8. Academic Press Inc., San Diego, New York. ISBN 0-12-715008-0

VASIL I.K. & HILDEBRANDT A.C. 1966a Variations of morphogenetic behaviour in plant tissue cultures. I. *Cichorium endivia*. Am. J. Bot. **53**, 860–869.

VASIL I.K. & HILDEBRANDT A.C. 1966b Variations of morphogenetic behaviour in plant tissue cultures. II. *Petroselinum hortense*. Am. J. Bot. **53**, 869–874.

VASIL I.K. & HILDEBRANDT A.C. 1966c Growth and chlorophyll production in plant callus tissues grown *in vitro*. Planta **68**, 69–82.

VASIL I.K. & NITSCH C. 1975 Experimental production of pollen haploids and their uses. Z. Pflanzenphysiol. **76**, 191–212.

VASIL I.K. & VASIL V. 1980a Embryogenesis and plantlet formation from protoplasts of pearl millet (*Pennisetum americanum*). pp. 255–259 *in* Ferenczy & Farkas (eds.) 1980 (*q.v.*).

VASIL V. & VASIL I.K. 1981a Somatic embryogenesis and plant regeneration from tissue cultures of *Pennisetum americanum* and *P. americanum* × *P. purpureum* hybrid. Am. J. Bot. **68**, 864–872.

VASIL V. & VASIL I.K. 1981b Somatic embryogenesis and plant regeneration from suspension cultures of pearl millet (*Pennisetum americanum*). Ann. Bot. **47**, 669–678.

VASIL V. & VASIL I.K. 1982a The ontogeny of somatic embryos of *Pennisetum americanum* (L.) K. Schum. I. In cultured immature embryos. Bot. Gaz. **143**, 454–465.

VAUGHN K.C. 1983 Chimeras and variegation: problems in propagation. HortScience **18**, 845–848.

VEGA M.A. & BOLAND R.L. 1986 Vitamin D-3 induces the *de novo* synthesis of calmodulin in *Phaseolus vulgaris* root segments growing *in vitro*. Biochim. Biophys. Acta **881**, 364–374.

VELIKY I.A. & MARTIN S.M. 1970 A fermenter for plant cell suspension cultures. Can. J. Microbiol. **16**, 223–226.

VENKETESWARAN S. & MAHLBERG P.G. 1962 Proliferation of albino and pigmented genetical strains of *Nicotiana* tissue culture. Physiol. Plant. **15**, 639–648.

VENVERLOO C. 1976 The formation of adventitious organs. III. A comparison of root and shoot formation on *Nautilocalyx* explants. Z. Pflanzenphysiol. **80**, 310–322.

VENVERLOO C.J. 1973 The formation of adventitious organs. I. Cytokinin-induced formation of leaves and shoots in callus cultures of *Populus nigra* L. 'Italica'. Acta Bot. Neerl. **22**, 390–398.

VERMA D.C. & DOUGALL D.K. 1979 Biosynthesis of *myo*- inositol and its role as a precursor of cell-wall polysaccharides in suspension cultures of wild-carrot cells. Planta **146**, 55–62.

VERMA D.C. & DURZAN D.J. 1980 Somatic embryogenesis in cell suspension cultures of wild carrot in a 'tissue culture cluster dish' (Costar). Plant Physiol. **65**, (Suppl.) 90 (Abst. 489).

VERMA D.C., LITVAY J.D., JOHNSON M.A. & EINSPHAR D.W. 1982 Media development for cell suspensions of conifers. pp. 59–60 *in* Fujiwara A. (ed.) 1982 (*q.v.*).

VERMA D.P.S. & VAN HUYSTEE R.B. 1971 Derivation, characteristics and large scale culture of a cell line from *Arachis hypogaea* L. cotyledons. Exp. Cell Res. **69**, 402–408.

VERMEER E. & EVERS P. 1987 b A new technique to reduce labour by refreshing liquid medium automatically with a new container. pp. 264–266 *in* Ducaté *et al.* (eds.) 1987 (*q.v.*).

VIEITEZ A.M. & VIEITEZ M.L. 1980b Culture of chestnut shoots from buds *in vitro*. Plant Physiol. **55**, 83–84.

VIEITEZ A.M., BARCIELA J. & BALLESTER A. 1989 Propagation of *Camellia japonica* cv. Alba Plena by tissue culture. J. Hort. Sci. **64**, 177–182.

VIEITEZ A.M., SAN-JOSE M.C. & VIEITEZ E. 1985a *In vitro* plantlet regeneration from juvenile and mature *Quercus robur* L. J. Hort. Sci. **60**, 99–106.

VIEITEZ F.J., SAN-JOSE C., BALLESTER A. & VIEITEZ A.M. 1990 Somatic embryogenesis in cultured immature zygotic embryos in chestnut. J. Plant Physiol. **136**, 253–256.

VILLALOBOS ARAMBULA V.M. 1984 Tissue culture technology applied to ornamental species. pp. 163, 165–168 *in* F.A.O. Plant Prodn. & Protection Paper 59.

VILLALOBOS V.M., FERREIRA P. & MORA A. 1991 The use of biotechnology in the conservation of tropical germplasm. Biotech. Adv. **9**, 197–215.

VILLALOBOS V.M., YEUNG E.C. & THORPE T.A. 1984 Origin of adventitious shoots in excised radiata pine cotyledons *in vitro*. Can. J. Bot. **63**, 2172–2176.

VINE S.J. & JONES O.P. 1969 The culture of shoot tips of hop (*Humulus lupulus*) to eliminate viruses. J. Hort. Sci. **44**, 281–284.

VISEUR J. 1987 Micropropagation of pear, *Pyrus communis* L., in a double-phase culture medium. Acta Hort. **212**, 117–124.

VISEUR J. & LIEVENS C. 1987 *In vitro* propagation and regeneration of plants from calluses of *Begonia* × *tuberhybrida*. Acta Hort. **212**, 705–709.

VISSER R.G.F. 1991 Regeneration and transformation of potato by *Agrobacterium tumefaciens*. Section B5 pp. 1–9 *in* Lindsey (ed.) 1991 (*q.v.*).

VON ARNOLD S. 1987 Effect of sucrose on starch accumulation in, and adventitous bud formation on, embryos of *Picea abies*. Ann. Bot. **59**, 15–22.

VON ARNOLD S. & ERIKSSON T. 1977 A revised medium for growth of pea mesophyll protoplasts. Physiol. Plant. **39**, 257–260.

VON ARNOLD S. & ERIKSSON T. 1978 Induction of adventitious buds on embryos of Norway spruce grown *in vitro*. Physiol. Plant. **44**, 283–287.

VON ARNOLD S. & ERIKSSON T. 1979a Induction of adventitious buds on buds of Norway spruce grown *in vitro*. Physiol. Plant. **45**, 29–34.

VON ARNOLD S. & ERIKSSON T. 1979b Bud induction on isolated needles of Norway spruce (*Picea abies* L. Karst) grown *in vitro*. Plant Sci. Lett. **15**, 363–372.

VON ARNOLD S. & ERIKSSON T. 1981 *In vitro* studies of adventitious shoot formation in *Pinus contorta*. Can. J. Bot. **59**, 870–874.

VON ARNOLD S. & ERIKSSON T. 1984 Effect of agar concentration on growth and anatomy of adventitious shoots of *Picea abies* L. Karst. Plant Cell Tiss. Organ Cult. **3**, 257–264.

VON ARNOLD S. & ERIKSSON T. 1985 Initial stages in the course of adventitious bud formation on embryos of *Picea abies*. Physiol. Plant. **60**, 41–47.

VOYIATZI C. & VOYIATZIS D.G. 1988 Shoot proliferation of the rose cv. (H.T.) Dr. Verhage as influenced by apical dominance regulating substances. Acta Hort. **226**, 671–674.

VREUGDENHIL D., BURGERS A., HARKES P.A.A. & LIBBENGA K.R. 1981 Modulation of the number of membrane bound auxin binding sites during the growth of batch cultured tobacco *Nicotiana tabacum* cultivar White Burley. Planta **152**, 415–419.

VUYLSTEKE D., SWENNEN R., WILSON G.F. & DE LANGHE E. 1988 Phenotypic variation among *in vitro* propagated plantain (*Musa* sp. cultivar 'AAB'). Scientia Hort. **36**, 79–88.

VYSKOT B. & BEZDEK M. 1984 Stabilization of synthetic media for plant tissue culture and cell cultures. Biol. Plant. **26**, 132–143.

VYSKOT B. & JARA Z. 1984 Clonal propagation of cacti through axillary buds *in vitro*. J. Hort. Sci. **59**, 449–452.

WADA K. & SHINOZAKI Y. 1985 Flowering response in relation to C and N contents of *Pharbitis nil* plants cultured in nitrogen-poor media. Plant Cell Physiol. **26**, 525–535.

WADDINGTON C.H. 1942 The epigenotype. Endeavour **1**, 18–20.

WAGENKNECHT A.C. & BURRIS R.H. 1950 Indoleacetic acid inactivating enzymes from bean roots and pea seedlings. Arch. Biochem. **25**, 30–53.

WAINWRIGHT H. & ENGLAND N. 1987 The micropropagation of *Prosopis juliflora* (Swartz) D.C.: establishment *in vitro*. Acta Hort. **212**, 49–53.

WAINWRIGHT H. & MARSH J. 1986 The micropropagation of watercress (*Rorippa nasturtium-aquaticum* L.). J. Hort. Sci. **61**, 251–256.

WAKASA K. 1979 Variation in the plants differentiated from the tissue culture of pineapple. Jap. J. Breed. **29**, 13–22.

WALDENMAIER S., PREIL W. & BUNEMANN G. 1986 Verwendung von antibiotiks in der mikrovermehrung. Gartenbau. **51**, 131–135.

WALKER K.A. & SATO S.J. 1981 Morphogenesis in callus tissue of *Medicago sativa*: the role of ammonium ion in somatic embryogenesis. Plant Cell Tiss. Organ Cult. **1**, 109–121.

WALKER P.N., HEUSER C.W. & HEINEMANN P.H. 1988 Micropropagation: studies in gaseous environments. Acta Hort. **230**, 145–152.

WALKEY D.G.A. 1976 High temperature inactivation of cucumber and alfalfa mosaic viruses in *Nicotiana rustica* cultures. Ann. Appl. Biol. **84**, 183–192.

WALKEY D.G.A. 1980 Production of virus-free plants by tissue culture. pp. 109–117 *in* Ingram and Helgeson (eds.) 1980 (*q.v.*).

WALKEY D.G.A. 1985 *Applied Plant Virology*. Heinemann, London. ISBN 0-434-92225-0

WALKEY D.G.A. & COOPER J. 1976 Growth of *Stellaria media, Capsella bursa-pastoris* and *Senecio vulgaris* plantlets from cultured meristem tips. Plant Sci. Lett. **7**, 179–186.

WALKEY D.G.A. & COOPER V.C. 1975 Effect of temperature on virus eradication and growth of infected tissue cultures. Ann. Appl. Biol. **80**, 185–190.

WALKEY D.G.A. & NEELY H.A. 1980 Virus inactivation in tissue culture. Nat. Veg. Res. Sta. U.K. Ann. Rep. 1980 **31**, p. 89.

WALKEY D.G.A. & WOOLFITT J.M.G. 1968 Clonal multiplication of *Nicotiana rustica* from shoot meristems in culture. Nature **220**, 1346–1347.

WALKEY D.G.A. & WOOLFITT J.M.G. 1970 Rapid clonal multiplication of cauliflower by shake culture. J. Hort. Sci. **45**, 203–206.

WALLACE R.H. 1928 Histogenesis of intumescences in the apple induced by ethylene gas. Am. J. Bot. **15**, 509–524.

WAN ABDUL R., GHANDIMATHI H., ROHANI O. & PARANJOTHY K. 1981 Recent developments in tissue culture of *Hevea*. International Rubber Res. Development Board Symposium, Haadyai, 1981.

WAN Y., SORENSEN E.L. & LIANG G.H. 1988a Genetic control of *in vitro* regeneration in alfalfa (*Medicago sativa* L.) Euphytica **39**, 3–9.

WANG A.S. 1989 Process for generating corn. U.S. Patent No. 4806483

WANG D. & YAN K. 1984 Somatic embryogenesis in *Echinochloa crusgalli*. Plant Cell Rep. **3**, 88–90.

WANG D.-Y. & VASIL I.K. 1982 Somatic embryogenesis and plant regeneration from inflorescence segments of *Pennisetum purpureum* Schum. (Napier or Elephant grass). Plant Sci. Lett. **25**, 147–154.

WANG H.F & HOLL F.B. 1988 *In vitro* culture and the incidence of somaclonal variation in regenerated plants of *Trifolium pratense* L. Plant Science **55**, 159–167.

WANG P. J. 1977 Regeneration of virus-free potato from tissue culture. pp. 386–391 *in* Barz *et al.* (eds.) 1977 (*q.v.*).

WANG P. J. & HU C. Y. 1980 Regeneration of virus-free plants through *in vitro* culture. pp. 61–99 *in* Fiechter A. (ed.) 1980b (*q.v.*).

WANG P.-J. & HU C.-H. 1982 *In vitro* mass tuberization and virus-free seed potato production in Taiwan. Am. Pot. J. **59**, 33–37.

WANG S.Y. & FAUST M. 1986 Effect of growth retardants on root formation and polyamine content in apple seedlings. J. Am. Soc. Hort. Sci. **111**, 912–917.

WANG W.C., TRONCHET M., LARROQUE N., DORION N. & ALBOUY J. 1988 Production of virus-free *Dahlia* by meristem culture and virus detection through cDNA probes and ELISA. Acta Hort. **234**, 421–428.

WANG Z., ZENG X., CHEN C., WU H., LI Q., FAN G. & LU W. 1980 Induction of rubber plantlets from anther of *Hevea brasiliensis* Muell. Arg. *in vitro*. Chinese J. Trop. Crops **1**, 16–26.

WANG Z., ZENG X., CHEN C., WU H., LI Q., FAN G. & LU W. 1981 Induction of plantlets from anthers of *Hevea in vitro*. Int. Rubber Res. Dev. Board Synposium, Haadyai 1981.

WARD H.B. & VANCE B.D. 1968 Effects of monochromatic radiations on growth of *Pelargonium* callus tissue. J. Exp. Bot. **19**, 119–124.

WARDLE K., DOBBS E.B. & SHORT K.C. 1983a *In vitro* acclimatization of aseptically cultured plantlets to humidity. J. Am. Soc. Hort. Sci. **108**, 386–389.

WAREING P.F. 1958 Interaction between indole-acetic acid and gibberellic acid in cambial activity. Nature **181**, 1744–1745.

WAREING P.F. 1979 What is the basis of the stability of apical meristems? pp. 1–9 *in* George E.F. (ed.) 1979 q.v.).

WARREN G.S. & FOWLER M.W. 1977 A physical method for the separation of the various stages in the embryogenesis of carrot cell cultures. Plant Sci. Lett. **9**, 71–76.

WARRINGTON K. 1933 The effect of length of day on the response of plants to boron. Ann. Bot. **47**, 429–458.

WASHER J., REILLY K.J. & BARNETT J.R. 1977 Differentiation in *Pinus radiata* callus culture: The effect of nutrients. N. Z. J. Forest Sci. **7**, 321–328.

WATANABE K., MITSUDA H. & YAMADA Y. 1983 Retention of metabolic and differentiation potentials of green *Lavandula vera* callus after freeze preservation. Plant Cell Physiol. **24**, 119–122.

WATANABE K., TANAKA K., ASADA K. & KASAL Z. 1971 The growth promoting effect of phytic acid on callus tissues of rice seed. Plant Cell Physiol. **12**, 161–164.

WATSON B. & HALPERIN W. 1981 Reinvestigation of the effects on hormones and sugars on xylogenesis in cultured Jerusalem artichoke (*Helianthus tuberosus*) tuber slices, with particular emphasis on the effects of different methods of media preparation and tissue analysis. Z. Pflanzenphysiol. **101**, 145–158.

WATTIMENA G., McCOWN B. & WEIS G. 1983 Comparative field performance of potatoes from microculture. Am. Potato J. **60**, 27–33.

WATTS J.W. & KING J.M. 1973a The use of antibiotics in the culture of non-sterile plant protoplasts. Planta **113**, 271–277.

WAZIZUKA T. & YAMAGUCHI T. 1987 The induction of enlarged apical domes *in vitro* and multi-shoot formation from finger millet (*Eleusine coracana*). Ann. Bot. **60**, 331–336.

WEATHERHEAD M.A., BURDON J. & HENSHAW G.G. 1978 Some effects of activated charcoal as an additive to plant tissue culture media. Z. Pflanzenphysiol. **89**, 141–147.

WEATHERHEAD M.A., BURDON J. & HENSHAW G.G. 1979 Effects of activated charcoal as an additive plant tissue culture media. Z. Pflanzenphysiol. **94**, 399–406.

WEATHERS P. & GILES K.L. 1987 Regeneration of many varieties of plants using a novel method of *in vitro* cell culture. In Vitro Cell Dev. Biol. **23**, 69A (Abst.).

WEATHERS P.J. & ZOBEL R.W. 1992 Aeroponics for the culture of organisms, tissues and cells. Biotech. Adv. **10**, 93–115.

WEBB D.T., ARIAS W. & DE HOSTOS E. 1986 Callus formation by *Ginkgo biloba* embryos on hormone-free media controlled by closures and media components. Phytomorph. **36**, 121–127.

WEBB J.K., BANTHORPE D.V. & WATSON D.G. 1984 Monoterpene synthesis in shoots regenerated from callus cultures. Phytochem. **23**, 903–904.

WEBB K.J., FAY M.F. & DALE P.J. 1987 An investigation of morphogenesis within the genus *Trifolium*. Plant Cell Tiss. Organ Cult. **11**, 37–46.

WEBER G., ROTH E.J. & SCHWEGER H.-G. 1983 Storage of cell suspensions and protoplasts of *Glycine max* (L.), *Datura innoxia* (Mill.) and *Daucus carota* (L.) by freezing. Z. Pflanzenphysiol. **109**, 29–39.

WEGG S.M. & TOWNSLEY P.M. 1983 Ascorbic acid in cultured tissue of Briar Rose, *Rosa rugosa* Thunb. Plant Cell Rep. **2**, 78–81.

WEHNER T.C. & LOCY R.D. 1981 *In vitro* adventitious shoot and root formation of cultivars and lines of *Cucumis sativus* L. HortScience **16**, 759–760.

WEI A.-M., KAMADA H. & HARADA H. 1986 Transformation of *Solanum nigrum* L. protoplasts by *Agrobacterium rhizogenes*. Plant Cell Rep. **5**, 93–96.

WEINSTEIN L.H. & GALSTON A.W. 1988 Prevention of a plant disease by specific inhibition of fungal polyamine biosynthesis. U.S. Patent No. 4818770.

WEINSTEIN L.H., MEISS A.N., UHLER R.L. & PURVIS E.R. 1956 Growth- promoting effects of ethylene-diamine tetra-acetic acid. Nature **178**, 1188.

WEINSTEIN L.H., ROBBINS W.R. & PERKINS H.F. 1951 Chelating agents and plant nutrition. Science **120**, 41–43.

WEIS J.S. 1967 Auxin inactivation by normal and derived tobacco tissue cultures. Adv. Front. Plant Sci. **18**, 155–161.

WEIS J.S. & JAFFE M.J. 1969 Photoenhancement by blue light of organogenesis in tobacco pith cultures. Physiol. Plant. **22**, 171–176.

WEISER C.J. 1959 Effect of boron on the rooting of clematis cuttings. Nature **183**, 559–560.

WEISER C.J. & BLANEY L.T. 1960 The effects of boron on the rooting of English Holly cuttings. Proc. Am. Soc. Hort. Sci. **75**, 704–710.

WELANDER M. 1987 *In vitro* culture of raspberry (*Rubus idaeus*) for mass propagation and virus elimination. Acta Hort. **212**, p. 610.

WELANDER M. 1988 Plant regeneration from leaf and stem segments of shoots raised *in vitro* from mature apple trees. J. Plant Physiol. **132**, 738–744.

WELANDER M. & HUNTRIESER I. 1981 The rooting ability of shoots raised '*in vitro*' from the apple rootstock A2 *in* juvenile and in adult growth phase. Physiol. Plant. **53**, 301–306.

WELANDER M. & SNYGG J.O. 1987 Effect of applied and endogenous auxin on callus and root formation of *in vitro* shoots of the apple rootstocks M26 and A2. Ann. Bot. **59**, 439–443.

WELANDER T. 1977 *In vitro* organogensis in explants from different cultivars of *Begonia* × *hiemalis*. Physiol. Plant. **41**, 142–145.

WELANDER T. 1978a *In vitro* propagation of clones from different cultivars of *Begonia hiemalis* sexual hybrid. Swed. J. Agric. Res. **8**, 181–186.

WELANDER T. 1978b Influence of nitrogen and sucrose in the medium and of irradiance of the stock plants on root formation in *Pelargonium* petioles grown *in vitro*. Physiol. Plant. **43**, 136–141.

WELANDER T. 1979 Influence of medium composition on organ formation in explants of *Begonia* × *hiemalis in vitro*. Swedish J.Agric.Res. **9**, 163-168.

WELSH K., SINK K.C. & DAVIDSON H. 1979 Progress on *in vitro* propagation of red maple. Comb. Proc. Int. Plant Proc. Soc., **29**, 382–386.

WELSH K.J. & SINK K.C. 1981 Morphogenetic responses of *Browallia* leaf sections and callus. Ann. Bot. **48**, 583–590.

WENCK A.R., CONGER B.V., TRIGIANO R.N. & SAMS C.E. 1988 Inhibition of somatic embryogenesis in Orchardgrass by endogenous cytokinins. Plant Physiol. **88**, 990–992.

WENZEL G., SCHIEDER O., PREZEWOZNY T., SOPORY S.K. & MELCHERS G. 1979 Comparison of single cell culture derived *Solanum tuberosum* L. plants and a model for their application in breeding programs. Theor. Appl. Genet. **55**, 49–55.

WERKER E. & LESHEM B. 1987 Structural changes during vitrification of carnation plantlets. Ann. Bot. **59**, 377–385.

WERNER E.M. & BOE A.A. 1980 *In vitro* propagation of Malling 7 apple rootstock. HortScience **15**, 509–510.

WERNICKE W., POTRYKUS I. & THOMAS E. 1982 Morphogenesis from cultured leaf tissue of *Sorghum bicolor* — The morphogenic pathways. Protoplasma **111**, 53–62.

WESTCOTT R.J. 1981a Tissue culture storage of potato germplasm. 1. Minimal growth storage. Potato Res., **24**, 331–342.

WESTCOTT R.J. 1981b Tissue culture storage of potato germplasm. 2. Use of growth retardants. Potato Res. **24**, 343–352.

WESTCOTT R.J., HENSHAW G.G. & GROUT B.W.W. 1977b Tissue culture methods and germplasm storage in potato. Acta Hort. **78**, 45–49.

WESTCOTT R.J., HENSHAW G.G. & ROCA W.M. 1977a Tissue culture storage of potato germplasm: callus initiation and plant regeneration. Plant Sci. Lett. **9**, 309–315.

WESTERHOF J., HAKKAART F.A. & VERSLUIJS J.M.A. 1984 Variation in two *Begonia* × *hiemalis* clones after *in vitro* propagation. Scientia Hort. **24**, 67–74.

WESTON G.D. & STREET H.E. 1968 Sugar absorption and sucrose inversion by excised tomato roots. Ann. Bot. **32**, 521–529.

WETHERELL D.F. 1969 Phytochrome in cultured wild carrot tissue. I. Synthesis. Plant Physiol. **44**, 1734–1737.

WETHERELL D.F. 1982 *Introduction to In Vitro Propagation.* Avery Publishing Group Inc., Wayne, New Jersey.

WETHERELL D.F. 1984 Enhanced adventive embryogenesis resulting from plasmolysis of cultured wild carrot cells. Plant Cell Tiss. Organ Cult. **3**, 221–227.

WETHERELL D.F. & DOUGALL D.K. 1976 Sources of nitrogen supporting growth and embryogenesis in cultured wild carrot tissue. Physiol. Plant. **37**, 97–103.

WETMORE R.H. & RIER J.P. 1963 Experimental induction of vascular tissues in callus of angiosperms. Am. J. Bot. **50**, 418–430.

WETTER L. R. & CONSTABEL F. (eds.) 1982 *Plant Tissue Culture Methods.* (2nd ed.) National Res. Council of Canada, Prairie Regional Lab., Saskatoon.

WETZSTEIN H.Y., AULT J.R. & MERKLE S.A. 1989 Further characterization of somatic embryogenesis and plantlet regeneration in pecan (*Carya illinoensis*). Plant Sci. **64**, 193–201.

WHITE M.C., DECKER A.M. & CHANEY R.L. 1981 Metal complexation in xylem fluid. I. Chemical composition of tomato and soybean stem exudate. Plant Physiol. **67**, 292–300.

WHITE P.R. 1932 Influence of some environmental conditions on the growth of excised root-tips of wheat seedlings in liquid media. Plant Physiol. **7**, 613-628.

WHITE P.R. 1933 Results of preliminary experiments on the culturing of isolated stem tips of *Stellaria media*. Protoplasma **19**, 97–116.

WHITE P.R. 1934a Potentially unlimited growth of excised tomato root tips in a liquid medium. Plant Physiol. **9**, 585–600.

WHITE P.R. 1934b Multiplication of the viruses of tobacco and aucuba mosaic in growing excised tomato roots. Phytopath. **24**, 1003–1011.

WHITE P.R. 1937a Survival of isolated tomato roots at sub-optimal and supra-optimal temperatures. Plant Physiol. **12**, 771–776.

WHITE P.R. 1937b Separation from yeast of materials essential for growth of excised tomato roots. Plant Physiol. **12**, 777–791.

WHITE P.R. 1938a Cultivation of excised roots of dicotyledonous plants. Am. J. Bot. **25**, 348–356.

WHITE P.R. 1938b Accessory salts in the nutrition of excised tomato roots. Plant Physiol. **13**, 391–398.

WHITE P.R. 1939a Potentially unlimited growth of excised plant callus in an artificial nutrient. Am. J. Bot. **26**, 59–64.

WHITE P.R. 1939b Glycine in the nutrition of excised tomato roots. Plant Physiol. **14**, 527–538.

WHITE P.R. 1942 Plant tissue cultures. Ann. Rev. Biochem. **11**, 615–628.

WHITE P.R. 1943a *A Handbook of Plant Tissue Culture.* The Jacques Catlell Press, Lancaster, Pa.

WHITE P.R. 1943b Nutrient deficiency studies and an improved inorganic nutrient for cultivation of excised tomato roots. Growth **7**, 53–65.

WHITE P.R. 1953 A comparison of certain procedures for the maintenance of plant tissue cultures. Am. J. Bot. **40**, 517–524.

WHITE P.R. 1954 *The Cultivation of Animal and Plant Cells.* 1st. edition. Ronald Press, New York.

WHITE P.R. 1963 *The Cultivation of Animal and Plant Cells.* 2nd edition. Ronald Press, New York.

WHITEHEAD H.C.M. & GILES K.L. 1977 Rapid propagation of poplars by tissue culture methods. N. Z. J. Forest Sci. **7**, 40–43.

WHITELEY E. & ABBOTT A.J. 1977 Microvegetative propagation of apples. Ann. Rep. Long Ashton Res. Sta. 1976 62–63.

WHITTEN G.H. 1988 Process for microplant propagation through increased multiple shoot formation. U.S. Patent No. 4762790.

WHITTIER D.P. 1964a The influence of cultural conditions on the induction of apogamy in *Pteridium gametophytes*. Am. J. Bot. **51**, 730–736.

WHITTIER D.P. 1964b The effect of sucrose on apogamy in *Cyrtomium falcatum* Presl. Am. Fern J. **54**, 20–25.

WHITTIER D.P. 1976 Tracheids, apogamous leaves and sporophytes in gametophytes of *Botrychium dissectum*. Bot. Gaz. **137**, 237–241.

WHITTIER D.P. & STEEVES T.A. 1960 The induction of apogamy in the bracken fern. Can. J. Bot. **38**, 925–930.

WHITTIER D.P. & STEEVES T.A. 1962 Further studies on induced apogamy of ferns. Can. J. Bot. **40**, 1525–1531.

WHITTINGHAM D.E., LYON M.F. & GLENISTER P.H. 1977 Long-term storage of mouse embryos at -196°C: the effect of background radiation. Genet. Res. **29**, 171–181.

WHITTINGTON W.J. 1959 The role of boron in plant growth. II. The effect on growth of the radicle. J. Exp. Bot. **10**, 93–103.

WICKHAM K., RODREGUEZ E. & ARDITTI J. 1980 Comparative phytochemistry of *Parthenium hysterophorus* L. (Compositae) tissue cultures. Bot. Gaz. **141**, 435–439.

WICKREMESINHE E.R.M., BLACKMON W.J. & REYNOLDS B.D. 1990a Adventitious shoot regeneration and plant production from explants of *Apios americana*. HortScience **25**, 1436–1439.

WICKSON M. & THIMANN K.V. 1958 The antagonism of auxin and kinetin in apical dominance. Physiol. Plant. **11**, 62–74.

WIERSEMA S.G., CABELLO R., TOUAR P. & DODDS J.H. 1987 Rapid seed multiplication by planting into beds, micro tubers and in vitro plants. Potato Res. **30**, 117–120.

WILCOX E.J., SELBY C. & WAIN R.L. 1978 Studies on plant growth-regulating substances. L. The cytokinin activity of some substituted benzyloxypurines. Ann. Appl. Biol. **88**, 439–444.

WILCOX E.J., SELBY C. & WAIN R.L. 1981 The cytokinin activities of 6-α-alkyl-benzyloxypurines. Ann. Appl. Biol. **97**, 221–226.

WILKINS C.P. & DODDS J.H. 1983 Effect of various growth regulators on growth *in vitro* of cherry shoot-tips. Plant Growth Reg. **1**, 209–216.

WILLIAMS C.P. & DODDS J.H. 1983 Conservation of woody species. pp. 113–136 *in* Dodds J.H. (ed.) 1983 (*q.v.*).

WILLIAMS E.G. & MAHESWARAN G. 1986 Somatic embryogenesis: factors influencing coordinated behaviour of cells as an embryogenic group. Ann. Bot. **57**, 443–462.

WILLIAMS L. & COLLIN H.A. 1976 Embryogenesis and plantlet formation in tissue cultures of celery. Ann. Bot. **40**, 325–332.

WILLIAMS R.R. & TAJI A.M. 1987 Effects of temperature, darkness and gelling agent on long-term storage of *in vitro* shoot cultures of Australian woody plant species. Plant Cell Tiss. Organ Cult. **11**, 151–156.

WILLIAMS R.R., TAJI A.A. & BOLTON J.A. 1984 *In vitro* propagation of *Dampiera diversifolia* and *Prostanthera rotundifolia*. Plant Cell Tiss. Organ Cult. **3**, 273–281.

WILLIAMS R.R., TAJI A.M. & BOLTON J.A. 1985 Specificity and interaction among auxins, light and pH in rooting of Australian woody species *in vitro*. HortScience **20**, 1052–1053.

WILLIAMSON C.E. 1950 Ethylene, a metabolic product of diseased or injured plants. Phytopath. **40**, 205–208.

WILLMER E.N. (ed.) 1966 *Cells and Tissues in Culture —Methods and Physiology* Vol 3. Academic Press, London, New York.

WILSON A.J., CHOUREY P.S. & SHARPE D.Z. 1985 Protoclones of *Sorghum bicolor* with unusually high mitochondrial DNA variation. pp. 368–369 *in* Henke *et al.* (eds.) 1985 (*q.v.*).

WILSON H.M., EISA M.Z. & IRWIN S.W.B. 1976 The effects of agitated liquid medium on *in vitro* cultures of *Hevea brasilensis*. Physiol. Plant. **36**, 399–402.

WILSON K.S. & CUTTER V.M. 1955 Localization of acid phosphatase in the embryo sac and endosperm of *Cocos nucifera*. Am. J. Bot. **42**, 116–119.

WILSON W.C. 1966 The possibilities of using ethylene gas to produce citrus fruit abscission under field conditions. Proc. Fla. State Hort. Soc. **79**, 301–304.

WIMBER D.E. 1965 Additional observations on clonal multiplication of *Cymbidiums* through culture of shoot meristems. Cymb. Soc. News **20**, (4) 7–10.

WINATA L. & HARVEY R.G. 1980 Effect of glyphosate on organ formation in alfalfa callus *in vitro*. Plant Physiol. **65**, (Suppl.) 89 (Abst. 487).

WINSTON D.W. & BATES D.H. 1960 Saturated solutions for the control of humidity in biological research. Ecology **41**, 232–237.

WINTON L.W. 1968b The rooting of liquid-grown aspen cultures. Am. J. Bot. **55**, 159–167.

WITHERS L.A. 1978 Freeze-preservation of cultured cells and tissues. pp. 297–306 *in* Thorpe T. A. (ed.) 1978 (*q.v.*).

WITHERS L.A. 1980a Preservation of germplasm. pp. 101–136 *in* Vasil I.K. (ed.) 1980b (*q.v.*).

WITHERS L.A. 1980b Cryopreservation of plant cell and tissue cultures. pp. 63–70 *in* Ingram and Helgeson (eds.) 1980 (*q.v.*).

WITHERS L.A. 1980c Low temperature storage of plant tissue cultures. pp. 102–150 *in* Fiechter A. (ed.) 1980b (*q.v.*).

WITHERS L.A. 1980d *Tissue Culture Storage for Genetic Conservation.* International Board for Plant Genetic Resources. Rome 1980 AGP: 1BPGR/80/8.

WITHERS L.A. 1984a Minimum requirements for receiving and maintaining tissue culture propagating material. pp. 191–217 *in Micropropagation of Selected Root Crops, Palms, Citrus and Ornamental Species.* FAO Plant Production and Protection Paper 59 FAO, Rome. ISBN 92-5-102157-0.

WITHERS L.A. 1984b Germplasm conservation *in vitro*: present state of research and its application. pp. 138–157 *in* Holden & Williams (eds.) 1984 (*q.v.*).

WITHERS L.A. 1985 Cryopreservation of cultures plant cells and protoplasts. pp. 243–268 *in* Kartha K.K. (ed.) 1985a (*q.v.*).

WITHERS L.A. 1987a Long-term preservation of plant cells, tissues and organs. Oxford Surveys of Plant Molecular & Cell Biol. **4**, 221–272.

WITHERS L.A. 1987b The low temperature preservation of plant cell tissue and organ cultures and seed for genetic conservation and improved agricultural practice. pp. 389–409 *in* Grout B.W.W. (ed.) *The Effects of Low Temperatures on Biological Systems.* Edward Arnold.

WITHERS L.A. 1988 Germplasm preservation. pp. 163–177 *in Applications of Plant Cell and Tissue Culture.* John Wiley. ISBN 0 471 91886 5

WITHERS L.A. & KING P.J. 1979 Proline: a novel cryoprotectant for the freeze preservation of cultured cells of *Zea mays* L. Plant Physiol. **64**, 675–678.

WITRZENS B., SCOWCROFT W.R., DONNES R.W. & LARKIN P.J. 1988 Tissue culture and plant regeneration from sunflower (*Helianthus annuus*) and interspecific hybrids (*H. tuberosus* × *H. annuus*). Plant Cell Tiss. Organ Cult. **13**, 61–76.

WITTENBACH V.A. & BUKOVAC M.J. 1980 *In vitro* culture of sour cherry fruits. J. Am. Soc. Hort. Sci. **105**, 277–279.

WOCHOK Z.S. 1987 Status of crop improvement through tissue culture. Comb. Proc. Int. Plant Prop. Soc. 1986 **36**, 72–77.

WOCHOK Z.S. & SLUIS C.J. 1980b Gibberellic acid promotes *Atriplex* shoot multiplication and elongation. Plant Sci. Lett. **17**, 363–369.

WOCHOK Z.S. & WETHERELL D.F. 1971 Supression of organised growth in cultured wild carrot tissue by 2-chloroethylphosphoric acid. Plant Cell Phyiol. **12**, 771–774.

WOLTER K.E. & SKOOG F. 1966 Nutritional requirements of *Fraxinus* callus cultures. Am. J. Bot. **53**, 263–269.

WOOD H.N. & BRAUN A.C. 1961 Studies on the regulation of certain essential biosynthetic systems in normal and crown-gall tumor cells. Proc. Nat. Acad. Sci. U.S.A. **47**, 1907–1913.

WOOD N.J. & LUNDERGAN C.A. 1981 Microwave sterilisation of tissue culture media. HortScience **16**, 417–418 (Abst. 136).

WOODWARD S., THOMSON R.J. & NEALE W. 1991 Observations on the propagation of carnivorous plants by *in vitro* culture. Newsletter Int. Plant Prop. Soc. Spring 1991.

WOOI K.C., WONG C.Y. & CORLEY R.H.V. 1982a Genetic stability of oil palm callus cultures. pp. 749–750 *in* Fujiwara A. (ed.) 1982 (*q.v.*).

WOOI K.C., WONG C.Y. & CORLEY R.H.V. 1982b Tissue culture of palms — a review. pp. 138–144 *in* Rao A.N. (ed.) 1982 (*q.v.*).

WOZNIAK J., HYNDMAN S.E., STRODE R.E. & OGLESBY R.P. 1982 Recent developments in *Gerbera* micropropagation. In Vitro **18**, 293.

WOZNY A., GWODZ E. & SWEYKOWSKA A. 1973 The effect of 3- indoleacetic acid on the differentiation of plastids in callus culturs of *Cichorium intybus* L. Protoplasma **76**, 109–114.

WRIGHT M.S., KOEHLER S.M., HINCHEE M.A. & CARNES M.G. 1986 Plant regeneration by organogenesis in *Glycine max*. Plant Cell Rep. **5**, 150–154.

WRIGHT N.A. & ALDERSON P.G. 1980 The growth of tulip tissues *in vitro*. Acta Hort. **109**, 263–270.

WRIGHT N.A., ALDERSON P.G. & RICE R.D. 1982 Towards the clonal propagation of tulip by tissue culture. pp. 697–698 *in* Fujiwara (ed.) 1982 (*q.v.*)

WU J.-H., HILDEBRANDT A.C. & RIKER A.J. 1960 Virus-host relationships in plant tissue culture. Phytopath. **50**, 587–594.

WU Y., YE D., INSTALLÉ P., JACOBS M. & NEGRUTIU I. 1990 Sex determination in the dioecious *Melandrium*: The *in vitro* culture approach. pp. 239–243 *in* Nijkamp *et al.* (eds.) 1990 (*q.v.*).

WULSTER G. & SACALIS J. 1980 Effects of auxins and cytokinins on ethylene evolution and growth of rose callus tissue in sealed vessels. HortScience **15**, 736–737.

WYN JONES R.G. & HUNT O.R. 1967 The function of calcium in plants. Bot. Rev. **33**, 407–426.

XIANG-CAN Z., JONES D.A. & KERR A. 1989 Regeneration of shoots on root explants of flax. Ann. Bot. **63**, 297–299.

YAE B.W., ZIMMERMAN R.H., FORDHAM I. & KO K.C. 1987 Influence of photoperiod, apical meristem and explant orientation on axillary shoot proliferation of apple cultivars *in vitro*. J. Am. Soc. Hort. Sci. **112**, 588–592.

YAKUWA H. & OKA S. 1988 Plant regeneration through meristem culture from vegetative buds of mulberry (*Morus bombycis* Koidz.) stored in liquid nitrogen. Ann. Bot. **62**, 79–82.

YAMADA T., SAKAI A., MATSUMURA T. & HIGUCHI S. 1991 Cryopreservation of apical meristems of white clover (*Trifolium repens* L.). Plant Science **73**, 111–116.

YAMADA Y., ZHI-QI Y. & DING-TAI T. 1986 Plant regeneration from protoplast-derived callus of rice (*Oryza sativa* L.). Plant Cell Rep. **5**, 85–88.

YAMAMOTO Y., MIZUGUCHI R. & SHIBATA T. 1990 Plant culture cell and use thereof. U.S. Patent No. 4970151.

YANAGAWA T. & SAKANISHI Y. 1980 Studies on the regeneration of excised bulb tissues of various tunicated bulbous ornamentals. I. Regenerative capacity of the segments from different parts of bulb scales. J. Jap. Soc. Hort. Sci. **48**, 405–502.

YANG H.-J. & CLORE W.J. 1973 Rapid vegetative propagation of asparagus through lateral bud culture. HortScience **8**, 141–143.

YANG H.-J. & CLORE W.J. 1974a Development of complete plantlets from moderately vigorous asparagus shoots of stock plants *in vitro*. HortScience **9**, 138–140.

YANG H.Y. & ZHOU C. 1990 *In vitro* gynogenesis. *in* Bhojwani S.S. (ed.) 1990 *Plant Tissue Culture. Applications and Limitations.*, Elsevier Science Publishers.

YANG N.-S. 1986 Medium for plant protoplast culture. U.S. Patent No. 4533636.

YANG N.-S. & PAAU A. 1986 Plant tissue culture device. U.S. Patent No. 4531324.

YANG Q.G., READ P.E., FELLMAN C.D. & HOSIER M.A. 1986 Effect of cytokinin, IBA and rooting regime on Chinese chestnut cultured *in vitro*. HortScience **21**, 133–134.

YANG S.F., ADAMS D.O., LIZADA C., YU Y., BRADFORD K.J., CAMERON A.C. & HOFFMAN N.E. 1980 Mechanism and regulation of ethylene biosynthesis. pp. 219–229 in Skoog F. (ed.) 1980 (q.v.).

YANG Y.W. & CHANG .C. 1979 In vitro plant regeneration from leaf explants of Stevia rebaudiana. Z. Pflanzenphysiol. 93, 337–343.

YAO D.-Y. & KRIKORIAN A.D. 1981 Multiplication of rice (Oryza sativa L.) from aseptically cultured nodes. Ann. Bot. 48, 255–259.

YASUDA T., FUJII Y. & YAMAGUCHI T. 1985 Embryogenic callus induction from Coffea arabica leaf explants by benzyladenine. Plant Cell Physiol. 26, 595–597.

YATAZAWA M., FURUHASHI K. & SHIMIZU M. 1967 Growth of callus tissue from rice root in vitro. Plant & Cell Physiol. 8, 363–373.

YEOMAN M.M. 1981 The mitotic cycle in higher plants. pp. 161–184 in John P.C.L. (ed.) 1981 The Cell Cycle. Cambridge University Press. London, New York.

YEOMAN M.M. & DAVIDSON A.W. 1971 Effect of light on cell division in developing callus cultures. Ann. Bot. 35, 1085–1100.

YEOMAN M.M. & FORCHE E. 1980 Cell proliferation and growth in callus cultures. pp. 1–24 in Vasil I.K. (ed.) 1980a (q.v.).

YEOMAN M.M. & STREET H.E. 1977 General cytology of cultured cells. pp. 137–176 in Street H.E. (ed.) 1977 (q.v.).

YEUNG E. C., THORPE T. A. & JENSEN C. J. 1981 In vitro fertilization and embryo culture. pp. 253–271 in Thorpe T. A. (ed.) 1981 (q.v.).

YIDANA J.A., WITHERS L.A. & IVINS J.D. 1987 Development of a simple method in the field for collecting germplasm. Tested procedure using nodal cuttings. Acta Hort. 212, 95–98.

YOCUM C.S. & HACKETT D.P. 1957 Participation of cytochromes in the respiration of the aroid spadix. Plant Physiol. 32, 186–191.

YORK W.S., DARVILL A.G. & ALBERSHEIM P. 1984 Inhibition of 2,4- dichlorophenoxyacetic acid-stimulated elongation of pea stem segments by a xyloglucan oligosaccharide. Plant Physiol. 75, 295–297.

YOSHIDA F. & KOHNO H. 1982 Effects of media containing NH4 as the sole nitrogen source on cultured cells of tobacco and rice. pp. 231–232 in Fujiwara A. (ed.) 1982 (q.v.).

YOSHIDA F., KOBAYASHI T. & YOSHIDA T. 1973 The mineral nutrition of cultured chlorophyllous cells of tobacco. I. Effects of π salts, π sucrose, Ca, Cl and B in the medium on the yield, friability, chlorophyll contents and mineral absorption of cells. Plant Cell Physiol. 14, 329–339.

YOSHINO M. & HASHIMOTO K. 1975 Occurrence of aphid-transmitted strawberry viruses in Saitama Prefecture and production of virus-free clones by means of meristem culture. Bull. Saitama Hort. Exp. Sta. 5, 46–61.

YOUNG P.M., HUTCHINS A.S. & CANFIELD M.L. 1984 Use of antibiotics to control bacteria in shoot cultures of woody plants. Plant Sci. Lett. 34, 203–209.

YOUNG R.E., PRATT H.K. & BIALE J.B. 1951 Identification of ethlene as a volatile product of the fungus Penicillium digitatum. Plant Physiol. 26, 304–309.

YU Y.-B. & YANG S.F. 1979 Auxin-induced ethylene production and its inhibition by aminoethoxyvinylglycine and cobalt ion. Plant Physiol. 64, 1074–1077.

YUSNITA S., GENEVE R.L. & KESTER S.T. 1990 Micropropagation of white Eastern Redbud (Cercis canadensis var. alba). HortScience 25, 1091 (Abst. 194).

ZADOR E., KOVES E. & SZABO M. 1985 Phenolic materials in auxin heterotroph and autotroph (habituated) tobacco callus tissues. Biochem. Physiol. Pflanz. 180, 125–131.

ZAGHMOUT O. & TORRES K.C. 1985 The effects of various carbohydrate sources and concentrations on the growth of Lilium longiflorum 'Harson' grown in vitro. HortScience 20, 660.

ZAGORSKA N.A., SHAMINA Z.B. & BUTENKO R.G. 1974 The relationship of morphogenetic potency of tobacco tissue culture and its cytogenetic features. Biol. Plant. 16, 262–274.

ZAITLIN M. 1959 Isolation of tobacco leaf cells capable of supporting virus multiplication. Nature 184, 1002–1003.

ZAKHLENYUK O.V. & KUNAKH V.A. 1987 Cytophysiological and cytogenetic effects of adenine derivatives in Haplopappus gracilis tissue culture. Fiziol. Rast. 34, 584–594.

ZAMSKI E. & UMIEL N. 1978 Streptomycin resistance in tobacco: II. Effects of the drug on the ultrastructure of plastids and mitochondria in callus cultures. Z. Pflanzenphysiol. 88, 317–325.

ZAMSKI E. & WYSE R.E. 1985 Stereospecificity of glucose carrier in sugar beet suspension cells. Plant Physiol. 78, 291–295.

ZAPATA F.J. & SINK K.C. 1980 Somatic embryogenesis in Lycopersicon peruvianum leaf protoplasts. HortScience 15, 415 (Abst. 313).

ZAPATA F.J., KHUSH G.S., CRILL J.P., NEU M.H., ROMERO R.O., TORRIZO L.B. & ALEJAR M. 1983 Rice anther culture at IRRI. pp. 27–46 in Anon 1983 (q.v.).

ZATYKO J.M. & MOLNAR I. 1986 Adventitious root formation of different fruit species influenced by the pH of medium. p. 29 in Abstracts VI Intl. Cong. Plant Tissue & Cell Culture. Minneapolis, Minn.

ZATYKO J.M., KISS G., RADICS Z. & SIMON I. 1989 Initiation of strawberry runner formation in vitro. Acta Hort. 265, 349–352.

ZATYKO J.M., SIMON I., SZALAY I. & MOLNAR I. 1982 Mixed culture of callus homogenates of different plant species in vitro. pp. 61–62 in Fujiwara A. (ed.) 1982 (q.v.).

ZEE S.-Y., & WU S.C. 1979 Embryogenesis in the petiole explants of Chinese celery. Z. Pflanzenphysiol. 93, 325–335.

ZEE S.-Y., WU S.C. & YUE S.B. 1979 Morphological and SDS- polyacrylamide gel electrophoretic studies of pro-embryoid formation in the petiole explants of Chinese celery. Z. Pflanzenphysiol. 95, 397–403.

ZELCER A., SOFERMAN O. & IZHAR S. 1983 Shoot regeneration in root cultures of Solanaceae. Plant Cell Rep. 2, 252–254.

ZELDIN E.L. & McCOWN B.H. 1986 Calcium gluconate can be used as a calcium source in plant tissue culture media. p. 57 in Somers et al. (eds.) 1986 (q.v.).

ZELITCH I. 1978 Improving the efficiency of photosynthesis. Science 188, 626–633.

ZENKTELER M. 1980 Intraovarian and in vitro pollination. pp. 137–156 in Vasil I.K. (ed.) 1980b (q.v.).

ZHANG B., STOLTZ L.P. & SNYDER J.C. 1986 In vitro proliferation and in vivo establishment of Euphorbia fulgens. HortScience 21, 859 (Abst.).

ZIESLIN N., KHAYAT E., YOGEV S. & SHOUB J. 1988 Promotion of cuttings production of Gerbera jamesonii by cytokinin. Acta Hort. 226, 425–429.

ZILIS M., ZWAGERMAN D., LAMBERTS D. & KURTZ L. 1979 Commercial propagation of herbacious perennials. Comb. Proc. Int. Plant Prop. Soc. 29, 404–414.

ZILIS M.R. & MEYER M.M. 1976 Rapid in vitro germination of immature, dormant embryos. Comb. Proc. Int. Plant Prop. Soc. 26, 272–275.

ZILIS M.R. & ZWAGERMAN D. 1980 In vitro characteristics of nucellar and adventitious embryos in the genus Hosta. HortScience 15, 3 (Abst. 327).

ZIMMER K. & PIEPER W. 1975 Weitere untersuchungen zur kultur in vitro von Aechmea. Gartenbauwiss. 40, 129–132.

ZIMMER K. & PIEPER W. 1976 Methods and problems of clonal propagation of bromeliads in vitro. Acta Hort. 64, 25–29.

ZIMMERMAN R.H. 1972 Juvenility and flowering in woody plants: a review. HortScience 7, 447–455.

ZIMMERMAN R.H. 1979 The laboratory of micropropagation at Cesena, Italy. Comb. Proc. Int. Plant Prop. Soc. 29, 398–400.

ZIMMERMAN R.H. 1981 Micropropagation of fruit plants. Acta Hort. 120, 217–222.

ZIMMERMAN R.H. 1982 Genetic stability of horticultural plants propagated by tissue culture. Comb. Proc. Int. Plant Prop. Soc. 1981 31, 118–121.

ZIMMERMAN R.H. 1983 Factors affecting in vitro propagation of apple cultivars. Acta Hort. 131, 171–178.

ZIMMERMAN R.H. 1984a Chapter 14 — Apple. pp. 369–395 in Sharp et al. (eds.) 1984 (q.v.).

ZIMMERMAN R.H. 1984b Rooting apple cultivars in vitro: interactions among light, temperature phloroglucinol and auxin. Plant Cell Tiss. Organ Cult. 3, 301–311.

ZIMMERMAN R.H. & BROOME O.C. 1980 Micropropagation of thornless blackberry. pp. 23–26 in Anon 1980 (q.v.).

ZIMMERMAN R.H. & BROOME O.C. 1981 Phloroglucinol and in vitro rooting of apple cultivar cuttings. J. Am. Soc. Hort. Sci. 106, 648–652.

ZIMMERMAN R.H. & FORDHAM I. 1989 Explant orientation affects axillary shoot proliferation of apple cultivars in vitro. HortScience 24, 351–352.

ZIMMERMAN R.H., GRIESBACH R.J., HAMMERSCHLAG F.A. & LAWSON R.H. (eds.) 1986 *Tissue Cultures as a Plant Production System for Horticultural Crops*. Martinus Nijhoff, Dordrecht/Boston/Lancaster. ISBN 90-247-3378-2

ZIMMERMAN T.W., ROGERS S.M. & COBB B.G. 1988a Controlling vitrification of *Petunia in vitro*. HortScience **23**, 758.

ZIMMERMAN T.W., ROGERS S.M. & COBB B.G. 1988b Physiological differences between normal and vitreous petunias grown *in vitro*. HortScience **23**, 780.

ZIMMERMANN E.S. & READ P.E. 1986 Micropropagation of *Typha* species. HortScience **21**, 1214–1216.

ZIMNY J. & LÖRZ H. 1986 Plant regeneration and initiation of cell suspensions from root-tip derived callus of *Oryza sativa* L. (rice). Plant Cell Rep. **5**, 89–92.

ZINK M.W. & VELIKY I.A. 1979 Acid phosphatases of *Ipomoea* sp. cultured *in vitro*. 1. Influence of pH and inorganic phosphate on the formation of phosphotases. Can. J. Bot. **57**, 739–753.

ZINK M.W. & VELIKY I.A. 1982 Separation and some properties of two acid phosphatases from suspension cultures of *Ipomoea* sp. Plant Cell Tiss. Organ Cult. **1**, 265–273.

ZIV M. & HALEVY A.H. 1972 Organs and plantlets regeneration of gladiolus through tissue culture. Proc. Int. Hort. Cong. 18 (1970) **1**, 211–212.

ZIV M., HALEVY H. & SHILO R. 1970 Organs and plantlets regeneration of gladiolus through tissue culture. Ann. Bot. **34**, 671–676.

ZIV M., MEIR G. & HALEVY A.H. 1981 Hardening carnation plants regenerated from shoot tips cultured *in vitro*. Env. Exp. Bot. **21**, 423 (Abst.).

ZIV M., MEIR G. & HALEVY A.H. 1983 Factors influencing the production of hardened glaucous carnation plantlets *in vitro*. Plant Cell Tiss. Organ Cult. **2**, 55–65.

ZOBEL R.W. & ROBERTS L.W. 1978 Effects of low concentrations of ethylene on cell division and cytodifferentiation in lettuce pith explants. Can. J. Bot. **56**, 987–990.

ZREIN M., BURCKARD J. & VAN REGENMORTEL M.H.V. 1986 Use of the biotin-avidin system for detecting a broad range of serologically related plant virus by ELISA. J. Virol. Meth. **13**, 121–128.

ZUCKER H., STARK H. & RAMBECK W.A. 1980 Light-dependent synthesis of cholecalciferol in a green plant. Nature **283**, 68–69.

ZWAR J.A. & BRUCE M.I. 1970 Cytokinins from apple extract and coconut milk. Aust. J. Biol. Sci. **23**, 289–297.

ZWAR J.A., KEFFORD N.P., BOTTOMLEY W. & BRUCE M.I. 1963 A comparison of plant cell division inducers from coconut milk and apple fruitlets. Nature **200**, 679–680.

Taxonomic Index

Subject index